Read It—links to eBook pages

If students don't have their textbook with them as they complete their online homework, all they have to do is click the *Read It* link under a problem. The link opens a relevant excerpt from the text that relates to the exercise.

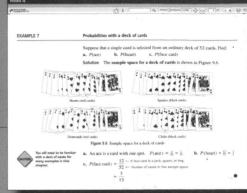

Watch It—video reinforcement

The *Watch It* feature allows students to see and hear additional instruction for almost every example in the text via 1- to 4-minute videos that correlate to the homework problems.

Master It—step-by-step tutorials

If students need even more help while solving a homework problem, they can click the *Master It* link to access a tutorial that walks them through the solution to a similar problem in multiple steps, providing feedback along the way. Students can then return to the original problem.

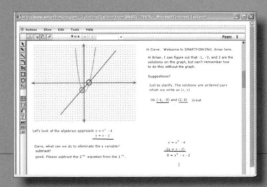

Chat About It—live online tutoring

Students can also click the *Chat About It* link for one-on-one tutoring (via whiteboarding, email, and instant messaging) from a mathematics instructor.

Screenshots shown here are for illustrative purposes only.

EDITION 9

MATHEMATICS
ITS POWER AND UTILITY

KARL J. SMITH

Santa Rosa Junior College

THOMSON
™
BROOKS/COLE

Australia • Brazil • Canada • Mexico • Singapore • Spain • United Kingdom • United States

THOMSON
BROOKS/COLE

Mathematics: Its Power and Utility, **Ninth Edition**
Karl J. Smith

Mathematics Editor: Carolyn Crockett
Development Editor: Kristin Marrs
Assistant Editor: Natasha Coats
Editorial Assistant: Lynh Pham
Technology Project Manager: Donna Kelley
Marketing Manager: Amanda Jellerichs
Marketing Assistant: Ashley Pickering
Marketing Communications Manager: Darlene Amidon-Brent
Project Manager, Editorial Production: Hal Humphrey
Art Director: Vernon Boes
Print Buyer: Barbara Britton

Permissions Editor: Roberta Broyer
Production Service: Matrix Productions
Text Designer: Diane Beasley
Photo Researcher: Terri Wright
Copy Editor: Susan Reiland
Illustrator: Lori Heckelman
Cover Designer: Gopa & Ted 2
Cover Image: Earth: © Jupiter Images; Light bulb: © Getty Images
Cover Printer: R.R. Donnelley/Willard
Compositor: ICC Macmillan Inc.
Printer: R.R. Donnelley/Willard

Library of Congress Control Number: 2007928593

Student Edition:
ISBN-13: 978-0495-38913-2
ISBN-10: 0-495-38913-7

Thomson Higher Education
10 Davis Drive
Belmont, CA 94002-3098
USA

For more information about our products, contact us at:
Thomson Learning Academic Resource Center
1-800-423-0563

For permission to use material from this text or product, submit a request online at **http://www.thomsonrights.com.**
Any additional questions about permissions can be submitted by e-mail to **thomsonrights@thomson.com.**

*I dedicate this book, with love,
to my grandson (my super guy),
Søren Sovndal.*

CONTENTS

(II) Applications: The Utility of Mathematics 331

PREFACE

The motive for the study of mathematics is insight into the nature of the universe. . . . As literature develops emotion, understanding, and sympathy, so mathematics develops observation, imagination, and reason.

W. E. Chancellor,
A Theory of Motives, Ideals and Values in Education (1907)

In this book we look at the *power* of mathematics, not the drudgery of number crunching. We look at it in historical perspective, and we see how mathematics has revolutionized the world. We also look at the *utility* of mathematics, and you are not told that you should do this just because it might be useful *someday*. The first part of the book, "The Power of Mathematics," develops some ideas in arithmetic, algebra, and geometry, and the second part of the book, "The Utility of Mathematics," develops the ideas around mathematics that you will use outside of the classroom.

If you are a student reading this preface, welcome! Each section of the book begins with an **IN THIS WORLD—Problem of the Day.** For example, here is the way we begin Section 1.1:

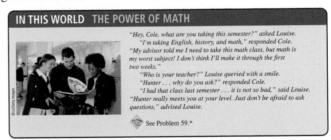

IN THIS WORLD   THE POWER OF MATH

"Hey, Cole, what are you taking this semester?" asked Louise.
"I'm taking English, history, and math," responded Cole. "My advisor told me I need to take this math class, but math is my worst subject! I don't think I'll make it through the first two weeks."
"Who is your teacher?" Louise queried with a smile.
"Hunter . . . why do you ask?" responded Cole.
"I had that class last semester . . . it is not so bad," said Louise. "Hunter really meets you at your level. Just don't be afraid to ask questions," advised Louise.

See Problem 59.*

If someone asked you today, "What are you taking this semester?" you might respond, "Well, I'm taking English and history, and I made the swimming team. Oh, I forgot, I also **have** to take math." What? You have to take math? How about, "You get to take math!"? 🛑 There is a message for you on page 1. Take the time to read that introductory page.

The first section of the book is entitled "Math Anxiety," and I have explained why I have written this book, and for whom it is intended. I hope you will begin reading this book with an open mind, and without bringing any bad experiences from past mathematics classes. You may be saying to yourself, "I wish I did not have to take this course; I'm not a math major," or "I don't know why I'm required to take a mathematics course." Regardless of your academic major, you should learn *something* from this book that will make life easier, less costly, or more efficient. This book is not about "doing math" or "completing the homework." It is not even about "doing well on exams." It is about learning essential skills for living!

Education is much more than books, classrooms, teachers, and requirements—it is about knowledge, and being able to use that knowledge. In 1958, when I was just starting to study high school mathematics, E.G. Begle, the leader of the School

Mathematics Study Group (SMSG), wrote something which, at the time, meant little to me: "The world of today demands more mathematical knowledge on the part of more people than the world of yesterday, and the world of tomorrow will demand even more." Well, today **is** the world of tomorrow, and that prediction is absolutely true. It is my belief that it is even more true for the next generation as we enter the 21st century. As you progress through the pages of this book, relax and enjoy, and along the way you will learn some useful mathematics.

To the Instructor

The rest of this preface is written for the instructor. As a teacher and author, I am faced with transferring some knowledge of the power, the beauty, and the utility of mathematics to my students. However, I can't instruct until my students have overcome their initial fears and attitudes about mathematics and are *ready* to listen.

I have often wondered why, when I tell people that I'm a math teacher, more often than not I hear about their unpleasant experiences in mathematics. Why is it that we *get* to participate in sports, or art, or music but **have** to take mathematics? For most people, mathematics is presented as the ultimate lesson in delayed gratification. Year after year, the students are told, "You must learn this thoroughly so you can do your math tomorrow, next week, next month, or next year." The implication is that in 20 or so years, we'll let you see the benefit of what you have been learning.

As I began to write this book, I asked myself, "What do my students *need?* Why should there be a new mathematics book in this world? What can I hope to present that is not already available?" This book was written to give the student who has previously not been successful with mathematics a fresh and innovative approach to arithmetic, beginning algebra, and geometry in order to satisfy basic competencies in mathematics in today's world. I have long believed that, if students have avoided or have been unsuccessful with a particular aspect of mathematics in the past, simply to present it to them again in the same way will generally not meet with a great deal more success. Nevertheless, because of the tremendous importance of mathematics, a student must have some degree of mathematical competency to be successful in almost any discipline. Therefore, even though I have presented the essential ideas of arithmetic, beginning algebra, and geometry, I have presented them in settings different from the usual or traditional ones.

My students need to be able to relate to the real world. You will find this book filled with practical information rather than abstract (and meaningless) made-up word problems.

For example, when we are looking at graphs we consider graphs showing the blood alcohol level and its effects on driving when drinking or political graphs taken from a newspaper.

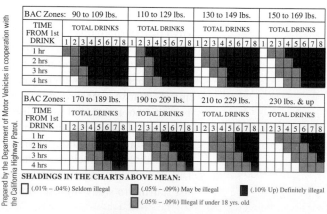

Blood Alcohol Concentration.

© David Young-Wolff/PhotoEdit

*My students need to be able to solve problems **outside** the classroom.* Take a look at the word problems we consider in Section 3.6. You will *not* find the usual mixture, distance, and age problems. Instead, we develop a *procedure* and work problems dealing with miles per gallon, price comparisons, and money exchange. We seek to develop higher-order reasoning in which the student needs to use, explain, and exploit newly learned knowledge. For example, we motivate probability by considering a Monopoly® game.

My students need to be able to estimate. I believe this is one of the most avoided topics in mathematics textbooks. I have spent a great deal of effort discussing this topic, and you will notice that many of the problem sets have multiple-choice questions that ask the students to estimate, not calculate. My students need to develop a *number sense,* which is different from "getting right answers." Answers in the back of the book are, of course, desirable and necessary, but in the book of life and problem solving there are no "answers in the back."

My students need money sense. Why do we learn to solve equations, but do not learn how to handle credit cards or purchase a car or home? (See Chapter 7.) I believe both skills are important in today's world.

RIGHT OR WRONG? LEVEL 3

Explain what is wrong, if anything, with the statements in Problems 55–60. Explain your reasoning.

55. $4 + 6 \times 8 = 80$

56. $2 + 8 \times 10 = 82$

57. $2 \times (3 + 4) = 14$ is an example of the distributive property.

58. The correct order of operations (for an expression with no parentheses) when simplifying is first multiply, then divide, then add, then subtract.

59. The number 0 is a natural number.

60. All natural numbers are also whole numbers.

have a trade-in with a value of $7,500. Here is a list of sales contract:

Sales price of Honda:	$19,800.00
Destination charges:	200.00
Subtotal:	20,000.00
Tax (7%) rate:	1,400.00
Less trade-in:	7,500.00
Amount to be financed:	13,900.00

We now calculate several key amounts:

$$\text{Interest: } I = Prt = 13,900(0.08)(4) = 4,448$$

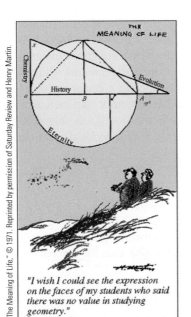

"The Meaning of Life," © 1971. Reprinted by permission of Saturday Review and Henry Martin.

"I wish I could see the expression on the faces of my students who said there was no value in studying geometry."

My students need to develop communication skills and think critically. In many of the sections of this book I have assigned problems that solicit a written paper or a book report. Problems designated **IN YOUR OWN WORDS** help encourage students to communicate mathematical ideas by using their own words. Students need to *communicate* in mathematics, and should not stop after they can "find a few right answers." Throughout the book, problems encourage a higher-order reasoning. For example, we analyze the lyrics of "By the Time I Get to Phoenix" and look for the errors in Anacin and Saab advertisements. Finally, throughout the book, I have included problems labeled Right or Wrong?, which include many common mistakes that must be avoided in order to understand the material.

Finally, *my students need to develop an appreciation for mathematics, its beauty, and its applications.* The applications taught in this course should not be limited to money-oriented applications. I have written this material with the goal that students walk away from this course with the feeling that mathematics can be pleasant, useful, and practical—and enjoyed for its own sake.

I believe we (teachers and authors) have done a disservice to most of our past students. We have taught mathematics as if we were preparing them for a career in mathematics, when instead we should have been teaching them an appreciation of mathematics. It is not necessary to learn all the technical details in order to use and appreciate math. For example, most people like music of some kind; almost anyone can find a radio station playing something they like to hear. Suppose we were to learn about music in the same way we learn about mathematics. Suppose we said that before you listen to the radio, you had to take three years of sand blocks and recorder, followed by five years of practice piano (graded by your proficiency at scales and rhythm), and finally after some high school courses on theory of music, you would be allowed to hear your first composed piece. On the contrary, composers, musicians, conductors, and music teachers see themselves as engaged in a common enterprise of bringing music to the world, and they believe that the techniques they are trying to teach should always be in the context of the wonderful sound of music. We should expect no less of mathematics.

I do not believe that students completely learn the material by working a particular type of problem only once. However, as a college instructor, I am well aware of time constraints and the amount of material that must be covered. I have therefore developed the idea of *uniform problem sets* for this edition, which means that each section contains 60 problems separated into Drill Problems and Application Problems. This uniformity makes it easy for an instructor to make "standard assignments" consisting of the same problems being assigned from section to section. For example, one instructor might assign odd problems (answers in the back of the book) or even problems (no answers in the back of the book). If an instructor wants some answers provided and others not, then an appropriate assignment might be the multiples of three (20 problems per assignment), or multiples of five (12 problems per assignment). You will notice that these standard assignments will include both Level 1 and Level 2 problems (with an occasional Level 3 challenge).

This book is published in two versions. The *student version* has a glossary and answers to the odd-numbered problems at the back of the book. The *instructor's version,* called the *Annotated Instructor's Edition* (AIE) includes *all* the answers. Most answers in this edition are included right next to the problem for easy reference, but the graphs and longer answers and solutions are included in an instructor's appendix called *Instructor's Answer Section* (IAS).

A Note on Calculator Usage

I believe that students in every college mathematics course should have calculator access, and this book makes that assumption. The proper use of calculators is best taught in the context of learning mathematics. As we progress through the material of this book, you will find many calculator exercises, but since *all* problems might benefit from the use of a calculator, we have not designated specific calculator problems. We also assume that the reader of this book has had *no* prior experience with calculators. Because the technology changes so rapidly, we have given only generic instructions on calculator usage, allowing students to use their individual calculators, regardless of brand.

Organization of This Book

The main theme throughout the book is *problem solving*. In "The Power of Mathematics" we begin by discussing math anxiety and how to formulate the problem. The most difficult first step for many students is to determine exactly the nature of

Math Anxiety Bill of Rights*
by Sandra L. Davis

1. I have the right to learn at my own pace and not feel put down or stupid if I'm slower than someone else.
2. I have the right to ask whatever questions I have.
3. I have the right to need extra help.
4. I have the right to ask a teacher or TA for help.
5. I have the right to say I don't understand.
6. I have the right not to understand.
7. I have the right to feel good about myself regardless of my abilities in math.
8. I have the right not to base my self-worth on my math skills.
9. I have the right to view myself as capable of learning math.
10. I have the right to evaluate my math instructors and how they teach.
11. I have the right to relax.
12. I have the right to be treated as a competent adult.
13. I have the right to dislike math.
14. I have the right to define success in my own terms.

the problem. All too often we try to solve a problem before we are even sure what we are trying to solve. Techniques from arithmetic, algebra, and geometry are all applied to problem solving.

These techniques of problem solving are then used in the second part of the book, "The Utility of Mathematics." Each topic in this part of the book was selected because of its usefulness to the student. The topics include managing money using the ideas of interest, installment buying, credit card buying, inflation, buying a car or home, sets, probability, contests, statistics, surveys, and the influence of these topics on our lives.

The material of this book can be adapted to almost any course arrangement. Chapter 1 on calculators and arithmetic is required for the rest of the book, but it may be treated lightly or skipped by those familiar with its contents. Topics from beginning algebra are presented in Chapters 2, 3, and 4 and are then used in developing much of the material that follows. For example, percents in Chapter 5 are described with proportions and simple equations. Chapter 6 introduces the ideas of geometry and measurement in a practical and down-to-earth manner. Chapters 7–11 give the students a chance to use mathematics in a variety of ways including interest, consumer applications, sets, logic, probability, statistics, and graphs. I have written this book with the idea that different classes will pick different topics as interest and competency requirements dictate. These chapters are independent and can be covered in any order. For example, many people using this book prefer to teach Chapter 7 (Applications of Percent) immediately after Chapter 4 (Percents and Problem Solving).

What Is New to This Edition

This book has been very successful, and most users and reviewers offered only minor suggestions. A major change I've made in this edition is added attention to applied problems. As the title implies, the book is divided into two parts: "The Power of Mathematics" and "The Utility of Mathematics," but that does not imply that you need to wait until Part II to investigate interesting applications. I have added many new application problems, especially to Part I, so that *every section* has problems designated as APPLICATION PROBLEMS. This is in keeping with the main theme: *problem solving.*

There is a fun, new feature called **Tergiversation,** which provides a numerical puzzle useful in checking answers.

In this edition I have expanded a popular feature in the previous edition. Every section now begins with **In This World—Problem of the Day.** You can use these problems to motivate the introduction to each section. I have revised the problem sets in this edition so that the problems are designated Level 1—essential ideas, Level 2—drill and practice, Level 2—applications, and Level 3—Right or Wrong?

I have added lists of essential ideas (chapter-by-chapter) to the chapter reviews, and have expanded the Research Projects.

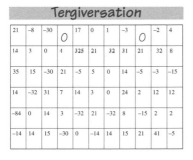

Tergiversation

21	−8	−30	O	17	0	1	−3	O	−2	4
14	3	0	4	325	21	32	31	21	32	8
35	15	−30	21	−5	5	0	14	−5	−3	−15
14	−32	31	7	14	3	0	24	2	12	12
−84	0	14	3	−32	21	−32	8	−15	2	2
−14	14	15	−30	0	−14	14	15	21	41	−5

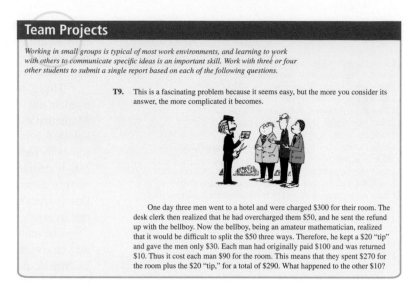

Team Projects

Working in small groups is typical of most work environments, and learning to work with others to communicate specific ideas is an important skill. Work with three or four other students to submit a single report based on each of the following questions.

T9. This is a fascinating problem because it seems easy, but the more you consider its answer, the more complicated it becomes.

One day three men went to a hotel and were charged $300 for their room. The desk clerk then realized that he had overcharged them $50, and he sent the refund up with the bellboy. Now the bellboy, being an amateur mathematician, realized that it would be difficult to split the $50 three ways. Therefore, he kept a $20 "tip" and gave the men only $30. Each man had originally paid $100 and was returned $10. Thus it cost each man $90 for the room. This means that they spent $270 for the room plus the $20 "tip," for a total of $290. What happened to the other $10?

Help for the Instructor

Annotated Instructor's Edition

The instructor's version of the complete student text contains answers to all the exercises in the text.

Test Bank

The Test Bank includes multiple tests per chapter as well as final exams. The tests are made up of a combination of multiple-choice, free-response, and fill-in-the-blank questions.

ExamView® Computerized Testing

Create, deliver, and customize tests—both print and online—in minutes with this easy-to-use assessment and tutorial system, which contains questions from the Test Bank in electronic format. The new algorithmic functionality offers a unique feature for recalculating questions, allowing professors to generate larger numbers of questions with the option for the exams to differ every time.

Enhanced WebAssign®

WebAssign®, the most widely used homework system in higher education, allows you to assign, collect, grade, and record homework assignments via the Web. Through a partnership between WebAssign and Thomson Brooks/Cole, this proven homework system has been enhanced to include links to textbook sections, video examples, and problem-specific tutorials.

ThomsonNOW™

Designed by instructors for instructors, ThomsonNOW™ *features the most intuitive, easy-to-use interface on the market* and offers a flexible online suite of services and resources. ThomsonNOW is designed to understand what you want to do, how you want to do it. ThomsonNOW is your source for results NOW! Go to www.thomsonedu. com/ThomsonNOW to try it out today.

Website

www.thomsonedu.com/math/smithpower
When you adopt a Thomson Brooks/Cole mathematics text, you and your students will have access to a variety of teaching and learning resources. This website features everything from book-specific resources to newsgroups. It's a great way to make teaching and learning an interactive and intriguing experience.

Help for the Student

Student Survival and Solutions Manual

Authored by Karl Smith, this manual is intended to help the students achieve success. It contains the complete solutions for approximately half of the problems in the text. Also available are sample tests, not only in hard-copy form, but also in electronic form for both IBM and Macintosh formats.

ThomsonNOW™

ThomsonNOW™ is an online suite of services and resources providing you with the choices and tools you need to improve your grade. ThomsonNOW is your source for results NOW! Go to www.thomsonedu.com/thomsonnow to try it out today.

Acknowledgments

I am most grateful to those who have assisted me in the development of this material: to my students who made many valuable suggestions about the material, and especially to those students who were bold enough to share their fears and anxieties with me; to my colleagues who shared ideas and teaching suggestions; and to the reviewers who offered many valuable suggestions.

I would also like to thank the reviewers of previous editions: Nizar Abudiab, Calhoun Community College; Carol Achs, Mesa Community College; Julia Arnold, Tidewater Community College; Dwight Atkins, Surry Community College; Mari Jo Baker, Illinois Central College; Carole Bergen, Mercy College; Elton Beougher, Fort Hays State University; John Beris, John Tyler Community College; Eugene Brown, Northern Virginia Community College; James W. Brown, Northern Essex Community College; Sharon Butler, Pikes Peak Community College; Kevin Chouinard, Northern Virginia Community College; Mary Clarke, Cerritos College; Stephan DeLong, Front Range Community College; Gary Donica, Florence-Darlington Technical College; William Durand, Henderson State College; Carolyn Ehr, Fort Hays State University; Rebecca Farrow, John Tyler Community College; Margaret Finster, Erie Community College; Ben V. Flora, Jr., Moorehead State University; Elton Fors, Northern State College, South Dakota; P.S. Gadiyaran, Southside Virginia Community College; Roy E. Garland, Minnersville State College; Barbara Gee, Cuesta College; Armando Gingras, Metropolitan State College, Denver; Donald K. Hostetler, Mesa Community College; Dorothy Johnson, Cleveland State University; Glenn E. Johnston, Moorehead State University; Joe Jordan, John Tyler Community College; Keith S. Joseph, Metropolitan State College, Denver; Joe Jordan, John Tyler Community College; Virginia Keen, Western Michigan University; Roxanne King, Prince

George's Community College; Michael Kirby, Tidewater Community College; Genevieve M. Knight, Hampton Institute; Harvey Lambert, University of Nevada, Reno; Lara Langdon, J. Sargeant Reynolds Community College; Robert Levine, Community College of Allegheny County; Ann Loving, J. Sargeant Reynolds Community College; Chicha Lynch, Capuchino High School; Tucker Maney, Northern Virginia Community College; Sandra Manigault, Northern Virginia Community College–Annendale Campus; Carl Miller, TESST Technology Institute; DeAnne Miller, Western New Mexico University; Glen E. Mills, Pensacola Junior College; Deloria Nanze-Davis, University of Texas at Brownsville; Carol B. Olmstead, University of Nevada, Reno; Charles Peselnick, DeVry Institute; Maryanne C. Petruska, Pensacola Junior College; Diana Pors, Eastside Union High School; Jane Rood, Eastern Illinois University; George C. Sethares, Bridgewater State College; Peter Stomieroski, Delaware Technical Community College; Clifford Tremblay, Pembroke State College; Elizabeth Wade, Pellissippi Community College; Richard Watkins, Tidewater Community College; Charles Wheeler, Montgomery College; Erma Williams, Hampton University; Martha Wilson, Hagerstown Business College; and Susan Wood, J. Sargeant Reynolds Community College.

The staff at Brooks/Cole and their freelancers also deserve special credit, especially Carolyn Crockett, senior acquisitions editor; Kristin Marrs, associate development editor; Mandy Jellerichs, marketing manager; Natasha Coats, supplements editor; Lynh Pham, editorial assistant; Ashley Pickering, marketing assistant; Sara Planck of Matrix Productions, production editor; Diane Beasley, interior designer; Lori Heckelman, illustrator; and Talia Wise, advertising project manager. And, as always, it was a pleasure to work with Susan Reiland, to whom I give my most heartfelt thanks for her exceptional work.

Karl J. Smith
Sebastopol, California

smithkjs@mathnature.com

FOUNDATIONS
The Power of Mathematics

Historically, the prime value of mathematics has been that it enables us to answer basic questions about our physical world, to comprehend the complicated operations of nature, and to dissipate much of the mystery that envelops life. The simplest arithmetic, algebra, and geometry suffice to determine the circumference of the earth, the distances to the moon and the planets, the speeds of sound and light, and the reasons for eclipses of the sun and moon. But the supreme value of mathematics, insofar as understanding the world about us is concerned, is that it reveals order and law where mere observation shows chaos. . . .

Morris Kline

Mathematics: An Introduction to Its Spirit and Use, San Francisco: W. H. Freeman, 1979, p. 1.

The first part of this book, The Power of Mathematics, attempts to develop an appreciation for mathematics by displaying the intrinsic **power** of the subject. We will begin by looking at some of the causes and effects of *math anxiety*. We take natural steps—small at first, and then a little larger as you gain confidence—to review and learn about calculators, fractions, percents, algebra, equations, metrics, and geometry.

Most people view mathematics as a series of techniques useful only to the scientist, the engineer, or the specialist. In fact, the majority of our population could be classified as math-avoiders, who consider the assertion that mathematics can be creative, beautiful, and significant not only as an "impossible dream," but also as something they don't even want to discuss.

At each turn of the page, I hope you will find something new and interesting. I want you to participate and become involved with the material. I want you to experience what I mean when I speak of the *beauty* of mathematics. I hope you are now ready to begin your study of a new course; I wish you success.

CHAPTER **1**

Arithmetic, Calculators, and Problem Solving

The only way I can distinguish proper from improper fractions is by their actions.

Ogden Nash

ANTICIPATE

- *Overview each chapter before you begin.*
- *Look over the chapter contents.*
- *Important terms are listed on page 72.*
- *Essential ideas are listed on page 72.*
- *Learning outcomes are listed on page 73.*
- *Attitude—you may have some unpleasant memories surrounding arithmetic in elementary school. In acknowledging that this is true for many people, we begin by discussing math anxiety. What is the message? Relax . . . it will not be as bad as you might think!*

1.1 Math Anxiety

IN THIS WORLD THE POWER OF MATH

"Hey, Cole, what are you taking this semester?" asked Louise.

"I'm taking English, history, and math," responded Cole. "My advisor told me I need to take this math class, but math is my worst subject! I don't think I'll make it through the first two weeks."

"Who is your teacher?" Louise queried with a smile.

"Hunter . . . why do you ask?" responded Cole.

"I had that class last semester . . . it is not so bad," said Louise. "Hunter really meets you at your level. Just don't be afraid to ask questions," advised Louise.

 See Problem 59.*

There are many reasons for reading a book, but the best reason is because you want to read it. Although you are probably reading this first page because you were requested to do so by your instructor, it is my hope that in a short while you will be reading this book because you want to read it.

Peanuts reprinted by permission of United Feature Syndicate, Inc.

Do you think that you are reasonably successful in other subjects but are unable to do math? Do you make career choices based on avoidance of mathematics courses? If so, you have *math anxiety*. If you reexamine your negative feelings toward mathematics, you can overcome them. In this book, I'll constantly try to help you overcome these feelings.

This book was written for people who are math-avoiders, people who think they can't work math problems, and people who think they are never going to use math. Do you see yourself making any of these statements shown in Figure 1.1?

Sheila Tobias, an educator, feminist, and founder of an organization called Overcoming Math Anxiety, has become one of our nation's leading spokespersons on math

*Each section begins with a reference to a specific problem in the Problem Set that we call "Problem of the Day." It relates the "In This World" commentary with a specific problem.

Figure 1.1 Math quotations—sound familiar?

anxiety. She is not a mathematician, and in fact she describes herself as a math-avoider. She has written a book titled *Overcoming Math Anxiety* (New York: W. W. Norton & Company, 1978; available in paperback). I recommend this book to anyone who has ever said, "I'm no good at numbers." In this book, she describes a situation that characterizes anxiety (p. 45):

> Paranoia comes quickly on the heels of the anxiety attack. "Everyone knows," the victim believes, "that I don't understand this. The teacher knows. Friends know. I'd better not make it worse by asking questions. Then everyone will find out how dumb I really am." This paranoid reaction is particularly disabling because fear of exposure keeps us from constructive action. We feel guilty and ashamed, not only because our minds seem to have deserted us but because we believe that our failure to comprehend this one new idea is proof that we have been "faking math" for years.

The reaction described in this paragraph sets up a vicious cycle. The more we avoid math, the less able we feel; and the less able we feel, the more we avoid it. The cycle can also work in the other direction. What do you like to do? Chances are, if you like it, you do it. The more you do something, the better you become at it. In fact, you've probably thought, "I like to do it, but I don't get to do it as often as I'd like to." This is the normal reaction toward something you like to do. In this book, I attempt to break the negative cycle concerning math and replace it with a positive cycle. However, I will need your help and willingness to try.

The central theme in this book is problem solving. Through problem solving I'll try to dispel your feelings of panic. Once you find that you are capable of doing mathematics, we'll look at some of its foundations and uses. There are no prerequisites for this book; and as we progress through the book, I'll include a review of the math you never quite learned in school—from fractions, decimals, percents, and metrics to algebra and geometry. I hope to answer the questions that, perhaps, you were embarrassed to ask.

At the end of each section in this book is a problem set. This first problem set is built around 12 math myths. These myths are in another book on math anxiety, *Mind Over Math,* by Stanley Kogelman and Joseph Warren (New York: Dial Press, 1978), which I highly recommend. These commonly believed myths have resulted in false impressions about how math is done, and they need to be dispelled.

> **Math Anxiety Bill of Rights***
> *by Sandra L. Davis*
>
> 1. I have the right to learn at my own pace and not feel put down or stupid if I'm slower than someone else.
> 2. I have the right to ask whatever questions I have.
> 3. I have the right to need extra help.
> 4. I have the right to ask a teacher or TA for help.
> 5. I have the right to say I don't understand.
> 6. I have the right not to understand.
> 7. I have the right to feel good about myself regardless of my abilities in math.
> 8. I have the right not to base my self-worth on my math skills.
> 9. I have the right to view myself as capable of learning math.
> 10. I have the right to evaluate my math instructors and how they teach.
> 11. I have the right to relax.
> 12. I have the right to be treated as a competent adult.
> 13. I have the right to dislike math.
> 14. I have the right to define success in my own terms.

*From *Overcoming Math Anxiety*, by Sheila Tobias, pp. 236–237.

Throughout this book, I will take off my author hat and put on my teacher hat to write you notes about the material in the book. These notes will explain steps or give you hints on what to look for as you are reading the book. These notes are printed in this font.

When you see the stop sign, you should stop for a few moments and study the material next to the stop sign. It is a good idea to memorize this material.

When you see the caution sign, you should make a special note of the material next to the caution sign because it will be used throughout the rest of the book.

When you see the yield sign, it means that you need to remember only the stated result and that the derivation is optional.

When you see the bump sign, some unexpected or difficult material follows, and you will need to slow down to understand the discussion.

CONQUER
ANXIETY
Many people using this book have what has been characterized as "math anxiety," and we have built in helps and hints to help you conquer this anxiety. When you see this symbol, you should follow the directions, or work the problem if you have been suffering from anxiety.

Hints for Success

Mathematics is different from other subjects. One topic builds on another, and you need to make sure that you understand *each* topic before progressing to the next one.

You must make a commitment to attend each class. Obviously, unforeseen circumstances can come up, but you must plan to attend class regularly. Pay attention to what your teacher says and does, and take notes. If you must miss class, write an outline of the text corresponding to the missed material, including working out each text example on your notebook paper.

You must make a commitment to daily work. Do not expect to save up and do your mathematics work once or twice a week. It will take a daily commitment on your part, and you will find mathematics difficult if you try to "get it done" in spurts. You could not expect to become proficient in tennis, soccer, or playing the piano by practicing once a week, and the same is true of mathematics. Try to schedule a regular time to study mathematics each day.

You must read the text carefully. Many students expect to get through a mathematics course by beginning with the homework problems, then reading some examples, and reading the text only as a desperate attempt to find an answer. This procedure is backward; do your homework only *after* reading the text.

You must ask questions. Part of learning mathematics involves frustration. Don't put off asking questions when you don't understand something, or if you feel an anxiety attack coming. STOP and put this book aside for a while. Talk to your instructor, or call me. My telephone number is

(707) 829-0606

I care about your progress with the course, and I'd like to hear your reactions to this book. I can be reached by e-mail at

smithkjs@mathnature.com

I have included road signs throughout this book to help you successfully get through it.

Direct Your Focus

Read the following story. No questions are asked, but try to imagine yourself sitting in a living room with several others who share your feelings about math. Your job is to read the story and make up a problem you know how to solve from any part of the story. You should have a pencil and paper, and you can have as much time as you want; nobody will look at what you are doing, but I want you to keep track of your feelings as your read the story and follow the directions.

Try reading this to your class and then do this subsection of the text as a classroom exercise.

On the way to the market, which is 12 miles from home, I stopped at the drugstore to pick up a get-well card. I selected a series of cards with puzzles on them. The first one said, "A bottle and a cork cost $1.10 and the bottle is a dollar more than the cork. How much is the bottle and how much is the cork?" I thought that would be a good card for Joe, so I purchased it for $1.75, along with a six-pack of cola for $2.79. The total bill was $4.81, which included 6% sales tax. My next stop was the market, which was exactly 3.4 miles from the drugstore. I bought $15.65 worth of groceries and paid with a $20 bill. I deposited the change in a charity bank on the counter and left the store. On the way home I bought 8.5 gallons of gas for $22.10. Because I had gone 238 miles since my last fill-up, I was happy with the mileage on my new car. I returned home and made myself a ham and cheese sandwich.

Have you spent enough time on the story? Take time to reread it (spend at least 10 minutes with this exercise). Now, write down a math question, based on this story, that you could answer without difficulty. Can you summarize your feelings? If my experiences in doing this exercise with my students apply to you, I would guess that you encountered some difficulty, some discomfort, perhaps despair or anger, or even indifference. Most students tend to focus on the more difficult questions (perhaps a miles-per-gallon problem) instead of following the directions to formulate a problem that will give you no difficulty.

How about the question: What is the round-trip distance from home to market and back?

Answer:

$$2 \times 12 \text{ miles} = 24 \text{ miles}$$

You say, "What does this have do with mathematics?" The point is that you need to learn to *focus on what you know,* rather than to focus on what you do not know. You may surprise yourself with the amount that you do know, and what *you* can bring to the problem-solving process.

Math anxiety builds on focusing on what you can't do rather than on what you can do. This leads to anxiety and frustration. Do you know what is the most feared thing in our society? It is the fear of speaking in public. And the fear of letting others know you are having trouble with this problem is related to that fear of speaking in public.

If you focus on a problem that is too difficult, you will be facing a blank wall. This applies to all hobbies or subjects. If you play tennis or golf, has your game improved since you started? If you don't play these games, how do you think you would feel trying to learn in front of all your friends? Do you think you would feel foolish?

Mathematicians don't start with complicated problems. If a mathematician runs into a problem that she can't solve, she will probably rephrase the problem as a simpler related problem that she can't solve. This problem is, in turn, rephrased as yet a simpler problem, and the process continues until the problem is manageable, and she has a problem that she *can* solve.

Writing Mathematics

The fundamental objective of education always has been to prepare students for life. A measure of your success with this book is a measure of its usefulness to you in your life. What are the basics for your knowledge "in life"? In this information age with access to a world of knowledge on the Internet, we still would respond by saying that the basics remain "reading, 'riting, and 'rithmetic." As you progress through the material in this book, we will give you opportunities to read mathematics and to consider some of the great ideas in the history of civilization, to develop your problem-solving skills ('rithmetic), and to communicate mathematical ideas to others ('riting). Perhaps you think of mathematics as "working problems" and "getting answers," but it is so much more. Mathematics is a way of thought that includes all three Rs, and to strengthen your skills you will be asked to communicate your knowledge in written form.

Journals

To begin building your skills in writing mathematics, you might keep a journal summarizing each day's work. Keep a record of your feelings and perceptions about what happened in class. How long did the homework take? What time of the day or night did I spend working and studying mathematics? What is the most important idea from the day's lesson? To help you with your journals, you will find problems in this text designated **IN YOUR OWN WORDS**. (For example, look at Problems 13–24 in Problem Set 1.1.) There are no right answers or wrong answers to this type of problem, but you are encouraged to look at these for ideas of what you might write in your journal.

PhotoDisk/Getty

Journal ideas

Write in your journal every day.

Include important ideas.

Include new words, ideas, formulas, or concepts.

Include questions that you want to ask later.

If possible, carry your journal with you so you can write in it anytime you get an idea.

Reasons for keeping a journal

It will record ideas you might otherwise forget.

It will keep a record of your progress.

If you have trouble later, it may help you diagnose areas for change or improvement.

It will build your writing skills.

PROBLEM SET 1.1

ESSENTIAL IDEAS LEVEL 1

In Problems 1–4, describe the meaning of each of the symbols, which you will find throughout the book.

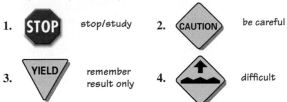

1. STOP — stop/study
2. CAUTION — be careful
3. YIELD — remember result only
4. — difficult

In this section, there are some hints for success. **IN YOUR OWN WORDS,** *discuss the statements in Problems 5–10 which refer to these hints.*

5. You must make a commitment to attend each class. Do you think this means each and every class?

6. If it is impossible to attend class (doctor's visit, for example), it is acceptable to skip over the day's activities and pick up with the material when you return.

7. If it is impossible to turn in one or two assignments (because of illness, for example), it is acceptable to skip those assignments and pick up with the material when you return.

8. You must make a commitment to do daily work. Do you think this means turning in each and every assignment?

9. You must read the text carefully. Do you think this means read every word?

10. You must ask questions.

11. **IN YOUR OWN WORDS** Some hints for success are listed on page 6. Have you used any other strategies for success that have worked for you?

12. **IN YOUR OWN WORDS** Consider the hints for success listed on page 6. Is there any reason why you don't think one of these strategies for success will work for you?

DRILL AND PRACTICE LEVEL 2

IN YOUR OWN WORDS *In Problems 13–24, comment on each math myth.*

13. Myth 1: Men are better than women in math.

14. Myth 2: Math requires logic, not intuition.

15. Myth 3: You must always know how you got the answer.

16. Myth 4: Math is not creative.

17. Myth 5: There is a best way to do a math problem.

18. Myth 6: It's always important to get the answer exactly right.

19. Myth 7: It's bad to count on your fingers.

20. Myth 8: Mathematicians do problems quickly, in their heads.

21. Myth 9: Math requires a good memory.

22. Myth 10: Math is done by working intensely until the problem is solved.

23. Myth 11: Some people have a "math mind" and some don't.

24. Myth 12: There is a magic key to doing math.

25. **IN YOUR OWN WORDS** Summarize your math experiences in elementary school.

26. **IN YOUR OWN WORDS** Summarize your math experiences in high school.

27. **IN YOUR OWN WORDS** Summarize your feelings today about this course.

28. **IN YOUR OWN WORDS** Describe a good experience you have had concerning mathematics.

29. **IN YOUR OWN WORDS** Describe an unpleasant experience you have had concerning mathematics.

30. **IN YOUR OWN WORDS** There are eight math quotations in Figure 1.1. Which one best describes your feelings about math today? Give reasons.

31. **IN YOUR OWN WORDS** There are eight math quotations in Figure 1.1. Which one is least like your feelings about math today? Give reasons.

CONQUER ANXIETY

The questions in Problems 32–40 are taken from the book **Conquering Math Anxiety: A Self-help Workbook, Second Edition** *(Pacific Grove, CA: Brooks/Cole, 2003), by Cynthia Arem. Answer these questions* **IN YOUR OWN WORDS.**

32. List one realistic math success goal.

33. What is a realistic target date for achieving this goal?

34. Which of the following criteria does this goal meet?

   Clearly stated?
   Do I value it?
   Do I believe I can do it?
   Do I want to do it?
   Will I find it personally fulfilling?
   Am I clear that this goal is what I want?
   Is it realistic?
   Do I envision a plan of action for achieving it?

35. I want to achieve my goal because of the following benefits and potential satisfactions.

36. Make a list of possible barriers and steps I will take to overcome each.

37. Make a list of positive forces and abilities.

38. Name people who can help.

39. List action steps and target dates.

40. What is my reward when I achieve this goal?

APPLICATIONS **LEVEL 2**

Symbols similar to the ones used in this book are common on the highways, and now we are seeing "universal" nonverbal symbols for other things. Problems 41–46 show universal traffic signs. See if you can guess what each symbol means.

41. women's rest room

42. handicapped

43. restaurant

44. stop ahead

45. kangaroo crossing

46. construction ahead

In Problems 47–52, symbols used in the classified section of a newspaper are shown. Match each symbol to one of the following classifications:

A. Announcements   B. Employment

C. Rentals   D. Merchandise

E. Recreation   F. Transportation medium

47. B

48. F

49. A

50. D

51. E

52. C

IN YOUR OWN WORDS *In Problems 53–54, read the story, and make up a problem you can solve from some part of the story.*

53. Yesterday, I purchased five calves at the auction for $95 each, so my herd now consists of nineteen cows, one bull, twenty-six steers, and thirteen calves. The auction yard charged me $35 to deliver the calves to my ranch, but I figured it was a pretty good deal since I live 42 miles from the auction yard. Today, twelve tons of hay were delivered, and I paid $780 for it plus $10 a ton delivery charge. Yes, sir, if my crops do well, this will be a very good year.

54. Tickets for the concert go on sale for $65 each tomorrow; each person is allowed to purchase no more than 4 tickets. I really don't mind paying for the tickets, but why do they need to add a $3-per-ticket service charge? I am going to pick up Jane at 5:00 A.M. so we can get in line early; the only problem is that Jane lives 23 miles from me and the ticket office is only 4 miles from my house. That means that we will not be able to line up before 6:00 A.M. Do you think that is early enough?

55. IN YOUR OWN WORDS Use Problem 53 to make up a second problem.

56. IN YOUR OWN WORDS Use Problem 54 to make up a second problem.

57. IN YOUR OWN WORDS Describe some of your feelings as you worked Problem 53.

58. IN YOUR OWN WORDS Describe some of your feelings as you worked Problem 54.

59. IN YOUR OWN WORDS* What is your math history? Briefly describe your chronological history in terms of the negative and positive experiences you've had with math. Include your earliest memories, as well as memories of how your teachers and your family influenced you in math. Describe how your family members approached math and describe their attitude toward your math ability. Include a description of how you've dealt with recent situations involving math in other classes, on the job, or in daily life situations. End with a discussion of how math could help you in accomplishing your educational objectives, in earning more money, in choosing a career, or in any other aspect of your life.

60. IN YOUR OWN WORDS We printed a "Math Anxiety Bill of Rights," by Sandra L. Davis, in this section. Turn in your own list of "Math Rights."

---

*These problems are taken from Exercise 2-1 in *Conquering Math Anxiety: A Self-help Workbook, Second Edition,* (Pacific Grove, CA: Brooks/Cole, 2003), by Cynthia Arem.

1.2 Formulating the Problem

IN THIS WORLD THE POWER OF MATH

"Look here," Alfonso explained patiently, *"if you divide these numbers, you will see that you can finish the problem."*

"Do you have a calculator?" asked Jerry.

"No, do I need one for this class?" cried Teresa.

"It will sure help!" cried Alfonso and Jerry in unison.

In this section, you will learn about formulating the problem as well as about some of what we call *elementary operations*. You will also be encouraged to use a calculator for working problems in this book.

See Problem 47.

In mathematics, we generally focus our attention on some particular sets of numbers. The simplest of these sets is the set we use to count objects and the first set that a child learns. It is called the set of *counting numbers* or *natural numbers*.*

Natural Numbers and Whole Numbers

> The set of numbers $\{1, 2, 3, 4, \ldots\}$ is called the set of **counting numbers** or the set of **natural numbers.** If the number zero is included, then the set $\{0, 1, 2, 3, 4, \ldots\}$ is called the set of **whole numbers.**

Order of Operations

Addition, subtraction, multiplication, and division are called the **elementary operations** for the whole numbers, and it is assumed that you understand these operations. However, certain agreements in dealing with these operations are necessary. Consider this arithmetic example:

$$Find: \quad 2 + 3 \times 4$$

LET'S SEE... ONE...
TWO... THREE...

There are two possible approaches to solve this problem:

$$Left\ to\ right: \quad 2 + 3 \times 4 = 5 \times 4 = 20$$
$$Multiplication\ first: \quad 2 + 3 \times 4 = 2 + 12 = 14$$

Because there are different results to this arithmetic example, it is necessary for us all to agree on one method or the other. At this point, you might be thinking, "Why

---

*In mathematics, we use the word *set* as an undefined term. Although sets are discussed in Chapter 8, we assume that you have an intuitive idea of the word *set*. It is used to mean a collection of objects or numbers. Braces are used to enclose the elements of a set, and three dots (called ellipses) are used to indicate that some elements are not listed. We use three dots only if the elements not listed are clear from the given numbers.

on earth would I start at the right and do the multiplication first?" Consider the following example.

EXAMPLE 1

Order of operations

Suppose that you sold a $2 benefit ticket on Monday and three $4 tickets on Tuesday. What is the total amount collected?

Solution   (SALES ON MONDAY) + (SALES ON TUESDAY) = (TOTAL SALES)

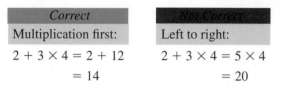

$$\$2 + 3 \times \$4 = \text{(TOTAL SALES)}$$

Correct	*Not Correct*
Multiplication first:	Left to right:
$2 + 3 \times 4 = 2 + 12$	$2 + 3 \times 4 = 5 \times 4$
$= 14$	$= 20$

Do you see why the correct result to Example 1 requires multiplication before addition?

Many of you may use a calculator to help you work problems in this book. If you do use a calculator, it is important that you use a calculator that carries out the correct order of operations, as we illustrate with the next example.

EXAMPLE 2

Order of operations using a calculator

In Example 1, we agreed that the correct simplification of the arithmetic problem

$$2 + 3 \times 4$$

is 14. Illustrate the correct buttons to press on a calculator, and check with the calculator you will use in this class to make sure you obtain the correct result.

Solution   You want the calculator you use in this class to accept the input of arithmetic problems in the same fashion as you would write it on your paper. Thus, the correct sequence of keys to press is

If you are using a calculator with this book, be sure you actually check out this answer.

Some calculators use a key labeled ENTER instead of the equal sign. The correct answer is 14, but some calculators will display the incorrect answer of 20. What is going on with a calculator that gives the answer 20? Such a calculator works from left to right without regard to the order of operations. For this book, you want to have a calculator that has been programmed to use the order of operations correctly.

If the operations are mixed, we agree to do multiplication and division *first* (from left to right) and *then* addition and subtraction from left to right.

EXAMPLE 3

Order of operations

Perform the indicated operations.

a. $7 + 2 \times 6$ **b.** $3 \times 5 + 2 \times 5$ **c.** $1 + 3 \times 2 + 4 - 3 + 6 \times 3$

Solution

a. $7 + 2 \times 6 = 7 + 12$ Multiplication first

$ = 19$ Addition next

b. $3 \times 5 + 2 \times 5 = 15 + 10$ Multiplication first

$ = 25$ Addition next

c. $1 + 3 \times 2 + 4 - 3 + 6 \times 3 = 1 + 6 + 4 - 3 + 18$

$ = 7 + 4 - 3 + 18$

$ = 11 - 3 + 18$

$ = 8 + 18$

$ = 26$ ●

If the order of operations is to be changed from this agreement, then parentheses are used to indicate this change.

EXAMPLE 4

Order of operations with parentheses

Perform the indicated operations.

a. $10 + 6 + 2$ **b.** $10 + (6 + 2)$ **c.** $10 - 6 - 2$ **d.** $10 - (6 - 2)$

e. Show the buttons you would press to work part **d** with a calculator.

Solution

a. $10 + 6 + 2 = (10 + 6) + 2$ Work from left to right; parentheses are understood.

$ = 16 + 2$

$ = 18$

b. $10 + (6 + 2) = 10 + 8$ Parentheses change the order of operations.

$ = 18$

Notice that parts **a** and **b** illustrate different problems that have the same answer. This is not the case with parts **c** and **d**.

c. $10 - 6 - 2 = (10 - 6) - 2$ Parentheses understood.

$ = 4 - 2$

$ = 2$

d. $10 - (6 - 2) = 10 - 4$ Parentheses given.

$ = 6$

e. Most calculators have parentheses keys. The one labeled $($ is the open parenthesis (this one comes first) and the one labeled $)$ is the close parenthesis (this one comes last). Locate these keys on your calculator. Also note that the operations keys are usually found at the right side. These are labeled $\div$ $\times$ $-$ $+$. Do not confuse subtraction $-$ with other keys labeled $(-)$ or $+/-$. The correct sequence of buttons to press for this example is

$$\boxed{10}\ \boxed{-}\ \boxed{(}\ \boxed{6}\ \boxed{-}\ \boxed{2}\ \boxed{)}\ \boxed{=}$$

Check the output of your calculator to make sure it gives the result shown in part **d**, namely, 6.   ●

We can now summarize the correct **order of operations,** including the use of parentheses.

Order of Operations

In doing arithmetic with mixed operations, we agree to proceed by following these steps:

Step 1   Parentheses first

Step 2   Multiplications and divisions, reading from left to right

Step 3   Additions and subtractions, reading from left to right

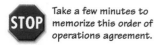 *Take a few minutes to memorize this order of operations agreement.*

You can remember this by using the mnemonic "**P**lease **M**ind **D**ear **A**unt **S**ally." The first letters will remind you of "**P**arentheses, **M**ultiplication and **D**ivision, **A**ddition and **S**ubtraction." However, if you use this mnemonic, remember that the order is *left to right* for pairs of operations: multiplication and division (as they occur) and *then* addition and subtraction (as they occur).

EXAMPLE 5

Mixed operations

Perform the indicated operations.

a. $12 + 9 \div 3$ **b.** $(12 + 9) \div 3$

c. $2 \times 15 + 9 \div 3 - 7 \times 2$ **d.** $2 \times (15 + 9) \div 3 - 7 \times 2$

Solution

a. $12 + 9 \div 3 = 12 + 3$ Multiplications/divisions before additions/subtractions

$= 15$ Additions/subtractions as they occur from left to right

b. $(12 + 9) \div 3 = 21 \div 3$ Parentheses first

$= 7$ Division next

Note the effect of the parentheses by comparing parts a and b.

c. $2 \times 15 + 9 \div 3 - 7 \times 2 = 30 + 3 - 14$ Multiplications/divisions

$= 33 - 14$ Additions/subtractions

$= 19$

d. $2 \times (15 + 9) \div 3 - 7 \times 2 = 2 \times 24 \div 3 - 7 \times 2$ Parentheses first

$= 48 \div 3 - 7 \times 2$ Multiplication ⎫

$= 16 - 7 \times 2$ Division   ⎬ left to right

$= 16 - 14$ Multiplication ⎭

$= 2$ Subtraction   ●

Simplify a Numerical Expression

The expressions in Example 5 are called *numerical expressions*. A **numerical expression** is one or more numbers connected by valid mathematical operations (such as *addition, subtraction, multiplication,* or *division*). To **simplify a numerical expression** means to carry out all the operations, according to the order of operations, and to write the answer as a single number.

EXAMPLE 6   **Simplifying a numerical expression**

Simplify $2[56 - 4(2 + 8)] + 5 - 4(2 + 1)$.

Solution   If there are parentheses inside parentheses (or brackets), the order of operations directs us to begin with the interior set of parentheses (shown in color):

$$2[56 - 4(2 + 8)] + 5 - 4(2 + 1) = 2[56 - 4(10)] + 5 - 4(2 + 1) \quad \text{Interior parentheses first}$$

$$= 2[56 - 40] + 5 - 4(3) \quad \text{Parentheses next}$$

$$= 2[16] + 5 - 12 \quad \text{All parentheses should be completed before continuing; note that the brackets are used as parentheses.}$$

$$= 32 + 5 - 12 \quad \text{Multiplications/divisions next}$$

$$= 25 \quad \text{Additions/subtractions}$$

Pólya's Problem-Solving Method

The model for problem solving that we will use was first published in 1945 by the great, charismatic mathematician George Pólya. His book *How to Solve It* (Princeton University Press, 1973) has become a classic. In Pólya's book, you will find this problem-solving model as well as a treasure trove of strategy, know-how, rules of thumb, good advice, anecdotes, history, and problems at all levels of mathematics. His problem-solving model is as follows.

Problem Solving

The problem-solving guidelines known as **Pólya's method** set forth the following steps.

Step 1   *Understand the problem.* Ask questions, experiment, or otherwise rephrase the question in your own words.

Step 2   *Devise a plan.* Find the connection between the data and the unknown. Look for patterns, relate to a previously solved problem or a known formula, or simplify the given information to give you an easier problem.

Step 3   *Carry out the plan.* Check the steps as you go.

Step 4   *Look back.* Examine the solution obtained. In other words, check your answer.

We will use this procedure as we develop the problem-solving idea throughout the book. However, we are not ready to tackle real problem solving, but need to start at the beginning with small steps. One of these small steps is developing skill in **translating** from English into math symbolism. The term **sum** is used to indicate the result obtained from addition, **difference** for the result from subtraction, **product** for the result of a multiplication, and **quotient** for the result of a division. When a problem involves mixed operations, it is classified as a sum, difference, product, or quotient according to the *last* operation performed, when using the order-of-operations agreement.

EXAMPLE 7 **Translating and classifying arithmetic operations**

Write each verbal description in math symbols, and then use your calculator to simplify.

a. The sum of the first five natural numbers

b. The product of the first five natural numbers

c. The sum of 5 and twice the number 53

d. The product of 5 and twice the number 4

e. The product of 5 and the sum of 2 and 4

f. The sum of 5 and the product of 2 and 4

g. The difference of 7 and 2 (or, equivalently, the difference of 2 from 7)

Solution

a. $1 + 2 + 3 + 4 + 5 = 15$ **b.** $1 \times 2 \times 3 \times 4 \times 5 = 120$

c. $5 + (2 \times 53) = 111$ **d.** $5 \times (2 \times 4)$ or $5 \times 2 \times 4 = 40$

e. $5 \times (2 + 4) = 5 \times 6 = 30$

In this book we will generally write such a calculation as $5(2 + 4)$. The multiplication written this way is called **juxtaposition** with the multiplication between the 5 and the parentheses understood. If you are using a calculator, check to see whether your calculator recognizes juxtaposition. Try:

No times sign required: $\boxed{5}\ \boxed{(}\ \boxed{2}\ \boxed{+}\ \boxed{4}\ \boxed{)}\ \boxed{=}$

The correct answer is 30. If your calculator does not display this result, then you will need to remember to input a times sign.

Times sign required: $\boxed{5}\ \boxed{\times}\ \boxed{(}\ \boxed{2}\ \boxed{+}\ \boxed{4}\ \boxed{)}\ \boxed{=}$

f. $5 + (2 \times 4) = 13$

The times sign *is* required for this problem, because otherwise it would be $5 + 24 = 29$.

g. $7 - 2 = 5$

Pay attention to the wording on subtraction problems. Part g is not the same as $2 - 7$.

EXAMPLE 8

Comparing order of operations

Simplify, classify as a sum or a product, and then compare answers.

a. $4 \times (3 + 2)$ **b.** $4 \times 3 + 4 \times 2$

Solution

a. $4 \times (3 + 2) = 4 \times 5$ Parentheses

$= 20$ Multiplication

This is a product, since the last operation is multiplication.

b. $4 \times 3 + 4 \times 2 = 12 + 8$ Multiplication before addition

$= 20$

This is a sum, since the last operation is addition.

Note that the answers to parts **a** and **b** are the same.   ●

Example 8 illustrates a combined property of addition and multiplication called the **distributive property for multiplication over addition:**

$$4 \times (3 + 2) = 4 \times 3 + 4 \times 2$$
$$\uparrow \qquad\qquad \uparrow \qquad \uparrow$$

Number outside parentheses

Number outside parentheses is **distributed** to **each** number inside parentheses.

This property holds for all whole numbers.

EXAMPLE 9

Distributive property

Write each expression without parentheses by using the distributive property.

a. $8 \times (7 + 10)$ **b.** $3 \times (400 + 20 + 5)$

Solution

a. $8 \times (7 + 10) = 8 \times 7 + 8 \times 10$

b. $3 \times (400 + 20 + 5) = 3 \times 400 + 3 \times 20 + 3 \times 5$ ●

The ability to recognize the difference between reasonable answers and unreasonable ones is important not only in mathematics, but whenever you are doing problem solving. This ability is even more important when you use a calculator, because pressing the incorrect key can often cause very unreasonable answers. Whenever you find an answer, you should ask yourself whether it is reasonable. How do you decide whether an answer is reasonable? One way is to **estimate** an answer. Webster's *New World Dictionary* tells us that as a verb, to *estimate* means "to form an opinion or a judgment about" or to calculate "approximately." In the *1986 Yearbook* of the National Council of Teachers of Mathematics, we find:

The broad *mathematical context* for an estimate is usually one of the following types:
A. An exact value is known but for some reason an estimate is used.
B. An exact value is possible but is not known and an estimate is used.
C. An exact value is impossible.

We will work on building your estimation skills throughout this book.

EXAMPLE 10 Estimation

If your salary is $9.75 per hour, your annual salary is approximately

A. $5,000   B. $10,000   C. $15,000   D. $20,000   E. $25,000

Solution Problem solving often requires some assumptions about the problem. For this problem, we are not told how many hours per week you work, or how many weeks per year you are paid. We assume a 40-hour week, and we also assume that you are paid for 52 weeks per year.

Estimate: Your hourly salary is about $10 per hour. A 40-hour week gives us $40 \times \$10 = \$400$ per week. For the estimate, we calculate the wages for 50 weeks instead of 52: 50 weeks yields $50 \times \$400 = \$20,000$. The answer is D.   ●

There are two important reasons for estimation: (1) to form a reasonable opinion (as in Example 10), or (2) to check the reasonableness of an answer. If reason (1) is our motive, we should not think it necessary to follow an estimation like the one in Example 10 by direct calculation. To do so would defeat the purpose of the estimation. On the other hand, if we are using the estimate for reason (2)—to see whether an answer is reasonable—we might perform the estimate as a check on the answer for Example 10 by calculator: *Display:* 20280. The actual annual salary is $20,280. In this case, our estimate confirms that our precise calculation does not contain a widely erroneous keying mistake.

PROBLEM SET (1.2)

ESSENTIAL IDEAS   LEVEL 1

1. State the order of operations.   See p. 14.

2. **IN YOUR OWN WORDS** Explain the distributive property.

DRILL AND PRACTICE   LEVEL 2

Simplify the numerical expressions given in Problems 3–16, and classify each as a sum, difference, product, or quotient.

3. **a.** $5 + 6 \times 2$ 17; sum

   b. $8 + 2 \times 3$ 14; sum

4. **a.** $20 - 4 \times 2$ 12; difference

   b. $10 - 5 \times 2$ 0; difference

5. **a.** $12 \div 6 + 3$ 5; sum

   b. $100 \div 10 \div 2$ 5; quotient

6. **a.** $12 + 6 \div 3$ 14; sum

   b. $100 \div (10 \times 2)$ 5; quotient

7. **a.** $15 + 6 \div 3$ 17; sum

   b. $16 - 6 \div 3$ 14; difference

8. **a.** $(15 + 6) \div 3$ 7; quotient

   b. $(15 - 6) \div 3$ 3; quotient

9. **a.** $4 \times 3 + 4 \times 5$ 32; sum

   b. $8 \times 2 + 8 \times 5$ 56; sum

10. **a.** $4 \times (3 + 5)$ 32; product

    b. $8 \times (2 + 5)$ 56; product

11. **a.** $2 + 15 \div 3 \times 5$ 27; sum

    b. $5 + 12 \div 3 \times 2$ 13; sum

12. **a.** $2 + 15 \times 3 \div 5$ 11; sum

    b. $5 + 12 \times 3 \div 2$ 23; sum

13. **a.** $(20 - 8) \div 4 \times 2 + 3$ 9; sum

    b. $20 - 8 \div 4 \times 2 + 3$ 19; sum

14. **a.** $2 + 3 \times 4 - 12 \div 2$ 8; difference

    b. $15 \div 5 \times 2 + 6 \div 3$ 8; sum

15. **a.** $2 \times 18 + 9 \div 3 - 5 \times 2$ 29; difference

    b. $2 \times (18 + 9) \div 3 - 5 \times 2$ 8; difference

16. **a.** $4 \times (12 - 8) \div 2$ 8; quotient

    b. $4 \times 12 - 8 \div 2$ 44; difference

Write out the expressions in Problems 17–20, without parentheses, by using the distributive property.

17. **a.** $3 \times (4 + 8)$ 3 × 4 + 3 × 8

    b. $7 \times (9 + 4)$ 7 × 9 + 7 × 4

18. a. $8 \times (50 + 5)$ $8 \times 50 + 8 \times 5$

  b. $6 \times (90 + 7)$ $6 \times 90 + 6 \times 7$

19. a. $4 \times (300 + 20 + 7)$ $4 \times 300 + 4 \times 20 + 4 \times 7$

  b. $6 \times (500 + 30 + 3)$ $6 \times 500 + 6 \times 30 + 6 \times 3$

20. a. $5 \times (800 + 60 + 4)$ $5 \times 800 + 5 \times 60 + 5 \times 4$

  b. $4 \times (700 + 10 + 5)$ $4 \times 700 + 4 \times 10 + 4 \times 5$

Translate each of the word statements in Problems 21–28 to numerical statements, and then simplify.

21. The sum of three and the product of two and four $3 + 2 \times 4$

22. The product of three and the sum of two and four $3(2 + 4)$

23. Ten times the sum of five and six $10 (5 + 6)$

24. Ten times the product of five and six $10 (5 \cdot 6)$

25. Eight times five plus ten $8 \times 5 + 10$

26. Eight times the difference of seven and five $8 (7 - 5)$

27. Eight times the difference of nine from eleven $8 (11 - 9)$

28. The product of the sum of three and four with the sum of five and six $(3 + 4)(5 + 6)$

Perform the indicated operations in Problems 29–44 on your calculator, and classify each as a sum, difference, product, or quotient.

29. $716 - 5 \times 91$ 261; difference

30. $143 + 12 \times 14$ 311; sum

31. $8 \times 14 + 8 \times 86$ 800; sum

32. $15 \times 27 + 15 \times 73$ 1,500; sum

33. $12 \times 63 + 12 \times 27$ 1,080; sum

34. $19 \times 250 + 19 \times 750$ 19,000; sum

35. $(18 + 2)(82 - 2)$ 1,600; product

36. $(34 - 4)(16 + 4)$ 600; product

37. $5 + 3 \times 7 + 65 - 8 \times 4$ 59; difference

38. $12 + 6 \times 9 - 5 \times 2 + 5 \times 14$ 126; sum

39. $27 \times 550 - 27 \times 450$ 2,700; difference

40. $23 \times 237 + 23 \times 763$ 23,000; sum

41. $1,214 - 18 \times 14 + 35 \times 8,121$ 285,197; sum

42. $862 + 328 \times 142 - 168$ 47,270; difference

43. $62 \times (48 - 12) + 13 \times (12 - 5)$ 2,323; sum

44. $12 \times (125 - 72) - 3 \times (18 - 3 \times 5)$ 627; difference

---

First estimate your answer in Problems 45–54, and then calculate the exact answer.   Estimates may vary.

45. How many hours are there in 360 days?   8,640 hours

46. How many pages are necessary to make 1,850 copies of a manuscript that is 487 pages long? (Print on one side only.)   900,950

***47.** In 2005, the Internal Revenue Service allowed a $3,200 deduction for each dependent. In 1997, it was $2,650. If a family has four dependents, what is the allowed deduction in 1997? $10,600

48. If your payroll deductions are $255.83 per week and your weekly gross wages are $1,025.66, what is your net pay? $769.83

49. If your monthly salary is $1,543, what is your annual salary? $18,516

50. The minimum wage in California will be $8.00 per hour in 2008. If you are paid $7.25 per hour today, what is your annual salary? $15,080

51. If you are paid $18.00 per hour, what is your annual salary? $37,440

52. If you are paid $31,200 per year, what is your hourly salary? $15.00

53. If your car gets 23 miles per gallon, how far can you go on 15 gallons of gas?   345 miles

54. If your car travels 492 miles on 12 gallons of gas, what is the number of miles per gallon?   41

Explain what is wrong, if anything, with the statements in Problems 55–60. Explain your reasoning.

55. $4 + 6 \times 8 = 80$ wrong or F; multiplication first; 52

56. $2 + 8 \times 10 = 82$ right or T

57. $2 \times (3 + 4) = 14$ is an example of the distributive property.   F; $2 \times (3 + 4) = 2 \times 3 + 2 \times 4$ is an example.

58. The correct order of operations (for an expression with no parentheses) when simplifying is first multiply, then divide, then add, then subtract.   F; first, multiply and divide (left to right), then add and subtract (left to right)

59. The number 0 is a natural number.   F; it is a whole number

60. All natural numbers are also whole numbers.   T

---

*The Problem of the Day problems are included to answer the question students sometimes ask, "When am I ever going to use this?" Each section in this part of the book begins with a problem that relates the material of the section to something you are likely to encounter outside the classroom. You are then asked to discuss or answer that question in the problem set. These problems are marked with the logo:

(1.3) Fractions and Decimals

IN THIS WORLD THE POWER OF MATH

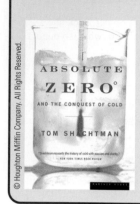

"My teacher told us today that we can't divide by zero!" exclaimed Carol. "I don't have a clue what she means. If you divide zero into a number, and come out with nothing, then you should be able to divide by zero and get nothing."

"Wait a minute," chimed Tom. "It is easy to understand. Look at it this way . . ."

In this section, we will not only learn about fractions and decimals, we will also see why we can't divide by zero.

 See Problem 3.

In the previous section, the symbol ÷ was used for division (for example, $10 \div 5$). However, more often a division bar is used, as in $\frac{10}{5}$.

EXAMPLE 1

Division notation and division by 0

Simplify (that is, perform the indicated operations).

a. $\frac{30}{6}$ **b.** $\frac{3,965}{305}$ **c.** $\frac{0}{5}$ **d.** $\frac{5}{0}$

e. $\frac{10 + 8}{7 + 2}$ **f.** $\frac{10}{3}$

Solution

a. $\frac{30}{6} = 5$ *Check by multiplication:* $6 \times 5 = 30$

b. If the division is lengthy, as in the case of $\frac{3,965}{305}$, you may need to do long division or use a calculator:

$$
\begin{array}{r}
13 \\
305\overline{)3965} \\
\underline{305} \\
915 \\
\underline{915} \\
0
\end{array}
$$
  Check: $305 \times 13 = 3,965$

Thus, $\frac{3,965}{305} = 13$.

c. $\frac{0}{5} = 0$ *Check by multiplication:* $5 \times 0 = 0$

d. $\frac{5}{0}$ To do this division, you would need to find a number such that, when it is multiplied by zero, the result is 5. There is no such number. For this reason, we say **division by zero is impossible.**

STOP *Remember, division by 0 is impossible.*

e. **The division bar also acts like a grouping symbol.** This division problem implies that we are to find the sum of 10 and 8 and then divide that answer by the sum of 7 and 2:

$$\frac{10 + 8}{7 + 2} = \frac{18}{9} = 2$$

You might wish to simplify this expression by using a calculator. When entering expressions such as this, if the one on top (or the one on the bottom) is more than a single number, then you must insert parentheses:

 By calculator, think of this as $\frac{(10 + 8)}{(7 + 2)}$:

f. $\frac{10}{3}$ There is no answer to this division in the set of whole numbers. ●

The reason there is no answer to $\frac{10}{3}$ in the set of whole numbers in part **f** of Example 1 is that there is no whole number that can be multiplied by 3 to give 10. If you do long division for this problem, there will be a **remainder** that is not zero:

$$\begin{array}{r} 3 \\ 3\overline{)10} \\ \underline{9} \\ 1 \end{array} \leftarrow \text{Remainder}$$

What does this remainder mean? In this example, the remainder 1 is still to be divided by 3, so it can be written as $\frac{1}{3}$. Such an expression is called a **fraction** or a **rational number.*** The word *fraction* comes from a Latin word meaning "to break." A fraction involves two numbers: one "upstairs," called the **numerator,** and one "downstairs," called the **denominator.** The denominator tells us into how many parts the whole has been divided, and the numerator tells us how many of those parts we have.

Fraction

A **fraction** is a number that is the quotient of a whole number divided by a counting number. A fraction is usually written as

$$\frac{\text{NUMERATOR}}{\text{DENOMINATOR}} \begin{array}{l} \leftarrow \text{A whole number} \\ \leftarrow \text{Divided by} \\ \leftarrow \text{A counting number (so that division by zero is} \\ \quad \text{excluded)} \end{array}$$

A fraction is called

- A **proper fraction** if the numerator is less than the denominator.
- An **improper fraction** if the numerator is greater than the denominator.
- A **whole number** if the denominator divides evenly into the numerator—that is, with remainder zero.

*Rational numbers are discussed in Section 2.6.

CAUTION Don't forget that the division bar in a fraction is used as a grouping symbol.

EXAMPLE 2

Classifying fractions

Classify each example as a proper fraction, an improper fraction, or a whole number.

a. $\frac{6}{7}$ **b.** $\frac{6}{8}$ **c.** $\frac{7}{6}$ **d.** $\frac{0}{4}$ **e.** $\frac{6}{3}$ **f.** $\frac{4}{0}$

Solution   **a.** $\frac{6}{7}$ Proper   **b.** $\frac{6}{8}$ Proper   **c.** $\frac{7}{6}$ Improper

    d. $\frac{0}{4}$ Whole number   **e.** $\frac{6}{3}$ Whole number

    f. $\frac{4}{0}$ None of these   *(Don't forget, you can't divide by zero.)*   ●

Improper fractions that are not whole numbers can also be written in a form called **mixed numbers** by carrying out the division and leaving the remainder as a fraction. A mixed number thus has two parts: a counting number part and a proper fraction part.

EXAMPLE 3

Writing an improper fraction as a mixed number

Write $\frac{23}{5}$ as a mixed number.

Solution
$$\begin{array}{r} 4 \quad \leftarrow \textit{Counting number part} \\ 5\overline{)23} \\ \underline{20} \\ 3 \quad \leftarrow \textit{Remainder means 3 to be divided by 5, or } \frac{3}{5}. \end{array}$$

$\frac{23}{5} = 4 + \frac{3}{5}$ or $4\frac{3}{5}$.   ●

EXAMPLE 4

Writing a mixed number as an improper fraction

Write $4\frac{3}{5}$ as an improper fraction.

Solution   Reverse the procedure in Example 3. The remainder is 3, the quotient is 4, and the divisor is 5. Thus,

$$\underset{\textit{Whole number}}{\underset{\downarrow}{4}} \times \underset{\textit{Numerator}}{\underset{\downarrow}{5}} + 3 = 23$$

$\uparrow$

This is the divisor (the denominator of the fraction).

$$4\frac{3}{5} = \frac{23}{5} \quad \leftarrow 23 = 4 \times 5 + 3$$

$\uparrow$

This is the divisor (or the denominator of the fraction).   ●

We find certain fractions to be of special interest in our study of arithmetic. These are fractions with denominators that are powers of 10 (10, 100, 1,000, 10,000, . . .).

Tenths: $\quad \frac{1}{10}, \frac{2}{10}, \frac{3}{10}, \frac{4}{10}, \frac{5}{10}, \frac{6}{10}, \frac{7}{10}, \frac{8}{10}, \frac{9}{10}, \frac{10}{10}, \frac{11}{10}, \cdots$

Hundredths: $\quad \frac{1}{100}, \frac{2}{100}, \frac{3}{100}, \frac{4}{100}, \frac{5}{100}, \frac{6}{100}, \cdots$

Thousandths: $\quad \frac{1}{1,000}, \frac{2}{1,000}, \frac{3}{1,000}, \frac{4}{1,000}, \frac{5}{1,000}, \cdots$

Each of these fractions can be written in **decimal form:**

$$\frac{1}{10} = 0.1 \qquad \frac{1}{100} = 0.01 \qquad \frac{1}{1,000} = 0.001$$

The word *fraction* is used with both forms. If we want to be specific, fractions written in the form

$$\frac{1}{10} \qquad \frac{1}{3} \qquad \frac{2}{5}$$

are called **common fractions,** and fractions written in the form

$$0.1 \qquad 0.5 \qquad 0.6$$

are called **decimal fractions.** When we simply use the word *fraction,* we are referring to a common fraction.

We will use division to show the relationship between fractions written as common fractions or as decimal fractions, but first let's look again at the positional notation of our number system:

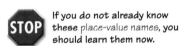

If you *do* not already know these place-value names, you should learn them now.

Trillions	Hundred billions	Ten billions	Billions	Hundred millions	Ten millions	Millions	Hundred thousands	Ten thousands	Thousands	Hundreds	Tens	Units	Decimal point	Tenths, $\frac{1}{10}$	Hundredths, $\frac{1}{100}$	Thousandths, $\frac{1}{1,000}$	Ten-thousandths, $\frac{1}{10,000}$	Hundred-thousandths, $\frac{1}{100,000}$	Millionths, $\frac{1}{1,000,000}$
1,	2	3	4,	5	6	7,	8	9	1,	2	3	4	.	8	9	0	1	2	3

Every whole number can be written in decimal form:

$$0 = 0. = 0.0 = 0.00 = 0.000 = 0.0000 = 0.00000 = \cdots$$
$$1 = 1. = 1.0 = 1.00 = 1.000 = 1.0000 = \cdots$$
$$2 = 2. = 2.0 = 2.00 = 2.000 = \cdots$$
$$3 = 3. = 3.0 = 3.00 = \cdots$$
$$4 = 4. = 4.0 = \cdots$$
$$5 = 5. = \cdots$$
$$\vdots$$

A period, called a **decimal point** in the decimal system, is used to separate the fractional part from the whole part. Sometimes zeros are placed after the decimal point or after the last digit to the right of the decimal point, as in

$$3.21 = 3.210 = 3.2100 = 3.21000 = 3.21\underbrace{0000} \ldots$$

These are called **trailing zeros.**

Now let's carry out division, bringing the decimal point straight up from the dividend to the quotient:

$$
\begin{array}{r}
0.1 \\
 \quad \leftarrow \text{Decimal point is carried straight up from dividend to quotient.} \\
10\overline{)1.0} \\
\underline{1\ 0} \\
0
\end{array}
$$

EXAMPLE 5 **Changing to decimal fractions by division**

Write the given fractions as decimals by performing long division.

a. $\frac{3}{10}$ **b.** $\frac{7}{100}$ **c.** $\frac{137}{1,000}$

Solution

a. $\frac{3}{10}$;

$$
\begin{array}{r}
0.3 \\
10\overline{)3.0} \\
\underline{3\ 0} \\
0
\end{array}
$$

b. $\frac{7}{100}$;

$$
\begin{array}{r}
0.07 \\
100\overline{)7.00} \\
\underline{7\ 00} \\
0
\end{array}
$$

c. $\frac{137}{1,000}$;

$$
\begin{array}{r}
0.137 \\
1,000\overline{)137.000} \\
\underline{100\ 0} \\
37\ 00 \\
\underline{30\ 00} \\
7\ 000 \\
\underline{7\ 000} \\
0
\end{array}
$$

Place as many trailing zeros are necessary.

Do you see a pattern in Example 5? Look at the next example.

EXAMPLE 6 **Changing to decimal fractions by inspection**

Write the given fractions in decimal form without doing any calculations.

a. $\frac{6}{10}$ **b.** $\frac{6}{100}$ **c.** $\frac{243}{1,000}$ **d.** $\frac{47}{10}$ **e.** $\frac{47}{100}$ **f.** $\frac{47}{1,000}$

Solution

a. $\frac{6}{10} = 0.6$ Tenths indicate one decimal place.

b. $\frac{6}{100} = 0.06$ Hundredths indicate two decimal places.

c. $\frac{243}{1,000} = 0.243$ Thousandths indicate three decimal places.

d. $\frac{47}{10} = 4.7$ **e.** $\frac{47}{100} = 0.47$ **f.** $\frac{47}{1,000} = 0.047$

You can see that fractions with denominators of 10, 100, 1,000, and so on are what we've called *decimal fractions* or simply **decimals.** On the other hand, *any fraction,* even one whose denominator is not a power of 10, can be written in decimal form by dividing.

EXAMPLE 7 **Changing common fractions into decimals by using division**

Write the given fractions in decimal form.   **a.** $\frac{3}{8}$ **b.** $\frac{7}{5}$ **c.** $2\frac{3}{4}$

Solution

a. $\frac{3}{8}$;

$$
\begin{array}{r}
0.375 \\
8\overline{)3.000} \\
\underline{2\ 4} \\
60 \\
\underline{56} \\
40 \\
\underline{40} \\
0
\end{array}
$$

Remember, the decimal point is moved straight up from the dividend to the quotient. Otherwise, carry out the division in the usual fashion.

You may keep adding trailing zeros here as long as you wish.

Cartoon courtesy of Patrick J. Boyle.

Thus, $\frac{3}{8} = 0.375$.   You can obtain this result using a calculator. If a zero remainder is obtained, the decimal is called a **terminating decimal.**

b. $\frac{7}{5}$;
$$
\begin{array}{r}
1.4 \\
5\overline{)7.0} \\
\underline{5} \\
20 \\
\underline{20} \\
0
\end{array}
$$

Thus, $\frac{7}{5} = 1.4$.

c. $2\frac{3}{4}$;   Since $2\frac{3}{4} = \frac{11}{4}$, we divide 4 into 11:

$$
\begin{array}{r}
2.75 \\
4\overline{)11.00} \\
\underline{8} \\
30 \\
\underline{28} \\
20 \\
\underline{20} \\
0
\end{array}
$$

An alternative method is to notice that

$$2\frac{3}{4} = 2 + \frac{3}{4}$$

Divide 4 into 3:

$$
\begin{array}{r}
0.75 \\
4\overline{)3.00}
\end{array}
$$

and then add 0.75 to 2.

Thus, $2\frac{3}{4} = 2.75$.

We noted in part **a** of Example 7 that you can append as many trailing zeros after the 3.0 as you wish. For some fractions, you could continue to append zeros forever and never complete the division. Such fractions are called **repeating decimals.**

EXAMPLE 8

Changing common fractions (repeating decimals)

Write $\frac{2}{3}$ in decimal form.

Solution

$$
\begin{array}{r}
0.666 \\
3\overline{)2.000} \\
\underline{1\,8} \\
20 \\
\underline{18} \\
20 \\
\underline{18} \\
2
\end{array}
$$

← The same remainder keeps coming up, so the process is never finished.

When you write repeating decimals, be careful to include three dots or the overbar.

CAUTION

This is a *repeating decimal* and is indicated by three trailing dots or by a bar over the repeating digits:

$$\frac{2}{3} = 0.666\ldots \qquad \text{or} \qquad \frac{2}{3} = 0.\overline{6}$$

You cannot correctly write

$$\frac{2}{3} = 0.6666 \qquad \text{or} \qquad \frac{2}{3} = 0.6667 \qquad \text{ These are wrong!}$$

because $3 \times 0.6666 = 1.9998$ and $3 \times 0.6667 = 2.0001$. You can correctly write

$$\frac{2}{3} \approx 0.6666 \qquad \text{or} \qquad \frac{2}{3} = 0.\overline{6}$$

The symbol $\approx$ means **approximately equal to.**

All fractions have a decimal form that either terminates (as in Example 7) or repeats (as in Example 8). Any number of digits may repeat; consider Example 9.

Calculators do not write repeating decimals, but finding $\frac{2}{3}$ on your calculator can be instructive.

Press: [2] [÷] [3] [=]

The display may vary. If you see 0.666666667, then your calculator *rounds* the last decimal place, whereas if you see 0.666666666, then your calculator *truncates* (cuts off) at the last decimal place. You should remember whether your calculator rounds or truncates. You should also count the number of decimal places shown in your calculator's display. The number of places shown by this example indicates the accuracy of your calculator. The one shown here is accurate to eight decimal places. (Note that the ninth decimal place is not accurate because of possible rounding.)

EXAMPLE 9   **Changing a mixed fraction to a decimal fraction**

Write $3\frac{5}{11}$ in decimal form.

Solution   First, write $\frac{5}{11}$ as a decimal:

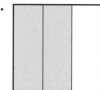

$$
\begin{array}{r}
0.45\ldots \\
11\overline{)5.00} \\
4\,4 \\
\hline
60 \\
55 \\
\hline
5 \quad \leftarrow\text{Repeats}
\end{array}
$$

By calculator: [3] [+] [5] [÷] [11] [=]

Display: 3.4545454545

Remember, a calculator does not show beyond its display; for this one, you must notice that it is a repeating decimal when you write $3.\overline{45}$.

Thus, $3\frac{5}{11} = 3 + \frac{5}{11} = 3 + 0.\overline{45} = 3.\overline{45}$. ●

EXAMPLE 10   **Estimating parts using common fractions**

Estimate the size of each shaded portion as a common fraction.

a.

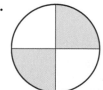

b.

Solution

a. The square is divided into 3 parts, and 2 of the 3 parts are shaded, so we estimate that $\frac{2}{3}$ of the square is shaded.

b. The circle is divided into 4 parts, and 2 of the 4 parts are shaded, so we estimate that $\frac{2}{4}$ or $\frac{1}{2}$ of the circle is shaded. ●

EXAMPLE 11 **Estimating parts using decimal fractions**

Estimate the size of each shaded portion as a decimal.

a. 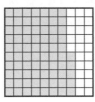   b.

Solution

a. Divide the square in half: b. Divide the square into thirds:

If you resort to counting squares, you are not estimating.

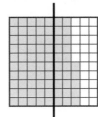   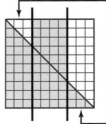

It looks as if half the remaining half is shaded, so we estimate that 75 of the 100 squares are shaded. The shaded portion is 0.75.

It appears that the number of squares not shaded in the first third is about the same as the number of small squares shaded in the last third, so we estimate the size of the shaded squares to be $\frac{2}{3}$ or $0.\overline{6}$. ●

EXAMPLE 12 **Application to a stock purchase**

Several years ago you purchased 400 shares of Disney stock selling at $29\frac{5}{8}$ per share. What is the total price you paid for this stock?

Solution First convert the stock price to dollars and cents by changing the mixed number to dollars and cents; then multiply by the number of shares.

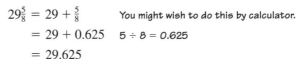
Do not round until you are ready to state your answer.

$$29\frac{5}{8} = 29 + \frac{5}{8} \qquad \text{You might wish to do this by calculator.}$$
$$= 29 + 0.625 \qquad 5 \div 8 = 0.625$$
$$= 29.625$$

Thus, the total price is $400 \times \$29.625 = \$11,850$. ●

PROBLEM SET 1.3

ESSENTIAL IDEAS **LEVEL 1**

1. **IN YOUR OWN WORDS** What is a fraction?

2. **IN YOUR OWN WORDS** Use a calculator to carry out the following sets of calculations.

   a. $\boxed{1} \boxed{\div} \boxed{1} \boxed{=}$

   b. $\boxed{1} \boxed{\div} \boxed{.} \boxed{1} \boxed{=}$

   c. $\boxed{1} \boxed{\div} \boxed{.} \boxed{0} \boxed{1} \boxed{=}$

   d. $\boxed{1} \boxed{\div} \boxed{.} \boxed{0} \boxed{0} \boxed{1} \boxed{=}$

   e. $\boxed{1} \boxed{\div} \boxed{.} \boxed{0} \boxed{0} \boxed{0} \boxed{1} \boxed{=}$

Describe the pattern of problems and answers. Does this lead you to any conclusion?

 3. IN YOUR OWN WORDS Explain why division by zero is not permitted.

4. Distinguish between a common fraction and a decimal fraction.

5. Give the names of the positional columns from trillions to millionths.

DRILL AND PRACTICE **LEVEL 2**

Classify each fraction as proper, improper, or a whole number, and then show the keystrokes required to enter each of the fractions in Problems 6–7 into a calculator.

6. a. $\frac{3}{2}$ improper; ⟦3⟧ ⟦÷⟧ ⟦2⟧ ⟦=⟧

   b. $\frac{15}{5}$ whole number; ⟦15⟧ ⟦÷⟧ ⟦5⟧ ⟦=⟧

7. a. $\frac{8}{13}$ proper; ⟦8⟧ ⟦÷⟧ ⟦13⟧ ⟦=⟧

   b. $\frac{17}{21}$ proper; ⟦17⟧ ⟦÷⟧ ⟦21⟧ ⟦=⟧

Show the keystrokes required to enter each of the mixed numbers in Problems 8–9 into a calculator.

8. a. $14\frac{3}{4}$ ⟦14⟧ ⟦+⟧ ⟦3⟧ ⟦÷⟧ ⟦4⟧ ⟦=⟧

   b. $3\frac{2}{7}$ ⟦3⟧ ⟦+⟧ ⟦2⟧ ⟦÷⟧ ⟦7⟧ ⟦=⟧

9. a. $4\frac{3}{7}$ ⟦4⟧ ⟦+⟧ ⟦3⟧ ⟦÷⟧ ⟦7⟧ ⟦=⟧

   b. $2\frac{1}{2}$ ⟦2⟧ ⟦+⟧ ⟦1⟧ ⟦÷⟧ ⟦2⟧ ⟦=⟧

Write each of the improper fractions in Problems 10–15 as a mixed number or a whole number.

10. a. $\frac{3}{2}$ $1\frac{1}{2}$ **b.** $\frac{4}{3}$ $1\frac{1}{3}$

   c. $\frac{5}{4}$ $1\frac{1}{4}$ **d.** $\frac{19}{2}$ $9\frac{1}{2}$

11. a. $\frac{16}{3}$ $5\frac{1}{3}$ **b.** $\frac{25}{4}$ $6\frac{1}{4}$

   c. $\frac{141}{10}$ $14\frac{1}{10}$ **d.** $\frac{163}{10}$ $16\frac{3}{10}$

12. a. $\frac{1,681}{10}$ $168\frac{1}{10}$ **b.** $\frac{1,493}{10}$ $149\frac{3}{10}$

   c. $\frac{833}{100}$ $8\frac{33}{100}$ **d.** $\frac{1,457}{100}$ $14\frac{57}{100}$

13. a. $\frac{27}{16}$ $1\frac{11}{16}$ **b.** $\frac{177}{10}$ $17\frac{7}{10}$

   c. $\frac{33}{16}$ $2\frac{1}{16}$ **d.** $\frac{27}{7}$ $3\frac{6}{7}$

14. a. $\frac{41}{12}$ $3\frac{5}{12}$ **b.** $\frac{61}{5}$ $12\frac{1}{5}$

   c. $\frac{118}{15}$ $7\frac{13}{15}$ **d.** $\frac{89}{21}$ $4\frac{5}{21}$

15. a. $\frac{83}{5}$ $16\frac{3}{5}$ **b.** $\frac{42}{3}$ 14

   c. $\frac{18}{3}$ 6 **d.** $\frac{125}{4}$ $31\frac{1}{4}$

Write each of the mixed numbers in Problems 16–27 as an improper fraction.

16. a. $2\frac{1}{2}$ $\frac{5}{2}$ **b.** $1\frac{2}{3}$ $\frac{5}{3}$ **17. a.** $1\frac{3}{4}$ $\frac{7}{4}$ **b.** $3\frac{3}{5}$ $\frac{18}{5}$

18. a. $4\frac{3}{8}$ $\frac{35}{8}$ **b.** $5\frac{1}{4}$ $\frac{21}{4}$ **19. a.** $3\frac{2}{3}$ $\frac{11}{3}$ **b.** $5\frac{1}{5}$ $\frac{26}{5}$

20. a. $6\frac{1}{2}$ $\frac{13}{2}$ **b.** $3\frac{2}{5}$ $\frac{17}{5}$ **21. a.** $1\frac{3}{10}$ $\frac{13}{10}$ **b.** $4\frac{2}{5}$ $\frac{22}{5}$

22. a. $2\frac{2}{5}$ $\frac{12}{5}$ **b.** $3\frac{7}{10}$ $\frac{37}{10}$ **23. a.** $17\frac{2}{3}$ $\frac{53}{3}$ **b.** $12\frac{4}{5}$ $\frac{64}{5}$

24. a. $11\frac{3}{8}$ $\frac{91}{8}$ **b.** $2\frac{9}{10}$ $\frac{29}{10}$ **25. a.** $1\frac{14}{15}$ $\frac{29}{15}$ **b.** $2\frac{13}{17}$ $\frac{47}{17}$

26. a. $19\frac{3}{5}$ $\frac{98}{5}$ **b.** $17\frac{1}{8}$ $\frac{137}{8}$ **27. a.** $18\frac{7}{8}$ $\frac{151}{8}$ **b.** $3\frac{11}{12}$ $\frac{47}{12}$

Change the fractions and mixed numbers in Problems 28–39 into decimal fractions.

28. a. $\frac{1}{8}$ 0.125   **b.** $\frac{3}{8}$ 0.375

29. a. $\frac{5}{6}$ $0.8\overline{3}$ **b.** $\frac{7}{6}$ $1.1\overline{6}$

30. a. $\frac{3}{5}$ 0.6   **b.** $\frac{7}{8}$ 0.875

31. a. $2\frac{1}{2}$ 2.5   **b.** $5\frac{1}{3}$ $5.\overline{3}$

32. a. $\frac{3}{7}$ $0.\overline{428571}$ **b.** $3\frac{1}{6}$ $3.1\overline{6}$

33. a. $6\frac{1}{12}$ $6.08\overline{3}$ **b.** $6\frac{2}{3}$ $6.\overline{6}$

34. a. $\frac{5}{9}$ $0.\overline{5}$ **b.** $\frac{7}{9}$ $0.\overline{7}$

35. a. $7\frac{5}{6}$ $7.8\overline{3}$ **b.** $4\frac{1}{15}$ $4.0\overline{6}$

36. a. $3\frac{1}{30}$ $3.0\overline{3}$ **b.** $\frac{2}{7}$ $0.\overline{285714}$

37. a. $2\frac{2}{3}$ $2.\overline{6}$ **b.** $4\frac{1}{6}$ $4.1\overline{6}$

38. a. $\frac{7}{15}$ $0.4\overline{6}$ **b.** $\frac{8}{9}$ $0.\overline{8}$

39. a. $4\frac{3}{8}$ 4.375   **b.** $3\frac{1}{9}$ $3.\overline{1}$

Estimate as a common fraction the size of the shaded portion of the regions in Problems 40–41.

40. a. 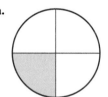 **b.**

    $\frac{1}{4}$ $\frac{1}{2}$

41. a.   **b.**

    $\frac{82}{100}$ or $\frac{41}{50}$ $\frac{5}{8}$

Estimate as a decimal fraction the shaded portions for each of the regions in Problems 42–43. **Answers vary.**

42. a. 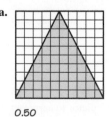 **b.**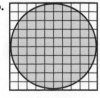

   0.50   0.80

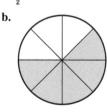

43. a.

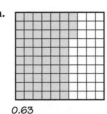

0.63

b.

0.82

In Problems 44–46, use a calculator to write each fraction in decimal form. Give the exact decimal value, if possible. If you can't give the exact value, indicate that the answer you are giving is approximate.

44. a. $\frac{1}{11}$ $0.\overline{09}$

b. $\frac{1}{12}$ $0.08\overline{3}$

45. a. $\frac{7}{15}$ $0.4\overline{6}$

b. $\frac{7}{22}$ $0.3\overline{18}$

46. a. $\frac{5}{19}$ 0.2631578947 (approx.)

b. $\frac{3}{17}$ 0.1764705882 (approx.)

Stock prices used to be quoted using eighths of a dollar. Find the total price of each transaction in Problems 47–52.

47. 100 shares of Citicorp at $52\frac{1}{2}$ $5,250

48. 100 shares of Liz Claiborne at $18\frac{3}{4}$ $1,875

49. 200 shares of Apple Computer at $42\frac{1}{4}$ $8,450

50. 300 shares of National Semi at $126\frac{1}{2}$ $37,950

51. 100 shares of Delta at $63\frac{1}{8}$ $6,312.50

52. 100 shares of Genentech at $60\frac{5}{8}$ $6,062.50

Explain what is wrong, if anything, with the statements in Problems 53–60. Explain your reasoning.

53. $\frac{0}{2} = 0$ T

54. $\frac{10}{0} = 0$ F; can't divide by 0

55. $0.05 = 0.050$ T

56. 0.75 is a fraction   T

57. $\frac{1}{3} = 0.333333333$ F; $\frac{1}{3} = 0.\overline{3}$

58. $0.\overline{6} = 0.666666666$ F; $0.\overline{6} = 0.666\ldots$

59. $238 \div 8.5 = 28$ T

60. $238 \div 8.51 = 27.9670$

F; by calculator, approximately 27.96709753

1.4 Rounding and Estimation

IN THIS WORLD   THE POWER OF MATH

"*Calling my family in Mexico is costing me a fortune,*" *said Rico.* "*It cost me over $40 last month on my phone bill!*"

"*You should get an international phone card,*" *advised Sally.* "*But be careful, some are better than others. Some cards have a maintenance fee, some have a service charge for each call, and others have one-minute, two-minute, or three-minute rounding.*"

"*What do you mean, three-minute rounding?*" *asked Rico.*

"*Well, it means if you make a call that lasts three minutes two seconds, they will charge you for six minutes.*"

In this section we will consider the process of rounding.

 See Problem 2.

Very large or very small numbers are difficult to comprehend. Most of us are accustomed to hearing about millions, billions, and even trillions, but do we really understand the magnitude of these numbers?

If you were to count one number per second, nonstop, it would take about 278 hours, or approximately $11\frac{1}{2}$ days, to count to a million. Not a million days have elapsed since the birth of Christ (a million days is about 2,700 years). A large book of about 700 pages contains about a million letters. A million bottle caps placed in a single line would stretch about 17 miles.

But the age in which we live has been called the age of billions. How large is a billion? How long would it take you to count to a billion? Go ahead—make a guess.

To get some idea about how large a billion is, let's compare it to some familiar units:

- If you gave away $1,000 *per day,* it would take you more than 2,700 *years* to give away a billion dollars.
- A stack of a billion $1 bills would be more than 59 miles high.
- At 8% interest, a billion dollars would earn you $219,178.08 interest *per day*!
- A billion seconds ago, *Godfather* came out and the video game *Pong* was released.
- A billion minutes ago, was about A.D. 100.
- A billion hours ago, people had not yet appeared on the earth.

To carry out the calculations necessary to make the preceding statements, we need two ideas. The first is rounding (discussed in this section), and the second is scientific notation (discussed in the next section). Rounding, estimation, and scientific notation can help increase the clarity of our understanding of numbers. For example, a budget of $252,892,988.18 for 99,200 students can be approximated as a $250 million budget for 100,000 students. A measurement of $19\frac{15}{16}$ inches might be recorded as 20 inches. You are often required to round decimals (for example, when you work with money). Estimates for the purpose of clarity are almost always found by rounding.

What do we mean by **rounding**? The following procedure should help explain.

Rounding a Decimal

To round a number in decimal form:

Step 1 **Locate the rounding digit.** This is identified by the column name. (These are listed on page 23.) Also, we sometimes refer to *two-place accuracy* and mean that the decimal should be accurate to two digits after the decimal point, and similarly for *three-place accuracy, four-place accuracy,* . . . .

Step 2 **Determine the rounding place digit.**
- It stays the same if the first digit to its right is a 0, 1, 2, 3, or 4.
- It increases by 1 if the digit to the right is a 5, 6, 7, 8, or 9. (If the rounding place digit is a 9 and 1 is added, there will be a carry in the usual fashion.)

Step 3 **Change digits.**
- All digits to the left of the rounding digit remain the same (unless there is a carry).
- All digits to the right of the rounding digit are changed to zeros.

> **Step 4   Drop zeros.**
> - If the rounding place digit is to the left of the decimal point, drop all trailing zeros.
> - If the rounding place digit is to the right of the decimal point, drop all trailing zeros to the right of the rounding place digit.

EXAMPLE 1   **Rounding**

Round 46.8217 to the nearest hundredth.

Solution

   Step 1. The rounding place digit is in the hundredths column.

   Step 2.

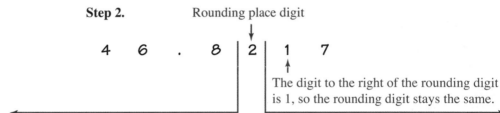

   Step 3. These digits stay the same.

   Step 4. These digits are changed into 0s; drop them (trailing zeros).

   The rounded number is 46.82.

EXAMPLE 2   **Rounding with a carry**

Round 13.6992 to the nearest hundredth.

Solution

   Step 1. The rounding place digit is in the hundredths column.

   Step 2.

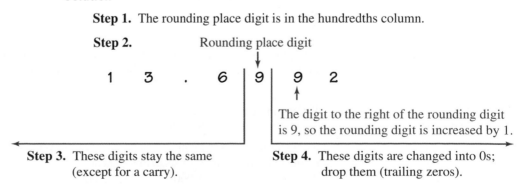

   Step 3. These digits stay the same (except for a carry).

   Step 4. These digits are changed into 0s; drop them (trailing zeros).

   The rounded number is 13.70. Notice that the zero that appears as the rounding place digit is *not* deleted.

EXAMPLE 3   **Rounding; drop trailing zeros**

Round 72,416.921 to the nearest hundred.

Solution

      Step 1. The rounding place digit is in the hundreds column.

      Step 2.   Rounding place digit

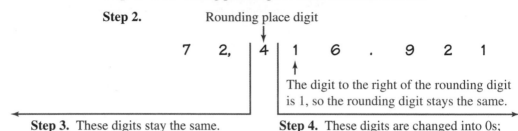

                                     The digit to the right of the rounding digit
                                     is 1, so the rounding digit stays the same.

     Step 3. These digits stay the same.   **Step 4.** These digits are changed into 0s;
                                             drop them (trailing zeros).

$$72{,}400.\underset{\uparrow}{\underbrace{000}}$$

Delete these trailing zeros.

The rounded number is 72,400.

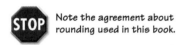 **STOP** *Note the agreement about rounding used in this book.*   In this book, we will round answers dealing with money to the nearest cent, and you should do the same in your work. Otherwise, you should not round any of your answers unless you are instructed to do so. This means, for example, that if you are converting fractions to decimals, you must include all decimal places until the decimal terminates or repeats (and you show this with an overbar). If you are using a calculator, you will need to interpret the display as representing either a terminating or a repeating decimal, if possible.

    Rounding is often used as a means of estimation. Throughout this book we will provide multiple-choice estimation questions so that you can practice and strengthen your estimating skills.

EXAMPLE 4   **Estimation by rounding**

Divide $858.25 into three shares. Which of the following is the best estimate of one share?
A. $90   B. $300   C. $900

Solution   Mentally round $858.25 to the nearest hundred dollars ($900); then divide by 3 to obtain $300. Thus, the best estimate is B.

EXAMPLE 5   **Estimating by rounding**

A theater has 53 rows with 39 seats in each row. Which of the following is the best estimate of the number of seats in the theater?
A. 100   B. 1,000   C. 2,000

Solution   Mentally round to the nearest ten: 50 rows of 40 seats each would give $50 \times 40 = 2{,}000$ seats. Thus, the best estimate is C.

PROBLEM SET (1.4)

ESSENTIAL IDEAS   LEVEL 1

STOP Don't forget to look at all of these essential ideas throughout the book.

1. IN YOUR OWN WORDS What is a rounding place digit?

2. IN YOUR OWN WORDS Describe the process of rounding.

DRILL AND PRACTICE   LEVEL 2

Round the numbers in Problems 3–24 to the given degree of accuracy.

3. 2.312; nearest tenth   2.3

4. 14.836; nearest tenth   14.8

5. 6,287.4513; nearest hundredth   6,287.45

6. 342.355; nearest hundredth   342.36

7. 5.291; one decimal place   5.3

8. 5.291; two decimal places   5.29

9. 6,287.4513; nearest hundred   6,300

10. 6,287.4513; nearest thousand   6,000

11. 12.8197; two decimal places   12.82

12. 813.055; two decimal places   813.06

13. 4.81792; nearest thousandth   4.818

14. 1.396; nearest unit   1

15. 4.8199; nearest whole number   5

16. 48.5003; nearest whole number   49

17. $12.993; nearest cent $12.99

18. $6.4312; nearest cent $6.43

19. $14.998; nearest cent $15.00

20. $6.9741; nearest cent $6.97

21. 694.3814; nearest ten   690

22. 861.43; nearest hundred   900

23. $86,125; nearest thousand dollars $86,000

24. $125,500; nearest thousand dollars $126,000

Round the calculator display shown in Problems 25–30.

```
2/3
        .6666666667
2/17
      .1176470588
7/51
        .137254902
```

```
1/3
        .3333333333
5/11
        .4545454545
19/53
        .358490566
```

25. 2/3; 3-place accuracy   0.667

26. 1/3; 4-place accuracy   0.3333

27. 2/17; 3-place accuracy   0.118

28. 5/11; 4-place accuracy   0.4545

29. 7/51; 3-place accuracy   0.137

30. 19/53; 4-place accuracy   0.3585

APPLICATIONS   LEVEL 2

A baseball player's batting average is found by dividing the number of hits by the number of times at bat. This number is then rounded to the nearest thousandth. Find each player's batting average in Problems 31–36.

31. Cole Becker was at bat 6 times with 2 hits.   0.333

32. Hannah Becker was at bat 20 times with 7 hits.   0.350

33. Theron Sovndal had 5 hits in 12 times at bat.   0.417

34. Jeff Tredway had 98 hits in 306 times at bat.   0.320

35. Hal Morris had 152 hits in 478 times at bat.   0.318

36. Tony Gwynn had 168 hits in 530 times at bat.   0.317

Estimate answers for Problems 37–42, choosing the most reasonable answer. You should not do any pencil-and-paper or calculator arithmetic for these problems.

37. The distance to school is 4.82 miles, and you must make the trip to school and back five days a week. Estimate how far you drive each week.

A. 9.64 miles
B. 50 miles
C. 482 miles   B; (Think: 4.82 ≈ 5 mi; round trip; 5 × 10 = 50.)

38. The length of a lot is 279 ft, and you must order fencing material that requires six times the length of the lot. Estimate the amount of material you should order.   A; (Think: 279 ≈ 300 and 300 × 6 = 1,800; choice A.)
A. 1,600 ft   B. 50 ft   C. 10,000 ft

39. If a person's annual salary is $35,000, estimate the monthly salary.   C; (Think: $35,000 ≈ $36,000; divide by 12: $3,000.)
A. $500   B. $1,000   C. $3,000

40. If 500 shares of a stock cost $19,087.50, estimate the value of each share of stock.
A. $40   B. $400   C. $4,000
A; (Think: $19,087.50 ≈ $20,000 and $20,000 ÷ 500 = $200 ÷ 5 = $40.)

41. If you must pay back $1,000 in 12 monthly installments, estimate the amount of each payment.
A. $25   B. $100   C. $12,000
B; (Think: $1,000 ≈ $1,200 and $1,200 ÷ 12 = $100.)

42. If an estate of $22,000 is to be divided equally among three children, estimate each child's share.
A. $7,000   B. $733.33   C. $65
A; (Think: $22,000 ≈ $21,000 and $21,000 ÷ 3 = $7,000.)

First give an estimate before answering each question in Problems 43–52.

43. If a person's annual salary is $15,000, what is the monthly salary?   **$1,250**

44. If a person's annual tax is $512, how much is that tax per month?   **$42.67**

45. If the sale of 150 shares of PERTEC stock grossed $1,818.75, how much was each share worth?   **$12.13**

46. If an estate of $22,000 is to be divided equally among three children, what is each child's share?   **$7,333.33**

47. If you must pay back $850 in 12 monthly payments, what is the amount of each payment?   **$70.83**

48. If you must pay back $1,000 in 12 monthly payments, what is the amount of each payment?   **$83.33**

49. A businesswoman bought a copy machine for her office. If it cost $674 and the useful life is six years, what is the cost per year?   **$112.33**

50. A businessman bought a fax machine for his office. If it cost $890 and the useful life is seven years, what is the cost per year?   **$127.14**

51. On December 5, 1985, a million balloons were released at Disneyland by the city of Anaheim, California. If the balloons were released at the rate of 100 per second, how long did it take to release the million balloons?   *Answers vary; almost 3 hours.*

52. Estimate the distance that would be covered by 1,000,000 textbooks, laid end to end.   *Answers vary; about 150–200 miles.*

53. **IN YOUR OWN WORDS**   Describe the size of a million.

54. **IN YOUR OWN WORDS**   Describe the size of a billion.

RIGHT OR WRONG?   **LEVEL 3**

Explain what is wrong, if anything, with the statements in Problems 55–60. Explain your reasoning.

55. 30.05 rounded to the nearest tenth is 30.   F; 30.1

56. 625.97555 rounded to the nearest hundredth is 600.   F; 625.98

57. 3,684,999 rounded to the nearest ten thousand is 3,690,000.   F; 3,680,000

58. 12,456.9099 rounded to the nearest tenth is 12,456.9000.   F; 12,456.9

59. If a jar contains 23 jelly beans, then 12 similar jars will contain about 250 jelly beans.   T

60. If a box contains 144 pencils, then obtaining 1,000 pencils will require about 7 boxes.   T

1.5 Exponents and Prime Factorization

IN THIS WORLD   THE POWER OF MATH

"I just read that our national debt is about $9 trillion," moaned Anita. "It just keeps growing and growing. Can we ever get it paid off?"

"It is not as bad as you think," said Rita. "Don't think of it in terms of absolute dollars, but as a percentage of gross national product."

"This is way too complicated for me. . . ."

In this section we will devise a way to handle big numbers, such as those dealing with national debt.

 See Problem 56.

We often encounter numbers that are made by repeated multiplication of the same numbers. For example,

$$10 \times 10 \times 10 \qquad 6 \times 6 \times 6 \times 6 \times 6$$
$$15 \times 15 \times 15 \times 15 \times 15 \times 15 \times 15 \times 15 \times 15 \times 15 \times 15 \times 15 \times 15$$

These numbers can be written more simply by inventing a new notation:

$$10^3 = \underbrace{10 \times 10 \times 10}_{3 \text{ factors}}$$

$$6^5 = \underbrace{6 \times 6 \times 6 \times 6 \times 6}_{5 \text{ factors}}$$

$$15^{13} = \underbrace{15 \times 15 \times \cdots \times 15}_{13 \text{ factors}}$$

We call this **power** or **exponential notation.** The number that is multiplied as a repeated factor is called the **base,** and the number of times the base is used as a factor is called the **exponent.** To use your calculator for exponents, locate the $\boxed{y^x}$, $\boxed{x^y}$, or $\boxed{\sim}$ keys. For example, to find the value of 6^5,

$$\boxed{6} \; \boxed{\sim} \; \boxed{5} \; \boxed{=}$$

You should see 7,776 displayed.

EXAMPLE 1	**Definition of exponent**

Tell what each of the given expressions means, and then expand (multiply out). Use your calculator where appropriate.

a. 6^2 **b.** 10^3 **c.** 7^5 **d.** 2^{15}

Solution

a. $6^2 = 6 \times 6$ or 36

   The base is 6; the exponent is 2; this is pronounced "six squared."

b. $10^3 = 10 \times 10 \times 10 = 1,000$

   The base is 10; the exponent is 3; this is pronounced "ten cubed."

c. $7^5 = 7 \times 7 \times 7 \times 7 \times 7 = 16,807$ (by calculator)

   The base is 7; the exponent is 5; this is pronounced "seven to the fifth power."

d. $2^{15} = \underbrace{2 \times 2 \times 2 \times \cdots \times 2 \times 2}_{15 \text{ factors}} = 32,768$

We now use this notation to observe a pattern for **powers of 10:**

$$10^1 = 10$$
$$10^2 = 10 \times 10 = 100$$
$$10^3 = 10 \times 10 \times 10 = 1,000$$
$$10^4 = 10 \times 10 \times 10 \times 10 = 10,000$$

Do you see a relationship between the exponent and the number?

$$10^{\underset{\uparrow}{5}} = \underbrace{100,000}_{5 \text{ zeros}}$$

Exponent is 5.

Notice that the exponent and the number of zeros are the same.

Could you write 10^{12} without actually multiplying?*

*Answer: 1,000,000,000,000

There is a similar pattern for multiplication of any number by a power of 10. Consider the following examples, and notice what happens to the decimal point:

$9.42 \times 10^1 = 94.2$ We find these answers by direct multiplication.

$9.42 \times 10^2 = 942.$

$9.42 \times 10^3 = 9,420.$

$9.42 \times 10^4 = 94,200.$

Do you see a pattern? If we multiply 9.42×10^5, how many places to the right will the decimal point be moved?

$$9.42 \times 10^5 = 942,000$$

5 places →

This answer is found by observing the pattern, not by directly multiplying.

Using this pattern, can you multiply the following *without direct calculation*?*

$$9.42 \times 10^{12}$$

We will investigate one final pattern of 10s, this time looking at smaller values in this pattern.

$$\vdots$$

$$100,000 = 10^5$$

$$10,000 = 10^4$$

$$1,000 = 10^3$$

$$100 = 10^2$$

$$10 = 10^1$$

Continuing with the same pattern, we have

$1 = 10^0$ We interpret the zero exponent as "decimal point moves 0 places."

$0.1 = 10^{-1}$ We will define negative numbers in Chapter 2.

$0.01 = 10^{-2}$ For now, we use the symbols −1, −2, −3, . . . as exponents to show

$0.001 = 10^{-3}$ position of decimal point.

$0.0001 = 10^{-4}$

$0.00001 = 10^{-5}$

$$\vdots$$

When we multiply some number by a power of 10, a pattern emerges:

$9.42 \times 10^2 = 942.$

$9.42 \times 10^1 = 94.2$

$9.42 \times 10^0 = 9.42$ Decimal moves 0 places.

$9.42 \times 10^{-1} = 0.942$ These answers are found by direct multiplication: $9.42 \times 0.1 = 0.942$.

$9.42 \times 10^{-2} = 0.0942$

$9.42 \times 10^{-3} = 0.00942$

*Answer: 9,420,000,000,000

Do you see that the same pattern holds for multiplying by a negative exponent? Can you multiply 9.42×10^{-6} *without direct calculation*? The solution is as follows:

$$9.42 \times 10^{-6} = 0.00000\,9\,42$$

$\leftarrow$ *Moved 6 places to the left.*

These patterns lead to a useful way of writing large and small numbers, called **scientific notation.**

Scientific Notation

> The **scientific notation** of a number is that number written as a power of 10 or as a decimal number between 1 and 10 times a power of 10.

EXAMPLE 2   **Writing numbers in scientific notation**

Write the given numbers in scientific notation.

a. 123,600   **b.** 0.000035   **c.** 48,300   **d.** 0.0821
e. 1,000,000,000,000   **f.** 7.35

Solution

a. $123{,}600 = 1.\,236 \times 10^?$

   Step 1 Fix the decimal point after the first nonzero digit.

   Step 2 From this number, count the number of decimal places to restore the number to its given form:

$$123{,}600 = 1.23600 \times 10^?$$

Move decimal point 5 places to the right $\rightarrow$

   Step 3 The exponent is the same as the number of decimal places needed to restore scientific notation to the original given number:

$$123{,}600 = 1.236 \times 10^5$$

b. $0.000035 = 3.5 \times 10^?$

   Step 1 Let's fix the decimal point.

   Step 2 $0.000035 = 000003.5 \times 10^?$

$\leftarrow$ *5 places to the left; this is* -5.

   Step 3 $0.000035 = 3.5 \times 10^{-5}$

c. $48{,}300 = 4.83 \times 10^4$

d. $0.0821 = 8.21 \times 10^{-2}$

e. $1{,}000{,}000{,}000{,}000 = 10^{12}$

f. $7.35 = 7.35 \times 10^0$ or just 7.35 ●

When working with very large or very small numbers, it is customary to use scientific notation. For example, suppose we wish to expand 2^{63}. A calculator can help us with this calculation:

The result is larger than can be handled with a calculator display, so your calculator will automatically output the answer in scientific notation, using one of the following formats:

$$9.223372037E18 \qquad 9.223372037\ 18 \qquad 9.223372037 \times 10^{18}$$

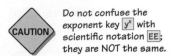

Do not confuse the exponent key y^x with scientific notation $\boxed{EE}$; they are NOT the same.

If you wish to enter a very large (or small) number into a calculator, you can enter these numbers using the scientific notation button on most calculators. Use the key labeled $\boxed{EE}$, $\boxed{EXP}$, or $\boxed{SCI}$. Whenever we show the $\boxed{EE}$ key, we mean press the scientific notation key on your brand of calculator.

Number	Scientific Notation	Calculator Input	Calculator Display
468,000	4.68×10^5	$\boxed{4.68}\ \boxed{EE}\ \boxed{5}$	4.68 05 or 4.68 E5
93,000,000,000	9.3×10^{10}	$\boxed{9.3}\ \boxed{EE}\ \boxed{10}$	9.3 10 or 9.3 E10

EXAMPLE 3 Operations with scientific notation

If the federal budget is $1.5 trillion (1,500,000,000,000), how much does it cost each individual, on average, if there are 240,000,000 people?

Solution   We must divide the budget by the number of people. We will use scientific notation and a calculator:

$$1,500,000,000,000 = 1.5 \times 10^{12} \qquad \text{and} \qquad 240,000,000 = 2.4 \times 10^8$$

The desired calculation is $\dfrac{1.5 \times 10^{12}}{2.4 \times 10^8}$.

We carry out this calculation using the appropriate scientific notation keys:

$$\boxed{1.5}\ \boxed{EE}\ \boxed{12}\ \boxed{\div}\ \boxed{2.4}\ \boxed{EE}\ \boxed{8}\ \boxed{=}$$

The answer is $6,250 per person.   ●

When you multiply numbers, the numbers being multiplied are called **factors.** The process of taking a given number and writing it as the product of two or more other numbers is called **factoring,** with the result called a **factorization** of the given number.

EXAMPLE 4 Finding factors

Find the factors of the given numbers.

a. 1 **b.** 2 **c.** 3 **d.** 4

e. 5 **f.** 6 **g.** 7 **h.** 8

Solution

a. $1 = 1 \times 1$ The factor is 1.
b. $2 = 2 \times 1$ Factors: 1, 2
c. $3 = 3 \times 1$ Factors: 1, 3
d. $4 = 4 \times 1$ or 2×2 Factors: 1, 2, 4

e. $5 = 5 \times 1$ Factors: 1, 5

f. $6 = 6 \times 1$ or 2×3 Factors: 1, 2, 3, 6

g. $7 = 7 \times 1$ Factors: 1, 7

h. $8 = 8 \times 1$ or 4×2 or $2 \times 2 \times 2$ Factors: 1, 2, 4, 8

Let's categorize the numbers listed in Example 4:

	PRIMES	*COMPOSITES*
Fewer than two factors:	*Exactly two factors:*	*More than two factors:*
1	2	4
	3	6
	5	8
	7	

A **prime** number is a natural number with exactly two distinct factors, and a **composite** number is a number with more than two factors. Will any number besides 1 have fewer than two factors? The primes smaller than 100 are listed in the box.

Primes Smaller Than 100

> 2, 3, 5, 7, 11, 13, 17, 19, 23, 29, 31, 37, 41, 43, 47, 53, 59, 61, 67, 71, 73, 79, 83, 89, 97

A **prime factorization** of a number is a factorization that consists exclusively of prime numbers.

EXAMPLE 5

Prime factorization of a number

Find the prime factorization of 36.

Solution

Step 1 From your knowledge of the basic multiplication facts, write any two numbers whose product is the given number. Circle any prime factor.

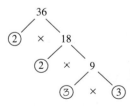

This process for finding a prime factorization is called a **factor tree.**

Step 2 Repeat the process for uncircled numbers.

Step 3 When all the factors are circled, their product is the *prime factorization.*

$$36 = 2 \times 2 \times 3 \times 3 = 2^2 \times 3^2$$

EXAMPLE 6   **Prime factorization of a number**

Find the prime factorization of 48.

Solution

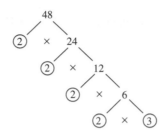

$$48 = 2 \times 2 \times 2 \times 2 \times 3 = 2^4 \times 3$$

If you cannot readily find the prime factors of a number, you should look at the list of prime factors from the smallest to the larger numbers, as illustrated in Example 7.

EXAMPLE 7   **Prime factorization of a large number**

Find the prime factorization of 34,153.

Solution   First, try 2; you might notice that 34,153 is not an even number, so 2 is not a factor. Next, try 3 (the next prime after 2); 3 does not divide evenly into 34,153, so 3 is not a factor. Next, try 5; it is also not a factor.

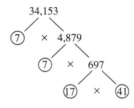

The next prime to try is 7 (by calculator or long division; calculator display is 4879). Now, focus on 4,879. Previously tried numbers cannot be factors, but since 7 *was* a factor, it might be again: 4,879 = 7 × 697.

Continue this process: 697 is not divisible (evenly) by 7, so try 11 (doesn't divide evenly), 13 (doesn't divide evenly), and 17 (does). The remaining number, 41, is a prime, so the process is complete:

$$34{,}153 = 7^2 \times 17 \times 41$$

PROBLEM SET **1.5**

ESSENTIAL IDEAS   **LEVEL 1**

1. **IN YOUR OWN WORDS** What is an exponent?

2. **IN YOUR OWN WORDS** What is scientific notation?

3. **IN YOUR OWN WORDS** Describe a process for finding the prime factorization of a number.

4. **IN YOUR OWN WORDS** Describe the difference between the y^x and $\boxed{\text{EE}}$ calculator keys.

5. Consider the number 10^6.

   a. What is the common name for this number?   *one million*

   b. What is the base?   *10*

   c. What is the exponent?   *6*

   d. According to the definition of exponential notation, what does the number mean?
   10 × 10 × 10 × 10 × 10 × 10

6. Consider the number 10^3.

   a. What is the common name for this number? *one thousand*

   b. What is the base? *10*

   c. What is the exponent? *3*

   d. According to the definition of exponential notation, what does the number mean? *10 × 10 × 10*

7. Consider the number 10^{-1}.

   a. What is the common name for this number? *one-tenth*

   b. What is the base? *10*

   c. What is the exponent? *−1*

   d. According to the definition of exponential notation, what does the number mean? *0.1*

8. Consider the number 10^{-2}.

   a. What is the common name for this number? *one-hundredth*

   b. What is the base? *10*

   c. What is the exponent? *−2*

   d. According to the definition of exponential notation, what does the number mean? *0.01*

DRILL AND PRACTICE   LEVEL 2

Write each of the numbers in Problems 9–16 in scientific notation.

9. a. 3,200   *3.2 × 10³*   **b.** 25,000   *2.5 × 10⁴*

   c. 18,000,000   *1.8 × 10⁷*   **d.** 640   *6.4 × 10²*

10. a. 0.004   *4 × 10⁻³*   **b.** 0.02   *2 × 10⁻²*

   c. 0.0035   *3.5 × 10⁻³*   **d.** 0.00000 045   *4.5 × 10⁻⁷*

11. a. 5,624   *5.624 × 10³*   **b.** 15,824   *1.5824 × 10⁴*

   c. 23.79   *2.379 × 10*   **d.** 0.000817   *8.17 × 10⁻⁴*

12. a. 35,000,000,000   *3.5 × 10¹⁰*

   b. 63,000,000   *6.3 × 10⁷*

   c. 0.00001   *10⁻⁵*

   d. 0.00000 00000 00000 00003 5   *3.5 × 10⁻²⁰*

13. a. 0.00000 421   *4.21 × 10⁻⁶*   **b.** 92,000,000   *9.2 × 10⁷*

   c. 1   *1 or 10⁰*   **d.** $1\frac{1}{2}$ *1.5 × 10⁰*

14. a. 0.00008 61   *8.61 × 10⁻⁵*   **b.** 249,000,000   *2.49 × 10⁸*

   c. 100   *10²*   **d.** $11\frac{1}{2}$ *1.15 × 10*

15. a. 634 E9   *6.34 × 10⁹*

   b. 5.2019 E11   *5.2019 × 10¹¹*

   c. 4.093745 08   *4.093745 × 10⁸*

   d. 8.291029292 12   *8.291029292 × 10¹²*

16. a. 2.029283 −03   *2.029283 × 10⁻³*

   b. 5.209 E−05   *5.209 × 10⁻⁵*

   c. 3.56 −10   *3.56 × 10⁻¹⁰*

   d. 3.8928 E−14   *3.8928 × 10⁻¹⁴*

Write each of the numbers in Problems 17–30 without using exponents.

17. a. 7.2×10^{10} *72,000,000,000*   **b.** 4.5×10^3 *4,500*

18. a. 3.1×10^2 *310*   **b.** 6.8×10^8 *680,000,000*

19. a. 2.1×10^{-3} *0.0021*   **b.** 4.6×10^{-7} *0.00000 046*

20. a. 2.05×10^{-1} *0.205*   **b.** 3.013×10^{-2} *0.03013*

21. a. 3.2×10^0 *3.2*   **b.** 8.03×10^{-4} *0.00080 3*

22. a. 5.06×10^3 *5.060*   **b.** 6.81×10^0 *6.81*

23. a. 7^2 *49*   **b.** 5^2 *25*

24. a. 2^6 *64*   **b.** 6^3 *216*

25. a. 2^8 *256*   **b.** 8^2 *64*

26. a. 4^3 *64*   **b.** 2^5 *32*

27. a. 10^4 *10,000*   **b.** 3^4 *81*

28. a. 4^5 *1,024*   **b.** 9^3 *729*

29. a. 2.18928271 10   *21,892,827,100*   **b.** 0.0000329 07   *329*

30. a. 0.00029214 E12   *292,140,000*   **b.** 1.29436732478 E19   *42,943,673,247,800,000,000*

Find the prime factorization (written with exponents) for the numbers in Problems 31–39.

31. a. 12   *2² × 3*   **b.** 20   *2² × 5*

32. a. 120   *2³ × 3 × 5*   **b.** 24   *2³ × 3*

33. a. 256   *2⁸*   **b.** 18   *2 × 3²*

34. a. 150   *2 × 3 × 5²*   **b.** 105   *3 × 5 × 7*

35. a. 400   *2⁴ × 5²*   **b.** 1,000   *2³ × 5³*

36. a. 10,000   *2⁴ × 5⁴*   **b.** 720   *2⁴ × 3² × 5*

37. a. 4,459   *7³ × 13*   **b.** 229,333   *13² × 23 × 59*

38. a. 2,098,987   *11³ × 19 × 83*   **b.** 803,257   *7² × 13² × 97*

39. a. 45,733   *19 × 29 × 83*   **b.** 29,791   *31³*

Estimate answers for Problems 40–45 by choosing the most reasonable answer. You should not do any pencil-and-paper or calculator arithmetic for these problems.

40. The number of marbles that could be placed into a bathtub is about:

   A. 10^3 B. 10^4 C. 10^9 *B*

41. The number of seconds since you have been born is about:

   A. 10^9 B. 10^{70} C. 10^{700} *A*

42. The cost of a pack (15 sticks) of gum (in dollars) is closest to:

   A. 10^{-2} B. 10^{-1} C. 10^0 *C*

43. In a restaurant, the cost of a cup of coffee (in dollars) is closest to:

   A. 10^{-2} B. 10^{-1} C. 10^0 *C*

44. The distance from the earth to the sun (in miles) is closest to:
A. 10^3 B. 10^7 C. 10^{18} B

45. The number of grains of sand on the earth is closest to:
A. 10^{50} B. 10^{-50} C. 10^{100} A

APPLICATIONS   LEVEL 2

46. A **googol** is a very large number that is defined in the cartoon. Write a googol in scientific notation. 10^{100}

Peanuts reprinted by permission of United Feature Syndicate, Inc.

47. A thermochemical calorie is about 41,840,000 ergs. Write this number in scientific notation. 4.184×10^7

48. The estimated age of the earth is about 5×10^9 years. Write this number without using an exponent.   5,000,000,000

49. The mass of the sun is about 3.33×10^5 times the mass of the earth. Write this without using an exponent.   333,000

50. a. The world's largest library, the Library of Congress, has approximately 59,000,000 items. Write this number in scientific notation. 5.9×10^7

b. If my local library has 54,000 volumes, how many times larger is the Library of Congress?   1,093 times larger

51. a. Saturn is about 8.86×10^8 miles from the sun. Write this distance without using an exponent.   886,000,000

b. Earth is 93,000,000 miles from the sun. How many times farther from the sun is Saturn than earth is from the sun?   9.5 times farther

52. a. The sun develops about 5×10^{23} horsepower per second. Write this without using an exponent.
500,000,000,000,000,000,000,000

b. Convert this to horsepower per year. 1.5855×10^{16}

53. a. A light-year is the distance that light travels in 1 year; this is about 5,869,713,600 miles. Write this distance in scientific notation. 5.8697136×10^9

b. If a spacecraft could travel at 82,300 mi/hr, how long would it take (in hours) for this craft to travel one light-year?   71,321

c. Estimate the time it would take (to the nearest year).   8 years

54. Estimate the total price of the following grocery items:
1 tube toothpaste, $1.89;
1 lb peaches, $0.79;
1 lb elbow macaroni, $1.39;
3 yogurts, $1.61;
lettuce, $0.59;
sliced turkey, $2.50;
chips, $1.89;
paper towels, $0.99;
half gallon of orange juice, $1.97;
1 lb cheddar cheese, $1.99;
3 cucumbers, $0.99;
1 lb frozen corn, $1.09;
2 bars soap, $1.79. $20; no calculator

55. Estimate the total cost of the following plumbing items:
120 $1\frac{1}{4}$-in. PVC pipe, $76.80;
$1\frac{1}{4}$-in. ball valve, $17.89;
$1\frac{1}{4}$-in PVC fittings, $24.28;
1-in. PVC fitting, $14.16;
$\frac{3}{4}$-in. PVC fittings, $6.48;
1-in. ball valve, $12.84. $150; no calculator

56. a. The national debt is about $9,200,000,000,000. Write this number in scientific notation. 9.2×10^{12}

b. Suppose that there are 301,000,000 people in the United States. Write this number in scientific notation. 3.01×10^8

c. If the debt is divided equally among the people, how much (rounded to the nearest hundred dollars) is each person's share? $30,600

RIGHT OR WRONG?   LEVEL 3

Explain what is wrong, if anything, with the statements in Problems 57–60. Explain your reasoning.

57. $5^2 = 10$ F; $5^2 = 5 \times 5 = 25$

58. 2^3 means $2 + 2 + 2$ F; 2^3 means $2 \times 2 \times 2$

59. 4^3 means multiply 4 by itself 3 times   F; $4^3 = 4 \times 4 \times 4$ (two multiplications)

60. A number is in scientific notation when it is written as a number between 1 and 10 times a power of 10.   F; it can also be a power of ten; moreover, it should be in decimal form.

1.6 Common Fractions

IN THIS WORLD   THE POWER OF MATH

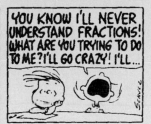

"Is Dr. Smith home?" asked Mary.

"Just a minute, I'll check," answered Shannon. *"Hey, Mom, do you know if Dad is home?"*

In everyday life, we use different names or titles for ourselves, depending on the context or situation. For example, in some situations I'm called Karl, in others Dr. Smith or Professor Smith, and in other places I'm Shannon's dad. We learn to deal with different names quite effectively in everyday situations, and we need to transfer this concept to numbers.

 See Problem 1.

A common fraction may have different names or representations, each of which is better than others in a certain context. For example, $\frac{1}{2}$, 0.5, $\frac{50}{100}$, and $\frac{8}{16}$ all name the same common fraction. We call $\frac{1}{2}$ the **reduced form,** but any of these may be the preferred form depending on what we want to do. In this section, when we refer to a fraction, we are referring to a common fraction. We say that a fraction is **reduced** if no counting number other than 1 divides evenly into both the numerator and the denominator. The process of reducing a fraction relies on the **fundamental property of fractions** and on the process of factoring introduced in Section 1.5.

Fundamental Property of Fractions

> If you multiply or divide both the numerator and the denominator by the same nonzero number, the resulting fraction will be the same.

 Reducing fractions is essential to working with fractions; study this procedure.

We will use this fundamental property first to reduce fractions, and then to multiply fractions. Let's begin by stating the procedure for **reducing fractions.**

Reducing Fractions

> In order to reduce a fraction:
>
> **Step 1** Find all common factors (other than 1) between the numerator and denominator.
>
> **Step 2** Divide out the common factors using the fundamental property of fractions.

EXAMPLE 1 Reduce a common fraction

Reduce $\frac{36}{48}$.

Solution

Step 1 Completely factor both numerator and denominator. We did this in the previous section.

Step 2 Write the numerator and denominator in factored form:

$$\frac{36}{48} = \frac{2 \times 2 \times 3 \times 3}{2 \times 2 \times 2 \times 2 \times 3}$$

Step 3 Use the fundamental property of fractions to eliminate the common factors. This process is sometimes called **canceling.***

$$\frac{36}{48} = \frac{2 \times 2 \times 3 \times \cancel{3}}{2 \times 2 \times 2 \times 2 \times \cancel{3}}$$

Step 4 Multiply the remaining factors. Treat the canceled factors as 1s.

$$
\begin{array}{c}
1 \times 1 \times 3 \times 1 = 3 \\
\uparrow \quad \uparrow \qquad \uparrow \\
\frac{36}{48} = \frac{2 \times 2 \times 3 \times \cancel{3}}{2 \times 2 \times 2 \times 2 \times \cancel{3}} = \frac{3}{4} \qquad \text{Notice how slashes are used as 1s.} \\
\downarrow \quad \downarrow \qquad \downarrow \\
1 \times 1 \times 2 \times 2 \times 1 = 4
\end{array}
$$

This process is rather lengthy and can sometimes be shortened by noticing common factors that are larger than prime factors. For example, you might have noticed that 12 is a common factor in Example 1, so that

$$\frac{36}{48} = \frac{3 \times \cancel{12}}{4 \times \cancel{12}} = \frac{3}{4}$$

$$\uparrow$$
Remember, this is 1.

EXAMPLE 2 Reducing fractions

Reduce the fractions. **a.** $\frac{4}{8}$ **b.** $\frac{75}{100}$ **c.** $\frac{35}{55}$ **d.** $\frac{160}{180}$ **e.** $\frac{1,200}{9,000}$

Solution

a. $\dfrac{4}{8} = \dfrac{1 \times 4}{2 \times 4}$ **b.** $\dfrac{75}{100} = \dfrac{3 \times 25}{4 \times 25}$ **c.** $\dfrac{35}{55} = \dfrac{7 \times 5}{11 \times 5}$

$\qquad = \dfrac{1}{2}$ $= \dfrac{3}{4}$ $= \dfrac{7}{11}$

If the fractions are complicated, you may reduce them in several steps.

d. $\dfrac{160}{180} = \dfrac{10 \times 16}{10 \times 18}$ **e.** $\dfrac{1,200}{9,000} = \dfrac{12 \times 100}{90 \times 100}$

$\qquad = \dfrac{2 \times 8}{2 \times 9}$ $= \dfrac{6 \times 2}{6 \times 15}$

$\qquad = \dfrac{8}{9}$ $= \dfrac{2}{15}$

*Notice that *cancel* does not mean "cross out or delete" factors. It means "use the fundamental property to eliminate common factors."

In this book, all fractional answers should be reduced unless you are otherwise directed.

We say that a fraction is **completely reduced** when there are no common factors of both the numerator and the denominator.

We now include fractions as part of the simplification process. To **simplify a fractional expression** means to carry out all the operations, according to the order of operations, and to write the answer as a single number or a completely reduced fraction.

We now turn to multiplying fractions.

Multiplying Fractions

> In order to **multiply fractions**, multiply numerators and multiply denominators.

EXAMPLE 3

Multiplying fractions

Simplify (that is, multiply the given numbers):

a. $\frac{1}{3} \times \frac{2}{5}$ **b.** $\frac{2}{3} \times \frac{4}{7}$ **c.** $5 \times \frac{2}{3}$ **d.** $3\frac{1}{2} \times 2\frac{3}{5}$

Solution

a. $\dfrac{1}{3} \times \dfrac{2}{5} = \boxed{\dfrac{1 \times 2}{3 \times 5}}$ ← This step can often be done in your head.

$= \dfrac{2}{15}$

b. $\dfrac{2}{3} \times \dfrac{4}{7} = \dfrac{8}{21}$

c. When multiplying a whole number and a fraction, as with $5 \times \frac{2}{3}$, write the whole number as a fraction and then multiply:

$$\frac{5}{1} \times \frac{2}{3} = \frac{10}{3} \text{ or } 3\frac{1}{3}$$

Both $\frac{10}{3}$ (in part c) and $\frac{91}{10}$ (in part d) are reduced fractions. Recall that a fraction is reduced if there is no number (other than 1) that divides into both the numerator and denominator evenly.

d. When multiplying mixed numbers, as with $3\frac{1}{2} \times 2\frac{3}{5}$, write the mixed numbers as improper fractions and then multiply:

$$\frac{7}{2} \times \frac{13}{5} = \frac{91}{10} \text{ or } 9\frac{1}{10}$$ ●

Multiplication of fractions can be visualized by considering the meaning of fractions as shown in Figure 1.2.

Don't fall into the trap of saying, "Why do I need to do this? I can find $\frac{4}{5}$ of $\frac{2}{3}$ by

$\frac{4}{5} \times \frac{2}{3} = \frac{8}{15}$

and that's all there is to it!" Figure 1.2 shows why multiplication of fractions works the way it does.

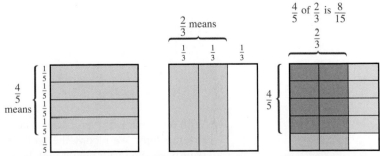

Figure 1.2 Geometrical justification of fractional multiplication

EXAMPLE 4　　　　　　　　**Illustrating the meaning of fractional multiplication**

Show that $\frac{3}{4}$ of $\frac{2}{3}$ is $\frac{6}{12}$.

Solution　　　　　　　　　　　　　　　　　The result is $\frac{6}{12}$ (6 shaded parts out of 12 parts).

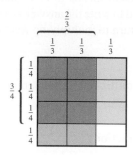

After the multiplication has been done, the product is often a fraction (such as the answer in Example 4) that can and should be reduced. Remember, a fraction is in reduced form if the only counting number that can divide evenly into both the numerator and the denominator is 1.

EXAMPLE 5　　　　　　　　**Multiplying fractions**

Simplify (that is, multiply the following numbers):

a. $\frac{3}{4} \times \frac{2}{3}$　　**b.** $\frac{2}{5} \times \frac{3}{4}$　　**c.** $\frac{3}{5} \times \frac{1}{3}$　　**d.** $3\frac{2}{3} \times 2\frac{2}{5}$　　**e.** $\frac{4}{5} \times \frac{3}{8} \times \frac{2}{5}$

Solution

a. $\dfrac{3}{4} \times \dfrac{2}{3} = \dfrac{6}{12}$　but　$\dfrac{6}{12} = \dfrac{3 \times \overset{1}{2}}{\underset{2}{4} \times 3} = \dfrac{1}{2}$

Notice that the actual multiplication was a wasted step because the answer was simply factored again in order to reduce it! Therefore, the proper procedure is cancel common factors before you do the multiplication. Also, it is *not* necessary to write out prime factors. To reduce $\frac{6}{12}$, notice that 6 is a common factor.

These little numbers mean that →
6 divides into 6 one time,
and 6 divides into 12 twice. →　　$\dfrac{\overset{1}{6}}{\underset{2}{12}} = \dfrac{1}{2}$　6 is the common factor.

b. $\dfrac{2}{5} \times \dfrac{3}{4} = \dfrac{\overset{1}{2} \times 3}{5 \times \underset{2}{4}} = \dfrac{3}{10}$

Notice that this is very similar to the original multiplication as stated to the left of the equal sign. You can save a step by canceling with the original product, as shown in the next part.

c. $\dfrac{\overset{1}{3}}{5} \times \dfrac{1}{\underset{1}{3}} = \dfrac{1}{5}$

d. $3\dfrac{2}{3} \times 2\dfrac{2}{5} = \dfrac{11}{\underset{1}{3}} \times \dfrac{\overset{4}{12}}{5} = \dfrac{44}{5}$ or $8\frac{4}{5}$

e. With a more lengthy problem, such as $\frac{4}{5} \times \frac{3}{8} \times \frac{2}{5}$, you may do your canceling in several steps. We recopy the problem at each step for the sake of clarity, but in your work the result would look like the last step only.

Step 1 $\dfrac{\overset{1}{\cancel{4}}}{5} \times \dfrac{3}{\underset{2}{\cancel{8}}} \times \dfrac{2}{5}$

Step 2 $\dfrac{\overset{1}{\cancel{4}}}{5} \times \dfrac{3}{\underset{\underset{1}{2}}{\cancel{8}}} \times \dfrac{\overset{1}{\cancel{2}}}{5}$

Step 3 $\dfrac{\overset{1}{\cancel{4}}}{5} \times \dfrac{3}{\underset{\underset{1}{2}}{\cancel{8}}} \times \dfrac{\overset{1}{\cancel{2}}}{5} = \dfrac{3}{25}$

When you want to find the fractional part of any number, you can do so by multiplication. That is, the word *of* is often translated into multiplication:

$\frac{4}{5}$ of $\frac{2}{3}$ is $\frac{4}{5} \times \frac{2}{3} = \frac{8}{15}$ and $\frac{3}{4}$ of $\frac{2}{3}$ is $\frac{3}{4} \times \frac{2}{3} = \frac{6}{12} = \frac{1}{2}$

The following example shows how you can use this idea with an applied problem.

EXAMPLE 6

Finding a sale price

If a store is having a "$\frac{1}{3}$-*OFF*" sale, you must pay $\frac{2}{3}$ of the original price. What is the sale price of a suit costing $355?

Solution We want to know "What is $\frac{2}{3}$ of 355?"

$$\frac{2}{3} \text{ of } 355 = \frac{2}{3} \times 355 = \frac{710}{3}$$

This mixed operation can easily be done by calculator:

$$\boxed{2} \ \boxed{\times} \ \boxed{355} \ \boxed{\div} \ \boxed{3} \ \boxed{=}$$

Since this is a problem involving a money answer, we want to write the answer in decimal form, rounded to the nearest cent. To do this, we divide 3 into 710 (and round) to obtain $236.67.

If the product of two numbers is 1, then those numbers are called **reciprocals.** To find the reciprocal of a given number, write the number in fractional form and then **invert,** as shown in Example 7.

EXAMPLE 7

Finding reciprocals

Find the reciprocal of each number, and then prove it is the correct reciprocal by multiplication.

Solution

a. $\frac{5}{11}$ Invert for reciprocal: $\frac{11}{5}$ *Check:* $\frac{5}{11} \times \frac{11}{5} = 1$

b. 3   Write as a fraction: $\frac{3}{1}$ Invert for reciprocal: $\frac{1}{3}$ *Check:* $3 \times \frac{1}{3} = 1$

   Using a calculator, find the key labeled $\boxed{1/x}$ *or* $\boxed{x^{-1}}$ *to find the reciprocal of a number in the display. For Example 7b, the reciprocal of 3 can be found:* $\boxed{3}$ $\boxed{1/x}$. *Calculator reciprocals are given as decimal fractions.*

c. $2\frac{3}{4}$ Write as a fraction: $\frac{11}{4}$ Invert for reciprocal: $\frac{4}{11}$ *Check:* $2\frac{3}{4} \times \frac{4}{11} = 1$

d. 0.2   Write as a fraction: $\frac{2}{10} = \frac{1}{5}$ Invert for reciprocal: $\frac{5}{1} = 5$

Check: $0.2 \times 5 = 1$

e. Zero is the only whole number that does not have a reciprocal because any number multiplied by zero is zero (and not 1). ●

The process of division is very similar to the process of multiplication. To divide fractions, you must understand these three ideas:

- **How to multiply fractions**
- **Which term is called the *divisor***
- **How to find the reciprocal of a number**

In the expression $10 \div 5$, the divisor is 5; that is, the **divisor** is the quantity (5) by which the given number (10) is divided.

EXAMPLE 8   Finding the divisor

Name the divisor: **a.** $4 \div 2$ **b.** $2 \div 4$ **c.** $\frac{6}{5} \div \frac{2}{3}$ **d.** $\frac{0}{8}$ **e.** $\frac{8}{0}$

Solution   **a.** 2   **b.** 4   **c.** $\frac{2}{3}$ **d.** 8   **e.** 0   ●

Dividing Fractions

To **divide fractions,** multiply by the reciprocal of the divisor. This is sometimes phrased as "invert and multiply."

EXAMPLE 9   Dividing fractions

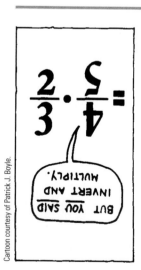

Cartoon courtesy of Patrick J. Boyle.

Simplify (that is, divide the following numbers):

a. $\frac{2}{3} \div \frac{4}{5}$ **b.** $\frac{3}{5} \div \frac{9}{20}$ **c.** $\frac{5}{8} \div 3$ **d.** $0 \div \frac{6}{7}$

Solution

a. $\dfrac{2}{3} \div \dfrac{4}{5} = \dfrac{2}{3} \times \dfrac{5}{4}$

$= \dfrac{\overset{1}{2}}{3} \times \dfrac{5}{\underset{2}{4}}$

$= \dfrac{5}{6}$

b. $\dfrac{3}{5} \div \dfrac{9}{20} = \dfrac{\overset{1}{3}}{\underset{1}{5}} \times \dfrac{\overset{4}{20}}{\underset{3}{9}}$

$= \dfrac{4}{3} \text{ or } 1\dfrac{1}{3}$

c. $\dfrac{5}{8} \div 3 = \dfrac{5}{8} \times \dfrac{1}{3}$

$= \dfrac{5}{24}$

d. $0 \div \dfrac{6}{7} = 0 \times \dfrac{7}{6}$

$= 0$ ●

We have discussed how to change a fraction to a decimal by division. The reverse procedure—changing a terminating decimal to a fraction—can be viewed as a multiplication problem involving fractions. This process is summarized in the following box.

Decimals to Fractions

Procedure for changing a terminating decimal into a fraction:

Step 1   Multiply the given number without its decimal point by the decimal name of the last digit.

Step 2   By the decimal name of the last digit, we mean:
One place is tenth, or $\frac{1}{10}$.
Two places is hundredth, or $\frac{1}{100}$.
Three places is thousandth, or $\frac{1}{1,000}$.
$\vdots$

EXAMPLE 10   **Changing a terminating decimal to a fraction**

Change the given decimal fractions to common fractions.

a. 0.4   **b.** 0.75   **c.** 0.0014   **d.** $0.12\frac{1}{2}$ **e.** $0.3\frac{1}{3}$

Solution

4 tenths; decimal position is tenth.

a. $0.4 = 4 \times \dfrac{1}{10} = \dfrac{\overset{2}{\cancel{4}}}{1} \times \dfrac{1}{\underset{5}{\cancel{10}}} = \dfrac{2}{5}$

75 hundredths; decimal position is hundredth.

b. $0.75 = \overset{3}{\cancel{75}} \times \dfrac{1}{\underset{4}{\cancel{100}}} = \dfrac{3}{4}$

14 ten-thousandths; decimal position is ten-thousandth.

c. $0.0014 = \overset{7}{\cancel{14}} \times \dfrac{1}{\underset{5,000}{\cancel{10,000}}} = \dfrac{7}{5,000}$

$12\frac{1}{2}$ hundredths; decimal position is hundredth.

d. $0.12\dfrac{1}{2} = 12\dfrac{1}{2} \times \dfrac{1}{100} = \dfrac{\overset{1}{\cancel{25}}}{2} \times \dfrac{1}{\underset{4}{\cancel{100}}} = \dfrac{1}{8}$

$3\frac{1}{3}$ tenths; decimal position is tenth.

e. $0.3\dfrac{1}{3} = 3\dfrac{1}{3} \times \dfrac{1}{10} = \dfrac{\overset{1}{\cancel{10}}}{3} \times \dfrac{1}{\underset{1}{\cancel{10}}} = \dfrac{1}{3}$

Numbers in which decimal and fractional forms are mixed, as in parts **d** and **e** of Example 10, are called **complex decimals.**

PROBLEM SET 1.6

ESSENTIAL IDEAS   LEVEL 1

1. IN YOUR OWN WORDS State the fundamental property of fractions, and explain why you think it is so "fundamental."

2. IN YOUR OWN WORDS Explain a procedure for reducing fractions.

3. IN YOUR OWN WORDS How do you know when a fraction is reduced?

4. IN YOUR OWN WORDS Explain a procedure for multiplying fractions.

5. IN YOUR OWN WORDS Explain a procedure for dividing fractions.

6. IN YOUR OWN WORDS Explain a procedure for changing a terminating decimal to a fraction.

DRILL AND PRACTICE   LEVEL 2

Completely reduce the fractions in Problems 7–14.

7. a. $\frac{2}{4}$ $\frac{1}{2}$ **b.** $\frac{3}{9}$ $\frac{1}{3}$ **c.** $\frac{4}{16}$ $\frac{1}{4}$ **d.** $\frac{2}{10}$ $\frac{1}{5}$

8. a. $\frac{3}{9}$ $\frac{1}{3}$ **b.** $\frac{6}{9}$ $\frac{2}{3}$ **c.** $\frac{2}{10}$ $\frac{1}{5}$ **d.** $\frac{4}{10}$ $\frac{2}{5}$

9. a. $\frac{3}{12}$ $\frac{1}{4}$ **b.** $\frac{4}{12}$ $\frac{1}{3}$ **c.** $\frac{6}{12}$ $\frac{1}{2}$ **d.** $\frac{8}{12}$ $\frac{2}{3}$

10. a. $\frac{14}{7}$ 2 **b.** $\frac{38}{19}$ 2 **c.** $\frac{92}{2}$ 46 **d.** $\frac{160}{8}$ 20

11. a. $\frac{72}{15}$ $\frac{24}{5}$ **b.** $\frac{42}{14}$ 3 **c.** $\frac{16}{24}$ $\frac{2}{3}$ **d.** $\frac{128}{256}$ $\frac{1}{2}$

12. a. $\frac{18}{30}$ $\frac{3}{5}$ **b.** $\frac{70}{105}$ $\frac{2}{3}$ **c.** $\frac{50}{400}$ $\frac{1}{8}$ **d.** $\frac{35}{21}$ $\frac{5}{3}$

13. a. $\frac{140}{420}$ $\frac{1}{3}$ **b.** $\frac{75}{50}$ $\frac{3}{2}$ **c.** $\frac{240}{672}$ $\frac{5}{14}$ **d.** $\frac{5,670}{12,150}$ $\frac{7}{15}$

14. a. $\frac{12}{432}$ $\frac{1}{36}$ **b.** $\frac{150}{1,000}$ $\frac{3}{20}$ **c.** $\frac{2,500}{10,000}$ $\frac{1}{4}$ **d.** $\frac{105}{120}$ $\frac{7}{8}$

Illustrate the given parts of a whole in Problems 15–20.

15. $\frac{2}{5}$ of $\frac{3}{4}$

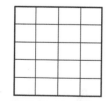

Shade 6 out of 20

16. $\frac{3}{5}$ of $\frac{5}{6}$

Shade 15 out of 30

17. $\frac{4}{5}$ of $\frac{1}{3}$

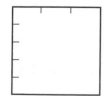

Shade 4 out of 15

18. $\frac{3}{5}$ of $\frac{3}{4}$

Shade 9 out of 20

19. $\frac{1}{6}$ of $\frac{2}{3}$

Shade 2 out of 18

20. $\frac{3}{5}$ of $\frac{1}{2}$

Shade 3 out of 10

In Problems 21–24, first name the divisor, and then find the answer by direct division. Finally, find the answer by multiplying by the reciprocal. Both answers should be the same.

21. a. $15 \div 5$ divisor, 5; 3; 3

b. $6 \div 3$ divisor, 3; 2; 2

22. a. $0 \div 3$ divisor, 3; 0; 0

b. $14 \div 2$ divisor, 2; 7; 7

23. a. $20 \div 4$ divisor, 4; 5; 5

b. $240 \div 16$ divisor, 16; 15; 15

24. a. $5 \div 0.2$ divisor, 0.2; 25; 25

b. $2.4 \div 0.6$ divisor, 0.6; 4; 4

Simplify the numerical expressions given in Problems 25–35. Give your answers in reduced form.

25. a. $\frac{1}{4} \times \frac{1}{6}$ $\frac{1}{24}$ **b.** $\frac{2}{3} \times \frac{4}{5}$ $\frac{8}{15}$

c. $\frac{3}{4} \times \frac{1}{6}$ $\frac{1}{8}$ **d.** $\frac{7}{20} \times \frac{100}{14}$ $\frac{5}{2}$

e. $\frac{5}{9} \times \frac{18}{25}$ $\frac{2}{5}$ **f.** $\frac{2}{3} \times \frac{3}{8}$ $\frac{1}{4}$

26. a. $\frac{4}{5} \times \frac{13}{16}$ $\frac{13}{20}$ **b.** $\frac{18}{25} \times \frac{5}{36}$ $\frac{1}{10}$

c. $\frac{4}{5} \times \frac{3}{8}$ $\frac{3}{10}$ **d.** $\frac{4}{7} \times \frac{14}{9}$ $\frac{8}{9}$

e. $\frac{5}{12} \times \frac{4}{15}$ $\frac{1}{9}$ **f.** $\frac{9}{16} \times \frac{4}{27}$ $\frac{1}{12}$

27. a. $\frac{1}{2} \div \frac{1}{3}$ $\frac{3}{2}$ **b.** $\frac{1}{3} \div \frac{1}{2}$ $\frac{2}{3}$

c. $\frac{2}{3} \div \frac{1}{2}$ $\frac{4}{3}$ **d.** $\frac{3}{4} \div \frac{2}{3}$ $\frac{9}{8}$

e. $\frac{2}{5} \times \frac{15}{8}$ $\frac{3}{4}$ **f.** $\frac{5}{3} \times \frac{9}{15}$ 1

28. a. $\frac{3}{5} \times \frac{20}{27}$ $\frac{4}{9}$ **b.** $\frac{3}{8} \div \frac{15}{16}$ $\frac{2}{5}$

c. $\frac{2}{3} \div \frac{5}{6}$ $\frac{4}{5}$ **d.** $\frac{4}{5} \div \frac{3}{10}$ $\frac{8}{3}$

e. $\frac{4}{7} \div \frac{4}{5}$ $\frac{5}{7}$ **f.** $\frac{5}{6} \div \frac{1}{3}$ $\frac{5}{2}$

29. a. $\frac{4}{5} \div \frac{4}{5}$ 1 **b.** $\frac{7}{9} \div \frac{7}{9}$ 1

c. $\frac{8}{3} \div \frac{8}{3}$ 1 **d.** $\frac{4}{5} \times 5$ 4

e. $\frac{3}{5} \div \frac{3}{7}$ $\frac{7}{5}$ **f.** $\frac{6}{7} \div \frac{2}{3}$ $\frac{9}{7}$

30. a. $\frac{4}{9} \div \frac{3}{4}$ $\frac{16}{27}$ **b.** $\frac{2}{3} \times 3$ 2

c. $\frac{5}{6} \times 18$ 15 **d.** $\frac{3}{8} \times 24$ 9

e. $\frac{5}{8} \times 8$ 5 **f.** $\frac{6}{7} \times 7$ 6

31. a. $\frac{2}{5} \div 3$ $\frac{2}{15}$ **b.** $\frac{3}{8} \div 3$ $\frac{1}{8}$

   c. $\frac{3}{5} \div 5$ $\frac{3}{25}$ **d.** $3 \div \frac{1}{6}$ 18

   e. $2\frac{1}{2} \div 3$ $\frac{5}{6}$ **f.** $6\frac{1}{2} \div 3$ $\frac{13}{6}$

32. a. $3\frac{4}{5} \div 0$ impossible   **b.** $7 \times \frac{9}{14}$ $\frac{9}{2}$

   c. $5 \div 1\frac{1}{2}$ $\frac{10}{3}$ **d.** $4 \div 2\frac{2}{3}$ $\frac{3}{2}$

   e. $6 \div 1\frac{5}{6}$ $\frac{36}{11}$ **f.** $52 \times \frac{5}{13}$ 20

33. a. $2\frac{2}{5} \times 1\frac{4}{5}$ $\frac{108}{25}$ **b.** $5\frac{1}{2} \times 3\frac{2}{3}$ $\frac{121}{6}$

   c. $4\frac{1}{6} \times 3\frac{3}{8}$ $\frac{225}{16}$ **d.** $1\frac{1}{6} \times 2\frac{1}{3}$ $\frac{49}{18}$

   e. $6\frac{1}{2} \times \frac{5}{6}$ $\frac{65}{12}$ **f.** $3\frac{4}{5} \times \frac{1}{2}$ $\frac{19}{10}$

34. a. $2\frac{2}{5} \div 1\frac{2}{3}$ $\frac{36}{25}$ **b.** $5\frac{1}{2} \div 1\frac{4}{5}$ $\frac{55}{18}$

   c. $2\frac{2}{3} \div 1\frac{1}{3}$ 2 **d.** $5 \times \frac{3}{5}$ 3

   e. $2\frac{1}{2} \times \frac{3}{4}$ $\frac{15}{8}$ **f.** $4\frac{1}{2} \div 9\frac{1}{2}$ $\frac{9}{19}$

35. a. $\frac{1}{2} \times \frac{8}{9} \times \frac{3}{16}$ $\frac{1}{12}$ **b.** $\frac{2}{3} \times \frac{5}{8} \times \frac{16}{100}$ $\frac{1}{15}$

   c. $\frac{2}{3} \times \frac{4}{5} \times \frac{15}{16}$ $\frac{1}{2}$ **d.** $2\frac{1}{2} \times 3\frac{1}{6} \times 1\frac{1}{5}$ $\frac{19}{2}$

   e. $\left(\frac{1}{2} \div \frac{1}{2}\right) \div \frac{1}{4}$ 4 **f.** $\frac{1}{2} \div \left(\frac{1}{3} \div \frac{1}{4}\right)$ $\frac{3}{8}$

Write the decimals in Problems 36–43 in fractional form.

36. a. 0.7 $\frac{7}{10}$ **b.** 0.9 $\frac{9}{10}$ **c.** 0.8 $\frac{4}{5}$

37. a. 0.25 $\frac{1}{4}$ **b.** 0.87 $\frac{87}{100}$ **c.** 0.375 $\frac{3}{8}$

38. a. 0.18 $\frac{9}{50}$ **b.** 0.48 $\frac{12}{25}$ **c.** 0.54 $\frac{27}{50}$

39. a. 0.78 $\frac{39}{50}$ **b.** 0.85 $\frac{17}{20}$ **c.** 0.246 $\frac{123}{500}$

40. a. 0.505 $\frac{101}{200}$ **b.** 0.015 $\frac{3}{200}$ **c.** 0.005 $\frac{1}{200}$

41. a. $0.66\frac{2}{3}$ $\frac{2}{3}$ **b.** $0.87\frac{1}{2}$ $\frac{7}{8}$ **c.** $0.16\frac{2}{3}$ $\frac{1}{6}$

42. a. $0.37\frac{1}{2}$ $\frac{3}{8}$ **b.** $0.8\frac{8}{9}$ $\frac{8}{9}$ **c.** $0.000\frac{1}{3}$ $\frac{1}{3,000}$

43. a. $0.1\frac{1}{9}$ $\frac{1}{9}$ **b.** $0.5\frac{5}{9}$ $\frac{5}{9}$ **c.** $0.08\frac{1}{3}$ $\frac{1}{12}$

APPLICATIONS   LEVEL 2

Some experts tell us that the amount of savings we need is $\frac{1}{10}$ times our age times our current salary. Calculate the amount of savings necessary in Problems 44–47.

44. age 20, salary $24,000 $48,000

45. age 30, salary $46,000 $138,000

46. age 25, salary $25,000 $62,500

47. age 50, salary $125,000 $625,000

48. If two thirds of a person's body weight is water, what is the weight of water in a person who weighs 180 pounds? 120 pounds

49. If Karl owns $\frac{3}{16}$ of a mutual water system and a new well is installed at a cost of $12,512, how much does Karl owe for his share? $2,346

50. What would 100 shares of Xerox stock cost when it is selling for $56.63 per share? $5,663.00

51. If you received $227.00 for selling 20 shares of Brunswick stock, what is the price per share? $11.35

52. A recipe calls for $\frac{5}{8}$ cup of sugar, one egg, and $\frac{7}{8}$ cup of flour. How much of each ingredient is needed to double this mixture? $1\frac{1}{4}$ cups of sugar, 2 eggs, $1\frac{3}{4}$ cups of flour

53. If $4\frac{2}{5}$ acres sell for $44,000, what is the price per acre? $10,000

RIGHT OR WRONG?   LEVEL 3

Explain what is wrong, if anything, with the statements in Problems 54–60. Explain your reasoning.

54. $\frac{9}{2}$ is a reduced fraction.   T

55. If I want to find $\frac{1}{2}$ of 16, the correct operation is to divide 16 by $\frac{1}{2}$.   F; multiply 16 by $\frac{1}{2}$.

56. $8 \times \frac{3}{2} = \frac{8 \times 3}{8 \times 2} = \frac{24}{16} = \frac{3}{2}$ F; $8 \times \frac{3}{2} = \frac{24}{2} = 12$

57. To find the reciprocal of any number, write $\dfrac{1}{\text{the number}}$.   F; all numbers except 0

58. $\frac{2}{3} \div \frac{4}{5} = \frac{4}{5} \div \frac{2}{3}$ F; $\frac{2}{3} \div \frac{4}{5} = \frac{2}{3} \times \frac{5}{4} = \frac{5}{6}$ but $\frac{4}{5} \div \frac{2}{3} = \frac{4}{5} \times \frac{3}{2} = \frac{6}{5}$

59. "Invert and multiply" means that a division problem can be carried out by changing the division to a multiplication, and then multiplying by the reciprocal of the divisor.   T

60. The following advertisement recently appeared in a Kansas newspaper: "Divide your age by one-half and that is the percent discount you will receive for this sale!"   If you are 20, then $20 \div \frac{1}{2} = 40$, 40% off; but if you are 50, then $50 \div \frac{1}{2} = 100$ or 100% off. (It's free?)

1.7 Adding and Subtracting Fractions

IN THIS WORLD THE POWER OF MATH

"Every time I cut one of these I'm off by about a sixteenth of an inch," stated Jim, a carpenter apprentice.

"You must take into account the width of the cut," coached Arnie. *"If you are making only one cut, then it will probably be okay because you'll discard the short piece, but if you want to make more than one cut, you'll need to add into your measurements the thickness of the blade. Let me show you . . ."*

In this section, you will learn how to work with fractions—namely, adding and subtracting them.

 See Problems 3 and 4.

If the fractions you are adding or subtracting are similar (all halves, thirds, fourths, fifths, sixths, and so on), then the procedure is straightforward: Add or subtract the numerators. In this case, we say that the fractions have **common denominators.** If the fractions are not similar, then you *cannot* add or subtract them directly; you must change the form of the fractions so that they are similar. This process is called *finding common denominators.*

Adding/Subtracting Fractions

In order to **add** or **subtract fractions** with common denominators, add or subtract the numerators. The denominator of the sum or difference is the same as the common denominator.

EXAMPLE 1

Adding and subtracting fractions with common denominators

Simplify the given numerical expressions.

a. $\frac{1}{5} + \frac{3}{5}$ **b.** $\frac{5}{9} - \frac{4}{9}$ **c.** $\frac{3}{2} + \frac{7}{2}$ **d.** $3\frac{2}{3} + 1\frac{2}{3} + \frac{1}{3} + 4\frac{2}{3}$

Solution

a. $\frac{1}{5} + \frac{3}{5} = \frac{4}{5}$

1 fifth   +   3 fifths   =   4 fifths

b. $\dfrac{5}{9} - \dfrac{4}{9} = \dfrac{1}{9}$

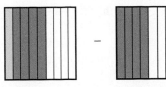

5 ninths $-$ 4 ninths $=$ 1 ninth

c. $\dfrac{3}{2} + \dfrac{7}{2} = \dfrac{10}{2} = 5$ This example could also be added in the form of mixed numbers:

Add fraction part first.

$$\begin{array}{r} 1\frac{1}{2} \\ +\,3\frac{1}{2} \\ \hline 4\frac{2}{2} \end{array}$$

↑ *Next, add whole number part.*

Since $\frac{2}{2} = 1$, it follows that $4\frac{2}{2} = 4 + \frac{2}{2} = 4 + 1 = 5$.

d.
$$\begin{array}{r} 3\frac{2}{3} \\ 1\frac{2}{3} \\ \frac{1}{3} \\ +\,4\frac{2}{3} \\ \hline 8\frac{7}{3} = 10\frac{1}{3} \end{array}$$

Notice that the carry may be more than 1. In this example, $\frac{7}{3} = 2\frac{1}{3}$.

Sometimes when doing subtraction, you must borrow from the units column to have enough fractional parts to carry out the subtraction. Remember,

 CAUTION $1 = \frac{2}{2} = \frac{3}{3} = \frac{4}{4} = \frac{5}{5} = \frac{6}{6} = \frac{7}{7} = \frac{8}{8} = \frac{9}{9} = \frac{10}{10} = \cdots$

EXAMPLE 2

Subtraction with common denominators and borrowing

Borrow 1 from the units column and combine with the fractional part.

a. $3\frac{1}{3}$ **b.** $5\frac{3}{5}$ **c.** $3\frac{1}{2}$ **d.** $1\frac{1}{3}$ **e.** $14\frac{4}{5}$

Solution

a. $3\frac{1}{3}$: You would do the following steps in your head and write only the answer:

 CAUTION Study this to understand rewriting numbers to carry out subtraction with mixed numbers and borrowing.

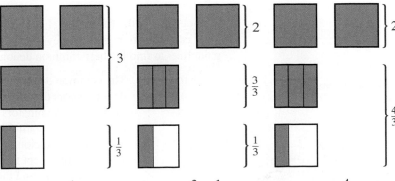

These all represent the same number: $3 + \dfrac{1}{3}$ $2 + \dfrac{3}{3} + \dfrac{1}{3}$ $2 + \dfrac{4}{3}$

Thus, $3\frac{1}{3} = 2\frac{4}{3}$.

b. $5\frac{3}{5} = 4\frac{8}{5}$ **c.** $3\frac{1}{2} = 2\frac{3}{2}$ **d.** $1\frac{1}{3} = \frac{4}{3}$ **e.** $14\frac{4}{5} = 13\frac{9}{5}$

Using the idea shown in Example 2, we can carry out some subtractions with mixed numbers.

EXAMPLE 3

Subtraction of mixed numbers with common denominators

Simplify the given numerical expressions. **a.** $3\frac{1}{3} - 1\frac{2}{3}$ **b.** $4\frac{3}{5} - 2\frac{4}{5}$ **c.** $1\frac{1}{3} - \frac{2}{3}$

Solution

$$
\textbf{a.}\quad
\begin{array}{r}
3\dfrac{1}{3} = 2\dfrac{4}{3} \\[4pt]
-\,1\dfrac{2}{3} = -\,1\dfrac{2}{3} \\[2pt]
\hline
1\dfrac{2}{3}
\end{array}
\qquad
\textbf{b.}\quad
\begin{array}{r}
4\dfrac{3}{5} = 3\dfrac{8}{5} \\[4pt]
-\,2\dfrac{4}{5} = -\,2\dfrac{4}{5} \\[2pt]
\hline
1\dfrac{4}{5}
\end{array}
\qquad
\textbf{c.}\quad
\begin{array}{r}
1\dfrac{1}{3} = \dfrac{4}{3} \\[4pt]
-\,\dfrac{2}{3} = -\,\dfrac{2}{3} \\[2pt]
\hline
\dfrac{2}{3}
\end{array}
$$

If the fractions to be added or subtracted do not have common denominators, the sum or difference is not as easy to find. For example, consider the sum $\frac{1}{5} + \frac{3}{4}$.

$$\frac{1}{5} \qquad + \qquad \frac{3}{4} \qquad = \qquad \frac{1}{5}\ \ \frac{3}{4}$$

1 fifth + 3 fourths = ?

What unit? Fifths?
Fourths?

We need to use the fundamental property of fractions to change the form of one or more of the fractions so that they do have the same denominators. Use the following guidelines to find the best common denominator.

STOP *Pay attention here:*

First: The common denominator should be a number that all the given denominators divide into evenly. This means that the product of the given denominators will always be a common denominator. Many students learn this and *always* find the common denominator by multiplication. Even though this works for all numbers, it is inefficient except for small numbers. Therefore, we have a second condition to find the best common denominator.

Second: The common denominator should be as small as possible. This number is called the **lowest common denominator,** denoted by **LCD.**

Lowest Common Denominator

The procedure for finding the lowest common denominator (LCD) is:

Step 1   Factor all given denominators into prime factors; write each factorization using exponents.

Step 2   List each different prime factor you found in the prime factorization of the denominator.

Step 3   On each prime in the list from step 2, place the largest exponent that appears on that prime factor anywhere in the factorization of the denominators.

Step 4   The LCD is the product of the prime factors with the exponents in step 3.

EXAMPLE 4

Finding the lowest common denominator

Find the LCD for the given denominators.

a. 6 and 8   **b.** 8 and 12   **c.** 24 and 30   **d.** 8, 24, and 60   **e.** 300 and 144

Solution

a. 6; 8
$$6 = 2 \times 3$$
$$8 = 2^3 \quad \text{Largest exponent on prime factor 3 is 1 (remember } 3 = 3^1 \text{).}$$
$$\downarrow$$
$$\text{LCD:} \quad 2^3 \times 3 = 8 \times 3 = 24$$
$$\uparrow$$
Largest exponent on prime factor 2 is 3.

b. 8; 12
$$8 = 2^3$$
$$12 = 2^2 \times 3$$
$$\text{LCD:} \quad 2^3 \times 3 = 8 \times 3 = 24$$

c. 24; 30
$$24 = 2^3 \times 3$$
$$30 = 2 \times 3 \times 5$$
$$\text{LCD:} \quad 2^3 \times 3 \times 5 = 8 \times 3 \times 5 = 120$$

d. 8; 24; 60   The same procedure works no matter how many denominators are given.
$$8 = 2^3$$
$$24 = 2^3 \times 3$$
$$60 = 2^2 \times 3 \times 5$$
$$\text{LCD:} \quad 2^3 \times 3 \times 5 = 8 \times 3 \times 5 = 120$$

e. 300; 144   If the numbers are larger, you may need factor trees:

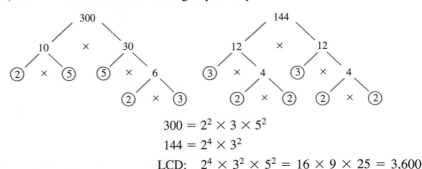

$$300 = 2^2 \times 3 \times 5^2$$
$$144 = 2^4 \times 3^2$$
$$\text{LCD:} \quad 2^4 \times 3^2 \times 5^2 = 16 \times 9 \times 25 = 3{,}600$$

Notice the proper procedure for carrying out the order of operations in Example 4, which mixes exponents and multiplication. Since an exponent is an indicated multiplication, the proper procedure is first to simplify the exponent and then to carry out the multiplication. This leads to an **extended order-of-operations** agreement.

Order of Operations Extended

This is essential for almost all that follows. You must make its application second nature.

In doing arithmetic with mixed operations, we agree to proceed by following these steps:

Step 1 Parentheses first

Step 2 Perform any operations that involve raising to a power.

Step 3 Multiplications and divisions, reading from left to right.

Step 4 Additions and subtractions, reading from left to right

---

EXAMPLE 5   **Using the extended order of operations**

Simplify $2^4 + 3(5 + 6)$.

Solution
$$\begin{aligned}
2^4 + 3(5 + 6) &= 2^4 + 3(11) && \text{Parentheses first} \\
&= 16 + 3(11) && \text{Powers next} \\
&= 16 + 33 && \text{Multiplications/divisions} \\
&= 49 && \text{Additions/subtractions}
\end{aligned}$$

We now turn to adding and subtracting fractions by finding the lowest common denominator.

Adding/Subtracting

In order to add or subtract fractions that do not have common denominators, carry out the following procedure:

Step 1 Find the LCD.

Step 2 Change the forms of the fractions to obtain forms with common denominators.

Step 3 Add or subtract the numerators of the fractions with common denominators.

EXAMPLE 6   **Addition and subtraction of fractions**

Simplify:

a. $\frac{1}{6} + \frac{3}{4}$ **b.** $\frac{4}{9} - \frac{1}{4}$ **c.** $2\frac{1}{6} + 5\frac{3}{8}$

d. $12\frac{7}{24} - 5\frac{4}{30}$ **e.** $\frac{3}{8} + \frac{11}{12} + \frac{3}{20}$ **f.** $16\frac{1}{3} - 4\frac{1}{2}$

Solution

a. Write in column form:

$$\frac{1}{6}$$

$$+\frac{3}{4}$$

Find the LCD: $6 = 2 \times 3$

$$4 = 2^2$$

LCD: $2^2 \times 3 = 12$

Next, change form:

$$\frac{1}{6} = \frac{2}{12}$$

$$+\frac{3}{4} = \frac{9}{12}$$

Add: $\frac{11}{12}$

In this example, you are asked to write

$$\frac{3}{4} \quad \text{as} \quad \frac{9}{12}$$

and we are reminded of the cartoon in the margin.

Cartoon courtesy of Patrick J. Boyle

b. Combining the steps outlined in part **a**, you'll obtain

$$\frac{4}{9} = \frac{16}{36}$$

$$-\frac{1}{4} = -\frac{9}{36}$$

$$\frac{7}{36}$$

Find the LCD: $9 = 3^2$

$$4 = 2^2$$

LCD: $2^2 \times 3^2 = 36$

c.

$$2\frac{1}{6} = 2\frac{4}{24}$$

$$+5\frac{3}{8} = 5\frac{9}{24}$$

$$7\frac{13}{24}$$

Find the LCD: $6 = 2 \times 3$

$$8 = 2^3$$

LCD: $2^3 \times 3 = 24$

d.

$$12\frac{7}{24} = 12\frac{35}{120}$$

$$-5\frac{4}{30} = -5\frac{16}{120}$$

$$7\frac{19}{120}$$

Find the LCD: $24 = 2^3 \times 3$

$$30 = 2 \times 3 \times 5$$

LCD: $2^3 \times 3 \times 5 = 120$

e.

$$\frac{3}{8} = \frac{45}{120}$$

$$\frac{11}{12} = \frac{110}{120}$$

$$\frac{3}{20} = \frac{18}{120}$$

$$\frac{173}{120} = 1\frac{53}{120}$$

Find the LCD: $8 = 2^3$

$$12 = 2^2 \times 3$$

$$20 = 2^2 \times 5$$

LCD: $2^3 \times 3 \times 5 = 120$

Borrow so that you can complete the subtraction.

$\downarrow$

f.
$$16\frac{1}{3} = 16\frac{2}{6} = 15\frac{8}{6}$$
$$-4\frac{1}{2} = -4\frac{3}{6} = -4\frac{3}{6}$$
$$\overline{11\frac{5}{6}}$$

The order of operations is the same for fractions as it is for whole numbers.

EXAMPLE 7   Mixed operations with fractions

Simplify: **a.** $\frac{3}{4} \times \frac{1}{3} + \frac{3}{4} \times \frac{2}{3}$ **b.** $\frac{3}{4}\left(\frac{1}{3} + \frac{2}{3}\right)$

Solution   Remember the correct order of operations.

a. $\dfrac{3}{4} \times \dfrac{1}{3} + \dfrac{3}{4} \times \dfrac{2}{3} = \dfrac{1}{4} + \dfrac{1}{2}$ **b.** $\dfrac{3}{4}\left(\dfrac{1}{3} + \dfrac{2}{3}\right) = \dfrac{3}{4} \times 1$

$$= \dfrac{1}{4} + \dfrac{2}{4} \qquad\qquad\qquad\qquad = \dfrac{3}{4}$$

$$= \dfrac{3}{4}$$

Recall that juxtaposition implies multiplication.

The distributive property tells us that the answers to parts **a** and **b** in Example 7 must be equal.

EXAMPLE 8   Mixed operations using juxtaposition for multiplication

Simplify: **a.** $\frac{5}{6}\left(\frac{3}{4} + \frac{1}{2}\right) + \frac{2}{3} \times \frac{9}{10}$ **b.** $\frac{1}{2} \div \frac{1}{3} \div \left(\frac{3}{4} + \frac{3}{5}\right)$

Solution

a. $\dfrac{5}{6}\left(\dfrac{3}{4} + \dfrac{1}{2}\right) + \dfrac{2}{3} \times \dfrac{9}{10} = \dfrac{5}{6}\left(\dfrac{3}{4} + \dfrac{2}{4}\right) + \dfrac{2}{3} \times \dfrac{9}{10}$ *Common denominator, parentheses first*

$$= \dfrac{5}{6}\left(\dfrac{5}{4}\right) + \dfrac{\overset{1}{2}}{\underset{1}{\cancel{3}}} \times \dfrac{\overset{3}{\cancel{9}}}{\underset{5}{\cancel{10}}}$$

$$= \dfrac{25}{24} + \dfrac{3}{5}$$

$$= \dfrac{125}{120} + \dfrac{72}{120}$$

$$= \dfrac{197}{120} \text{ or } 1\dfrac{77}{120}$$

$$\textbf{b.}\ \frac{1}{2} \div \frac{1}{3} \div \left(\frac{3}{4} + \frac{3}{5} \right) = \frac{1}{2} \div \frac{1}{3} \div \left(\frac{15}{20} + \frac{12}{20} \right)$$

$$= \frac{1}{2} \div \frac{1}{3} \div \frac{27}{20}$$

$$= \frac{1}{2} \times \frac{3}{1} \div \frac{27}{20} \qquad \text{Multiplication and division from left to right}$$

$$= \frac{3}{2} \div \frac{27}{20}$$

$$= \frac{\overset{1}{\cancel{3}}}{2} \times \frac{\overset{10}{\cancel{20}}}{\underset{9}{\cancel{27}}}$$

$$= \frac{10}{9} \text{ or } 1\frac{1}{9}$$

PROBLEM SET (1.7)

ESSENTIAL IDEAS   LEVEL 1

1. **IN YOUR OWN WORDS** What is the extended order-of-operations agreement?

2. **IN YOUR OWN WORDS** State a procedure for finding the lowest common denominator for a set of fractions.

3. **IN YOUR OWN WORDS** Describe a procedure for adding fractions that do not have common denominators.

4. **IN YOUR OWN WORDS** Describe a procedure for subtracting fractions that do not have common denominators.

DRILL AND PRACTICE   LEVEL 2

Estimate (do not calculate) the answers in Problems 5–12.

5. $\frac{19}{40}$ is about the same as

   A. $\frac{1}{2}$ B. $\frac{1}{3}$ C. $\frac{5}{4}$ D. $\frac{1}{5}$ A

6. $\frac{3}{10}$ is about the same as

   A. $\frac{1}{2}$ B. $\frac{1}{3}$ C. $\frac{5}{4}$ D. $\frac{1}{5}$ B

7. $\frac{19}{40} - \frac{3}{10}$ is about the same as

   A. $\frac{1}{2}$ B. $\frac{1}{3}$ C. $\frac{5}{4}$ D. $\frac{1}{5}$ D

8. $\frac{1}{2} + \frac{1}{4} + \frac{1}{8} + \frac{1}{16} + \frac{1}{32}$ is about equal to

   A. $\frac{1}{2}$ B. 1   C. $\frac{3}{2}$ D. 1,000   B

9. If I multiply a given nonzero number by $\frac{2}{3}$, the answer _____ B _____ than the given number.

   A. is larger

   B. is smaller

   C. could be either larger or smaller

10. If I multiply a given nonzero number by $\frac{3}{2}$, the answer _____ A _____ than the given number

    A. is larger

    B. is smaller

    C. could be either larger or smaller

11. If I divide a given nonzero number by $\frac{2}{3}$, the answer _____ A _____ than the given number.

    A. is larger

    B. is smaller

    C. could be either larger or smaller

12. If I divide a given nonzero number by $\frac{3}{2}$, the answer _____ B _____ than the given number.

    A. is larger

    B. is smaller

    C. could be either larger or smaller

Simplify the numerical expressions given in Problems 13–15. Give your answers in reduced form.

13. **a.** $\frac{2}{5} + \frac{1}{5}$ $\frac{3}{5}$ **b.** $\frac{3}{7} + \frac{5}{7}$ $\frac{8}{7}$ **c.** $\frac{5}{11} + \frac{3}{11}$ $\frac{8}{11}$

    d. $\frac{3}{2} + \frac{5}{2}$ 4   **e.** $\frac{7}{3} - \frac{4}{3}$ 1   **f.** $\frac{5}{9} + \frac{1}{9}$ $\frac{2}{3}$

14. **a.** $\frac{9}{13} - \frac{5}{13}$ $\frac{4}{13}$ **b.** $\frac{6}{23} - \frac{5}{23}$ $\frac{1}{23}$ **c.** $\frac{9}{7} - \frac{2}{7}$ 1

    d. $\frac{13}{15} + \frac{2}{15}$ 1   **e.** $\frac{7}{12} - \frac{1}{12}$ $\frac{1}{2}$ **f.** $\frac{5}{8} - \frac{3}{8}$ $\frac{1}{4}$

15. **a.** $2\frac{2}{3}$ **b.** $6\frac{4}{5}$ **c.** $8\frac{3}{8}$

    $+ 1\frac{1}{3}$ $+ 2\frac{1}{5}$ $+ 4\frac{5}{8}$

    $\overline{4}$ $\overline{9}$ $\overline{13}$

d. $5\frac{1}{3}$ **e.** $14\frac{1}{8}$ **f.** $6\frac{1}{4}$

$-3\frac{2}{3}$ $-8\frac{5}{8}$ $-5\frac{3}{4}$

$\overline{1\frac{2}{3}}$ $\overline{5\frac{1}{2}}$ $\overline{\frac{1}{2}}$

Find the LCD for the denominators given in Problems 16–19.

16. a. 4; 8 *8* **b.** 2; 6 *6*

c. 2; 5 *10* **d.** 5; 12 *60*

17. a. 4; 12 *12* **b.** 12; 90 *180*

c. 12; 336 *336* **d.** 90; 210 *630*

18. a. 6; 8; 10 *120* **b.** 9; 12; 14 *252*

c. 60; 18 *180* **d.** 450; 15 *450*

19. a. 735; 1,125 *55,125* **b.** 315; 735 *2,205*

c. 420; 450 *6,300* **d.** 600; 90; 30 *1,800*

Simplify the numerical expressions given in Problems 20–31. Remember that fractions are not considered simplified unless they are reduced.

20. a. $\frac{1}{2}+\frac{2}{3}$ *$\frac{7}{6}$* **b.** $\frac{1}{2}+\frac{3}{8}$ *$\frac{7}{8}$*

c. $\frac{1}{2}-\frac{1}{6}$ *$\frac{1}{3}$* **d.** $\frac{1}{2}+\frac{2}{5}$ *$\frac{9}{10}$*

e. $\frac{1}{2}-\frac{2}{5}$ *$\frac{1}{10}$* **f.** $\frac{5}{6}+\frac{2}{3}$ *$\frac{3}{2}$*

21. a. $\frac{5}{6}-\frac{1}{3}$ *$\frac{1}{2}$* **b.** $\frac{5}{6}+\frac{5}{8}$ *$\frac{35}{24}$*

c. $\frac{5}{8}-\frac{1}{3}$ *$\frac{7}{24}$* **d.** $\frac{3}{4}-\frac{5}{12}$ *$\frac{1}{3}$*

e. $\frac{3}{5}+\frac{1}{6}$ *$\frac{23}{30}$* **f.** $\frac{3}{4}+\frac{1}{12}$ *$\frac{5}{6}$*

22. a. $\frac{2}{45}+\frac{1}{6}$ *$\frac{19}{90}$* **b.** $\frac{41}{45}-\frac{5}{6}$ *$\frac{7}{90}$*

c. $\frac{4}{9}-\frac{5}{12}$ *$\frac{1}{36}$* **d.** $\frac{3}{5}+\frac{1}{12}$ *$\frac{41}{60}$*

e. $\frac{5}{24}-\frac{2}{15}$ *$\frac{3}{40}$* **f.** $\frac{5}{27}+\frac{1}{90}$ *$\frac{53}{270}$*

23. a. $2\frac{1}{2}$ **b.** $1\frac{2}{3}$ **c.** $3\frac{3}{8}$

$+4\frac{3}{4}$ $+5\frac{1}{2}$ $+5\frac{1}{2}$

$\overline{7\frac{1}{4}}$ $\overline{7\frac{1}{6}}$ $\overline{8\frac{7}{8}}$

24. a. $5\frac{1}{8}$ **b.** $17\frac{1}{2}$ **c.** $12\frac{1}{3}$

$-3\frac{3}{4}$ $-6\frac{2}{3}$ $-4\frac{1}{2}$

$\overline{1\frac{3}{8}}$ $\overline{10\frac{5}{6}}$ $\overline{7\frac{5}{6}}$

25. a. $\frac{1}{8}+2\frac{2}{3}+\frac{1}{6}$ *$2\frac{23}{24}$*

b. $\frac{4}{5}+\frac{3}{7}+\frac{3}{10}$ *$1\frac{37}{70}$*

26. a. $6\frac{1}{8}+3\frac{2}{5}+1\frac{1}{4}$ *$10\frac{31}{40}$*

b. $5\frac{1}{2}+6\frac{3}{4}+4\frac{1}{8}$ *$16\frac{3}{8}$*

27. a. $7\frac{2}{3}+5\frac{1}{2}+12\frac{1}{6}$ *$25\frac{1}{3}$*

b. $12\frac{3}{8}+2\frac{1}{2}+5\frac{1}{8}$ *20*

28. a. $\frac{1}{2}+\frac{2}{3}\times\frac{1}{5}$ *$\frac{19}{30}$*

b. $\frac{1}{2}\div\left(\frac{1}{3}\div\frac{1}{4}\right)$ *$\frac{3}{8}$*

29. a. $\frac{1}{2}\times\frac{2}{3}+\frac{1}{5}$ *$\frac{8}{15}$*

b. $\frac{1}{5}\div\frac{1}{3}\div\frac{1}{4}$ *$\frac{12}{5}$*

30. a. $\frac{3}{4}\left(\frac{9}{13}+\frac{4}{13}\right)$ *$\frac{3}{4}$*

b. $\frac{4}{5}\left(\frac{5}{16}+\frac{11}{16}\right)$ *$\frac{4}{5}$*

31. a. $\dfrac{3\times3+5\times2}{5\times3}$ *$\frac{19}{15}$*

b. $\dfrac{3\times5+7\times4}{7\times5}$ *$\frac{43}{35}$*

Perform the indicated operations in Problems 32–37. You may use your calculator and leave answers in decimal form.

32. $\dfrac{3}{4}\times\dfrac{119}{200}+\dfrac{3}{4}\times\dfrac{81}{200}$ *0.75*

33. $\dfrac{4}{5}\times\dfrac{17}{95}+\dfrac{4}{5}\times\dfrac{78}{95}$ *0.8*

34. $\dfrac{7}{8}\times\dfrac{107}{147}+\dfrac{7}{8}\times\dfrac{40}{147}$ *0.875*

35. $\left(\dfrac{4}{5}+\dfrac{2}{3}\right)\div\dfrac{1}{5}+2$ *$9.\overline{3}$*

36. $\dfrac{19}{300}+\dfrac{55}{144}+\dfrac{25}{108}$ *0.6767592593 (approx.)*

37. $\dfrac{15}{253}+\left(\dfrac{53}{104}-\dfrac{25}{208}\right)$ *0.4487116145 (approx.)*

APPLICATIONS   LEVEL 2

Estimate the portion of each square occupied by the indicated letter in Problems 38–49.

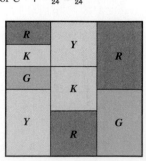

38. *A* $\frac{1}{2}\cdot\frac{1}{4}+\frac{1}{3}\cdot\frac{1}{2}=\frac{7}{24}$

39. *B* $\frac{1}{2}\cdot\frac{1}{4}+\frac{1}{3}\cdot\frac{1}{2}=\frac{7}{24}$

40. *C* $\frac{1}{4}+\frac{1}{3}\cdot\frac{1}{2}=\frac{5}{12}$

41. *A or B*

$\frac{1}{4}+\frac{2}{3}\cdot\frac{1}{2}=\frac{7}{12}$

or can find portion that is not C:

$1-\frac{5}{12}=\frac{7}{12}$

42. *B or C* $1-\frac{7}{24}=\frac{17}{24}$ **43.** *A or C* $1-\frac{7}{24}=\frac{17}{24}$

44. *R* $\frac{1}{6}\cdot\frac{1}{3}+\frac{1}{3}\cdot\frac{1}{3}+\frac{1}{2}\cdot\frac{1}{3}=\frac{1}{3}$

45. *K* $\frac{1}{6}\cdot\frac{1}{3}+\frac{1}{3}\cdot\frac{1}{3}=\frac{1}{6}$

46. *G* $\frac{1}{6}\cdot\frac{1}{3}+\frac{1}{2}\cdot\frac{1}{3}=\frac{2}{9}$

47. *Y* $\frac{1}{2}\cdot\frac{1}{3}+\frac{1}{3}\cdot\frac{1}{3}=\frac{5}{18}$

48. *R or K or G* not Y: $1-\frac{5}{18}=\frac{13}{18}$

49. *R or G or Y* not K: $1-\frac{1}{6}=\frac{5}{6}$

50. A recipe calls for $\frac{2}{3}$ cup milk and $\frac{1}{2}$ cup water.

a. What is the total amount of liquid? $1\frac{1}{6}$ cup

b. If you wish to make one-fourth of this recipe, how much of each ingredient is needed, and what is the total amount of liquid? $\frac{1}{6}$ cup milk; $\frac{1}{8}$ cup water; $\frac{7}{24}$ cup total

51. Suppose you have items to mail that weigh $1\frac{1}{4}$ lb, $2\frac{2}{3}$ lb, and $3\frac{1}{2}$ lb. What is the total weight of these packages? $7\frac{5}{12}$ pounds

52. Loretta received three boxes of candy for her birthday: a $1\frac{1}{2}$-lb box, a $\frac{3}{4}$-lb box, and a $2\frac{15}{16}$-lb box. What is the total weight of the candy she received? $5\frac{3}{16}$ pounds

53. Suppose you are installing molding around a table and you need pieces $5\frac{1}{4}$ in., $7\frac{1}{2}$ in., and $5\frac{3}{16}$ in. long. If the saw chews up $\frac{1}{16}$ in. of material each time a cut is made, what is the smallest single length of molding that can be used to do this job? $18\frac{1}{16}$ in.

54. If the outside diameter of a piece of tubing is $\frac{15}{16}$ in. and the wall is $\frac{3}{16}$ in. thick, what is the inside diameter? $\frac{9}{16}$ in.

RIGHT OR WRONG? **LEVEL 3**

Explain what is wrong, if anything, with the statements in Problems 55–60. Explain your reasoning.

55. $\dfrac{3}{8} + \dfrac{4}{8} = \dfrac{3+4}{8+8} = \dfrac{7}{16}$
F; do not add the denominators. Answer is $\frac{7}{8}$.

56. $3\frac{5}{8} - 2\frac{7}{8} = 1\frac{2}{8} = 1\frac{1}{4}$ F; write $3\frac{5}{8} - 2\frac{7}{8} = 2\frac{13}{8} - 2\frac{7}{8} = \frac{6}{8} = \frac{3}{4}$

57. $\dfrac{3}{8} \times \dfrac{5}{8} = \dfrac{3 \times 5}{8 \times 8} = \dfrac{15}{64}$ T

58. $\dfrac{3}{8} \div \dfrac{5}{8} = \dfrac{8}{3} \times \dfrac{5}{8} = \dfrac{5}{3}$ F; invert the divisor

59. $\dfrac{3}{8} + \dfrac{2}{5} = \dfrac{3 \times 5 + 2 \times 8}{8 \times 5} = \dfrac{15 + 16}{40} = \dfrac{31}{40}$ T

60. $\dfrac{3}{5} + \dfrac{2}{5} \times \dfrac{1}{2} = 1 \times \dfrac{1}{2} = \dfrac{1}{2}$ F; multiplication first: $\frac{3}{5} + \frac{1}{5} = \frac{4}{5}$

1.8 Hindu–Arabic Numeration System

IN THIS WORLD THE POWER OF MATH

From Margarita Philosophica Nova, 1523. Courtesy of the Museum of the History of Science, University of Oxford

"Look here, Boethius, you need to quit being so old-fashioned," proclaimed Pythagoras. *"Certainly, you can see the benefits of using decimals!"*

"You are a heretic!" exclaimed Boethius. *"You will rot in hell for your beliefs. I've used the numerals of the Roman church all of my life, and I'm not about to change now."*

"Can't you see Arithmetica *in her beautiful robes looking over our competition?"* asked Pythagoras. *"Why do you think she is smiling at me?"*

In this section, we will look at the numeration system we use every day—it is called the *Hindu–Arabic* numeration system.

 See Problem 3.

The system in common use today for naming numbers (the one we have been calling the decimal system) has ten symbols—namely, 0, 1, 2, 3, 4, 5, 6, 7, 8, and 9. The selection of ten digits was, no doubt, a result of our having ten fingers (digits).

The symbols originated in India about 300 B.C. However, because the early specimens do not contain a zero or use a positional system, this numeration offered no advantage over other systems then in use in India.

The date of the invention of the zero symbol is not known. The symbol did not originate in India, but probably came from the late Babylonian period via the Greek

HISTORICAL NOTE

Hindu 300 B.C.

Arabic 10th century

Arabic 15th century

European 15th century

20th century typewriter

1 2 3 4 5 6 7 8 9 0

20th century bank check

The symbols used in the Hindu–Arabic numeration system have changed considerably over the centuries. The most recent variation is the bar codes that can be read by a computer.

world. By the year A.D. 750, the zero symbol and the idea of a positional system had been brought to Baghdad and translated into Arabic. We are not certain how these numerals were introduced into Europe, but is likely that they came via Spain in the 8th century. Gerbert, who later became Pope Sylvester II, studied in Spain, and was the first European scholar known to have taught these numerals. Because of the origins, these numerals are called the **Hindu–Arabic numerals.** Since ten basic symbols are used, the Hindu–Arabic numeration system is also called the *decimal numeration system,* from the Latin word *decem,* meaning "ten."

At an early age, we learn our numbers as we learn to count, but if we are asked to define what we mean by *number,* we are generally at a loss. There are many different kinds of numbers, and one type of number is usually defined in terms of more primitive types of numbers. The word *number* is taken as one of our primitive (or undefined) words, but it is used to answer the question "How many?" For example, if we asked how many stars are in this list: ★★★ ★★, you would answer "five," but someone else might answer "cinq," or "cinco," or "fünf." Someone else might respond by saying, "There are '3 + 2' stars." In other words, there is one number 5, but there might be many symbols used to represent the idea of "five." The concept of "fiveness" is called a **number;** the symbol used to represent the concept is called a **numeral.**

A **numeration system** consists of a set of basic symbols and some rules for making other symbols from them, the purpose being the identification of all numbers. In the first sections of this book, we have assumed a knowledge of the Hindu–Arabic (decimal) numeration system. The invention of a precise and "workable" way of putting together a set of symbols that is easily learned to represent the multitude of possible numbers is one of the greatest inventions of humanity. It is certainly equal to the invention of the alphabet, which takes 26 letters and uses them to carry the knowledge of one generation to the next.

In this section, we take a deeper look at the Hindu–Arabic numeration system:

- It uses ten symbols, called digits.
- Larger numbers are expressed in terms of powers of 10.
- It is positional.

Consider how we count objects:

■ ■ ■ ■ ■ ■ ■ ■ ■ ■
1 2 3 4 5 6 7 8 9 ?

At this point we could invent another symbol as the Egyptians did (you might suggest 0, but remember that 0 represents no objects), or we could reuse the digit symbols by repeating them or by altering their positions. We agree to use 10 to mean 1 group of

We call this group a **ten.** The symbol 0 was invented as a placeholder to show that the 1 here is in a different position from the 1 representing ■. We continue to count:

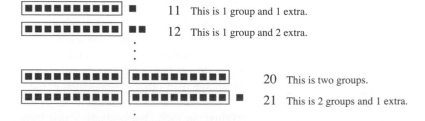

We continue in the same fashion until we have 9 groups and 9 extra. What's next? It is 10 groups or a group of groups:

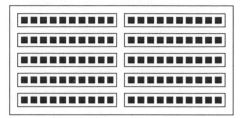

We call this group of groups a $10 \cdot 10$ or 10^2 or a **hundred.** We again use position and repeat the symbol 1 with still different meaning: 100.

EXAMPLE 1   **Meaning of a number given in decimal form**

What does 134 mean?

Solution   **134** means that we have **1** group of 100, **3** groups of 10, and **4** extra. In symbols,

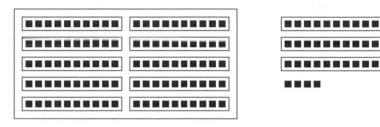

We denote this more simply by writing:

These represent the number in each group.

$$(\mathbf{1} \ \times \ \underbrace{10^2}) + (\mathbf{3} \ \times \ \underbrace{10}) + \mathbf{4}$$

These are the names of the groups.

This leads us to the meaning *one hundred, three tens, four ones.*   ●

The representation, or the meaning, of the number 134 in Example 1 is called **expanded notation.**

EXAMPLE 2   **Writing a decimal numeral in expanded notation**

Write 52,613 in expanded form.

Solution $52{,}613 = 50{,}000 + 2{,}000 + 600 + 10 + 3$
$= 5 \times 10^4 + 2 \times 10^3 + 6 \times 10^2 + 1 \times 10 + 3$ ●

EXAMPLE 3   **Writing an expanded numeral in decimal notation**

Write $4 \times 10^8 + 9 \times 10^7 + 6 \times 10^4 + 3 \times 10 + 7$ in decimal form.

Solution You can use the order of operations and multiply out the digits, but you should be able to go directly to decimal form if you remember what place value means:

$$4\ 9\ 0\ 0\ 6\ 0\ 0\ 3\ 7 = 490{,}060{,}037$$

Notice that there were no powers of 10^6, 10^5, 10^3, or 10^2.

The positions to the right of the decimal point are fractions:

$$\frac{1}{10} = 10^{-1}, \qquad \frac{1}{100} = 10^{-2}, \qquad \frac{1}{1{,}000} = 10^{-3}$$

To complete the pattern, we also sometimes write $10 = 10^1$ and $1 = 10^0$.

EXAMPLE 4   **Writing a decimal numeral with fractional parts in expanded form**

Write 479.352 using expanded notation.

Solution $479.352 = 400 + 70 + 9 + 0.3 + 0.05 + 0.002$

$$= 400 + 70 + 9 + \frac{3}{10} + \frac{5}{100} + \frac{2}{1{,}000}$$

$$= 4 \times 10^2 + 7 \times 10^1 + 9 \times 10^0 + 3 \times 10^{-1}$$
$$+ 5 \times 10^{-2} + 2 \times 10^{-3}$$

PROBLEM SET (1.8)

ESSENTIAL IDEAS   **LEVEL 1**

1. **IN YOUR OWN WORDS** Discuss the difference between "number" and "numeral."

2. **IN YOUR OWN WORDS** What is expanded notation?

3. **IN YOUR OWN WORDS** What do we mean by a decimal numeration system?

4. **IN YOUR OWN WORDS** What is a Hindu–Arabic numeral?

5. What is a group of groups in:

   a. base 10   *100*   **b.** base 20   *400*

6. What is a group of groups in:

   a. base 2   *2*   **b.** base 8   *64*

DRILL AND PRACTICE   **LEVEL 2**

Explain each of the concepts or procedures in Problems 7–10.
See IAS for meanings.

7. Illustrate the meaning of 123.

8. Illustrate the meaning of 145.

9. Illustrate the meaning of 1,234 by showing the appropriate groupings.

10. Illustrate the meaning of 1,326 by showing the appropriate groupings.

Give the meaning of the numeral 5 in each of the numbers in Problems 11–16.

11. 805   *5 units*

12. 508   *5 hundreds*

13. 0.00567   *5 thousandths*

14. 0.00765   *5 hundred-thousandths*

15. 5×10^4 *5 ten thousands*

16. 58,000,000   *5 ten millions*

Write the numbers in Problems 17–30 in decimal notation.

17. **a.** 10^5 *100,000*   **b.** 10^3 *1,000*

18. **a.** 10^6 *1,000,000*   **b.** 10^4 *10,000*

19. **a.** 10^{-4} *0.0001*   **b.** 10^{-3} *0.001*

20. **a.** 10^{-2} *0.01*   **b.** 10^{-6} *0.000001*

21. **a.** 5×10^3 *5,000*   **b.** 5×10^2 *500*

22. **a.** 8×10^{-4} *0.0008*   **b.** 7×10^{-3} *0.007*

23. **a.** 6×10^{-2} *0.06*   **b.** 9×10^{-5} *0.00009*

24. a. 5×10^{-6} 0.000005

b. 2×10^{-9} 0.000000002

25. a. $1 \times 10^4 + 0 \times 10^3 + 2 \times 10^2 + 3 \times 10^1 + 4 \times 10^0$ 10,234

b. $6 \times 10^1 + 5 \times 10^0 + 0 \times 10^{-1} + 8 \times 10^{-2} + 9 \times 10^{-3}$ 65.089

26. a. $5 \times 10^5 + 2 \times 10^4 + 1 \times 10^3 + 6 \times 10^2 + 5 \times 10^1 + 8 \times 10^0$ 521,658

b. $6 + 10^7 + 4 \times 10^3 + 1 \times 10^0$ 60,004,001

27. a. $7 \times 10^6 + 3 \times 10^{-2}$ 7,000,000.03

b. $6 \times 10^9 + 2 \times 10^{-3}$ 6,000,000,000.002

28. $5 \times 10^5 + 4 \times 10^2 + 5 \times 10^1 + 7 \times 10^0 + 3 \times 10^{-1} + 4 \times 10^{-2}$ 500,457.34

29. $3 \times 10^3 + 2 \times 10^1 + 8 \times 10^0 + 5 \times 10^{-1} + 4 \times 10^{-2} + 2 \times 10^{-4}$ 3,028.5402

30. $2 \times 10^4 + 6 \times 10^2 + 4 \times 10^{-1} + 7 \times 10^{-3} + 6 \times 10^{-4} + 9 \times 10^{-5}$ 20,600.40769

Write each of the numbers in Problems 31–38 in expanded notation.

31. a. 741 $7 \times 10^2 + 4 \times 10 + 1$

b. 728,407 $7 \times 10^5 + 2 \times 10^4 + 8 \times 10^3 + 4 \times 10^2 + 7$

32. a. 0.096421
$9 \times 10^{-2} + 6 \times 10^{-3} + 4 \times 10^{-4} + 2 \times 10^{-5} + 1 \times 10^{-6}$
b. 27.572 $2 \times 10 + 7 + 5 \times 10^{-1} + 7 \times 10^{-2} + 2 \times 10^{-3}$

33. a. 47.00215 $4 \times 10^1 + 7 + 2 \times 10^{-3} + 1 \times 10^{-4} + 5 \times 10^{-5}$

b. 521 $5 \times 10^2 + 2 \times 10 + 1$

34. a. 6,245 $6 \times 10^3 + 2 \times 10^2 + 4 \times 10^1 + 5$

b. 2,305,681
$2 \times 10^6 + 3 \times 10^5 + 5 \times 10^3 + 6 \times 10^2 + 8 \times 10^1 + 1$
35. a. 428.31 $4 \times 10^2 + 2 \times 10^1 + 8 + 3 \times 10^{-1} + 1 \times 10^{-2}$

b. 5,245.5 $5 \times 10^3 + 2 \times 10^2 + 4 \times 10^1 + 5 + 5 \times 10^{-1}$

36. a. 0.00000527 $5 \times 10^{-6} + 2 \times 10^{-7} + 7 \times 10^{-8}$

b. 100,000.001 $1 \times 10^5 + 1 \times 10^{-3}$

37. a. 893.0001 $8 \times 10^2 + 9 \times 10^1 + 3 + 1 \times 10^{-4}$

b. 8.00005 $8 + 5 \times 10^{-5}$

38. a. 678,000.01 $6 \times 10^5 + 7 \times 10^4 + 8 \times 10^3 + 1 \times 10^{-2}$

b. 57,285.9361 $5 \times 10^4 \mid 7 \times 10^3 + 2 \times 10^2 \times 8 \times 10^1 + 5 + 9 \times 10^{-1} + 3 \times 10^{-2} + 6 \times 10^{-3} + 1 \times 10^{-4}$

APPLICATIONS   **LEVEL 2**

One of the oldest devices used for calculation is the abacus, as shown in Figure 1.3. Each rod names one of the positions we use in counting. Each bead on the bottom represents one unit in that column and each bead on the top represents 5 units in that column. The number illustrated in Figure 1.3 is 1,734. What number is illustrated by the drawings in Problems 39–44?

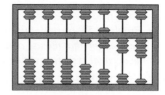

Figure 1.3 Abacus

39. 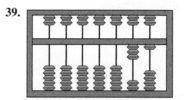   31

40. 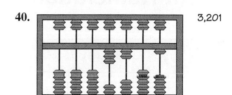   3,201

41. 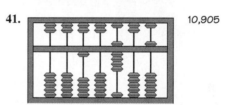   10,905

42. 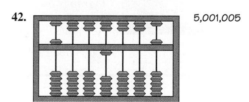   5,001,005

43. 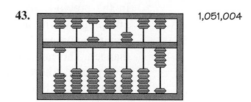   1,051,004

44. 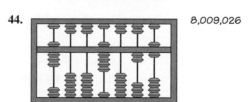   8,009,026

Sketch an abacus to show the numbers given in Problems 45–52.
See IAS.

45. 132   **46.** 849   **47.** 3,214   **48.** 9,387

49. 1,998   **50.** 2,001   **51.** 3,000,400   **52.** 8,007,009

Some applications do not lend themselves to the decimal numeration system. Problems 53–60 are of this type, and we will see in the following section that the use of numeration systems other than the decimal system might be appropriate.

53. Add 5 years, 7 months to 6 years, 8 months.
12 years, 3 months

54. Add 3 years, 10 months to 2 years, 5 months.
6 years, 3 months

55. Add 10 ft, 7 in. to 7 ft, 10 in.   18 ft, 5 in.

56. Add 6 ft, 8 in. to 9 ft, 5 in.   16 ft, 1 in.

57. Add 2 gross, 3 dozen, 4 units to 5 gross, 9 dozen, 10 units.
8 gross, 1 dozen, 2 units

58. Add 1 gross, 9 dozen, 7 units to 2 gross, 8 dozen, 8 units.
4 gross, 6 dozen, 3 units

59. If you keep one investment for 1 year, 7 months, 11 days, and then roll it over into another investment for 1 year, 6 months, 26 days, how long was the total investment (if you assume that all months are 30 days long)?
3 years, 2 months, 7 days

60. If you keep one investment for 3 years, 4 months, 21 days, and then roll it over into another investment for 1 year, 6 months, 15 days, how long was the total investment (if you assume that all months are 30 days long)?
4 years, 11 months, 6 days

1.9   Different Numeration Systems

IN THIS WORLD   THE POWER OF MATH

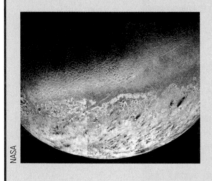

"Do you know what my teacher said today?" asked George. "He wanted me to add 1 + 1 in something called base two, whatever that is. Well, he just stared at me so I had to say something, so I blurted out sarcastically, '2.' And THEN he had the nerve to say, 'No, the answer is 10.'"

"Well, George, he was right. In base 2, 1 + 1 = 10," said Bill.

"Why would we ever use a base other than base 10?" exclaimed George.

"I can name one obvious example. Do you remember those photographs we just saw of Triton, Neptune's largest moon?" asked Bill. "When photographs are sent back from space, they are sent using a binary numeration system."

 See Problem 60.

In the previous section, we discussed the Hindu–Arabic numeration system and grouping by tens. However, we could group by twos, fives, twelves, or any other counting number. In this section, we summarize numeration systems with bases other than ten. This not only will help you understand our own numeration system, but will give you insight into the numeration systems used with computers, namely, base 2 (**binary**), base 8 (**octal**), and base 16 (**hexadecimal**).

Number of Symbols

The number of symbols used in a particular base depends on the method of grouping for that base. For example, in base ten the grouping is by tens, and in base five the grouping is by fives. Suppose we wish to count

■■■■■■■■■■■

in various bases. Let's look for patterns in Table 1.1. Note the use of the subscript following the numeral to keep track of the base in which we are working.

TABLE 1.1	Grouping in Various Bases		
Base	**Symbols**	**Method of Grouping**	**Notation**
two	0, 1		1011_{two}
three	0, 1, 2		102_{three}
four	0, 1, 2, 3		23_{four}
five	0, 1, 2, 3, 4		21_{five}
six	0, 1, 2, 3, 4, 5		15_{six}
seven	0, 1, 2, 3, 4, 5, 6		14_{seven}
eight	0, 1, 2, 3, 4, 5, 6, 7		13_{eight}
nine	0, 1, 2, 3, 4, 5, 6, 7, 8		12_{nine}
ten	0, 1, 2, 3, 4, 5, 6, 7, 8, 9		11_{ten}

Do you see any patterns? Suppose we wish to continue this pattern. Can we group by elevens or twelves? We can, provided new symbols are "invented." For base eleven (or higher bases), we use the symbol T to represent ■■■■■■■■■■. For base twelve (or higher bases), we use E to stand for ■■■■■■■■■■■. For bases larger than twelve, other symbols can be invented.

For example, $2T_{twelve}$ means that there are two groupings of twelve and T (ten) extra:

We continue with the pattern from Table 1.1 by continuing beyond base ten in Table 1.2.

TABLE 1.2	Grouping in Various Bases		
Base	**Symbols**	**Method of Grouping**	**Notation**
eleven	0, 1, 2, 3, 4, 5, 6, 7, 8, 9, T		10_{eleven}
twelve	0, 1, 2, 3, 4, 5, 6, 7, 8, 9, T, E		E_{twelve}
thirteen	0, 1, 2, 3, 4, 5, 6, 7, 8, 9, T, E, U		$E_{thirteen}$
fourteen	0, 1, 2, 3, 4, 5, 6, 7, 8, 9, T, E, U, V		$E_{fourteen}$

Do you see more patterns? Can you determine the number of symbols in each base system?

Change from Some Base to Base Ten

To change from base b to base ten, we write the numerals in expanded notation. The resulting number is in base ten.

EXAMPLE 1 **Changing to base ten**

Change each number to base ten.

a. 1011.01_{two} **b.** 1011.01_{four} **c.** 1011.01_{five}

Solution

a. $1011.01_{two} = 1 \times 2^3 + 0 \times 2^2 + 1 \times 2^1 + 1 \times 2^0 + 0 \times 2^{-1} + 1 \times 2^{-2}$
$$= 8 + 0 + 2 + 1 + 0 + 0.25$$
$$= 11.25$$

b. $1011.01_{four} = 1 \times 4^3 + 0 \times 4^2 + 1 \times 4^1 + 1 \times 4^0 + 0 \times 4^{-1} + 1 \times 4^{-2}$
$$= 64 + 0 + 4 + 1 + 0 + 0.0625$$
$$= 69.0625$$

c. $1011.01_{five} = 1 \times 5^3 + 0 \times 5^2 + 1 \times 5^1 + 1 \times 5^0 + 0 \times 5^{-1} + 1 \times 5^{-2}$
$$= 125 + 0 + 5 + 1 + 0 + 0.04$$
$$= 131.04$$

Change from Base Ten to Some Base

To see how to change from base ten to any other valid base, let's again look for a pattern:

To change from base ten to base two, group by twos.

To change from base ten to base three, group by threes.

To change from base ten to base four, group by fours.

To change from base ten to base five, group by fives.

$$\vdots$$

The groupings from this pattern are summarized in Table 1.3.

TABLE 1.3	Place-Value Chart					
Base			**Place Value**			
2	$2^5 = 32$	$2^4 = 16$	$2^3 = 8$	$2^2 = 4$	$2^1 = 2$	$2^0 = 1$
3	$3^5 = 243$	$3^4 = 81$	$3^3 = 27$	$3^2 = 9$	$3^1 = 3$	$3^0 = 1$
4	$4^5 = 1,024$	$4^4 = 256$	$4^3 = 64$	$4^2 = 16$	$4^1 = 4$	$4^0 = 1$
5	$5^5 = 3,125$	$5^4 = 625$	$5^3 = 125$	$5^2 = 25$	$5^1 = 5$	$5^0 = 1$
6	$6^5 = 7,776$	$6^4 = 1,296$	$6^3 = 216$	$6^2 = 36$	$6^1 = 6$	$6^0 = 1$
7	$7^5 = 16,807$	$7^4 = 2,401$	$7^3 = 343$	$7^2 = 49$	$7^1 = 7$	$7^0 = 1$
8	$8^5 = 32,768$	$8^4 = 4,096$	$8^3 = 512$	$8^2 = 64$	$8^1 = 8$	$8^0 = 1$
10	$10^5 = 100,000$	$10^4 = 10,000$	$10^3 = 1,000$	$10^2 = 100$	$10^1 = 10$	$10^0 = 1$
12	$12^5 = 248,832$	$12^4 = 20,736$	$12^3 = 1,728$	$12^2 = 144$	$12^1 = 12$	$12^0 = 1$

The next example shows how we can interpret this grouping process in terms of a simple division.

EXAMPLE 2   **Changing to base two**

Convert 42 to base two.

Solution Using Table 1.3, we see that the largest power of two smaller than 42 is 2^5, so we begin with $2^5 = 32$:

$$42 = 1 \times 2^5 + 10$$
$$10 = 0 \times 2^4 + 10$$
$$10 = 1 \times 2^3 + 2$$
$$2 = 0 \times 2^2 + 2$$
$$2 = 1 \times 2^1 + 0$$
$$0 = 0 \times 2^0$$

We could now write out 42 in expanded notation:

$$42 = 1 \times 2^5 + 0 \times 2^4 + 1 \times 2^3 + 0 \times 2^2 + 1 \times 2^2 + 0 \times 2^0 = 101010_{two}$$

Instead of carrying out the steps by using Table 1.3, we will begin with 42 and carry out repeated division, saving each remainder as we go. We are changing to base 2, so we do repeated division by 2:

$$\begin{array}{r} 21 \\ 2\overline{)42} \end{array} \quad \text{r. } 0 \quad \leftarrow \text{ Save remainder.}$$

Next, we need to divide 21 by 2, but instead of rewriting our work we work our way up:

$$\begin{array}{r} 10 \\ 2\overline{)21} \\ 2\overline{)42} \end{array} \quad \begin{array}{l} \text{r. } 1 \quad \leftarrow \text{ Save all remainders.} \\ \text{r. } 0 \quad \leftarrow \text{ Save remainder.} \end{array}$$

Continue by doing repeated division.

Stop when you get a zero here.
↓

$$\begin{array}{r} 0 \\ 2\overline{)\ 1} \\ 2\overline{)\ 2} \\ 2\overline{)\ 5} \\ 2\overline{)10} \\ 2\overline{)21} \\ 2\overline{)42} \end{array} \quad \begin{array}{l} \text{r. } 1 \\ \text{r. } 0 \\ \text{r. } 1 \\ \text{r. } 0 \\ \text{r. } 1 \\ \text{r. } 0 \end{array} \quad \left| \begin{array}{l} \text{Answer is found by reading down.} \\ \\ \\ \downarrow \end{array} \right.$$

Thus, $42 = 101010_{two}$.
You can check by using expanded notation:

$$101010_{two} = 1 \times 2^5 + 1 \times 2^3 + 1 \times 2 = 32 + 8 + 2 = 42 \qquad \bullet$$

EXAMPLE 3   **Changing from base 10 to other bases**

Write 42 in: **a.** base three   **b.** base four

Solution

a. Begin with $3^3 = 27$ (from Table 1.3):

$$\begin{array}{l} 42 = 1 \times 3^3 + 15 \\ 15 = 1 \times 3^2 + 6 \\ 6 = 2 \times 3^1 + 0 \\ 0 = 0 \times 3^0 \end{array} \qquad \text{or} \qquad \begin{array}{r} 0 \\ 3\overline{)\ 1} \\ 3\overline{)\ 4} \\ 3\overline{)14} \\ 3\overline{)42} \end{array} \quad \begin{array}{l} \text{r. } 1 \\ \text{r. } 1 \\ \text{r. } 2 \\ \text{r. } 0 \end{array}$$

Thus, $42 = 1120_{three}$.

b. Begin with $4^2 = 16$ (from Table 1.3):

$$42 = 2 \times 4^2 + 10 \qquad \text{or}$$
$$10 = 2 \times 4^1 + 2$$
$$2 = 2 \times 4^0$$

$$
\begin{array}{r}
0 \quad \text{r. } 2 \\
4\overline{)\ 2} \quad \text{r. } 2 \\
4\overline{)10} \quad \text{r. } 2 \\
4\overline{)42}
\end{array}
$$

Thus, $42 = 222_{four}$.

EXAMPLE 4   **Applied number base problem**

Suppose you need to purchase 1,000 name tags and can buy them by the gross (144), the dozen (12), or individually. The name tags cost $0.50 each, $4.80 per dozen, and $50.40 per gross. How should you order to minimize the cost?

Solution   If you purchase 1,000 tags individually, the cost is $0.50 \times 1,000 = \$500$. This is not the least cost possible, because of the bulk discounts. We must find the maximum number of gross, the number of dozens, and then purchase the remainder individually. We will proceed by repeated division by 12, which we recognize as equivalent to changing the number to base twelve. Change 1,000 to base 12:

$$
\begin{array}{r}
0 \quad \text{r. } 6 \\
12\overline{)\quad 6} \quad \text{r. } 11, \text{ or } E \text{ in base twelve} \\
12\overline{)\quad 83} \quad \text{r. } 4 \\
12\overline{)1{,}000}
\end{array}
$$

Thus, $1,000 = 6E4_{twelve}$ so you must purchase 6 gross, 11 dozen, and 4 individual tags. Let's check: The cost is $6 \times \$50.40 + 11 \times \$4.80 + 4 \times \$0.50 = \$357.20$. As you can see, this is considerably less expensive than purchasing the individual name tags.

PROBLEM SET (1.9)

ESSENTIAL IDEAS   LEVEL 1

1. IN YOUR OWN WORDS Explain the process of changing from base eight to base ten.

2. IN YOUR OWN WORDS Explain the process of changing from base sixteen to base ten.

3. IN YOUR OWN WORDS Explain the process of changing from base ten to base eight.

4. IN YOUR OWN WORDS Explain the process of changing from base ten to base sixteen.

DRILL AND PRACTICE   LEVEL 2

5. Count the number of people in the indicated base.

a. base ten   9
b. base five 14_{five}
c. base three 100_{three}
d. base eight 11_{eight}
e. base two 1001_{two}
f. base nine 10_{nine}

6. Count the number of people in the indicated base.

   a. base ten   13   **b.** base five 23_{five}

   c. base thirteen $10_{thirteen}$ **d.** base eight 15_{eight}

   e. base two 1101_{two} **f.** base twelve 11_{twelve}

In Problems 7–16, write the numbers in expanded notation.

7. 643_{eight} $6 \times 8^2 + 4 \times 8^1 + 3 \times 8^0$

8. 5387.9_{twelve} $5 \times 12^3 + 3 \times 12^2 + 8 \times 12^1 + 7 \times 12^0 + 9 \times 12^{-1}$

9. 110111.1001_{two} $1 \times 2^5 + 1 \times 2^4 + 1 \times 2^2 + 1 \times 2^1 + 1 \times 2^0 + 1 \times 2^{-1} + 1 \times 2^{-4}$

10. 5411.1023_{six} $5 \times 6^3 + 4 \times 6^2 + 1 \times 6^1 + 1 \times 6^0 + 1 \times 6^{-1} + 2 \times 6^{-3} + 3 \times 6^{-4}$

11. 64200051_{eight} $6 \times 8^7 + 4 \times 8^6 + 2 \times 8^5 + 5 \times 8^1 \times 1 \times 8^0$

12. 1021.221_{three} $1 \times 3^3 + 2 \times 3^1 + 1 \times 3^0 + 2 \times 3^{-1} + 2 \times 3^{-2} + 1 \times 3^{-3}$

13. 323000.2_{four} $3 \times 4^5 + 2 \times 4^4 + 3 \times 4^3 + 2 \times 4^{-1}$

14. 234000_{five} $2 \times 5^6 + 3 \times 5^4 + 4 \times 5^3$

15. 3.40231_{five} $3 \times 5^0 + 4 \times 5^{-1} + 2 \times 5^{-3} + 3 \times 5^{-4} + 1 \times 5^{-5}$

16. 2033.1_{four} $2 \times 4^3 + 3 \times 4^1 + 3 \times 4^0 + 1 \times 4^{-1}$

Change the numbers in Problems 17–30 to base ten.

17. 527_{eight} 343   **18.** 527_{twelve} 751

19. $25TE_{twelve}$ 4,307   **20.** 1101.11_{two} 13.75

21. 431_{five} 116   **22.** 65_{eight} 53

23. 1011.101_{two} 11.625

24. 11101000110_{two} 1,862

25. 573_{twelve} 807   **26.** 4312_{eight} 2,250

27. 2110_{three} 66   **28.** 4312_{five} 582

29. 537.1_{eight} 351.125   **30.** 3731_{eight} 2,009

31. Change 724 to base five. 10344_{five}

32. Change 628 to base four. 21310_{four}

33. Change 256 to base two. 100000000_{two}

34. Change 427 to base twelve. $2E7_{twelve}$

35. Change 412 to base five. 3122_{five}

36. Change 615 to base eight. 1147_{eight}

37. Change 5,133 to base twelve. $2E79_{twelve}$

38. Change 615 to base two. 1001100111_{two}

39. Change 512 to base two. 1000000000_{two}

40. Change 795 to base seven. 2214_{seven}

41. Change 52 to base three. 1221_{three}

42. Change 4,731 to base twelve. $28T3_{twelve}$

43. Change 602 to base eight. 1132_{eight}

44. Change 76 to base four. 1030_{four}

APPLICATIONS   **LEVEL 2**

Use number bases to answer the questions given in Problems 45–58.

45. Change 158 hours to days and hours.   6 days, 14 hours

46. Change 52 days to weeks and days.   7 weeks, 3 days

47. Change 39 ounces to pounds and ounces.   2 lb, 7 oz

48. Change 55 inches to feet and inches.   4 ft, 7 in.

49. Change $4.59 to quarters, nickels, and pennies.
18 quarters, 1 nickel, 4 pennies

50. Change 500 to gross, dozens, and units.
3 gross, 5 doz, 8 units

51. Suppose you have two quarters, four nickels, and two pennies. Use base five to write a numeral to indicate your financial status. 242_{five}; financial status is $0.72

52. Using only quarters, nickels, and pennies, what is the minimum number of coins needed to make $0.84?
$84 = 314_{five}$, so 8 coins

53. Change $8.34 to the smallest number of coins consisting of quarters, nickels, and pennies.
33 quarters, 1 nickel, 4 pennies

54. A bookstore ordered 9 gross, 5 dozen, and 4 pencils. Write this number in base twelve and in base ten.
$954_{twelve} = 1,360$ pencils

55. Change 54 months to years and months.
$54 = 46_{twelve}$; 4 years, 6 months

56. Change 44 days to weeks and days.
$44 = 62_{seven}$; 6 weeks, 2 days

57. Change 49 hours to days and hours.
$49 = 21_{twenty-four}$; 2 days, 1 hour

58. Change 29 hours to days and hours.
$29 = 15_{twenty-four}$; 1 day, 5 hours

59. IN YOUR OWN WORDS The *duodecimal numeration system* refers to the base twelve system, which uses the symbols 0, 1, 2, 3, 4, 5, 6, 7, 8, 9, *T*, *E*. Historically, a numeration system based on 12 is not new. There were 12 tribes in Israel and 12 Apostles of Christ. In Babylon, 12 was used as a base for the numeration system before it was replaced by 60. In the 18th and 19th centuries, Charles XII of Sweden and Georg Buffon (1707–1788) advocated the adoption of the base twelve system. Even today there is a Duodecimal Society of America that advocates the adoption of this system. According to the Society's literature, no one "who thought long enough—three to 17 minutes—to grasp the central idea of the duodecimal system ever failed to concede its superiority." Study the duodecimal system from 3 to 17 minutes, and comment on whether you agree with the Society's statement.

60. IN YOUR OWN WORDS Discuss the binary (base two) numeration system.

1.10 Chapter 1 Summary and Review

Take some time getting ready to work the review problems in this section. First, look back at the definition and property boxes. You will maximize your understanding of this chapter by working the problems in this section only after you have studied the material.

IMPORTANT TERMS
Numbers refer to sections of this chapter.

Spending some time with the terms and objectives of this chapter will pay dividends in assuring your success.

Abacus [1.8]
Addition [1.2, 1.7]
Approximately equal to symbol [1.3]
Base [1.5]
Binary [1.9]
Canceling [1.6]
Column names [1.3]
Common denominator [1.7]
Common fraction [1.3]
Completely reduced fraction [1.6]
Complex decimal [1.6]
Composite [1.5]
Counting number [1.2]
Cubed [1.5]
Decimal [1.3]
Decimal fraction [1.3]
Decimal numeration system [1.9]
Decimal point [1.3]
Denominator [1.3]
Difference [1.2]
Distributive property (for multiplication over addition) [1.2]
Divide fractions [1.6]
Division by zero [1.3]
Divisor [1.6]
Elementary operations [1.2]
Estimation [1.2]
Expanded notation [1.8]

Exponent [1.5]
Exponential notation [1.5]
Extended order of operations [1.7]
Factor [1.5]
Factoring [1.5]
Factorization [1.5]
Factor tree [1.5]
Fraction [1.3]
Fundamental property of fractions [1.6]
Googol [1.5]
Hexadecimal [1.9]
Hindu–Arabic numerals [1.8]
Hundred [1.3]
Improper fraction [1.3]
Invert [1.6]
Juxtaposition [1.2]
LCD [1.7]
Lowest common denominator [1.7]
Mixed number [1.3]
Multiply fractions [1.6]
Natural number [1.2]
Number [1.8]
Numeral [1.8]
Numeration system [1.8]
Numerator [1.3]
Numerical expression [1.2]
Octal [1.9]
Order of operations [1.2]

Place-value chart [1.9]
Place-value names [1.3]
Power [1.5]
Powers of ten [1.5]
Prime factorization [1.5]
Prime number [1.5]
Product [1.2]
Proper fraction [1.3]
Quotient [1.2]
Rational number [1.3]
Reciprocal [1.6]
Reduced fraction [1.6]
Reducing fractions [1.6]
Remainder [1.3]
Repeating decimal [1.3]
Rounding money [1.4]
Rounding numbers [1.4]
Scientific notation [1.5]
Simplify a fractional expression [1.6]
Simplify a numerical expression [1.2]
Squared [1.5]
Subtraction of fractions [1.7]
Sum [1.2]
Ten [1.3]
Terminating decimal [1.3]
Trailing zeros [1.3]
Translation [1.2]
Whole numbers [1.2]

Essential Ideas

[1.1] Problems 1–4	Road sign warnings	
Problems 5–10	Behavior for success in this course	
[1.2] Problem 1	Order of operations	
Problem 2	Distributive property	
[1.3] Problems 1, 4	Meaning of fractions	
Problems 2–3	Division by zero	
Problem 5	Place-value meanings	

[1.4] Problem 1	Rounding place digit
Problem 2	Process of rounding
[1.5] Problems 1; 5–8	Definition of exponent; terminology of power notation
Problem 2	Scientific notation
Problem 3	Prime factorization
Problem 4	Distinguish exponent and EE calculator keys
[1.6] Problem 1	Fundamental property of fractions
Problems 2–3	Reducing fractions
Problems 4–5	Multiplying and dividing fractions
Problem 6	Changing decimals to fractions
[1.7] Problem 1	Extended order of operations
Problems 2–4	Adding and subtracting fractions
[1.8] Problem 1	Contrast number/numeral
Problem 2	Expanded notation
Problems 3–6	Meaning of Hindu–Arabic numerals
[1.9] Problems 1–4	Changing from one base to another

LEARNING OUTCOMES

The material in this chapter is reviewed in the following list of learning outcomes. A self-test (with answers and suggestions for additional study) is given. This self-test is constructed so that each problem number corresponds to a related objective. For example, Problem 7 is testing Objective 1.7. This self-test is followed by a practice test with the questions in mixed order.

[1.1]	*Objective* 1.1	Know some of the symptoms and possible cures for math anxiety.
[1.2]	*Objective* 1.2	Use the order-of-operations agreement to carry out calculations with mixed operations. Classify an expression as a sum, difference, product, or quotient.
[1.2]	*Objective* 1.3	Use the distributive property to eliminate parentheses.
[1.2]	*Objective* 1.4	Translate from words into math symbols.
[1.2–1.7]	*Objective* 1.5	Estimate answers to arithmetic problems.
[1.3]	*Objective* 1.6	Classify a fraction as proper, improper, or a whole number and be able to enter a fraction into a calculator. Recognize whether the fraction is reduced.
[1.3]	*Objective* 1.7	Write an improper fraction as a mixed number or a whole number.
[1.3]	*Objective* 1.8	Write a mixed number as an improper fraction.
[1.3]	*Objective* 1.9	Change a common fraction to a decimal fraction.
[1.4]	*Objective* 1.10	Round a decimal fraction to a specified degree of accuracy.
[1.5]	*Objective* 1.11	Write a number in scientific notation.
[1.5]	*Objective* 1.12	Write a number without exponents.
[1.5]	*Objective* 1.13	Find the prime factorization of a given number.
[1.6]	*Objective* 1.14	Reduce a common fraction.
[1.6]	*Objective* 1.15	Understand the meaning of multiplying and dividing fractions.
[1.6]	*Objective* 1.16	Multiply and divide common fractions.
[1.6]	*Objective* 1.17	Change a decimal fraction to a common fraction.
[1.7]	*Objective* 1.18	Add and subtract common fractions with common denominators.
[1.7]	*Objective* 1.19	Find the LCD for some given denominators.
[1.7]	*Objective* 1.20	Add and subtract common fractions.

[1.7]	*Objective* 1.21	Carry out mixed operations with fractions, including those using juxtaposition.
[1.8]	*Objective* 1.22	Explain (or illustrate) the meaning of a number.
[1.8]	*Objective* 1.23	Write a number in expanded notation as a decimal numeral.
[1.8]	*Objective* 1.24	Write a decimal number in expanded notation.
[1.9]	*Objective* 1.25	Count objects using various bases.
[1.9]	*Objective* 1.26	Write numbers in various bases in expanded notation.
[1.9]	*Objective* 1.27	Change numerals in various bases to base ten.
[1.9]	*Objective* 1.28	Change base ten numerals to a given base.
[1.2–1.9]	*Objective* 1.29	Work applied problems. (See Problems 29–30.)

Self-Test

Each question of this self-test is related to the corresponding objective listed above.

1. Describe what is meant by math anxiety.

2. Simplify $40 + 20 \div 5 \times 3$, and classify as a sum, difference, product, or quotient.

3. Rewrite $8(500 + 60 + 7)$ using the distributive property.

4. Find (translate) and then simplify:
   a. the sum of the squares of three and eleven
   b. the square of the sum of three and eleven

5. If you spend $1.85 per day on tolls, estimate the amount you spend each year.

6. Classify each fraction as proper, improper, or a whole number, and then show the keystrokes required to enter each fraction into a calculator. State which of these fractions are reduced.
   a. $\frac{5}{2}$ b. $\frac{6}{2}$ c. $\frac{2}{5}$ d. $\frac{2}{6}$

7. Write $\frac{85}{6}$ as a mixed number.

8. Write $7\frac{3}{8}$ as an improper fraction.

9. Change $6\frac{1}{3}$ to decimal form.

10. Round $85.255 to the nearest cent.

11. Write 93,500,000 in scientific notation.

12. Write 8.92×10^{-9} without exponents.

13. Find the prime factorization of 1,330.

14. Reduce $\frac{1,330}{1,881}$.

15. a. Name the divisor in $18 \div 6$.
    b. Find $18 \div 6$ by direct division, and then multiply by the reciprocal.

16. a. Simplify: $5\frac{3}{8} \times 2\frac{2}{3}$
    b. Simplify: $\frac{12}{35} \div \frac{4}{7}$

17. Write $0.8\frac{1}{3}$ as a fraction.

18. Simplify $12\frac{2}{5} - 5\frac{4}{5}$.

19. Find the lowest common denominator for the numbers 120 and 700.

20. Simplify $\frac{3}{10} + \frac{4}{15} + \frac{5}{12}$.

21. Simplify $\frac{2}{3}\left(\frac{3}{8} - \frac{1}{8} \times 2\right)$.

22. Illustrate the meaning of 243.

23. Write $5 \times 10^3 + 6 \times 10^2 + 3 \times 10^{-2}$ in decimal notation.

24. Write 10,063,002 in expanded notation.

25. Count ★★★★★★★★★ in
    a. base 10   **b.** base 5   **c.** base 8   **d.** base 2

26. Write 101111.01_{two} in expanded notation.

27. Change $65ET_{twelve}$ to base ten.

28. Change 57 to base two.

29. A recipe calls for $\frac{2}{3}$ lb of Colombian coffee and $\frac{1}{2}$ lb of another coffee.
    a. What is the total weight of the mixture?
    b. If you give away one quarter of the mixture, what is the weight of the gift?

30. Change 70 months to years and months. Represent your answer using base 12 notation.

STUDY HINTS *Compare your solutions and answers to the self-test. For each problem you missed, work some additional problems in the section listed in the margin. After you have worked these problems, you can test yourself with the practice test.*

Additional Problems

[1.1] Problems 13–24; 32–40

[1.2] Problems 3–16; 29–44

[1.2] Problems 17–20

[1.2] Problems 21–28

[1.2] Problems 45–54;
[1.3] Problems 40–43;
[1.4] Problems 37–54;
[1.5] Problems 40–45;
[1.7] Problems 5–12; 38–49

[1.3] Problems 6–9

[1.3] Problems 10–15

[1.3] Problems 16–27

[1.3] Problems 28–39; 44–46

[1.4] Problems 3–30

[1.5] Problems 9–16

[1.5] Problems 17–30

Complete Solutions to the Self-Test

1. Answers vary: fear; inability to take constructive action; guilt; the more we avoid math, the less able we feel, and the less able we feel, the more we avoid it.

2. $40 + 20 \div 5 \times 3 = 40 + 4 \times 3$ *Remember the order of operations.*
   $$= 40 + 12$$
   $$= 52$$
   This is a sum.

3. $8(500 + 60 + 7) = 8(500) + 8(60) + 8(7)$.
   Use the distributive property; do not carry out the arithmetic

4. **a.** $3^2 + 11^2 = 130$ **b.** $(3 + 11)^2 = 196$

5. $\$1.85 \times 365 \approx \$2 \times 350 = \$700$; you would spend about $700 per year on tolls. Calculator check: $1.85 \times 365 = 675.25$.

6. **a.** reduced improper fraction   **b.** whole number
   c. reduced proper fraction   **d.** proper fraction

7. $\frac{85}{6} = 14\frac{1}{6}$. Find $85 \div 6 = 14$ with remainder 1.

8. $7\frac{3}{8} = \frac{59}{8}$. Find $8 \times 7 + 3 = 59$.

9. $6.\overline{3}$.
   Do not round your answer; 6.3333333 is not correct; $6.33\frac{1}{3}$ is not a simplified form.

10. $85.26. The rounding place digit is the hundredth column: 85.2\boxed{5}$5.

11. 9.35×10^7. Count 7 decimal places to the right to restore the number to its given form.

12. 0.00000 00089 2. Count 9 decimal places to the left.

[1.5] Problems 31–39

[1.6] Problems 7–14

[1.6] Problems 15–24

[1.6] Problems 25–35

[1.6] Problems 36–43

[1.7] Problems 13–15

[1.7] Problems 16–19

[1.7] Problems 20–31

[1.7] Problems 32–37

13. $2 \times 5 \times 7 \times 19$. Use a factor tree:

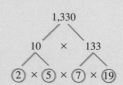

14. $\dfrac{1,330}{1,881} = \dfrac{2 \times 5 \times 7 \times \cancel{19}}{3 \times 3 \times 11 \times \cancel{19}}$ The factor tree for 1,330 is shown in Problem 13. The other tree is:

$$= \dfrac{2 \times 5 \times 7}{3 \times 3 \times 11}$$

$$= \dfrac{70}{99}$$

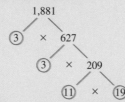

15. a. Divisor is 6.
   b. $18 \div 6 = 3$; $18 \div 6 = 18 \times \frac{1}{6} = \frac{18}{1} \times \frac{1}{6} = \frac{18}{6} = 3$
   Note that the answers are the same.

16. a. $5\frac{3}{8} \times 2\frac{2}{3} = \frac{43}{8} \times \frac{8}{3} = \frac{43}{3}$ You can also write this answer as $14\frac{1}{3}$.

   b. $\dfrac{12}{35} \div \dfrac{4}{7} = \dfrac{\overset{3}{\cancel{12}}}{\underset{5}{\cancel{35}}} \times \dfrac{\overset{1}{\cancel{7}}}{\underset{1}{\cancel{4}}} = \dfrac{3}{5}$

17. $0.8\frac{1}{3} = 8\frac{1}{3} \times \frac{1}{10} = \dfrac{\overset{5}{\cancel{25}}}{3} \times \dfrac{1}{\underset{2}{\cancel{10}}} = \dfrac{5}{6}$

18. $12\frac{2}{5} - 5\frac{4}{5} = 6\frac{3}{5}$ Write: $12\frac{2}{5} = 11\frac{7}{5}$

$$- 5\frac{4}{5} = -5\frac{4}{5}$$
$$\overline{\phantom{-5\frac{4}{5} = -}6\frac{3}{5}}$$

19. $120 = 2^3 \times 3 \times 5$
$700 = 2^2 \times 5^2 \times 7$
LCD: $2^3 \times 3 \times 5^2 \times 7 = 4,200$

20. $\dfrac{3}{10} = \dfrac{18}{60}$

$ \dfrac{4}{15} = \dfrac{16}{60}$

$+ \dfrac{5}{12} = \dfrac{25}{60}$
$$\overline{\phantom{+ \dfrac{5}{12} = \;}\dfrac{59}{60}}$$

21. $\dfrac{2}{3}\left(\dfrac{3}{8} - \dfrac{1}{8} \times 2\right) = \dfrac{2}{3}\left(\dfrac{3}{8} - \dfrac{2}{8}\right)$ Remember order of operations.

$$= \dfrac{2}{3}\left(\dfrac{1}{8}\right)$$

$$= \dfrac{1}{12}$$ Parentheses and juxtaposition (no operation symbol) mean multiplication.

22. 243 is $200 + 40 + 3$ or 2 hundreds, 4 tens, and 3 units:

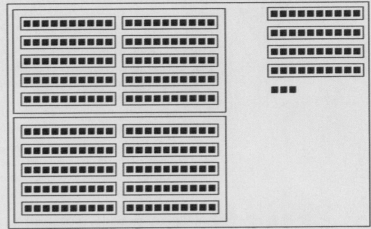

23. $5 \times 10^3 + 6 \times 10^2 + 3 \times 10^{-2} = 5{,}000 + 600 + \dfrac{3}{100} = 5{,}600.03$

24. $10{,}063{,}002 = 1 \times 10^7 + 0 \times 10^6 + 0 \times 10^5 + 6 \times 10^4$
$\qquad\qquad\qquad + 3 \times 10^3 + 0 \times 10^2 + 0 \times 10^1 + 2 \times 10^0$
$\qquad\qquad = 1 \times 10^7 + 6 \times 10^4 + 3 \times 10^3 + 2 \times 10^0$

25. a. 8

b. $\boxed{\bigstar\bigstar\bigstar\bigstar\bigstar}\ \bigstar\bigstar\bigstar$; 13_{five}

c. $\boxed{\bigstar\bigstar\bigstar\bigstar\bigstar\bigstar\bigstar\bigstar}$; 10_{eight}

d. $\boxed{\bigstar\bigstar\,|\,\bigstar\bigstar}\ \boxed{\bigstar\bigstar\,|\,\bigstar\bigstar}$; 1000_{two}

26. $101111.01_{two} = 1 \times 2^5 + 0 \times 2^4 + 1 \times 2^3 + 1 \times 2^2$
$\qquad\qquad\qquad\qquad + 1 \times 2^1 + 1 \times 2^0 + 0 \times 2^{-1} + 1 \times 2^{-2}$

27. $65ET_{twelve} = 6 \times 12^3 + 5 \times 12^2 + 11 \times 12^1 + 10 \times 12^0 = 11{,}230$

28. Use repeated division:

$$
\begin{array}{l}
\ 0 \quad \text{r. 1} \\
2)\overline{\ 1\ } \quad \text{r. 1} \\
2)\overline{\ 3\ } \quad \text{r. 1} \\
2)\overline{\ 7\ } \quad \text{r. 0} \\
2)\overline{14} \quad \text{r. 0} \\
2)\overline{28} \quad \text{r. 1} \\
2)\overline{57}
\end{array}
$$

The result is found (reading down): 111001_{two}.

29. a. $\frac{2}{3} + \frac{1}{2} = \frac{4}{6} + \frac{3}{6} = \frac{7}{6}$ The total weight is $\frac{7}{6}$ or $1\frac{1}{6}$ lb.

b. $\frac{1}{4}$ of $\frac{7}{6} = \frac{1}{4} \times \frac{7}{6} = \frac{7}{24}$ The size of the gift is $\frac{7}{24}$ lb.

 Note: In studying for the exam, be sure you look at several different types of word problems.

30. Divide 70 by 12 and save the remainder:

$$
\begin{array}{l}
\ 5 \quad \text{r. 10} \\
12)\overline{70}
\end{array}
$$

It is 5 years and 10 months, or in base 12: $5T_{twelve}$.

Chapter 1 Review Questions

*To prepare for a chapter test, first study the chapter; then, read each term from the important terms list above and make sure you know the meaning of each word; finally, review the chapter objectives. **After** these steps, take the self-test and correct all your answers. The following review questions can be used for extra practice.*

1. **IN YOUR OWN WORDS**
   a. List a symptom of math anxiety that you have experienced at some time in your life.
   b. How do you think someone with a severe case of math anxiety could learn to deal with this anxiety?
   c. Name a math myth that is easy for you to accept as a myth.
   d. Name a math myth that is difficult for you not to believe in, even if you know it is a myth.

2. a. A box of oranges contains approximately 96 oranges. If the U.S. annual production of oranges is 186,075,000 boxes, estimate the number of oranges produced each year in the United States. Leave your answer in scientific notation. $96 \times 186{,}075{,}000 \approx 10^2 \times$
   b. Your answer for part **a** is about $\qquad$ $1.86 \times 10^8 = 1.86 \times 10^{10}$
      A. 2 million   B. 20 million   C. 2 trillion   D. 2 billion   E. 20 billion   E
   c. Estimate the portion of the square that is shaded. $\frac{1}{12}$

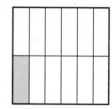

   d. Illustrate the meaning of 138.   *See IAS.*

3. Eliminate the parentheses, but do not carry out the arithmetic.
   a. $5(8 + 2)$ $5 \times 8 + 5 \times 2$
   b. $2(25 + 35)$ $2 \times 25 + 2 \times 35$
   c. $3(200 + 50 + 6)$ $3 \times 200 + 3 \times 50 + 3 \times 6$
   d. $5(400 + 50 + 9)$
      $5 \times 400 + 5 \times 50 + 5 \times 9$

4. a. Write the sum of the cubes of 2 and 3. $2^3 + 3^3 = 35$
   b. Write the cube of the sum of 2 and 3. $(2 + 3)^3 = 125$
   c. Change 13,335 seconds to hours, minutes, and seconds.   *3 hr, 42 min, 15 sec*
   d. Use a calculator to estimate 3 trillion dollars divided by the population of the United States, 215 million.   ⬛3⬛ ⬛EE⬛ ⬛12⬛ ⬛÷⬛ ⬛2.15⬛ ⬛EE⬛ ⬛8⬛ ⬛=⬛   *Answer is about $14,000/person.*

5. Write each as a mixed number.
   a. $\frac{114}{7}$ $16\frac{2}{7}$
   b. $\frac{25}{3}$ $8\frac{1}{3}$
   c. $\frac{167}{10}$ $16\frac{7}{10}$
   d. $\frac{153}{100}$ $1\frac{53}{100}$

6. Write each as an improper fraction.
   a. $4\frac{2}{3}$ $\frac{14}{3}$
   b. $1\frac{5}{8}$ $\frac{13}{8}$
   c. $3\frac{3}{4}$ $\frac{15}{4}$
   d. $12\frac{5}{9}$ $\frac{113}{9}$

7. Write in decimal form.
   a. $\frac{7}{8}$ 0.875
   b. $\frac{5}{6}$ $0.8\overline{3}$
   c. $8\frac{2}{3}$ $8.\overline{6}$
   d. $2\frac{4}{5}$ 2.8

8. a. Round 6.149 to the nearest tenth.   6.1
   b. Round 45.5 to the nearest unit.   46
   c. Round $45.31499 to the nearest dollar. $45
   d. Round $104.996 to the nearest cent. $105.00

9. Write in scientific notation.
   a. 0.0034 3.4×10^{-3}
   b. 4,000,300 4.0003×10^6
   c. 17,400 1.74×10^4
   d. 5   5

10. Write without exponents.
    a. 4^3 64
    b. 9^2 81
    c. 5.79×10^{-4} 0.000579
    d. 4.01×10^5 401,000

11. Write the prime factorization.
    a. 86 2×43
    b. 72 $2^3 \times 3^2$
    c. 486 2×3^5
    d. 1,372 $2^2 \times 7^3$

12. Reduce each fraction.
    a. $\frac{15}{25}$ $\frac{3}{5}$
    b. $\frac{32}{16}$ 2
    c. $\frac{192}{240}$ $\frac{4}{5}$
    d. $\frac{128}{384}$ $\frac{1}{3}$

13. Write in fractional form.

a. 0.333 $\frac{333}{1,000}$ b. $0.2\frac{2}{9}$ $\frac{2}{9}$ c. 0.95 $\frac{19}{20}$ d. $0.00\frac{1}{2}$ $\frac{1}{200}$

14. Find the LCD.

a. $12; 15$ 60 b. $6; 10$ 30 c. $10; 15; 6$ 30 d. $24; 30; 18$ 360

15. Simplify and classify each as a sum, difference, product, or quotient.

a. $12 + 20 \div 2$ $22;$ sum b. $(12 + 20) \div 2$ $16;$ quotient
c. $8 + 3 \times 6 \div 2$ $17;$ sum d. $(8 + 3) - (6 \div 2)$ $8;$ difference

Simplify the expressions in Problems 16–20.

16. a. $\frac{3}{5} \times \frac{25}{27}$ $\frac{5}{9}$ b. $\frac{4}{9} \times 27$ 12 c. $4\frac{1}{6} \times 3\frac{2}{5}$ $\frac{85}{6}$ d. $2\frac{3}{4} \times \frac{4}{5}$ $\frac{11}{5}$

17. a. $\frac{5}{8} \div \frac{1}{2}$ $\frac{5}{4}$ b. $\frac{14}{25} \div \frac{7}{5}$ $\frac{2}{5}$ c. $1\frac{1}{2} \div \frac{3}{4}$ 2 d. $6\frac{1}{2} \div 3\frac{3}{4}$ $\frac{26}{15}$

18. a. $\frac{5}{7} + \frac{3}{7}$ $\frac{8}{7}$ b. $\frac{6}{11} - \frac{2}{11}$ $\frac{4}{11}$ c. $12\frac{4}{5} + 6\frac{3}{5}$ $19\frac{2}{5}$ d. $5\frac{1}{3} - 1\frac{2}{3}$ $3\frac{2}{3}$

19. a. $\frac{3}{8} + \frac{1}{6}$ $\frac{13}{24}$ b. $\frac{7}{12} - \frac{2}{15}$ $\frac{9}{20}$ c. $7\frac{2}{15} - 3\frac{7}{12}$ $3\frac{11}{20}$ d. $\frac{4}{10} + \frac{7}{15} - \frac{5}{6}$ $\frac{1}{30}$

20. a. $\frac{2}{3} + \frac{4}{5} \div \frac{1}{2}$ $\frac{34}{15}$ b. $\dfrac{2 \times 8 + 3 \times 5}{3 \times 8}$ $\frac{31}{24}$ c. $\frac{4}{5} \times \frac{12}{23} - \frac{4}{5} \times \frac{2}{23}$ $\frac{8}{23}$ d. $\frac{4}{5}\left(\frac{12}{23} - \frac{2}{23}\right)$ $\frac{8}{23}$

21. Rework Problem 20 using a calculator; leave your answer in decimal form. Classify each as a sum, difference, product, or quotient.

a. $2.26666666667;$ sum
b. $1.29166666667;$ quotient
c. $0.347826087;$ difference
d. $0.347826087;$ product

22. a. Change 11011_{two} to base ten. 27
b. Change 716_{eight} to base ten. 462
c. Change one million to base five. 224000000_{five}
d. Change one million to base two. $11110100001001000000_{two}$

23. Write each number in decimal notation.

a. $4 \times 10^3 + 6 \times 10^1 + 3 \times 10^0 + 2 \times 10^{-2}$ $4,063.02$
b. $4 \times 8^3 + 6 \times 8^1 + 3 \times 8^0 + 2 \times 8^{-2}$ $2,009.03125$
c. $1 \times 2^3 + 1 \times 2^0 + 1 \times 2^{-1}$ 9.5
d. $3 \times 12^2 + 4 \times 12^1 + 3 \times 12^0$ 483

24. If you join a book club and agree to buy six books at $24.95 each plus $3.50 postage and handling for each book, what is the total cost to fulfill this agreement? $170.70

25. Enter your favorite number (a counting number from 1 to 9) into a calculator. Multiply by 259; then multiply this result by 429. What is your answer? Try it for three different choices. Favorite digit repeated six times.

Individual Projects

Learning to use sources outside your classroom and textbook is an important skill, and here are some ideas for extending some of the ideas in this chapter.

PROJECT 1.1 **Start a Journal** Create a first entry in your journal. Write down five ideas concerning your commitment to keeping a journal. Tomorrow, write in your journal several reasons for keeping a journal. After that, write in your journal within 24 hours of each math class that you attend.

PROJECT 1.2 It is stated in *Everybody Counts,* "Mathematics is alive and constantly changing. As we complete the last decade of this century, we stand on the threshold of major changes in the mathematics curriculum in the United States." Report on some of these recent changes.

REFERENCES Lynn Steen, *Everybody Counts: A Report to the Nation on the Future of Mathematics Education.* (Washington, D.C.: National Academy Press, 1989).

(Continued)

See also *Curriculum and Evaluation Standards for School Mathematics* from the National Council of Teachers of Mathematics (Reston, VA: NCTM, 1989).

PROJECT 1.3 Insert appropriate operation signs ($+$, $-$, $\times$, or $\div$) between consecutive digits so that the following becomes a true statement: Answers vary;

$$1 \quad 2 \quad 3 \quad 4 \quad 5 \quad 6 \quad 7 \quad 8 \quad 9 = 100 \qquad 1+2+3+4+5+6+7+8\times 9 = 100$$

PROJECT 1.4 Imagine that you have written the numbers from 1 to 1,000,000. What is the total number of zeros you have recorded? 488,895

PROJECT 1.5 A rubber ball is known to rebound half the height it drops.

If the ball is dropped from a height of 100 feet, how far will it have traveled by the time it hits the ground for:

a. The first time? 100 ft   **b.** The second time? 200 ft

c. The third time? 250 ft   **d.** The fourth time? 275 ft

e. The fifth time? 287.5 ft

f. Look for a pattern, and decide whether there is a maximum distance the ball will travel if we assume that it will bounce indefinitely. 300 ft

PROJECT 1.6 Look for a pattern in the following problem. Verify by division (show your work).

a. $\frac{1}{9} = 0.111\ldots$ **b.** $\frac{2}{9} = 0.222\ldots$ **c.** $\frac{3}{9} = 0.333\ldots$

d. $\frac{4}{9} = 0.444\ldots$ **e.** $\frac{8}{9} = 0.888\ldots$ a–e. show your work

f. What is $\frac{9}{9}$ according to the pattern? 0.999...

PROJECT 1.7 Can you find a pattern?

$$0, \ 1, \ 2, \ 10, \ 11, \ 12, \ 20, \ 21, \ 22, \ 100, \ldots$$

The pattern continues: 101, 102, 110, 111, 112, 120, ...

PROJECT 1.8 Notice the following pattern for multiplication by 11:

$$14 \times 11 = 1\_4 \qquad 51 \times 11 = 5\_1$$

First, copy the first and last digits of the number to be multiplied by 11. Leave a space between these digits. Then, insert the sum of the original two digits between those original digits:

$$14 \times 11 = 1\,\mathbf{5}\,4 \qquad\qquad 51 \times 11 = 5\,\mathbf{6}\,1$$
$$\uparrow \qquad\qquad\qquad\qquad \uparrow$$
$$1 + 4 = 5 \qquad\qquad\quad 5 + 1 = 6$$

Use expanded notation to show why this pattern "works." Answers vary.

Team Projects

Working in small groups is typical of most work environments, and learning to work with others to communicate specific ideas is an important skill. Work with three or four other students to submit a single report based on each of the following questions.

T1. Working with others can be beneficial not only on the job, but also in the classroom. For this team project, introduce yourself to three or four classmates, and work with them for this problem. Spend at least 30 minutes getting to know one another, specifically focusing on these statements about your previous mathematics experiences:

"Everybody knows what to do, except me!"
"I got the right answer, but I don't know how!"
"I'm sure I learned it, but I can't remember what to do!"
"This may be a stupid question, but . . . ."
"I'm no good at numbers!"
"Math is unrelated to my life!"
"Math is my worst subject!"
"I don't have a math mind!"   *Answers vary.*

Write a paper summarizing your discussion, and submit one paper for your team.

T2. If it takes 1 second to say each number, how long would it take (to the nearest year) to count to a billion? Assume nonstop counting.   *About 32 years*

T3. If it takes 1 second to write down each digit, how long would it take to write all the numbers from 1 to 1,000,000?   *5,888,896 digits; about 68 days.*

T4. In the *B.C.* cartoon, Peter has a mental block against 4s. See whether you can handle 4s by writing the numbers from 1 to 10 using four 4s for each.

B.C. cartoon reprinted by permission of Johnny Hart and Creators Syndicate, Inc.

Here are the first three completed for you:

$$\frac{4}{4} + 4 - 4 = 1 \qquad \frac{4}{4} + \frac{4}{4} = 2 \qquad \frac{4 + 4 + 4}{4} = 3$$

More than one answer is possible. For example,

$$\frac{4}{4 + 4 - 4} = 1 \qquad \text{and} \qquad 4 - \frac{4 + 4}{4} = 2$$

Answers vary; $4 = 4 + (4 - 4) \div 4$;
$5 = (4 \times 4 + 4) \div 4$;
$6 = 4 + (4 + 4) \div 4$;
$7 = (44 \div 4) - 4$;
$8 = 4 + 4 + 4 - 4$;
$9 = 4 + 4 + (4 \div 4)$;
$10 = (44 - 4) \div 4$

CHAPTER **2**

Sets of Numbers

Algebra is generous, she often gives more than is asked of her.

Jean D'Alembert

ANTICIPATE

- *Overview; check out contents, terms, essential ideas, and learning outcomes.*
- *Integers—have you worked with positive and negative numbers before?*
- ***Algebra*** *is defined as a generalization of arithmetic and has been described as one of the best labor-saving devices invented by the human mind.*
- *Don't go into "symbol shock" when you work in this chapter.*

2.1 Symbol Shock

IN THIS WORLD   THE POWER OF MATH

"Look, Jeff, you just fill in the grid so that every row, every column, and every box contains the digits 1 through 9," explained Mary.

"I'm not very good at math!" cried Jeff.

"Oh, no, this is a SUDOKU puzzle—these are great fun, and there is no math involved. The grid has numbers, but nothing has to add up to anything else. You solve this puzzle with reasoning and logic."

"Great, I love puzzles! Let me try it."

In this section, we will learn the power of math by using symbols to represent numbers using what we call *variables*. This goes way beyond the SUDOKU puzzle. In the problem set you will find a SECRET MESSAGE puzzle—try it, you'll like it!

See Problem 56.

Our society is filled with symbols that we've learned to use intuitively. Books have been written to help us interpret the symbols of body language, we can learn to interpret our dreams, and the very language we use is a symbolic representation. For example, the letters FACE can stand for a variety of ideas, depending on the context in which they are used, as illustrated here.

FACE

FACE

F A C E

In algebra, we use letters of the alphabet to represent numbers with unknown values. A letter used in this way is called a **variable.**

EXAMPLE 1   **Using variables**

Think of a counting number from one to ten. Add five. Multiply the result by two. Subtract six. Divide by two. Subtract the original number. Let me guess the result: It is two. How did I know the result, even though you were allowed to begin with *any* number? Why does this number trick work?

Solution   We answer this question twice, one way without using variables and other way with variables.

Without Variables	*With Variables*
Let ☐ represent the number you have chosen (its value is unknown to me). Let stars (∗ ∗ ...) represent the numbers stated in the question (known numbers).	Let n = UNKNOWN NUMBER.

Think of a number:

☐ n

Add five:

☐ ∗ ∗ ∗ ∗ ∗ $n + 5$

Multiply by two:

☐ ∗ ∗ ∗ ∗ ∗

☐ ∗ ∗ ∗ ∗ ∗ $2(n + 5) = 2n + 10$

Subtract six:

☐ ∗ ∗ ∗ ∗ ∗ = ☐ ∗ ∗

☐ ∗ ∗ ∗ ∗ ∗ = ☐ ∗ ∗ $\begin{aligned} 2n + 10 - 6 &= 2n + 4 \\ &= 2(n + 2) \quad \text{Distributive property} \end{aligned}$

Divide by two:

$\dfrac{☐\ ∗\ ∗}{☐\ ∗\ ∗} = ☐\ ∗\ ∗$ $\dfrac{2(n + 2)}{2} = n + 2$

Subtract the original number:

☐ ∗ ∗ = ∗ ∗ $n + 2 - n = 2$

In either case, the final result is two!   ●

As you look at Example 1, which solution seems easier: the one with or the one without variables? At this point, it may be that the one without variables is easier for you to understand. Our study of algebra is a study in becoming familiar enough with the variables to feel comfortable with manipulations like those shown at the right in Example 1.

A variable represents a number from a given set of numbers called the **domain** of the variable. To express the idea "sum of a number and two," you can write

$$n + 2$$

Go slowly here! We are setting up some very important ideas about algebra.

where n represents the unknown number. If an expression contains at least one variable, it is called a **variable expression.** The domain for this variable expression is the set of all numbers, because there is no reason to restrict the possible replacement of n (that is, n can be 6, 3, $\frac{1}{3}$, or any other number that comes to mind). On the other hand, if n represents the number of people on an elevator, then $n + 2$ represents the idea that two additional people board the elevator, and the domain for n is the set of whole numbers up to some maximum capacity of the elevator. If the domain $D = \{0, 1, 2, 3, \ldots, 30\}$, then the possible number of people on the elevator after the two additional people board is $\{2, 3, 4, \ldots, 32\}$.

EXAMPLE 2   Variable expression

Let x be the variable and let $D = \{0, 1, 5, 10\}$ be the domain. What are the possible values for the variable expression $x + 7$?

Solution   When we find the possible values for a variable expression, we replace the variable by a particular value. When we do this, we say that we *substitute* a value for the variable.

Consider the variable expression: $x + 7$

If $x = 0$, we substitute the value 0 for the variable x to obtain:

$$0 + 7 = 7$$

We continue:
$$1 + 7 = 8 \quad \text{if} \quad x = 1$$
$$5 + 7 = 12 \quad \text{if} \quad x = 5$$
$$10 + 7 = 17 \quad \text{if} \quad x = 10$$

Thus, the possible values for the variable expression are $\{7, 8, 12, 17\}$. The variable expression *cannot* represent $9 + 7 = 16$ because 9 is not in the domain. ●

Some terms involving the operations with which you should be familiar are summarized in Table 2.1.

TABLE 2.1	Translating into Algebra
Symbol	**Verbal Description**
$=$	Two expressions are **equal** if they are the same. Is equal to; is the same as; is; was; becomes; will be; results in.
$+$	The numbers being added are called **terms,** and the result is called the **sum. Plus;** the sum of; added to; more than; greater than; increased by; taller; longer; larger; heavier.
$-$	The numbers being subtracted are called **terms,** and the result is called the **difference. Minus;** the difference of; the difference between; is subtracted from; less than; smaller than; decreased by; is diminished by; shorter; smaller; lighter.
$\times$	A **times** sign is used primarily in arithmetic.
$\cdot$	A raised dot is used to indicate multiplication in algebra, as in $11 \cdot 7$ or $x \cdot 1$.
$(\ )$	Parentheses are used to indicate multiplication in algebra, as in $3(x + 2)$.
no symbol ⬦ CAUTION Be careful to distinguish between *term* and *factor*.	**Juxtaposition** (no symbol) is used to indicate multiplication, as in $3x$. The numbers being multiplied are called **factors,** and the result is called the **product.** Times; product; is multiplied by; of; twice; double.
$\div$ fractional bar	The division symbol is used primarily in arithmetic. The fractional bar, as in $\frac{3}{4}$ (meaning 3 divided by 4) or $\frac{x}{y}$ (meaning x divided by y) is used in algebra. The x is called the **dividend,** y is called the **divisor,** and the result is called the **quotient.** Divided by; quotient of; per.

EXAMPLE 3

Translating an English expression into a variable expression

Choose a letter to represent the variable, and write a mathematical statement to express the idea.

a. The sum of a number and 13

b. The difference of a number subtracted from 10

c. The quotient of two numbers

d. The product of two consecutive numbers

Solution   With an example such as this, we do not want to belabor an obvious answer. On the other hand, we realize the necessity of "building a procedure" for translating from English into algebra. In building this procedure and taking careful steps, we must also prevent "symbol shock" or undue avoidance of symbols.

a. "The sum of a number and 13"   Sum indicates addition, so the statement is

$$(\text{NUMBER}) + (\text{THIRTEEN})$$

Now select some variable (your choice)—say, $n = \text{NUMBER}$. Then the symbolic statement is

$$n + 13$$

b. "The difference of a number subtracted from 10"

$$(\text{TEN}) - (\text{NUMBER})$$

Let $x = \text{NUMBER}$. Then the variable expression is

$$10 - x$$

c. "The quotient of two numbers"

$$\frac{\text{NUMBER}}{\text{ANOTHER NUMBER}}$$

If there is more than one unknown in a problem, more than one variable may be needed. Let $m = \text{NUMBER}$ and $n = \text{ANOTHER NUMBER}$; then

$$\frac{m}{n}$$

d. "The product of two consecutive numbers"

$$(\text{NUMBER})\,(\text{NEXT CONSECUTIVE NUMBER})$$

If there is more than one unknown in a problem, but a relationship between those unknowns is given, then *do not choose* more than you need for the problem. In this problem, a "consecutive number" means one more than the first number:

$$(\text{NUMBER})\,(\text{NUMBER} + 1)$$

Let $y = \text{NUMBER}$. Then the variable expression is

$$y(y + 1)$$ ●

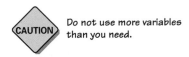

Do not use more variables than you need.

In Chapter 1, you simplified numerical expressions. If $x = a$, then x and a name the same number; x may be replaced by a in any expression, and the value of the expression remains unchanged. When you replace variables by given numerical values and then simplify the resulting numerical expression, the process is called **evaluating an expression**.

This is the second of the main algebraic processes. The first was simplify and the second is evaluate.

EXAMPLE 4   **Evaluating an expression**

Evaluate $a + cb$, where $a = 2$, $b = 11$, and $c = 3$.

Solution $a + cb$ Remember, *cb* means *c* times *b*.

Step 1   Replace each variable with the corresponding numerical value. You may need

$$
\begin{array}{ccc}
a & c & \cdot\; b \\
\downarrow & \downarrow & \downarrow\;\downarrow \\
2\; + & 3\; & (\;11\;)
\end{array}
$$

← Parentheses are necessary so that the product *cb* is not changed to 311.

Step 2   Simplify: $2 + 3(11) = 2 + 33$ Multiplication before addition
$$= 35$$

EXAMPLE 5   **Sum of squares and square of a sum**

Evaluate the following where $a = 3$ and $b = 4$.   **a.** $a^2 + b^2$ **b.** $(a + b)^2$

Solution

a. $a^2 + b^2 = 3^2 + 4^2$ This is called a *sum of squares.*
$$= 9 + 16$$
$$= 25$$ Remember the order of operations; multiplication comes first.

b. $(a + b)^2 = (3 + 4)^2$ This is called the *square of a sum.*
$$= 7^2$$
$$= 49$$ Order of operations; parentheses first

STOP Spend some time with this example. It is important because: (1) It illustrates the ideas of evaluation; and (2) you need to remember that $(a + b)^2 \neq a^2 + b^2$.

Remember that a particular variable is replaced by a single value when an expression is evaluated. You should also be careful to write capital letters differently from lowercase letters, because they often represent different values. This means that, just because $a = 3$ in Example 5, you should not assume that $A = 3$. On the other hand, it is possible that other variables *might* have the value 3. For example, just because $a = 3$, do not assume that another variable—say, t—cannot also have the value $t = 3$.

EXAMPLE 6   **Number puzzle**

Let $a = 1$, $b = 3$, $c = 2$, and $d = 4$. Find the value of the given capital letters.

a. $G = bc - a$ **b.** $H = 3c + 2d$ **c.** $I = 3a + 2b$

d. $R = a^2 + b^2d$ **e.** $S = \dfrac{2(b + d)}{2c}$ **f.** $T = \dfrac{3a + bc + b}{c}$

Solution   After you have found the value of a capital letter, write it in the box that corresponds to its numerical value. This exercise will help you check your work.

37	9	5	14	6

a. $G = bc - a$
  $= 3(2) - 1$
  $= 6 - 1$
  $= 5$

b. $H = 3c + 2d$
  $= 3(2) + 2(4)$
  $= 6 + 8$
  $= 14$

c. $I = 3a + 2b$
  $= 3(1) + 2(3)$
  $= 3 + 6$
  $= 9$

d. $R = a^2 + b^2 d$
  $= 1^2 + 3^2(4)$
  $= 1 + 9(4)$
  $= 37$

e. $S = \dfrac{2(b + d)}{2c}$
  $= \dfrac{2(3 + 4)}{2(2)}$
  $= \dfrac{2(7)}{4}$
  $= \dfrac{7}{2}$

f. $T = \dfrac{3a + bc + b}{c}$
  $= \dfrac{3(1) + 3(2) + 3}{2}$
  $= \dfrac{3 + 6 + 3}{2}$
  $= \dfrac{12}{2}$
  $= 6$

After you have filled in the appropriate boxes, the result is

37	9	5	14	6
R	I	G	H	T

PROBLEM SET 2.1

ESSENTIAL IDEAS   LEVEL 1

 CAUTION
Remember, working these problems marked "essential" will pay major dividends when working through the book. You should work these problems even if not assigned by your instructor.

1. Numbers or variables that are added are called __terms__ .

2. Numbers or variables that are multiplied are called __factors__ .

3. Give at least three translations for each of the following symbols:

  a. $+$ plus, sum, added to, will be

  b. $-$ minus, difference, subtracted from

  c. $\times$ times, product, multiplied by

  d. $\div$ divided by, quotient, per

  e. $=$ equals, same as, is, results in

4. What is a variable?
   a symbol used to represent an unknown value
5. What does it mean to "evaluate an expression"?
   Replace a variable by a given numerical value and then simplify.
6. Give an example of:

  a. difference of squares of a and b $a^2 - b^2$

  b. square of a difference of b from a $(a - b)^2$

DRILL AND PRACTICE   LEVEL 2

Let x be the variable and let $D = \{0, 1, 3, 7\}$ *be the domain. Find the values for the variable expressions in Problems 7–9.*

7. $2x + 1$
  1, 3, 7, 15

8. x^2
  0, 1, 9, 49

9. $50 - x^2$
  50, 49, 41, 1

Let y be the variable and let $D = \{0, 2, 3, 10\}$ *be the domain. Find the values for the variable expressions in Problems 10–12.*

10. $y + 8$ 8, 10, 11. 18

11. $(10 + y)^2$ 100, 144, 169, 400

12. $10 + y^2$ 10, 14, 19, 110

In Problems 13–37, let $w = 2$, $x = 1$, $y = 2$, *and* $z = 4$ *to evaluate the given expressions to find the values of the given capital letters.*

13. $A = x + z + 8$ 13

14. $B = 5x + y - z$ 3

15. $C = 10 - w$ 8

16. $D = 3z$ 12

17. $E = 25 - y^2$ 21

18. $F = w(y - x + wz)$ 18

19. $G = 5x + 3z + 2$ 19

20. $H = 3x + 2w$ 7

21. $I = 5y - 2z$ 2

22. $J = 2w - z$ 0

23. $K = wxy$ 4

24. $L = x + y^2$ 5

25. $M = (x + y)^2$ 9

26. $N = x^2 + 2xy + y^2 + 1$ 10

27. $P = y^2 + z^2$ 20

28. $Q = w(x + y)$ 6

29. $R = z^2 - y^2 - x^2$ 11

30. $S = (x + y + z)^2$ 49

31. $T = x^2 + y^2 z$ 17

32. $U = \dfrac{w + y}{z}$ 1

33. $V = \dfrac{3wyz}{x}$ 48

34. $W = \dfrac{3w + 6z}{xy}$ 15

35. $X = (x^2 z + x)^2 z$ 100

36. $Y = (wy)^2 + w^2 y + 3x$ 27

37. $Z = 2w - xy^2 + (xy)^2$ 4

38. This problem will help you check your work in Problems 13–37. Fill in the capital letters from Problems 13–37 to correspond with their numerical values (O has been filled in for you). Some letters may not appear in the boxes. When you are finished, darken all the blank spaces to separate the words in the secret message. Some of the blank spaces have also been filled in to help you.

Tergiversation

13	5	19	21	3	11	13	14	2	49	22	50
17	7	21	23	19	11	21	13	17	21	49	17
5	13	3	O	11		49	13	48	2	10	19
12	21	48	2	8	21	26	21	48	21	11	22
2	10	48	21	10	17	21	12				

ALGEBRA_IS_ _THE_GREATEST LABOR_SAVING DEVICE_EVER_INVENTED_ _ _

Problem of the Day

APPLICATIONS **LEVEL 2**

An essential skill in working applied problems is the ability to choose a variable to represent an unknown quantity. You are asked to practice this skill in Problems 39–50. Choose a letter to represent the variable, and write a mathematical expression for the idea; you do not need to simplify.

39. A number plus five $n + 5$

40. Twice a number $2n$

41. Five minus a number $5 - n$

42. A number minus five $n - 5$

43. A number x plus 3 divided by 2 $x + \frac{3}{2}$

44. The sum of $x + 3$ divided by 2 $\frac{x + 3}{2}$

45. The difference of a number subtracted from 1 $1 - n$

46. The difference of 1 subtracted from a number $n - 1$

47. The product of seven and a number $7n$

48. The product of a number and five
   $5n$ (Note: $n5$ is correct, $5n$ is customary.)
49. The quotient of five divided by a number $\frac{5}{n}$

50. The quotient of a number divided by five $\frac{n}{5}$

51. Think of a counting number less than 20. Add six. Double the result. Subtract eight. Divide by two. Subtract your original number. The answer is 2. Explain why this trick works. $x; x + 6; 2x + 12; 2x + 4; x + 2; 2$

52. The pictures here describe a number trick. Describe it in words.

(1) ☐   (2) ☐ * * *   (3) ☐ * * *   (4) ☐ * *   (5) * *
                            ☐ * * *   ☐ * *   * *

Pick a number; add 3; double it; subtract 2; subtract twice the original number; the answer is 4.

53. The algebraic steps below describe a number trick. Describe it in words.

(1) x (2) $x + 7$

(3) $2(x + 7) = 2x + 14$

(4) $2x + 14 - 4 = 2x + 10 = 2(x + 5)$

(5) $\frac{2(x + 5)}{2} = x + 5$ Pick a number; add 7; double it; subtract 4; divide by 2; subtract the original num-

(6) $x + 5 - x = 5$ ber; the answer is 5.

54. Translate the following symbolic messages:

EZ4NE12CYU $\dfrac{R}{WEIGHT}$ Easy for anyone to see why you are overweight.

U8N8N8N8NR $\dfrac{2}{ACTIVE}$ You ate and ate and ate and ate and are too overactive.

55. **IN YOUR OWN WORDS** My favorite number is 7. Make up a number trick in which you ask someone to think of a number and carry on some operations, with the final answer always 7.

56. **SUDOKU Puzzle** Fill in the grid so that every row, every column, and every three-by-three box contains the digits 1 through 9.

9	6	3	1	7	4	2	5	8
1	7	8	3	2	5	6	4	9
2	5	4	6	8	9	7	3	1
8	2	1	4	3	7	5	9	6
4	9	6	8	5	2	3	1	7
7	3	5	9	6	1	8	2	4
5	8	9	7	1	3	4	6	2
3	1	7	2	4	6	9	8	5
6	4	2	5	9	8	1	7	3

RIGHT OR WRONG? **LEVEL 3**

Explain what is wrong, if anything, with the statements in Problems 57–60. Explain your reasoning.

57. If $x = 10$ or 20, then $x + 9$ is 19 or 29. The domain is x.
F; the domain is 10, 20, not x.

58. The quotient of 30 divided by 6 is the same as the quotient of 6 divided by 30.   F; $30 \div 6 \neq 6 \div 30$

59. Numbers that are added are called terms.   T

60. Numbers that are multiplied are called terms.
F; they are called factors.

2.2 Addition of Integers

"Hey, Freddie, what does five mean?" asked Carl. "Can you define that more precisely for me?"

"Well, it is not easy. Everyone thinks they know what five means—until they try to define it or explain it. Do you know what we mean by a cardinal number?" asked Freddie. *

"Yes I know, but you will never get your ideas across unless you say it so everyone knows what you mean!" said Carl. †

It is not easy to understand the nature of the positive and negative numbers. You have, no doubt, used negative numbers many times: when you are playing a card game and lose more points than you gain; or when you are watching a football game and your team loses more yards than it gains; or when the temperature drops below zero degrees; or when the profit for a product changes to a loss.

 See Problem 51.

You have probably seen the need for numbers to represent quantities less than zero many times. Some common examples are temperatures below zero, card scores that are "in the hole," business debts, and altitudes below sea level. To represent these ideas, we introduce **signed numbers.**

- With each counting number, we associate a **positive sign:**

$$1 = +1 \qquad 2 = +2 \qquad 3 = +3 \quad \ldots$$

    Although the symbolism is the same as that of an addition sign, remember that addition requires two numbers, for example, $6 + 5$. Using positive signs, this addition problem would look like this: $(+6) + (+5)$.

- For each counting number, we define a *new number,* called its *opposite,* by using a **negative sign.**

    The opposite of 1 is denoted by -1.

    The opposite of 2 is denoted by -2.

    The opposite of 3 is denoted by -3.

    And so on.

CAUTION Do NOT confuse the $\boxed{(-)}$ opposite key with the minus key $\boxed{-}$.

The negative (or opposite) sign on a calculator is labeled $\boxed{(-)}$ or $\boxed{+/-}$ or $\boxed{\text{CHS}}$.

---

*The German logician and mathematician F. L. G. Frege (1848–1925) tried to define numbers precisely in 1884 with what he called a cardinal number. He amplified his views in several volumes, but he was largely ignored during his life.

†Here is the way that the historian Carl B. Boyer stated this idea: "History shows that novelty in ideas is more readily accepted if couched in relatively conventional form."

The **positive numbers** and **negative numbers** are separated by a number called **zero.** The **opposite** of a given number is defined to be the number that, when added to the given number, gives a sum of zero:

Given positive number   *Opposite*   *Given negative number*   *Opposite*

$$+1 + (-1) = 0$$
$$+2 + (-2) = 0$$
$$+3 + (-3) = 0$$
$$\vdots$$

$$(-1) + 1 = 0$$
$$(-2) + 2 = 0$$
$$(-3) + 3 = 0$$
$$\vdots$$

The opposite of a positive number is negative.   *The opposite of a negative number is positive.*

Since $0 + 0 = 0$, the opposite of zero is zero.

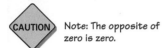 Note: The opposite of zero is zero.

The counting numbers, along with their opposites and the number 0, form a set called the **integers.**

Integers

> The set of **integers** is the set
> $$\{\ldots, -4, -3, -2, -1, 0, 1, 2, 3, 4, \ldots\}$$

HISTORICAL NOTE

Girolamo Cardano
(1501–1576)

Karl Smith library

Historically, the negative integers were developed quite late. There are indications that the Chinese had some knowledge of negative numbers as early as 200 B.C., and in the 7th century A.D., the Hindu Brahmagupta stated the rules for operations with positive and negative numbers. The Chinese represented negative integers by putting them in red (compare with the present-day accountant), and the Hindus represented them by putting a circle or a dot over the number. However, as late as the 16th century, some European scholars were calling numbers such as (−1) absurd. In 1545, Girolamo Cardano, an Italian scholar who presented the elementary properties of negative numbers, called the positive numbers "true" numbers and the negative numbers "fictitious" numbers. However, they did become universally accepted; and as a matter of fact, the word *integer* that we use to describe this set is derived from "numbers with integrity."

The easiest way to understand the operations and properties of integers is to represent them on a **number line,** as shown in Figure 2.1.

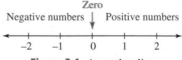

Figure 2.1 A number line

To draw a number line, locate any two convenient points; label the one on the left 0 (zero) and the one on the right $+1$ (positive one). The distance between these points is called a **unit scale** and can be used to mark off equal distances in both directions. These points correspond to the integers, as shown in Figure 2.1. A number line can be used to order numbers using three **order symbols,** $<$, $>$, and $=$.

Order Symbols

> **Less than** (symbol $<$) means *to the left* on a number line.
> **Greater than** (symbol $>$) means *to the right* on a number line.
> **Equal to** (symbol $=$) means *the same point* on a number line.

EXAMPLE 1   **Comparing the sizes of numbers**

Write $<$, $>$, or $=$ in the blank.

a. 2 _____ 5   **b.** 6 _____ 3   **c.** 4 _____ 4

d. -2 _____ -3 **e.** 0 _____ -2

Solution

a. $2 < 5$, since 2 is to the left of 5 on a number line.

b. $6 > 3$ **c.** $4 = 4$ **d.** $-2 > -3$, since -2 is to the right of -3.

e. $0 > -2$ ●

With the introduction of negative values, we also need to introduce a symbol to represent distance, because distances are nonnegative.

Absolute Value

> The **absolute value** of a number is the distance of that number from 0 on the number line.
>
>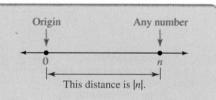

To **evaluate an absolute value** means to write it without absolute value symbols, as shown in the following example.

EXAMPLE 2   **Evaluating an absolute value**

Evaluate: **a.** $|5|$ **b.** $|-5|$ **c.** $|-3|$ **d.** $|0|$ **e.** $|-349|$

Solution

a. The absolute value of 5, symbolized by $|5|$, is 5 because 5 is 5 units from 0.

b. The absolute value of -5, symbolized by $|-5|$, is 5 because -5 is 5 units from 0.

c. $|-3| = 3$ **d.** $|0| = 0$ **e.** $|-349| = 349$ ●

You will find an absolute value key on many calculators. You might wish to try to use your calculator for the evaluations in Example 2.

EXAMPLE 3   **Finding the larger absolute value**

Tell which number is larger. Then show the larger absolute value.

a. $2; 5$ **b.** $-2; -5$ **c.** $-8; 10$ **d.** $8; -10$

Solution		*Larger Number*	*Larger Absolute Value*
a.	2; 5	5	5
b.	−2; −5	−2	5
c.	−8; 10	10	10
d.	8; −10	8	10

A number line is also used to illustrate the addition of integers. It is agreed that adding a positive number means moving to the right, and that adding a negative number means moving to the left. This process is illustrated in Example 4. Adding zero means no move at all.

EXAMPLE 4   **Addition using a number line**

Add on a number line:
a. $2 + 6$ **b.** $6 + (−4)$ **c.** $(−10) + 6$ **d.** $(−2) + (−8)$

Solution

a. Positive + Positive: $2 + 6$

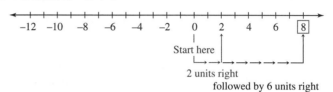

Ending point is 8.

To avoid confusion, negative numbers are often enclosed in parentheses when combined with other operations.

b. Positive + Negative: $6 + (−4)$

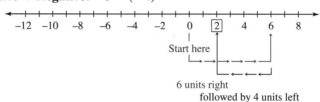

Ending point is 2.

c. Negative + Positive: $(−10) + 6$

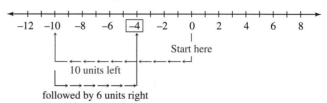

Ending point is −4.

d. Negative + Negative: $(−2) + (−8)$

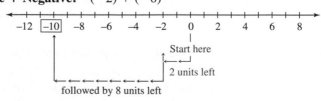

Ending point is −10.

The method of adding on a number line shown in Example 4 is not practical for continued use, so we use it to lead us to the following rules for the **addition of two nonzero integers.** This procedure is summarized as a flowchart in Figure 2.2.

Adding Integers

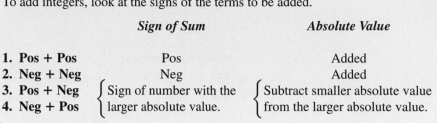

To add integers, look at the signs of the terms to be added.

	Sign of Sum	*Absolute Value*
1. Pos + Pos	Pos	Added
2. Neg + Neg	Neg	Added
3. Pos + Neg	Sign of number with the	Subtract smaller absolute value
4. Neg + Pos	larger absolute value.	from the larger absolute value.

STOP You absolutely must have this procedure committed to memory.

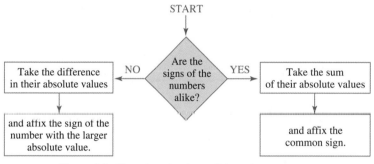

Figure 2.2 Flowchart for the addition of two integers

In order to add zero to any number, n, we use the following property, called the **identity property for addition.** It states that adding zero to any number does not change the value of that number. In symbols,

$$0 + n = n + 0 = n$$

EXAMPLE 5   **Adding integers**

Simplify the given numerical expressions. Note the use of parentheses.

a. $45 + 27$ Positive + Positive   **b.** $-18 + (-21)$ Negative + Negative
c. $13 + (-5)$ Positive + Negative   **d.** $-13 + 5$ Negative + Positive
e. $-8 + 12$ **f.** $-48 + 53$
g. $127 + (-127)$ **h.** $5 + (-3) + (-4)$
i. $-2 + [3 + (-5)]$

Solution

a. $45 + 27 = 72$ *Positives are understood.*

b. $-18 + (-21) = -39$ *Add absolute values:* $18 + 21 = 39$
   ↑   ↑

    Neg + Neg is negative

c. $13 + (-5) = +8$ *Subtract absolute values:* $13 - 5 = 8$
   ↑   ↑

    Pos + Neg; use the sign of the number with the larger absolute value.

d. $-13 + 5 = -8$ *Subtract absolute values:* $13 - 5 = 8$
↑
Sign of the number with the larger absolute value

e. $-8 + 12 = +4$ *Subtract absolute values:* $12 - 8 = 4$
↑
Sign of the number with the larger absolute value

f. $-48 + 53 = 5$
↑
Positive sign understood

g. $127 + (-127) = 0$ *Remember, adding opposites gives 0.*

h. $5 + (-3) + (-4) = 2 + (-4)$ For more than two numbers, add two at a time.
$= -2$

i. $-2 + [3 + (-5)] = -2 + (-2)$
$= -4$

PROBLEM SET 2.2

ESSENTIAL IDEAS   LEVEL 1

1. What is the set of integers? $\{\ldots, -3, -2, -1, 0, 1, 2, 3, \ldots\}$

2. IN YOUR OWN WORDS Describe how you add two positive integers.

3. IN YOUR OWN WORDS Describe how you add two negative integers.

4. IN YOUR OWN WORDS Describe how you add a positive and a negative integer.

5. IN YOUR OWN WORDS What is absolute value, and why do we need it to describe addition and subtraction of integers?

6. Certain words describe basic algebraic processes: simplify a numerical expression, evaluate a variable expression, and evaluate an absolute value. Which one of these was introduced in this section? Define this process.
Evaluate an absolute value; it means to write an expression without absolute value symbols.

Tell whether the "−" is a minus sign or an opposite sign in Problems 7–12.

7. $-(+4)$ opposite

8. $6 - 4$ minus

9. $12 - 456$ minus

10. $-(34)$ opposite

11. $-y$ opposite

12. $-x$ opposite

DRILL AND PRACTICE   LEVEL 2

Compare the size of the given numbers by filling in $<$, $>$, or $=$ in the blanks in Problems 13–16.

13. a. $8 \underline{\quad < \quad} 14$ **b.** $14 \underline{\quad > \quad} 8$
c. $-8 \underline{\quad < \quad} 14$ **d.** $-14 \underline{\quad < \quad} -8$

14. a. $-6 \underline{\quad < \quad} 6$ **b.** $6 \underline{\quad > \quad} -6$
c. $-6 \underline{\quad = \quad} -6$ **d.** $-6 \underline{\quad < \quad} -(-6)$

15. a. $|4| \underline{\quad = \quad} |-4|$ **b.** $-|4| \underline{\quad < \quad} |4|$
c. $|-4| \underline{\quad > \quad} -|-4|$ **d.** $-|4| \underline{\quad < \quad} 0$

16. a. $|0| \underline{\quad < \quad} |-5|$ **b.** $-|5| \underline{\quad < \quad} |5|$
c. $-|-5| \underline{\quad = \quad} -|5|$ **d.** $-|5| \underline{\quad < \quad} 0$

Evaluate the given absolute values in Problems 17–20.

17. a. $|7|$ 7   **b.** $|-10|$ 10
c. $|0|$ 0   **d.** $-|10|$ −10

18. a. $-|7|$ −7   **b.** $|-7|$ 7
c. $-|0|$ 0   **d.** $-|-10|$ −10

19. a. $|8 - 5|$ 3   **b.** $|5 - 8|$ 3
c. $|5| - |8|$ −3   **d.** $|8| - |5|$ 3

20. a. $|14 - 9|$ 5   **b.** $|9 - 14|$ 5
c. $|9| - |14|$ −5   **d.** $|14| - |9|$ 5

In Problems 21 and 22, (i) give the larger value, and (ii) give the larger absolute value.

21. a. $9, 6$ i. 9; ii. 9   **b.** $-9, -6$ i. −6; ii. 9
c. $-9, 6$ i. 6; ii. 9   **d.** $9, -6$ i. 9; ii. 9

22. a. $1, 3$ i. 3; ii. 3   **b.** $-1, 3$ i. 3; ii. 3
c. $-1, -3$ i. −1; ii. 3   **d.** $1, -3$ i. I; ii. 3

Use a number line in Problems 23–28.

23. Start at 0 and move -3 units. Then move $+8$ units. Then move -6 units. What is the ending point?   −1

24. Start at 0 and move $+5$ units. Then move $+2$ units. Then move -10 units. What is the ending point? -3

25. Start at 0, move -5 units, move $+12$ units, and then move -6 units. What is the ending point?   1

26. Start at 0, move $+3$ units, move -5 units, and then move -1 unit. What is the ending point? -3

27. Start at 0, move $+6$ units, move -8 units, move $+5$ units, and then move -9 units. What is the ending point? -6

28. Start at 0, move -3 units, move -2 units, move $+8$ units, and then move $+2$ units. What is the ending point?   5

Find the sums in Problems 29–36.

29. a. $-5 + 9$ 4
  b. $5 + (-9)$ -4
  c. $-(5) + 9$ 4
  d. $-5 + (-9)$ -14

30. a. $-7 + 6$ -1
  b. $7 + 6$ 13
  c. $-7 + (-6)$ -13
  d. $7 + (-6)$ 1

31. a. $-9 + (-4)$ -13
  b. $-9 + 4$ -5
  c. $9 + 4$ 13
  d. $9 + (-4)$ 5

32. a. $8 + (-6)$ 2
  b. $-8 + (-6)$ -14
  c. $-8 + 6$ -2
  d. $8 + 6$ 14

33. a. $-62 + 79$ 17
  b. $71 + (-32)$ 39
  c. $-9 + 15$ 6
  d. $-82 + (-41)$ -123

34. a. $162 + (-27)$ 135
  b. $-15 + 83$ 68
  c. $-14 + 27$ 13
  d. $42 + (-121)$ -79

35. a. $-64 + 64$ 0
  b. $247 + (-247)$ 0
  c. $-18 + (-4 + 3)$ -19
  d. $[-18 + (-4)] + 3$ -19

36. a. $(-8 + 6) + (6 + 8)$ 12
  b. $-8 + (6 + 6) + 8$ 12
  c. $62 + (-62)$ 0
  d. $-128 + 128$ 0

37. Suppose you are given the following number line:

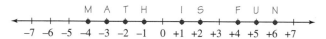

  a. Explain why a move from H to N is described by $+7$.
  The point N is seven units to the right of H.
  b. Describe a move from T to F. $+6$
  c. Describe a move from U to A. -8
  d. Describe a move from A to U. $+8$

38. Suppose you are given the following number line:

  a. Explain why a move from T to A is described by $+7$.
  The point A is seven units to the right of T.
  b. Describe a move from T to H. $+6$
  c. Describe a move from D to S. -10
  d. Describe a move from U to R. $+7$

Show the sums requested in Problems 39–44 on a number line.
Show number lines.
39. $(+5) + (+3)$ 8
40. $(-5) + (+3)$ -2
41. $(+4) + (-7)$ -3
42. $(+3) + (+5)$ 8
43. $(-3) + (+5)$ 2
44. $(-2) + (-4)$ -6

Perform the indicated operations in Problems 45–48 on your calculator.

45. a. $561 + (-453)$ 108
  b. $-12,852 + 8,152$ $-4,700$

46. a. $-993 + (-482)$ $-1,475$
  b. $-50 + (-2,050)$ $-2,100$

47. a. $-459 + (-340)$ -799
  b. $-459 - (-340)$ -119

48. a. $78 + 3,450 + (-583)$ 2,945
  b. $0 + (-689) + 482$ -207

APPLICATIONS   **LEVEL 2**

49. In a game of rummy, a player's scores for five hands were 25, -120, 45, -10, and 60. What is the player's total score?   0

50. In a game of rummy, a player's scores for six hands were 45, 55, -30, -85, 35, and 50. What is the player's total score?   70

51. What is the final temperature in a freezer if at 9:00 A.M. it is $-5°C$ and then it goes up by $10°$, drops by $15°$, drops by $6°$, and finally goes up by $7°$? $-9°C$

52. What is the final temperature if it is $-8°C$ at 7:00 A.M., rises by $14°C$, rises by $23°C$, falls by $14°C$, and then falls by $28°C$? $-13°C$

53. The Rams took the kickoff on the 1-yard line, gained 22 yards, lost 4 yards, gained 5 yards, and then lost 8 yards. Where did the Rams finish this drive?   16-yard line

AP/Wide World Photos

54. If a football drive begins on the 12-yard line, gains 15 yards, gains 3 yards, loses 8 yards, gains 4 yards, and finally gains 0 yards, where does this drive end?   26-yard line

RIGHT OR WRONG? **LEVEL 3**

Explain what is wrong, if anything, with the statements in Problems 55–60. Explain your reasoning.

55. The sum of a positive and a negative is negative.
F; the sign depends on the numbers being added.
56. The sum of two negatives is positive.
F; it is negative.
57. For $-6 + (-3)$ the larger number is -3. T

58. The expression -10 symbolizes negative 10, the opposite of 10, but not minus 10.
T; minus is an operation requiring two numbers.
59. The expression -5 symbolizes negative 5, the opposite of 5, but not minus 5.
T; minus is an operation requiring two numbers.
60. The sum of opposites is positive.
F; it is 0.

2.3 Subtraction of Integers

IN THIS WORLD THE POWER OF MATH

© JAX LTD, INC., www.iaxgames.com

"Have you ever played the 'take away' game, Jerry?" asked Tommy. *"My teacher brought it to school yesterday, and I thought it was another stupid trick, but we played it for awhile and I loved it! I'm asking my mom to buy it for me."*

Many children play "take away" games. "What is 6 take away 4?" Holding up six fingers, the child simply counts off "5, 4, 3, 2 is 6 take away 4." To take away, the child does not subtract but simply counts backward.

 See Problem 47.

Determining the amount of change a customer should receive from a purchase certainly uses subtraction. If the purchase is $1.65 and you give the clerk $2.00, the operation is $2.00 - 1.65 = 0.35$, or 35¢ change. But that is *not* the way a clerk determines your change. Usually, the clerk hands you a dime and a quarter and says, "That's $1.65, $1.75, and $2.00." The necessary subtraction is done by adding: $1.65 + 0.10 + 0.25 = 2.00$.

On the number line, subtraction involves going back in the opposite direction instead of going ahead as in addition. Let's look at the child's "take away" game using a number line. For $6 - 4$:

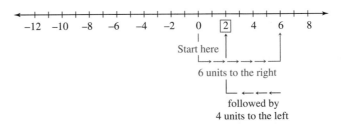

Start here

6 units to the right

followed by
4 units to the left

Notice that this looks the same as $6 + (-4)$; see Example 4b of the previous section. That is,

$$\left.\begin{array}{l} 6 - 4 = 2 \\ 6 + (-4) = 2 \end{array}\right\}$$ Result is the same location.

But what if we have negative numbers? Negative already indicates "going back" or to the left. Does subtracting a negative mean going to the right?

Look again at a sequence of problems and find the most logical solutions. Subtract each problem:

$$5 - 5 = 0$$
$$5 - 4 = 1$$
$$5 - 3 = 2$$
$$5 - 2 = 3$$
$$5 - 1 = 4$$
$$5 - 0 = 5$$
$$5 - (-1) = ?$$
$$5 - (-2) = ?$$
$$5 - (-3) = ?$$

It does seem that subtracting successively smaller numbers from 5 should give successively larger differences. On the number line, $5 - (-3)$ means "going in the opposite direction from -3," but instead of trying to do subtraction on a number line, we look at a pattern:

$$5 - 1 = 4$$
$$5 - 0 = 5$$
$$5 - (-1) = ? \; \leftarrow \text{From the pattern, this is 6: } 5 - (-1) = 5 + 1 = 6$$
$$5 - (-2) = ? \; \leftarrow \text{From the pattern, this is 7: } 5 - (-2) = 5 + 2 = 7$$
$$5 - (-3) = ? \; \leftarrow \text{From the pattern, this is 8: } 5 - (-3) = 5 + 3 = 8$$

It does look as if $5 - (-3)$ is equal to 8. We note that this is the same as $5 + 3$.

Guided by these results, we define **subtraction of integers** as follows.

Subtracting Integers

The procedure for subtracting integers has only one step:

To subtract, add the opposite of the number to be subtracted. In symbols,

$$a - b = a + (-b)$$

EXAMPLE 1   Subtraction by adding the opposite

Find $7 - 10$.

Solution   *Subtraction*
$$\downarrow$$
$$7 - 10 = 7 + (-10)$$
$$\uparrow \; \uparrow$$
Add the opposite.
$$= -3 \quad \text{Use the rules of } \textit{addition} \text{ to obtain this result.}$$

EXAMPLE 2   Subtraction of integers

Simplify the following.

a. $7 - (-10)$ **b.** $4 - (-8)$ **c.** $-2 - (-9)$ **d.** $2 - (-9)$

e. $-2 - 9$ **f.** $-345 - 527$ **g.** $8 - (-5) - 14 + (-3) - (-2)$

Solution

a. $7 - (-10) = 7 + (+10) = 17$ b. $4 - (-8) = 4 + 8 = 12$

c. $-2 - (-9) = -2 + 9 = 7$ d. $2 - (-9) = 2 + 9 = 11$

e. $-2 - 9 = -2 + (-9) = -11$ f. $-345 - 527 = -345 + (-527)$
$$= -872$$

g. With more than two additions or subtractions, work from left to right. It is customary first to change all of the subtractions to additions by adding the opposites, and then to add the positive numbers as well as the negative numbers, and finally to carry out the addition.

$$8 - (-5) - 14 + (-3) - (-2) = 8 + 5 + (-14) + (-3) + 2$$
$$= [8 + 5 + 2] + [(-14) + (-3)]$$
$$= 15 + (-17)$$
$$= -2$$

 Much of your work will be simplified if your thinking on this point is clear.

There are three uses for the symbol "−":

- **Minus** is used to indicate subtraction, an operation symbol.
- **Negative** is used to indicate those numbers to the left of the origin on a number line.
- **Opposite** is used to signify an equivalent distance from the origin, but in an opposite direction. This is a number that can be either positive or negative.

For example, $5 - [-(-2)]$ means

$$5 \ minus \text{ the } opposite \text{ of } negative \ 2$$
$$5 - [- (-2)]$$

On a calculator, the key for the minus symbol is denoted by ⊟ and is usually located at the right (above the plus key). The negative and opposite symbols are denoted by (−) or +/− and should not be confused with the minus key. Locate these keys on your calculator. The next example illustrates the three different uses for the symbol "−".

EXAMPLE 3

Practice with the "−" symbol

Indicate whether "minus," "negative," or "opposite" best describes the use of "−" in each expression:

a. $(-2) + (+9)$ b. $-(+6) + (+4)$ c. $(+4) - (+7)$ d. $-x$ e. $x - y$

Solution

a. $(-2) + (+9)$ **Negative**

b. $-(+6) + (+4)$ **Opposite**

c. $(+4) - (+7)$ **Minus**

d. $-x$ **Opposite;** *when the "−" symbol appears alone in front of a variable, as in this example, it always means opposite.*

e. $x - y$ **Minus;** *when the "−" symbol appears between two variables, as in this example, it always means subtraction (minus).*

Opposite Symbol

> The symbol $-x$ is read "the <u>opposite</u> of x" and should not be read "negative x" or "minus x."

If you remember the information in this box you will save yourself a great deal of confusion.

When evaluating an expression involving negative numbers, you may sometimes need to use additional sets of parentheses to keep the meaning of the expression clear. This is illustrated in Example 4.

EXAMPLE 4

Evaluation of expression with negative numbers

Evaluate the given expressions, where $a = -2$ and $b = -4$.   **a.** $a + b$ **b.** $a - b$

Solution

a. $a + b = -2 + (-4)$
$$= -6$$

b. $a - b = -2 - (-4)$
$$= -2 + 4$$
$$= 2$$

PROBLEM SET 2.3

ESSENTIAL IDEAS   LEVEL 1

1. IN YOUR OWN WORDS Explain the procedure for subtracting integers.

2. IN YOUR OWN WORDS Contrast the three uses for the "−" symbol—namely, minus, negative, and opposite.

DRILL AND PRACTICE   LEVEL 2

Find the differences in Problems 3–10. Show your solutions as two steps: First rewrite the subtraction as addition; then carry out the addition to find the answer.

3. a. $8 - 5$ $8 + (-5) = 3$

   b. $12 - 7$ $12 + (-7) = 5$

   c. $15 - (-15)$ $15 + 15 = 30$

   d. $15 - 15$ $15 + (-15) = 0$

4. a. $46 - (-46)$ $46 + 46 = 92$

   b. $46 - 46$ $46 + (-46) = 0$

   c. $15 - (-8)$ $15 + 8 = 23$

   d. $22 - (-8)$ $22 + 8 = 30$

5. a. $-7 - (-18)$ $-7 + 18 = 11$

   b. $-7 - 18$ $-7 + (-18) = -25$

   c. $7 - 18$ $7 + (-18) = -11$

   d. $7 - (-18)$ $7 + 18 = 25$

6. a. $9 - (-5)$ $9 + 5 = 14$

   b. $-9 - 5$ $-9 + (-5) = -14$

   c. $-9 - (-5)$ $-9 + 5 = -4$

   d. $9 - 5$ $9 + (-5) = 4$

7. a. $17 - (-8)$ $17 + 8 = 25$

   b. $-17 - 8$ $-17 + (-8) = -25$

   c. $17 - 8$ $17 + (-8) = 9$

   d. $-17 - (-8)$ $-17 + 8 = -9$

8. a. $-21 - 7$ $-21 + (-7) = -28$

   b. $-21 - (-7)$ $-21 + 7 = -14$

   c. $21 - (-7)$ $21 + 7 = 28$

   d. $21 - 7$ $21 + (-7) = 11$

9. a. $-13 - (-6)$ $-13 + 6 = -7$

   b. $13 - 6$ $13 + (-6) = 7$

   c. $13 - (-6)$ $13 + 6 = 19$

   d. $-13 - 6$ $-13 + (-6) = -19$

10. a. $8 - 23$ $8 + (-23) = -15$

   b. $-8 - (-23)$ $-8 + 23 = 15$

   c. $-8 - 23$ $-8 + (-23) = -31$

   d. $8 - (-23)$ $8 + 23 = 31$

Simplify the numerical expressions given in Problems 11–16.

11. a. $-4 - (-5) + 8$ 9

   b. $-8 + 9 - (-7)$ 8

   c. $8 - 6 - (-5)$ 7

   d. $-4 + 8 - (-2)$ 6

12. a. $-4 - 5 - (-6)$ -3

   b. $4 - 5 - 6$ -7

   c. $4 - 5 - (-6)$ 5

   d. $4 - (-5) - 6$ 3

13. a. $-8 - 7 - 6$ -21

   b. $-8 - 7 - (-6)$ -9

   c. $8 - 7 - (-6)$ 7

   d. $-8 - (-7) - 6$ -7

14. a. $-6 - 7 - (-9)$ -4

   b. $4 - 7 - 5$ -8

   c. $-7 - 3 - (-8)$ -2

   d. $6 - (-3) - 7$ 2

15. a. $-8 - 4 - 3$ -15

   b. $-8 - 4 - 5$ -17

   c. $11 - 14 - (-16)$ 13

   d. $-11 + (-5) - 5$ -21

16. a. $-21 - 14 - (-52)$ 17

   b. $37 + (-15) - 21$ 1

   c. $-2 - 3 - 7 - 10$ -22

   d. $21 - 37 - (-10)$ -6

Write out each of the statements in Problems 17–24 in words.

17. a. $5 - 3$ five minus three

   b. $5 - (-3)$ five minus negative three

18. a. $-2 - 5$ negative two minus five

   b. $-2 - (-5)$ negative two minus negative five

19. a. $-(3)$ the opposite of three

   b. $-(-3)$ the opposite of negative three

20. a. -3 negative three

   b. $2 - (-3)$ two minus negative three

21. a. $x + (-y)$ x plus the opposite of y

   b. $-x - y$ opposite of x minus y

22. a. $x - y$ x minus y

   b. $-y$ the opposite of y

23. a. $-[6(-1)] - 1$
   opposite of six times negative one minus one

   b. $6 - [-(-1)]$
   six minus the opposite of negative one

24. a. $-(2) - (-3)$
   opposite of two minus negative three

   b. $-2 - [-(-3)]$
   negative two minus the opposite of negative three

In Problems 25–38, let $x = -2, y = -1,$ and $z = -3$ to evaluate the given expression to find the values of the given capital letters.

25. $A = x + y$ -3

26. $B = x - z$ 1

27. $C = z - y$ -2

28. $D = y - z$ 2

29. $E = x - y$ -1

30. $F = -y$ 1

31. $G = -x$ 2

32. $H = -z$ 3

33. $I = x + y + z$ -6

34. $J = -x + (-y) + (-z)$ 6

35. $K = y + z - x$ -2

36. $L = z - x - z$ 2

37. $M = z - x - y$ 0

38. $N = x - y - z$ 2

Perform the indicated operations in Problems 39–46 on your calculator.

39. $487 - 843$ -356

40. $-381 - (-843)$ 162

41. $-1,439 - 816$ $-2,255$

42. $-125,409 - (-34,817)$ $-90,592$

43. $-4,567 + (-3,891) + 458$ $-8,000$

44. $-982 - (-458) + (-402)$ -926

45. $4,987 + (-4,583) - 478 + (-5,670)$ $-5,744$

46. $-8,211 - 9 - 10,209 + 4,511 - (-4,529)$ $-9,389$

APPLICATIONS   LEVEL 2

47. In Death Valley, California, the temperature can vary from 134°F above zero to 25°F below zero. What is the difference between these temperature extremes?   159°F

48. What is the difference in elevation between the top of a mountain 8,520 ft above sea level and a point in a valley 253 ft below sea level?   8,773 ft

49. What is the difference in elevation between a plane flying at 25,400 ft above sea level and a submarine traveling 450 ft below sea level?   25,850 ft

50. IBM stock had the following changes during a certain week: $+1, +3, -2, -1,$ and -3. What is the *net* change for the week?   down 2 or -2

The questions in Problems 51–53 are based on the following weather map.

51. What is the difference in temperature between Huntsville, AL, and Memphis, TN? 3°

52. What is the difference in temperature between Salt Lake City, UT, and Grand Rapids, MI? 5°

53. What is the difference in temperature between Colorado Springs, CO, and Huntsville, AL? 25°

54. **IN YOUR OWN WORDS** Applications are a major part of every mathematics course, but for most students they are often the least understood portion of the course.

CONQUER ANXIETY

In her book, *Conquering Math Anxiety: A Self-help Workbook, Second Edition* (Pacific Grove, CA: Brooks/Cole, 2003), Cynthia Arem discusses building internal barriers and walls when faced with word problems. Share your thoughts and feelings about working word problems.

RIGHT OR WRONG? **LEVEL 3**

Explain what is wrong, if anything, with the statements in Problems 55–60. Explain your reasoning.

55. The opposite of -3 is 3. T

56. $a - b$ means "a minus b" and $a + (-b)$ means "a plus the opposite of b." T

57. "Add the opposite" applied to the expression $-5 - 3$ means $5 + 3$. F; it means $-5 + (-3)$.

58. The symbol "$-a$" is read "minus a."
F; it is "the opposite of a."

59. The symbol $-b$ means that b is negative.
F; b can be positive, negative, or zero.

60. $5 - (-15) = -10$ F; it is 20.

2.4 Multiplication of Integers

IN THIS WORLD THE POWER OF MATH

HOW DO I PILE -4 BLOCKS?

2 blocks 3 blocks -4 blocks

"Hey, Ein, what's up?" asked Charlie. "I thought you had all those big ideas, but now you are playing with my kid's blocks."

"Vell, your boy asked me to explain negative numbers to him, und I am trying to do zat." replied Ein. "I know zat should be easy, but I've always had trouble with my arithmetic."

In this section you will learn how to multiply both positive and negative numbers. As you progress through this section, think by looking for patterns.

 See Problem 5.

What is multiplication? We really should answer that question before considering *how* to multiply. What actually happens when we multiply? Well, what does "three times four" mean? "Twelve" you answer proudly. That *is* the product—the answer— but how did you get that value? What did you do to multiply? You probably memorized that answer long ago, using a multiplication table, but what if you could no longer use that table or you forgot that particular entry? You might have to think about the meaning of multiplication.

For the whole numbers, multiplication can be defined as repeated addition, since we say that 4×3 means

$$\underbrace{3 + 3 + 3 + 3}_{4 \text{ addends}}$$

However, this *cannot* be done for all integers, since $(-4) \times 3$ or

$$\underbrace{3 + 3 + \cdots + 3}_{-4 \text{ addends}}$$

doesn't "make sense." Thus, it is necessary to generalize the definition of multiplication to include all integers. There are four cases to consider.

Positive Times a Positive

Positive integers are the same as the natural numbers, so the previous definition of repeated addition applies: **The product of two positive numbers is a positive number.**

Positive Times a Negative

Now consider $(+3) \times (-4)$ by looking at a pattern:

$$(+3) \times (+4) = \mathbf{+12}$$
$$(+3) \times (+3) = \mathbf{+9}$$
$$(+3) \times (+2) = \mathbf{+6}$$

Would you know what to write next? Here it is:

$$(+3) \times (+1) = \mathbf{+3}$$
$$(+3) \times (0) = \mathbf{0}$$

What comes next? Do you see the pattern? *As the second factor decreases by* 1, *the product decreases by* 3:

$$(+3) \times (-1) = \mathbf{-3}$$
$$(+3) \times (-2) = \mathbf{-6}$$
$$(+3) \times (-3) = \mathbf{-9}$$
$$(+3) \times (-4) = \mathbf{-12}$$

Do you see how to continue? Try building a few more such patterns using different numbers. What do you see about the product of a positive and a negative number? **The product of a positive number and a negative number is a negative number.**

Negative Times a Positive

The order in which two numbers are multiplied has no effect on the product, so

$$(-3) \times (+4) = (+4) \times (-3)$$
$$= \mathbf{-12}$$

The product of a negative number and a positive number is a negative number.

Negative Times a Negative

Consider the final example: the product of two negative integers, say, $(-3) \times (-4)$. Once again, we begin by looking for a pattern. Start with

$$(-3) \times (+4) = -12$$
$$(-3) \times (+3) = -9$$
$$(-3) \times (+2) = -6$$

What would you write next? Here it is:

$$(-3) \times (+1) = -3$$
$$(-3) \times (0) = 0$$

What comes next? You should notice that, as the second factor *decreases by* 1, *the product increases by* 3:

$$(-3) \times (-1) = \mathbf{+3}$$
$$(-3) \times (-2) = \mathbf{+6}$$
$$(-3) \times (-3) = \mathbf{+9}$$
$$(-3) \times (-4) = \mathbf{+12}$$

The product of two negative numbers is a positive number.

Finally, we note that if one (or both) of the integers is zero, then the product is zero. We now summarize these results for **multiplication of nonzero integers** in the following box.

Multiplying Integers

To multiply nonzero integers, look at the signs of the factors and then determine the sign of the product before multiplying the integers.

	Sign of product	Absolute values
Pos × Pos	+	Multiplied
Pos × Neg	−	Multiplied
Neg × Pos	−	Multiplied
Neg × Neg	+	Multiplied

To summarize what we have just established for multiplying two integers, we look at the signs of the numbers. If the signs are different, the product is negative. If the signs are alike, the product is positive. Using a flowchart, such as Figure 2.3, we can break the process down into a few simple steps.

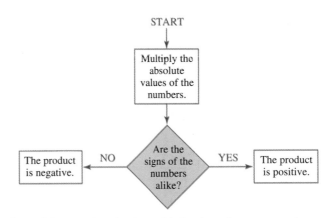

Figure 2.3 Flowchart for the multiplication of two nonzero integers

EXAMPLE 1   **Multiplying integers**

Simplify the following.

a. 6×9 b. $6 \times (-2)$ c. $(-3)7$

d. $(-8)(-9)$ e. $-2(-3)(-4)$ f. $-2(-3)5$

Solution

a. $6 \times 9 = 54$ b. $6 \times (-2) = -12$
   Positive understood

c. $(-3)7 = -21$ Remember that numbers in parentheses written right next to each other mean multiplication.

d. $(-8)(-9) = 72$

e. $-2(-3)(-4) = 6(\ 4)$ Work from left to right.
   $= -24$

f. $-2(-3)5 = 30$ From left to right: $-2(-3)5 = 6(5) = 30$

Before leaving the topic of multiplication, we will consider one more example. Certainly $(-4) = (4)(-1) = (-1)(4)$, which can be shown on a number line:

This example would seem to apply for any integer n.

Opposite Property

$$(-1)n = -n$$

Negative one times a number is the opposite of that number.

Examples 2 and 3 illustrate the process of evaluating expressions with integers.

EXAMPLE 2

Evaluating algebraic expressions with integers

Evaluate $a^2 - 2ab + b^2$, where $a = -2$ and $b = -1$.

Solution
$$\begin{aligned}
a^2 - 2ab + b^2 &= (-2)^2 - 2(-2)(-1) + (-1)^2 \\
&= 4 - 4 + 1 \\
&= 1
\end{aligned}$$

EXAMPLE 3

Evaluating algebraic expressions dealing with opposites

Evaluate $-a$, a^2, $-a^2$, and $(-a)^2$ for $a = 2$ and $a = -3$.

Solution If $a = 2$ (the variable is a positive number):

$-a = -2$	The opposite of a is negative two.
$a^2 = (2)^2 = 2 \cdot 2 = 4$	The square of a is four.
$-a^2 = -2^2 = -(2 \cdot 2) = -4$	The opposite of a squared is negative four.
$(-a)^2 = (-2)^2 = (-2)(-2) = 4$	The square of the opposite of a is four.

An important principle is illustrated in Example 3, and it involves an idea often missed by beginning algebra students—that is, the difference between
$$-2^2 \text{ and } (-2)^2$$
$$-3^2 \text{ and } (-3)^2$$
$$a^2 \text{ and } -a^2 \ (a \neq 0)$$

If $a = -3$ (the variable is a negative number):

$-a = -(-3) = 3$	The opposite of a is three.
$a^2 = (-3)^2 = (-3)(-3) = 9$	The square of a is nine.
$-a^2 = -(-3)^2 = -(-3)(-3) = -9$	The opposite of a squared is negative nine.
$(-a)^2 = (3)^2 = 3 \cdot 3 = 9$	The square of the opposite of a is nine.

Multiplication by zero is done using a property called the **zero multiplication property.** If n is any number, then

$$n \cdot 0 = 0 \cdot n = 0$$

That is, any number multiplied by zero is equal to zero.

Example 3 illustrates an important distinction:

$$-2^2 = -4 \qquad -3^2 = -9 \qquad -a^2 \text{ is negative } (a \neq 0).$$
$$(-2)^2 = 4 \qquad (-3)^2 = 9 \qquad a^2 \text{ is positive } (a \neq 0).$$

PROBLEM SET 2.4

ESSENTIAL IDEAS LEVEL 1

1. What does m times n mean? $\underbrace{n + n + n + \cdots + n}_{m \text{ addends}}$, that is, m addends of n; that is,

2. State the opposite property. $(-1)n = -n$

3. State the zero multiplication property. $n \cdot 0 = 0 \cdot n = 0$

4. IN YOUR OWN WORDS Explain how to multiply two positive integers.

5. IN YOUR OWN WORDS Explain how to multiply two negative integers.

6. IN YOUR OWN WORDS Explain how to multiply a positive and a negative integer.

DRILL AND PRACTICE LEVEL 2

Perform the indicated operations in Problems 7–22.

7. a. $6 \times (-9)$ −54
   b. $3 \times (-5)$ −15
   c. $(-2) \times 4$ −8
   d. $4 \times (-2)$ −8

8. a. $4 \times (-5)$ −20
   b. $8 \times (-8)$ −64
   c. $-6 \times (-11)$ 66
   d. $-7 \times (-4)$ 28

9. a. $6(-8)$ −48
   b. $(-4)(-7)$ 28
   c. $7(5)$ 35
   d. $3(9)$ 27

10. a. $(-7)(4)$ −28
    b. $9(-9)$ −81
    c. $5(0)$ 0
    d. $(-8)(4)$ −32

11. a. $(-6)(-9)$ 54
    b. $7(-6)$ −42
    c. $5(-2)(-5)$ 50
    d. $(-5)3(5)$ −75

12. a. $-8(-9)(2)$ 144
    b. $3(-6)(-1)$ 18
    c. $2(9)(-3)$ −54
    d. $(-4)(8)(-5)$ 160

13. a. $5(-4)(-2)$ 40
    b. $(-2)(-1)3$ 6
    c. $4(-7)3$ −84
    d. $(-4)(2)(-1)$ 8

14. a. -4^2 −16
    b. $(-4)^2$ 16
    c. $-4^2 + (-4)^2$ 0
    d. $-4^2 - (-4)^2$ −32

15. a. $(-5)^2$ 25
    b. -5^2 −25
    c. $(-5)^2 - 5^2$ 0
    d. $5^2 - (-5)^2$ 0

16. a. -6^2 −36
    b. $(-6)^2$ 36
    c. $-6^2 + (-6)^2$ 0
    d. $-6^2 - (-6)^2$ −72

17. a. $(-7)^2$ 49
    b. -7^2 −49
    c. $(-7)^2 - 7^2$ 0
    d. $-7^2 - (-7)^2$ −98

18. a. $(-8)^2$ 64
    b. -8^2 −64
    c. $-8^2 - 8^2$ −128
    d. $-8^2 - (-8)^2$ −128

19. a. $(-8)(-2)(-2)$ −32
    b. $(-8)(-8)(-2)$ −128
    c. $(-1)(-5)(-6)$ −30
    d. $(-8)(-2)(-1)$ −16

20. a. $(-3)^2 - (-4)^2$ −7
    b. $(-2)^2 - (-3)^2$ −5
    c. $(-2)^2 - (-1)^2$ 3
    d. $(-5)^2 - (-3)8$ 49

21. a. $-3(4 - 9)^2$ −75
    b. $-2(6 - 10)^2$ −32
    c. $(-5)(-4) - (-3)^2$ 11
    d. $2(-8) - (-3)^2$ −25

22. a. $-6 - 3(-5)$ 9
    b. $-8 + 4(-2)$ −16
    c. $(-2)(8 - 3) - (-1 - 7)^2$ −74
    d. $2(-5 + 3)^2 - (-4)5$ 28

In Problems 23–38, let $x = -3$, $y = 2$, and $z = -1$ to evaluate the given expression to find the values of the given capital letters.

23. $A = xy$ −6
24. $B = xz$ 3
25. $C = yz$ −2
26. $D = xyz$ 6
27. $E = x^2 + y^2$ 13
28. $F = (x + y)^2$ 1
29. $G = (x - y)^2$ 25
30. $H = x^2 - y^2$ 5
31. $I = -x^2$ −9
32. $J = -y^2$ −4
33. $K = z^2 - x^2$ −8
34. $L = (z - x)^2$ 4
35. $M = x^2 - 2xy + y^2$ 25
36. $N = x^2 + 2xy + y^2$ 1
37. $P = (x - y - z)^2$ 16
38. $Q = (x - y + z)^2$ 36

APPLICATIONS LEVEL 2

39. Walk to the right 15 steps three times in a row; then walk to the left 8 steps; repeat this eight-step move four more times. What is the net change from your starting position? 5 or 5 steps to the right

40. Walk to the left 12 steps; then walk to the right 20 steps; then walk to the left 7 steps; finally, repeat this last seven-step move a total of six more times. What is the net change from your starting position? −41 or 41 steps to the left

41. Tim was not a very good card player and obtained a score of −23 four times in a row. What is Tim's final score? −92

42. Rebaldo obtained a score of 28, but then received three 25-point penalties. What is Rebaldo's final score? **−47**

43. Rose went down 5 floors three times in a row, and then turned around and reversed her steps. If 25 calories are used for each floor, what is the total number of calories Rose consumed? **750 calories**

44. Linda was climbing down a cliff and went down a 20-ft distance eight times, but then went up a 15-ft distance three times. What is the net change from her starting position? **−115, or down 115 ft**

45. What is the opposite of moving to the left 5 units a total of three times? **moving to the right 15 units**

46. What is the opposite of moving down 20 units a total of 18 times? **moving up 360**

47. What is the net result of the opposite of gaining $150 from each of three people? **losing a total of $450 or −$450**

48. What is the net result of the opposite of losing $150 to each of five people? **gaining $750**

RIGHT OR WRONG? **LEVEL 3**

Explain what is wrong, if anything, with the statements in Problems 49–60. Explain your reasoning.

49. The sum of two positives is positive. T

50. The sum of a positive and a negative is negative.
F; the sum may be positive or negative.

51. The sum of two negatives is negative. T

52. The product of two positives is positive. T

53. The product of a positive and a negative is negative. T

54. The product of two negatives is negative. F; it is positive.

55. $-6^2 = 36$ F; $-6^2 = -36$

56. $-10^2 = 100$ F; $-10^2 = -100$

57. $-8^2 = 64$ F; $-8^2 = -64$

58. $(-6)^2 = 36$ T

59. $(-10)^2 = 100$ T

60. $(-8)^2 = 64$ T

2.5) Division of Integers

IN THIS WORLD **THE POWER OF MATH**

Courtesy of Herman Cain

"What can you do with mathematics? I don't want to be a mathematician, nor do I want to teach!" said Marcy. "Why do I need to take a math course in order to graduate?"

"I'm glad I majored in mathematics because it provided me a foundation for my current business career," said Herman, CEO and President of T.H.E., Inc., a leadership company, and former CEO of Godfather's Pizza, Inc.

"Wow, you were a math major?" asked Marcy. "I didn't know that! What did you enjoy most about mathematics?"

*"It is everywhere in daily life—in both my personal life and my business life. Mathematics has allowed me to make complex 'things' simple. I call it **focus,** which allows me to solve business problems of all types."**

In this section we will discuss division of integers. We consider division of positives and negatives, as well as division by zero.

 See Problem 2.

The story of Herman Cain's career is a story of work, determination, and a unique recipe for success: **focus. He graduated from Morehouse College with a B.S. in mathematics and then earned his Master's Degree in Computer Science from Purdue University.*

Since division can be thought of as multiplying by the reciprocal of a number, it follows that division can be written as a multiplication. For example,

$$(-10) \div 2 = (-10) \times \frac{1}{2} \quad \textit{Negative times positive is negative.}$$
$$= -5$$

This fact means that the rules for **division of nonzero integers** are identical to those for multiplication.

Dividing Integers

> To divide nonzero integers, look at the signs of the factors and then determine the sign of the quotient before dividing the integers.
>
> | | *Sign of quotient* | *Absolute values* |
> |---|---|---|
> | Pos ÷ Pos | + | Divided |
> | Pos ÷ Neg | − | Divided |
> | Neg ÷ Pos | − | Divided |
> | Neg ÷ Neg | + | Divided |

STOP

EXAMPLE 1

Division of integers

Simplify the following.

a. $10 \div 5$ **b.** $10 \div (-5)$ **c.** $(-10) \div 5$ **d.** $(-10) \div (-5)$

e. $90 \div (-9)$ **f.** $-282 \div (-6)$ **g.** $0 \div 10$ **h.** $10 \div 0$

Solution

a. $10 \div 5 = 2$ **b.** $10 \div (-5) = -2$ **c.** $(-10) \div 5 = -2$

d. $(-10) \div (-5) = 2$ **e.** $90 \div (-9) = -10$ **f.** $-282 \div (-6) = 47$

g. $0 \div 10 = 0$ **This checks since 10 × 0 = 0.**

h. $10 \div 0$ **Impossible;** you can't divide by zero because, if there were some number (say, x), then $\frac{10}{0} = x$ means $0 \cdot x = 10$. But $0 \times x = 0$ and is not 10 for *any* value of x. ●

Pay particular attention to parts *g* and *h* of Example 1. Students often confuse the two, so it is important that you specifically remember that *division by zero is impossible.* Sometimes we say that *division by zero is undefined.*

In algebra, we rarely use the ÷ symbol; instead we use the fraction bar introduced in Section 1.3. The fraction bar is also used as a grouping symbol. For example,

$$\frac{2+3}{5} \quad \text{means} \quad (2+3) \div 5$$

whereas

$$2 + \frac{3}{5} \quad \text{means} \quad 2 + (3 \div 5)$$

This distinction is particularly important when you are evaluating expressions. Consider how you would use a calculator to evaluate these expressions.

For $\dfrac{2+3}{5}$, *press:* (2 + 3) ÷ 5 = *Display:* 1

Note: You must press the equal key to group the numbers above the fractional bar before doing the division. Contrast this with the next sequence:

For $2 + \frac{3}{5}$, *press:* 2 + 3 ÷ 5 = *Display:* 2.6

EXAMPLE 2   **Evaluating expressions with a fractional grouping bar**

Evaluate the following expressions, where $x = -6$, $y = 3$, and $z = -3$.

a. $\dfrac{x - y}{x - z}$ **b.** $\dfrac{x^2 - y^2}{x + y}$

Solution

a.
$$\dfrac{x - y}{x - z} = \dfrac{-6 - 3}{-6 - (-3)}$$
$$= \dfrac{-9}{-6 + 3}$$
$$= \dfrac{-9}{-3}$$
$$= 3$$

b.
$$\dfrac{x^2 - y^2}{x + y} = \dfrac{(-6)^2 - 3^2}{-6 + 3}$$
$$= \dfrac{36 - 9}{-3}$$
$$= \dfrac{27}{-3}$$
$$= -9$$

●

Another common use of division of integers is in finding the **average** of a set of numbers. The average we are considering is sometimes called the **mean** and is defined as the *sum* of the quantities being averaged divided by the *number* of quantities being averaged.

EXAMPLE 3   **Average test score**

If a student's test scores are 72, 85, 79, and 92, what is this student's average test score?

Solution

$$\text{AVERAGE} = \dfrac{72 + 85 + 79 + 92}{4}$$ ← Divide by 4 because there are 4 scores being averaged.

$$= \dfrac{328}{4}$$ *Press:* (72 + 85 + 79 + 92) ÷ 4 =

$$= 82$$

Don't forget that the fractional bar is a grouping symbol, so group the numbers on the top before doing the division.

●

Averages can also include negative numbers, as in finding the average low temperature for a week of very cold days.

EXAMPLE 4   **Finding an average**

Find the average of 5, -7, 3, 0, 4, -15, and -4.

Solution $\text{AVERAGE} = \dfrac{5 + (-7) + 3 + 0 + 4 + (-15) + (-4)}{7}$

$$= \dfrac{-14}{7}$$
$$= -2$$

●

PROBLEM SET 2.5

ESSENTIAL IDEAS LEVEL 1

1. **IN YOUR OWN WORDS** Describe a procedure for dividing integers.

2. **IN YOUR OWN WORDS** Discuss why we say division by 0 is impossible.

3. **IN YOUR OWN WORDS** Describe the difference between $2 - \frac{3}{4}$ and $\frac{2-3}{4}$.

4. **IN YOUR OWN WORDS** Describe the difference between $7 - 5/2$ and $(7-5)2$.

DRILL AND PRACTICE LEVEL 2

Find the quotient in Problems 5–12.

5. **a.** $42 \div 7$ 6 **b.** $63 \div 9$ 7
   c. $56 \div 8$ 7 **d.** $110 \div 10$ 11

6. **a.** $-51 \div 17$ −3 **b.** $100 \div (-5)$ −20
   c. $48 \div -4$ −12 **d.** $-15 \div 5$ −3

7. **a.** $-56 \div 8$ −7 **b.** $-88 \div (-8)$ 11
   c. $-24 \div 4$ −6 **d.** $28 \div (-7)$ −4

8. **a.** $(-8) \div 0$ impossible **b.** $0 \div (-8)$ 0
   c. $0 \div 0$ undefined **d.** $0 \div 10$ 0

9. **a.** $\dfrac{-63}{-9}$ 7 **b.** $\dfrac{-15}{-3}$ 5
   c. $\dfrac{-90}{3}$ −30 **d.** $\dfrac{85}{-5}$ −17

10. **a.** $\dfrac{92}{-2}$ −46 **b.** $\dfrac{-528}{-4}$ 132
    c. $\dfrac{-450}{-10}$ 45 **d.** $\dfrac{-105}{-5}$ 21

11. **a.** $\dfrac{15}{0}$ impossible **b.** $\dfrac{0}{-5}$ 0
    c. $\dfrac{73}{0}$ impossible **d.** $\dfrac{19}{0}$ impossible

12. **a.** $\dfrac{10}{-5}$ −2 **b.** $\dfrac{-6}{-3}$ 2
    c. $\dfrac{0}{12}$ 0 **d.** $\dfrac{-6}{0}$ impossible

Find the value of each of the expressions in Problems 13–16. Show the keys you would press to evaluate the expression using a calculator, and then verify that the calculator answer agrees with your first answer.

13. **a.** $\dfrac{12-4}{2}$ 4 ⎡(12 − 4)⎤ ÷ 2 =
    b. $12 - \frac{4}{2}$ 10 12 − 4 ÷ 2 =

14. **a.** $18 - \frac{6}{3}$ 16 18 − 6 ÷ 3 =
    b. $\dfrac{18-6}{3}$ 4 ⎡(18 − 6)⎤ ÷ 3 =

15. **a.** $\dfrac{6+21}{-3}$ −9 ⎡(6 + 21)⎤ ÷ (−) 3 =
    b. $6 + \frac{21}{-3}$ −1 6 + 21 ÷ (−) 3 =

16. **a.** $\dfrac{2+(-8)}{2}$ −3 ⎡(2 + (−) 8)⎤ ÷ 2 =
    b. $2 + \frac{-8}{2}$ −2 2 + (−) 8 ÷ 2 =

Find the value of each of the expressions in Problems 17–30.

17. $(-6)(-6) \div (+9)$ 4 18. $2 \cdot (-14) \div (-4)$ 7

19. $(-20)(+3) \div (-5)$ 12 20. $5 \cdot 8 \div (-10)$ −4

21. $(3 +12) \div (-3)$ −5 22. $3 + 12 \div (-3)$ −1

23. $\dfrac{8 + (-3) - (-7)}{-4}$ −3 24. $\dfrac{-7 - (-2) - 9}{-2}$ 7

25. $\dfrac{-11 + 9 - 6 - 8}{(-2)(2)}$ 4 26. $\dfrac{7 - 2 + 8 - 1}{(-1)(-3)}$ 4

27. $\dfrac{(-7) - (-5)(-3)}{2 - (-9)}$ −2 28. $\dfrac{(-5) - (-7)(-3)}{8 - (-5)}$ −2

29. $\dfrac{12 - (-2)(-3)}{2}$ 3 30. $\dfrac{5 - (-4)(-3)}{2 - (-5)}$ −1

Given that $u = -1$, $v = 2$, $w = -3$, and $x = -5$, evaluate each of the expressions in Problems 31–46 in order to find the value of the capital letter.

31. $A = w + vx$ −13 32. $B = u + wx$ 14

33. $C = w + \dfrac{x}{u}$ 2 34. $D = \dfrac{w}{u} + x$ −2

35. $E = \dfrac{w}{x + v}$ 1 36. $F = \dfrac{x}{v - w}$ −1

37. $G = \dfrac{x + u}{w}$ 2 38. $H = \dfrac{u - v}{v + x}$ 1

39. $I = \dfrac{x + w}{u - x}$ −2 40. $J = \dfrac{w + x}{u}$ 8

41. $K = \dfrac{w + x}{v}$ −4 42. $L = \dfrac{v^2 w}{x + u}$ 2

43. $M = \dfrac{u - w^2}{u - w}$ −5 44. $N = \dfrac{x^2 - v^2}{v + x}$ −7

45. $P = \dfrac{u + v + w + x}{7} \quad -1$

46. $Q = \dfrac{4(u + v) - (w + x)}{4} \quad 3$

47. Find the average of the first 9 positive integers.   5

48. Find the average of 6, -10, 14, -25, and 0. -3

49. Find the average of 2, -5, 4, -7, and -4. -2

50. Find the average of -7, -18, 4, -9, and 5. -5

51. Find the average of -3, -6, 5, 8, 0, -2, and 5.   1

52. Find the average of 21, 0, -34, 45, and -12.   4

Explain what is wrong, if anything, with the statements in Problems 53–60. Explain your reasoning.

53. In $5 \div 20$, the divisor (the number we are dividing by) is 5.   F; the divisor is 20.

54. $0 \div 2$ is impossible.   F; it is 0.

55. $5 \div 0 = 0$ F; can't divide by 0.

56. A negative divided by a negative is negative. F; it is positive.

57. An average must be positive. F; an average can be positive, negative, or zero.

58. $6 \div 3 + 3 = 1$ F; it is 5 (division before addition).

59. $2 + 6 \div 2 = 4$ F; it is 5 (division before addition).

60. $9 + 12 \div 3$ means $\dfrac{9 + 12}{3}$.   F; it means $9 + \frac{12}{3}$.

2.6 Rational and Irrational Numbers

IN THIS WORLD   THE POWER OF MATH

"I'm reattaching my TV antenna, which just blew over in the storm," said Terry. "I need some guy wires and some electrical connectors that look like this."

"No problem," said the clerk. "Let me show you how these connectors work."

Your number world expands considerably in this section. The book has traced your number history: first came the counting numbers, then the fractions and decimals, and in this section we learn about numbers that are not fractions, to form what are called the *real numbers*.

 See Problem 41.

The integers provide a set of numbers that includes all possible answers for addition, multiplication, and subtraction.* In the same way, we wish to consider a set of numbers that includes all possible answers for the operation of division. We start with the integers, and we also include the set of all possible fractions. With this larger set, we can add, subtract, multiply, and divide any two numbers (except division by zero) and get answers in the set.

*In more advanced work, this idea is summarized by what is called *closure*. We say that the set of integers is closed for the operation of subtraction (for example) if any two elements in the set can be subtracted and the result is an integer.

This enlarged set is called the set of **rational numbers** and is denoted by $\mathbb{Q}$. (It is called $\mathbb{Q}$ because it is formed by considering all quotients, except those involving division by 0.) The set $\mathbb{Q}$ consists of integers and fractions—that is, numbers that can be written as $\frac{p}{q}$, where p is an integer and q is a nonzero integer. These sets are shown in Figure 2.4.

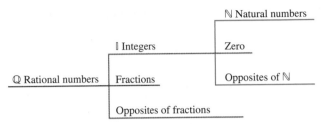

Figure 2.4 Relationships among sets of numbers

Consider any number in the set $\mathbb{N}$, say, 5. Then 5 is also contained in $\mathbb{I}$ and $\mathbb{Q}$. Consider some number in $\mathbb{Q}$, say, $\frac{1}{2}$. Since $\frac{1}{2}$ is in $\mathbb{Q}$ but not in $\mathbb{I}$, we say that $\frac{1}{2}$ is a rational number that is not an integer.

Because the signs of the numerator and denominator of a fraction may be either positive or negative, there are several equivalent forms of any fraction. Suppose p and q are positive integers; then

$$\frac{p}{q} = \frac{-p}{-q} = -\frac{-p}{q} = -\frac{p}{-q}$$

Likewise, the fraction itself can be negative; then

$$-\frac{p}{q} = \frac{-p}{q} = \frac{p}{-q} = -\frac{-p}{-q}$$

Because of this variety of possible forms, we call $\frac{p}{q}$ and $\frac{-p}{q}$ the standard forms of a fraction, and we reduce all other forms to one of these.

Standard-Form Fraction

> If p and q are positive integers, then $\frac{p}{q}$ and $\frac{-p}{q}$ are called the **standard forms of a fraction. A reduced fraction** is a fraction in standard form such that there is no integer (other than 1 or -1) that divides into both p and q.

EXAMPLE 1   **Standard forms of a fraction**

Write each nonstandard form in standard form.

a. $\dfrac{-5}{-7}$ b. $\dfrac{5}{-7}$ c. $-\dfrac{-5}{7}$ d. $-\dfrac{5}{-7}$ e. $-\dfrac{5}{7}$ f. $-\dfrac{-5}{-7}$

Solution

a. $\dfrac{-5}{-7} = \dfrac{5}{7}$ b. $\dfrac{5}{-7} = \dfrac{-5}{7}$ c. $-\dfrac{-5}{7} = \dfrac{5}{7}$

d. $-\dfrac{5}{-7} = \dfrac{5}{7}$ e. $-\dfrac{5}{7} = \dfrac{-5}{7}$ f. $-\dfrac{-5}{-7} = \dfrac{-5}{7}$

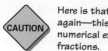

Here is that word *simplify* again—this time for numerical expressions with fractions.

To **simplify** a numerical expression containing a rational number means to carry out all of the operations, according to the order-of-operations agreement, and to write your answer as a single number or a reduced fraction.

EXAMPLE 2   Operations with rational numbers

Simplify the given numerical expressions.

a. $\dfrac{-3}{2} \cdot \dfrac{1}{2}$ b. $\dfrac{4}{-9} \cdot \dfrac{-15}{8}$ c. $\dfrac{\frac{-2}{3}}{\frac{-5}{3}}$

d. $\dfrac{-2}{3} + \dfrac{5}{-3}$ e. $\dfrac{-3}{4} - \dfrac{1}{-5}$ f. $\dfrac{4}{5} + \dfrac{1}{5} \cdot \dfrac{-1}{2}$

Solution

a. $\dfrac{-3}{2} \cdot \dfrac{1}{2} = \dfrac{-3}{4}$

b. $\dfrac{4}{-9} \cdot \dfrac{-15}{8} = \dfrac{2 \cdot 2 \cdot (\cancel{-1}) \cdot 3 \cdot 5}{(\cancel{-1}) \cdot 3 \cdot 3 \cdot 2 \cdot 2 \cdot 2}$

$$= \dfrac{5}{3 \cdot 2}$$

$$= \dfrac{5}{6}$$

c. $\dfrac{\frac{-2}{3}}{\frac{-5}{3}} = \dfrac{-2}{3} \div \dfrac{-5}{3}$

$$= \dfrac{-2}{3} \cdot \dfrac{3}{-5}$$

$$= \dfrac{2}{5}$$

d. $\dfrac{-2}{3} + \dfrac{5}{-3} = \dfrac{-2}{3} + \dfrac{-5}{3}$

$$= \dfrac{-7}{3}$$

e. $\dfrac{-3}{4} - \dfrac{1}{-5} = \dfrac{-3}{4} - \dfrac{-1}{5}$

$$= \dfrac{-3}{4} \cdot \dfrac{5}{5} - \dfrac{-1}{5} \cdot \dfrac{4}{4}$$

$$= \dfrac{-15}{20} - \dfrac{-4}{20}$$

$$= \dfrac{-15 - (-4)}{20}$$

$$= \dfrac{-15 + 4}{20}$$

$$= \dfrac{-11}{20}$$

f. $\dfrac{4}{5} + \dfrac{1}{5} \cdot \dfrac{-1}{2} = \dfrac{4}{5} + \dfrac{-1}{10}$

$$= \dfrac{8}{10} + \dfrac{-1}{10}$$

$$= \dfrac{7}{10}$$

Don't forget the correct order of operations: multiplication first, then addition.

For centuries it was thought that the set of rational numbers was complete in the sense that no other numbers existed or were needed, since all additions, subtractions, multiplication, and nonzero divisions result in rational numbers. The first indication that numbers other than rational numbers exist came from ancient Greece.

There is a silly pun based on the Pythagorean theorem as shown at the right in italic: Three bunnies are proudly sitting side by side. The first, a 5-lb hare, sits on a buffalo skin. The second, a 7-lb hare, is on a deer skin. The third, papa hare, who weighs 12 lb, is on a hippopotamus skin. Therefore, *the hare on the hippopotamus is equal to the sum of the hares on the other two hides.*

Pythagorean Theorem

This is one of the most famous results in all of elementary mathematics. You should spend some time studying this theorem.

The secret Greek society called the Pythagoreans (see the accompanying Historical Note) is credited with discovering the famous property of square numbers that today bears Pythagoras' name (even though it was known to the Chinese long before). They found that, if they constructed squares on each of the legs of a right triangle, the area of the largest square was equal to the sum of the areas of the smaller squares. We will state the **Pythagorean theorem** algebraically by saying that, if a and b are the lengths of the legs of a right triangle and c is the length of the **hypotenuse** (the longest side of the right triangle), then *the square of the length of the hypotenuse is equal to the sum of the squares of the lengths of the other two sides.*

> For any right triangle ABC, with sides of length a, b, and c,
> $$a^2 + b^2 = c^2$$
> where c is the length of the side opposite the right angle. Also, if
> $$a^2 + b^2 = c^2$$
> then the ΔABC is a right triangle.

This property leads to a revolutionary idea in mathematics—one that caused the Pythagoreans many problems. It is the idea that there exist numbers that are not rational.

Consider a right triangle with each leg 1. Then the hypotenuse must be
$$1^2 + 1^2 = c^2$$
$$2 = c^2$$

If we denote the number whose square is 2 by $\sqrt{2}$, we have $\sqrt{2} = c$. The symbol $\sqrt{2}$ is read "**square root** of two," and the symbol "$\sqrt{\ }$" is called a **square root symbol** or a **radical.** This means that $\sqrt{2}$ is that number such that, when multiplied by itself, as in

$$\sqrt{2} \times \sqrt{2}$$

the product is 2. You might notice your calculator has a button marked $\boxed{\sqrt{\ }}$. Some calculators require that you press the square root button first, and then the number, whereas others find the square root of the previously pressed number; you should try this on your calculator to see which way to do it:

$$\boxed{\sqrt{\ }}\ \boxed{2} \qquad \text{or} \qquad \boxed{2}\ \boxed{\sqrt{\ }}$$

Note that the display 1.414213562 is an approximation for the square root of 2, since if we actually square this number, we obtain a number close to 2, but not actually the number 2 as required for the square root of two:

$$1.414213562 \times 1.414213562 = 1.999999998944727844$$

We see that a calculator is no help in deciding whether $\sqrt{2}$ is rational or irrational.

The question for the Pythagoreans was whether $\sqrt{2}$ is rational. That is, does there exist a fractional or decimal representation for $\sqrt{2}$? We will now consider this question.

EXAMPLE 3   **Using the definition of square root**

Use the definition of square root to find the following numbers.

a. $\sqrt{3} \times \sqrt{3}$ **b.** $\sqrt{4} \times \sqrt{4}$ **c.** $\sqrt{5} \times \sqrt{5}$

d. $\sqrt{15} \times \sqrt{15}$ **e.** $\sqrt{16} \times \sqrt{16}$ **f.** $\sqrt{155} \times \sqrt{155}$

g. $\sqrt{x} \times \sqrt{x}$ (x positive)

Solution

a. $\sqrt{3} \times \sqrt{3} = 3$ **b.** $\sqrt{4} \times \sqrt{4} = 4$ **c.** $\sqrt{5} \times \sqrt{5} = 5$

d. $\sqrt{15} \times \sqrt{15} = 15$ **e.** $\sqrt{16} \times \sqrt{16} = 16$ **f.** $\sqrt{155} \times \sqrt{155} = 155$

g. $\sqrt{x} \times \sqrt{x} = x$ ●

By considering the results of Example 3, we can show that some square roots are rational. From part **b** of Example 3, we have

$$\sqrt{4} \times \sqrt{4} = 4$$

and we know that $2 \times 2 = 4$, so it seems reasonable that $\sqrt{4} = 2$. But wait! We also know that $(-2) \times (-2) = 4$, so isn't it just as reasonable that $\sqrt{4} = -2$? Mathematicians have agreed that the *square root symbol be used to denote only nonnegative numbers,* so that $\sqrt{4} = 2$ (*not* -2). If we want to indicate a negative root, we write

$$-\sqrt{4} = -2$$

From Example 3, you should notice that the square roots of natural numbers that are perfect squares will be rational. Look at this list of perfect squares:

$$1^2 = 1$$
$$2^2 = 4$$
$$3^2 = 9$$
$$4^2 = 16$$
$$5^2 = 25$$
$$\vdots$$

STOP Note these perfect squares.

The **perfect squares** you should know for this book are 1, 4, 9, 16, 25, 36, 49, 64, 81, 100, 121, 144, 169, and 196.

EXAMPLE 4   **Finding square roots**

Find the positive square root of each of the given numbers.

a. 4   **b.** 49   **c.** $\frac{1}{4}$ **d.** -9 **e.** 324

Solution

a. $\sqrt{4} = 2$, since $2 \times 2 = 4$

b. $\sqrt{49} = 7$, since $7 \times 7 = 49$

c. $\sqrt{\frac{1}{4}} = \frac{1}{2}$, since $\frac{1}{2} \times \frac{1}{2} = \frac{1}{4}$

d. $\sqrt{-9}$ This **does not exist** because no number squared can be negative:*

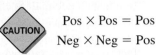

$$\text{Pos} \times \text{Pos} = \text{Pos}$$
$$\text{Neg} \times \text{Neg} = \text{Pos}$$

e. If the number is not one you recognize from the times table, such as $\sqrt{324}$, you can sometimes find it by trial-and-error multiplication:

$$10^2 = 100$$
$$20^2 = 400, \quad \text{so } \sqrt{324} \text{ is between 10 and 20}$$
$$15^2 = 225, \quad \text{so } \sqrt{324} \text{ is between 15 and 20}$$
$$19^2 = 361, \quad \text{so } \sqrt{324} \text{ is between 17 and 19}$$
$$18^2 = 324, \quad \text{so } \sqrt{324} = 18.$$ ●

Example 4 illustrates finding the square roots of perfect squares. What if the number is not a perfect square? To answer this question, we need to note that rational numbers can be written in a decimal form that either terminates or repeats, as shown by Example 5.

EXAMPLE 5   **Writing a rational number as a decimal**

Show that each number is rational by representing it as a terminating or a repeating decimal.

a. 3   **b.** $\frac{1}{2}$ **c.** $\frac{1}{3}$ **d.** $\frac{1}{7}$ **e.** $-6\frac{1}{18}$ **f.** $\dfrac{2}{-35}$

Solution

a. $3 = 3$ terminating decimal; rational

b. $\frac{1}{2} = 0.5$ terminating decimal; rational

c. $\frac{1}{3} = 0.\overline{3}$ repeating decimal; rational

d. $\frac{1}{7} = 0.\overline{142857}$ repeating decimal; rational

e. $-6\frac{1}{18} = -6.0\overline{5}$ repeating decimal; rational

f. $\dfrac{2}{-35} = -0.0\overline{571428}$ repeating decimal; rational ●

Now consider the square root of a number that is not a perfect square—say, $\sqrt{2}$. You might try to represent this square root as a decimal, but you would not be successful:

$$1^2 = 1$$
$$2^2 = 4, \qquad \text{so } \sqrt{2} \text{ is between 1 and 2} \qquad \text{Try 1.5 next; it is halfway between 1 and 2.}$$
$$1.5^2 = 2.25, \quad \text{so } \sqrt{2} \text{ is between 1 and 1.5} \qquad \text{Try 1.4 next; it is between 1 and 1.5.}$$
$$1.4^2 = 1.96, \quad \text{so } \sqrt{2} \text{ is between 1.4 and 1.5}$$
$$\vdots$$

You may even turn to a calculator to obtain the display 1.414213562, but $1.414213562^2 \neq 2$, so even this number is not equal to the square root of 2. It is proved in more

*Actually, there are numbers whose squares are negative, but such numbers are outside the scope of this course.

advanced courses that $\sqrt{2}$ **is not rational** and cannot be represented as a repeating or terminating decimal! Such a number is called an **irrational number** and is written as $\sqrt{2}$. Notice that at first we used the symbol $\sqrt{}$ to indicate a process (square root), but now we use it to indicate a *number*. Square roots of counting numbers that are not perfect squares are irrational numbers. Some irrational numbers are listed here:

$$\sqrt{2}, \sqrt{3}, \sqrt{5}, \sqrt{6}, \sqrt{7}, \sqrt{8}, \sqrt{10}, \sqrt{11}, \sqrt{12}, \sqrt{13}, \sqrt{14}, \sqrt{15}, \sqrt{17}$$

EXAMPLE 6

Classifying radicals as rational or irrational

Classify each given number as rational or irrational. If it is irrational, place it between two integers.

a. $\sqrt{64}$ **b.** $\sqrt{65}$ **c.** $\sqrt{441}$ **d.** $\sqrt{965}$

Solution

a. $\sqrt{64}$ **Rational** because $8^2 = 64$

b. $\sqrt{65}$ **Irrational** because 65 is not a perfect square; since $8^2 = 64$ and $9^2 = 81$, $\sqrt{65}$ is between 8 and 9. *Note:* Your calculator shows $\sqrt{65} \approx 8.062257748$, but that does not answer the question asked because the *calculator* display 8.062257748 is a terminating decimal and terminating decimals are rational. The correct response, however, is that $\sqrt{65}$ is irrational because 65 is not a perfect square.

c. $\sqrt{441}$ $20^2 = 400$
  $30^2 = 900,$ so $\sqrt{441}$ is between 20 and 30
  $25^2 = 625,$ so $\sqrt{441}$ is between 20 and 25
  $22^2 = 484,$ so $\sqrt{441}$ is between 20 and 22
  $21^2 = 441$ **Rational** because $\sqrt{441} = 21$

d. $\sqrt{965}$ $30^2 = 900$
  $40^2 = 1,600,$ so $\sqrt{965}$ is between 30 and 40
  $32^2 = 1,024,$ so $\sqrt{965}$ is between 30 and 32
  $31^2 = 961,$ so $\sqrt{965}$ is between 31 and 32
  ↑   ↑
  Consecutive counting numbers,
  so 965 is not a perfect square.

Irrational; $\sqrt{965}$ is between 31 and 32 and cannot be represented as a repeating or terminating decimal. ●

  Given a problem like Example 6, but one in which the number under the radical is a fraction, you can determine whether it is a rational or an irrational number by writing it as a common fraction and then handling the numerator and denominator separately, as shown in Example 7.

EXAMPLE 7

Classifying radicals with decimals as rational or irrational

Classify each number as rational or irrational.

a. $\sqrt{0.25}$ **b.** $\sqrt{1.5625}$

Solution

a. $\sqrt{0.25} = \sqrt{\dfrac{25}{100}}$ **b.** $\sqrt{1.5625} = \sqrt{\dfrac{15,625}{10,000}}$ 15,625: $100^2 = 10,000$
$200^2 = 40,000$
$125^2 = 15,625$

$= \dfrac{5}{10}$ $= \dfrac{125}{100}$

$= \dfrac{1}{2}$ **Rational** $= \dfrac{5}{4}$ **Rational**

EXAMPLE 8

Using a calculator to classify a radical

Classify each number as rational or irrational. You may use a calculator.

a. $\sqrt{20.4304}$ **b.** $\sqrt{3.525}$

Solution

a. $\sqrt{20.4304} = \sqrt{\dfrac{204,304}{10,000}}$ Calculator display: $\sqrt{204,304} = 452$
$\sqrt{10,000} = 100$

$= \dfrac{452}{100}$

$= 4.52$ **Rational**

b. $\sqrt{3.525} = \sqrt{\dfrac{3,525}{1,000}}$

$= \sqrt{\dfrac{141}{40}}$ This fraction is reduced, and neither
141 nor 40 is a perfect square.

Irrational

After studying Example 8, you might wonder why you shouldn't simply use a calculator to answer the question, but you must keep in mind the directions. You were not asked to *perform the operation* of square root, but rather to *classify the numbers* as rational or irrational. Calculators *always* make irrational numbers look like rational numbers because they represent them as terminating decimals. If the numerator and denominator of the reduced form of the number under the radical sign can be written as perfect squares, then the number is rational; if not, the number is irrational.

We will sometimes find it necessary to limit our work to the set of rational numbers; in these cases, we'll need to approximate an irrational number with a rational number. You can do this by successive approximations (trial-and-error multiplication) or by using your calculator.

EXAMPLE 9

Approximating an irrational number as a rational

Approximate $\sqrt{18}$ with a rational number of two decimal places.

Solution

Method I.   Use a calculator: $\boxed{\sqrt{\ }}$ $\boxed{18}$ *Display*:   4.242640687
Round to two decimal places: 4.24

Method II. This method can be used if you have a calculator without a square root key.

$4^2 = 16$
$5^2 = 25$ so $\sqrt{18}$ is between 4 and 5; *try some numbers between 4 and 5.*
$4.2^2 = 17.64$
$4.3^2 = 18.49$ so $\sqrt{18}$ is between 4.2 and 4.3; *try some numbers between 4.2 and 4.3.*

$4.24^2 = 17.9776$
$4.25^2 = 18.0625$ so $\sqrt{18}$ is between 4.24 and 4.25
$4.245^2 = 18.020025$ so $\sqrt{18}$ is closer to 4.24 than to 4.25

Round to two decimal places: 4.24 ●

In algebra, we group together all the rational numbers and all the irrational numbers into a set called the **real numbers.** The real numbers may be classified in several ways, as indicated in the next box.

Real Numbers

> The real numbers can be characterized in various ways:
> * Positive, negative, or zero
> * Rational or irrational
> * Terminating, repeating, or nonterminating/nonrepeating
>   If it terminates, it is rational.
>   If it repeats, it is rational.
>   If it does not terminate or repeat, it is irrational.

STOP *Note the three different characterizations of real numbers.*

When you first consider this third characterization of the real numbers, it may be hard to imagine a decimal that does not terminate or repeat. All of the rational numbers we have considered have decimal representations that either terminate or repeat:

$$\frac{1}{2} = 0.5 \qquad \frac{5}{8} = 0.625 \qquad \frac{1}{3} = 0.333\ldots \qquad \frac{1}{6} = 0.1666\ldots$$

In fact, the Pythagoreans knew of numbers like $\sqrt{2}$ but they believed them to be rational (that is, a number whose decimal representation either terminates or repeats).

Legend tells us that one day while the Pythagoreans were at sea, one of their group came up with an argument that $\sqrt{2}$ could not be a rational number. This result shattered the Pythagorean philosophy, which said that all numbers were rational. This member of the group proved logically that $\sqrt{2}$ was not a rational number, so they were forced to change their philosophy or deny logic. Legend has it that they took the latter course: They set the man who discovered it to sea alone in a small boat and pledged themselves to secrecy.

Irrational numbers are needed when working with the Pythagorean theorem. Since the theorem asserts that $a^2 + b^2 = c^2$, and since c is the positive number whose square is $a^2 + b^2$, we see that

$$c = \sqrt{a^2 + b^2}$$

Also, if you want to find the length of one of the legs—say, a—when you know both b and hypotenuse c, you can use the formula

$$a = \sqrt{c^2 - b^2}$$

Examples 10 and 11 use this Pythagorean relationship.

EXAMPLE 10   **Determining a length using the pythagorean relationship**

If a 13-ft ladder is placed against a building so that the base of the ladder is 5 ft away from the building, how high up does the ladder reach?

Solution

Consider Figure 2.5. Let h be the height of the ladder on the building. Since h is one of the legs of a right triangle, use the formula

$$a = \sqrt{c^2 - b^2}$$
$$h = \underset{\underset{unknown}{\uparrow}}{\sqrt{13^2 - 5^2}} \quad \textit{Substitute.}$$

$$= \sqrt{169 - 25}$$
$$= \sqrt{144}$$
$$= 12$$

13 ft. ladder

5 ft.

Figure 2.5 Ladder problem

Thus, the ladder reaches 12 ft up the side of the building.

     Your answer to Example 10 was rational. But suppose that the result were irrational. You could either leave your result in radical form or estimate your result, as shown in Example 11.

EXAMPLE 11   **Estimating distances using the pythagorean theorem**

Suppose that you need to attach several guy wires to your TV antenna, as shown in Figure 2.6. If one guy wire is attached 20 ft away from a 30-ft antenna, what is the exact length of that guy wire, and what is the length to the nearest foot?

Solution

The length of the guy wire is the length of the hypotenuse of a right triangle:

$$c = \sqrt{a^2 + b^2}$$
$$= \sqrt{20^2 + 30^2}$$
$$= \sqrt{1,300}$$

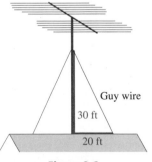

Guy wire

30 ft

20 ft

Figure 2.6

The exact length of the guy wire is $\sqrt{1,300}$; it is irrational, since 1,300 is not a perfect square.

Estimate the length: $30^2 = 900$ *1,300 is between 900 and 1,600 so $\sqrt{1,300}$ is between 30 and 40.*

$$40^2 = 1,600$$

For a better approximation, you can use a calculator: $c \approx 36.05551275$. The guy wire is 36 ft long (to the nearest ft). *Note:* If the application will not allow any length less than $\sqrt{1,300}$ (as in real life), then instead of rounding, take the *next larger* foot, namely, 37 ft.

PROBLEM SET (2.6)

ESSENTIAL IDEAS — LEVEL 1

1. **IN YOUR OWN WORDS** What is a reduced fraction? Include as part of your answer what is meant by the standard form of a fraction.

2. **IN YOUR OWN WORDS** State the Pythagorean theorem. Draw a picture of a right triangle, and describe in words what it means for a triangle to be a right triangle.

3. **IN YOUR OWN WORDS** Discuss different ways of characterizing the set of real numbers. Give examples of each type.

4. List the perfect squares less than 200.
   1, 4, 9, 16, 25, 36, 49, 64, 81, 100, 121, 144, 169, 196

5. What does $\sqrt{4}$ mean? *Hint:* Do not answer 2.
   It is the positive number that squared is 4.

6. What does $\sqrt{9}$ mean? *Hint:* Do not answer 3.
   It is the positive number that squared is 9.

7. What does $\sqrt{2}$ mean? *Hint:* Do not answer 1.4142 . . . .
   It is the positive number that squared is 2.

8. What does $\sqrt{3}$ mean? *Hint:* Do not answer 1.732 . . . .
   It is the positive number that squared is 3.

DRILL AND PRACTICE — LEVEL 2

Write each fraction in Problems 9–12 in standard form.

9. **a.** $-\dfrac{7}{8}$ $\frac{-7}{8}$ **b.** $\dfrac{5}{-8}$ $\frac{-5}{8}$

   c. $-\dfrac{-7}{-9}$ $\frac{-7}{9}$ **d.** $\dfrac{-a}{-b}$ $\frac{a}{b}$

10. **a.** $\dfrac{-6}{-11}$ $\frac{6}{11}$ **b.** $-\dfrac{1}{-2}$ $\frac{1}{2}$

    c. $-\dfrac{2}{3}$ $\frac{-2}{3}$ **d.** $\dfrac{a}{-b}$ $\frac{-a}{b}$

11. **a.** $\dfrac{-x}{-y}$ $\frac{x}{y}$ **b.** $\dfrac{-y}{-3}$ $\frac{y}{3}$

    c. $\dfrac{1}{-x}$ $\frac{-1}{x}$ **d.** $-\dfrac{a}{-b}$ $\frac{a}{b}$

12. **a.** $-\dfrac{5}{-z}$ $\frac{5}{z}$ **b.** $\dfrac{-ab}{-cd}$ $\frac{-ab}{cd}$

    c. $-\dfrac{xy}{-2z}$ $\frac{xy}{2z}$ **d.** $\dfrac{-2wx}{-3z}$ $\frac{2wx}{3z}$

Simplify the expressions in Problems 13–16.

13. **a.** $\dfrac{-5}{14} + \dfrac{-3}{21}$ $\frac{-1}{2}$ **b.** $\dfrac{-5}{14} \cdot \dfrac{21}{-3}$ $\frac{5}{2}$

    c. $\dfrac{3}{-10} + \dfrac{-5}{14}$ $\frac{-23}{35}$ **d.** $\dfrac{1}{9} - \dfrac{-2}{3}$ $\frac{7}{9}$

14. **a.** $\dfrac{-5}{7} \cdot \dfrac{14}{-10}$ 1   **b.** $\dfrac{5}{-2} \div \dfrac{-2}{6}$ $\frac{15}{2}$

    c. $\dfrac{-2}{3} + \dfrac{1}{2}$ $\frac{-1}{6}$ **d.** $\dfrac{-5}{8} - \dfrac{1}{12}$ $\frac{-17}{24}$

15. **a.** $\dfrac{3}{-10} + \dfrac{-1}{5} - \dfrac{-1}{3}$ $\frac{-1}{6}$ **b.** $\dfrac{2}{-15} - \dfrac{1}{-3} + \dfrac{-1}{2}$ $\frac{-3}{10}$

    c. $\dfrac{1}{-2} + \dfrac{-1}{4} - \dfrac{-3}{8}$ $\frac{-3}{8}$ **d.** $\dfrac{-1}{2} + \dfrac{1}{-4} - \dfrac{-3}{8}$ $\frac{-3}{8}$

16. **a.** $-6 + \dfrac{1}{6}$ $\frac{-35}{6}$ **b.** $-3 - \dfrac{2}{3}$ $\frac{-11}{3}$

    c. $-5 - \dfrac{1}{5}$ $\frac{-26}{5}$ **d.** $2 - \dfrac{1}{-2}$ $\frac{5}{2}$

Find the positive square root of each of the numbers in Problems 17–22.

17. **a.** 9   3   **b.** 1   1

    c. 0   0   **d.** -9 impossible

18. **a.** 36   6   **b.** 25   5

    c. -16 impossible   **d.** 625   25

19. **a.** 81   9   **b.** -25 impossible

    c. 169   13   **d.** 196   14

20. **a.** 225   15   **b.** $\dfrac{25}{36}$ $\frac{5}{6}$

    c. $\dfrac{100}{144}$ $\frac{5}{6}$ **d.** $\dfrac{9}{49}$ $\frac{3}{7}$

21. **a.** 1,225   35   **b.** 2,025   45

    c. 9,604   98   **d.** 6,084   78

22. **a.** 10,000   100   **b.** 1,089   33

    c. 10,404   102   **d.** 3,364   58

Approximate each irrational number in Problems 23–26 with a rational number to two decimal places.

23. **a.** $\sqrt{15}$ 3.87   **b.** $\sqrt{17}$ 4.12

    c. $\sqrt{20}$ 4.47   **d.** $\sqrt{50}$ 7.07

24. **a.** $\sqrt{30}$ 5.48   **b.** $\sqrt{40}$ 6.32

    c. $\sqrt{80}$ 8.94   **d.** $\sqrt{130}$ 11.40

25. **a.** $\sqrt{190}$ 13.78   **b.** $\sqrt{1,000}$ 31.62

    c. $\sqrt{2,000}$ 44.72   **d.** $\sqrt{3,000}$ 54.77

26. **a.** $\sqrt{250}$ 15.81   **b.** $\sqrt{875}$ 29.58

    c. $\sqrt{4,210}$ 64.88   **d.** $\sqrt{5,284}$ 72.69

Classify each of the numbers in Problems 27–32 as rational or irrational. If the number is rational, write it as a terminating or repeating decimal. If it is irrational, estimate it by placing it between two integers.

27. **a.** 5   rational; 5   **b.** $\sqrt{5}$ irrational; $2 < \sqrt{5} < 3$

    c. $\sqrt{25}$ rational; 5   **d.** $\frac{1}{4}$ rational; 0.25

28. a. $\sqrt{\frac{1}{4}}$ rational; 0.5

   b. $\sqrt{\frac{1}{9}}$ rational; $0.\overline{3}$

   c. $-2\frac{7}{10}$ rational; -2.7

   d. $\sqrt{0.49}$ rational; 0.7

29. a. $\sqrt{10}$ irrational; $3 < \sqrt{10} < 4$

   b. $\sqrt{15}$ irrational; $3 < \sqrt{15} < 4$

   c. $\sqrt{16}$ rational; 4

   d. $\sqrt{17}$ irrational; $4 < \sqrt{17} < 5$

30. a. $\frac{1}{36}$ rational; $0.02\overline{7}$

   b. $\sqrt{784}$ rational; 28

   c. $\sqrt{580}$ irrational; $24 < \sqrt{580} < 25$

   d. $\sqrt{18.49}$ rational; 4.3

31. a. $\sqrt{2,400}$ irrational; $48 < \sqrt{2,400} < 49$

   b. $\sqrt{2,401}$ rational; 49

   c. $\sqrt{2,402}$ irrational; $49 < \sqrt{2,402} < 50$

   d. $\sqrt{\frac{1}{10}}$ irrational; $0 < \sqrt{\frac{1}{10}} < 1$

32. a. $\sqrt{12.3904}$ rational; 3.52

   b. $\sqrt{12.4}$ irrational; $3 < \sqrt{12.4} < 4$

   c. $\sqrt{1.2}$ irrational; $1 < \sqrt{1.2} < 2$

   d. $\sqrt{1.2321}$ rational; 1.11

APPLICATIONS   **LEVEL 2**

33. How far from the base of a building must a 26-ft ladder be placed so that it reaches 24 ft up the wall?   10 ft

34. How far from the base of a building must a 10-ft ladder be placed so that it reaches 8 ft up the wall?   6 ft

35. How high up on a wall does a 26-ft ladder reach if the bottom of the ladder is placed 10 ft from the building?   24 ft

36. How high up on a wall does a 10-ft ladder reach if the bottom of the ladder is placed 6 ft from the building?   8 ft

37. What is the exact length of the hypotenuse if the legs of a right triangle are 2 in. each? $\sqrt{8}$ (or $2\sqrt{2}$) in.

38. What is the exact length of the hypotenuse if the legs of a right triangle are 3 ft each? $\sqrt{18}$ (or $3\sqrt{2}$) ft

39. An empty rectangular lot is 400 ft by 300 ft. How many feet would you save by walking diagonally across the lot instead of walking the length and width?   200 ft

40. An empty rectangular lot is 80 ft by 60 ft. How many feet would you save by walking diagonally across the lot instead of walking the length and the width?   40 ft

41. A television antenna is to be erected and held by guy wires.

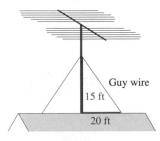

If the guy wires are 20 ft from the base of the antenna and the antenna is 15 ft high, what is the exact length of each guy wire? If four guy wires are to be attached, how many feet of wire should be purchased if it can't be bought by a fraction of a foot?   Length is 25 ft each; would need to purchase 100 ft.

42. A television antenna is to be erected and held by guy wires. If the guy wires are 25 ft from the base of the antenna and the antenna is 15 ft high, what is the exact length of each guy wire? What is the length of each guy wire to the nearest foot? If four guy wires are to be attached, how many feet of wire should be purchased if it can't be bought by a fraction of a foot?   Exact length is $\sqrt{850}$; this is approx. 29 ft; $4\sqrt{850} \approx 116.6$, so would need to purchase 117 ft

43. A television antenna is to be erected and held by guy wires. If the guy wires are 15 ft from the base of the antenna and the antenna is 10 ft high, what is the exact length of each guy wire? What is the length of each guy wire to the nearest foot? If four guy wires are to be attached, how many feet of wire should be purchased if it can't be bought by a fraction of a foot?   Exact length is $\sqrt{325}$; this is approx. 18 ft; $4\sqrt{325} \approx 72.11$, so would need to purchase 73 ft.

RIGHT OR WRONG?   **LEVEL 3**

Explain what is wrong, if anything, with the statements in Problems 44–60. Explain your reasoning.

44. $-\frac{1}{2}$ is a reduced form.   F; must be in standard form: $\frac{-1}{2}$.

45. $\frac{-12}{5}$ is a reduced form.   T

46. $a^2 + b^2 = c^2$ F; true if and only if a right triangle with sides a and b and hypotenuse c.

47. $\sqrt{2} = 1.414213562$ F; $\sqrt{2}$ is an irrational number.

48. $\sqrt{3} = 1.732050808$ F; $\sqrt{3}$ is an irrational number.

49. $\frac{1}{3} = 0.3333333333$ F; $\frac{1}{3} = 0.\overline{3}$

50. $\frac{2}{3} = 0.6666666666$ F; $\frac{2}{3} = 0.\overline{6}$

51. $\sqrt{225}$ is an irrational number.   F; $\sqrt{225} = 15$

52. $\sqrt{100}$ is an irrational number.   F; $\sqrt{100} = 10$

53. $0.454545\ldots$ is an irrational number.   F; repeating decimals are rational.

54. $\sqrt{9}$ is equal to both 3 and -3.   F; $\sqrt{9} = 3$

55. $\sqrt{16}$ is equal to both 4 and -4.   F; $\sqrt{16} = 4$

56. For a right triangle with sides a and b and hypotenuse c, $c^2 - a^2 = b^2$.   T

57. $\sqrt{8}$ is an irrational number between 2 and 3. T

58. $\sqrt{10}$ is an irrational number between 2 and 3.
F; it is between 3 and 4.

59. $\sqrt{280}$ is an irrational number between 10 and 20. T

60. $\sqrt{441}$ is an irrational number between 20 and 30.
F; it is rational.

2.7 Chapter 2 Summary and Review

Take some time getting ready to work the review problems in this section. First, look back at the definition and property boxes. You will maximize your understanding of this chapter by working the problems in this section only after you have studied the material.

IMPORTANT TERMS

Numbers refer to sections of this chapter.

Spending some time with the terms and objectives of this chapter will pay dividends in assuring your success.

Absolute value [2.2]
Addition of integers [2.2]
Algebra [2.0]
Average [2.5]
Difference [2.1]
Dividend [2.1]
Division by zero [2.5]
Division of integers [2.5]
Divisor [2.1]
Domain [2.1]
Equal to [2.1; 2.2]
Evaluate an absolute value [2.2]
Evaluating an expression [2.1]
Factor [2.1]
Greater than [2.2]
Hypotenuse [2.6]
Identity for addition [2.2]

Integer [2.2]
Irrational number [2.6]
Less than [2.2]
Mean [2.5]
Minus [2.1]
Multiplication of integers [2.4]
Negative number [2.2]
Negative sign [2.2]
Number line [2.2]
Opposite [2.2]
Opposite property [2.4]
Order symbols [2.2]
Perfect square [2.6]
Plus [2.1]
Positive number [2.2]
Positive sign [2.2]
Product [2.1]
Pythagorean theorem [2.6]

Quotient [2.1]
Radical [2.6]
Rational number [2.6]
Real number [2.6]
Reduced fraction [2.6]
Signed number [2.2]
Square root [2.6]
Square root symbol [2.6]
Standard form of a fraction [2.6]
Subtraction of integers [2.3]
Sum [2.1]
Term [2.1]
Unit scale [2.2]
Variable [2.1]
Variable expression [2.1]
Zero [2.2]
Zero multiplication property [2.4]

Essential Ideas

[2.1] Problems 1–2	Add terms, multiply factors
Problem 3	Translations for operation symbols
Problem 4	Meaning of a variable
Problem 5	Evaluate an expression
Problem 6	Difference of squares/square of a difference
[2.2] Problem 1	Set of integers
Problems 2–5	Procedure for adding integers
Problem 6	Evaluate an absolute value
[2.3] Problem 1	Procedure for subtracting integers
Problem 2	Three uses of the "−" symbol: minus, negative, and opposite
[2.4] Problem 1	Define multiplication
Problem 2	Opposite property

Problem 3	Zero multiplication property
Problems 4–6	Procedure for multiplying integers
[2.5] Problem 1	Procedure for dividing integers
Problem 2	Reason why division by zero is impossible
Problems 3–4	Using a fractional bar for division
[2.6] Problem 1	Standard forms of a reduced fraction
Problem 2	Pythagorean theorem
Problem 3	Characterizations of the real numbers
Problem 4	Perfect squares less than 200
Problems 5–8	Meaning of square root

LEARNING OUTCOMES

The material in this chapter is reviewed in the following list of learning outcomes. A self-test (with answers and suggestions for additional study) is given. This self-test is constructed so that each problem number corresponds to a related objective. For example, Problem 7 is testing Objective 2.7. This self-test is followed by a practice test with the questions in mixed order.

[2.1]	*Objective* 2.1	Given an algebraic expression and a domain, evaluate the expression.
[2.1]	*Objective* 2.2	Evaluate an algebraic expression using whole numbers.
[2.1]	*Objective* 2.3	Choose a letter to represent the variable, and write a mathematical statement to express an idea
[2.2]	*Objective* 2.4	Be able to describe addition of integers.
[2.2]	*Objective* 2.5	Distinguish between a minus sign and an opposite sign.
[2.2]	*Objective* 2.6	Compare the size of two given integers.
[2.2]	*Objective* 2.7	Evaluate a given absolute value statement.
[2.2]	*Objective* 2.8	Be able to add integers using a number line.
[2.2]	*Objective* 2.9	Add integers.
[2.3]	*Objective* 2.10	Contrast the three uses for the "−" sign.
[2.3]	*Objective* 2.11	Be able to describe subtraction of integers, as well as to carry out the operation of subtraction of integers.
[2.4]	*Objective* 2.12	Be able to describe multiplication of integers, as well as to carry out the operation of multiplication of integers.
[2.5]	*Objective* 2.13	Be able to describe division of integers, as well as to carry out the operation of division of integers.
[2.3–2.5]	*Objective* 2.14	Simplify expressions with mixed operations.
[2.2–2.5]	*Objective* 2.15	Perform operations with integers using a calculator.
[2.5]	*Objective* 2.16	Find the average of a given set of numbers.
[2.3–2.5]	*Objective* 2.17	Evaluate an algebraic expression using integers.
[2.6]	*Objective* 2.18	Simplify fractional operations with positive and negative numerators and denominators. Leave answers in standard form.
[2.6]	*Objective* 2.19	Explain the meaning of square root.
[2.6]	*Objective* 2.20	Find the positive square root of a given number.
[2.6]	*Objective* 2.21	Approximate an irrational number with a rational number to a given number of decimal places.
[2.6]	*Objective* 2.22	Classify a number as rational or irrational.
[2.2–2.6]	*Objective* 2.23	Work applied problems. (See Problems 23–25.)

Self-Test

Each question of this self-test is related to the corresponding objective listed above.

1. If $D = \{0, 3, 9\}$, find the values for $100 - x^2$.

2. Evaluate $x^2 - 2xy + y^2$ for $x = 5$ and $y = 2$.

3. Write a mathematical statement for the product of two consecutive integers.

4. In your own words, describe how to add any two integers.

5. Tell whether the "−" is a minus sign or an opposite sign.
   a. $7 - 4$ **b.** $-(+2)$ **c.** $-t$ **d.** $1 - t$

6. Compare the size of the given numbers by filling in $>$, $<$, or $=$ in the blanks.
   a. -8 _____ -12 **b.** $-(-5)$ _____ 5 **c.** -4 _____ 0
   d. -3 _____ -10

7. Evaluate the given absolute values.
   a. $|12 - 15|$ **b.** $|12| - |15|$ **c.** $-|12 - 15|$ **d.** $-|12| - |15|$

8. On a number line, start at 0 and move $+6$ units. Then move -4, followed by $+2$, and then -8. What is the ending point?

9. Add the given integers.
   a. $12 + (-14)$ **b.** $-12 + (-14)$ **c.** $12 + 14$ **d.** $-12 + 14$

10. Write out the following statements in words.
    a. -4 **b.** $-x$ **c.** $5 - 3$ **d.** $10 - [-(-3)]$

Simplify the numerical expressions given in Problems 11–14.

11. **a.** $20 - 32$ **b.** $-35 - (-58)$ **c.** $-48 - 56$ **d.** $93 - (-7)$

12. **a.** -5^2 **b.** $(-5)^2$ **c.** $-(2)(-5)$ **d.** $(-1)(-2)(-5)$

13. **a.** $125 \div (-5)$ **b.** $\dfrac{0}{-200}$ **c.** $\dfrac{-35}{0}$ **d.** $\dfrac{0}{0}$

14. **a.** $10 - (-3)(-2)$ **b.** $10 - \dfrac{-3}{2}$ **c.** $\dfrac{6(-2) + 10}{-2}$ **d.** $6(-2) + \dfrac{10}{-2}$

15. Show the calculator steps to evaluate each numerical expression and also show the simplified result.
    a. $3 - (-8)$ **b.** $\dfrac{-10}{2(5)}$ **c.** $4 + \dfrac{8}{2}$ **d.** $\dfrac{4 + 8}{2}$

16. Find the average of $7, -4, -3, 0$, and 10.

17. Evaluate $-x^2 + y^2$ for $x = -3$ and $y = -4$.

18. **a.** $\dfrac{-2}{3} + \dfrac{4}{-5}$ **b.** $\dfrac{-2}{3} \cdot \dfrac{4}{-5}$ **c.** $\dfrac{-3}{12} - \dfrac{4}{-15}$ **d.** $\dfrac{-3}{12} \div \dfrac{4}{-15}$

19. What does $\sqrt{20}$ mean?

20. Find the positive square root of 2,025.

21. Approximate $\sqrt{8.25}$ with a rational number to two decimal places.

22. Classify $\sqrt{1.69}$ as rational or irrational. If it is rational, write it as a terminating or repeating decimal. If it is irrational, place it between two consecutive integers.

23. A diagonal brace is to be placed in the wall of a room. The height of the wall is 8 ft, and the wall is 20 ft long. What is the exact length of the brace? What is the length of the brace to the nearest foot?

24. If the Dow Jones Industrial Average of 30 stock prices for a particular week has the following changes, what is the *net* change for the week?

    Monday, $+9$; Tuesday, -15; Wednesday, -29; Thursday, $+7$; Friday, $+6$

25. Telescope Peak (11,049 ft) is the highest point in Death Valley. What is the difference in elevation between this peak and Death Valley's lowest point in Badwater Basin (-282 ft)?

STUDY HINTS *Compare your solutions and answers to the self-test. For each problem you missed, work some additional problems in the section listed in the margin. After you have worked these problems, you can test yourself with the practice test.*

Additional Problems

[2.1] Problems 7–12

[2.1] Problems 13–37

[2.1] Problems 39–50; 51–54

[2.2] Problems 2–4; 21–22

[2.2] Problems 7–12

[2.2] Problems 13–16

[2.2] Problems 17–20

[2.2] Problems 23–28; 37–44

[2.2] Problems 29–36; 45–48

Complete Solutions to the Self-Test

1. If $x = 0$, then $100 - x^2 = 100 - 0 = 100$.
   If $x = 3$, then $100 - x^2 = 100 - 9 = 91$.
   If $x = 9$, then $100 - x^2 = 100 - 81 = 19$.

2. $x^2 - 2xy + y^2 = 5^2 - 2(5)(2) + 2^2$
$$= 25 - 20 + 4$$
$$= 9$$

3. Let $x = $ AN INTEGER; then
   $x + 1 = $ NEXT CONSECUTIVE INTEGER.
   $x(x + 1)$ represents the product of two consecutive integers.

4. Answers vary; see page 95.

5. a. minus, since it is between two numbers
   b. opposite, since it is in front of a number
   c. opposite, since it is in front of a variable
   d. minus, since it is between a number and a variable

6. a. 8 is to the right of -12 on a number line, so the correct statement is $-8 > -12$.
   b. $-(-5) = 5$, so the numbers are equal and the correct symbol is the equal symbol.
   c. -4 is to the left of 0, so the correct statement is $-4 < 0$.
   d. -3 is to the right of -10, so the correct statement is $-3 > -10$.

7. a. $|12 - 15| = |-3|$ Subtract, then absolute value.
$$= 3$$
   b. $|12| - |15| = 12 - 15$ Absolute value, then subtract.
$$= -3$$
   c. $-|12 - 15| = -|-3|$ Subtract first.
$$= -(3)$$ Absolute value next.
$$= -3$$ Opposite of 3 is -3.
   d. $-|12| - |15| = -12 - 15$ Absolute value, then subtract.
$$= -27$$

8. a. -4

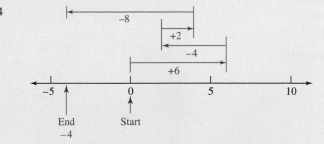

End
-4

Start

9. a. $12 + (-14) = -2$ Positive + Negative; $|12| = 12$ and $|-14| = 14$; the larger absolute value is 14, so the answer is negative (subtract absolute values).

   b. $-12 + (-14) = -26$ Negative + Negative (add absolute values).
   c. $12 + 14 = 26$ Positive + Positive (add absolute values).
   d. $-12 + 14 = 2$ Negative + Positive; the larger absolute value is 14, so the answer is positive (subtract absolute values).

[2.3] Problems 2; 17–24

10. a. negative four
 b. opposite of x
 c. five minus three
 d. ten minus the opposite of negative three

[2.3] Problems 1; 3–16

11. a. $20 - 32 = 20 + (-32)$ **b.** $-35 - (-58) = -35 + 58$
       $= -12$ $= 23$
 c. $-48 - 56 = -104$ **d.** $93 - (-7) = 93 + 7$
                                 $= 100$

[2.4] Problems 4–6; 7–22

12. a. $-5^2 = -25$ **b.** $(-5)^2 = 25$
 c. $-(2)(-5) = 10$ **d.** $(-1)(-2)(-5) = -10$

[2.5] Problems 1–2; 5–12

13. a. $125 \div (-5) = -25$ **b.** 0
 c. Not defined (impossible) **d.** Not defined

[2.5] Problems 17–30

14. a. $10 - (-3)(-2) = 10 - 6$
               $= 4$
 b. $10 - \dfrac{-3}{2} = \dfrac{20}{2} + \dfrac{3}{2}$

             $= \dfrac{23}{2}$
 c. $\dfrac{6(-2) + 10}{-2} = \dfrac{-12 + 10}{-2}$

             $= \dfrac{-2}{-2}$

             $= 1$
 d. $6(-2) + \dfrac{10}{-2} = -12 + (-5)$

               $= -17$

[2.2] Problems 45–48
[2.3] Problems 39–46
[2.5] Problems 13–16

15. a. $\boxed{3}\ \boxed{-}\ \boxed{(-)}\ \boxed{8}\ \boxed{=}$ *Display:* 11
 b. $\boxed{(-)}\ \boxed{10}\ \boxed{\div}\ \boxed{(}\ \boxed{2}\ \boxed{\times}\ \boxed{5}\ \boxed{)}\ \boxed{=}$ *Display:* -1
 c. $\boxed{4}\ \boxed{+}\ \boxed{8}\ \boxed{\div}\ \boxed{2}\ \boxed{=}$ *Display:* 8
 d. $\boxed{(}\ \boxed{4}\ \boxed{+}\ \boxed{8}\ \boxed{)}\ \boxed{\div}\ \boxed{2}\ \boxed{=}$ *Display:* 6

[2.5] Problems 47–52

16. $\dfrac{7 + (-4) + (-3) + 0 + 10}{5} = 2$

[2.3] Problems 25–38
[2.4] Problems 23–38
[2.5] Problems 31–46

[2.6] Problems 9–16

17. $-x^2 + y^2 = -(-3)^2 + (-4)^2$
            $= -9 + 16$
            $= 7$

18. a. $\dfrac{-2}{3} + \dfrac{4}{-5} = \dfrac{-2}{3} \cdot \dfrac{5}{5} + \dfrac{-4}{5} \cdot \dfrac{3}{3}$ **b.** $\dfrac{-2}{3} \cdot \dfrac{4}{-5} = \dfrac{-8}{-15} = \dfrac{8}{15}$

             $= \dfrac{-10 + (-12)}{15}$

             $= \dfrac{-22}{15}$

 c. $\dfrac{-3}{12} - \dfrac{4}{-15} = \dfrac{-1}{4} \cdot \dfrac{15}{15} - \dfrac{-4}{15} \cdot \dfrac{4}{4}$ **d.** $\dfrac{-3}{12} \div \dfrac{4}{-15} = \dfrac{-1}{4} \cdot \dfrac{-15}{4}$

             $= \dfrac{-15 - (-16)}{60}$ $= \dfrac{15}{16}$

             $= \dfrac{1}{60}$

[2.6] Problems 5–8

[2.6] Problems 17–22

[2.6] Problems 23–26

[2.6] Problems 27–32

Applications

[2.1] Problems 39–50
[2.2] Problems 49–54
[2.3] Problems 47–53
[2.4] Problems 39–48
[2.5] Problems 47–52
[2.6] Problems 33–43

19. $\sqrt{20}$ is that number so that $\sqrt{20} \times \sqrt{20} = 20$.

20. $40^2 = 1{,}600$ Thus, $\sqrt{2{,}025} = 45$.
$50^2 = 2{,}500$
$45^2 = 2{,}025$

21. $\sqrt{8.25} \approx 2.872281323$ (by calculator); to two places, 2.87.

22. Rational; $\sqrt{1.69} = \sqrt{\dfrac{169}{100}}$
$= \dfrac{13}{10}$
$= 1.3$

23. $\sqrt{8^2 + 20^2} = \sqrt{64 + 400}$
$= \sqrt{464}$
This is the exact length.
$\sqrt{464}$ is between 21 and 22, so to the nearest foot, it is 22 ft.

24. $(+9) + (-15) + (-29) + (+7) + (+6) = -22$
The net change for the week is down 22 points.

25. $11{,}049 - (-282) = 11{,}049 + 282$
$= 11{,}331$
The difference in the elevations is 11,331 ft.

Chapter 2 Review Questions

YIELD

CAUTION

Two of the essential processes of algebra are *simplify* and *evaluate*. These processes are the subject of Problems 3–4.

To prepare for a chapter test, first study the chapter; then, read each term from the important terms list above and make sure you know the meaning of each word; finally, review the chapter objectives. **After** *these steps, take the self-test and correct all your answers. The following review questions can be used for extra practice.*

1. **IN YOUR OWN WORDS** Describe how to add, subtract, multiply, and divide integers.

2. **IN YOUR OWN WORDS** Characterize the set of real numbers.

3. **a.** Define what it means to *simplify* a numerical expression.   Carry out all operations according to the order-of-operations agreement and write your answer as a single number.
   b. Define what it means to *simplify* a rational expression. Carry out all operations according to the order-of-operations agreement and write your answer as a reduced standard-form fraction.

4. **a.** Define what it means to *evaluate* a variable expression.   Replace the designated variables with given numbers and then simplify the resulting numerical expression.
   b. Define what it means to *evaluate* an absolute value.   Write the expression without absolute values and simplify the resulting numerical expression.

Simplify the expressions in Problems 5–10.

5. **a.** $5 + 123$ 128
   d. $-34 + (-27)$ −61
   g. $41 + (-14)$ 27
   j. $61 + 0$ 61

   b. $-56 + 87$ 31
   e. $3 + 19$ 22
   h. $-4 + (-6)$ −10

   c. $93 + (-45)$ 48
   f. $-3 + 5$ 2
   i. $-5 + 4$ −1

6. **a.** $-43 + (-21)$ −64
   d. $81 + 23$ 104
   g. $5 - 23$ −18
   j. $-3 - (-8)$ 5

   b. $73 + (-47)$ 26
   e. $-19 + 41$ 22
   h. $-5 - 9$ −14

   c. $-61 + (-3)$ −64
   f. $77 + (-53)$ 24
   i. $14 - (-10)$ 24

7. **a.** $-6 - 8$ −14
   d. $-13 - (-63)$ 50
   g. $15 - 23$ −8
   j. $6(5)$ 30

   b. $42 - (-27)$ 69
   e. $-3 - (-15)$ 12
   h. $-15 - 23$ −38

   c. $0 - 47$ −47
   f. $7 - (-32)$ 39
   i. $14(-2)$ −28

8. a. $-3(-12)$ *36*
    b. $-5(4)$ *−20*
    c. $-4(-6)$ *24*

  d. $0(-6)$ *0*
    e. $-10(60)$ *−600*
    f. $5(-30)$ *−150*

  g. -4^2 *−16*
    h. $(-4)^2$ *16*
    i. $(-1)(-3)(-2)$ *−6*

  j. $(-1)(3)(6)$ *−18*

9. a. $15 \div 3$ *5*
    b. $125 \div (-5)$ *−25*
    c. $-48 \div (-4)$ *12*

  d. $-32 \div 8$ *−4*
    e. $\dfrac{-14}{-7}$ *2*
    f. $\dfrac{121}{-11}$ *−11*

  g. $\dfrac{-19}{-19}$ *1*
    h. $\dfrac{1{,}001}{13}$ *77*
    i. $\dfrac{-56}{8}$ *−7*

  j. $\dfrac{0}{-18}$ *0*

10. a. $(-4) + (-2)(-5)$ *6*
    b. $[-4 + (-2)](-5)$ *30*
    c. $\dfrac{-24}{0}$ *impossible*

  d. $\dfrac{0}{0}$ *impossible*
    e. $\dfrac{-24 + 14}{-2}$ *5*
    f. $-24 - 14 \div (-2)$ *−17*

  g. $\dfrac{-5}{12}\left(\dfrac{-2}{-25}\right)$ *$\frac{-1}{30}$*
    h. $\dfrac{-5}{12} + \dfrac{5}{-15}$ *$\frac{-3}{4}$*
    i. $\dfrac{3}{-7} - \dfrac{-10}{21}$ *$\frac{1}{21}$*

  j. $\dfrac{-4}{5} \div \dfrac{-1}{4}$ *$\frac{16}{5}$*

Evaluate the expressions in Problems 11–13 for $x = -3$, $y = 5$, and $z = 1$.

11. a. $x - y - z$ *−9*
    b. $(xy - z)x$ *48*

  c. $\dfrac{y^2 - x^2}{x + y}$ *8*
    d. $-x^2 + (-x)^2$ *0*

12. a. $(x + y)^2$ *4*
    b. $x^2 + y^2$ *34*

  c. $\dfrac{x^2 - y^2}{z - x}$ *−4*
    d. $-y^2 + (-y)^2$ *0*

13. a. $x + y - 5z$ *−3*
    b. $3x + y - 10z$ *−14*

  c. $-x$ *3*
    d. $-y$ *−5*

14. Find the positive square roots.
  a. 100 *10*
    b. -16 *doesn't exist*
  c. 0 *0*
    d. 7,569 *87*

15. Classify the numbers as rational or irrational. If a number is rational, write it as a terminating or repeating decimal. If it is irrational, place it between two consecutive integers.

  a. $\sqrt{529}$ *rational, 23*
    b. $\sqrt{1{,}000}$ *irrational; $31 < \sqrt{1{,}000} < 32$*

  c. $\sqrt{\frac{4}{9}}$ *rational, $\frac{2}{3} = 0.\overline{6}$*
    d. $\sqrt{6.76}$ *rational; 2.6*

Write a mathematical statement to express the ideas in Problems 16–19.

16. The sum of a number and 20 *$n + 20$*

17. The quotient of a number divided by the next consecutive integer *$\frac{n}{n+1}$*

18. The product of a number and 3 *$3n$*

19. The difference of a number subtracted from 50 *$50 - n$*

20. Find the average of the sets of numbers.
  a. $6, -5, -3, 2$ *0*
        b. $14, -5, -8, -11, 0$ *−2*
  c. $12, 0, -40, 21, -9, -5, 0$ *−3*
        d. $86, 90, 88, 72$ *84*

21. A rectangular field measures 250 ft by 600 ft. If you walk across the field along the diagonal, how much shorter is the trip than if you walk along the edges? It is 200 ft shorter.

22. If a 12-ft ladder is placed against a building so that the base of the ladder is 4 ft away from the building, how high up does the ladder reach (rounded to the nearest foot)? 11 ft

23. A diagonal brace is to be placed on a gate. If the height of the gate is 6 ft and the width is 4 ft, what is the exact length of the brace? What is the length of the brace to the nearest foot? $\sqrt{52}$ or $2\sqrt{13}$; 7 ft

24. What is the exact length of the hypotenuse if the legs of a right triangle are 4 in. each? $\sqrt{32}$ or $4\sqrt{2}$

25. A balloon rises at a rate of 40 ft per minute when the wind is blowing horizontally at a rate of 30 ft per minute. After three minutes, how far away from the starting point, in a direct line, is the balloon? 150 ft

Individual Projects

Learning to use sources outside your classroom and textbook is an important skill, and here are some ideas for extending some of the ideas in this chapter.

PROJECT 2.1 **Update your Journal** Project 1.1 suggested that you start a journal. If you did not do that, begin a journal now. If you did start a journal at the beginning of this course, have you been keeping it up to date? How many math classes have you had since the beginning of class? It was suggested that you write in your journal within 24 hours of each class. Now, that you have been in class awhile, write about your classroom experiences to date. Has the class lived up to your expectations? Why or why not?

PROJECT 2.2 Write a paper or prepare an exhibit illustrating the Pythagorean theorem.

PROJECT 2.3 Consider a square as shown in Figure 2.7. What is the total length of the segments making up the stairs in each part of the figure? Look for a pattern to answer the question: Does the number of stairs matter? 2 in.; no

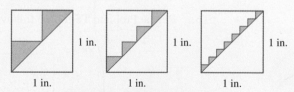

1 in.　　　1 in.　　　1 in.

1 in.　　　1 in.　　　1 in.

Figure 2.7 Find the length of steps

PROJECT 2.4 Find an irrational number with the requested property.

a. Between 1 and 3　1.2323323332...

b. Between 0.53 and 0.54　0.53353335...

c. Between $\frac{1}{11}$ and $\frac{1}{10}$　0.0919919991...

PROJECT 2.5 A person wants to board a plane with a 5-ft-long steel rod, but airline regulations say that the maximum length of any object or parcel permitted to be checked on board is 4 ft. Without bending or cutting the rod or altering it in any way, how did the person check it through without violating the rule? Put it diagonally in a box with dimensions 3 ft by 4 ft.

Team Projects

Working in small groups is typical of most work environments, and learning to work with others to communicate specific ideas is an important skill. Work with three or four other students to submit a single report based on each of the following questions.

T5. The Pythagorean theorem tells us that the sum of the squares of the lengths of the legs of a right triangle is equal to the square of the length of the hypotenuse. Verify that the theorem is true by tracing the squares and fitting them onto the pattern of the upper two squares shown in Figure 2.8.

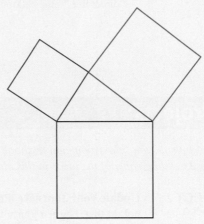

Figure 2.8 Pythagorean theorem squares

Next, cut the squares along the lines and rearrange the pieces so that the pieces all fit into the large square in Figure 2.8.

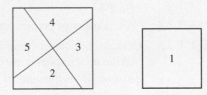

T6. Repeat Problem **T5** for the following squares.

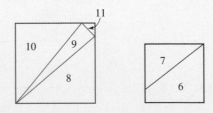

CHAPTER 3

Introduction to Algebra

The human mind has never invented a labor-saving machine equal to algebra.

THE NATIONS, Vol. 33, p. 327

ANTICIPATE

- *Overview; check out contents, terms, essential ideas, and learning outcomes.*
- *In the first two chapters, we considered simplifying numerical expressions involving fractions and integers.*
- *If you have previously studied algebra, then some of the material of this chapter may be familiar to you. The essential idea of this chapter is learning to solve simple equations.*

3.1 Polynomials

We will now turn our attention to simplifying variable expressions. Recall from Section 2.1 that a variable expression is an expression that contains at least one variable and at least one defined operation. Let's begin with multiplication. From arithmetic we know that the order in which we multiply numbers does not affect the answer we obtain. This means that, if we multiply numbers such as

$$2(3) \quad \text{or} \quad 3(2)$$

we obtain the same answer—namely, 6. The same is true if we multiply variables (remember that *juxtaposition* means multiplication):

$$xy \quad \text{or} \quad yx$$

The difference between the numerical expression and the variable expression is that $2(3)$ can be written more simply as 6, whereas xy is considered to be in simplified form. Also, even though

$$xy = yx$$

it is customary to write the letters in alphabetical order, as xy.

If you are multiplying a number and a variable, as in $3x$, the numerical part is usually written first and the juxtaposition tells us that it means 3 times x. In algebra we usually do not use a multiplication symbol, because to write

$$3 \times x$$

would cause confusion between the times sign and the variable x. For the product of a number and a variable, the form $3x$ is considered simplified form. In a product of two or more factors, any collection of factors is said to be the **coefficient** of the rest of the factors. Thus, in $5a$, 5 is the coefficient of a, and a is the coefficient of 5. The constant factor is called the **numerical coefficient.** An expression may have many

*"On Algebra," *Washington Post*, February 18, 2006.

factors, such as $15x^2yz$. We say that 15 is the numerical coefficient, x^2 is the coefficient of $15yz$, $15y$ is the coefficient of x^2z, and so on. If no constant factor is shown, as in ab, we say that the numerical coefficient is 1, since $ab = 1 \cdot ab$.

Numerical Coefficient

> If no constant factor appears in an expression, the numerical coefficient is understood to be 1.

This seems like an easy idea, but one that is often forgotten.

To multiply variables, you will need to remember the meaning of an exponent. Consider the following example.

EXAMPLE 1

Multiplication with variables

Use the definition of exponent to multiply the given algebraic expressions:

a. x^2x^3 **b.** y^4y^5 **c.** $x^2y(xy^4)$

Solution

a. $x^2x^3 = xx \cdot xxx = x^5$

b. $y^4y^5 = yyyy \cdot yyyyy = y^9$

c. $x^2y(xy^4) = xxy \cdot xyyyy$

$\qquad\qquad = xxxyyyy$ Remember, you can rearrange the order of multiplication.

$\qquad\qquad = x^3y^5$ ●

The product of two powers with the same base is a power with that base and with an exponent that is the sum of the exponents. We call this the **addition law of exponents.**

Addition Law

> $$b^m \cdot b^n = b^{m+n}$$
> To *multiply* two numbers with like bases, add the exponents.

The bases MUST be the same.

EXAMPLE 2

Using the addition law of exponents

Write the solutions in exponent form, applying the addition law of exponents whenever possible.   **a.** $2^2 \cdot 2^3$ **b.** x^3x^4 **c.** yy^2 **d.** x^2y^3

Solution

a. $2^2 \cdot 2^3 = 2^{2+3} = 2^5$ Note: $2^2 \cdot 2^3 \neq 4^5$

b. $x^3x^4 = x^{3+4} = x^7$

c. $yy^2 = y^1y^2 = y^{1+2} = y^3$

d. x^2y^3 cannot be simplified further.   ●

Not only can you rearrange the order of the factors in multiplication, but you can actually associate them to simplify an expression. When multiplying, you should mentally group together the numerical coefficients as well as any variables that are the same. Multiply together the numerical coefficients and use the law of exponents on all base numbers that are the same, as illustrated in Example 3.

EXAMPLE 3

Multiplying variable expressions

Multiply the given variable expressions.

a. $(-3x)(5x)$ **b.** $2a(3b)(4c)$ **c.** $(-2xy)(3x^2)(-y^3)$

Solution

a. $(-3x)(5x) = -3(5)xx$ Do this step mentally.

$$= -15x^2$$

b. $2a(3b)(4c) = 2(3)(4)abc$

$$= 24abc$$

c. $(-2xy)(3x^2)(-y^3) = -2(3)(-1)xx^2yy^3$

$$= 6x^3y^4$$

    In the previous chapter, we defined the word *term* as a number that is being added or subtracted. In algebra, we need an expanded definition. Examples 1–3 illustrate the multiplication of numbers and variables. The answer in each case was still an indicated multiplication. Such expressions are called *terms*.

Term

> A **term** is a number, a variable, or a product of numbers and variables.

 CAUTION This is an important word to know in algebra.

EXAMPLE 4

Naming terms

Decide whether the following are terms.

a. 10   **b.** x **c.** $10x$ **d.** $x + 10$ **e.** $10abcd$ **f.** $\frac{10}{x}$ **g.** $\frac{10}{3}$ **h.** $\frac{x}{10}$

Solution

a. 10 is a **term** because it is a single number.

b. x is a **term** because it is a single variable.

c. $10x$ is a **term** because it is the product of a number and a variable.

d. $x + 10$ is **not a single term** because it is not a product; this is actually classified as a two-term expression.

e. $10abcd$ is a **term.**

f. $\frac{10}{x}$ is **not a term** because it is not a product. (It is a quotient of a number and a variable.)

g. $\frac{10}{3}$ is a **term** because it is a single number. Contrast this with part **f.** The number $\frac{10}{3}$ is a quotient, but it is also a single number.

h. $\frac{x}{10}$ is a **term** because it is the product of a number $\left(\frac{1}{10}\right)$ and a variable (x).

Terms are connected by addition or subtraction:

$$5x + 6 \qquad x^2 - x + 3 \qquad 2x + 7y - 3$$

We call expressions that consist of one or more terms *polynomials*. Think of subtractions as sums by adding the opposite.

Polynomial

> A **polynomial** is a term or a sum of terms.

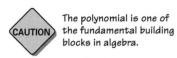

The polynomial is one of the fundamental building blocks in algebra.

A polynomial is classified by the number of terms it has, as indicated in the following box.

Classifications

> • A polynomial with one term is called a **monomial.**
> • A polynomial with two terms is called a **binomial.**
> • A polynomial with three terms is called a **trinomial.**

EXAMPLE 5

Classifying polynomials by terms

Classify each polynomial according to its number of terms.

a. $2x^2 + 3x - 5$ **b.** $15x^2y$ **c.** 6 **d.** $x^2 - y^2$

Solution

a. $2x^2 + 3x - 5$ is a trinomial.   **b.** $15x^2y$ is a monomial.

c. 6 is a monomial.   **d.** $x^2 - y^2$ is a binomial.   ●

A polynomial is also classified according to the *degree of its terms. Remember that terms are made up of numbers, variables, and products of numbers and variables.* The number of variable factors is called the **degree** of a term.

EXAMPLE 6

Degree of a term

Find the degree of each term.

a. $3x$ **b.** 5^3xy **c.** 10 **d.** $2x^2$ **e.** $9x^2y^3$

Solution

a. $3x$ is degree 1 (one variable factor).

b. 5^3xy is degree 2 (two variable factors).

c. 10 is degree 0 (no variable factors).

d. $2x^2$ is degree 2 (think what we mean by x^2; xx is two variable factors.)

e. $9x^2y^3$ is degree 5.   ●

A polynomial is the sum or difference of terms, and we also speak about the degree of a polynomial.

Degree | The **degree of a term** is the number of variable factors in that term. The **degree of a polynomial** is the largest degree of any of its terms.

EXAMPLE 7

Classifying polynomials by degree

Spend some time with this example.

Classify each of the following polynomials by degree.

a. $2x^2 + 3x - 5$ **b.** $15x^2y$ **c.** 6 **d.** $x^2 - y^2$ **e.** $5x^3 - 4x^2 + 2x - 10$

Solution

a. $2x^2 + 3x - 5$ is degree 2.

b. $15x^2y$ is degree 3.

c. 6 is degree 0.

d. $x^2 - y^2$ is degree 2.

e. $5x^3 - 4x^2 + 2x - 10$ is degree 3.

When writing polynomials, it is customary to arrange the terms from the highest-degree term to the lowest-degree term, as shown in parts **a** and **e** of Example 7. If terms have the same degree, as in part **d** of Example 7, the terms are usually listed in alphabetical order.

PROBLEM SET 3.1

ESSENTIAL IDEAS   LEVEL 1

1. IN YOUR OWN WORDS What is a term?

2. IN YOUR OWN WORDS What is a polynomial?

3. IN YOUR OWN WORDS State the addition law of exponents.

4. IN YOUR OWN WORDS What is the degree of a term?

DRILL AND PRACTICE   LEVEL 2

Give the degree and numerical coefficient of each term in Problems 5–10.

5. a. $3x^4$ 4; 3 **b.** $5x^2$ 2; 5

6. a. $8x^5$ 5; 8 **b.** $64x$ 1; 64

7. a. x 1; 1 **b.** $8x$ 1; 8

8. a. x^2 2; 1 **b.** $-5x^2$ 2; −5

9. a. x^3 3; 1 **b.** $-2x^4$ 4; −2

10. a. $-x$ 1; −1 **b.** $-x^5$ 5; −1

Identify each polynomial in Problems 11–16 as a monomial, binomial, or trinomial. Also, give the degree of the polynomial.

11. a. $x^2 + 5$ second-degree binomial

  b. $x^3 - 3$ third-degree binomial

12. a. $abcd$ fourth-degree monomial

  b. $a + b + c$ first-degree trinomial

13. a. 123,456 zero-degree monomial

  b. $4abc - d$ third-degree binomial

14. a. $5xy^3 + 5xy$ fourth-degree binomial

  b. $a - b - c$ first-degree trinomial

15. a. $2x^2 + 5x + 3$ second-degree trinomial

  b. $x^2 - 5x + 3$ second-degree trinomial

16. a. $x - 5$ first-degree binomial

  b. $x^2 + 5$ second-degree binomial

Use the definition of exponent and the addition law of exponents to multiply the algebraic expressions in Problems 17–34.

17. a. $yyyyyy$ y^6 **b.** $x^3x^4y^2y^3$ x^7y^5

18. a. $xxxxxxx$ x^7 **b.** $x^2x^3y^3y^3$ x^5y^6

19. a. xxy^3y x^2y^4 **b.** x^2xy^3y x^3y^4

20. a. $7x(3x)$ $21x^2$ **b.** $3x(7y)$ $21xy$

21. a. $(4x)(2y)$ 8xy **b.** $(9x)(-2y)$ −18xy

22. a. $(2x)(3y)$ 6xy **b.** $(-9x)(3x)$ $-27x^2$

23. a. $5(2x)(3x)$ $30x^2$ **b.** $-2(5x)(3y)$ −30xy

24. a. $x(4y)(3z)$ 12xyz **b.** $(-4a)(2y)(-c)$ 8acy

25. a. $(2x)^2$ $4x^2$ **b.** $(3y)^2$ $9y^2$

26. a. $-(3y)^2$ $-9y^2$ **b.** $(2x)(5y^2)$ $10xy^2$

27. a. $-(5x)^2$ $-25x^2$ **b.** $(2x)(5y)^2$ $50xy^2$

28. a. $(2x)^2(5y)$ $20x^2y$ **b.** $(2x^2)(5y)$ $10x^2y$

29. a. $(4x)(-2x)^2$ $16x^3$ **b.** $(2x)^2(-3x)$ $-12x^3$

30. a. $(4x)(-2x)^3$ $-32x^4$ **b.** $(2x^2)(-3x)$ $-6x^3$

31. a. $y^3(-5y^2)(-4y)$ $20y^6$ **b.** $y(-5y^2)(-4y^3)$ $20y^6$

32. a. $(-x^4)(-x^3)$ x^7 **b.** $-x^2(x^3)(6x)$ $-6x^6$

33. a. $-(2x)^2(3x)$ $-12x^3$ **b.** $-(3x)^2(-2x)$ $18x^3$

34. a. $-(4y)^2(-3y)$ $48y^3$ **b.** $-(-5x)^2(x^4)$ $-25x^6$

Make up an example of a polynomial that uses the variable x and satisfies the description given in Problems 35–40. **Examples vary.**

35. a. A first-degree trinomial

    b. A second-degree trinomial

36. a. A monomial of degree 0

    b. A fifth-degree monomial

37. a. A second-degree monomial

    b. A fourth-degree trinomial

38. a. A second-degree binomial

    b. A first-degree monomial

39. a. A third-degree monomial

    b. A third-degree binomial

40. a. A third-degree trinomial

    b. A first-degree binomial

Write each of the word phrases given in Problems 41–46 in symbols and simplify the numerical expressions.

CAUTION Spend some time on these word phrases. The problems are designed to help you "talk the talk" of mathematics.

41. a. The sum of two squared and three squared $2^2 + 3^2 = 13$

    b. The square of the sum of two and three $(2 + 3)^2 = 25$

42. a. The square of the sum of x and 5 $(x + 5)^2$

    b. The sum of x squared and 5 $x^2 + 5$

43. a. Three times the cube of a number $3x^3$

    b. The cube of three times a number $(3x)^3$

44. a. The square of a number plus four $x^2 + 4$

    b. The square of the sum of four and a number $(4 + x)^2$

45. a. The difference of squares $x^2 - y^2$

    b. The square of a difference $(x - y)^2$

46. a. The difference of cubes $x^3 - y^3$

    b. The cube of a difference $(x - y)^3$

APPLICATIONS **LEVEL 2**

47. Every day Karl jogs one minute longer than he did the day before.

    a. If he jogs for 40 minutes today, how long will he jog tomorrow? **41 minutes**

    b. If he jogs for 40 minutes today, how long did he jog a week ago? **33 minutes**

    c. If he jogs for x minutes today, how long will he jog in 3 days? $x + 3$

    d. If he jogs for y minutes today, how long did he jog yesterday? $y - 1$

48. A log is cut into two pieces.

    a. If the log is 10 ft long, and one piece is x feet long, how long is the other piece? $10 - x$

    b. If the log is 25 ft, and one piece is 12 ft, what is the length of the other piece? **13 ft**

    c. If the two pieces are x and y ft long, how long was the log? $x + y$

    d. If the log is x ft long and one piece is y ft long, how long is the other piece? $x - y$

49. If you have \$450 in a checking account, indicate the amount of money in this account after the given action:

    a. You write a check for \$25. **\$425**

    b. You write a check for x dollars. **\$(450 − x)**

    c. You write a check for \$12, and then another check for y dollars. **\$(438 − y)**

    d. You make a deposit of d dollars. **\$(450 + d)**

50. The school band marches in a rectangular array of rows and columns.

    a. If there are 72 people who march in eight rows, how many columns are there? **9**

    b. If there are x rows and y columns, how many are in the band? xy

    c. If there are 10 rows and t people in the band, how many columns are there? $t \div 10$ or $\frac{t}{10}$

    d. If there are T people in the band, and there are x rows, how many columns are there? $T \div x$ or $\frac{T}{x}$

RIGHT OR WRONG? **LEVEL 3**

Explain what is wrong, if anything, with the statements in Problems 51–58. Explain your reasoning.

51. $x^4x^2 = x^8$ **F; add the exponents: x^6**

52. $y^3y^2 = y^6$ **F; add the exponents: y^5**

53. $x^2 + x^3 = x^5$ **F; expression $x^2 + x^3$ is simplified**

54. $y^3 + y^4 = y^7$ **F; expression $y^3 + y^4$ is simplified**

55. $2^3 \cdot 2^4 = 4^7$ **F; add the exponents: 2^7**

56. $4^2 \cdot 4^3 = 16^5$ F; add the exponents: 4^5

57. $2^2 \cdot 3^2 = 6^{2+2} = 6^4$ F; $2^2 \cdot 3^2 = 4 \cdot 9 = 36$

58. $3^2 \cdot 2^3 = 6^5$ F; $3^2 \cdot 2^3 = 9 \cdot 8 = 72$

CONQUER ANXIETY

You might want to consult the book **Conquering Math Anxiety: A Self-help Workbook, Second Edition** *(Pacific Grove, CA: Brooks/Cole, 2003), by Cynthia Arem.*

59. IN YOUR OWN WORDS Creating a positive attitude toward mathematics is an important part of conquering math anxiety. Consider the following checklist* that measures your progress away from anxiety. List the ones that apply to you and then comment on the exercise.

1. I'm becoming a good math student.
2. I'm learning more math each day.
3. I'm capable of learning math.
4. I have good abilities in math.
5. I allow myself to relax when I study math.
6. I remember more math each day.
7. I'm relaxed, calm, alert, and confident in math.
8. My math improves every day.
9. I can understand math if I give myself a chance.
10. I enjoy math more each day.
11. I like math because it's useful in everyday life.
12. Working out math problems is fun.
13. Math is more and more exciting each day.
14. Math is creative.
15. Math is stimulating.
16. My way of doing math is a good one.
17. Math helps me get to where I want to go.
18. Math is my friend.
19. I'm feeling better about math.
20. Math methods help me solve everyday problems.
21. Add some of your own positive affirmations.

60. IN YOUR OWN WORDS Comment on the following quotation.[†] "Algebra traditionally has been a gatekeeper course leading to further study of mathematics in secondary school, to college entrance, and to jobs in technical fields."

*From *Conquering Math Anxiety: A Self-help Workbook, Second Edition* (Pacific Grove, CA: Brooks/Cole, 2003), by Cynthia Arem.

[†]Dr. Patricia I. Wright, Virginia Department of Education, *Algebra Proficiency for All.*

3.2 Similar Terms

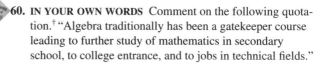

IN THIS WORLD   THE POWER OF MATH

WHAT DO YOU SAY WE PLAY SOMETHING DIFFERENT?

"Hey, Ein! Let's go!" shouted the Hippo as she stepped onto the teeter-totter.

"But zat is impossible!" proclaimed the professor. *"The laws of mathematics and physics do not allow us to play together. Vat can vee do?"*

"Oh chill out . . . ," chided the Hippo. *"I've had algebra and I can prove to you that we can play together."*

In this section we will look at some rules of algebra which may help Hippo prove to the professor that they can play together on the teeter-totter.

 See Problem 55.

One of the most difficult tasks for students beginning to study algebra is to recognize the form of the expected answer. In the previous section, we saw that numbers or variables can be multiplied to form a single new term by using the definition of exponents and the addition law of exponents. Now we turn our attention to addition and subtraction.

The key to multiplication is the **distributive property,** which was introduced in Section 1.2. We will restate it here for easy reference.

Distributive Property

$$a(b + c) = ab + ac$$

> **STOP** This property is a virtual powerhouse property in algebra. You will use it almost every time you use algebra.

If the variable parts of the individual terms are the same (both in variable and in degree), then the distributive property can be used to carry out addition:

$$2x + 3x = (2 + 3)x \quad \text{Distributive property}$$
$$= 5x$$

On the other hand, if the variable (or degree) parts are not the same, then the distributive property does not apply, as with the following sums:

$$2x + 3y \qquad 2x^2 + 5x \qquad 5x^2 + 4x - 5$$

EXAMPLE 1

Using the distributive property to combine terms

Find the indicated sums: **a.** $3a + 7a$ **b.** $2x^2 + 5x^2$ **c.** $5x + 4y + 4x$

Solution

a. $3a + 7a = (3 + 7)a$ Use the distributive property; you should do this in your head.
$$= 10a$$

b. $2x^2 + 5x^2 = 7x^2$

c. $5x + 4y + 4x = 9x + 4y$ Mentally: $5x + 4x = (5 + 4)x$

You cannot use the distributive property on $9x + 4y$.   ●

We need some terminology to describe what we are doing in Example 1. We refer to terms that can be added together as **similar** or **like terms.**

Similar Terms

If two or more terms are exactly alike except for their numerical coefficients, we call them **similar terms.**

EXAMPLE 2

Recognizing similar terms

Which of the following are sets of similar terms?

a. $5x, -3x, 9x$ **b.** $2x^2, 2x$ **c.** abc, abc^2, ab^2c **d.** $-3x^2y, -5x^2y, 14x^2y$

Solution

a. $5x, -3x,$ and $9x$ are **similar** terms.

b. $2x^2$ and $2x$ are **not similar** terms.

c. $abc, abc^2,$ and ab^2c are **not similar** terms.

d. $-3x^2y, -5x^2y,$ and $14x^2y$ are **similar** terms.   ●

> **STOP** Make SURE you study this paragraph until you really understand what is being said here.

To add or subtract variable expressions, add or subtract by using the distributive property. You can usually do this in your head, but you need to be especially careful when the coefficients are integers rather than counting numbers. Note how we simplify the expressions in Example 3.

EXAMPLE 3   Adding and subtracting algebraic expressions

Find the indicated sums and differences:

a. $-12x - (-5x)$ **b.** $-3x - 6x$ **c.** $4x - 5x + 2x$

d. $(2x + 3y) + (5x - 2y)$ **e.** $(x - y) + (x - 5y)$

Solution

a. $-12x - (-5x) = -7x$ Mentally, $-12 - (-5) = -12 + 5 = -7$.

b. $-3x - 6x = -9x$ Mentally, $-3 - 6 = -3 + (-6) = -9$.

c. $4x - 5x + 2x = x$ Mentally, $4 - 5 + 2 = 4 + (-5) + 2 = 1$.

d. $(2x + 3y) + (5x - 2y) = 7x + y$ Mentally, $2x + 5x + 3y - 2y$.

e. $(x - y) + (x - 5y) = 2x - 6y$ Mentally, $x + x - y - 5y$.

PROBLEM SET 3.2

ESSENTIAL IDEAS   LEVEL 1

1. State the distributive property. $a(b + c) = ab + ac$

2. What is meant by "similar terms"?   Terms that are exactly the same except for the numerical coefficients

In Problems 3–8, pick out the similar terms, if any.

3. $3x, 5xy, 2x^2y, 10x, 3xy^2, 4y$ 3x and 10x

4. $3x, 5xy, 2x^2y, 3xy^2, 7xy, 4y$ 5xy and 7xy

5. $3x, 5xy, 2x^2y, 3xy^2, 4y, 6x^2y$ 2x²y and 6x²y

6. $4x, 6x^2y, 5xy, 4y, 12x, 3xy^2, 4xz$ 4x and 12x

7. $4x, 6x^2y, 5xy, 4y, 3xy^2, 12x^2y, 4xz$ 6x²y and 12x²y

8. $4x, 6x^2y, 5xy^2, 4y, 3xy^2, 4xz$ 5xy² and 3xy²

DRILL AND PRACTICE   LEVEL 2

Combine similar terms in Problems 9–18.

9. a. $2x + 5x$ 7x   **b.** $3y + 5y$ 8y

10. a. $9z + 2z$ 11z   **b.** $7x - 3x$ 4x

11. a. $3y - 2y$ y   **b.** $8z - 2z$ 6z

12. a. $-3x + 5x$ 2x   **b.** $-5x + 2x$ −3x

13. a. $-3z + z$ −2z   **b.** $4x - 9x$ −5x

14. a. $3x - (-2)x$ 5x   **b.** $5x - (-8x)$ 13x

15. a. $-6x - (8x)$ −14x   **b.** $-5x - (-2x)$ −3x

16. a. $-7x - (-5x)$ −2x   **b.** $5x - 5x$ 0

17. a. $-x + x$ 0   **b.** $-4x + 4x$ 0

18. a. $2x + 3y$ 2x + 3y   **b.** $5 - 2x$ −2x + 5

Find the indicated sums and differences in Problems 19–48.

19. a. $4x + 2x + 7x$ 13x   **b.** $2x + 3x + 8x$ 13x

20. a. $6x + 7x + (-4)x$ 9x   **b.** $9y + 2y + (-7)y$ 4y

21. a. $-2x + 3y + 2x$ 3y   **b.** $2x + 3y - 3y$ 2x

22. a. $3y - 2y - y$ 0   **b.** $5z + 2z - 8z$ −z

23. a. $5x + 15 - 15$ 5x   **b.** $x - 36 + 36$ x

24. a. $2y + 8 - 8$ 2y   **b.** $3x + 5 - 3x$ 5

25. a. $2y + 8 - 2y$ 8   **b.** $5x - 7 - 5x$ −7

26. a. $5x + 12 - 5x$ 12   **b.** $8t + 1 - 8t$ 1

27. $5x + 4y + (-8)x$ −3x + 4y

28. $3a + (-5)a + (-2)a$ −4a

29. $2b + (-9)b + 6b$ −b

30. $-2c + (-5)c + 9c$ 2c

31. $-4a + 7b + (-5)b$ −4a + 2b

32. $8x + 3y - 10x$ −2x + 3y

33. $5x + 3 - 4x + 5$ x + 8

34. $6x + 3 - 5x + 7$ x + 10

35. $10 - 3x - 17 + 5x$ 2x − 7

36. $12x - 9 + 5x - 8$ 17x − 17

37. $7y + 6 - 11y - 4$ −4y + 2

38. $7x + 3y - 5y + 2y - 8$ 7x − 8

39. $8y - 2x + 3 - 5x + 15$ −7x + 8y + 18

40. $(2x + 3y) + (5x - 6y)$ 7x − 3y

41. $(x - 2y) + (3x - 5y)$ 4x − 7y

42. $(x - y) + (2x - 3y)$ **3x − 4y**

43. $(x + y) + (3x - 5y)$ **4x − 4y**

44. $(2x - y) + (x - 3y) + 5y$ **3x + y**

45. $(3x + 2y) + (x - 3y) + 5y$ **4x + 4y**

46. $(2x^2 - 1) + (3x - 4) + (x^2 - 3x + 3)$ **3x² − 2**

47. $(3x^2 + 4) + (2x - 5) + (x^2 - 5x)$ **4x² − 3x − 1**

48. $(8x^2 - 3) + (5x + 3) + (x^2 - 8)$ **9x² + 5x − 8**

APPLICATIONS　　**LEVEL 2**

In Problems 49–55, add the items.

49. You have 18 apples and 4 oranges, and your brother has 3 apples and 16 oranges. When you get home, you put all of your fruit into a bin. How many apples and oranges are in the bin?   **21 apples and 20 oranges**

50. You have x apples and y oranges, and your brother has 5 apples and 6 oranges. When you get home, you put all of your fruit into a bin. How many apples and oranges are in the bin?   **x + 5 apples and y + 6 oranges**

51. You have 4 x's and 9 y's and your brother has 7 x's and 8 y's. When you get home, you put all of your x's and y's into a bin. How many x's and y's are in the bin?
11 x's and 17 y's

52. You have a jar of 140 nuts and 60 bolts, and you dump this into a can that has 80 bolts and 95 nuts. How many nuts and bolts are now in the can?   **235 nuts and 140 bolts**

53. You have a jar of 45 n's and 23 b's, and you dump this into a can that has 40 b's and 19 n's. How many n's and b's are now in the can?   **63 b's and 64 n's**

54. Cole has 185 p's and 19 q's, while Hannah has 13 q's and 105 p's. What is the total number of p's and q's that the two have together?   **290 p's and 32 q's**

 55. In the "In This World" problem at the beginning of this section (see p. 140), there seem to be two variables. Define these variables.   **H = weight of hippo**
p = weight of professor

RIGHT OR WRONG?　　**LEVEL 3**

Explain what is wrong, if anything, with the statements in Problems 56–60. Explain your reasoning.

56. $x + x + x = x^3$ **F; x + x + x = 3x**

57. $2x^2 + 3x^2 = 5x^4$ **F; 2x² + 3x² = 5x²**

58. $6y + 2y = 8y^2$ **F; 6y + 2y = 8y**

59. $5x^2 + 3x + 1 = 9x^3$ **F; the left side is simplified**

60. $3x^2 - 2x + 4 = 5x^3$ **F; the left side is simplified**

(3.3) Simplification

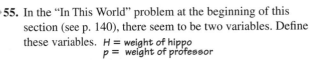

IN THIS WORLD THE POWER OF MATH

© CBS/Photofest

"Larry, I'm going to give you the same advice I give to all the geniuses I know," said Alan. *

　"Which is?" asked Larry.

　"Don't be an idiot," retorted Alan.

Numb3rs is a CBS television show that opens each week with the statement, "We all use math every day . . ." *Numb3rs* depicts the confluence of police work and mathematics in solving crime. An FBI agent recruits his mathematical genius brother to help solve crimes in Los Angeles.

　In this section, we consider one of the most important topics in mathematics—namely, the simplification of a polynomial.

　See Problem 2.

*"Spree" from *Numb3rs* first aired September 22, 2006.

In the previous section, we discussed the addition and subtraction of polynomials by using the idea of similar terms. In this section, we consider multiplication of polynomials by using the distributive property. First, consider a monomial times a polynomial.

EXAMPLE 1

Using the distributive property to multiply polynomials

Glenn R. Steiner

Carry out the indicated operations:

a. $5(x + 3)$ **b.** $2x(x - y)$ **c.** $3x^2y(5xy^3 + x^2y)$ **d.** $(-1)(5x^2 - 2x + 3)$

Solution

a. $5(x + 3) = 5x + 15$ **b.** $2x(x - y) = 2x^2 - 2xy$

c. $3x^2y(5xy^3 + x^2y) = 3x^2y(5xy^3) + 3x^2y(x^2y)$
$$= 15x^3y^4 + 3x^4y^2$$

d. $(-1)(5x^2 - 2x + 3) = -5x^2 + 2x - 3$

You should pay particular attention to part **d** of Example 1. It is common to multiply a polynomial by -1, but this is often done in connection with a property of -1 that was stated in Chapter 2:

$$(-1)n = -n$$

This means that, if you are subtracting polynomials such as

$$(6x^2 + 2x - 10) - (5x^2 - 2x + 3)$$

you need to remember that subtraction requires that you first add the opposite:

$$(6x^2 + 2x - 10) + (-1)(5x^2 - 2x + 3)$$

Next, use the distributive property as shown in part **d** of Example 1:

$$6x^2 + 2x - 10 + (-5)x^2 + 2x + (-3)$$

Finally, add the similar terms:

$$x^2 + 4x - 13$$

$6x^2 + (-5)x^2 = x^2$ $(-10) + (-3) = -13$

$2x + 2x = 4x$

EXAMPLE 2

Adding polynomials

Add: $(3x^2 + 3x - 5) + (2x^2 - 5x - 10)$

Solution $(3x^2 + 3x - 5) + (2x^2 - 5x - 10) = 5x^2 \qquad -2x \qquad -15$

$3x^2 + 2x^2 = 5x^2$

$3x - 5x = (3 - 5)x = -2x$

$-5 + (-10) = -15$

EXAMPLE 3   **Subtracting polynomials**

Subtract: $(3x^2 + 3x - 5) - (2x^2 - 5x - 10)$

Solution $(3x^2 + 3x - 5) - (2x^2 - 5x - 10) = 3x^2 + 3x - 5 - 2x^2 + 5x + 10$

$\uparrow \qquad \uparrow \quad \uparrow$

Watch these signs.

$$= x^2 + 8x + 5$$

Mentally eliminate parentheses by thinking:

$$3x^2 + 3x - 5 + (-1)(2x^2 - 5x - 10)$$

Distribute and write the result as shown above. Finally, mentally associate (group together) the similar terms:

$$3x^2 + (-2)x^2 = x^2$$
$$3x + 5x = 8x$$
$$-5 + 10 = 5$$

●

Now we combine both multiplication and addition. Be sure you remember the correct extended order of operations:

Parentheses first

Exponents next

Multiplication and division next

Addition and subtraction last

We now define what the word *simplify* means when applied to polynomials.

Simplify   A polynomial is **simplified** if all operations are completed according to the order-of-operations agreement, all similar terms have been combined, and the terms of the polynomial are written in order of descending degree.

EXAMPLE 4   **Simplifying polynomials (multiplication and addition)**

Simplify: **a.** $2(x - 3) + 4(x + 2)$ **b.** $2x(x - y) + 3y(x + 1)$
                  c. $3x(x + 2y) + 2y(y - 3)$

Solution

a. $2(x - 3) + 4(x + 2) = 2x - 6 + 4x + 8$ Parentheses first (distribute).

$\qquad\qquad\qquad\qquad = 6x + 2$ Similar terms next (add/subtract).

b. $2x(x - y) + 3y(x + 1) = 2x^2 - 2xy + 3xy + 3y$

$\qquad\qquad\qquad\qquad = 2x^2 + xy + 3y$

c. $3x(x + 2y) + 2y(y - 3) = 3x^2 + 6xy + 2y^2 - 6y$

Note: In this example, the first three terms are degree 2, so we list those terms first (in alphabetical order).

●

EXAMPLE 5 **Simplifying polynomials (multiplication and subtraction)**

Simplify: **a.** $2(4x - 5) - 4(3x - 7)$ **b.** $3(2x^2 - 4x + 9) - (x^2 + 5x - 6)$

Solution

a. $2(4x - 5) - 4(3x - 7) = 8x - 10 - 12x + 28$ Distributive property

↑ ↑

Watch signs.

$= -4x + 18$ Combine similar terms.

b. $3(2x^2 - 4x + 9) - (x^2 + 5x - 6) = 6x^2 - 12x + 27 - x^2 - 5x + 6$

$= 5x^2 - 17x + 33$ ●

The distributive property is also used to multiply polynomials. In this course we will consider the product of two binomials, but the method illustrated here could be extended to any polynomials. Consider the product

$$(2x + 3)(3x + 5)$$

Recall the distributive property:

$$A(B + C) = AB + AC$$

Distribute the outside number $(2x + 3)$ to each number inside the parentheses:

$(2x + 3)(3x + 5) = (2x + 3)3x + (2x + 3)5$

$= 2x(3x) + 3(3x) + (2x)(5) + 3(5)$

Use the distributive property again.

$= 6x^2 + 9x + 10x + 15$

$= 6x^2 + 19x + 15$

EXAMPLE 6 **Multiplying binomials**

Simplify: **a.** $(5x + 3)(2x + 3)$ **b.** $(x - 7)(x + 4)$

c. $(2x + 3)(x - 5)$ **d.** $(x - 5)(x - 3)$

Solution

a. $(5x + 3)(2x + 3) = (5x + 3)2x + (5x + 3)(3)$

$= 10x^2 + 6x + 15x + 9$

$= 10x^2 + 21x + 9$

b. $(x - 7)(x + 4) = (x - 7)x + (x - 7)4$

$= x^2 - 7x + 4x - 28$

$= x^2 - 3x - 28$

c. $(2x + 3)(x - 5) = (2x + 3)x + (2x + 3)(-5)$

$= 2x^2 + 3x + (-10)x + (-15)$

$= 2x^2 - 7x - 15$

d. $(x - 5)(x - 3) = (x - 5)x + (x - 5)(-3)$

$= x^2 - 5x + (-3)x + 15$

$= x^2 - 8x + 15$ ●

STOP Confusion of the words "simplify" and "evaluate" is common. These are two of the most important processes in algebra.

It is particularly important that you understand the correct use of two terms in algebra: *simplify* and *evaluate*. We compare these terms here:

Simplify	To **simplify** means to carry out all operations, according to the order-of-operations agreement, and to write the answer in a specified form:
	if it is a numerical expression, write as a single number;
	if it is a numerical expression including a fraction, write as a single number or as a reduced fraction;
	if it is a polynomial (or an algebraic expression), write the answer with similar terms combined and in order of descending degree.
Evaluate	To **evaluate** an algebraic expression means to replace the variables by specified values and then to simplify the resulting numerical expression.

PROBLEM SET 3.3

ESSENTIAL IDEAS LEVEL 1

1. State the distributive property. $a(b + c) = ab + ac$

2. What does it mean to simplify a polynomial? **See box above.**

DRILL AND PRACTICE LEVEL 2

Simplify the algebraic expressions in Problems 3–34.

3. $6(x + 1) + 3(x + 2)$ $9x + 12$

4. $3(x + 2) + 2(x + 3)$ $5x + 12$

5. $5(x + 3) + 2(x + 4)$ $7x + 23$

6. $6(x + 1) + 2(x + 4)$ $8x + 14$

7. $3(x - 5) + 2(x + 1)$ $5x - 13$

8. $2(x + 5) + (x - 4)$ $3x + 6$

9. $4(x - 2) + 6(x - 2)$ $10x - 20$

10. $(x - 6) + 2(x - 8)$ $3x - 22$

11. $(2x + 3y) + (5x - 6y)$ $7x - 3y$

12. $(x - 2y) + (3x - 5y)$ $4x - 7y$

13. $(x - y) + (2x - 3y)$ $3x - 4y$

14. $(x + y) + (3x - 5y)$ $4x - 4y$

15. $6(x + 2) - 3(x + 5)$ $3x - 3$

16. $3(x + 2) - 2(x + 1)$ $x + 4$

17. $5(x + 3) - 2(x + 8)$ $3x - 1$

18. $6(x + 1) - 2(x + 6)$ $4x - 6$

19. $3(x - 5) - 2(x + 1)$ $x - 17$

20. $2(x + 5) - (x - 4)$ $x + 14$

21. $4(x - 2) - 6(x - 2)$ $-2x + 4$

22. $(x - 6) - 2(x - 8)$ $-x + 10$

23. $(2x + 3y) - (5x - 6y)$ $-3x + 9y$

24. $(3x - 5y) - (x - 2y)$ $2x - 3y$

25. $(x - y) - (2x - 3y)$ $-x + 2y$

26. $(x + y) - (3x - 5y)$ $-2x + 6y$

27. $(x - 2y) - (3x - 5y)$ $-2x + 3y$

28. $(2x - y) - (x - 3y)$ $x + 2y$

29. $(3x + 2) - (2x + 1)$ $x + 1$

30. $(5x + 3) - (3x - 5)$ $2x + 8$

31. $(x - 3) - (2x + 4)$ $-x - 7$

32. $(x - 4) - (3x - 5)$ $-2x + 1$

33. $(3x - 5) - (2x + 3)$ $x - 8$

34. $(5x + 3) - (3x + 5)$ $2x - 2$

Simplify the algebraic expressions in Problems 35–50.

35. **a.** $(x + 1)(x + 2)$ $x^2 + 3x + 2$
    b. $(x + 3)(x + 3)$ $x^2 + 6x + 9$

36. **a.** $(x - 5)(x + 7)$ $x^2 + 2x - 35$
    b. $(x - 3)(x + 8)$ $x^2 + 5x - 24$

37. **a.** $(x + 3)(x - 2)$ $x^2 + x - 6$
    b. $(x + 2)(x - 5)$ $x^2 - 3x - 10$

38. **a.** $(x - 4)(x - 1)$ $x^2 - 5x + 4$
    b. $(x - 5)(x - 3)$ $x^2 - 8x + 15$

39. **a.** $(x + 2)(x - 2)$ $x^2 - 4$
    b. $(x - 3)(x + 2)$ $x^2 - x - 6$

40. **a.** $(x + 5)(x + 5)$ $x^2 + 10x + 25$
    b. $(x - 2)(x - 2)$ $x^2 - 4x + 4$

41. **a.** $(x - 3)^2$ $x^2 - 6x + 9$
    b. $(x + 2)^2$ $x^2 + 4x + 4$

42. a. $(2x + 1)^2$ $4x^2 + 4x + 1$

b. $(3x - 2)^2$ $9x^2 - 12x + 4$

43. $(3x^2 - 2x + 4) - (x^2 + 2x + 1)$ $2x^2 - 4x + 3$

44. $(3x^2 + 2x - 5) - (3x^2 - x + 3)$ $3x - 8$

45. $(x^2 + 4x - 1) - (3x^2 - 5x - 1)$ $-2x^2 + 9x$

46. $(5x^2 - 3x - 4) - (7x^2 + 3x - 4)$ $-2x^2 - 6x$

47. $2(x^2 + x - 1) + 4(x^2 - 2x + 3)$ $6x^2 - 6x + 10$

48. $4x^2(x^2 - x + 2) + 3x(x^2 + x - 1)$ $4x^4 - x^3 + 11x^2 - 3x$

49. $2(3x^3 + 2x - 1) + (5x^3 - 4x^2 + 3)$ $11x^3 - 4x^2 + 4x + 1$

50. $2(5x^3 - 4x^2 + 3x - 5) + 3(2x^2 - 5x - 6)$
$10x^3 - 2x^2 - 9x - 28$

51. If you have x pairs of athletic shoes and y pairs of loafers, and you have no other shoes, answer the following questions.

a. How many pairs of shoes do you own? $x + y$

b. How many shoes (written as a product) do you own?
$2(x + y)$

c. How many shoes (written as a sum) do you own? $2x + 2y$

52. Suppose that adult tickets to the 4H Chicken-Que on Friday and Saturday are $8.00, and children's tickets are $3.00.

a. If you sell 5 adult tickets on Friday and 4 adult tickets on Saturday, how much did you collect? $72

b. If you sell x children's tickets on Friday and y children's tickets on Saturday, how much (written as a product) did you collect? $3(x + y)$

c. If you sell x children's tickets on Friday and y children's tickets on Saturday, how much (written as a sum) did you collect? $3x + $3y$

d. If you sell m adult tickets on Friday, and x children's tickets on Friday, how much did you collect?
$8m + $3x$

Explain what is wrong, if anything, with the statements in Problems 53–60. Explain your reasoning.

53. $3(x + 5) = 3x + 5$ F; $3(x + 5) = 3x + 15$

54. $-(x + 3) = -x + 3$ F; $-(x + 3) = -x - 3$

55. $-x = (-1)x$ T

56. $x - y = x + (-1)y$ T

57. $(x + 5) - (x + 4) = 9$ F; 1

58. $(3y - 4) - (4 + 3y) = 0$ F; -8

59. $(x + 5)(x + 4) = x^2 + 5x + 20$ F; $x^2 + 9x + 20$

60. $(x - 3)(x - 2) = x^2 - 3x + 6$ F; $x^2 - 5x + 6$

3.4 Equations

IN THIS WORLD   THE POWER OF MATH

Can you tell who's who by their hair?

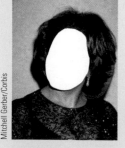

Mitchell Gerber/Corbis   Carlo Allegri/Getty Images   Lisa O'Connor/Zuma/Corbis   Reuters/Corbis   Reuters/Corbis

Just as you needed to look for visual clues to find the identities of the celebrities in these photographs, you must check the clues of a given equation to find the solution. Solving equations is as old as mathematics itself, but the use of the equal sign dates back to Robert Recorde in his book *The Whetstone of Witte* written in 1557. In this section, we will use numerical clues to find an unknown value for an equation.

 See Problem 1.

We now define one of the most important processes in algebra—namely, the idea of *solving an equation*. There are three types of equations:

$2 + 3 = 5$ is a *true equation.*

$2 + 3 = 9$ is a *false equation.*

$2 + x = 9$ is an *open equation.*

Equation

An **equation** is a statement of equality between two expressions, called the *left side* and the *right side*. There are three types of equations: *true, false,* and *open.*

An **open** (or **conditional**) equation is an equation that depends on the value of a variable. Values that make the conditional equation true are called the **solutions** or **roots** of the equation, and are said to **satisfy** the equation.

To **solve** an equation means to find the replacement for the unknown (that is, the variable or variables) that makes the equation true.

Do not confuse the words *evaluate, simplify,* and *solve.* We reviewed the correct use of the words *evaluate* and *simplify* at the end of the previous section. We *evaluate* an algebraic expression, we *simplify* a numerical expression or an algebraic expression, and we *solve* an equation. Keep in mind that an equation is *two* expressions connected by an equal sign.

The process of solving an equation is to look for things to do to both sides of an equation that do not affect the solution. The key ideas are those of *opposites* (for addition and subtraction) and *reciprocals* (for multiplication and division).

Opposites

Reciprocals

Two numbers whose sum is 0 are called **opposites.**

Two numbers whose product is 1 are called **reciprocals.**

EXAMPLE 1

Adding opposites

Use the idea of opposites to find the sums.

a. $5 + (-5)$ **b.** $-18 + 18$ **c.** $x + (-x)$

d. $x - x$ **e.** $175 + 7 + (-7)$ **f.** $14 + 23 - 23$

g. $x - 18 + 18$ **h.** $y + 10 - 10$ **i.** $x + y - x$

Solution

a. $5 + (-5) = 0$ **b.** $-18 + 18 = 0$ **c.** $x + (-x) = 0$

d. $x - x = x + (-x)$ **e.** $175 + 7 + (-7) = 175$ **f.** $14 + 23 - 23 = 14$

      $= 0$

g. $x - 18 + 18 = x$ **h.** $y + 10 - 10 = y$ **i.** $x + y - x = y$ ●

The goal in solving an equation is to *isolate the variable* on one side of the equation. To begin our study, we state the first of four properties about equation solving—namely, the **addition property of equations.**

Addition Property

> The solution of an equation is **unchanged** by **adding the same number to both sides of the equation.**

You will use this property to add some number to both sides of an equation so that, after it is simplified, the only expression on one side of the equation is the variable. If the solution of an equation is unchanged by some operation, then the resulting equation is said to be **equivalent** to the original equation.

EXAMPLE 2   **Using the addition property of equations**

Solve the given equations.

a. $x - 7 = 12$ **b.** $y - 10 = 5$ **c.** $z - 12 = -25$ **d.** $-108 = k - 92$

Solution   Remember that to *solve* an equation means to find the replacement of the variable that makes the equation true.

a. $x - 7 = 12$

The opposite of subtracting 7 is adding 7,
*so you **add 7 to both sides** of the equation.*

$x - 7 + 7 = 12 + 7$

$x = 19$ Simplify.

*This says that, **if** x is replaced by 19, the original equation is true (because they are equivalent equations). It does not say that x is always equal to 19. In fact, x is a variable, so it can be replaced by any number in the domain. For example, if x is replaced by 20, the equation is false. The form x = 19 is the desired form for the solution because in this form the solution is obvious.*

Check: $19 - 7 = 12$

Replace x by 19 to check.

b. $y - 10 = 5$ Given
$y - 10 + 10 = 5 + 10$ Add 10 to both sides.
$y = 15$ Simplify.   Can you check?

c. $z - 12 = -25$ Notice that, when solving equations, you
$z - 12 + 12 = -25 + 12$ write one equation under the other with
$z = -13$ the equal signs aligned.

d. $-108 = k - 92$ It doesn't matter whether the variable
$-108 + 92 = k - 92 + 92$ ends up on the left or the right side.
$-16 = k$

The addition property is used whenever some number is being subtracted from the variable. **If a number is being added to the variable, then the opposite is subtraction,** and you can use the following **subtraction property of equations.**

Subtraction Property

> The solution of an equation is **unchanged** by **subtracting the same number from both sides of the equation.**

EXAMPLE 3   **Using the subtraction property of equations**

Solve the given equations.

a. $x + 5 = 13$ **b.** $y + 8 = 5$ **c.** $17 = a + 12$ **d.** $19 = b + 48$

Solution

a. $\underbrace{x + 5}_{\uparrow} = 13$

The opposite of adding 5 is subtracting 5,
*so you **subtract 5 from both sides** of the equation.*

$$x + 5 \overset{\downarrow}{-\ 5} = 13 \overset{\downarrow}{-\ 5}$$

$$\underbrace{x = 8}_{\uparrow} \quad \text{Simplify.} \quad \text{Check:} \quad 8 + 5 = 13.$$

If x is equal to 8, then the equation is true

b. $y + 8 = 5$ Given.

$y + 8 - 8 = 5 - 8$ Subtract 8 from both sides.

$y = -3$ Simplify.   Can you check?

c. $17 = a + 12$

$17 - 12 = a + 12 - 12$

$5 = a$

d. $19 = b + 48$

$19 - 48 = b + 48 - 48$

$-29 = b$ ●

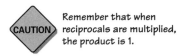 **CAUTION** Remember that when reciprocals are multiplied, the product is 1.

The idea of opposite operations extends to examples in which the variable is multiplied or divided by some number; that is, multiplication and division are opposite operations.

EXAMPLE 4   **Multiplying reciprocals**

Simplify cach expression.

a. $\dfrac{3x}{3}$ **b.** $\dfrac{5x}{5}$ **c.** $\dfrac{19p}{19}$ **d.** $\dfrac{-12q}{-12}$

e. $\left(\dfrac{x}{2}\right)(2)$ **f.** $\left(\dfrac{x}{7}\right)(7)$ **g.** $\left(\dfrac{t}{-3}\right)(-3)$

Solution   The definition of a reciprocal tells us that the product of a number and its reciprocal is 1. This means, for example, that $3\left(\tfrac{1}{3}\right) = 1$ and $\tfrac{5}{5} = 1$.

a. $\dfrac{3x}{3}$ *Think:*   "If some number x is multiplied by 3 and then the result is divided by 3, the result is the original number x." As you are thinking this, you write

$$\frac{3x}{3} = x$$

b. $\dfrac{5x}{5} = x$ **c.** $\dfrac{19p}{19} = p$ **d.** $\dfrac{-12q}{-12} = q$

e. $\left(\dfrac{x}{2}\right)(2)$ *Think:*   "If some number x is divided by 2 and then the result is multiplied by 2, the result is the original number x." As you are thinking this, you write

$$\left(\frac{x}{2}\right)(2) = x$$

f. $\left(\dfrac{x}{7}\right)(7) = x$ **g.** $\left(\dfrac{t}{-3}\right)(-3) = t$ ●

STOP   To solve an equation in which some number is dividing the variable, use the following **multiplication property of equations.**

Multiplication Property

> The solution of an equation is **unchanged** by **multiplying both sides of the equation by the same nonzero number.**

EXAMPLE 5   **Using the multiplication property of equations**

Solve each equation.

a. $\dfrac{x}{2} = 9$ **b.** $\dfrac{w}{8} = 7$ **c.** $\dfrac{r}{-5} = 12$ **d.** $-3 = \dfrac{m}{6}$ **e.** $0 = \dfrac{n}{4}$

Solution

a. $\dfrac{x}{2} = 9$

The opposite of dividing by 2 is multiplying by 2, so you ***multiply both sides*** *of the equation* ***by 2.***

$$\left(\frac{x}{2}\right)(2) = 9(2)$$

$x = 18$ **Simplify.**   *Check:* $\frac{18}{2} = 9$.

b. $\dfrac{w}{8} = 7$ **c.** $\dfrac{r}{-5} = 12$ **d.** $-3 = \dfrac{m}{6}$ **e.** $0 = \dfrac{n}{4}$

$\left(\dfrac{w}{8}\right)(8) = 7(8)$ $\dfrac{r}{-5}(-5) = 12(-5)$ $-3(6) = \left(\dfrac{m}{6}\right)(6)$ $0(4) = \left(\dfrac{n}{4}\right)(4)$

$w = 56$ $r = -60$ $-18 = m$ $0 = n$ ●

The last property of equations of this section is used if the variable is multiplied by some number; we call this the **division property of equations.**

Division Property

> The solution of an equation is **unchanged** by **dividing both sides of the equation by the same nonzero number.**

EXAMPLE 6   **Using the division property of equations**

Solve each equation.

a. $5a = 20$ **b.** $3b = 39$ **c.** $-7c = 42$ **d.** $-104 = 8d$

e. $-70 = -14e$

Solution

a. $5a = 20$

The opposite of multiplying by 5 is dividing by 5, so you divide both sides of the equation by 5.

$$\frac{5a}{5} = \frac{20}{5}$$

$a = 4$ Simplify.   *Check:* $5(4) = 20$.

b. $3b = 39$ **c.** $-7c = 42$

$$\frac{3b}{3} = \frac{39}{3}$$ $$\frac{-7c}{-7} = \frac{42}{-7}$$

$b = 13$ $c = -6$

d. $-104 = 8d$ **e.** $-70 = -14e$

$$\frac{-104}{8} = \frac{8d}{8}$$ $$\frac{-70}{-14} = \frac{-14e}{-14}$$

$-13 = d$ $5 = e$

The celebrities in the photographs on page 148 are Oprah Winfrey, Arnold Schwarzenegger, Jay Leno, Cher, and Julia Roberts.

PROBLEM SET (3.4)

ESSENTIAL IDEAS LEVEL 1

1. Explain what it means to "solve an equation." Find replacements for the variable that make the equation true.
2. State the four properties of equations. Addition, subtraction, multiplication, and division properties of equations
3. What is a solution of an equation? A value for the variable that makes the equation true
4. What is the goal when solving an equation? Opposite operations to isolate the variable on one side

DRILL AND PRACTICE LEVEL 2

Solve each equation in Problems 5–44. Show each step of the process until the variable is isolated. Be sure to keep your equal signs aligned.

5. a. $a - 5 = 10$ 15   **b.** $b - 8 = 14$ 22
6. a. $c - 2 = 0$ 2   **b.** $d - 9 = -7$ 2
7. a. $6 = g - 2$ 8   **b.** $0 = h - 112$ 112
8. a. $-5 = h - 4$ -1   **b.** $-40 = i - 92$ 52
9. a. $m + 2 = 7$ 5   **b.** $n + 8 = 12$ 4
10. a. $n + 19 = 20$ 1   **b.** $p + 8 = 2$ -6
11. a. $8 + s = 4$ -4   **b.** $12 + t = 15$ 3
12. a. $36 + u = 40$ 4   **b.** $18 + v = 10$ -8
13. $d - 7 = -10$ -3   **14.** $e - 1 = -35$ -34
15. $f - 3 = -12$ -9   **16.** $-10 + w = 14$ 24
17. $-12 + x = -6$ 6   **18.** $-137 = j - 49$ -88
19. $q + 7 = -15$ -22   **20.** $r + 6 = -14$ -20

 CAUTION Don't forget that capital letters and lowercase letters are not the same.

21. $\dfrac{A}{3} = 7$ 21   **22.** $\dfrac{B}{12} = 8$ 96
23. $\dfrac{C}{5} = -12$ -60   **24.** $\dfrac{D}{8} = -15$ -120
25. $\dfrac{E}{-4} = 11$ -44   **26.** $\dfrac{F}{-12} = 16$ -192
27. $\dfrac{G}{-13} = -3$ 39   **28.** $7 = \dfrac{H}{-8}$ -56
29. $-4 = \dfrac{I}{-10}$ 40   **30.** $-18 = \dfrac{J}{-4}$ 72
31. $\dfrac{K}{19} = 0$ 0   **32.** $\dfrac{L}{-9} = 0$ 0
33. $3M = 33$ 11   **34.** $4N = -48$ -12
35. $-8P = -96$ 12   **36.** $-Q = 5$ -5
37. $-R = 14$ -14   **38.** $-S = 19$ -19

39. $-12T = 168$ -14   **40.** $13U = -234$ -18
41. $-5V = 225$ -45   **42.** $-6W = -228$ 38
43. $13X = 0$ 0   **44.** $2Y = 0$ 0

APPLICATIONS LEVEL 2

45. IN YOUR OWN WORDS To solve $\frac{2}{3}x = 5$, do you think it would be easier to divide both sides by $\frac{2}{3}$ or to multiply both sides by $\frac{3}{2}$? Are both these steps permissible? Explain.

46. IN YOUR OWN WORDS To solve $5x = \frac{2}{3}$, do you think it would be easier to divide both sides by 5 or to multiply both sides by $\frac{1}{5}$? Are both these steps permissible? Explain.

47. A molecule of C_2H_6 consists of two carbon atoms and six hydrogen atoms, as shown in Figure 3.1.

Figure 3.1 Molecule

a. How many of each type of atom do x molecules contain? 2x carbon atoms and 6x hydrogen atoms
b. Write the total number of atoms in x molecules as a sum. $2x + 6x = 8x$ atoms
c. How many atoms does one molecule contain? 8
d. How many atoms do y molecules contain? 8y

48. In the "In This World" problem for Section 3.2, the hippo claimed to be able to show the professor that they could have fun on the teeter-totter. In Problem 55 of that section, you were asked to define two variables described in the problem. Use those two variables and a new variable in order to write an equation representing the teeter-totter problem. Let w be some weight so that $H = p + w$

RIGHT OR WRONG? LEVEL 3

Explain what is wrong, if anything, with the statements in Problems 49–60. Explain your reasoning.

49. $x - 5 = -6$
      $x = -11$ F; should be x = -1; add 5 to both sides.
50. $x + 2 = 8$
      $x = 10$ F; should be x = 6; subtract 2 from both sides.

51. $\dfrac{x}{5} = -10$

    $x = -2$ F; should be x = −50; multiply both sides by 5.

52. $3x = 2$

    $x = 6$ F; should be x = $\frac{2}{3}$; divide both sides by 3.

53. If you multiply reciprocals, the product is 0.   F; the product is 1.

54. The first step in solving $x + 8 = 5$ is to subtract 5 from both sides.   F; subtract 8 from both sides.

55. The first step in solving $x - 6 = 2$ is to subtract 2 from both sides.   F; add 6 to both sides.

56. The first step in solving $x - 5 = 11$ is to move the 5 to the other side.   F; add 5 to both sides.

57. The first step in solving $x + 3 = -14$ is to move the 3 to the other side.   F; subtract 3 from both sides.

58. To solve $5x = -20$, use the multiplication property of equations.   F; use the division property of equations.

59. To solve $\dfrac{x}{-8} = -3$, use the division property of equations.   F; use the multiplication property of equations.

60. *What is wrong,* if anything, with the following "proof"?

    i. 12 eggs = 1 dozen

    ii. 24 eggs = 2 dozen

          Multiply both sides of step i by 2.

    iii. 6 eggs $= \dfrac{1}{2}$ dozen

          Divide both sides of step i by 2.

    iv. 144 eggs = 1 dozen

          Multiply step iii by step ii (equals times equals).

    v. 12 dozen = 1 dozen

          Substitute, since 144 eggs = 12 dozen.

Cannot multiply equals times equals; can only multiply both sides by nonzero constant.

3.5 Solving Equations

IN THIS WORLD   THE POWER OF MATH

COMMUTATIVE PROPERTY
$a + b = b + a$
$ab = ba$

The formal development of algebra is beyond the scope of this book, but it depends on some properties that we have assumed without formal development. These properties are stated here.

The *commutative property* states that the order in which you add or multiply numbers does not change the result of the answer. For example,

    $3 + 5 = 8$ and $5 + 3 = 8$ *or* $3 \times 5 = 15$ and $5 \times 3 = 15$

ASSOCIATIVE PROPERTY
$(a + b) + c = a + (b + c)$
$(ab)c = a(bc)$

The *associative property* states that, when adding three numbers, you can add the third number to the sum of any pair of those numbers. For example,

    $(3 + 5) + 7 = 15$ and $3 + (5 + 7) = 15$

The same result holds for multiplication, namely,

    $(3 \times 5) \times 7 = 105$ and $3 \times (5 \times 7) = 105$

In this section, we use these algebraic properties to develop a procedure for solving equations.

 See Problem 9.

One of the most important tools in problem solving is solving equations. The equations we consider in this chapter are sometimes called *first-degree* equations. In this section, we'll take the fundamentals you learned in the previous section and apply them to more complicated equations. The first step is to learn to solve the equations from the previous section *mentally.*

EXAMPLE 1

Basic properties of solving equations

Solve each equation.

a. $7h = -56$ **b.** $j + 7 = -56$ **c.** $\frac{r}{7} = -56$ **d.** $s - 7 = -56$

Solution

a. $7h = -56$

$\quad\quad h = -8$

Mentally divide both sides by 7.

b. $j + 7 = -56$

$\quad\quad j = -63$

Mentally subtract 7 from both sides.

c. $\dfrac{r}{7} = -56$

$\quad\quad r = -392$

Mentally multiply both sides by 7.

d. $s - 7 = -56$

$\quad\quad s = -49$

Mentally add 7 to both sides.

> **CAUTION** Don't forget that whatever is done to an equation must be done to both sides.

Equations more difficult than those in Example 1 can now be considered. In these examples, you must simplify by adding similar terms.

EXAMPLE 2

Solving equations by first simplifying

Solve each equation.

a. $3x - 2 - 2x = 5 + 2x - 2x$ **b.** $4 + 5x - 5x = 7 + 6x - 5x$

c. $\frac{x}{2} + 4 - 4 = 5 - 4$ **d.** $4 - 10 = 10 - 3x - 10$

Solution

a. $3x - 2 - 2x = 5 + 2x - 2x$ Given.

$\quad\quad\quad x - 2 = 5$ First simplify.

$\quad\quad\quad\quad\quad x = 7$ Add 2 to both sides (done mentally).

b. $4 + 5x - 5x = 7 + 6x - 5x$ Given.

$\quad\quad\quad\quad 4 = 7 + x$ Simplify.

$\quad\quad\quad -3 = x$ Subtract 7 from both sides (mentally).

c. $\dfrac{x}{2} + 4 - 4 = 5 - 4$ Given.

$\quad\quad\quad\quad \dfrac{x}{2} = 1$ Simplify.

$\quad\quad\quad\quad x = 2$ Multiply both sides by 2.

d. $4 - 10 = 10 - 3x - 10$ Given.

$\quad\quad -6 = -3x$ Simplify.

$\quad\quad 2 = x$ Divide both sides by -3.

STOP Sometimes it is necessary to use more than one of the equation properties when solving a simple equation.

Sonja Kovalevsky
(1850–1891)

Sonja Kovalevsy, earlier known as Sofia Korvin-Krukovsky, was a gifted mathematician who did work in calculus and in algebra. She is thought to be the first woman to receive a doctorate in mathematics. Born in Moscow to Russian nobility, she left Russia in 1868 because universities were closed to women. She went to Germany since she wished to study with Karl Weierstraß in Berlin. The University of Berlin would also not accept women, so she studied privately with Weierstrass and in 1874 was awarded a doctoral degree in absentia from Göttingen, which excused her from oral examination on the basis of her outstanding thesis. She won the *Prix Bordin* because of the exceptional merit of her paper. It was said that her early interest in mathematics was aroused by an odd wallpaper that covered her room in a summer house. Fascinated, she spent hours trying to make sense of it. The paper turned out to be lecture notes on higher mathematics purchased by her father during his student days.

Solving Simple Equations

The procedure for solving simple equations consists of two steps:

Step 1 Simplify the left and right sides.

Step 2 Use equation properties to isolate the variable on one side.
a. First, use the addition or subtraction property.
b. Next, use the multiplication or division property.

 CAUTION Some of you may want to keep showing the intermediate steps (as we did in the previous section). However, this will get in your way as you progress through this material, so you are strongly encouraged to add, subtract, multiply, and divide entries in your head, as illustrated by the following examples.

EXAMPLE 3

Solving equations

Solve each equation.

a. $4x + 3 = 7$　　**b.** $2x - 7 = 13$　　**c.** $41 = \frac{x}{2} - 7$　　**d.** $-4 = \frac{x}{3} + 2$

Solution

a.
$4x + 3 = 7$	Given.
$4x = 4$	Subtract 3 from both sides.
$x = 1$	Divide both sides by 4.

b.
$2x - 7 = 13$	Given.
$2x = 20$	Add 7 to both sides.
$x = 10$	Divide both sides by 2.

c.
$41 = \dfrac{x}{2} - 7$	Given.
$48 = \dfrac{x}{2}$	Add 7 to both sides.
$96 = x$	Multiply both sides by 2.

d.
$-4 = \dfrac{x}{3} + 2$	Given.
$-6 = \dfrac{x}{3}$	Subtract 2 from both sides.
$-18 = x$	Multiply both sides by 3.

Sometimes you need to solve equations with the variable on both sides of the equal sign. In such cases, use equation properties to get the variable *on one side only*.

EXAMPLE 4 **Solving equations with a variable on both sides**

Solve each equation.

a. $4x + 3 = 3x + 8$ **b.** $2x - 4 = 5x + 2$

Solution

a. $4x + 3 = 3x + 8$ Given.

$x + 3 = 8$ Subtract 3x from both sides.

$x = 5$ Subtract 3 from both sides.

b. $2x - 4 = 5x + 2$ Given.

$-4 = 3x + 2$ Subtract 2x from both sides.

$-6 = 3x$ Subtract 2 from both sides.

$-2 = x$ Divide both sides by 3.

The last example illustrates equation solving with parentheses and algebraic simplification.

EXAMPLE 5 **Solving equations with parentheses**

Solve $3(x - 5) = 4(x + 2)$.

Solution $3(x - 5) = 4(x + 2)$ Given.

$3x - 15 = 4x + 8$ Distributive property

$-15 = x + 8$ Subtract 3x from both sides.

$-23 = x$ Subtract 8 from both sides.

PROBLEM SET (3.5)

ESSENTIAL IDEAS   LEVEL 1

Simplify the expressions in Problems 1–8. Note that these are not equations.

1. a. $3x + 2x$ **5x**   **b.** $5y + 2y$ **7y**

2. a. $9x - 5x$ **4x**   **b.** $12y - 5y$ **7y**

3. a. $y + 8 - 8$ **y**   **b.** $3x - 10 + 10$ **3x**

4. a. $6 - x + x$ **6**   **b.** $2x - 10 - 2x$ **−10**

5. a. $x - y - x$ **−y**   **b.** $10x - 5 - 10x$ **−5**

6. a. $10 - x + x$ **10**   **b.** $6 - x - 6$ **−x**

7. a. $3x + 5 + x - 5$ **4x**

  b. $9x + 8 - 2x - 8$ **7x**

8. a. $5x + 8 - 3x - 8$ **2x**

  b. $5 - 2x + 6 + 2x$ **11**

 9. IN YOUR OWN WORDS Present a procedure for solving simple equations.

10. IN YOUR OWN WORDS Explain the steps in solving $-x = -5$.

DRILL AND PRACTICE   LEVEL 2

Solve the equations in Problems 11–18. Show all your work and be sure to keep the equal signs aligned.

11. a. $2x + 1 = 9$ **4**   **b.** $3x + 4 = 19$ **5**

12. a. $5x + 7 = 47$ **8**   **b.** $4y - 3 = 77$ **20**

13. a. $\dfrac{z}{5} + 3 = 4$ **5**   **b.** $\dfrac{z}{3} + 1 = 0$ **−3**

14. a. $\dfrac{w}{-4} - 7 = 6$ **−52**   **b.** $\dfrac{w}{3} - 19 = 47$ **198**

15. a. $-s - 5 = 14$ **−19**   **b.** $-s - 7 = 10$ **−17**

16. a. $4 + (-u) = 17$ **−13**   **b.** $3 + (-s) = 15$ **−12**

17. a. $17 + (-s) = 21$ **−4**   **b.** $4 - s = 17$ **−13**

18. a. $3 - s = 15$ **−12**   **b.** $18 - s = 31$ **−13**

Solve the equations in Problems 19–25. Show all your work and be sure to keep the equal signs aligned. Notice that the variables here are capital letters. In algebra, lowercase and capital letters may have different values, so be careful that you write these variables as capital letters on your paper.

19. a. $3A + 7 = 49$ **14**   **b.** $2B + 5 = 65$ **30**

  c. $3C - 8 = 115$ **41**   **d.** $2D - 10 = 52$ **31**

20. a. $\dfrac{E}{7} + 12 = 12$ **0**   **b.** $\dfrac{F}{5} - 12 = 53$ **325**

  c. $9 = \dfrac{G}{2} + 5$ **8**   **d.** $-8 = \dfrac{H}{6} - 3$ **−30**

21. a. $4 + 3I = 67$ **21**   **b.** $2 - 5J = 62$ **−12**

  c. $\dfrac{K}{7} - 10 = 0$ **70**   **d.** $\dfrac{L}{12} + 4 = -3$ **−84**

22. a. $-M = 14$ **−14**   **b.** $6 + \dfrac{N}{2} = -10$ **−32**

  c. $-P + 5 = -12$ **17**   **d.** $7 + (-Q) = 15$ **22**

23. a. $8 - R = 5$ **3**   **b.** $5 - S = 10$ **−5**

  c. $10 - T = -5$ **15**   **d.** $4 - 2U = 8$ **−2**

24. a. $7 - 3V = 10$ **−1**   **b.** $6 - 5W = 26$ **−4**

  c. $1 - 5X = 126$ **−25**   **d.** $12 - 21Y = 75$ **−3**

25. $3(Z - 43) = 5(Z - 77)$ **128**

26. This problem will help you check your work in Problems 19–25. Fill in the capital letters from Problems 19–25 to correspond with their numerical values shown in the blanks. (The letter O has been filled in for you.) Some letters may not appear in the boxes. When you finish putting letters in the boxes, darken all the blank spaces to separate the words in the message.

Tergiversation

21	−8	−30	O	17	0	1	−3	O	−2	4
14	3	0	4	325	21	−32	31	21	−32	8
35	15	−30	21	−5	5	0	14	−5	−3	−15
14	−32	31	7	14	3	0	24	2	12	12
−84	0	14	3	−32	21	−32	8	−15	2	2
−14	14	15	−30	0	−14	14	15	21	41	−5

I_HOPE_YOU_ARE_FINDING_THIS_EASY_
AND_ARE _ _ _ _ LEARNING _ _ _
MATHEMATICS

Solve the equations in Problems 27–39. Show all your work and be sure to keep the equal signs aligned.

27. a. $2x + 3 = x + 5$ **2**

  b. $4x - 7 = 3x + 2$ **9**

28. a. $3x + 4 = 4x - 5$ **9**

  b. $2x + 1 = 3x + 8$ **−7**

29. a. $4x - 11 = 3x + 2$ **13**

  b. $6x + 4 = 7x - 3$ **7**

30. a. $3x + 2 = x + 6$ **2**

  b. $5x - 8 = 3x + 2$ **5**

31. a. $4x - 3 = 2x + 1$ **2**

  b. $5x - 6 = 2x + 3$ **3**

32. a. $6x - 2 = 3x - 11$ **−3**

  b. $5x - 3 = 7x + 5$ **−4**

33. a. $3x + 4 = 5x - 6$ **5**

  b. $2x - 3 = 4x - 1$ **−1**

34. a. $2(x - 5) = 3x + 2$ **−12**

  b. $6x - 5 = 5(x - 1)$ **0**

35. a. $3(x - 8) = 7x + 4$ **−7**

  b. $9x + 1 = 5(x - 3)$ **−4**

36. a. $5(x + 1) = 4(x - 1)$ **−9**

  b. $3(x - 2) = 2(x + 5)$ **16**

37. a. $4(x + 1) = 2(x - 1)$ **−3**

  b. $5(x - 3) = 3(x + 8) + 1$ **20**

38. a. $189(x - 2) = 4(x + 1) - 12$ **2**

  b. $9(x - 3) - 6 = 2(x + 1)$ **5**

39. a. $2(x + 1) + 1 = 1 - 2(x - 3)$ **1**

  b. $2 - 3(x - 1) = 4 - 2(x - 3)$ **−5**

40. IN YOUR OWN WORDS When solving $5x + 3 = 5$, as a first step, would you subtract 3 or 5 from both sides? Explain.

41. IN YOUR OWN WORDS When solving $\frac{x}{4} + 5 = 3$, as a first step, would you multiply both sides by 4 or subtract 5 from both sides? Explain.

42. IN YOUR OWN WORDS Explain the steps in solving $5x - 4 = 24$.

43. IN YOUR OWN WORDS Explain the steps in solving $\frac{x}{3} + 1 = 5$.

44. IN YOUR OWN WORDS Explain the steps in solving $x + 5 = 3x - 1$.

APPLICATIONS   LEVEL 2

Currency exchange rates fluctuate daily, but we will use Table 3.1 as the foreign currency exchange rate. To convert from a foreign currency into dollars, use the following equation:

$$\left(\begin{array}{c}\text{NUMBER OF}\\\text{U.S. DOLLARS}\end{array}\right)\left(\begin{array}{c}\text{EXCHANGE}\\\text{RATE}\end{array}\right) = \left(\begin{array}{c}\text{AMOUNT OF FOREIGN}\\\text{CURRENCY}\end{array}\right)$$

TABLE 3.1   Currency Exchange Rates*

Country	Currency	Rate
Australia	Dollar	1.31580
Britain	Pound	0.53273
Canada	Dollar	1.12482
European Union	Euro	0.79424
Japan	Yen	119.115
Mexico	Peso	10.7970
Switzerland	Franc	1.26483

*Conversion rates on October 25, 2006.

For example, if a ring costs 300 Euros in Germany, the equivalent amount in U.S. dollars is found as follows:

↓ From Table 3.1 (use local currency)

$$\left(\begin{array}{c}\text{NUMBER OF}\\\text{U.S. DOLLARS}\end{array}\right)(0.79424) = 300$$

$$\left(\begin{array}{c}\text{NUMBER OF}\\\text{U.S. DOLLARS}\end{array}\right) = 377.72$$

Divide both sides by 0.79434 (by calculator)

The ring costs $377.72 in U.S. dollars. Note that when working with money we round to the nearest cent.

Find the values of the items in Problems 45–52 expressed in U.S. dollars, assuming the given prices are in local currency.

45. A dinner in a Canadian restaurant is $15.00.   **$13.34**

46. A sweater sells for $125 in Canada.   **$111.13**

47. A hotel room in Mexico is 520 pesos.   **$48.16**

48. A prize tulip bulb in Holland (The Netherlands) is selling for €8.   **$10.07**

49. A German Black Forest clock is selling for €435.   **$547.69**

50. A set of bone china in England is £346.   **$649.48**

51. A tray in an Italian store is marked €24.   **$30.22**

52. One admission to EuroDisney is €49.   **$61.69**

RIGHT OR WRONG?   LEVEL 3

Explain what is wrong, if anything, with the statements in Problems 53–56. Explain your reasoning.

53. The best first step in solving $4x + 3 = 15$ is to divide both sides by 4.   **F; subtract 3 from both sides.**

54. The best first step in solving $2x - 5 = -4$ is to divide both sides by 2.   **F; add 5 to both sides.**

55. The best first step in solving $\frac{x}{3} + 5 = 2$ is to multiply both sides by 3.   **F; subtract 5 from both sides.**

56. The best first step in solving $\frac{x}{5} - 3 = 10$ is to multiply both sides by 5.   **F; add 3 to both sides.**

Solve the equations in Problems 57–60.

57. $2x + 5 = x - 10$

$x + 5 = -10$

$x = -5$ **F; subtract 5 from both sides; solution is $x = -15$.**

58. $3x + 4 = x - 8$

$4x + 4 = -8$

$4x = -12$

$x = -3$ **F; subtract x from both sides; solution is $x = -6$.**

59. $1 - x = 8$

$-x = 7$ **F; not finished, should be $x = -7$.**

60. $\frac{x}{3} + 5 = 6$

$x + 5 = 18$ **F; $x + 15 = 18$ or $\frac{x}{3} = 1$ (if you mult. both**

$x = 13$ **sides by 3); better to subtract 5 from both sides to obtain $\frac{x}{3} = 1$ or $x = 3$.**

3.6 Problem Solving with Algebra

IN THIS WORLD THE POWER OF MATH

Lauren Resnick (right) recognized at the SEEK-16 National Summit on Strategies for Engineering, Feb. 2005.

"We need to teach the students to be good problem solvers. Dr. Resnick, how do you think this can best be achieved?"

"Good problem solvers do not rush in to apply a formula or an equation," answered Dr. Resnick. *"Instead, they try to understand the problem situation; they consider alternative representations and relations among variables."*

"Agreed! But how do the students know when they are finished with the problem-solving process?"

"Only when satisfied that they understand the situation and all the variables in a qualitative way do they start to apply the quantification," continued Dr. Resnick.*

In this section, we look at using variables and algebra to work real-life problems—in other words, using the *power of math* IN THIS WORLD.

 See Problem 1.

Our goal in applying algebra to problem solving is to find solutions to a wide variety of problems. In the last two sections, you've seen techniques for solving equations. In this section, we'll introduce a *technique for solving problems.* Eventually, you want to be able to solve applied problems to obtain *answers;* but when beginning, we must start with simple problems—ones for which the answers are obvious or trivial. You must, therefore, keep in mind that we are seeking not answers in this section, but a strategy for attacking word problems. You should also pay particular attention to the way we translate from the words of the problem to the symbols of algebra, which leads to the use of algebraic variables.

We begin by considering an equation with more than one variable. An equation with more than one variable is called a **literal equation.** When working with literal equations, we carry out the same steps that were explained in the last section, except that we treat one variable as the unknown and the other variables as known quantities. To **solve** a literal equation for one of the variables means to write the equation in an equivalent form with the requested variable isolated on one side of the equation.

EXAMPLE 1

Solving a literal equation

Solve the equation $P = S - C$ for C.

Solution Since we are solving for C, we treat C as the unknown and the other variables as known quantities. This means that we wish to isolate C on one side.

*Adapted from an address by Lauren B. Resnick, National Convocation of Precollege Education in Mathematics, National Academy of Sciences and National Academy of Engineering, Washington, D.C., May 1982. (Quoted in *Science,* Vol. 220, No. 4596, April 26, 1983, p. 29.)

$$P = S - C \qquad \text{Given equation}$$
$$P + C = S - C + C \qquad \text{Add } C \text{ to both sides.}$$
$$P + C = S \qquad \text{Simplify.}$$
$$C = S - P \qquad \text{Subtract } P \text{ from both sides.}$$

Literal equations are often given as **formulas,** where each of the variables has a specific meaning. In Example 1, the given literal equation is sometimes remembered as the **profit formula,** where P represents the profit, S represents the selling price (or revenue), and C the cost (or overhead). Another example of a literal equation is the Pythagorean theorem, which we stated in Section 2.6: If $a^2 + b^2 = c^2$, then

$$a^2 = c^2 - b^2 \qquad \text{Subtract } b^2 \text{ from both sides.}$$

and

$$b^2 = c^2 - a^2 \qquad \text{Subtract } a^2 \text{ from both sides.}$$

EXAMPLE 2   **Solving a literal equation**

Stand firm in your refusal to remain conscious during algebra. In real life, I assure you, there is no such thing as algebra.

Solve the equation $2x + 3y - 6 = 0$ for y.

Solution
$$2x + 3y - 6 = 0 \qquad \text{Given equation}$$
$$2x + 3y = 6 \qquad \text{Add 6 to both sides.}$$
$$3y = -2x + 6 \qquad \text{Subtract 2x from both sides.}$$
$$y = \frac{-2}{3}x + 2 \qquad \text{Divide both sides by 3.}$$

When confronted with a word problem, many people begin by looking at the last sentence to see what is being asked for, declare that this quantity is the unknown, and then proceed to read the problem backward to come up with an equation. This procedure complicates the thinking process and can be frustrating. Instead, we begin with the problem as stated, using as many unknowns as we wish with our initial statement. We then let this relationship *evolve* until we have a statement with a single unknown. At *this* point, a variable is chosen as a natural result of the thinking process, and the resulting equation can be solved.

The first type of problem involves number relationships.

EXAMPLE 3   **Number problem**

If you add twelve to twice a number, the result is six. What is the number?

Solution

Step 1   Read the problem carefully. Make sure you know what is given and what is wanted.

Step 2   Write a verbal description of the problem using operations signs and an equal sign, but still using key words.

$$2(\text{A NUMBER}) + 12 = 6$$

Step 3   If there is a single unknown, choose a variable.

$$\text{Let} \quad n = \text{A NUMBER}$$

Step 4   Replace the verbal phrase by the variable. This is called **substitution.**

$$2n + 12 = 6$$

Step 5 Solve the equation and check the solution in the original problem to see whether it makes sense.

$$2n + 12 = 6$$
$$2n = -6 \quad \text{Subtract 12 from both sides.}$$
$$n = -3 \quad \text{Divide both sides by 2.}$$

Check: Add 12 to twice -3 and the result is 6.

Step 6 State the solution to the word problem in words: *The number is* -3.   ●

Notice that we illustrated a *procedure* with this example. We now give a summary of this procedure before we consider more examples.

Problem Solving

> The procedure for solving word problems is summarized by the following steps.
>
> **Step 1** **Read the problem.** Note what it is all about. Focus on processes rather than numbers. You can't work a problem you don't understand.
>
> **Step 2** **Restate the problem.** Write a verbal description of the problem using operations signs and an equal sign. Look for equality. If you can't find equal quantities, you will never formulate an equation.
>
> **Step 3** **Choose a variable.** If there is a single unknown, choose a variable.
>
> **Step 4** **Substitute.** Replace the verbal phrases by known numbers and by the variable.
>
> **Step 5** **Solve the equation.** This is the easy step. Be sure your answer makes sense by checking it with the original question in the problem. Use estimation to eliminate unreasonable answers.
>
> **Step 6** **State the answer.** There were no variables defined when you started, so $x = 3$ is not an answer. Pay attention to units of measure and other details of the problem. Remember to answer the question that was asked.

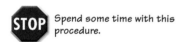 **STOP** Spend some time with this procedure.

The second type of problem involves consecutive numbers. If $n = $ A NUMBER, then

$$\text{THE NEXT CONSECUTIVE NUMBER} = n + 1$$
$$\text{THE THIRD CONSECUTIVE NUMBER} = n + 2$$

Also, if $E = $ AN EVEN NUMBER, then

$$E + 2 = \text{THE NEXT CONSECUTIVE EVEN NUMBER}$$

and if $F = $ AN ODD NUMBER, then

$$F + 2 = \text{THE NEXT CONSECUTIVE ODD NUMBER}$$

EXAMPLE 4   **Consecutive integer problem**

Find two consecutive even integers whose sum is 34.

Solution

Step 1 Read the problem.

Step 2 Write a verbal description of the problem, using operations signs and an equal sign. **Do not attempt to skip this step.**

$$\text{EVEN INTEGER} + \text{NEXT EVEN INTEGER} = \text{SUM}$$

Step 3 Choose a variable.

$$\text{Let} \quad E = \text{EVEN INTEGER}$$
$$E + 2 = \text{NEXT EVEN INTEGER}$$

Step 4 Substitute the variable into the verbal equation; also substitute known or given numbers (such as SUM is 34).

$$E + (E + 2) = 34$$

Step 5 Solve the equation.

$$2E + 2 = 34$$
$$2E = 32 \qquad \text{Simplify (combine terms).}$$
$$E = 16 \qquad \text{Divide both sides by 2.}$$

Thus, $E + 2 = 18$.

Step 6 State the solution to the word problem in words: The even integers are 16 and 18. ●

Examples 3 and 4 are good problems to help you learn the *procedure* for working with word problems, but the ultimate goal of problem solving is to work applied problems. One of the most common applications that we can consider at this point deals with the gasoline mileage of your car. The gasoline consumption of a car is measured in *miles per gallon* (mpg), and is related to the distance traveled by the following formula:

$$\begin{pmatrix} \text{MILES PER} \\ \text{GALLON} \end{pmatrix} \times \begin{pmatrix} \text{NUMBER OF} \\ \text{GALLONS} \end{pmatrix} = \begin{pmatrix} \text{DISTANCE} \\ \text{TRAVELED} \end{pmatrix}$$

Examples 5 and 6 illustrate how you might use this formula.

EXAMPLE 5　　　　　**Applied problem: MPG**

336	441
Miles per tankful Estimated city driving range EPA estimated MPG ⑯ CITY	Miles per tankful Estimated highway driving range EPA estimated 21 HIGHWAY

Example 5 uses the city mileage. You might show that you obtain the same answers if you use the highway mileage.

An advertisement for an Oldsmobile had the information shown. What is the size of the tank?

Solution

Step 1 Do you understand the question? Can you rephrase it in your own words?

Step 2 $\begin{pmatrix} \text{MILES PER} \\ \text{GALLON} \end{pmatrix} \times \begin{pmatrix} \text{NUMBER OF} \\ \text{GALLONS} \end{pmatrix} = \begin{pmatrix} \text{DISTANCE} \\ \text{TRAVELED} \end{pmatrix}$

Step 3 Let $g = $ NUMBER OF GALLONS.

Step 4 Substitute:

$$\begin{pmatrix} \text{MILES PER} \\ \text{GALLON} \end{pmatrix} \times \begin{pmatrix} \text{NUMBER OF} \\ \text{GALLONS} \end{pmatrix} = \begin{pmatrix} \text{DISTANCE} \\ \text{TRAVELED} \end{pmatrix}$$
$$\updownarrow \qquad\qquad\qquad\qquad\qquad \updownarrow$$
$$16 \quad \times \begin{pmatrix} \text{NUMBER OF} \\ \text{GALLONS} \end{pmatrix} = \quad 336$$
$$16g = 336$$

Step 5 $\qquad\qquad\qquad\qquad\qquad g = 21 \qquad \text{Divide both sides by 16.}$

Step 6 The car has a 21-gallon tank. ●

EXAMPLE 6   **Applied problem: MPG**

Suppose you take a trip in your car. At the beginning of the trip, the odometer reads 13,689.4, and at the end of the trip it reads 15,274.9. You used a total of 46.2 gallons of gasoline for the trip. What gas mileage (to the nearest $\frac{1}{10}$ gallon) did you get on this trip?

Solution   Divide both sides of the given MPG formula to solve for *miles per gallon:*

$$\begin{pmatrix} \text{MILES PER} \\ \text{GALLON} \end{pmatrix} \times \begin{pmatrix} \text{NUMBER OF} \\ \text{GALLONS} \end{pmatrix} = \begin{pmatrix} \text{DISTANCE} \\ \text{TRAVELED} \end{pmatrix}$$

Divide both sides by NUMBER OF GALLONS:

$$\begin{pmatrix} \text{MILES PER} \\ \text{GALLON} \end{pmatrix} = \frac{\text{DISTANCE TRAVELED}}{\text{NUMBER OF GALLONS}}$$

$$= \frac{1,585.5}{46.2} \quad \leftarrow \text{This is found by subtraction.}$$

$$\approx 34.318\ldots$$

To the nearest $\frac{1}{10}$, this number is 34.3. Thus, the car averaged 34.3 mpg for the trip.

Another application that requires problem-solving ability involves determining the best price for an item in a grocery store. Consider Example 7.

EXAMPLE 7   **Applied problem: price comparison**

Three prices for dog food are mentioned in the cartoon. What are the prices per can for the three types of dog food (assuming that all the cans are the same size)? If the boy buys 10 cans, what does he save by buying the least expensive as compared to the most expensive?

Solution $\begin{pmatrix} \text{NUMBER OF} \\ \text{CANS} \end{pmatrix} \begin{pmatrix} \text{PRICE PER} \\ \text{CAN} \end{pmatrix} = \begin{pmatrix} \text{TOTAL} \\ \text{COST} \end{pmatrix}$

Apply this general formula for each of the dog foods. Let a, b, and c be the prices per can for the three brands, respectively.

First Brand	*Second Brand*	*Third Brand*
$3\left(\begin{array}{c}\text{PRICE PER}\\\text{CAN}\end{array}\right) = 78$	$2\left(\begin{array}{c}\text{PRICE PER}\\\text{CAN}\end{array}\right) = 68$	$10\left(\begin{array}{c}\text{PRICE PER}\\\text{CAN}\end{array}\right) = 254$
$\updownarrow$	$\updownarrow$	$\updownarrow$
$3a \quad = 78$	$2b \quad = 68$	$10c \quad = 254$
$a = 26$	$b = 34$	$c = 25.4$

Notice that we worked in pennies (this is often easier than working in dollars). The third dog food is the cheapest.

$$\text{SAVINGS} = \left(\begin{array}{c}\text{TOTAL COST}\\\text{OF MOST}\\\text{EXPENSIVE}\end{array}\right) - \left(\begin{array}{c}\text{TOTAL COST}\\\text{OF LEAST}\\\text{EXPENSIVE}\end{array}\right)$$

$$= \left(\begin{array}{c}\text{NO. OF CANS}\\\text{OF MOST}\\\text{EXPENSIVE}\end{array}\right)\left(\begin{array}{c}\text{COST PER}\\\text{CAN OF MOST}\\\text{EXPENSIVE}\end{array}\right) - \left(\begin{array}{c}\text{NO. OF CANS}\\\text{OF LEAST}\\\text{EXPENSIVE}\end{array}\right)\left(\begin{array}{c}\text{COST PER}\\\text{CAN OF LEAST}\\\text{EXPENSIVE}\end{array}\right)$$

$$\qquad \updownarrow \qquad\qquad \updownarrow \qquad\qquad \updownarrow \qquad\qquad \updownarrow$$

$$= \quad (10) \qquad (34) \quad - \quad (10) \qquad (25.4)$$

$$= 340 - 254$$

$$= 86$$

The savings is $0.86.

The final example will test your problem-solving ability in a new setting to see whether you can use the techniques in a situation that is not exactly like one of the given types of problems. You will begin to be able to accomplish problem solving only when you begin to use it in a wide variety of contexts.

EXAMPLE 8

Applied problem

A dispatcher must see that 75,000 condensers are delivered immediately. He has two sizes of trucks: one will carry 15,000 condensers, the other will carry 12,000 condensers. How many smaller trucks are necessary if the dispatcher is required by union contract to use two of the larger trucks for this order?

Solution

$$\left(\begin{array}{c}\text{AMOUNT DELIVERED}\\\text{BY LARGER TRUCKS}\end{array}\right) + \left(\begin{array}{c}\text{AMOUNT DELIVERED}\\\text{BY SMALLER TRUCKS}\end{array}\right) = \left(\begin{array}{c}\text{TOTAL}\\\text{AMOUNT}\\\text{DELIVERED}\end{array}\right)$$

$$\swarrow \searrow \qquad\qquad \swarrow \searrow \qquad\qquad \updownarrow$$

$$\left(\begin{array}{c}\text{NO. OF}\\\text{LG. TRUCKS}\end{array}\right)\left(\begin{array}{c}\text{CAPACITY OF}\\\text{LG. TRUCKS}\end{array}\right) + \left(\begin{array}{c}\text{NO. OF SM.}\\\text{TRUCKS}\end{array}\right)\left(\begin{array}{c}\text{CAPACITY OF}\\\text{SM. TRUCKS}\end{array}\right) = 75{,}000$$

$$\updownarrow \qquad\qquad \updownarrow \qquad\qquad \updownarrow \qquad\qquad \updownarrow$$

$$2 \qquad (15{,}000) + \left(\begin{array}{c}\text{NO. OF SM.}\\\text{TRUCKS}\end{array}\right) (12{,}000) = 75{,}000$$

"Great scott! You got the order backwards! We wanted twenty 75,000-microfared condensers!"

Let n = NUMBER OF SMALLER TRUCKS.

$$2(15,000) + n(12,000) = 75,000$$
$$30,000 + 12,000n = 75,000$$
$$12,000n = 45,000$$
$$n = 3.75$$

Notice that the solution of the equation is not necessarily the answer to the problem. You must interpret this solution to answer the question that was asked. The dispatcher will need to send 4 smaller trucks.

Example 8 illustrates a key ingredient in problem solving. Look at your answers to make sure of the following:

1. **They are possible.** In Example 8, it is impossible to send 3.75 trucks. If a question asks how many people can get onto an elevator and you obtain the answer $25\frac{1}{4}$, you know that answer is not possible and must be rounded.

2. **They answer the question that is asked.**

3. **They are reasonable;** that is, make some estimation in your own mind about what the answer should be before you begin. For example, in Example 5, we asked for the size of the gas tank on an Oldsmobile. If the answer to your arithmetic had turned out to be 210 gallons or 2 gallons, you would know that these answers are not reasonable and you would begin looking for some error in your calculations. Problems 3–12 ask you to practice your estimation skills.

PROBLEM SET 3.6

ESSENTIAL IDEAS   LEVEL 1

1. **IN YOUR OWN WORDS** Explain the procedure for problem solving.

2. If E is an even integer, what is the next consecutive even integer?   **E + 2**

DRILL AND PRACTICE   LEVEL 2

Estimate answers for Problems 3–12 by choosing the most reasonable answer. You should not do any pencil-and-paper or calculator arithmetic for these problems.

3. Estimate the gas mileage you might obtain with a compact car.   **A**

   A. 28 mpg   B. 89 mpg   C. 12 mpg

4. Estimate the distance you might be able to drive on a full tank of gas.   **B**

   A. 50 mi   B. 250 mi   C. 850 mi

5. Estimate the price of a 12-oz can of corn.

   A. $0.25   B. $0.89   C. $1.49   **B**

6. Estimate the price of a twelve-pack of cola.

   A. $0.75   B. $3.49   C. $7.50   **B**

7. Estimate the price of dinner for two at an elegant restaurant.   **B**

   A. $12.00   B. $80.00   C. $350.00

8. Estimate the average price of a new home.   **B**

   A. $25,000   B. $165,000   C. $650,000

9. Estimate the average monthly rent for an apartment.   **B**

   A. $225   B. $550   C. $4,250

10. Estimate the starting wage for a new college graduate.   **B**

    A. $6.00/hr   B. $20.00/hr   C. $80.00/hr

11. If you add three consecutive numbers and the sum is 600, estimate the size of the first of the three numbers you are adding.   **C**

    A. 20   B. 50   C. 200

12. If you add two consecutive even numbers and the sum is 214, estimate the product of the numbers.   **C**

    A. 100   B. 200   C. 10,000

In Problems 13–30, *solve for the variable that is capitalized.*
Assume that none of the variables is 0.

13. $a + B = c$ $B = c - a$

14. $c = d + E$ $E = c - d$

15. $X - y = 5$ $X = y + 5$

16. $x - Y = 5$ $Y = x - 5$

17. $X - 2y = 7$ $X = 2y + 7$

18. $2x - Y = 7$ $Y = 2x - 7$

19. $i = Prt$ $P = \frac{i}{rt}$

20. $x = 5Yz$ $Y = \frac{x}{5z}$

21. $3x - Y + 2 = 0$ $Y = 3x + 2$

22. $5x - Y - 4 = 0$ $Y = 5x - 4$

23. $6x + Y - 5 = 0$ $Y = -6x + 5$

24. $2x + Y + 8 = 0$ $Y = -2x - 8$

25. $3x + 2Y + 4 = 0$ $Y = \frac{-3}{2}x - 2$

26. $5x + 3Y - 9 = 0$ $Y = \frac{-5}{3}x + 3$

27. $3x - 2Y + 4 = 0$ $Y = \frac{3}{2}x + 2$

28. $5x - 3Y - 9 = 0$ $Y = \frac{5}{3}x - 3$

29. $p = 2\ell + 2W$ $W = \frac{1}{2}p - \ell$ or $W = \frac{p-2\ell}{2}$

30. $p = 2L + 2w$ $L = \frac{1}{2}p - w$ or $L = \frac{p-2w}{2}$

APPLICATIONS   LEVEL 2

Solve Problems 31–43. *Because you are practicing a*
procedure, you must show all your work.
Note: Answers alone are NOT sufficient.

31. If you subtract 12 from twice a number, the result is 6. What is the number?   9

32. If you add 15 to twice a number, the result is 7. What is the number?   −4

33. If you subtract 9 from three times a number, the result is 0. What is the number?   3

34. If you multiply a number by 5 and then subtract −10, the difference is −30. What is the number?   −8

35. If you multiply a number by 4 and then subtract −4, the result is 0. What is the number?   −1

36. The sum of a number and 24 is equal to four times the number. What is the number?   8

37. The sum of 6 and twice a number is equal to four times the number. What is the number?   3

38. If 12 is subtracted from twice a number, the difference is four times the number. What is the number?   −6

39. If 6 is subtracted from three times a number, the difference is twice the number. What is the number?   6

40. Find two consecutive numbers whose sum is 117.   58, 59

41. Find two consecutive even numbers whose sum is 94.   46, 48

42. The Nissan Sentra sedan has an estimated MPG of 35, with a cruising range of 455 miles. What is the size of the tank?   13 gallons

43. The Rolls-Royce Silver Shadow I has an estimated MPG of 9, with a cruising range of 234 miles. What is the size of the tank?   26 gallons

© Ron Kimball Studios

Find the miles per gallon in Problems 44–51 *to the nearest*
tenth of a gallon. First estimate an answer; then calculate.

	Odometer Start	Odometer Finish	Gallons Used	
44.	02316	02480	13.4	12.2
	150 mi/15 gal ≈ 10 MPG			
45.	47341	47576	17.3	13.6
	200 mi/15 gal ≈ 13 MPG			
46.	19715	19932	9.2	23.6
	200 mi/10 gal ≈ 20 MPG			
47.	13719	14067	11.1	31.4
	350 mi/10 gal ≈ 35 MPG			
48.	21812	22174	8.7	41.6
	350 mi/10 gal ≈ 35 MPG			
49.	16975	17152	18.6	9.5
	200 mi/20 gal ≈ 10 MPG			
50.	23485	24433	48.4	19.6
	1,000 mi/50 gal ≈ 20 MPG			
51.	08271.6	10373.0	53.2	39.5
	2,000 mi/50 gal ≈ 40 MPG			

52. Libby's green beans cost $0.79 for 15 ounces and Diet Delight green beans cost $0.49 for 5 ounces. Which is the better buy, and by how much, rounded to the nearest $\frac{1}{10}$ cent?
Libby's is about 4.5¢/oz less expensive than Diet Delight.

53. Del Monte asparagus spears sell for $1.39 for 8 oz, and Green Giant asparagus spears cost $1.99 for 12 oz. Which is the better buy, and by how much, rounded to the nearest $\frac{1}{10}$ cent?
Green Giant asparagus spears are about 0.8¢/oz less expensive.

54. Palmolive liquid detergent is $3.99 for a 64-oz bottle, and $1.59 for a 22-oz bottle. Which is the better buy, and by how much, rounded to the nearest cent?
The 64 oz is the better buy; it is about $0.01 per ounce less.

55. An eight-pack of AA Duracell batteries is $8.09 and a four-pack is $3.79. Which is the better buy, and by how much, rounded to the nearest cent?
The 4-pack is the better buy, and is about $0.06/battery less.

56. Yuban coffee is $3.69 for a 12-oz size (reg) and $8.79 for a 24-oz size (decaf). What is the better buy, and by how much, rounded to the nearest cent?
The 12-oz reg coffee is the better buy, by $0.06 per ounce.

57. A box of Total cereal is $5.09 for 1 lb 2 oz, and $3.49 for the 12-oz size. Which box is less expensive, and by how much, rounded to the nearest tenth of a cent?
The 1-lb 2-oz = 18-oz box is $0.008 per ounce less expensive.

58. A cabinet shop produces two types of custom-made cabinets for a customer. If one cabinet costs four times as much as the other, and if the total price for both cabinets is $6,225, how much does each cabinet cost? *$1,245 and $4,980*

59. A house and a lot together are appraised at $216,000. If the house is worth five times the value of the lot, how much is the lot worth? *The value of the lot is $36,000.*

60. There are three grades of flooring adhesive. The first costs twice as much as the second, and the second costs three times as much as the third. If you purchase one of each, the cost is $45. How much is the most expensive adhesive? *$27.00*

3.7) Inequalities

IN THIS WORLD THE POWER OF MATH

Ancient Inequalities Found in Pompeii

"The rich got richer and the poor got poorer in ancient Pompeii," said Dr. Richard Jones from the University of Bradford's Department of Archaeological Sciences.

"Look at our team!" shouted Audrey. "How many similarities and differences can you find in the picture at the left?"

"Wait, Audrey. I'm trying to teach you something about ancient Pompeii, but you keep changing the subject," said Jones. "Look at the ruins; the rich used fountains and swimming pools to show off their wealth, but you are talking about shirt color. Let's take a break and see if this has anything to do with mathematical inequalities."

  See Problem 2.

The techniques of the previous sections can be applied to quantities that are not equal. If we are given any two numbers x and y, then either $x = y$ or $x \neq y$.

If $x \neq y$, then either $x < y$ or $x > y$. We call this the **comparison property.***

Comparison Property

For any two numbers x and y, exactly one of the following is true:
1. $x = y$; x is equal to (the same as) y
2. $x > y$; x is greater than (bigger than) y
3. $x < y$; x is less than (smaller than) y

*Sometimes this is called the trichotomy property.

This means that if two quantities are not exactly equal, we can relate them with a greater-than or a less-than symbol (called an **inequality symbol**). For the inequality

$$x < 3$$

there is more than one replacement for the variable that makes this statement true. In fact, we cannot even list all the numbers that make it true, because it is very impractical to write, "The answers are 2, 1, -110, 0, $2\frac{1}{2}$, 2.99, ..." Instead, we relate the answer to a number line, as shown in Figure 3.2. The fact that 3 is not included (since 3 is not less than 3), is indicated by an open circle at the point 3, as shown.

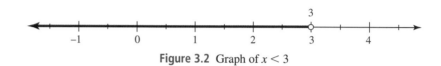

Figure 3.2 Graph of $x < 3$

If we want to include the endpoint $x = 3$ with the inequality $x < 3$, we write $x \le 3$ and say "x is less than or equal to 3." We define two additional inequality symbols:

$$x \ge y \quad \text{means} \quad x > y \text{ or } x = y$$
$$x \le y \quad \text{means} \quad x < y \text{ or } x = y$$

Our language translates inequalities in many ways, and the following list gives some of the more common translations:

Symbols	Comment	Translations	
$x > y$ or $y < x$	These symbolic statements have the same meaning.	x is greater than y x is bigger than y x is larger than y x is more than y	y is smaller than x y is less than x x is to right of y y is to the left of x
$x \ge y$ or $y \le x$	These symbolic statements have the same meaning.	x is greater than or equal to y x is bigger than or equal to y x is at least y	y is smaller than or equal to x y is less than or equal to x y is not more than x
$x > 0$		x is greater than 0 x is positive x is to the right of the origin	
$x \ge 0$		x is greater than or equal to 0 x is nonnegative x is not negative	
$x < 0$		x is less than 0 x is negative x is to the left of the origin	
$x \le 0$		x is less than or equal to 0 x is nonpositive x is not positive	

Karl Smith library

Karl Friedrich Gauss
(1777–1855)

Karl Smith library

Archimedes
(287–212 B.C.)

T he five most famous people in the history of mathematics include Karl Gauss, whose work has influenced almost every branch of mathematics. Gauss joked that he knew how to reckon before he could talk. He graduated from college at 15 and had his doctorate at 22. The next three are Leonhard Euler (1707–1783), who is known as one of the most prolific mathematicians in history; Isaac Newton (1642–1723), who entered the university when he was 18 and invented the calculus when the university closed for a year because of the bubonic plague; and Gottfried Leibniz (1646–1716), who is also credited with inventing the calculus and an early calculating machine, and at the age of 14 attempted to reform mathematics. The fifth person who is part of this distinguished company is the greatest mathematician of antiquity, Archimedes (287–212 B.C.). He developed many of our formulas for area and volume, calculated an approximation for π, found centers of gravity, invented engines and catapults, and formulated principles of levers. He was, in every sense of the word, the first universal mathematical genius.

To **solve an inequality** means to find all replacements for the variable (or variables) that make the inequality true. With inequalities, there may be many values that make the inequality true, so we define the **solution** of an inequality to be the set of all values that make the inequality true. This solution is shown using a graph, so solving inequalities is the same as graphing inequalities. The inequalities we solve in this chapter are sometimes called *first-degree* inequalities.

EXAMPLE 1

Graphing inequalities

Graph the solution for each given inequality.　**a.** $x \leq 3$　**b.** $x > 5$　**c.** $-2 \leq x$

Solution

a. Notice that, in this example, the endpoint is included because with $x \leq 3$, it is possible that $x = 3$. This is shown as a solid dot on the number line:

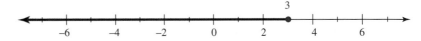

b. $x > 5$

c. $-2 \leq x$

Although you can graph this directly, you will have less chance of making a mistake when working with inequalities if you rewrite them so that the variable is on the left; that is, reverse the inequality to read $x \geq -2$. Notice that the direction of the arrow has been changed. This is because the symbol requires that the arrow always point to the smaller number. When you change the direction of the arrow, we say that you have *changed the order of the inequality*. For example, if $-2 \leq x$, then $x \geq -2$, and we say the order has been changed. The graph of $x \geq -2$ is shown on the following number line:

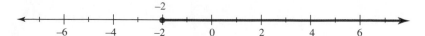

On a number line, if $x < y$, then x is to the left of y. Suppose the coordinates x and y are plotted as shown in Figure 3.3.

Figure 3.3 Number line showing two coordinates, x and y

If you add 2 to both x and y, you obtain $x + 2$ and $y + 2$. From Figure 3.4, you see that $x + 2 < y + 2$.

Figure 3.4 Number line with 2 added to both x and y

If you add some number c, there are two possibilities:
$c > 0$ ($c > 0$ is read "c is **positive**")
$c < 0$ ($c < 0$ is read "c is **negative**")

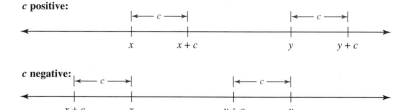

Figure 3.5 Adding positive and negative values to x and y

If $c > 0$, then $x + c$ is still to the left of $y + c$. If $c < 0$, then $x + c$ is still to the left of $y + c$, as shown in Figure 3.5. This argument justifies the following property.

Addition Property of Inequality

If $x < y$, then
$$x + c < y + c$$
Also,   if $x \leq y$, then $x + c \leq y + c$
if $x > y$, then $x + c > y + c$
if $x \geq y$, then $x + c \geq y + c$

Because this **addition property of inequality** is essentially the same as the addition property of equality, you might expect that there is also a multiplication property of inequality. We would hope that we could multiply both sides of an inequality by some number c without upsetting the inequality. Consider some examples. Let $x = 5$ and $y = 10$, so that $5 < 10$.

$$\begin{array}{llll}
\text{Let } c = 2: & 5 \cdot 2 < 10 \cdot 2 & & \\
& 10 < 20 & & \text{True} \\
\text{Let } c = 0: & 5 \cdot 0 < 10 \cdot 0 & & \\
& 0 < 0 & & \text{False} \\
\text{Let } c = -2: & 5(-2) < 10(-2) & & \\
& -10 < -20 & & \text{False}
\end{array}$$

You can see that you cannot multiply both sides of an inequality by a constant and be sure that the result is still true. However, if you restrict c to a positive value, then you can multiply both sides of an inequality by c. On the other hand, if c is a negative number, then the order of the inequality should be reversed. This is summarized by the **multiplication property of inequality.**

Multiplication Property of Inequality

Positive multiplication $(c > 0)$
If $x < y$, then
$$cx < cy$$
↑
Order unchanged

Also, for $c > 0$,
if $x \leq y$, then $cx \leq cy$
if $x > y$, then $cx > cy$
if $x \geq y$, then $cx \geq cy$

Negative multiplication $(c > 0)$
If $x < y$, then
$$cx > cy$$
↑
Order reversed

Also, for $c < 0$,
if $x \leq y$, then $cx \geq cy$
if $x > y$, then $cx < cy$
if $x \geq y$, then $cx \leq cy$

The same properties hold for positive and negative division. In summary, given $x < y$, $x \leq y$, $x > y$, or $x \geq y$, then a procedure for solving an inequality is stated in the following box.

Solving Inequalities

The procedure for solving inequalities is the same as the procedure for solving equations, except that, if you multiply or divide by a negative number, you reverse the order of the inequality.

The **inequality symbols are the *same*** if we

1. Add the same number to both sides.
2. Subtract the same number from both sides.
3. Multiply both sides by a positive number.
4. Divide both sides by a positive number.

This works the same as with equations.

The **inequality symbols are *reversed*** if we

1. Multiply both sides by a negative number.
2. Divide both sides by a negative number.
3. Interchange the x and the y.

This works the same as with equations, except reverse order.

EXAMPLE 2   **Solving inequalities**

Solve: **a.** $-x \geq 2$ **b.** $\dfrac{x}{-3} < 1$ **c.** $5x - 3 \geq 7$

Solution

a. $-x \geq 2$

$x \leq -2$ Multiply both sides by −1, and remember to reverse the order of the inequality.

b. $\dfrac{x}{-3} < 1$

$x > -3$ Multiply both sides by −3, and reverse the order.

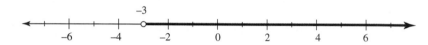

c. $5x - 3 \geq 7$ Given inequality.

$5x - 3 + 3 \geq 7 + 3$ Add 3 to both sides.

$5x \geq 10$ Simplify.

$\dfrac{5x}{5} \geq \dfrac{10}{5}$ Divide both sides by 5.

$x \geq 2$ Simplify.

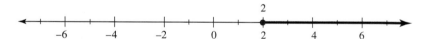

PROBLEM SET (3.7)

ESSENTIAL IDEAS   **LEVEL 1**

Translate each symbolic statement in Problems 1–6 into words.   **Verbal statements may vary.**

1. a. $19 > 4$ Nineteen is greater than four.

   b. $x < 8$ x is less than eight.

2.

a. $5 > 3$ Five is greater than three.

b. ■ $<$ ■   Blue box is smaller than green box.

3. a. $-5 \leq -2$ Negative five is less than or equal to negative two.

   b. $-x > 2$ The opposite of x is greater than two.

4. a. $k \geq -2$ k is greater than or equal to negative two.

   b. $m < -4$ m is less than negative four.

5. a. $x > 0$ x is positive.

   b. $y \leq 0$ y is not positive.

6. a. $w < 0$ w is negative.

   b. $t \geq 0$ t is nonnegative.

Translate each verbal statement in Problems 7–12 using inequality symbols $<, \leq, >,$ or $\geq$.

7. a. *P* is positive. $P > 0$

   b. *N* is negative. $N < 0$

8. a. Q is not positive. $Q \leq 0$

   b. R is not negative. $R \geq 0$

9. a. x is positive. $x > 0$

   b. x is not positive. $x \leq 0$

10. a. $-x$ is positive. $-x > 0$

   b. $-x$ is negative. $-x < 0$

11. a. M is no more than 4. $M \leq 4$

   b. Q is no less than 4. $Q \geq 4$

12. a. x is nonnegative. $x \geq 0$

   b. y is not positive. $y \leq 0$

DRILL AND PRACTICE   LEVEL 2

Graph the solution for each inequality given in Problems 13–24.   **See IAS.**

13. a. $x < 5$ **b.** $x \geq 6$

14. a. $x \geq -3$ **b.** $x \leq -2$

15. a. $1 > x$ **b.** $x \geq 100$

16. a. $4 \geq x$ **b.** $-1 < x$

17. a. $-5 \leq x$ **b.** $-3 > x$

18. a. $x < 50$ **b.** $x \geq -125$

19. a. $x \leq -75$ **b.** $-30 > x$

20. a. $45 \geq x$ **b.** $-40 < x$

21. a. $-50 \leq x$ **b.** $100 > x$

22. a. $\frac{x}{2} > 3$ **b.** $\frac{x}{2} > 50$

23. a. $4 < \frac{x}{2}$ **b.** $-2 > \frac{x}{-4}$

24. a. $40 < \frac{x}{2}$ **b.** $-20 > \frac{x}{4}$

Solve the inequalities in Problems 25–42.

25. $x + 7 \geq 3$ $x \geq -4$ **26.** $x - 2 \leq 5$ $x \leq 7$

27. $x - 2 \geq -4$ $x \geq -2$ **28.** $10 < 5 + y$ $y > 5$

29. $-4 < 2 + y$ $y > -6$ **30.** $-3 < 5 + y$ $y > -8$

31. $2 > -s$ $s > -2$ **32.** $-t \leq -3$ $t \geq 3$

33. $-m > -5$ $m < 5$ **34.** $5 \leq 4 - y$ $y \leq -1$

35. $3 > 2 - x$ $x > -1$ **36.** $5 \geq 1 - w$ $w \geq -4$

37. $2x + 6 \leq 8$ $x \leq 1$ **38.** $3y - 6 \geq 9$ $y \geq 5$

39. $3 > s + 9$ $s < -6$ **40.** $2 < 2s + 8$ $s > -3$

41. $4 \leq a + 2$ $a \geq 2$ **42.** $3 > 2b - 13$ $b < 8$

APPLICATIONS   LEVEL 2

43. If the opposite of a number must be less than 5, what are the possible numbers satisfying this condition?   **any number greater than −5**

44. If the opposite of a number must be greater than twice the number, what are the possible numbers?   **any number less than 0**

45. Suppose that three times a number is added to 12 and the result is negative. What are the possible numbers?
any number less than −4

46. Suppose that seven times a number is added to 35 and the result is positive. What are the possible numbers?
any number greater than −5

47. Suppose that twice a number is subtracted from 8 and the result is positive. What are the possible numbers?
any number less than 4

48. Suppose that five times a number is subtracted from 15 and the result is negative. What are the possible numbers?
any number greater than 3

49. If you solve an inequality and obtain $2 < 5$, what interpretation can you give to the solution?
All values in domain satisfy the inequality.

50. If you solve an inequality and obtain $2 > 5$, what interpretation can you give to the solution?
No values satisfy the inequality.

51. If a number is four more than its opposite, what are the possible numbers?   **The number is 2.**

52. If a number is six less than twice its opposite, what are the possible numbers?   **The number is −2.**

53. If a number is less than four more than its opposite, what are the possible numbers?   **The number is less than 2.**

54. If a number is less than six minus twice its opposite, what are the possible numbers?   **The number is greater than −6.**

RIGHT OR WRONG?   LEVEL 3

Explain what is wrong, if anything, with the statements in Problems 55–60. Explain your reasoning.

55. If $x \geq 5$, then the endpoint is an open dot.   **F; it is a solid dot.**

56. If $x < -5$, then the endpoint of the graph is an open dot.   **T**

57. If $-x > 5$, then $x > -5$.   **F; reverse inequality.**

58. If $-x \leq 5$, then $x \leq -5$.   **F; reverse inequality.**

59. $2 - 3x \leq 8$

    $-3x \leq 6$

       $x \leq -2$ **F; reverse inequality when dividing by a negative.**

60. $x + 3 > 2x - 5$

    $3 > x - 5$

    $8 > x$

    $x > 8$ **F; reverse inequality.**

3.8 Chapter 3 Summary and Review

Take some time getting ready to work the review problems in this section. First, look back at the definition and property boxes. You will maximize your understanding of this chapter by working the problems in this section only after you have studied the material.

IMPORTANT TERMS

Numbers refer to sections of this chapter.

Spending some time with the terms and objectives of this chapter will pay dividends in assuring your success.

Addition law of exponents [3.1]
Addition property of equations [3.4]
Addition property of inequality [3.7]
Binomial [3.1]
Coefficient [3.1]
Comparison property [3.7]
Conditional equation [3.4]
Degree [3.1]
Distributive property [3.2]
Division property of equations [3.4]
Equation [3.4]
Equation-solving procedure [3.5]

Equivalent equations [3.4]
Evaluate [3.3]
Formula [3.6]
Inequality symbols [3.7]
Like terms [3.2]
Literal equation [3.6]
Monomial [3.1]
Multiplication property of equations [3.4]
Multiplication property of inequality [3.7]
Negative [3.7]
Numerical coefficient [3.1]
Open equation [3.4]
Opposite [3.4]
Polynomial [3.1]

Positive [3.7]
Problem-solving procedure [3.6]
Profit formula [3.6]
Reciprocal [3.4]
Root of an equation [3.4]
Satisfy an equation [3.4]
Similar terms [3.2]
Simplify [3.3]
Solution [3.4]
Solve [3.4; 3.6; 3.7]
Substitution [3.6]
Subtraction property of equations [3.4]
Term [3.1]
Trinomial [3.1]

Essential Ideas

[3.1] Problems 1–2, 4	Know what we mean by a term, a polynomial, and degree.
Problem 3	Know the addition law of exponents
[3.2] Problem 1	State the distributive law.
Problem 2–8	Know what we mean by similar terms, and be able to pick them out.
[3.3] Problem 1	State the distributive law.*
Problem 2	What does it mean to simplify a polynomial?
[3.4] Problems 61, 63–64	What does it mean to solve an equation? What is its solution? What is the goal of equation solving?
Problem 62	Know the four properties of equations.
[3.5] Problems 1–8	Be able to simplify expressions.
[3.6] Problem 1	What is your problem-solving procedure?
Problem 2	Be able to make symbolic statements for even or odd integers.
[3.7] Problems 1–6	Know the verbal translations for inequality symbols.

LEARNING OUTCOMES

The material in this chapter is reviewed in the following list of learning outcomes. A self-test (with answers and suggestions for additional study) is given. This self-test is constructed so that each problem number corresponds to a related objective. For example, Problem 7 is testing Objective 3.7. This self-test is followed by a practice test with the questions in mixed order.

[3.1]	*Objective* 3.1	Give the degree and numerical coefficient of a term.
[3.1]	*Objective* 3.2	Identify a polynomial as a monomial, binomial, or trinomial, and give the degree of the polynomial.

*Yes, this is a repeat. What does that say to you about its importance?

Self-Test

Each question of this self-test is related to the corresponding objective listed above.

1. What are the degree and the numerical coefficient of $-2x^4$?

2. Identify each polynomial as a monomial, binomial, or trinomial, and give the degree.
   a. $2x - 3y$ **b.** $x^2 + y^3$ **c.** -5^2 **d.** $x^2 - x^2y^2 + y^2$

3. Simplify $(5x)^2(2y)^3$.

4. **a.** Write out a difference of the squares of a and b.
   b. Write out the square of the difference of a from b.

5. Simplify $5x - 3y + 5 - 8x + 3y - 12$.

6. Simplify $3(2x + 5) - (x + 3)$.

7. Simplify $(2x - y)(x + 3y)$.

8. Solve $-3 = x - 5$.

9. Solve $x + 8 = -2$.

10. Solve $\dfrac{x}{-5} = 13$.

11. Solve $8x = -32$.

12. Solve: **a.** $5x - 3 = 12$ **b.** $\dfrac{x}{2} + 8 = -2$

13. If you drive 243 miles and use 8.2 gallons of gasoline, estimate the miles per gallon.

14. Solve: **a.** $A = \ell w$ for w; $(\ell \neq 0)$ **b.** $6x - 2y - 4 = 0$ for y

15. Solve $-x > 5$.

16. Suppose that the exchange rate in Great Britain is 0.53273 pound per dollar. What is the cost (in dollars) for an item marked 250 pounds in Great Britain?

17. The Toyota Corolla has an estimated MPG of 22, with a cruising range of 286 miles. What is the size of the tank?

18. Chicken of the Sea tuna sells for $1.39 for a 7-oz can, whereas Star Kist diet pack costs $0.99 for a 5-oz can. Which is the better buy, and by how much, rounded to the nearest $\frac{1}{10}$ cent?

19. Which of the three sizes in the following ad is the least expensive per oz?

OXYDOL DETERGENT

20-oz. Pkg....................67¢

84-oz. Pkg...................2.61

49-oz. Pkg. Save 2¢:

1.57

20. Current postal regulations state that no package may be sent if its combined length, width, and height exceed 72 in. What are the possible dimensions of a box to be mailed with equal height and width if the length is four times the height?

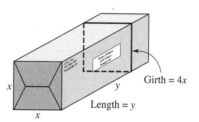

Girth = $4x$

Length = y

x y x

STOP

STUDY HINTS   *Compare your solutions and answers to the self-test. For each problem you missed, work some additional problems in the section listed in the margin. After you have worked these problems, you can test yourself with the practice test.*

Additional Problems

[3.1] Problems 5–10

[3.1] Problems 11–16; 35–40

[3.1] Problems 17–34

[3.1] Problems 41–46
[3.7] Problems 1–6
[3.2] Problems 9–48

[3.3] Problems 3–34; 43–50
[3.5] Problems 1–8

[3.3] Problems 35–42

[3.4] Problems 5–8; 13–18

Complete Solutions to the Self-Test

1. The degree is 4 and the numerical coefficient is -2.

2. a. first-degree binomial   **b.** third-degree binomial

c. zero-degree monomial   **d.** fourth-degree trinomial

3. $(5x)^2(2y)^3 = 5^2x^2(2^3y^3)$

$\qquad\qquad = 200x^2y^3 \quad$ $5^2 \cdot 2^3 = 25 \cdot 8 = 200$

4. a. $a^2 - b^2$ or $b^2 - a^2$ **b.** $(b - a)^2$

5. $5x - 3y + 5 - 8x + 3y - 12 = (5x - 8x) + (-3y + 3y) + (5 - 12)$

$\qquad\qquad$ This step should be done mentally.

$\qquad\qquad\qquad = -3x - 7$

6. $3(2x + 5) - (x + 3) = 6x + 15 - x - 3 \quad$ Don't forget to distribute the number -1.

$\qquad\qquad\qquad = 5x + 12$

7. $(2x - y)(x + 3y) = (2x - y)x + (2x - y)3y$

$\qquad\qquad\qquad = 2x^2 - xy + 6xy - 3y^2$

$\qquad\qquad\qquad = 2x^2 + 5xy - 3y^2$

8. $-3 = x - 5$

$\quad\; 2 = x \quad$ Add 5 to both sides.

Applications

9. $x + 8 = -2$
   $x = -10$ Subtract 8 from both sides.

10. $\dfrac{x}{-5} = 13$
    $x = -65$ Multiply both sides by −5.

11. $8x = -32$
    $x = -4$ Divide both sides by 8.

12. **a.** $5x - 3 = 12$ **b.** $\dfrac{x}{2} + 8 = -2$
    $5x = 15$ $\dfrac{x}{2} = -10$
    $x = 3$ $x = -20$

13. $\dfrac{243}{8.2} \approx \dfrac{240}{8} \approx 30$; estimate 30 mpg

14. **a.** $A = \ell w$ **b.** $6x - 2y - 4 = 0$
    $\dfrac{A}{\ell} = w$ $6x - 4 = 2y$
     $3x - 2 = y$

15. $-x > 5$
    $x < -5$ Multiply both sides by −1; don't forget to reverse the order of the inequality.

16.   (DOLLARS)(EXCHANGE RATE) = (AMOUNT OF FOREIGN CURRENCY)
    (NUMBER OF DOLLARS) (0.53273) = 250
               NUMBER OF DOLLARS = 469.280874
    The cost (in dollars) is $469.28.

17. (MPG)(NO. OF GAL) = (DISTANCE)
         22(NO. OF GAL) = 286
                $22g = 286$ Let g = NUMBER OF GAL.
                   $g = 13$
    The size of the tank is 13 gallons.

18. COST OF 1 OZ OF CHICKEN OF THE SEA = $1.39 ÷ 7 = $0.199
    COST OF 1 OZ OF STAR KIST = $0.99 ÷ 5 = $0.198
    Star Kist is about 0.1¢/oz less expensive than Chicken of the Sea.

19. COST OF 1 OZ OF 20-OZ PKG = $0.67 ÷ 20 = $0.0335
    COST OF 1 OZ OF 84-OZ PKG = $2.61 ÷ 84 = $0.0311
    COST OF 1 OZ OF 49-OZ PKG = $1.57 ÷ 49 = $0.0320
    The least expensive is the 84-oz size. I have no idea why the advertisement for the 49-oz size says, "Save 2¢."

20.   LENGTH + WIDTH + HEIGHT ≤ 72 in.
         LENGTH + HEIGHT + HEIGHT ≤ 72 in.   WIDTH = HEIGHT
    4(HEIGHT) + HEIGHT + HEIGHT ≤ 72 in.   LENGTH = 4(HEIGHT)
                $4h + h + h \le 72$ in.   Let h = HEIGHT
                        $6h \le 72$ in.   Similar terms
                          $h \le 12$ in.   Divide by 6.
                HEIGHT ≤ 12 in.
                WIDTH ≤ 12 in.   HEIGHT = WIDTH
                      $4h \le 48$ in.
                LENGTH ≤ 48 in.
    The height and width must each be 12 in. or less, and the length must be 48 in. or less.

Chapter 3 Review Questions

*To prepare for a chapter test, first study the chapter; then, read each term from the important terms list above and make sure you know the meaning of each word; finally, review the chapter objectives. **After** these steps, take the self-test and correct all your answers. The following review questions can be used for extra practice.*

1. Give the degree and the numerical coefficient.
a. $5x^3$ **3; 5** **b.** $2x$ **1; 2** **c.** x^4 **4; 1** **d.** $-3x^5$ **5; -3**

2. Identify each polynomial as a monomial, binomial, or trinomial, and give the degree.
a. $6x^2 + xy - 5y^2$ **second-degree trinomial** **b.** $xy - 1$ **second-degree binomial**
c. 6^2 **zero-degree monomial** **d.** $x^2 - y^2$ **second-degree binomial**

Simplify the expressions in Problems 3–7.

3. a. $x^2x^7y^3y^8$ **x^9y^{11}** **b.** $(3x)^2(4y)$ **$36x^2y$**
c. $3x^2(4y)^2$ **$48x^2y^2$** **d.** $(-x^2)(-xy)$ **x^3y**

4. a. $6x + 5 - 5$ **$6x$** **b.** $3x - 2 - 3x$ **-2**
c. $-6x - (-4)x$ **$-2x$** **d.** $3y - 2x + 5 - 3y + 4x$ **$2x + 5$**

5. a. $2(x + 3) + 4(x - 5)$ **$6x - 14$** **b.** $3(2x - 1) + 2(1 - 5x)$ **$-4x - 1$**
c. $(5x - 3y) - 2(x + 3y)$ **$3x - 9y$** **d.** $(3x + 2) - (5x + 3)$ **$-2x - 1$**

6. a. $(x - 5)(x + 4)$ **$x^2 - x - 20$** **b.** $(2x + 1)(x - 3)$ **$2x^2 - 5x - 3$**

7. a. $(3x + 4)(3x - 4)$ **$9x^2 - 16$** **b.** $(ab - c)(2ab + 3c)$ **$2a^2b^2 + abc - 3c^2$**

Solve the equations or inequalities in Problems 8–16.

8. a. $a - 10 = 40$ **50** **b.** $b - 6 = -31$ **−25**
c. $13 = c - 20$ **33** **d.** $-5 = d + 14$ **−19**

9. a. $A + 5 = 2$ **−3** **b.** $B + 23 = -8$ **−31**
c. $9 + C = 30$ **21** **d.** $-5 + D = -15$ **−10**

10. a. $\dfrac{E}{6} = 5$ **30** **b.** $\dfrac{F}{3} = 12$ **36**

c. $\dfrac{G}{-2} = 60$ **−120** **d.** $-12 = \dfrac{H}{-5}$ **60**

11. a. $2x = 46$ **23** **b.** $-x = 5$ **−5**

12. a. $-4x = 20$ **−5** **b.** $-25 = -5x$ **5**

13. a. $3x + 2 = 8$ **2** **b.** $1 - 5y = 101$ **−20**

14. a. $\dfrac{x}{2} - 5 = 4$ **18** **b.** $\dfrac{x - 5}{2} = 4$ **13**

15. a. $x + 2 > -1$ **$x > -3$** **b.** $2 - x < -1$ **$x > 3$**

16. a. $-x \le 25$ **$x \ge -25$** **b.** $6 \ge 3 - x$ **$x \ge -3$**

17. Solve $I = Prt$ for t. **$t = \dfrac{I}{Pr}$**

18. Solve $3x + 2y + 8 = 0$ for y. **$y = \dfrac{-3}{2}x - 4$**

19. Solve $2x - y = 0$ for y. **$y = 2x$**

20. Solve $2x - y = 0$ for x. **$x = \frac{1}{2}y$**

21. If you add three consecutive even numbers and the sum is 78, estimate the first of the three numbers. **The first number is 24; estimate by 75/3 = 25.**

22. If you subtract eight from twice a number and the result is equal to negative twelve, what is the number? **The number is −2.**

23. The Mercedes-Benz 560SL has an estimated MPG of 12 and a fuel tank capacity of 23.8 gallons. What is the estimated cruising range?
The estimated cruising range is about 10 × 25 = 250; by direct calculation it is 285.6 miles.

24. If a 32-oz bottle of ketchup costs \$0.99 and a 44-oz bottle costs \$1.49, which size is less expensive (per ounce), and by how much per ounce (rounded to the nearest tenth of a cent)?   *The 32-oz bottle is the less expensive, by 0.3¢ per ounce.*

25. Suppose that the odometer read 46312 at the start of your vacation and 48132 at the end. If your trip required 52 gallons of gas, what was the car's MPG for this trip?
The trip's MPG is 35.

Individual Projects

Learning to use sources outside your classroom and textbook is an important skill, and here are some ideas for extending some of the ideas in this chapter.

PROJECT 3.1   In the "In This World" problem of Section 3.2, a hippopotamus promised to algebraically show the professor that they could play on the teeter-totter. In Problem 55 of Section 3.2, you were asked to help the hippo identify the variables and then in Problem 48 of Section 3.4, you were asked to write an equation. "Now," says Ms. Hippo, "we let $H = $ WEIGHT OF HIPPOPOTAMUS and $p = $ WEIGHT OF PROFESSOR, with some weight w (probably very large) so that

$$H = p + w$$

Did you get this, Mister Professor?"

"Yes, but we still can't play while I'm stranded up here," said the professor. "Go on, I'm listening."

"Multiply both sides by $H - p$:

$$H(H - p) = (p + w)(H - p)$$

Then, we use the distributive property:

$$H^2 - Hp = pH + wH - p^2 - wp$$

You got that simplification? Good! Now subtract wH from both sides:

$$H^2 - Hp - wH = pH - p^2 - wp$$

Use the distributive property again:

$$H(H - p - w) = p(H - p - w)$$

Finally, divide both sides by $H - p - w$:

$$H = p$$

Now, since our weights are the same, we'll have no problem on the teeter-totter."

"Wait!" hollers the professor. "Obviously this is false."

Where is the error in the reasoning?
Notice that $H - p - w = 0$ and we can't divide both sides by zero.

PROJECT 3.2   One day Perry White sent Lois Lane and Clark Kent out to the Coliseum to cover a big story. On the way, Clark, disguised as Superman, made a quick trip to Wal-Mart to pick up a present for Lois. It took Lois 2 hours to reach the Coliseum from the *Daily Planet,* but it took Clark only 10 minutes, even though he traveled twice as far as Lois. If Lois drove at 50 mph, how fast did Clark (Superman) travel?
Superman traveled at 1,200 miles per hour.

Team Projects

Working in small groups is typical of most work environments, and learning to work with others to communicate specific ideas is an important skill. Work with three or four other students to submit a single report based on each of the following questions.

T7. *"When will I ever use algebra?"* With a team of two or three other classmates, each of you check the college catalogue of a nearby liberal arts college, a state college, a university, and a world-class university. (If you don't have access to the Internet, make a trip to your college library.)

Robert Holmes/Corbis

Compare the math requirements for at least 10 different baccalaureate degree programs.

T8. Form teams in which team members have an interest in a similar type of business. With your team, make an appointment with a manager of the business and schedule an interview. Ask specific questions about the qualifications for a career in that business, and in particular find out the amount of mathematics or algebra required.

CHAPTER 4

Percents and Problem Solving

Mathematics has beauties of its own—a symmetry and proportion in its results . . . the mental emotion should be that of enjoyment and beauty, not that of repulsion from the ugly and the unpleasant.

J. W. Young in Howard Eves, Mathematical Circles Squares,
Boston: Prindle, Weber and Schmidt, 1972.

ANTICIPATE

- *Overview; check out contents, terms, essential ideas, and learning outcomes.*
- *Ratios and proportions lead to understanding percents.*
- *Using percents in your everyday life is common and important.*

4.1 Ratio and Proportion

IN THIS WORLD THE POWER OF MATH

"*Take a look at this painting, called* George Washington Crossing the Delaware *by Leutze," said art critic Ambrose. "Can you pick out George Washington?"*

"*Sure, prof!" quipped Rita. "He is the dude that is taller than all the other guys."*

"*That is correct, Rita." said Ambrose. "In art, we call this* **proportion.** *Proportion refers to the way different elements in a painting refer to each other in terms of size. Leutze painted George Washington out of proportion because he is the subject of the painting. See if you can find an object in the foreground whose size seems too small."*

 See Problem 1.

A **ratio** expresses a size relationship between two sets and is defined as a quotient of two numbers. It is written using the word *to,* a colon, or a fraction; that is, if the ratio of men to women is 5 **to** 4, this could also be written as 5 : 4 or $\frac{5}{4}$. We will emphasize the idea that a ratio can be written as a fraction (or as a quotient of two numbers). Since a fraction can be reduced, a ratio can also be reduced.

EXAMPLE 1 **Writing a ratio in lowest terms**

Reduce the given ratios to lowest terms.

a. 4 to 52   **b.** 15 to 3   **c.** $1\frac{1}{2}$ to 2   **d.** $1\frac{2}{3}$ to $3\frac{3}{4}$

Solution

a. A ratio of 4 to 52

$$\frac{4}{52} = \frac{1}{13}$$

A ratio of 1 to 13 is a reduced ratio

b. A ratio of 15 to 3

$$\frac{15}{3} = 5$$

Write this as $\frac{5}{1}$ because a ratio compares two numbers. Lowest terms: A ratio of 5 to 1

c. A ratio of $1\frac{1}{2}$ to 2

$$\frac{1\frac{1}{2}}{2} = 1\frac{1}{2} \div 2$$

$$= \frac{3}{2} \times \frac{1}{2}$$

$$= \frac{3}{4}$$

Lowest terms: A ratio of 3 to 4

d. A ratio of $1\frac{2}{3}$ to $3\frac{3}{4}$

$$\frac{1\frac{2}{3}}{3\frac{3}{4}} = 1\frac{2}{3} \div 3\frac{3}{4}$$

$$= \frac{5}{3} \div \frac{15}{4}$$

$$= \frac{5}{3} \times \frac{4}{15} = \frac{4}{9}$$

Lowest terms: A ratio of 4 to 9

A **proportion** is a statement of equality between ratios. Notice that Ein (in the margin) is deciding whether the frogs in his hands are proportional. In mathematics, we use symbolism for this idea:

$$\frac{a}{b} = \frac{c}{d}$$

"a is to b" "as" "c is to d"

The notation used in some (older) books is $a : b :: c : d$. Even though we won't use this notation, we will use words associated with this notation to name the terms:

Extremes
Means
$a : b :: c : d$

In the more common fractional notation, we have

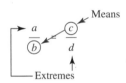

Means

$\frac{a}{\textcircled{b}} \quad \frac{\textcircled{c}}{d}$

Extremes

EXAMPLE 2   **Notation of proportions**

Read each proportion, and name the means and the extremes.

a. $\frac{2}{3} = \frac{10}{15}$ **b.** $\frac{10}{15} = \frac{2}{3}$ **c.** $\frac{m}{5} = \frac{3}{8}$

Solution

a. $\frac{2}{3} = \frac{10}{15}$
   Read: Two is to three as ten is to fifteen.
   Means: 3 and 10
   Extremes: 2 and 15

b. $\frac{10}{15} = \frac{2}{3}$
   Read: Ten is to fifteen as two is to three.
   Means: 15 and 2
   Extremes: 10 and 3

c. $\frac{m}{5} = \frac{3}{8}$
   Read: m is to five as three is to eight.
   Means: 5 and 3
   Extremes: m and 8

The following **property of proportions** is fundamental to our study of proportions and percents.

Property of Proportions

> If the product of the means equals the product of the extremes, then the ratios form a proportion.
>
> *Also,*
>
> If the ratios form a proportion, then the product of the means equals the product of the extremes.

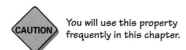

You will use this property frequently in this chapter.

The property of proportions can be stated in symbols:

$$\frac{a}{b} = \frac{c}{d}$$

$$\underbrace{b \times c}_{\uparrow} = \underbrace{a \times d}_{\uparrow}$$

Product of means = Product of extremes

Note that the product of the means equals the product of the extremes even if we interchange the left and right sides (as we did in Examples 2**a** and 2**b**).

EXAMPLE 3

Finding ratios that form a proportion

Tell whether each pair of ratios forms a proportion.   **a.** $\frac{3}{4}, \frac{36}{48}$ **b.** $\frac{5}{16}, \frac{7}{22}$

Solution **a.** *Means*   *Extremes*   **b.** *Means*   *Extremes*

4×36 3×48 16×7 5×22

$144 = 144$ $112 \neq 110$

Thus,   Thus,

$$\frac{3}{4} = \frac{36}{48}$$ $$\frac{5}{16} \neq \frac{7}{22}$$

They form a proportion.   They do not form a proportion.

PROBLEM SET 4.1

ESSENTIAL IDEAS   LEVEL 1

1. What is a ratio? What is a proportion? *A ratio is a quotient of two numbers; a proportion is a statement of equality between ratios.*
2. What is the property of proportions? *See box on p. 186.*

DRILL AND PRACTICE   LEVEL 2

Write the ratios given in Problems 3–13 as reduced fractions.

3. **a.** The ratio of "yes" to "no" answers is 3 to 2   3/2

   b. The vote was affirmative by a 5 to 4 margin.   5/4

4. **a.** The ratio of cars to people is 1 to 3.   1/3

   b. The ratio of taxis to cars is 1 to 20.   1/20

5. **a.** The ratio of cats to dogs is 4 to 7.   4/7

   b. The ratio of dogs to cats is 7 to 4.   7/4

6. **a.** The ratio of gallons to miles is 20 to 4.   5/1

   b. The ratio of miles to gallons is 25 to 1   25/1

7. **a.** The ratio of dollars to people is 92 to 4.   23/1

   b. The ratio of dollars to donuts is 5 to 6.   5/6

8. **a.** The ratio of wins to losses is 12 to 4.   3/1

   b. The ratio of losses to wins is 6 to 15.   2/5

9. **a.** The ratio of apples to oranges is 6 to 2.   3/1

   b. The ratio of peanuts to cashews is 10 to 2.   5/1

10. **a.** The ratio of sand to gravel is 2 to 5.   2/5

    b. The ratio of children to adults is $2\frac{1}{5}$ to 2.   11/10

11. **a.** The ratio of cars to people is 1 to $2\frac{1}{2}$.   2/5

    b. The ratio of adults to children is 500 to 150.   10/3

12. **a.** Find the ratio of $2\frac{3}{4}$ to $6\frac{1}{4}$.   11/25

    b. Find the ratio of $6\frac{1}{4}$ to $2\frac{3}{4}$.   25/11

13. **a.** Find the ratio of $5\frac{2}{3}$ to $2\frac{1}{3}$.   17/7

    b. Find the ratio of $6\frac{1}{3}$ to $4\frac{1}{3}$.   19/13

In Problems 14–21, read each proportion and name the means and extremes.

14. $\dfrac{5}{8} = \dfrac{35}{56}$ Means: 8, 35
Extremes: 5, 56
5 is to 8 as 35 is to 56

15. $\dfrac{94}{47} = \dfrac{2}{1}$ Means: 47, 2
Extremes: 94, 1
94 is to 47 as 2 is to 1

16. $\dfrac{5}{3} = \dfrac{2}{x}$ Means: 3, 2
Extremes: 5, x
5 is to 3 as 2 is to x

17. $\dfrac{5}{x} = \dfrac{1}{2}$ Means: x, 1
Extremes: 5, 2
5 is to x as 1 is to 2

18. $\dfrac{a}{2} = \dfrac{c}{3}$ Means: 2, c
Extremes: a, 3
a is to 2 as c is to 3

19. $\dfrac{8}{b} = \dfrac{c}{2}$ Means: b, c
Extremes: 8, 2
8 is to b as c is to 2

20. $\dfrac{a}{b} = \dfrac{c}{d}$ Means: b, c
Extremes: a, d
a is to b as c is to d

21. $\dfrac{w}{x} = \dfrac{y}{z}$ Means: x, y
Extremes: w, z
w is to x as y is to z

Tell whether each pair of ratios in Problems 22–37 forms a proportion.

22. $\dfrac{7}{1}, \dfrac{21}{3}$ yes

23. $\dfrac{6}{8}, \dfrac{9}{12}$ yes

24. $\dfrac{3}{6}, \dfrac{5}{10}$ yes

25. $\dfrac{7}{8}, \dfrac{6}{7}$ no

26. $\dfrac{9}{2}, \dfrac{10}{3}$ no

27. $\dfrac{6}{5}, \dfrac{42}{35}$ yes

28. $\dfrac{85}{18}, \dfrac{42}{9}$ no

29. $\dfrac{403}{341}, \dfrac{13}{11}$ yes

30. $\dfrac{20}{70}, \dfrac{4}{14}$ yes

31. $\dfrac{3}{4}, \dfrac{75}{100}$ yes

32. $\dfrac{2}{3}, \dfrac{67}{100}$ no

33. $\dfrac{5}{3}, \dfrac{7\frac{1}{3}}{4}$ no

34. $\dfrac{3}{2}, \dfrac{5}{3\frac{1}{2}}$ no

35. $\dfrac{5\frac{1}{5}}{7}, \dfrac{4}{5}$ no

36. $\dfrac{1}{3}, \dfrac{33\frac{1}{3}}{100}$ yes

37. $\dfrac{2}{3}, \dfrac{66\frac{2}{3}}{100}$ yes

38. Now that you have been using this book for some time, this would be a good place to give some feedback to the author. Send him an e-mail at **smithkjs@mathnature.com.** The activities in this problem are taken from Chapter 5 of *Conquering Math Anxiety: A Self-help Workbook, Second Edition* (Pacific Grove, CA: Brooks/Cole, 2003) by Cynthia Arem.

    a. List at least ten positive adjectives or nouns you can associate with success in math.

    b. List at least seven inspirational images that come to mind that you can relate to your conquest of math fears and success in math.

    c. Describe the growth-enhancing emotions you would like to experience as a result of overcoming math anxiety.

    d. Now, using the positive ideas, imagery, and emotions identified above, develop your own special positive metaphors.

    e. Write the metaphors on separate 3" × 5" cards and post them in the place where you study.

APPLICATIONS LEVEL 2

A baseball player's batting average is the ratio of hits to times at bat. For example, how many hits per times at bat does a player with a batting average of 0.275 have?

$$0.275 = \frac{275}{1,000} = \frac{11}{40}$$

This is a ratio of 11 to 40, which means the player has an average of 11 hits for every 40 times at bat. Find the average number of hits per times at bat (stated as a ratio) for the batting champions named in Problems 39–44.

39. Ty Cobb (Detroit, 1912); 0.390   39 to 100

40. Jake Daubert (Brooklyn, 1913); 0.350   7 to 20

41. Pete Runnels (Boston, 1960); 0.320   8 to 25

42. Ernie Lombardi (Boston, 1942); 0.330   33 to 100

43. Wade Boggs (Boston, 1988); 0.366   183 to 500

44. Julio Franco (Texas, 1991); 0.342   171 to 500

45. About 106 baby boys are born for every 100 baby girls.
   a. Write this as a simplified ratio of males to females.
     53 to 50
   b. Write a simplified ratio of females to males.   50 to 53

46. A cement mixture calls for 60 pounds of cement for 3 gallons of water.
   a. What is the ratio of cement to water?   20 to 1
   b. What is the ratio of water to cement?   1 to 20

47. A certain school has 40 freshmen, 30 sophomores, 15 juniors, and 10 seniors.
   a. What is the ratio of juniors to seniors?   3 to 2
   b. What is the ratio of juniors to those in school?   3 to 19

48. A certain school has 40 freshmen, 30 sophomores, 15 juniors, and 10 seniors.

   a. What is the ratio of sophomores to freshmen?   3 to 4
   b. What is the ratio of seniors to freshmen?   1 to 4

49. If you drive 119 miles on $8\frac{1}{2}$ gallons of gas, what is the simplified ratio of miles to gallons?   14 to 1

50. If Jesse can do a job in four hours and Mia can do the same job in three hours, what is ratio of the rate of work of Jesse to that of Mia?   4 to 3

51. If you drive 279 miles on $15\frac{1}{2}$ gallons of gas, what is the simplified ratio of miles to gallons?   18 to 1

52. If you drive 180 miles on $7\frac{1}{2}$ gallons of gas, what is the simplified ratio of miles to gallons?   24 to 1

53. If you drive 151.7 miles on 8.2 gallons of gas, what is the simplified ratio of miles to gallons?   37 to 2

54. What is the gear ratio (rear to front) of a bicycle that has 30 teeth on the rear sprocket and 52 teeth on the front sprocket?   15 to 26

RIGHT OR WRONG? LEVEL 3

Explain what is wrong, if anything, with the statements in Problems 55–60. Explain your reasoning.

55. A simplified form of a ratio of 6 to 4 is 1.5.
   F; ratios involve 2 numbers

56. A simplified form of a ratio of 6 to 1 is 6.
   F; ratios involve 2 numbers

57. The symbol $\frac{2}{3}$ is used to represent a division, a fraction, and a ratio.   T

58. The expression

$$\frac{6}{9} = \frac{2}{3}$$

   is a proportion.   T

59. A ratio of $2\frac{1}{2}$ to $6\frac{1}{3}$ is not permitted because a ratio cannot contain fractions.   F

60. A ratio of 12 to 4 is the same as the ratio of 3 to 1.   T

4.2 Problem Solving with Proportions

IN THIS WORLD THE POWER OF MATH

"Hey, Rick, how do you like your new truck?" asked Tom.
   "It is absolutely awesome. The acceleration is out of this world. My dog loves it! She feels it's a thrill ride each time we leave a stoplight," answered Rick.
   "Hold on—it is not about acceleration. Have you heard of global warming? You should be more concerned about your miles per gallon than you are about acceleration. Do you even know how to calculate it for your new truck?"

 See Problem 47.

In Section 4.1, we tested pairs of ratios to see whether they formed a proportion. In the usual setting for a proportion, however, three of the terms of the proportion are known and one of the terms is unknown. It is always possible to find the missing term.

EXAMPLE 1   Finding a missing term of a proportion

Find the missing term of each proportion.

a. $\frac{3}{4} = \frac{w}{20}$ **b.** $\frac{3}{4} = \frac{27}{y}$ **c.** $\frac{2}{x} = \frac{8}{9}$ **d.** $\frac{t}{15} = \frac{3}{5}$

Solution

a. $\dfrac{3}{4} = \dfrac{w}{20}$:   PRODUCT OF MEANS = PRODUCT OF EXTREMES

$$4w = 3(20) \qquad \text{Divide both sides by 4; notice that 4 is the number opposite the unknown.}$$

$$w = \frac{3(\overset{5}{\cancel{20}})}{\underset{1}{\cancel{4}}}$$

$$w = 15$$

b. $\dfrac{3}{4} = \dfrac{27}{y}$:   PRODUCT OF MEANS = PRODUCT OF EXTREMES

$$4(27) = 3y \qquad \text{Divide both sides by 3; notice that 3 is the number opposite the unknown.}$$

$$\frac{4(\overset{9}{\cancel{27}})}{\underset{1}{\cancel{3}}} = y$$

$$36 = y$$

c. $\dfrac{2}{x} = \dfrac{8}{9}$:   PRODUCT OF MEANS = PRODUCT OF EXTREMES

$$8x = 2(9) \qquad \text{Divide both sides by 8; notice that 8 is the number opposite the unknown.}$$

$$x = \frac{\overset{1}{\cancel{2}}(9)}{\underset{4}{\cancel{8}}}$$

$$x = \frac{9}{4}$$

d. $\dfrac{t}{15} = \dfrac{3}{5}$:   PRODUCT OF MEANS = PRODUCT OF EXTREMES

$$3(15) = 5t \qquad \text{Divide both sides by 5; notice that 5 is the number opposite the unknown.}$$

$$\frac{3(\overset{3}{\cancel{15}})}{\underset{1}{\cancel{5}}} = t$$

$$9 = t$$

Notice that the unknown term can be in any one of four proportions, as illustrated by the four parts of Example 1. But even though you can find the missing term of a proportion (called **solving the proportion**) by the technique used in Example 1, it is easier to think in terms of **the cross-product divided by the number opposite the unknown.** This method is easier than actually solving the equation because it can be done quickly using a calculator, as shown in the examples following the procedure box.

Solving Proportions

This procedure is essential not only for solving proportion, but also when working with percents in the remainder of this chapter.

> To solve a proposition, use this procedure:
>
> **Step 1** Find the product of the means or the product of the extremes, whichever does not contain the unknown term.
>
> **Step 2** Divide this product by the number that is opposite the unknown term.

EXAMPLE 2

Solving a proportion

Solve the proportion for the unknown term. **a.** $\frac{5}{6} = \frac{55}{y}$ **b.** $\frac{5}{b} = \frac{3}{4}$ **c.** $\frac{2\frac{1}{2}}{5} = \frac{a}{8}$

Solution

a. $\dfrac{5}{6} = \dfrac{55}{y}$

$$y = \frac{6 \times 55}{5} \quad \leftarrow \text{Product of the means} \\ \leftarrow \text{Number opposite the unknown}$$

$$= \frac{6 \times \overset{11}{\cancel{55}}}{\underset{1}{\cancel{5}}}$$

$$= 66$$

The procedure for solving a proportion is easy to carry out when using a calculator:

$\boxed{6}\ \boxed{\times}\ \boxed{55}\ \boxed{\div}\ \boxed{5}\ \boxed{=}$

b. $\dfrac{5}{b} = \dfrac{3}{4}$

$$b = \frac{5 \times 4}{3} \quad \leftarrow \text{Product of the extremes} \\ \leftarrow \text{Number opposite the unknown}$$

$$= \frac{20}{3} \quad \text{or} \quad 6\frac{2}{3}$$

c. $\dfrac{2\frac{1}{2}}{5} = \dfrac{a}{8}$

$$a = \frac{2\frac{1}{2} \times 8}{5} \quad \leftarrow \text{Product of the extremes} \\ \leftarrow \text{Number opposite the unknown}$$

$$= \frac{\frac{5}{2} \times 8}{5}$$

$$= \frac{20}{5}$$

$$= 4$$

Many applied problems can be solved using a proportion. Whenever you are working an applied problem, you should estimate an answer so that you will know whether the result you obtain is reasonable.

When setting up a proportion with units, be sure that like units occupy corresponding positions, as illustrated in Examples 3–5.

EXAMPLE 3   **Problem solving using proportions**

If 4 cans of cola sell for 89¢, how much will 12 cans cost?

Solution
$$\underset{\substack{\uparrow \\ \text{cents}}}{\overset{\substack{\text{cans} \\ \downarrow}}{\frac{4}{89}}} = \underset{\substack{\uparrow \\ \text{cents}}}{\overset{\substack{\text{cans} \\ \downarrow}}{\frac{12}{x}}}$$

$$x = \frac{89 \times \overset{3}{\cancel{12}}}{\underset{1}{\cancel{4}}}$$

$$= 267$$

The cost for 12 cans is $2.67.

EXAMPLE 4   **Problem solving using proportions—again**

If a 120-mile trip took $8\frac{1}{2}$ gallons of gas, how much gas is needed for a 240-mile trip?

Solution
$$\underset{\substack{\uparrow \\ \text{gallons}}}{\overset{\substack{\text{miles} \\ \downarrow}}{\frac{120}{8\frac{1}{2}}}} = \underset{\substack{\uparrow \\ \text{gallons}}}{\overset{\substack{\text{miles} \\ \downarrow}}{\frac{240}{x}}}$$

$$x = \frac{8\frac{1}{2} \times \overset{2}{\cancel{240}}}{\underset{1}{\cancel{120}}}$$

$$= 17$$

The trip will require 17 gallons.

EXAMPLE 5   **Problem solving using proportions—one last time**

If the property tax on a $65,000 home is $416, what is the tax on an $85,000 home?

Solution
$$\underset{\substack{\uparrow \\ \text{tax}}}{\overset{\substack{\text{value} \\ \downarrow}}{\frac{65,000}{416}}} = \underset{\substack{\uparrow \\ \text{tax}}}{\overset{\substack{\text{value} \\ \downarrow}}{\frac{85,000}{x}}}$$

$$x = \frac{416 \times 85,000}{65,000}$$

$$= 544 \quad \textit{You can do the arithmetic by canceling or by using a calculator.}$$

The tax is $544.

PROBLEM SET 4.2

ESSENTIAL IDEAS | LEVEL 1

Write a proportion for each statement in Problems 1–10, and then solve the proportion to find the value of the variable.

1. 9 is to 10 as x is to 20. $\frac{9}{10} = \frac{x}{20}; x = 18$

2. 6 is to 8 as x is to 24. $\frac{6}{8} = \frac{x}{24}; x = 18$

3. 4 is to 9 as y is to 18. $\frac{4}{9} = \frac{y}{18}; y = 8$

4. 4 is to 5 as y is to 10. $\frac{4}{5} = \frac{y}{10}; y = 8$

5. 3 is to t as 15 is to 20. $\frac{3}{t} = \frac{15}{20}; t = 4$

6. 12 is to 27 as t is to 9. $\frac{12}{27} = \frac{t}{9}; t = 4$

7. 12 is to 18 as 8 is to s. $\frac{12}{18} = \frac{8}{s}; s = 12$

8. 7 is to 10 as 84 is to s. $\frac{7}{10} = \frac{84}{s}; s = 120$

9. u is to 18 as 1 is to 2. $\frac{u}{18} = \frac{1}{2}; u = 9$

10. u is to 6 as 1 is to 3. $\frac{u}{6} = \frac{1}{3}; u = 2$

DRILL AND PRACTICE | LEVEL 2

Solve each proportion in Problems 11–18.

11. $\dfrac{6}{1} = \dfrac{x}{3}$ 18

12. $\dfrac{1}{5} = \dfrac{3}{x}$ 15

13. $\dfrac{x}{3} = \dfrac{4}{1}$ 12

14. $\dfrac{5}{x} = \dfrac{1}{6}$ 30

15. $\dfrac{6}{5} = \dfrac{x}{5}$ 6

16. $\dfrac{9}{5} = \dfrac{27}{x}$ 15

17. $\dfrac{4}{3} = \dfrac{x}{6}$ 8

18. $\dfrac{11}{5} = \dfrac{44}{x}$ 20

Solve each proportion in Problems 19–43.

19. $\dfrac{5}{1} = \dfrac{A}{6}$ 30

20. $\dfrac{1}{9} = \dfrac{4}{B}$ 36

21. $\dfrac{C}{2} = \dfrac{5}{1}$ 10

22. $\dfrac{7}{D} = \dfrac{1}{8}$ 56

23. $\dfrac{12}{18} = \dfrac{E}{12}$ 8

24. $\dfrac{12}{15} = \dfrac{20}{F}$ 25

25. $\dfrac{G}{24} = \dfrac{14}{16}$ 21

26. $\dfrac{4}{H} = \dfrac{3}{15}$ 20

27. $\dfrac{2}{3} = \dfrac{I}{24}$ 16

28. $\dfrac{4}{5} = \dfrac{3}{J}$ $\frac{15}{4}$

29. $\dfrac{3}{K} = \dfrac{2}{5}$ $\frac{15}{2}$

30. $\dfrac{L}{18} = \dfrac{5}{6}$ 15

31. $\dfrac{7\frac{1}{5}}{9} = \dfrac{M}{5}$ 4

32. $\dfrac{4}{2\frac{2}{3}} = \dfrac{3}{N}$ 2

33. $\dfrac{P}{4} = \dfrac{4\frac{1}{2}}{6}$ 3

34. $\dfrac{5}{2} = \dfrac{Q}{12\frac{3}{5}}$ $\frac{63}{2}$

35. $\dfrac{5}{R} = \dfrac{7}{12\frac{3}{5}}$ 9

36. $\dfrac{1\frac{1}{3}}{\frac{1}{9}} = \dfrac{S}{2\frac{2}{3}}$ 32

37. $\dfrac{33}{2\frac{1}{5}} = \dfrac{3\frac{3}{4}}{T}$ $\frac{1}{4}$

38. $\dfrac{U}{1\frac{1}{2}} = \dfrac{\frac{1}{2}}{\frac{3}{4}}$ 1

39. $\dfrac{\frac{1}{5}}{\frac{2}{3}} = \dfrac{\frac{3}{4}}{V}$ $\frac{5}{2}$

40. $\dfrac{\frac{3}{7}}{\frac{1}{3}} = \dfrac{W}{\frac{2}{9}}$ $\frac{2}{7}$

41. $\dfrac{\frac{3}{5}}{\frac{1}{2}} = \dfrac{X}{\frac{2}{3}}$ $\frac{4}{5}$

42. $\dfrac{9}{Y} = \dfrac{1\frac{1}{2}}{3\frac{2}{3}}$ 22

43. $\dfrac{Z}{2\frac{1}{3}} = \dfrac{1\frac{1}{2}}{4\frac{1}{5}}$ $\frac{5}{6}$

44. This problem will help you check your work in Problems 19–43. Fill in the capital letters from Problems 19–43 to correspond with their numerical values in the boxes. For example, if

$$\frac{W}{7} = \frac{10}{14}$$

then

$$W = \frac{7 \times 10}{14}$$

$$= 5$$

Now find the box or boxes with number 5 in the corner and fill in the letter *W*. This has already been done for you. (The letter O has also been filled in for you.) Some letters may not appear in the boxes. When you are finished filling in the letters, darken all the blank spaces to separate the words in the secret message. Notice that one of the blank spaces has also been filled in to help you.

Tergiversation

1/4	20	16	32		3	9	O	36	15	8	4
1	2	56	O	1	36	1/4	8	56	15	22	7
5 W	16	15	15	1/3	30	32	32	16	32	1/4	12/5
22	O	1	1/2	16	2	18	25	16	2	56	-
16	2	21	11	8	9	9	O	9	32	!	!

THIS_PROBLEM UNDOUBTEDLY_WILL_ASSIST_YOU_IN_FINDING_ERRORS!!

APPLICATIONS **LEVEL 2**

45. If 4 melons sell for $2.80, how much would 7 melons cost?
$4.90

46. If you can read a 120-page book in 4 hours, how long will it take to read 150 pages? 5 hours

47. If a 184-mile trip took $11\frac{1}{2}$ gallons of gas, how much gas is needed for a 160-mile trip? 10 gallons

48. If a 121-mile trip took $5\frac{1}{2}$ gallons of gas, how many miles can be driven with a full tank of 13 gallons? 286 miles

49. If Roger can type at a rate of 65 words per minute, at this rate, how long (to the nearest minute) will it take him to type a 559-word letter? 9 minutes

50. If Ginger can type a 15,120-word report in 4 hours, how many words per minute does Ginger type (assume a constant rate)? 63 words per minute

51. If a family uses $3\frac{1}{2}$ gallons of milk per week, how much milk will this family need for 4 days? 2 gallons

52. If 2 gallons of paint are needed for 75 ft of fence, how many gallons are needed for 900 ft of fence? 24 gallons

53. If Jack jogs 3 miles in 40 minutes, how long will it take him (to the nearest minute) to jog 2 miles at the same rate?
27 minutes

54. If Jill jogs 2 miles in 15 minutes, how long will it take her (to the nearest minute) to jog 5 miles at the same rate?
38 minutes

55. A moderately active 140-pound person will use 2,100 calories per day to maintain that body weight. How many calories per day are necessary to maintain a moderately active 165-pound person? 2,475 calories

56. You've probably seen advertisements for posters that can be made from any photograph. If the finished poster will be 2 ft by 3 ft, it's likely that part of your original snapshot will be cut off. Suppose that you send in a photo that measures 3 in. by 5 in. If the shorter side of the enlargement will be 2 ft, what size should the longer side of the enlargement be so that the entire snapshot is shown in the poster? $3\frac{1}{3}$ ft or 3 ft 4 in.

57. Suppose you wish to make a scale drawing of your living room, which measures 18 ft by 25 ft. If the shorter side of the drawing is 6 in., how long is the longer side of the scale drawing? $8\frac{1}{3}$ in.

58. If the property tax on a $180,000 home is $1,080, what is the tax on a $130,000 home? $780

RIGHT OR WRONG? **LEVEL 3**

Explain what is wrong, if anything, with the statements in Problems 59–60. Explain your reasoning.

59. To solve a proportion means to reduce the ratios.
F; it means to find the value of the missing or unknown quantity

60. To solve a proportion, a good method is to find the variable by finding the cross-product divided by the number opposite the unknown. T

4.3 Percent

IN THIS WORLD THE POWER OF MATH

"This fruit looks ready for shipment," said Cal. "Do you think we'll make enough to cover our expenses this year?"

"I have my doubts," answered Roberta. "I just read that the July numbers show that the Consumer Price Index rose by 0.4 percent."

We can pick up almost any newspaper and find some application of percent. In this section, we discuss percents and relate working with percents to solving proportions.

 See Problem 8.

Percent is a commonly used word, which you can find daily in any newspaper.

Percent | **Percent** is the ratio of a given number to 100. This means that a percent is the numerator of a fraction whose denominator is 100.

The symbol % is used to indicate percent. Consider some examples from one issue of a local newspaper.

EXAMPLE 1 Meaning of percent

Illustrate the meaning of percent in the following quotes.

a. "The President recommended an 8 percent cost-of-living raise in Social Security payments."

b. "$33\frac{1}{3}$% OFF"

Solution

a. "8 percent" means "the ratio of 8 to 100."

b. "$33\frac{1}{3}$%" means "the ratio of $33\frac{1}{3}$ to 100."

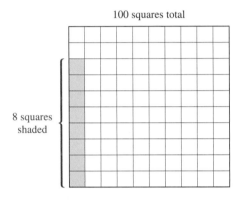

100 squares total

8 squares shaded

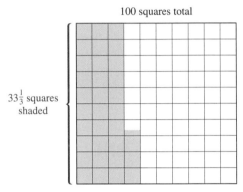

100 squares total

$33\frac{1}{3}$ squares shaded

Since a percent is a ratio, percents can easily be written in fractional form.

*31st Yearbook of the National Council of Teachers of Mathematics (1969), pp. 146–147.

EXAMPLE 2   **Writing percents as fractions**

Write the following percents as simplified fractions.

a. "Sale 75% OFF"   **b.** "SALARIES UP 6.8%"

Solution

a. 75% means a "ratio of 75 to 100": $\dfrac{75}{100} = \dfrac{3}{4}$

b. 6.8% means a "ratio of 6.8 to 100": $6.8 \div 100 = 6\dfrac{8}{10} \div 100$

$$= 6\dfrac{4}{5} \div 100$$

$$= \dfrac{\overset{17}{\cancel{34}}}{5} \times \dfrac{1}{\underset{50}{\cancel{100}}}$$

$$= \dfrac{17}{250}$$ ●

Percents can also be written as decimals. Since a percent is a ratio of a number to 100, we can divide by 100 by moving the decimal point, as we discussed in Chapter 1.

Percent to Decimal

> To express a percent as a decimal, shift the decimal point two places to the *left* and delete the % symbol. If the percent involves a fraction, write the fraction as a decimal; *then* shift the decimal point.

EXAMPLE 3   **Writing percents as decimals**

Write each percent in decimal form.

a. 8 percent   **b.** 6.8%   **c.** $33\frac{1}{3}\%$ **d.** $\frac{1}{2}\%$

Solution

a. 8%
　↑
　└ If a decimal point is not shown, it is always understood to be at the right of the whole number.
0.08 %
　↑┘ Shift the decimal point two places to the left; add zeros as placeholders, if necessary. Delete % symbol.

Answer: 8% = 0.08

b. 6.8%   *Think:*   6.8%
　　　　　　　　　　↑┘ Shift two places, add placeholders as necessary, and delete percent symbol.

Answer: 6.8% = 0.068

c. $33\dfrac{1}{3}\%$ *Think:* $33\dfrac{1}{3}\%$
　　　　　　　　　　　　　↑ └ Decimal point is understood.

Answer: $33\frac{1}{3}\% = 0.33\frac{1}{3}$ or   0.333...

d. $\frac{1}{2}\%$

$\dfrac{1}{2} = 0.5$,   so $\dfrac{1}{2}\% = 0.5\%$ *Think:*   00.5%
　　　　　　　　　　　　　　　　　　　　　　　　↑┘

Answer: 0.5% = 0.005   ●

TABLE 4.1	Fraction/Decimal/Percent Conversion Chart		
To: From:	**Fraction**	**Decimal**	**Percent**
Fraction		Divide the numerator (top) by the denominator (bottom). Write as a terminating or as a repeating decimal (bar notation).	First change the fraction to a decimal by carrying out the division to two decimal places and writing the remainder as a fraction. *Then* move the decimal point two places to the right, and affix a % symbol.
Terminating Decimal	Write the decimal without the decimal point, and multiply by the decimal name of the last digit (rightmost digit).		Shift the decimal point two places to the *right*, and affix a % symbol.
Percent	Write as the ratio to 100, and reduce the fraction. If the percent involves a decimal, first write the decimal in fractional form, and then delete the % symbol and multiply by $\frac{1}{100}$. If the percent involves a fraction, delete the % symbol and multiply by $\frac{1}{100}$.	Shift the decimal point two places to the *left*, and delete the % symbol. If the percent involves a fraction, first write the fraction as a decimal, and then shift the decimal point.	

Spend some time with this table. In fact, you may want to place a marker on this page for future reference.

The primary objective of this section is to develop the ability to express a number amount in any of three important forms, as summarized in Table 4.1.

As you can see from the examples, every number can be written in three forms: fraction, decimal, and percent. We discussed changing from fraction to decimal in Section 1.3 and changing from a terminating decimal to a fraction in Section 1.6, so we'll focus on the other transformations in this section.

EXAMPLE 4

Changing from decimal form

Write decimal forms as percents and fractions. **a.** 0.85 **b.** 2.485

Solution

a. Look in the terminating decimal row in Table 4.1, and follow the directions for changing a terminating decimal to a percent. We move the decimal point two places to the right and affix a % symbol: $0.85 = 85\%$

Decimal understood

To change to fractional form, we can convert the decimal to a fraction (see Section 1.3) or we can use Table 4.1 to change the percent to a fraction: 85% means $\frac{85}{100} = \frac{17}{20}$.

b. Change decimal to a percent (two places): $2.485 = 248.5\%$
Change percent to a fraction:

$$248.5\% \text{ means } 248.5 \times \frac{1}{100} = 248\frac{1}{2} \times \frac{1}{100} = \frac{497}{2} \times \frac{1}{100} = \frac{497}{200} \text{ or } 2\frac{97}{200}$$

EXAMPLE 5	**Changing fractions to percents**

Write each fraction in percent form.   **a.** $\frac{5}{8}$ **b.** $\frac{5}{6}$

Solution

a. Look in the fraction row in Table 4.1, and follow the directions for changing a fraction to a percent.

First, change the fraction to a decimal (use division or a calculator): $\frac{5}{8} = 0.625$

Then, move the decimal point two places to the right and affix a percent symbol:
$0.\,625 = 62.5\%$

b. Change the fraction to a decimal but stop after two places and save the remainder:
$$\frac{5}{6} = 0.83\tfrac{1}{3}$$

Then, move the decimal point: $0.83\tfrac{1}{3} = 83\tfrac{1}{3}\%.$

This decimal point is understood.

PROBLEM SET 4.3

ESSENTIAL IDEAS   LEVEL 1

1. What is a percent?   *Percent is the ratio of a number to 100.*

2. **IN YOUR OWN WORDS** How do you convert a percent to a decimal?

3. **IN YOUR OWN WORDS** How do you convert a percent to a fraction?

4. **IN YOUR OWN WORDS** How do you convert a terminating decimal to a percent?

5. **IN YOUR OWN WORDS** How do you convert a terminating decimal to a fraction?

6. **IN YOUR OWN WORDS** How do you convert a fraction to a percent?

7. **IN YOUR OWN WORDS** How do you convert a fraction to a decimal?

DRILL AND PRACTICE   LEVEL 2

Write the percents in Problems 8–14 as simplified fractions.

8. SALE 50% OFF $\frac{1}{2}$

9. At the beginning of the year there were two persons out of work in Luxembourg, and by the end of the year, unemployment had spiraled to 11, making the unemployment figure jump by 550%. $5\frac{1}{2}$ or $\frac{11}{2}$

10. There was a 13.4 percent increase in the use of electricity. $\frac{67}{500}$

11. The weight of a certain model of automobile was decreased by 3.7 percent. $\frac{37}{1,000}$

12. Ivory Soap is $99\frac{44}{100}\%$ pure. $\frac{1,243}{1,250}$

13. In 2006, the sales tax in Pennsylvania was 6%. $\frac{3}{50}$

14. In 2006, the stock market rose 15% during a one-month period. $\frac{3}{20}$

In Problems 15–55, change the given form into the two missing forms.

	Fraction	*Decimal*	*Percent*
15.	$\frac{1}{2}$	0.50	50%
16.	$\frac{1}{4}$	0.25	25%
17.	$\frac{1}{8}$	0.125	$12\frac{1}{2}\%$
18.	$\frac{3}{8}$	0.375	$37\frac{1}{2}\%$
19.	$\frac{1}{3}$	$0.\overline{3}$	$33\frac{1}{3}\%$
20.	$\frac{1}{5}$	0.2	20%
21.	$\frac{2}{5}$	0.4	40%

	Fraction	Decimal	Percent
22.	$\dfrac{3}{20}$	0.15	15%
23.	$\dfrac{2}{3}$	$0.\overline{6}$	$66\frac{2}{3}\%$
24.	$\dfrac{5}{6}$	$0.8\overline{3}$	$83\frac{1}{3}\%$
25.	$\dfrac{1}{12}$	$0.08\overline{3}$	$8\frac{1}{3}\%$
26.	$\dfrac{5}{36}$	$0.13\overline{8}$	$13\frac{8}{9}\%$
27.	$\dfrac{5}{9}$	$0.\overline{5}$	$55\frac{5}{9}\%$
28.	$\dfrac{1}{7}$	$0.\overline{142857}$	$14\frac{2}{7}\%$
29.	$\frac{3}{4}$	0.75	75%
30.	$\frac{1}{5}$	0.2	20%
31.	$\frac{17}{20}$	0.85	85%
32.	$\frac{19}{20}$	0.95	95%
33.	$\frac{9}{10}$	0.9	90%
34.	$\frac{1}{20}$	0.05	5%
35.	$\frac{3}{20}$	0.15	15%
36.	$\frac{7}{20}$	0.35	35%
37.	$\frac{13}{20}$	0.65	65%
38.	$\frac{7}{40}$	0.175	$17\frac{1}{2}\%$
39.	$\frac{3}{8}$	0.375	$37\frac{1}{2}\%$
40.	$\frac{3}{80}$	0.0375	3.75%
41.	$\frac{7}{8}$	0.875	$87\frac{1}{2}\%$
42.	$\frac{1}{400}$	0.0025	0.25%
43.	$\frac{2}{5}$	0.4	40%
44.	$\frac{4}{5}$	0.8	80%
45.	1	1	100%
46.	2	2	200%

	Fraction	Decimal	Percent
47.	$\frac{3}{5}$	0.6	60%
48.	$\frac{13}{20}$	0.65	65%
49.	$\frac{9}{20}$	0.45	45%
50.	$\frac{1}{25}$	0.04	4%
51.	$\frac{2}{25}$	0.08	8%
52.	$\frac{13}{200}$	0.065	$6\frac{1}{2}\%$
53.	$\frac{5}{8}$	0.625	$62\frac{1}{2}\%$
54.	$\frac{2}{9}$	$0.\overline{2}$	$22\frac{2}{9}\%$
55.	$\frac{1}{9}$	$0.\overline{1}$	$11\frac{1}{9}\%$

APPLICATIONS LEVEL 2

Grades in a classroom are often given according to the percentage score obtained by the student. Suppose that a teacher grades according to the following scheme, where all scores are rounded to the nearest percent:

A 90%–100%
B 80%–89%
C 65%–79%
D 50%–64%
F 0%–49%

To determine a percent grade, form a ratio of score received to possible score and then write this ratio as a percent. For example, if a student gets seven answers right out of a possible ten, his or her percent score is

$$\frac{7}{10} = 70\%$$

Calculate the percent (nearest percent) and determine the letter grade for each score given in Problems 56–59.

56. Possible 10 points

   a. 7   70%; C   **b.** 8   80%; B

   c. $7\frac{1}{2}$ 75%; C   **d.** $8\frac{1}{4}$ 82.5%; B

57. Possible 100 points

   a. 75   75%; C   **b.** 92   92%; A

   c. 38   38%; F   **d.** $66\frac{1}{2}$ 67%; C

58. Possible 200 points

   a. 160   80%   **b.** 150   75%; C

   c. 155   78%; C   **d.** 120   60%; D

59. Possible 1200 points

    a. 900   *75%; C*   **b.** 780   *65%; C*

    c. 816   *68%; C*   **d.** 1000   *83%; B*

RIGHT OR WRONG?   **LEVEL 3**

60. What is wrong, if anything, with the statement "the square root of 25% is 50%."   *Nothing is wrong; it is true.*

(4.4) Problem Solving with Percents

IN THIS WORLD   THE POWER OF MATH

"Hi, Guy," said Charley. "You will never believe how much I just paid for taxes."

"You've got to be kidding!" retorted Guy. "We paid $4,437 in taxes last year, and that was 29% of my income! Can you imagine that! Twenty-nine percent is almost one dollar out of every three dollars I earn."

We will discuss problem solving with percent problems in this section. In Example 8, we will ask the question, "What is Guy's total income?"

 See Problem 47.

TABLE 4.2	Fraction Comparison
Percent	**Fraction**
10%	$\frac{1}{10}$
25%	$\frac{1}{4}$
$33\frac{1}{3}$%	$\frac{1}{3}$
50%	$\frac{1}{2}$

Percent problems are very common. We begin this section with a discussion of estimation, and then we conclude with some percent calculations.

    The first estimation method is the **unit fraction-conversion method,** which can be used to estimate the common percents of 10%, 25%, $33\frac{1}{3}$%, and 50%. To estimate the size of a part of a whole quantity, which is sometimes called a **percentage,** rewrite the percent as a fraction (see Table 4.2) and mentally multiply, as shown in Example 1.

EXAMPLE 1   **Using the unit fraction-conversion method**

Use the unit fraction-conversion method to find the requested percentages.

    a. 50% of 800   **b.** 25% of 1,200   **c.** $33\frac{1}{3}$% of 600   **d.** 10% of 824

Solution   Mathematically, the word "of" means "multiply"; refer to Table 4.2 for the percents. The steps shown in this example should be done mentally, with no written work necessary.

$$50\% \text{ of } 800: \quad \tfrac{1}{2} \times 800 = 400; \quad \textit{Think: } 800 \div 2 = 400$$
$$25\% \text{ of } 1,200: \quad \tfrac{1}{4} \times 1,200 = 300; \quad \textit{Think: } 1,200 \div 4 = 300$$
$$33\tfrac{1}{3}\% \text{ of } 600: \quad \tfrac{1}{3} \times 600 = 200; \quad \textit{Think: } 600 \div 3 = 200$$
$$10\% \text{ of } 824: \quad \tfrac{1}{10} \times 824 = 82.4; \quad \textit{Think: } 824 \div 10 = 82.4 \qquad \bullet$$

    If the numbers for which you are finding a percentage are not as "nice" as those given in Example 1, you can estimate by rounding the number, as shown in Example 2.

EXAMPLE 2

Estimating percentages

Estimate the following percentages:

a. 25% of 312   **b.** 50% of 843   **c.** $33\frac{1}{3}$% of 1,856   **d.** 25% of 43,350

Solution

a. Estimate 25% of 312 by rounding 312 so that it is easily divisible by 4:
$$\frac{1}{4} \times 320 = 80 \quad \text{Find } 320 \div 4 = 80.$$

b. Estimate 50% of 843 by rounding 843 so that it is easily divisible by 2:
$$\frac{1}{2} \times 840 = 420 \quad \text{Find } 840 \div 2 = 420.$$

c. Estimate $33\frac{1}{3}$% of 1,856 by rounding 1,856 so that it is *easily* divisible by 3:
$$\frac{1}{3} \times 1,800 = 600 \quad \text{Find } 1,800 \div 3 = 600.$$

d. Estimate 25% of 43,350 by rounding 43,350 so that it is *easily* divisible by 4:
$$\frac{1}{4} \times 44,000 = 11,000$$

●

The second estimation procedure uses a multiple of a unit fraction. For example,

Think of 75% as $\frac{3}{4}$, which is $3 \times \frac{1}{4}$.

Think of $66\frac{2}{3}$% as $\frac{2}{3}$, which is $2 \times \frac{1}{3}$.

Think of 60% as $\frac{6}{10}$, which is $6 \times \frac{1}{10}$.

EXAMPLE 3

Estimating percents using multiples

Estimate the following percentages.

a. 75% of 943   **b.** $66\frac{2}{3}$% of 8,932   **c.** 60% of 954   **d.** 80% of 0.983

Solution

a. 75% of 943 $\approx \dfrac{3}{4} \times 1,000$ **b.** $66\frac{2}{3}$% of 8,932 $\approx \dfrac{2}{3} \times 9,000$

$\qquad = 3\left(\dfrac{1}{4} \times 1,000\right)$ $\qquad = 2\left(\dfrac{1}{3} \times 9,000\right)$

$\qquad = 750$ $\qquad = 6,000$

c. 60% of 954 $\approx \dfrac{6}{10} \times 1,000$ **d.** 80% of 0.983 $\approx \dfrac{8}{10} \times 1$

$\qquad = 6\left(\dfrac{1}{10} \times 1,000\right)$ $\qquad = 0.8$

$\qquad = 600$

●

Many percentage problems are more difficult than those thus far considered in this chapter. The following quotation was found in a recent publication: "An elected official is one who gets 51 percent of the vote cast by 40 percent of the 60 percent of voters who registered." Certainly, most of us will have trouble understanding the percents given in this quotation; but you can't pick up a newspaper without seeing dozens of examples of ideas that require some understanding of percents. A difficult job for most of us is knowing whether to multiply or divide by the given numbers. In this section, I provide you with a sure-fire method for knowing what to do. The first step is to understand what is meant by **the percent problem.**

The Percent Problem

Study this percent problem. If you learn this, you get a written guarantee for correctly working percent problems.

A	is $P\%$	of W
↓	↓	↓
This is the given amount.	The percent is written $\dfrac{P}{100}$	This is the whole quantity. It always follows the word "of."

The percent problem won't always be stated in this form, but notice that three quantities are associated with it:

CAUTION Read these three steps SLOWLY!

1. The *amount*—sometimes called the **percentage**

2. The *percent*—sometimes called the **rate**

3. The *whole quantity*—sometimes called the **base**

Now, regardless of the form in which you are given the percent problem, follow these steps to write a proportion:

1. Identify the *percent* first; it will be followed by the symbol % or the word *percent*. Write it as a fraction:

$$\frac{P}{100}$$

2. Identify the *whole quantity* next; it is preceded by the word *of*. It is the denominator of the second fraction in the proportion:

$$\frac{P}{100} = \frac{}{W} \quad \leftarrow \text{This is the quantity following the word "of."}$$

3. The remaining number is the partial amount; it is the numerator of the second fraction in the proportion:

$$\frac{P}{100} = \frac{A}{W} \quad \leftarrow \text{This is the last quantity to be inserted into the proportion.}$$

EXAMPLE 4

Identifying the parts of a percent problem

For each of the following cases, identify the percent, the whole quantity, and the amount (the percentage or part), and then write a proportion.

a. What number is 18% of 200?   **b.** 18% of 200 is what number?

c. 150 is 12% of what number?   **d.** 63 is what percent of 420?

e. 18% of what number is 72?   **f.** 120 is what percent of 60?

Solution

	Percent, P (%)	*Whole, W* ("of")	*Amount, A* (part)	*Proportion* $\dfrac{P}{100} = \dfrac{A}{W}$
a. What number is 18% of 200?	18	200	unknown	$\dfrac{18}{100} = \dfrac{A}{200}$
b. 18% of 200 is what number?	18	200	unknown	$\dfrac{18}{100} = \dfrac{A}{200}$

	Percent, P	Whole, W	Amount, A	Proportion
	(%)	("of")	(part)	$\dfrac{P}{100} = \dfrac{A}{W}$
c. 150 is 12% of what number?	12	unknown	150	$\dfrac{12}{100} = \dfrac{150}{W}$
d. 63 is what percent of 420?	unknown	420	63	$\dfrac{P}{100} = \dfrac{63}{420}$
e. 18% of what number is 72?	18	unknown	72	$\dfrac{18}{100} = \dfrac{72}{W}$
f. 120 is what percent of 60?	unknown	60	120	$\dfrac{P}{100} = \dfrac{120}{60}$

Regardless of the arrangement of the question, identify *P* first.

Second, identify the number following the word "of."

This number is identified last.

●

Since there are only three letters in the proportion

$$\frac{P}{100} = \frac{A}{W}$$

there are three types of percent problems. These possible types were illustrated in Example 4. To answer a question involving a percent, write a proportion and then solve the proportion. Try solving each proportion in Example 4. The answers are:
a. $A = 36$; **b.** $A = 36$; **c.** $W = 1,250$; **d.** $P = 15$; **e.** $W = 400$; **f.** $P = 200$.

EXAMPLE 5   Problem solving with percents

In a certain class there are 500 points possible. The lowest C grade is 65% of the possible points. How many points are equal to the lowest C grade?

Solution   What is 65% of 500 points?

$$\frac{65}{100} = \frac{A}{500} \quad \leftarrow \text{This is the quantity following the word "of."}$$

$$A = \frac{65 \times \overset{5}{500}}{\underset{1}{100}}$$

$$= 325$$

Check by estimation: 65% of 500 $\approx 6(\frac{1}{10} \times 500) = 300$. The lowest C grade is 325 points. ●

EXAMPLE 6   Problem solving with percents—again

If your monthly salary is \$4,500 and 21% is withheld for taxes and Social Security, how much money will be withheld from your check on payday?

Solution   How much is 21% of \$4,500?

$$\frac{21}{100} = \frac{A}{4,500} \quad \leftarrow \text{This is the last quantity to be inserted into the proportion.}$$

$$A = \frac{21 \times 4,500}{100} = 945$$

Check by estimation: 21% of 4,500 $\approx 2(\frac{1}{10} \times 4,500) = 900$. The withholding is \$945. ●

EXAMPLE 7

More problem solving with percents

You make a $25 purchase, and the clerk adds $2.25 for sales tax. This doesn't seem right to you, so you want to know what percent tax has been charged.

Solution   What percent of $25 is $2.25?

$$\frac{P}{100} = \frac{2.25}{25}$$

$$\frac{100 \times 2.25}{25} = P$$

$$9 = P$$

Check by estimation: 9% of $25 \approx \frac{1}{10} \times 25 = 2.50$. The tax charged was 9%.   ●

EXAMPLE 8

Problem solving with percents—again and again

Your neighbors tell you that they paid $4,437 in taxes last year, and this amounted to 29% of their total income. What was their total income? (See "In This World" at the beginning of this section.)

Solution   29% of total income is $4,437.

$$\frac{29}{100} = \frac{4,437}{W}$$

$$\frac{100 \times 4,437}{29} = W$$

$$15,300 = W$$

Check by estimation: 29% of $15,300 \approx 3(\frac{1}{10} \times 15,000) = 3(1,500) = 4,500$. Since $4,500 is an estimate for $4,437, we conclude the result is correct. Their total income was $15,300.   ●

EXAMPLE 9

Percent decrease followed by a percent increase

In 2000–2001, the Nasdaq experienced a decline from approximately 5,000 (5,048.62 on March 10, 2000) to approximately 1,600 (1,619.58 on April 1, 2001). What is the percent of this decline? What is the percent increase necessary for the Nasdaq to climb back to its previous high?

Solution   From 5,000 to 1,600 is a decline of 3,400 points, so we have "3,400 is what percent of 5,000?"

$$\frac{P}{100} = \frac{3,400}{5,000}$$

$$P = \frac{100 \times 3,400}{5,000}$$

$$= 68\%$$

The stock market decline was 68%.

To increase from 1,600 to 5,000 is an increase of 3,400, so we ask, "3,400 is what percent of 1,600?"

$$\frac{P}{100} = \frac{3,400}{1,600}$$

$$P = \frac{100 \times 3,400}{1,600}$$

$$= 212.5$$

To regain its previous level, the Nasdaq will need to increase by approximately 213%. Note that a 68% decline requires a 213% increase to restore the original amount. ●

WARNING!   You must be careful not to add percents. For example, suppose you have $100 and spend 50%. How much have you spent, and how much do you have left?

Amount spent	*Remainder*
$50	$50

Now, suppose you spend 50% of the remainder. How much have you spent, and how much is left?

New spending	*Old spending*	*Remainder*
$25	$50	$25

This means you have spent $75 or 75% of your original bankroll. A common ERROR is to say "50% spending + 50% spending = 100% spending." **Remember, if you add percents, you often obtain incorrect results.**

EXAMPLE 10   **A common error from a newspaper**

A newspaper headline proclaimed

> # Teen drug use soars 105%
>
> WASHINGTON – Teen drug use rose 105% between 1995 and 1997.
>   A national survey showed that between 1995 and 1996 youth drug use rose 30%, but between 1996 and 1997 usage soared to 75%.
>   Over the two year period, the rise of 105% was attributed to ...

What is wrong with this headline?

Solution   We are not given all the available numbers, but consider the following possibility:
Suppose there are 100 drug users, so a rise of

> 100 to 130 is a 30% increase
>
> 130 to 227 is a 75% increase
>
> 100 to 227 is a 127% increase, NOT 30% + 75% = 105%

Remember, adding percents can give faulty results. ●

PROBLEM SET (4.4)

ESSENTIAL IDEAS   LEVEL 1

1. **IN YOUR OWN WORDS** Describe the "percent problem."

2. **IN YOUR OWN WORDS** Explain what is meant by each of the following words: percentage, rate, base.

DRILL AND PRACTICE   LEVEL 2

Estimate the percentages in Problems 3–14.   Estimates vary.

3. 50% of 2,010   *1,000*

4. 25% of 415   *100*

5. 10% of 90,200   *9,000*

6. 10% of 88.6   *9*

7. 50% of 9,800   *5,000*

8. $33\frac{1}{3}$% of 3,060   *1,000*

9. 25% of 819   *200*

10. 25% of 790   *200*

11. 75% of 1,058   *750*

12. 75% of 94   *75*

13. $66\frac{2}{3}$% of 8,600   *6,000*

14. $66\frac{2}{3}$% of 35   *24*

Write each sentence in Problems 15–30 as a proportion, and then solve to answer the question.

15. What number is 15% of 64? $\frac{15}{100} = \frac{A}{64}$; 9.6

16. What number is 120% of 16? $\frac{120}{100} = \frac{A}{16}$; 19.2

17. 14% of what number is 21? $\frac{14}{100} = \frac{21}{w}$; 150

18. 40% of what number is 60? $\frac{40}{100} = \frac{60}{w}$; 150

19. 10 is what percent of 5? $\frac{P}{100} = \frac{10}{5}$; 200%

20. What percent of $20 is $1.20? $\frac{P}{100} = \frac{1.2}{20}$; 6%

21. 4 is what percent of 5? $\frac{P}{100} = \frac{4}{5}$; 80%

22. What percent of 12 is 9? $\frac{P}{100} = \frac{9}{12}$; 75%

23. What percent of 5 is 25? $\frac{P}{100} = \frac{25}{5}$; 500%

24. 49 is 35% of what number? $\frac{35}{100} = \frac{49}{w}$; 140

25. 3 is 12% of what number? $\frac{12}{100} = \frac{3}{w}$; 25

26. 21 is $66\frac{2}{3}$% of what number? $\frac{66\frac{2}{3}}{100} = \frac{21}{w}$; 31.5

27. 12 is $33\frac{1}{3}$% of what number? $\frac{33\frac{1}{3}}{100} = \frac{12}{w}$; 36

28. What is 8% of $2,425? $\frac{8}{100} = \frac{A}{2,425}$; $194

29. What is 6% of $8,150? $\frac{6}{100} = \frac{A}{8,150}$; $489

30. 400% of what number is 150? $\frac{400}{100} = \frac{150}{w}$; 37.5

APPLICATIONS   LEVEL 2

The book 100% American *(New York: Poseidon Press, 1988) by Daniel Evan Weiss is a book of "facts" about American opinions. The percentages in Problems 31–38 are taken from this book. In estimating the numbers in Problems 31–38, assume that the questions refer to the 180 million adult Americans.* Estimates vary.

31. 50% of American adults are men.
    90 million (think 180 ÷ 2)

32. 50% of American men (see Problem 31) are shorter than 5 ft 9 in.   45 million (think 90 ÷ 2)

33. 25% of Americans never exercise at all.
    45 million (think 180 ÷ 4)

34. 10% of Americans say the car is the greatest invention of all time.   18 million (think 180 ÷ 10)

35. 90% of Americans consider themselves happy people.
    162 million (think 9 × 18)

36. 40% of Americans do not think a college education is important to succeed in the business world.   72 million (think 4 × 18)

37. 3% of Americans think Elvis Presley was history's most exciting figure.   5.4 million (think: 1.8 × 3 ≈ 2 × 3 = 6)

38. 6% of Americans believe the single greatest element in happiness is great wealth. 12 million (think 1.8 × 6 ≈ 2 × 6 = 12 or can double the results of Problem 37 to estimate 10.8 million

39. If 11% of the 180 million adult Americans live in poverty, how many adult Americans live in poverty?   19.8 million

40. If 6.2% of the 180 million adult Americans are unemployed, how many adult Americans are unemployed?
    11.16 million

41. If the sales tax is 6% and the purchase price is $181, what is the amount of tax? $10.86

42. If the sales tax is 5.5% and purchase price is $680, what is the amount of tax? $37.40

43. If you were charged $151 in taxes on a $3,020 purchase, what percent tax were you charged?   5%

44. If a government worker will receive a pension of 80% of her present salary, what will the pension be if her monthly salary is $4,250? $3,400

45. Government regulations require that, for certain companies to receive federal grant money, 15% of the total number of employees must meet minority requirements. If a company employs 390 people, how many minority people should be employed to meet the minimum requirements?   59 (You can't employ half a person.)

46. If $14,300 has been contributed to the United Way fund drive and this amount represents 22% of the goal, what is the United Way goal? $65,000

47. If Brad's monthly salary is $8,200, and 32% is withheld for taxes and Social Security, how much money is withheld each month?   The tax withheld is $2,624.

48. A certain test is worth 125 points. How many points (rounded to the nearest point) are needed to obtain a score of 75%?
94 points

49. If you correctly answer 8 out of 12 questions on a quiz, what is your percentage right? $66\frac{2}{3}\%$

50. If Carlos answered 18 out of 20 questions on a test correctly, what was his percentage right? 90%

51. If Wendy answered 15 questions correctly and obtained 75%, how many questions were on the test? 20 questions

52. Shannon Sovndal received an 8% raise, which amounted to $100 per month. What was his old wage, and what will his new wage be? The old wage was $1,250 and the new wage is $1,350.

53. An advertisement for a steel-belted radial tire states that this tire delivers 15% better gas mileage. If the present gas mileage is 25.5 MPG, what mileage would you expect if you purchased these tires? Round your answer to the nearest tenth of a mile per gallon. 29.3 MPG

54. A drop from 50 to 10 is a loss of 80%; what is the percent gain from 10 to 50? 400%

55. What is the product of 5% and 20%? Write your answer as a percent. 1%

56. What is the quotient of 5% and 20%? Write your answer as a percent. 25%

RIGHT OR WRONG? LEVEL 3

Explain what is wrong, if anything, with the statements in Problems 57–60. Explain your reasoning.

57. The percent problem has three parts: the percent, the whole quantity, and the partial amount. T

58. The first quantity to be identified when solving the percent problem is the percent. It is the quantity preceding a percent symbol or the word "percent." T

59. The second quantity to be identified when solving the percent problem is the whole quantity. It is the quantity preceded by the word "of." T

60. The newspaper clipping shown here was printed in a newspaper as a letter to the editor during the 1998 military build-up in the Middle East. What is wrong with John's complaint about "the new math"? 50% of 50% is 25%. Multiply decimals, do not add; that is, "of" means multiply.

> ## Military math
>
> **Editor:** Let me see if I have this right. During the Gulf War, I kept hearing news reports that allied forces had destroyed 90 percent of Iraq's war-making capability. Then the news reports said that brave U.N. inspectors had forced Iraq to destroy another 90 percent several times. In the last few months news reports said that Iraq itself had destroyed 90 percent of its weapons at least a couple of times as a show of earnest good faith.
>
> All told, then, some 450 percent of the Iraqi military was wiped out, and yet somehow they are massing forces against Iran. Now I hear news reports say that Saddam Hussein is still a threat and that there may be another October surprise.
>
> Did I miss something in those news reports? Did the news people miss something? 450 percent? Must be the new math.
>
> JOHN
> Rohnert Park

4.5 Chapter 4 Summary and Review

Take some time getting ready to work the review problems in this section. First, look back at the definition and property boxes. You will maximize your understanding of this chapter by working the problems in this section only after you have studied the material.

IMPORTANT TERMS

Numbers refer to sections of this chapter.

Spending some time with the terms and objectives of this chapter will pay dividends in assuring your success.

Base [4.4]
~~Extremes [4.1]~~
Means [4.1]
Percent [4.3]
Percent problem [4.4]
Percentage [4.4]

Property of proportions [4.1]
Proportion [4.1]
Rate [4.4]
Ratio [4.1]
Solve a proportion [4.2]

Essential Ideas

[4.1] Problem 1   What is a ratio? What is a proportion?

    Problem 2   Know the property of proportions.

[4.2] Problems 1–10   Write a statement as a proportion and solve for an unknown.

[4.3] Problem 1   What is a percent?

    Problems 2–7   Know how to convert from one form to another:

         (1) fraction to a decimal

         (2) fraction to a percent

         (3) terminating decimal to a fraction

         (4) terminating decimal to a percent

         (5) percent to a fraction

         (6) percent to decimal

[4.4] Problem 1   Understand the percent problem.

    Problem 2   Understand the words *percentage, rate,* and *base.*

LEARNING OUTCOMES

The material in this chapter is reviewed in the following list of learning outcomes. A self-test (with answers and suggestions for additional study) is given. This self-test is constructed so that each problem number corresponds to a related objective. For example, Problem 7 is testing Objective 4.7. This self-test is followed by a practice test with the questions in mixed order.

[4.1]   *Objective* 4.1   Reduce a ratio to lowest terms.

[4.1]   *Objective* 4.2   Read a proportion, and name the means and extremes. Decide whether a given pair of ratios forms a proportion.

[4.1]   *Objective* 4.3   Solve applied ratio problems.

[4.2]   *Objective* 4.4   Solve a proportion.

[4.2]   *Objective* 4.5   Solve applied proportion problems.

[4.3]   *Objective* 4.6   Write percents as simplified fractions.

[4.3]   *Objective* 4.7   Change fractions to decimals and percents.

[4.3]   *Objective* 4.8   Change decimals to fractions and percents.

[4.3]   *Objective* 4.9   Change percents to fractions and decimals.

[4.4]   *Objective* 4.10   Estimate percentages.

[4.4]   *Objective* 4.11   Solve percent problems.

[4.3; 4.4] *Objective* 4.12   Solve applied percent problems (Problems 12–15).

Self-Test

Each question of this self-test is related to the corresponding objective listed above.

1. If the ratio of miles to gallons is 154 to 5.5, what is this as a reduced ratio?
2. Do $\frac{7}{2}$ and $\frac{21}{8}$ form a proportion?
3. The ratio of errors to correct answers is 4 per 100; write this as a simplified ratio.
4. Solve the proportion $\frac{25}{x} = \frac{575}{138}$.

5. If the ratio of wins to losses is 3 to 5, how many losses would you expect if there are 882 wins?

6. If a summer sale advertises 20% off, what is this discount written as a simplified fraction?

7. Write the fraction $\frac{5}{12}$ as a decimal and as a percent.

8. Write the decimal 0.005 as a fraction and as a percent.

9. Write the percent $8\frac{1}{2}\%$ as a fraction and as a decimal.

10. Estimate 25% of 412.

11. 85% of what number is 170?

12. The 2000 U.S. census set the population at 281,421,906. The Census Bureau estimates that from April 1, 2000, to October 1, 2006, the population increased by 6.6%. What is the U.S. population in October 2006 according to Census Bureau estimates?

13. In a certain class there are 500 possible points. The lowest B grade is 80%. How many points are needed to obtain the lowest B grade?

14. If inflation is 0.9% and your salary is $42,500, what should your salary be next year to keep pace with inflation?

15. A saleswoman complained to her friend that she had had a bad day. She had made only two sales, for $1,500 each. On the first sale she had made a profit of 30% on the cost price, but on the second one she had taken a 30% loss on the cost price. "That doesn't seem to be any loss at all," said the friend. "Your profit and loss balance each other." "On the contrary," said the saleswoman, "I lost almost $300, overall." Who was right, the saleswoman or the friend? Justify your answer.

 STOP

STUDY HINTS *Compare your solutions and answers to the self-test. For each problem you missed, work some additional problems in the section listed in the margin. After you have worked these problems, you can test yourself with the practice test.*

Additional Problems

[4.1] Problems 3–13

[4.1] Problems 14–37

[4.1] Problems 39–54

[4.2] Problems 11–43

Complete Solutions to the Self-Test

1. $\dfrac{154}{5.5} = \dfrac{1,540}{55} = \dfrac{28}{1}$; the ratio of miles to gallons is 28 to 1.

2. Means   Extremes

   2×21 7×8

   $42 \neq 56$

   These ratios do not form a proportion.

3. $\dfrac{\text{ERRORS}}{\text{CORRECT ANSWERS}} = \dfrac{4}{100}$

   $= \dfrac{1}{25}$

   The error rate is 1 to 25.

4. $\dfrac{25}{x} = \dfrac{575}{138}$

   $x = \dfrac{25 \times 138}{575}$

   $= 6$

   The value of x is 6.

5. Set up $\dfrac{\text{WINS}}{\text{LOSSES}}$; $\dfrac{3}{5} = \dfrac{882}{x}$

$$x = \dfrac{5 \times 882}{3}$$

$$= 1{,}470$$

We would expect 1,470 losses.

6. 20% off is $\dfrac{20}{100} = \dfrac{1}{5}$.

7. Divide; $5 \div 12 = 0.41666\ldots$ or $0.41\overline{6}$.

Divide; shift decimal two places to the right, and save the remainder:
$0.41\frac{2}{3} = 41\frac{2}{3}\%$.

8. 0.005 as a fraction is $\dfrac{5}{1{,}000} = \dfrac{1}{200}$. As a percent,

$0.005 = 0.5\%$ (move decimal point two places to the right).

9. $8\dfrac{1}{2}\% = 8\dfrac{1}{2} \times \dfrac{1}{100}$

$$= \dfrac{17}{2} \times \dfrac{1}{100}$$

$$= \dfrac{17}{200}$$

$8\frac{1}{2}\% = 8.5\% = 0.085$ (move decimal point two places to the left).

10. Think of 25% of 412 as $\frac{1}{4}$ of $412 \approx \frac{1}{4} \times 400 = 100$.

11. $\dfrac{85}{100} = \dfrac{170}{x}$

$$x = \dfrac{100 \times 170}{85} \quad \textit{Carry out this calculation on your calculator.}$$

$$= 200$$

The number is 200.

Here is an alternative solution:

We remember that "of" means multiplication:

$$0.85\,(\text{UNKNOWN NUMBER}) = 170$$

$$\text{UNKNOWN NUMBER} = \dfrac{170}{0.85} \quad \textit{Divide both sides by 0.85.}$$

$$= 200 \quad \textit{Use a calculator.}$$

The unknown number is 200.

12. We need to find 6.6% of 281,421,906, and we remember that "of" means multiply:
$0.066(281{,}421{,}906) = 18{,}573{,}845.796 \quad \textit{Use a calculator.}$

We now need to round the answer to the nearest person to find the increase in population. This increase is added to the beginning population:

$$281{,}421{,}906 + 18{,}573{,}846 = 299{,}995{,}752$$

Estimate the 2006 population to be 300,000,000.

13. $\dfrac{80}{100} = \dfrac{x}{500}$

$$x = \dfrac{80 \times 500}{100}$$

$$= 400$$

The lowest B grade is given for 400 points.

Applications

14. What is 0.9% of $42,500?

$$\frac{0.9}{100} = \frac{x}{42,500}$$

$$x = \frac{0.9 \times 42,500}{100} \qquad \textit{Use a calculator.}$$

$$= 382.5$$

The raise due to inflation is $382.50, so the expected salary is

$$\$42,500 + \$382.50 = \$42,882.50$$

15. First, find the profit for the first sale:

$$\text{COST} + \text{PROFIT} = \text{SELLING PRICE}$$
$$x + 0.30x = 1,500 \qquad \textit{Let } x = \text{COST.}$$
$$1.3x = 1,500$$
$$x = 1,153.85 \qquad \textit{Round to the nearest cent.}$$

Cost is $1,153.85, so the profit is

$$0.3(\$1,153.85) = \$346.15$$

Second, find the loss for the second sale:

$$\text{COST} - \text{LOSS} = \text{SELLING PRICE}$$
$$x - 0.30x = 1,500 \qquad \textit{Let } x = \text{COST.}$$
$$0.7x = 1,500$$
$$x = 2,142.86 \qquad \textit{Round to the nearest cent.}$$

Cost is $2,142.86, so the loss is

$$0.3(\$2,142.86) = \$642.86$$

Thus, for the day the results are:

$$\$346.15 + (-\$642.86) = -\$296.71$$

The saleswoman was correct.

Chapter 4 Review Questions

*To prepare for a chapter test, first study the chapter; then, read each term from the important terms list above and make sure you know the meaning of each word; finally, review the chapter objectives. **After** these steps, take the self-test and correct all your answers. The following review questions can be used for extra practice.*

1. Express the ideas as reduced ratios.
   a. The ratio of cement to water is 120 to 6.   20 to 1
   b. The gear ratio is 34 teeth to 17 teeth.   2 to 1
   c. The ratio of wins to losses is 155 to 75.   31 to 15
   d. The ratio of miles to gallons is 117 to $6\frac{1}{2}$.   18 to 1

2. a. Read $\frac{5}{8} = \frac{x}{2}$ as a proportion.   5 is to 8 as x is to 2
   b. What are the means in the proportion $\frac{4}{y} = \frac{19}{7}$?   y and 19
   c. What are the extremes in the proportion $\frac{x}{2} = \frac{1}{12}$?   x and 12
   d. Do $\frac{3}{2}$ and $\frac{9}{6}$ form a proportion?   yes

3. Change the fractions to decimals and percents.
   a. $\frac{3}{5}$ 0.6; 60%   **b.** $\frac{3}{2}$ 1.5; 150%   **c.** $\frac{4}{3}$ $1.\overline{3}$; $133\frac{1}{3}\%$ **d.** $\frac{1}{6}$ $0.1\overline{6}$; $16\frac{2}{3}\%$

4. Change the decimals to fractions and percents.
   a. 0.25 $\frac{1}{4}$; 25%   **b.** 0.8 $\frac{4}{5}$; 80%   **c.** 1.05 $\frac{21}{20}$; 105%   **d.** 0.125 $\frac{1}{8}$; 12.5%

5. Change the percents to fractions and decimals.

    a. 35% $\frac{7}{20}$; 0.35   **b.** 240% $\frac{12}{5}$; 2.4   **c.** 6% $\frac{3}{50}$; 0.06   **d.** $37\frac{1}{2}$% $\frac{3}{8}$; 0.375

Solve each proportion in Problems 6–9.

6. $\dfrac{5}{8} = \dfrac{A}{2}$ $\frac{5}{4}$ or 1.25   **7.** $\dfrac{4}{5} = \dfrac{3}{B}$ $\frac{15}{4}$ or 3.75

8. $\dfrac{C}{100} = \dfrac{2}{3}$ $\frac{200}{3}$ or $66.\overline{6}$ **9.** $\dfrac{12}{D} = \dfrac{4}{5}$ 15

Write a proportion for each statement in Problems 10–17 and then answer the question.

10. 45% of 120 is what number? $\frac{45}{100} = \frac{A}{120}$; 54

11. 82% of 85 is what number? $\frac{82}{100} = \frac{A}{85}$; 69.7

12. 60 is what percent of 80? $\frac{P}{100} = \frac{60}{80}$; 75%

13. 1,450 is what percent of 3,000? $\frac{P}{100} = \frac{1,450}{3,000}$; $48\frac{1}{3}$

14. 90 is 120% of what number? $\frac{120}{100} = \frac{90}{W}$; 75

15. 603 is 250% of what number? $\frac{250}{100} = \frac{603}{W}$; 241.2

16. What number is 25% of 300? $\frac{25}{100} = \frac{A}{300}$; 75

17. What number is 45% of 490? $\frac{45}{100} = \frac{A}{400}$; 220.5

Answer each question in Problems 18–25.

18. If a car went 351 miles on $13\frac{1}{2}$ gallons of gas, how many miles will it go on 5 gallons of gas? 130 miles

19. If 1 gallon of paint covers 250 sq ft, how many gallons are needed for 1,250 sq ft? 5 gal

20. If rolls are sold at 12 for $3.50, how much do 3 rolls cost?
                                          $0.88 (round $0.875 to the nearest cent)

21. If the ratio of cement to water is 120 lb to 6 gallons, how many gallons should be added to 150 lb of cement? 7.5 gallons

22. Suppose you get 16 out of 20 on a test. What is your score, expressed as a percent? 80%

23. If you received 85% on a test consisting of 20 items, how many questions did you get correct? 17

24. If your gross taxable income is $35,240 and the tax rate is 32%, what is the amount of tax due? $11,276.80

25. If the sales tax rate on a $59 item is 6%, what is the total price, including tax? $62.54

Individual Projects

*Learning to use sources outside your classroom and textbook is an important skill, and
here are some ideas for extending some of the ideas in this chapter.*

PROJECT 4.1   A man goes into a store and says to the salesperson, "Give me as much money as I have with me and I will spend $10 here." It is done. The operation is repeated in a second and a third store, after which he has no money left. How much did he have originally? $8.75: see Instructor's Manual for the solution.

PROJECT 4.2   At a certain hamburger stand, the owner sold soft drinks out of two 16-gallon barrels. At the end of the first day, she wished to increase her profit, so she filled the soft-drink barrels with water, thus diluting the drink served. She repeated the procedure at the end of the second and third days. At the end of the fourth day, she had 10 gallons remaining in the barrels, but they contained only 1 pint of pure soft drink. How much pure soft drink was served in the four days?
Since she started with 32 gallons and ended with 1 pt (of pure soft drink) the amount of soft drink served was 31 gal, 3 qt, and 1 pt.

© Antonio Mo/Taxi/Getty Images

Team Projects

*Working in small groups is typical of most work environments, and learning to work
with others to communicate specific ideas is an important skill. Work with three or four
other students to submit a single report based on each of the following questions.*

T9. This is a fascinating problem because it seems easy, but the more you consider its
answer, the more complicated it becomes.

One day three men went to a hotel and were charged $300 for their room. The
desk clerk then realized that he had overcharged them $50, and he sent the refund
up with the bellboy. Now the bellboy, being an amateur mathematician, realized
that it would be difficult to split the $50 three ways. Therefore, he kept a $20 "tip"
and gave the men only $30. Each man had originally paid $100 and was returned
$10. Thus it cost each man $90 for the room. This means that they spent $270 for
the room plus the $20 "tip," for a total of $290. What happened to the other $10?

They spent $270 for the room,
minus the $20 "tip" = $250.
The hotel received $250 and the
bellboy received $20. This
accounts for the $270.

T10. With a team of two or three others, keep track of each time any team member sees
a fraction or percent being used outside the classroom (for example, a half-off sale,
or a bank interest rate, or a recipe calling for $2\frac{1}{2}$ tablespoons of an ingredient). Make
up a master list for the team (eliminate duplications), and discuss why a fraction or
percent is used, rather than a whole number. Also comment on why a fraction is
used rather than a percent, or vice versa.

Introduction to Geometry

CHAPTER 5

Poetry is as exact a science as geometry.

Gustave Flaubert

ANTICIPATE

- *Overview; check out contents, terms, essential ideas, and learning outcomes.*
- ***Geometry,** or "earth measure," was one of the first branches of mathematics.*
- *Both the Egyptians and the Babylonians needed geometry for construction, land measurement, and commerce.*
- *Formal development utilizes deductive logic (which is discussed in Chapter 8), beginning with certain assumptions, called **axioms, postulates,** or **premises.***

5.1 Euclidean Geometry

IN THIS WORLD THE POWER OF MATH

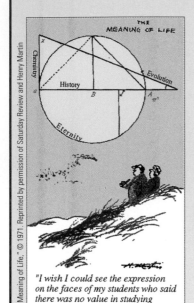

"The Meaning of Life." © 1971. Reprinted by permission of Saturday Review and Henry Martin

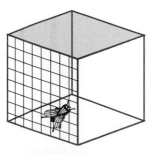

"I wish I could see the expression on the faces of my students who said there was no value in studying geometry."

"What are you going to do when you retire, Martin?" asked Mary. "When my husband, Dan, retired he absolutely drove me crazy!"

"Well, what did he do? Play golf and watch television? I think the most important thing to do is to keep busy," answered Martin. "I'm trying to discover the meaning of life."

"Meaning of life! Are you kidding?" quipped Mary. "How do you get from being a geometry teacher to the meaning of life?"

"Well, they really are not too far apart," said Martin. "Geometry deals with one of the oldest branches of mathematics. Euclid collected all the material that was known at that time and organized it in a book known as Euclid's Elements. *I'm using logic, but I really am looking for some inspiration. I don't know if I'll ever get that connection—maybe if I gaze up into the sky I'll see it."*

In this section we discuss the terminology of geometry, introduce Euclid's postulates, and develop some of the basic geometric constructions.

See Problem 8.

Geometry involves **points** and sets of points called **lines, planes,** and **surfaces.** Certain concepts in geometry are called **undefined terms.** For example, what is a line? You might say, "I know what a line is!" But try to define a line. Is it a set of points? Any set of points? What is a point?

1. A point is something that has no length, width, or thickness.

2. A point is a location in space.

Certainly these are not satisfactory definitions because they involve other terms that are not defined. We will therefore take the terms *point, line,* and *plane* as undefined.

We often draw physical models or pictures to represent these concepts; however, we must be careful not to try to prove assertions by looking at pictures, since a picture may contain hidden assumptions or ambiguities. For example, is the fly in Figure 5.1 inside or outside the cube? Now, consider Figure 5.2 on page 217. If you look at Figure 5.2(a), you might call it a square. If you look at Figure 5.2(b), you might say it is something else. But what if we have in mind a cube, as shown in Figure 5.2(c)? Even if you view this object as a cube, do you see the same cube as everyone else?

These examples illustrate that, although we may use a figure to help us understand a problem, we cannot prove results by this technique.

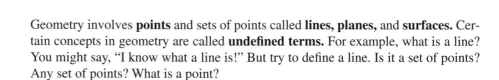

Figure 5.1 Fly on a cube

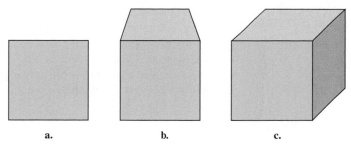

Figure 5.2 Three views of the same object

What do you see? A square? A cube? Figures can be ambiguous (not clear, or with hidden meaning).

Geometry can be separated into two broad categories:

1. Traditional (which is the geometry of Euclid)

2. Transformational (which is more algebraic than Euclid's traditional approach)

In the remainder of this section, we will briefly consider each of the categories of geometry.

When Euclid was formalizing traditional geometry, he based it on five postulates known today as **Euclid's postulates.** In mathematics, a result that is proved on the basis of some agreed-upon postulates is called a **theorem.**

𝔈𝔲𝔠𝔩𝔦𝔡'𝔰 𝔓𝔬𝔰𝔱𝔲𝔩𝔞𝔱𝔢𝔰

1. A straight line can be drawn from any point to any other point.

2. A straight line extends infinitely far in either direction.

3. A circle can be described with any point as center and with a radius equal to any finite straight line drawn from the center.

4. All right angles are equal to each other.

5. Given a straight line and any point not on this line, there is one and only one line through that point that is parallel to the given line.*

The first four of these postulates were obvious and noncontroversial, but the fifth one was different. The fifth postulate is about parallel lines. Two straight lines in the same plane are said to be **parallel** if they do not intersect. This fifth postulate looked more like a theorem than a postulate. It was much more difficult to understand than the other four postulates, and for more than 20 centuries mathematicians tried to derive it from the other postulates or to replace it by a more acceptable equivalent. Today we can either accept Postulate 5 (without proof) or we can deny it. If it is accepted, then the geometry that results is consistent with our everyday experiences and is called **Euclidean geometry.** If it is denied, it turns out that no contradiction results; in fact, if it is not accepted, other *non-Euclidean geometries* result.

Let's look at each of Euclid's postulates. The first one says that a straight line can be drawn from any point to any other point. To connect two points, you need a device

*The fifth postulate stated here is the one usually found in high school geometry books. It is sometimes called Playfair's axiom and is equivalent to Euclid's original statement as translated from the original Greek by T. L. Heath: "If a straight line falling on two straight lines makes the interior angle on the same side less than two right angles, the two straight lines, if produced infinitely, meet on that side on which the angles are less than the two right angles."

called a **straightedge** (a device that we assume has no markings on it; you will use a ruler, but not to measure, when you are treating it as a straightedge). The portion of the line that connects points A and B in Figure 5.3 is called a **line segment.** We write this line segment as $\overline{AB}$ (or $\overline{BA}$). We contrast this notation with $\overleftrightarrow{AB}$, which is used to name the line passing through the points A and B. We use the symbol $|\overline{AB}|$ for the length of the segment $\overline{AB}$.

Figure 5.3 A line segment

The second postulate says that we can draw a straight line. This seems straightforward and obvious, but we should point out that we will indicate a line by putting arrows on each end. If the arrow points in only one direction, then the figure is called a **ray.** We write $\overrightarrow{AB}$ or $\overleftarrow{BA}$ for the ray with endpoint A passing through B, as shown in Figure 5.4.

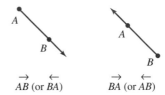

Figure 5.4 Two rays

If we consider a point on a line, that point separates the line into parts: two **half-lines** and the point itself, as shown in Figure 5.5.

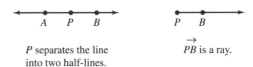

P separates the line into two half-lines.

$\overrightarrow{PB}$ is a ray.

Figure 5.5 Half-lines and rays

For certain geometric constructions, we need a device called a **compass,** Figure 5.6 shows a compass, which is used to mark off and duplicate lengths, but not to measure them. If objects have exactly the same size and shape, they are called **congruent.**

To **construct** a figure means to use a straightedge and compass to create a figure that meets certain requirements. To *construct a line segment congruent to a given line segment,* copy a segment $\overline{AB}$ on any line ℓ. First, fix the compass so that the pointer is on point A and the pencil is on B, as shown on Figure 5.7(a). Then on line ℓ, choose a point C. Next, without changing the compass setting, place the pointer on C and strike an arc at D, as shown in Figure 5.7(b).

Pointer   Pencil

Figure 5.6 A compass

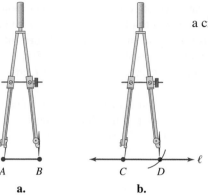

Euclid's third postulate leads us to a second construction. The task is to construct a circle, given its center and radius. These steps are summarized in Figure 5.8.

a. **b.**

Figure 5.7 Constructing a line segment

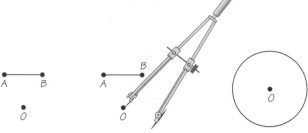

a. Given: a point and a radius of length $\overline{AB}$.

b. Set the legs of the compass on ends of radius $\overline{AB}$; move pointer to point O without changing the setting.

c. Hold the pointer at point O, and move the pencil end to draw the circle.

Figure 5.8 Construction of a circle

We will demonstrate the fourth postulate in the next section when we consider angles.

The final construction of this section will demonstrate the fifth postulate. The task is to construct a line through a point P parallel to a given line ℓ, as shown in Figure 5.9.

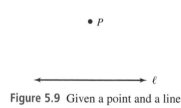

Figure 5.9 Given a point and a line

First, draw any line through P that intersects ℓ at a point A, as shown in Figure 5.10(a). Now, draw an arc with the pointer at A and radius $\overline{AP}$, and label the point of intersection of the arc and the line X, as shown in Figure 5.10(b). With the same opening of the compass, draw an arc first with the pointer at P and then with the pointer at X. This will determine a point Y. Draw the line through both P and Y. This line is parallel to ℓ, as shown in Figure 5.10(c).

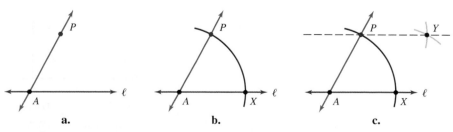

a. **b.** **c.**

Figure 5.10 Construction of a line through a given point parallel to a given line

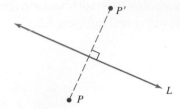

Figure 5.11 A reflection

We now turn our attention to the second category of geometry. The transformational category is quite different from traditional geometry. It begins with the idea of a **transformation.** For example, one way to transform one geometric figure into another is by a *reflection*. Given a line L and a point P, as shown in Figure 5.11, we call the point P' the **reflection** of P about the line if $\overline{PP'}$ is perpendicular to L and is also bisected by L.

Each point in the plane has exactly one reflection point corresponding to a given line L. A reflection is called a *reflection transformation,* and the line of reflection is called the **line of symmetry.** The easiest way to describe a line of symmetry is to say that if you fold a figure along its line of symmetry, then the figure will fold onto itself to form a perfect match, as shown in Figure 5.12.

Figure 5.12 Line symmetry of the maple leaf of canada

Other transformations include *translations, rotations, dilations,* and *contractions,* which are illustrated in Figure 5.13.

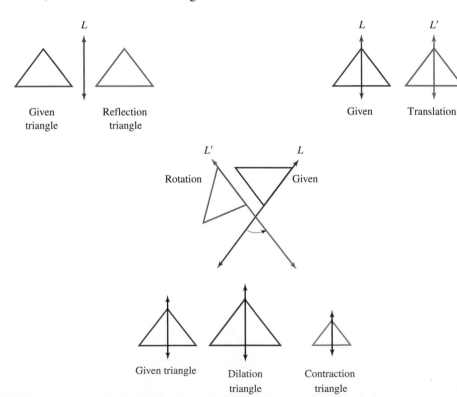

Figure 5.13 Transformations of a fixed geometric figure

PROBLEM SET 5.1

ESSENTIAL IDEAS   LEVEL 1

1. **IN YOUR OWN WORDS** Describe what you see in the following illustration.

2. **IN YOUR OWN WORDS** Why do you think Problem 1 is included in this problem set? How does this question relate to working problems in geometry?

3. **IN YOUR OWN WORDS** Describe a procedure for constructing a line segment congruent to a given segment.

4. **IN YOUR OWN WORDS** Describe a procedure for constructing a circle with a radius congruent to a given segment.

5. **IN YOUR OWN WORDS** Describe what it means to be an undefined term.

6. **IN YOUR OWN WORDS** Describe line symmetry.

7. **IN YOUR OWN WORDS** What is the difference between an axiom and a theorem?

8. What are the two categories into which geometry is usually separated?
Traditional (Euclidean geometry) and transformational

DRILL AND PRACTICE   LEVEL 2

Using only a straightedge and a compass, reproduce the figures in Problems 9–20. See IAS.

9. A line segment

A   B

10. A line segment

C

D

11. A line segment

E   F

12. A line segment

G

H

13. A circle (given radius)

S   T

14. A circle (given radius)

U   V

15. A circle (given radius)

W   X

16. A circle (given radius)

Y   Z

17. A line through *P* parallel to ℓ

18. A line through *S* parallel to *k*

ℓ

P

S

k

19. A line through *R* parallel to *n*

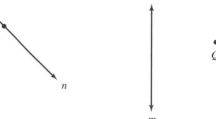

n

R

20. A line through *Q* parallel to *m*

Q

m

Use the illustration in Figure 5.14 to draw the figures requested in Problems 21–29. **See IAS.**

Figure 5.14 A given line

21. $\overline{PQ}$

22. $\overline{RS}$

23. $\overleftrightarrow{PQ}$

24. $\overleftrightarrow{RS}$

25. $\overrightarrow{PQ}$

26. $\overrightarrow{SR}$

27. $\overrightarrow{PQ}$

28. $\overrightarrow{RS}$

29. $\overleftrightarrow{RS}$

Study the patterns shown in Figure 5.15. When folded, they will form cubes spelling CUBE. Letter each pattern in Problems 30–35. Answers are not unique. **See IAS.**

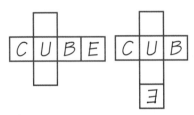

Figure 5.15 Fold-ups form cubes

30.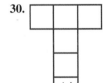

31.

32.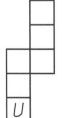

33.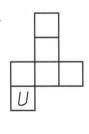

34.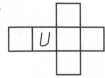

35.

In Problems 36–37, label each drawing as illustrating a reflection, translation, rotation, dilation, or a contraction.

36.

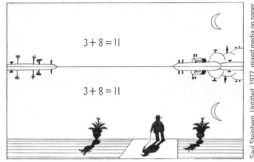

reflection

37.

rotation

Find at least one line of symmetry for each of the illustrations in Problems 38–45. **See IAS.**

38.

39.

40.

41.

42.

43.

44.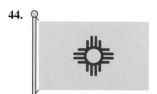

45.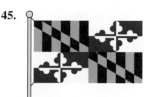

Which of the pictures in Problems 46–53 illustrate a line symmetry?

46. Chambered nautilus

not symmetric

47. Butterfly

symmetric

52. Eiffel tower

53. Empire State Building

symmetric

symmetric

48. *Dodecahedron*, by Leonardo da Vinci

not symmetric

49. Human circulatory system

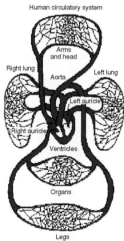

Human circulatory system

Arms and head

Right lung   Left lung

Aorta

Left auricle

Right auricle

Ventricles

Organs

Legs

not symmetric

54. **IN YOUR OWN WORDS** Many curves can be illustrated by using only straight line segments. The basic design is drawn by starting with an angle, as shown in Figure 5.16.

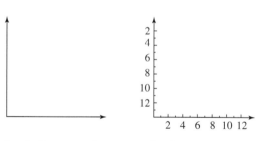

Step 1: Draw an angle with two sides of equal length.

Step 2: Mark off equally distant units on both rays, using a compass.

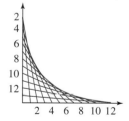

Step 3: Connect 1 to 1, connect 2's, connect 3's ... .

Figure 5.16 Constructing an angle design

The result is called *aestheometry* and is depicted in Figure 5.17. Make up your own angle design.

50. Human brain

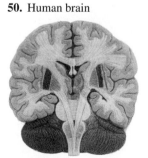

not symmetric

51. Restaurant at Los Angeles International Airport

symmetric

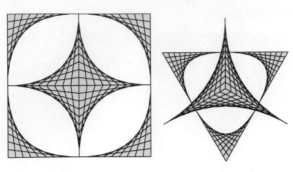

a. Angle design **b.** Angle design

Figure 5.17 Aestheometry angle designs

55. **IN YOUR OWN WORDS** A second basic *aestheometric* design (see Problem 54) begins with a circle as in Figure 5.18.

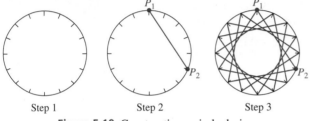

Figure 5.18 Constructing a circle design

Step 1 Draw a circle (step 1) and mark off equally spaced points.

Step 2 Choose any two points and connect them.

Step 3 Connect succeeding points around the circle.

Make up your own design using circles or parts of a circle. An example is shown in Figure 5.19.

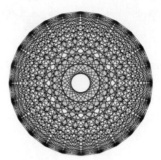

Figure 5.19 Circle design

RIGHT OR WRONG? LEVEL 3

Explain what is wrong, if anything, with the statements in Problems 56–60. Explain your reasoning.

56. Every fact in mathematics can be proved, if only we are careful enough and take our time. F; some words are undefined, some facts are assumed (axioms), and some facts are proved (theorems).

57. Two lines are parallel if they never intersect. F; the lines must be in the same plane.

58. A construction allows only a straightedge and a compass. T

59. The most well known of Euclid's postulates is the first one. F; it is the fifth one (the parallel postulate).

60. If we are given a square and look at a dilation and a contraction of that square, we are looking at an example of a reflection. F; we are looking at larger and smaller squares.

5.2 Polygons and Angles

A **polygon** is a geometric figure that has three or more straight sides, all of which lie on a flat surface or plane so that the starting point and the ending point are the same. Polygons can be classified according to their number of sides, as shown in Figure 5.20.

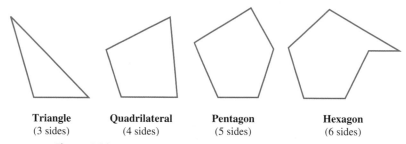

| Triangle | Quadrilateral | Pentagon | Hexagon |
| (3 sides) | (4 sides) | (5 sides) | (6 sides) |

Figure 5.20 Polygons classified according to number of sides

Polygons (not pictured)

Heptagon (7 sides)

Octagon (8 sides)

Nonagon (9 sides)

Decagon (10 sides)

Dodecagon (12 sides)

***n*-gon** (*n* sides)

A connecting point of two sides is called a **vertex** (plural **vertices**) and is usually designated by a capital letter. An **angle** is composed of two rays or segments with a common endpoint. The angles between the sides of a polygon are sometimes also de-noted by a capital letter, but other ways of denoting angles are shown in Figure 5.21.

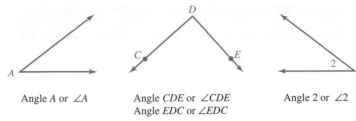

Angle A or $\angle A$ Angle CDE or $\angle CDE$ Angle 2 or $\angle 2$
Angle EDC or $\angle EDC$

This notation for angles is used throughout all of mathematics. CAUTION

Figure 5.21 Ways of denoting angles

EXAMPLE 1

Locating angles

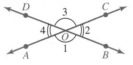

Figure 5.22

Name the given angles in Figure 5.22 in at least two ways.

a. $\angle 1$ **b.** $\angle 2$ **c.** $\angle 3$ **d.** $\angle 4$

Solution

a. $\angle AOB$ or $\angle BOA$ **b.** $\angle COB$ or $\angle BOC$

c. $\angle COD$ or $\angle DOC$ **d.** $\angle AOD$ or $\angle DOA$ ●

To construct an angle with the same size as a given angle B, first draw a ray from B', as shown in Figure 5.23(a). Next, mark off an arc with the pointer at the vertex of the given angle and label the points A and C. Without changing the compass, mark off a similar arc with the pointer at B', as shown in Figure 5.23(b). Label the point C' where this arc crosses the ray from B'. Place the pointer at C and set the compass to the distance from C to A. Without changing the compass, put the pointer at C' and strike an arc to make a point of intersection A' with the arc from C', as shown in Figure 5.23(c). Finally, draw a ray from B' through A'.

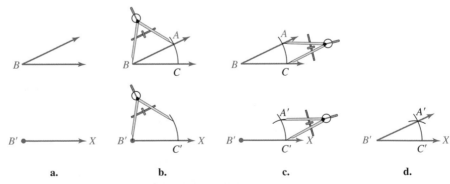

a.   **b.**   **c.**   **d.**

Figure 5.23 Construction of an angle congruent to a given angle

Two angles are said to be **equal** if they describe the same angle. If we write m in front of an angle symbol, we mean the measure of the angle rather than the angle it-self. Notice that in the solution to each part of Example 1, we used the *same angle;* thus, in part **a**, for example, $\angle AOB = \angle BOA$. Also notice the single and double arcs used to mark the angles in Example 1; these are used to denote angles with equal measure, so $m\angle COB = m\angle AOD$ and $m\angle COD = m\angle AOB$, but $\angle COD \neq \angle AOB$ (since they are not the same angle). Denoting an angle by a single letter is preferred except in the case (as shown by Example 1) where several angles share the same vertex.

Angles are usually measured using a unit called a **degree**, which is defined to be $\frac{1}{360}$ of a full revolution. The symbol ° is used to designate degrees. To measure an angle, you can use a **protractor**, but in this book the angles whose measures we need will be labeled as in Figure 5.24.

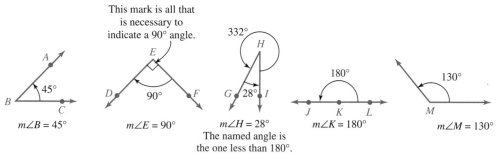

Figure 5.24 Labeling angles

Angles are sometimes classified according to their measures, as shown in Table 5.1. Experience leads us to see the plausibility of Euclid's fourth postulate that all right angles are congruent to one another.

STOP *Remember these names for types of angles.*

TABLE 5.1	Types of Angles
Angle Measure	**Classification**
Less than 90°	**Acute**
Equal to 90°	**Right**
Between 90° and 180°	**Obtuse**
Equal to 180°	**Straight**

EXAMPLE 2   Classification of angles

Label the angles B, E, H, K, and M in Figure 5.24 by classification.

Solution $\angle B$ is acute; $\angle E$ is right; $\angle H$ is acute; $\angle K$ is straight; $\angle M$ is obtuse.   ●

Two angles with the same measure are said to be **congruent.** If the sum of the measures of two angles is 90°, they are called **complementary angles,** and if the sum is 180°, they are called **supplementary angles.**

Consider any two (different) intersecting lines in a plane, and let O be the point of intersection, as shown in Figure 5.25.

These lines must form four angles. Angles with a common ray, common vertex, and on opposite sides of their common sides are called **adjacent angles.** We say that $\angle 1$ and $\angle 2$, $\angle 2$ and $\angle 3$, $\angle 3$ and $\angle 4$, as well as $\angle 4$ and $\angle 1$ are pairs of adjacent angles. We also say that $\angle 1$ and $\angle 3$ as well as $\angle 2$ and $\angle 4$ are pairs of **vertical angles**—that is, two angles for which each side of one angle is a prolongation through the vertex of a side of the other.

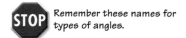

Figure 5.25 Angles formed by intersecting lines

EXAMPLE 3   Naming angles formed by intersecting lines

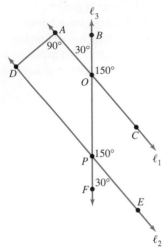

Figure 5.26 Classifying angles

Classify the named angles in Figure 5.26.

a. $\angle AOB$ **b.** $\angle BOC$ **c.** $\angle DAO$

Next, classify the following named pairs of angles shown in Figure 5.26.

d. $\angle AOB$ and $\angle BOC$ **e.** $\angle BOC$ and $\angle OPE$ **f.** $\angle AOB$ and $\angle COP$

g. $\angle FPE$ and $\angle EPO$

Solution

a. Acute   **b.** Obtuse   **c.** Right

d. Supplementary and adjacent   **e.** Congruent   **f.** Vertical

g. Supplementary and adjacent

      A polygon with four sides is a **quadrilateral.** Some other classifications are given in the following box.

Quadrilaterals

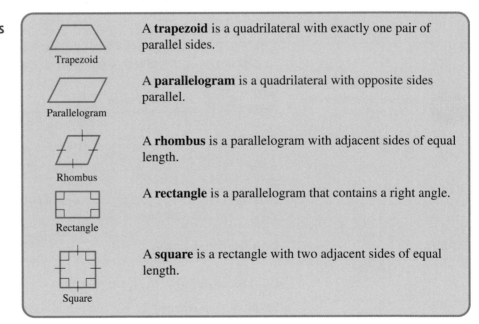

A **trapezoid** is a quadrilateral with exactly one pair of parallel sides.

A **parallelogram** is a quadrilateral with opposite sides parallel.

A **rhombus** is a parallelogram with adjacent sides of equal length.

A **rectangle** is a parallelogram that contains a right angle.

A **square** is a rectangle with two adjacent sides of equal length.

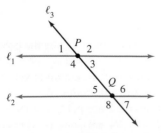

Figure 5.27 Parallel lines cut by a transversal

      Consider three lines arranged similarly to those shown in Figure 5.26. Suppose that two of the lines, say, ℓ_1 and ℓ_2, are **parallel** (that is, they lie in the same plane and never intersect), and also that a third line ℓ_3 intersects the parallel lines at points P and Q, as shown in Figure 5.27. The line ℓ_3 is called a **transversal.**
      We make some observations about angles:

Vertical angles are congruent.

Alternate interior angles are pairs of angles whose interiors lie between the parallel lines, but on opposite sides of the transversal, each having one of the lines for one of its sides. *Alternate interior angles are congruent.*

Alternate exterior angles are pairs of angles that lie outside the parallel lines, but on opposite sides of the transversal, each with one side adjacent to each parallel. *Alternate exterior angles are congruent.*

Corresponding angles are two nonadjacent angles whose interiors lie on the same side of the transversal such that one angle lies between the parallel lines and the other does not. *Corresponding angles are congruent.*

EXAMPLE 4   Classifying pairs of angles

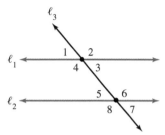

Figure 5.28 Angles formed by parallel lines and a transversal

Consider Figure 5.28.

a. Name the vertical angles.   **b.** Name the alternate interior angles.
c. Name the corresponding angles.   **d.** Name the alternate exterior angles.

Solution

a. The vertical angles are: $\angle 1$ and $\angle 3$; $\angle 2$ and $\angle 4$; $\angle 5$ and $\angle 7$; $\angle 6$ and $\angle 8$.
b. The alternate interior angles are: $\angle 4$ and $\angle 6$; $\angle 3$ and $\angle 5$.
c. The corresponding angles are: $\angle 1$ and $\angle 5$; $\angle 2$ and $\angle 6$; $\angle 3$ and $\angle 7$; $\angle 4$ and $\angle 8$.
d. The alternate exterior angles are: $\angle 1$ and $\angle 7$; $\angle 2$ and $\angle 8$.   ●

To summarize the results from Example 4, notice that the following angles are congruent (the symbol "$\simeq$" means "is congruent to"):

$$\angle 1 \simeq \angle 3 \simeq \angle 5 \simeq \angle 7 \qquad \text{and} \qquad \angle 2 \simeq \angle 4 \simeq \angle 6 \simeq \angle 8$$

Also, all pairs of adjacent angles are supplementary.

EXAMPLE 5   Finding congruent angles

Find the measures of the eight numbered angles in Figure 5.28, where ℓ_1 and ℓ_2 are parallel. Assume that $m\angle 5 = 50°$.

Solution $m\angle 1 = 50°$ Corresponding angles
$m\angle 2 = 180° - 50° = 130°$ $\angle 1$ and $\angle 2$ are supplementary.
$m\angle 3 = 50°$ $\angle 3$ and $\angle 1$ are vertical angles.
$m\angle 4 = 130°$ Vertical angles
$m\angle 5 = 50°$ Given
$m\angle 6 = 130°$ Supplementary angles
$m\angle 7 = 50°$ Vertical angles
$m\angle 8 = 130°$ Supplementary angles   ●

If two lines intersect so that the adjacent angles are equal, then the lines are **perpendicular.** Simply, lines that intersect to form angles of 90° (right angles) are called perpendicular lines. In Figure 5.29, lines ℓ_3 and ℓ_4 intersect to form a right angle, and therefore they are perpendicular lines.

In a diagram on a printed page, any line that is parallel to the top and bottom edge of the page is considered **horizontal.** Lines that are perpendicular to a horizontal line are considered to be **vertical.** In Figure 5.30, line ℓ_5 is a horizontal line and line ℓ_6 is a vertical line.

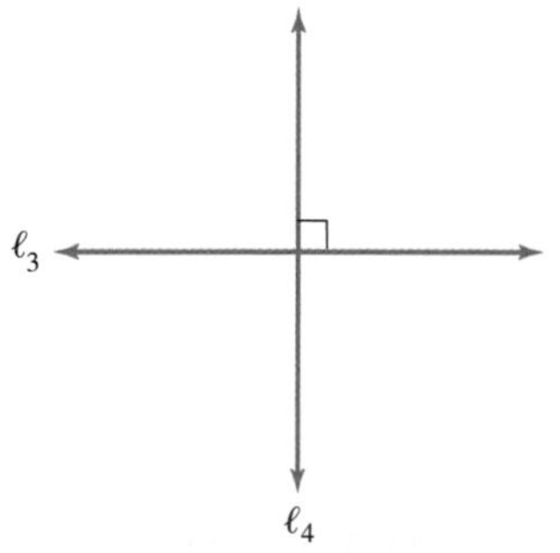

Figure 5.29 Perpendicular lines

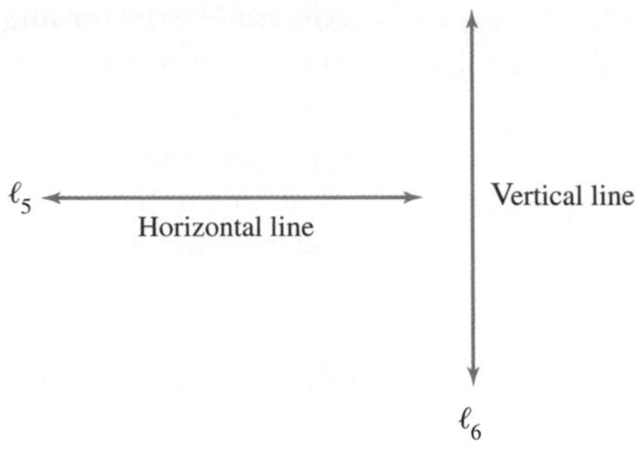

$\ell_5 \longleftrightarrow$ Horizontal line $\qquad$ Vertical line

ℓ_6

Figure 5.30 Horizontal and vertical lines

EXAMPLE 6

Perpendicular, horizontal, and vertical lines

The diagram in Figure 5.31 shows lines in the same plane. Which of the given statements are true?

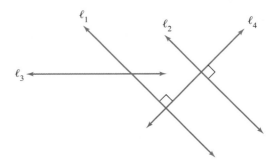

Figure 5.31 Classifying lines

a. Lines ℓ_1 and ℓ_2 are parallel and horizontal.

b. Lines ℓ_4 and ℓ_2 are intersecting and not perpendicular.

c. Lines ℓ_2 and ℓ_3 are intersecting lines.

Solution

a. Lines ℓ_1 and ℓ_2 are parallel, but they are not horizontal. Thus, the statement is false.

b. Lines ℓ_4 and ℓ_2 are both intersecting and perpendicular. The statement is false.

c. Lines ℓ_2 and ℓ_3 are intersecting. Recall that the arrows on ℓ_3 indicate that it goes on without end in both directions, so it will intersect ℓ_2. This statement is true. ●

PROBLEM SET 5.2

ESSENTIAL IDEAS **LEVEL 1**

1. What is an angle? *Two rays with a common endpoint*

2. Distinguish between equal angles and congruent angles.
Equal angles are the same angle, and congruent angles are the same size (that is, have the same measure).

3. What is a quadrilateral? Describe five different classifications of quadrilaterals. *See p. 228.*

4. Distinguish between horizontal and vertical lines. *See p. 229.*

5. Describe right angles, acute angles, and obtuse angles. *See p. 217.*

6. Describe adjacent and vertical angles. *See p. 227.*

7. Describe parallel lines. *See p. 228.*

8. Name four pairs of congruent angles formed by parallel lines cut by a transversal. *vertical; alternate interior angles; alternate exterior angles; corresponding angles*

DRILL AND PRACTICE LEVEL 2

Name the polygons in Problems 9–14 according to the number of sides.

9. a. 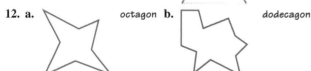 quadrilateral **b.** pentagon

10. a.  octagon **b.** decagon

11. a.  triangle **b.** hexagon

12. a.  octagon **b.** dodecagon

13. a. 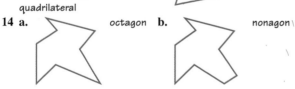 **b.** heptagon

quadrilateral

14 a. 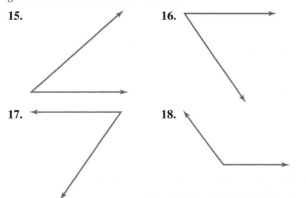 octagon **b.** nonagon

Using only a straightedge and a compass, reproduce the angles given in Problems 15–20. *See IAS.*

15. **16.**

17. **18.**

19. 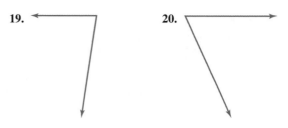 **20.**

21. Consider Figure 5.32.

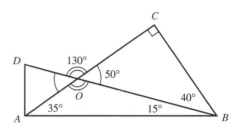

Figure 5.32 Angles in a triangle

Classify the angles as acute, right, straight, or obtuse.

a. ∠DOC obtuse   **b.** ∠AOB obtuse

c. ∠DBC acute   **d.** ∠CAB acute

e. ∠DOB straight   **f.** ∠C right

g. ∠COB acute   **h.** ∠AOC straight

i. ∠DOA acute

j. Name a pair of angles that have the same measure.
m∠COB = m∠DOA or m∠DOC = m∠AOB

k. Name an angle congruent to ∠DOB. ∠AOC

22. Consider Figure 5.33.

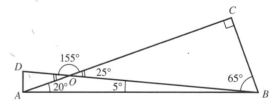

Figure 5.33 Angles in a triangle

Classify the angles as acute, right, straight, or obtuse.

a. ∠DOC obtuse

b. ∠AOB obtuse

c. ∠DBC acute

d. ∠CAB acute

e. ∠DOB straight

f. ∠C right

g. ∠COB acute

h. ∠AOC straight

i. ∠DOA   acute

j. Name a pair of angles that have the same measure.
   m∠COB = m∠DOA or m∠DOC = m∠AOB
k. Name an angle congruent to ∠DOB.   ∠AOC

In Problems 23–27, classify the requested angles shown in Figure 5.34, where ℓ₁ and ℓ₂ are parallel.

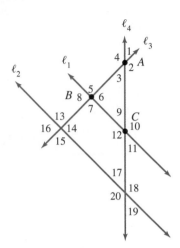

Figure 5.34 Classifying angles

23. a. ∠BAC if m∠1 is 30°   acute

b. ∠ABC if m∠5 is 90°   right

24. a. ∠18 if m∠17 is 105°   acute

b. ∠19 if m∠11 is 70°   acute

25. a. ∠10 if m∠11 is 90°   right

b. ∠16 if m∠15 is 30°   obtuse

26. a. ∠CBA if m∠16 is 120°   obtuse

b. ∠BCA if m∠19 is 110°   obtuse

27. a. ∠1 if m∠2 is 130°   acute

b. ∠5 if m∠15 is 88°   acute

In Problems 28–31, classify the pairs of angles shown in Figure 5.34.

28. a. ∠2 and ∠4   vertical

b. ∠13 and ∠14   adj. and supp.

29. a. ∠9 and ∠12   adj. and supp.

b. ∠9 and ∠10   adj. and supp.

30. a. ∠9 and ∠17   corresponding

b. ∠9 and ∠11   vertical

31. a. ∠12 and ∠18   alternate interior angles

b. ∠7 and ∠13   alternate interior angles

In Problems 32–35, find the measures of all the angles in Figure 5.35.

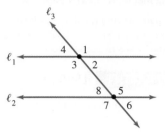

Figure 5.35 ℓ₁ is parallel to ℓ₂
   m∠1 = m∠3 = m∠5 = m∠7
   m∠2 = m∠4 = m∠6 = m∠8

32. a. Given m∠7 = 110°   m∠8 = 70°

b. Given m∠2 = 65°   m∠1 = 115°

33. a. Given m∠6 = 19°   m∠7 = 161°

b. Given m∠1 = 153°   m∠2 = 27°

34. a. Given m∠5 = 120°   m∠6 = 60°

b. Given m∠3 = 163°   m∠4 = 17°

35. a. Given m∠8 = 42°   m∠7 = 138°

b. Given m∠4 = 48°   m∠3 = 132°

Each of the four diagrams in Figure 5.36 shows lines in the same plane. Classify each of the statements in Problems 36–41 as true or false.

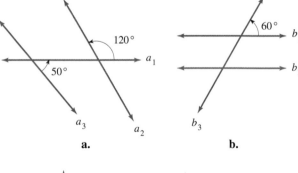

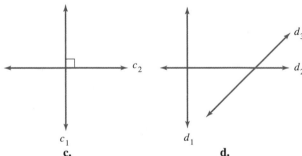

Figure 5.36 Intersecting lines

36. The lines a₁ and a₃ are both intersecting and parallel.   F

37. The lines b₁ and b₂ are vertical.   F

38. The lines c_1 and c_2 are not intersecting.   F

39. The lines d_1 and d_3 are intersecting.   T

40. The lines c_2 and d_2 are horizontal.   T

41. The lines a_2 and a_3 are both vertical and parallel.   F

Determine whether each sentence in Problems 42–46 is true or false.

42. a. Every square is a rectangle.   T

   b. Every square is a parallelogram.   T

43. a. Every square is a rhombus.   T

   b. Every rhombus is a square.   F

44. a. Every square is a quadrilateral.   T

   b. A parallelogram is a rectangle.   F

45. a. A rectangle is a parallelogram.   T

   b. A trapezoid is a quadrilateral.   T

46. a. A quadrilateral is a trapezoid.   F

   b. A parallelogram is a trapezoid.   F

For the quadrilaterals named in Problems 47–51, answer "yes" or "no" to indicate whether each of the following properties is satisfied:

   a. opposite sides parallel

   b. opposite sides have equal length

   c. opposite angles have equal measure

   d. interior angles are right angles

   e. diagonals have equal length

47. rectangle   yes, yes, yes, yes, yes

48. square   yes, yes, yes, yes, yes

49. parallelogram   yes, yes, yes, no, no

50. trapezoid   no, no, no, no, no

51. rhombus   yes, yes, yes, no, no

APPLICATIONS   **LEVEL 2**

52. Most buildings form what kind of angles with the ground on which they are built?   right angle

53. Classify the angle that the Leaning Tower of Pisa leans when viewed from the direction in which the tower leans. (See "In This World" at the beginning of this section.)   acute

54. Classify the angle that the Leaning Tower of Pisa leans when viewed from the direction from which the tower leans.   obtuse

55. The operation of telescopes depends on the reflection of light on mirrors within the telescope. Such a reflection is shown in Figure 5.37.

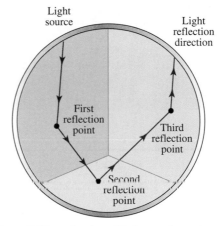

Figure 5.37 Reflection of light rays in a telescope

Identify the three angles shown in Figure 5.37, and then classify each angle.   two obtuse angles and one right angle

RIGHT OR WRONG?   **LEVEL 3**

Explain what is wrong, if anything, with the statements in Problems 56–60. Explain your reasoning.

56. Two angles are said to be congruent if they have the same measure.   T; if two angles are congruent, then they must have the same measure.

57. A right angle is an angle whose measure is 180°.   F; a right angle has a measure of 90°.

58. If the rays of an angle point in opposite directions so that the rays form a straight line, we say the angle is a straight angle.   T

59. All rectangles are parallelograms.   T

60. Vertical angles are supplementary.   F; vertical angles have the same measure.

5.3 Triangles

IN THIS WORLD THE POWER OF MATH

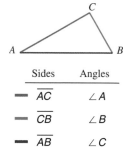

"Did you hear that there is a new production of Fame *at the Beenleigh Theatre?" asked Tom.*

"Yes, and I hear it is wonderful," answered Betty. "My friend Gina is in it. She even has a number where she is playing the triangle."

"A triangle? What are you talking about?" asked Tom. "I know about triangles from geometry but what is a triangle in music?"

We will investigate triangles in this section and will note many important properties of triangles. In fact, the Problem of the Day even relates a mathematical triangle to a musical one.

See Problem 2.

One of the most frequently encountered polygons is the *triangle*. Every triangle has six parts: three sides and three angles. We name the sides by naming the endpoints of the line segments, and we name the angles by identifying the vertex (see Figure 5.38).

Triangles are classified both by sides and by angles:

Sides	Angles
— $\overline{AC}$	$\angle A$
— $\overline{CB}$	$\angle B$
— $\overline{AB}$	$\angle C$

Figure 5.38 A standard triangle showing the six parts

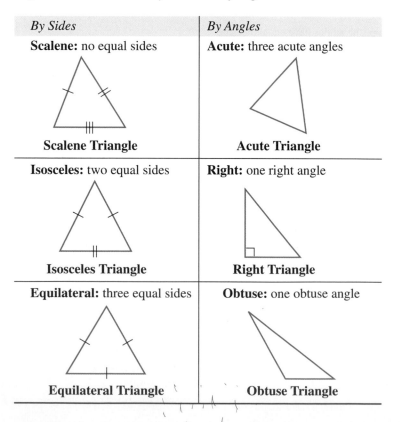

By Sides	By Angles
Scalene: no equal sides	**Acute:** three acute angles
Scalene Triangle	Acute Triangle
Isosceles: two equal sides	**Right:** one right angle
Isosceles Triangle	Right Triangle
Equilateral: three equal sides	**Obtuse:** one obtuse angle
Equilateral Triangle	Obtuse Triangle

We say that two triangles are **congruent** if they have the same size and shape. Suppose that we wish to construct a triangle with vertices D, E, and F, congruent to $\triangle ABC$ as shown in Figure 5.38. We would proceed as follows:

Step 1 Mark off segment $\overline{DE}$ so that it is congruent to $\overline{AB}$. We write this as $\overline{DE} \simeq \overline{AB}$.

Step 2 Construct angle E so that it is congruent to angle B. We write this as $\angle E \simeq \angle B$.

Step 3 Mark off segment $\overline{EF} \simeq \overline{BC}$, as shown in Figure 5.39.

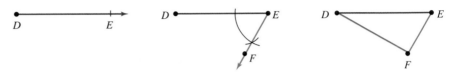

Figure 5.39 Constructing congruent triangles

You can now see that, if you connect points D and F with a straightedge, the resulting $\triangle DEF$ has the same size and shape as $\triangle ABC$. The procedure we used here is called SAS, meaning we constructed two sides and an *included* angle (an angle between two sides) congruent to two sides and an included angle of another triangle. We call these **corresponding parts.** There are other procedures for constructing congruent triangles. Some of these are discussed in Problem Set 5.3. For this example, we say $\triangle ABC \simeq \triangle DEF$. From this we conclude that all six corresponding parts are congruent.

$$\triangle ABC \qquad \simeq \qquad \triangle DEF$$

A corresponds to D
B corresponds to E
C corresponds to F

EXAMPLE 1 **Finding corresponding parts of a given triangle**

Name the corresponding parts of the given triangles.

a. $\triangle ABC \simeq \triangle A'B'C'$ **b.** $\triangle RST \simeq \triangle UST$

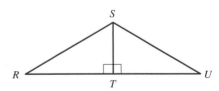

Solution

a. $\overline{AB}$ corresponds to $\overline{A'B'}$
$\overline{AC}$ corresponds to $\overline{A'C'}$
$\overline{BC}$ corresponds to $\overline{B'C'}$
$\angle A$ corresponds to $\angle A'$
$\angle B$ corresponds to $\angle B'$
$\angle C$ corresponds to $\angle C'$

b. $\overline{RS}$ corresponds to $\overline{US}$
$\overline{RT}$ corresponds to $\overline{UT}$
$\overline{ST}$ corresponds to $\overline{ST}$
$\angle R$ corresponds to $\angle U$
$\angle RTS$ corresponds to $\angle UTS$
$\angle RST$ corresponds to $\angle UST$

One of the most basic properties of triangles involves the sum of the measures of the angles of a triangle. To discover this property for yourself, place a pencil with an eraser along one side of any triangle as shown in Figure 5.40(a).

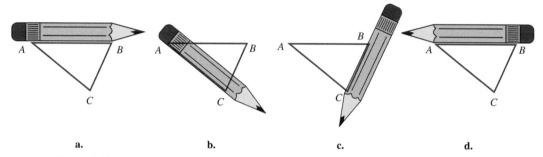

a. b. c. d.

Figure 5.40 Demonstration that the sum of the measures of the angles in a triangle is 180°

Now rotate the pencil to correspond to the size of $\angle A$, as shown in Figure 5.40(b). You see your pencil is along side $\overline{AC}$. Next, rotate the pencil through $\angle C$, as shown in Figure 5.40(c). Finally, rotate the pencil through $\angle B$. Notice that the pencil has been rotated the same amount as the sum of the angles of the triangle. Also, notice that the orientation of the pencil is exactly reversed from the starting position. This leads us to the following important property, called the **sum of angles of a triangle** theorem.

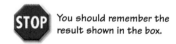

You should remember the result shown in the box.

Sum of Angles Property

The sum of the measures of the angles in any triangle is 180°.

EXAMPLE 2

Finding a missing angle of a triangle

Find the missing angle measure in the triangle in Figure 5.41.

Solution Let x represent the missing angle's measure.

$$65° + 82° + x = 180°$$
$$147° + x = 180°$$
$$x = 33°$$

The missing angle's measure is 33°.

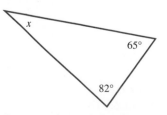

Figure 5.41 What is x?

EXAMPLE 3   **Using algebra to find the angles of a triangle**

Find the measures of the angles of a triangle if it is known that the measures are x, $2x - 15°$, and $3(x + 17°)$.

Solution   Using the theorem for the sum of the measures of the angles in a triangle, we have:

$$x + (2x - 15°) + 3(x + 17°) = 180° \quad \text{Eliminate parentheses.}$$
$$6x + 36° = 180° \quad \text{Combine similar terms.}$$
$$6x = 144° \quad \text{Subtract 36 from both sides.}$$
$$x = 24° \quad \text{Divide both sides by 6.}$$

Now find the angle measures:

$$x = 24°$$
$$2x - 15° = 2(24°) - 15° = 33°$$
$$3(x + 17°) = 3(24° + 17°) = 123°$$

The angles have measures of 24°, 33°, and 123°.   ●

An **exterior angle** of a triangle is the angle on the other side of an extension of one side of the triangle. An example is the angle whose measure is marked as x in Figure 5.42.

Note that the following relationships are true for any $\triangle ABC$ with exterior angle x:

$$m\angle A + m\angle B + m\angle C = 180° \quad \text{and} \quad m\angle C + x = 180°$$

Thus,

$$m\angle A + m\angle B + m\angle C = m\angle C + x$$
$$m\angle A + m\angle B = x \quad \text{Subtract } m\angle C \text{ from both sides.}$$

We summarize this with the **exterior angle formula.**

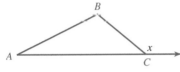

Figure 5.42 Exterior angle x

| **Exterior Angle Formula** | The measure of an exterior angle of a triangle equals the sum of the measures of the two opposite interior angles. |

EXAMPLE 4   **Finding an exterior angle**

Find the value of x in Figure 5.43.

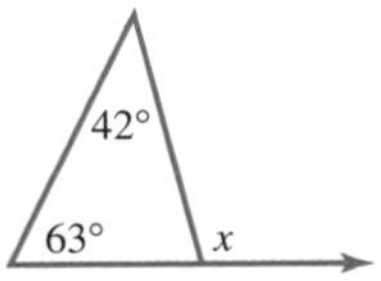

Figure 5.43 What is x?

$$\overbrace{\text{Sum of interior angles}} \qquad \underset{\downarrow}{\text{Exterior angle}}$$

Solution $63° + 42° \quad = \quad x$

$$105° = x$$

The measure of the exterior angle is 105°.   ●

PROBLEM SET (5.3)

ESSENTIAL IDEAS **LEVEL 1**

1. What is a triangle? a polygon with three sides (which also has three angles)

Problem of the Day **2. IN YOUR OWN WORDS** Explain why the musical instrument called a "triangle" (see Figure 5.44) is not a good example of a geometric triangle.

Figure 5.44 A musical instrument

3. IN YOUR OWN WORDS Show that *the sum of the measures of the interior angles of any triangle is* 180° by carrying out the following steps.

a. Draw three triangles: one with all acute angles, one with a right angle, and a third with an obtuse angle. A triangle with all acute angles is shown in Figure 5.45.

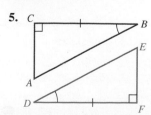

Figure 5.45 Triangle

b. Tear apart the angles of each triangle you've drawn.

c. Place the pieces together to form a straight angle.

4. What is the sum of the measures of the acute angles of a right triangle? **90°**

DRILL AND PRACTICE **LEVEL 2**

Name the corresponding parts of the triangles in Problems 5–10.

5.

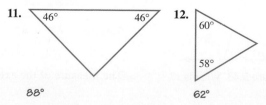

$\overline{AB} \simeq \overline{ED}$; $\overline{AC} \simeq \overline{EF}$; $\overline{CB} \simeq \overline{FD}$; $\angle A \simeq \angle E$; $\angle B \simeq \angle D$; $\angle C \simeq \angle F$

6.

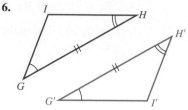

$\overline{GH} \simeq \overline{G'H'}$; $\overline{GI} \simeq \overline{G'I'}$; $\overline{HI} \simeq \overline{H'I'}$; $\angle G \simeq \angle G'$; $\angle H \simeq \angle H'$; $\angle I \simeq \angle I'$

7.

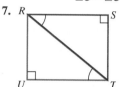

$\overline{RS} \simeq \overline{TU}$; $\overline{RT} \simeq \overline{TR}$; $\overline{ST} \simeq \overline{UR}$; $\angle SRT \simeq \angle UTR$; $\angle S \simeq \angle U$; $\angle STR \simeq \angle URT$

8.

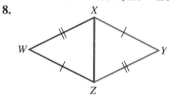

$\overline{WX} \simeq \overline{YZ}$; $\overline{WZ} \simeq \overline{YX}$; $\overline{XZ} \simeq \overline{ZX}$; $\angle W \simeq \angle Y$; $\angle WXZ \simeq \angle YZX$; $\angle WZX \simeq \angle YXZ$

9.

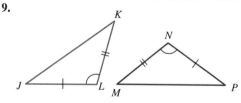

$\overline{KL} \simeq \overline{MN}$; $\overline{KJ} \simeq \overline{MP}$; $\overline{JL} \simeq \overline{PN}$; $\angle J \simeq \angle P$; $\angle K \simeq \angle M$; $\angle L \simeq \angle N$

10.

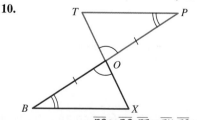

$\overline{PO} \simeq \overline{BO}$; $\overline{PT} \simeq \overline{BX}$; $\overline{TO} \simeq \overline{XO}$; $\angle T \simeq \angle X$; $\angle P \simeq \angle B$; $\angle BOX \simeq \angle POT$

In Problems 11–16, find the measure of the third angle in each triangle.

11.

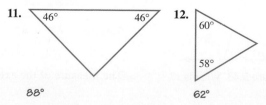

46° 46°

88°

12.

60°

58°

62°

13.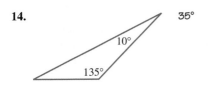

14.

15. 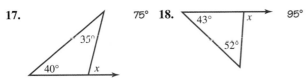 **16.**

Find the measure of the indicated exterior angle in each of the triangles in Problems 17–22.

17. 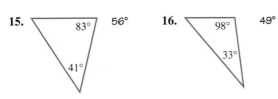 **18.**

19. 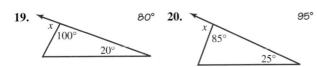 **20.**

21. 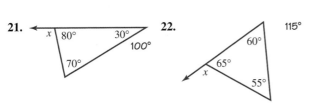 **22.**

Using only a straightedge and a compass, reproduce the triangles given in Problems 23–28. See IAS.

23. 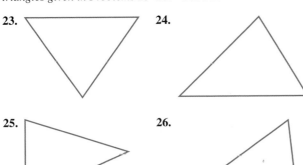 **24.**

25. **26.**

27. 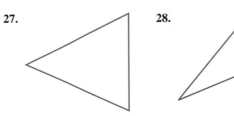 **28.**

Use algebra to find the value of x in each of the triangles in Problems 29–34. Notice that the measurement of the angle is not necessarily the same as the value of x.

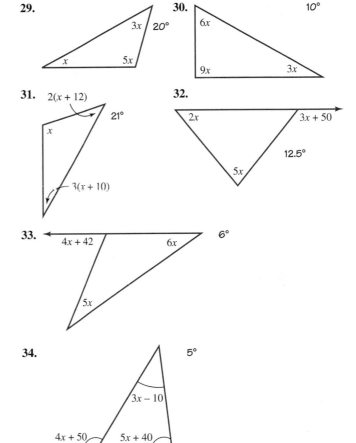

29. **30.**

31. $2(x + 12)$ **32.**

33.

34.

Draw an example of each of the triangles described in Problems 35–42. If you think the figure cannot exist, write "impossible." See IAS.

35. acute scalene

36. acute isosceles

37. acute equilateral

38. right scalene

39. right isosceles

40. right equilateral impossible

41. obtuse scalene

42. obtuse isosceles

43. Find the measures of the angles of a triangle if it is known that the measures of the angles are x, $2x$, and $3x$.   30°, 60°, 90°

44. Find the measures of the angles of a triangle if it is known that the measures of the angles are x, x, and $2x$.   45°, 45°, 90°

45. Find the measures of the angles of a triangle if it is known that the measures of the angles are x, $x + 10°$, and $x + 20°$. **50°, 60°, 70°**

46. Find the measures of the angles of a triangle if it is known that the measures of the angles are $2x + 30°$, $3x - 50°$, and $4x + 20°$. **70°, 10°, 100°**

47. Find the measures of the angles of a triangle if it is known that the measures of the angles are x, $14° + 3x$, and $3(x + 25°)$. **13°; 53°; 114°**

48. Find the measures of the angles of a triangle if it is known that the measures of the angles are x, $3x - 10°$, and $3(55° - x)$. **25°; 65°; 90°**

49. In the text we constructed congruent triangles by using SAS. Reproduce the triangle shown in Problem 25 by using SSS. This means to construct the triangle by using the lengths of the three sides. *See Problem 25.*

50. In the text we constructed congruent triangles by using SAS. Reproduce the triangle shown in Problem 26 by using SSS. This means to construct the triangle by using the lengths of the three sides. *See Problem 26.*

51. In the text we constructed congruent triangles by using SAS. Reproduce the triangle shown in Problem 27 by using ASA. This means to construct the triangle by using a side included between two angles. *See Problem 27.*

52. In the text we constructed congruent triangles by using SAS. Reproduce the triangle shown in Problem 28 by using ASA. This means to construct the triangle by using a side included between two angles. *See Problem 28.*

APPLICATIONS   LEVEL 2

In Problems 53–58, assume that the given angles have been measured, and calculate the angles (marked as x) that could not be found by direct measurement.

53.

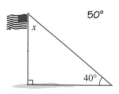

50°

40°

54.

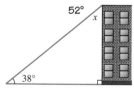

52°

38°

55.

120° **56.**

57.

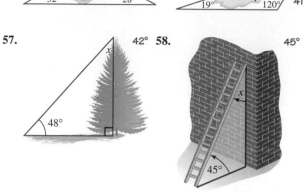

42° **58.**

45°

59. The legs of a picnic table form a triangle where $\overline{AC}$ and $\overline{BC}$ have the same length, as shown in Figure 5.46.

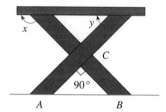

Figure 5.46 Picnic table

Find the measures of angles x and y so that the top of the table will be parallel to the ground. $x = 135°$; $y = 45°$

60. Repeat Problem 59, except assume that the angle marked 90° is not really a right angle, but instead is 92°.
$x = 136°$; $y = 44°$

5.4 Similar Triangles

"Have you looked at our flag lately? It is all ragged. We need to buy a new one," said Carol. *"How big a flag should I buy?"*

"Well, it should be proportional to the size of the flagpole." answered Terry. *"How tall is that pole?"*

"I don't have a clue. I think you should shinny up the pole and drop a line so that we can determine its height!"

In this section we will introduce the idea of similar triangles, which will enable us to measure distances indirectly, without the need (or inconvenience) of taking a direct measurement.

 See Problem 48.

Congruent figures have exactly the same size and shape. However, it is possible for figures to have exactly the same shape without having the same size. Such figures are called **similar figures.** In this section, we will focus on **similar triangles.** If $\triangle ABC$ is similar to $\triangle DEF$, we write

$$\triangle ABC \sim \triangle DEF$$

Similar triangles are shown in Figure 5.47.

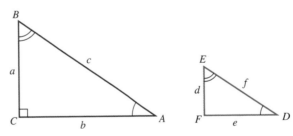

Figure 5.47 Similar triangles

Since these figures have the same shape, we talk about **corresponding angles** and **corresponding sides.** The corresponding angles of similar triangles are those angles that are equal. The corresponding sides are those sides that are opposite equal angles.

$m\angle A = m\angle D$, so these are corresponding angles.

$m\angle B = m\angle E$, so these are corresponding angles.

$m\angle C = m\angle F$, so these are corresponding angles.

Side $\overline{BC}$ is opposite $\angle A$ and side $\overline{EF}$ is opposite $\angle D$, so we say that $\overline{BC}$ corresponds to $\overline{EF}$.

$\overline{AC}$ corresponds to $\overline{DF}$.

$\overline{AB}$ corresponds to $\overline{DE}$.

Even though corresponding angles are equal, corresponding sides do not need to have the same length. If they do have the same length, the triangles are congruent. However, when they are not the same length, we can say they are proportional. From Figure 5.47, we see that the lengths of the sides are labeled a, b, and c and d, e, and f. When we say the sides are proportional, we mean

Primary ratios   *Reciprocals*

$$\frac{a}{b} = \frac{d}{e} \qquad \frac{a}{c} = \frac{d}{f} \qquad \frac{b}{c} = \frac{e}{f} \qquad\qquad \frac{b}{a} = \frac{e}{d} \qquad \frac{c}{a} = \frac{f}{d} \qquad \frac{c}{b} = \frac{f}{e}$$

Similar Triangle Property

> Two triangles are similar if two angles of one triangle are equal to two angles of the other triangle. If the triangles are similar, then their corresponding sides are proportional.

EXAMPLE 1

Corresponding parts of similar triangles

Identify pairs of triangles that are similar in Figure 5.48.

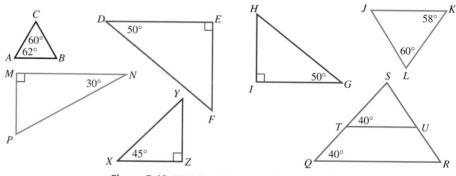

Figure 5.48 Which of these triangles are similar?

Solution $\triangle ABC \sim \triangle JKL$; $\triangle DEF \sim \triangle GIH$; $\triangle SQR \sim \triangle STU$ ●

EXAMPLE 2

Finding lengths of sides of similar triangles

Given the similar triangles in Figure 5.49, find the unknown lengths marked b' and c'.

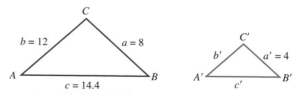

Figure 5.49 Given $\triangle ABC \sim \triangle A'B'C'$

Solution   Since corresponding sides are proportional (other proportions are possible), we have

$$\frac{a'}{a} = \frac{b'}{b} \qquad\qquad \frac{a}{c} = \frac{a'}{c'}$$

$$\frac{4}{8} = \frac{b'}{12} \qquad\qquad \frac{8}{14.4} = \frac{4}{c'}$$

$$b' = \frac{4 \times 12}{8} \qquad\qquad c' = \frac{14.4 \times 4}{8}$$

$$b' = 6 \qquad\qquad c' = 7.2$$

HISTORICAL NOTE

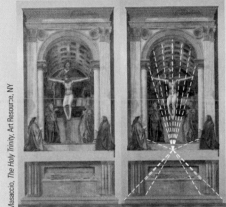

Masaccio, *The Holy Trinity*, Art Resource, NY

Masaccio
(1401–1428)

As Europe passed from the Middle Ages to the Renaissance, artists were at the forefront of the intellectual revolution. No longer satisfied with flat-looking scenes, they wanted to portray people and objects as they looked in real life. The artist's problem was one of dimension, and dimension is related to mathematics. The first great painter of the Italian Renaissance was Masaccio, whose painting (left) shows mathematical perspective. At the right is another drawing by Masaccio showing the structure of perspective. The ideas of shapes, rectangles, triangles, and circles, and how these figures relate to each other were of importance not only to mathematicians, but also to artists and architects.

Finding similar triangles is simplified even further if we know that the triangles are right triangles, because then the triangles are similar if one of the acute angles of one triangle has the same measure as an acute angle of the other.

EXAMPLE 3

Problem solving with similar triangles

Suppose that a tree and a yardstick are casting shadows as shown in Figure 5.50. If the shadow of the yardstick is 3 yards long and the shadow of the tree is 12 yards long, use similar triangles to estimate the height h of the tree if you know that $m\angle S = m\angle S'$.

Solution   Since $\angle G$ and $\angle G'$ are right angles, and since $m\angle S = m\angle S'$, we know that $\triangle SGT \sim \triangle S'G'T'$. Therefore, corresponding sides are proportional.

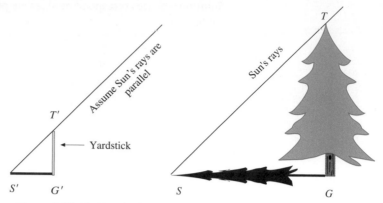

Figure 5.50 Finding the height of a tall object by using similar triangles

$$\frac{\text{LENGTH OF YARDSTICK}}{\text{DISTANCE FROM } S' \text{ TO } G'} = \frac{\text{HEIGHT OF TREE}}{\text{DISTANCE FROM } S \text{ TO } G}$$

$$\frac{1}{3} = \frac{h}{12} \quad \text{You solved proportions like this in Chapter 4.}$$

$$h = \frac{1 \times 12}{3}$$

$$h = 4$$

The tree is 4 yards (or 12 ft) tall. ●

There is a relationship between the sizes of the angles of a right triangle and the ratios of the lengths of the sides. In a right triangle, the side opposite the right angle is called the **hypotenuse.** Each of the acute angles of a right triangle has one side that is the hypotenuse. The other side of that angle is called the **adjacent side.** Finally, the side that is neither of the sides of an angle is called the **opposite side.**

EXAMPLE 4

Sides of a right triangle

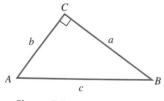

Figure 5.51 A right triangle

Consider $\triangle ABC$ with right angle at C, as shown in Figure 5.51.

Name the hypotenuse and the sides adjacent to the acute angles. Finally, name the side opposite each of the acute angles.

Solution The hypotenuse is c, the side adjacent to $\angle A$ is b, and the side adjacent to $\angle B$ is a. The side opposite $\angle A$ is a, and the side opposite $\angle B$ is b. ●

You might recall the Pythagorean theorem, introduced in Chapter 2, which we now expand to help us decide whether a given triangle is a right triangle.

Pythagorean Theorem

> For any right triangle with sides a and b and hypotenuse c,
>
> $$a^2 + b^2 = c^2$$
>
> Furthermore, if $a^2 + b^2 = c^2$ for three sides of a triangle, then the triangle is a right triangle.

HISTORICAL NOTE

Courtesy of the British Library, London

The Egyptians and the Chinese knew of the Pythagorean theorem before the Pythagoreans (but they didn't call it the Pythagorean theorem, of course, since Pythagoras was not born yet). An early example is shown at left. It is attributed to Chou Pei, who was probably a contemporary of Pythagoras. At right is a copy from a Muslim manuscript, written in 1258, that shows the Pythagorean theorem.

Courtesy of the British Library, London

EXAMPLE 5   **Problem solving using the pythagorean theorem**

A carpenter wants to make sure that the corner of a room is square (a right angle). If she measures out sides of 3 feet and 4 feet, how long should she make the diagonal (hypotenuse)?

Solution   The hypotenuse is the unknown, so use the Pythagorean theorem:

$$c^2 = a^2 + b^2 \qquad \text{Pythagorean theorem}$$

$$c = \sqrt{a^2 + b^2} \qquad \text{In Chapter 2, we noted that if } c^2 = a^2 + b^2, \text{ then } c = \sqrt{a^2 + b^2}.$$

$$= \sqrt{3^2 + 4^2} \qquad \text{The sides are 3 and 4.}$$

$$= \sqrt{9 + 16}$$

$$= \sqrt{25}$$

$$= 5$$

If she makes the diagonal 5 feet long, then the triangle will be a right triangle, and the corner of the room will be square.

If we look at the right triangle shown in Figure 5.51, we can give names to the primary ratios because it turns out that these ratios are very useful for finding a variety of facts about a given triangle. The names that we give to the primary ratios in a right triangle are called **trigonometric ratios** and are defined in the following box.

Trigonometric Ratios

In a right triangle ABC with right angle at C,

$\sin A$ (pronounced "**sine** of A") is the ratio $\dfrac{\text{opposite side of } A}{\text{hypotenuse}}$

$\cos A$ (pronounced "**cosine** of A") is the ratio $\dfrac{\text{adjacent side of } A}{\text{hypotenuse}}$

$\tan A$ (pronounced "**tangent** of A") is the ratio $\dfrac{\text{opposite side of } A}{\text{adjacent side of } A}$

STOP Pay attention to this definition and to the next example.

EXAMPLE 6   **Finding sides of a triangle using trigonometric ratios**

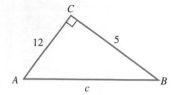

Figure 5.52 Triangle ABC

Given a right triangle with sides 5 and 12, find the trigonometric ratios for the angles A and B. Show your answers in both common-fraction and decimal-fraction form, with decimals rounded to four places.

Solution   First, draw $\triangle ABC$ as shown in Figure 5.52 and then use the Pythagorean theorem to find the length of the hypotenuse:

$$c = \sqrt{5^2 + 12^2}$$
$$= \sqrt{25 + 144}$$
$$= \sqrt{169}$$
$$= 13$$

$\sin A = \frac{5}{13} \approx 0.3846; \quad \cos A = \frac{12}{13} \approx 0.9231; \quad \tan A = \frac{5}{12} \approx 0.4167$

$\sin B = \frac{12}{13} \approx 0.9231; \quad \cos B = \frac{5}{13} \approx 0.3846; \quad \tan B = \frac{12}{5} \approx 2.4$ ●

Tables of ratios for different angles are available (see, for example, Table I in Appendix B). Certain calculators have keys for the sine, cosine, and tangent ratios.

EXAMPLE 7   **Finding trigonometric ratios**

Find the trigonometric ratios by using either Table I in Appendix B or a calculator. (Round calculator answers to four decimal places.)

a. $\sin 45°$ **b.** $\cos 32°$ **c.** $\tan 19°$

Solution

a. $\sin 45° \approx 0.7071$ from Table I or by calculator

b. $\cos 32° \approx 0.8480$ from Table I or by calculator

c. $\tan 19° \approx 0.3443$ from Table I or by calculator   ●

Trigonometric ratios are useful in a variety of situations, as illustrated in the next example.

EXAMPLE 8   **Problem solving with trigonometric ratios**

The angle from the ground to the top of the Great Pyramid of Cheops is 52° if a point on the ground directly below the top is 351 ft away, as shown in Figure 5.53. What is the height of the pyramid (rounded to the nearest foot)?

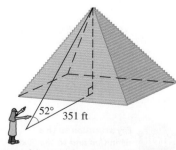

Figure 5.53 Calculating the height of the great pyramid

Solution From Figure 5.53, we see that for height h:

$$\tan 52° = \frac{h}{351}$$

Solving for h by multiplying both sides by 351, we obtain

$$h = 351 \tan 52°$$
$$\approx 351(1.2799) \quad \text{By table}$$
$$\approx 449.2449 \quad \text{By calculator, } 351 \tan 52° \approx 449.2595129.$$

Notice that the calculator and table answers in Example 8 are not identical. This is because both the table and the calculator give approximations of the exact value of $\tan 52°$.

The height of the pyramid is about 449 ft.

PROBLEM SET 5.4

ESSENTIAL IDEAS LEVEL 1

1. What are similar triangles?   Triangles with the same shape

2. What is the important property regarding similar triangles?   Similar triangle property

3. Explain the Pythagorean theorem.   See p. 244.

4. What are the trigonometric ratios?   sine, cosine, and tangent

Use the right triangle in Figure 5.54 to answer the questions in Problems 5–15.

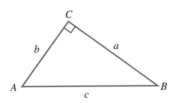

Figure 5.54 $\triangle ABC$

5. What is the side opposite $\angle A$?   a
6. What is the side opposite $\angle B$?   b
7. What is the side adjacent $\angle A$?   b
8. What is the side adjacent $\angle B$?   a
9. What is the hypotenuse?   c
10. What is $\sin A$? $\frac{a}{c}$
11. What is $\sin B$? $\frac{b}{c}$
12. What is $\cos A$? $\frac{b}{c}$
13. What is $\cos B$? $\frac{a}{c}$
14. What is $\tan A$? $\frac{a}{b}$
15. What is $\tan B$? $\frac{b}{a}$

DRILL AND PRACTICE LEVEL 2

Find the trigonometric ratios in Problems 16–21 by using either Table I in Appendix B or a calculator. Round your answers to four decimal places.

16. **a.** $\sin 56°$ 0.8290
    b. $\cos 90°$ 0
    c. $\tan 24°$ 0.4452
17. **a.** $\sin 15°$ 0.2588
    b. $\cos 34°$ 0.8290
    c. $\tan 52°$ 1.2799
18. **a.** $\sin 61°$ 0.8746
    b. $\cos 54°$ 0.5878
    c. $\tan 75°$ 3.7321
19. **a.** $\sin 82°$ 0.9903
    b. $\cos 8°$ 0.9903
    c. $\tan 79°$ 5.1446
20. **a.** $\sin 14°$ 0.2419
    b. $\cos 76°$ 0.2419
    c. $\tan 26°$ 0.4877
21. **a.** $\sin 18°$ 0.3090
    b. $\cos 18°$ 0.9511
    c. $\tan 89°$ 57.2900

In Problems 22–27, tell whether it is possible to conclude that the pairs of triangles are similar. If they are similar, list the proportional parts.

22.

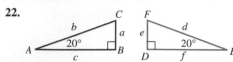

similar; $\overline{AB} \cong \overline{ED}$; $\overline{AC} \cong \overline{EF}$; $\overline{CB} \cong \overline{FD}$; $\angle A \cong \angle E$; $\angle B \cong \angle D$; $\angle C \cong \angle F$

23.

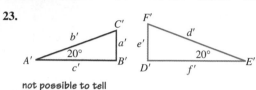

not possible to tell

24.

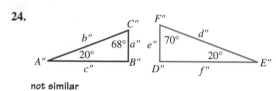

not similar

25.

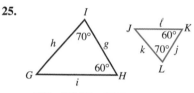

similar; $\overline{GH} \cong \overline{JK}$; $\overline{GI} \cong \overline{JL}$; $\overline{IH} \cong \overline{LK}$; $\angle G \cong \angle J$; $\angle H \cong \angle K$; $\angle I \cong \angle L$

26.

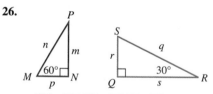

similar; $\overline{MN} \cong \overline{SQ}$; $\overline{MP} \cong \overline{SR}$; $\overline{PN} \cong \overline{RQ}$; $\angle M \cong \angle S$; $\angle P \cong \angle R$; $\angle N \cong \angle Q$

27.

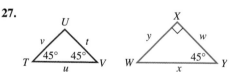

similar; $\overline{TV} \cong \overline{WY}$; $\overline{TU} \cong \overline{WX}$; $\overline{VU} \cong \overline{YX}$; $\angle T \cong \angle W$; $\angle U \cong \angle X$; $\angle V \cong \angle Y$

Given two similar triangles, as shown in Figure 5.55, find the unknown lengths in Problems 28–37.

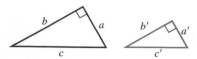

Figure 5.55 Similar triangles

28. $a = 4, b = 8$; find c. $\sqrt{80}$

29. $a' = 7, b' = 3$; find c'. $\sqrt{58}$

30. $a' = 2, c' = 9$; find b'. $\sqrt{77}$

31. $b = 6, c = 15$; find a. $\sqrt{189}$

32. $a = 4, b = 8, a' = 2$; find b'. 4

33. $b = 5, c = 15, b' = 3$; find c'. 9

34. $c = 6, a = 4, c' = 8$; find a'. $\frac{16}{3}$

35. $a' = 7, b' = 3, a = 5$; find b. $\frac{15}{7}$

36. $b' = 8, c' = 12, c = 4$; find b. $\frac{8}{3}$

37. $a' = 2, c' = 9, c = 5$; find a. $\frac{10}{9}$

In Problems 38–42, find the sine, cosine, and tangent for the angle A. Answers show sine, cosine, and tangent, respectively.

38. a.   **b.**

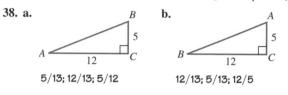

5/13; 12/13; 5/12   12/13; 5/13; 12/5

39. a.   **b.**

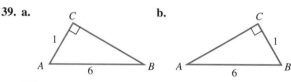

a. $\sqrt{35}/6 \approx 0.9860$; $1/6 \approx 0.1667$; $\sqrt{35}/1 \approx 5.9161$
b. $1/6 \approx 0.1667$; $\sqrt{35}/6 \approx 0.9860$; $1/\sqrt{35} \approx 0.1690$

40. a. A   **b.** B

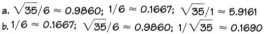
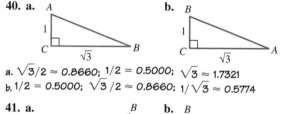

a. $\sqrt{3}/2 \approx 0.8660$; $1/2 = 0.5000$; $\sqrt{3} \approx 1.7321$
b. $1/2 = 0.5000$; $\sqrt{3}/2 \approx 0.8660$; $1/\sqrt{3} \approx 0.5774$

41. a.   **b.** B

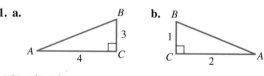

a. 3/5; 4/5; 3/4
b. $1/\sqrt{5} \approx 0.4472$; $2/\sqrt{5} \approx 0.8944$; $1/2 = 0.5000$

42. a.   **b.** B

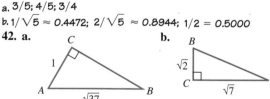

a. $6/\sqrt{37} \approx 0.9864$; $1/\sqrt{37} \approx 0.1644$; $6/1 = 6.0000$
b. $\sqrt{2}/3 \approx 0.4714$; $\sqrt{7}/3 \approx 0.8819$; $\sqrt{2}/\sqrt{7} \approx 0.5345$

APPLICATIONS   **LEVEL 2**

43. The mathematics of the early Egyptians was practical and centered around surveying, construction, and record keeping. They used a simple device to aid surveying—a rope with 12 equal divisions marked by knots, as shown in Figure 5.56.

Figure 5.56 Egyptian measuring rope

When the rope was stretched and staked so that a triangle was formed with sides 3, 4, and 5, the angle formed by the shorter sides was a right angle.

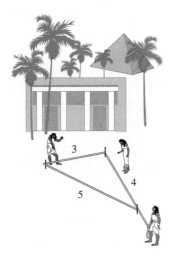

This method was extremely useful in Egypt, where the Nile flooded the rich lands close to the river each year. The lands had to be resurveyed when the waters subsided. Which of the following ropes would form right triangles?

a. Rope A: 30 knots (sides 5, 12, and 13)   **yes**

b. Rope B: 9 knots (sides 2, 3, and 4)   **no**

44. Use similar triangles and a proportion to find the length of the lake shown in Figure 5.57.   **125 ft**

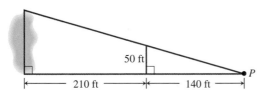

Figure 5.57 Determining the length of a lake

45. Use similar triangles and a proportion to find the length of the swamp shown in Figure 5.58.   **45 ft**

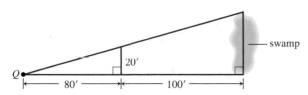

Figure 5.58 Determine the distance across a swamp

46. Use similar triangles and a proportion to find the height of the building shown in Figure 5.59.   **35 ft**

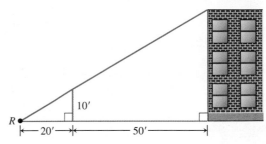

Figure 5.59 Determining the height of a building

47. Use similar triangles and a proportion to find the height of the house shown in Figure 5.60.   **24 ft**

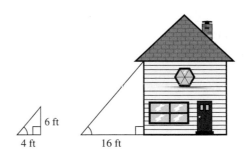

Figure 5.60 Determining the height of a house

48. Find the height of a flagpole as shown in Figure 5.61, if it casts a shadow of 10 ft at the same time that the shadow of a 6-ft person is 5 ft.   **12 ft**

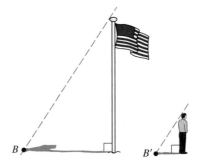

Figure 5.61 Determining the height of a flagpole

49. Find the height of a flagpole (rounded to the nearest foot) as shown in Figure 5.61 if it casts a shadow of 15 ft at the same time that the shadow of a 5-ft person is 4 ft.   **19 ft**

50. If a carpenter wants to make sure that the corner of a room is square and measures 5 ft and 12 ft along the walls, how long should he make the diagonal?   **13 ft**

© Bill Varie/Corbis

51. If a carpenter wants to be sure that the corner of a building is square and measures 6 ft and 8 ft along the sides, how long should the diagonal be?   10 ft

52. If a tree casts a shadow of 12 ft at the same time that a 6-ft person casts a shadow of $2\frac{1}{2}$ ft, find the height of the tree (to the nearest foot).   29 ft

53. If the angle from the horizontal to the top of a building is 38° and the horizontal distance from its base is 90 ft, what is the height of the building (to the nearest foot)?
$90(\tan 38°) \approx 70$ ft

54. If the angle from the horizontal to the top of a tower is 52° and the horizontal distance from its base is 85 ft, what is the height of the tower (to the nearest foot)?
$85(\tan 52°) \approx 109$ ft

RIGHT OR WRONG?   **LEVEL 3**

Explain what is wrong, if anything, with the statements in Problems 55–60. Explain your reasoning.

55. If $\triangle ABC \sim \triangle A'B'C'$, then $\frac{a}{c} = \frac{a'}{b'}$.   F; $\frac{a}{c} = \frac{a'}{c'}$

56. If $\triangle ABC \sim \triangle A'B'C'$, then $\overline{BC}$ and $\overline{AB}$ are corresponding parts.   F; $\overline{BC}$ and $\overline{B'C'}$

57. If two angles of one triangle are congruent to two angles of another triangle, then the triangles are similar.   T

58. In a right triangle ABC with right angle at C,

$$\sin B = \frac{\text{opposite side of } B}{\text{hypotenuse}}$$ T

59. In a right triangle ABC with right angle at C,

$$\cos B = \frac{\text{opposite side of } B}{\text{hypotenuse}}$$ F; $\cos B = \frac{\text{adjacent side of } B}{\text{hypotenuse}}$

60. In a right triangle ABC with right angle at C,

$$\tan B = \frac{\text{opposite side of } B}{\text{adjacent side of } B}$$ T

(5.5) Chapter 5 Summary and Review

STOP

Take some time getting ready to work the review problems in this section. First, look back at the definition and property boxes. You will maximize your understanding of this chapter by working the problems in this section only after you have studied the material.

IMPORTANT TERMS

Numbers refer to sections of this chapter.

CAUTION

Spending some time with the terms and objectives of this chapter will pay dividends in assuring your success.

Acute angle [5.3]	Congruent [5.1]	Degree [5.2]
Adjacent angle [5.2]	Congruent angles [5.2]	Dodecagon [5.2]
Adjacent side [5.4]	Congruent triangles [5.3]	Equal angles [5.2]
Alternate exterior angle [5.2]	Construction [5.1]	Euclidean geometry [5.1]
Alternate interior angle [5.2]	Corresponding angles [5.2]	Euclid's postulates [5.1]
Angle [5.2]	Corresponding parts [5.3]	Exterior angle [5.3]
Axiom [5.5]	Corresponding sides [5.4]	Exterior angle formula [5.3]
Compass [5.1]	Cosine [5.4]	Geometry [5.1]
Complementary angles [5.2]	Decagon [5.2]	Half-line [5.1]
		Heptagon [5.2]

Hexagon [5.2]
Horizontal line [5.2]
Hypotenuse [5.4]
Line [5.1]
Line of symmetry [5.1]
Line segment [5.1]
n-gon [5.2]
Nonagon [5.2]
Obtuse angle [5.2]
Octagon [5.2]
Opposite side [5.4]
Parallel lines [5.2]
Parallelogram [5.2]
Pentagon [5.2]
Perpendicular lines [5.2]
Plane [5.1]
Point [5.1]
Polygon [5.2]

Postulate [5.5]
Premise [5.5]
Protractor [5.2]
Pythagorean theorem [5.4]
Quadrilateral [5.2]
Ray [5.1]
Rectangle [5.2]
Reflection [5.1]
Rhombus [5.2}
Right angle [5.1]
Scalene triangle [5.3]
Similar figures [5.4]
Similar triangle
    property [5.4]
Similar triangles [5.4]
Sine [5.4]
Square [5.2]
Straight angle [5.2]

Straightedge [5.1]
Sum of the measures of the
    angles of a triangle [5.3]
Supplementary
    angles [5.2]
Surface [5.1]
Tangent [5.4]
Theorem [5.1]
Transformation [5.1]
Transversal [5.2]
Trapezoid [5.2]
Triangle [5.2, 5.3]
Trigonometric ratios [5.4]
Undefined terms [5.1]
Vertex [5.2]
Vertical angles [5.2]
Vertical line [5.2]

Essential Ideas

[5.1] Problems 1–2	We cannot reason from the way a figure looks. We can reason only from the given, or known, information.
Problems 3–4	Be able to construct (with a straightedge and compass only) a segment congruent to a given segment and a circle with a radius congruent to a given segment.
Problem 5	What is an undefined term and why is it necessary to have undefined terms?
Problem 6	Know what is meant by line symmetry.
Problem 7	Distinguish axioms and theorems.
[5.2] Problems 1; 5	Define an angle; distinguish right, acute, and obtuse angles.
Problem 2	Distinguish between equal and congruent angles.
Problem 3	Define a quadrilateral; be familiar with five different classifications of quadrilaterals.
Problem 4	Distinguish horizontal and vertical lines.
Problems 6–8	Describe parallel lines; describe the various pairs of angles associated with parallel lines.
[5.3] Problems 1–2	Define a triangle.
Problems 3–4	Remember that the sum of the measures of a triangle is 180°.
[5.4] Problem 1	Define similar triangles.
Problem 2	State the similar triangle property.
Problem 3	State the Pythagorean theorem.
Problem 4	What are the trigonometric ratios, and how can we use them?

LEARNING OUTCOMES

The material in this chapter is reviewed in the following list of learning outcomes. A self-test (with answers and suggestions for additional study) is given. This self-test is constructed so that each problem number corresponds to a related objective. For example, Problem 7 is testing Objective 5.7. This self-test is followed by a practice test with the questions in mixed order.

[5.1] *Objective* 5.1	Using a straightedge and a compass, construct a line segment congruent to a given segment.
[5.1] *Objective* 5.2	Using a straightedge and a compass, construct a circle with a given radius.
[5.1] *Objective* 5.3	Construct a line through a given point parallel to a given line.
[5.1] *Objective* 5.4	Identify line symmetry in a given picture or figure.
[5.1] *Objective* 5.5	Recognize and distinguish the notation for segments, lines, and rays.
[5.1] *Objective* 5.6	Recognize examples of translations, rotations, dilations, and contractions.
[5.1] *Objective* 5.7	Visualize transformations.
[5.2] *Objective* 5.8	Classify polygons according to the number of sides.
[5.2] *Objective* 5.9	Construct an angle congruent to a given angle.
[5.2] *Objective* 5.10	Classify angles as acute, right, straight, or obtuse.
[5.2] *Objective* 5.11	Find the measures of angles formed by parallel lines cut by a transversal.
[5.2] *Objective* 5.12	Classify quadrilaterals using the definitions of a rectangle, square, parallelogram, trapezoid, and rhombus.
[5.2] *Objective* 5.13	Classify pairs of angles formed by intersecting lines.
[5.2] *Objective* 5.14	Recognize intersecting, parallel, perpendicular, vertical, and horizontal lines.
[5.3] *Objective* 5.15	Name the corresponding parts of congruent triangles.
[5.3] *Objective* 5.16	Find the measure of the third angle of a triangle.
[5.3] *Objective* 5.17	Find the measure of an exterior angle of a triangle.
[5.3] *Objective* 5.18	Construct a triangle congruent to a given triangle.
[5.3] *Objective* 5.19	Use algebra to find the angles of a triangle.
[5.3] *Objective* 5.20	Correctly use the terminology for classifying triangles.
[5.4] *Objective* 5.21	Identify the parts of a correctly labeled triangle, and identify the sine, cosine, and tangent of an angle.
[5.4] *Objective* 5.22	Find a trigonometric ratio by using either Table I (Appendix B) or a calculator.
[5.4] *Objective* 5.23	Determine whether two triangles are similar.
[5.4] *Objective* 5.24	Use proportions and similar triangles to find the length of a side of a triangle.
[5.4] *Objective* 5.25	Use the sine, cosine, or tangent to find the length of a side in a right triangle.
[5.4] *Objective* 5.26	Work applied geometry problems. That is, use similar triangles, the Pythagorean theorem, or trigonometric ratios to find an unknown distance (Problems 26–30).

Self-Test

Each question of this self-test is related to the corresponding objective listed above.

1. Construct a segment congruent to the given segment.

_____

2. Draw a circle with radius equal to the length of the segment given in Problem 1.
3. Construct a line through the given point parallel to the given line.

• *P*

⟷

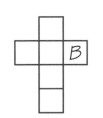

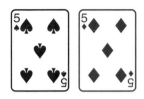

Figure 5.62 Form a cube spelling "CUBE"

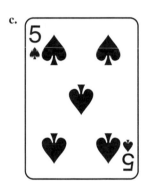

Figure 5.63 Two cards

4. Decide which of the given pictures illustrate line symmetry.

a.

b.

c.

d.
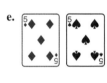

5. Draw an example of each of the following geometrical figures.
  a. $\overrightarrow{PQ}$ **b.** $\overleftarrow{PQ}$ **c.** $\overline{PQ}$ **d.** $\overleftrightarrow{PQ}$

6. Fill in the missing letters to form the word "CUBE" when the pattern in Figure 5.62 is folded to form a cube.

7. Start with the cards shown in Figure 5.63.
    Identify each part as a translation, rotation, dilation, or contraction.

a.

b.

c.

d.

e.

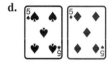

8. Identify the name of the polygon with the given number of sides.
  a. six   **b.** four   **c.** eight   **d.** three   **e.** five

9. Construct an angle congruent to $\angle POS$ in Figure 5.64.

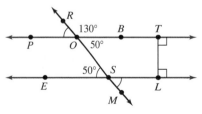

Figure 5.64

10. In Figure 5.64, classify the given angle as acute, right, straight, or obtuse.
  a. $\angle BOS$ **b.** $\angle ESM$ **c.** $\angle ROS$ **d.** $\angle BTL$ **e.** $\angle POS$

11. Find the measures of the angles in Figure 5.64.
  a. $\angle POS$ **b.** $\angle RSL$ **c.** $\angle LSM$ **d.** $\angle BTL$

12. Define the named quadrilateral.
  a. rectangle   **b.** parallelogram   **c.** trapezoid   **d.** rhombus   **e.** square

13. Suppose ℓ_1 and ℓ_2 are parallel lines. Classify the pairs of angles shown in Figure 5.65.

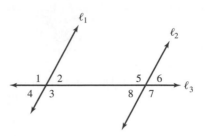

Figure 5.65 Parallel lines cut by a transversal

  a. $\angle 1$ and $\angle 5$ **b.** $\angle 5$ and $\angle 6$ **c.** $\angle 2$ and $\angle 4$
  d. $\angle 2$ and $\angle 8$ **e.** $\angle 1$ and $\angle 7$ **f.** $\angle 1$ and $\angle 3$

14. Classify any of the lines ℓ_1, ℓ_2, or ℓ_3 in Figure 5.65 as parallel, perpendicular, horizontal, or vertical.

15. If $\triangle TRI \simeq \triangle ARI$ in Figure 5.66, name the corresponding parts.

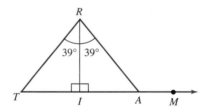

Figure 5.66 Congruent triangles

16. What is the measure of $\angle T$ in Figure 5.66?

17. What is the measure of $\angle RAM$ in Figure 5.66?

18. Construct a triangle congruent to $\triangle TAR$ in Figure 5.66.

19. Find the angles of a triangle if it is known that the measures of the angles are $2x + 10°$, $5x - 60°$, and $x - 10°$.

20. **a.** Draw a correctly labeled right triangle.
    b. Draw a scalene obtuse triangle.
    c. Draw an isosceles right triangle.

21. In a correctly labeled triangle $\triangle TOP$, with right angle $\angle TOP$, use the definition of the trigonometric ratios to find the requested ratios.
      a. $\sin T$ **b.** $\cos T$ **c.** $\tan T$

22. Find the values of the given trigonometric ratios by using Table I (Appendix B) or a calculator. Round your answers to four decimal places.
      a. $\sin 59°$ **b.** $\tan 0°$ **c.** $\cos 18°$ **d.** $\tan 82°$

23. Is $\triangle AIR \sim \triangle TIR$ in Figure 5.66? Tell why or why not.

24. If $\triangle ABC \sim \triangle A'B'C'$ and $a' = 5$, $b' = 12$, and $a = 7\frac{1}{2}$, what is b?

25. If $\overline{RI}$ in Figure 5.66 is 5 in., what is the length of $\overline{AI}$ (to the nearest inch)?

26. The legs of a picnic table form a triangle where $\overline{AC}$ and $\overline{BC}$ have the same length, as shown in Figure 5.67. If $m\angle ACB = 89°$, find the measures of angles x and y so that the top of the table will be parallel to the ground.

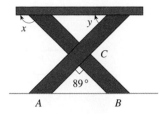

Figure 5.67 Picnic table

27. Find the measures of a triangle if it is known that the measures of the angles are x, $4x$, and $5x$.

28. If a tree casts a shadow of 12 ft at the same time that a 6-ft person casts a shadow of $2\frac{1}{2}$ ft, find the height of the tree (to the nearest foot).

29. Use similar triangles and a proportion to find the height of the cliff shown in Figure 5.68.

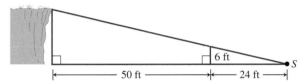

Figure 5.68 Determining the height of a cliff

30. The world's most powerful lighthouse is on the coast of Brittany, France, and is about 160 ft tall. Suppose you are in a boat just off the coast, as shown in Figure 5.69. Determine your distance (to the nearest foot) from the base of the lighthouse if $m\angle B = 12°$.

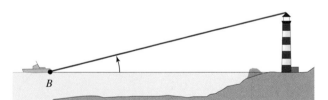

Figure 5.69 Distance from ship to shore

STOP   **STUDY HINTS**   *Compare your solutions and answers to the self-test. For each problem you missed, work some additional problems in the section listed in the margin. After you have worked these problems, you can test yourself with the practice test.*

Additional Problems

[5.1] Problems 9–12
[5.1] Problems 13–16

Complete Solutions to the Self-Test

1.

2.

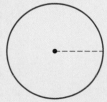

3.

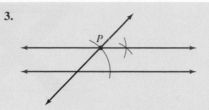

4. a. not symmetric (look at the eagle's head)

    b. symmetric

    c. flag is symmetric; not if pole is included

    d. not symmetric

5. a.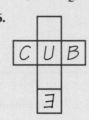

6.

7. a. rotation   **b.** translation   **c.** dilation

    d. contraction   **e.** rotation and contraction

8. a. hexagon   **b.** quadrilateral   **c.** octagon

    d. triangle   **e.** pentagon

9.

10. a. acute   **b.** obtuse   **c.** straight   **d.** right   **e.** obtuse

11. a. 130° (vertical angles)   **b.** 130° (corresponding angles)

    c. 50° (vertical angles)   **d.** 90° (right angle mark)

12. a. A rectangle is a parallelogram that contains a right angle.

    b. A parallelogram is a quadrilateral with opposite sides parallel.

    c. A trapezoid is a quadrilateral with exactly one pair of parallel sides.

    d. A rhombus is a parallelogram with adjacent sides of equal length.

    e. A square is a rectangle with two adjacent sides of equal length.

13. a. corresponding angles   **b.** supplementary angles

    c. vertical angles   **d.** alternate interior angles

    e. alternate exterior angles   **f.** vertical angles

14. ℓ_1 and ℓ_2 are parallel; ℓ_3 is horizontal.

15. $\angle T \simeq \angle A$; $\angle TIR \simeq \angle AIR$; $\angle TRI \simeq \angle ARI$; $\overline{TI} \simeq \overline{AI}$; $\overline{TR} \simeq \overline{AR}$; $\overline{RI} \simeq \overline{RI}$

[5.3] Problems 11–16

16. Since the sum of the measures of the angles is 180°,
$$m\angle T = 180° - 90° - 39° = 51°$$

[5.3] Problems 17–22

17. $m\angle RAM = 90° + 39° = 129°$

[5.3] Problems 23–28; 49–52

18.

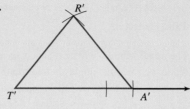

[5.3] Problems 29–34; 43–48

19. Since the sum of the measures of the angles is 180°,
$$(2x + 10°) + (5x - 60°) + (x - 10°) = 180°$$
$$2x + 5x + x + 10° - 60° - 10° = 180°$$
$$8x - 60° = 180°$$
$$8x = 240°$$
$$x = 30°$$

The angles are:
$$2x + 10° = 2(30°) + 10° = 70°$$
$$5x - 60° = 5(30°) - 60° = 90°$$
$$x - 10° = 30° - 10° = 20°$$

[5.3] Problems 35–42

20. a.

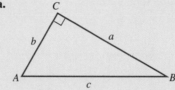

b.   **c.**

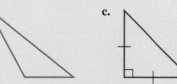

[5.4] Problems 5–15

21. a. $\sin T = \dfrac{|\overline{PO}|}{|\overline{PT}|}$ **b.** $\cos T = \dfrac{|\overline{TO}|}{|\overline{PT}|}$ **c.** $\tan T = \dfrac{|\overline{PO}|}{|\overline{TO}|}$

[5.4] Problems 16–21

22. a. $\sin 59° = 0.8572$ **b.** $\tan 0° = 0$
c. $\cos 18° = 0.9511$ **d.** $\tan 82° = 7.1154$

[5.4] Problems 22–27

23. They are similar because two angles of one triangle are equal to two angles of the other.

[5.4] Problems 28–37

24. Since the triangles are similar, corresponding sides are proportional.
$$\frac{a'}{b'} = \frac{a}{b}$$
$$\frac{5}{12} = \frac{7\frac{1}{2}}{b}$$
$$b = \frac{12 \times 7.5}{5}$$
$$= 18 \quad \textbf{By calculator}$$

Applications

25. $\tan 39° = \dfrac{\text{opposite side}}{\text{adjacent side}} = \dfrac{|\overline{AI}|}{|\overline{RI}|} = \dfrac{|\overline{AI}|}{5}$

$5 \tan 39° = |\overline{AI}|$ **Multiply both sides by 5.**

$4.0489 = |\overline{AI}|$ **By table or calculator**

This side is 4 in.

26. The upper triangle will also have a base angle with measure 89°, so to keep the top level, the other angles in that triangle must have the same measure.

$$y + y + 89° = 180° \quad \textbf{Sum of the measures of a triangle is 180°.}$$
$$2y = 91° \quad \textbf{Subtract 89° from both sides.}$$
$$y = 45.5°$$

Finally, since x and y are supplementary,

$$x + y = 180°$$
$$x + 45.5° = 180° \quad \textbf{Substitute the value of y.}$$
$$x = 134.5°$$

The top will be parallel if the measure of angle x is 134.5° and the measure of angle y is 45.5°.

27. $x + 4x + 5x = 180°$ **Sum of the measures is 180°.**

$10x = 180°$

$x = 18°$

The angles are 18°, $4x = 4(18°) = 72°$, and $5x = 5(18°) = 90°$.

28.

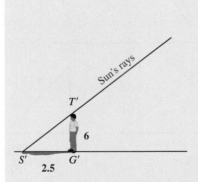
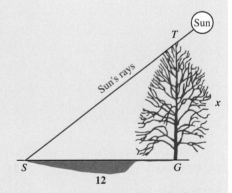

Because the sun's rays are parallel, the triangle formed by the man, shadow, and sun's ray is proportional to the triangle formed by the tree, shadow, and sun's ray. Thus,

$$\frac{6}{2.5} = \frac{x}{12} \quad \textbf{Corresponding parts of similar triangles}$$

$$72 = 2.5x$$

$$28.8 = x \quad \textbf{Divide both sides by 2.5.}$$

The tree is about 29 ft tall (correct to the nearest foot).

29. Use proportional parts.

$$\frac{6}{24} = \frac{h}{50 + 24}$$ Let *h* be the height of the cliff.

$$h = \frac{6 \times 74}{24}$$ Note: 50 + 24 = 74.

$$h = 18.5$$ By calculator

The height of the cliff is 18.5 ft.

30. Use the definition of the tangent ratio.

$$\tan 12° = \frac{160}{d}$$ Let *d* be the distance to the lighthouse.

$$d \tan 12° = 160$$ Multiply both sides by *d*.

$$d = \frac{160}{\tan 12°}$$

$$= 753$$ By calculator: 752.7408175

By table: Use 0.2126 for tan 12°.

The distance from the boat to the lighthouse is approximately 753 ft.

Chapter 5 Review Questions

To prepare for a chapter test, first study the chapter; then, read each term from the important terms list above and make sure you know the meaning of each word; finally, review the chapter objectives. **After** these steps, take the self-test and correct all your answers. The following review questions can be used for extra practice.

Using only a straightedge and compass, carry out the requested constructions in Problems 1–4. Verify constructions by looking at the given parts.

1. Construct a segment congruent to the given segment: ————

2. Construct a circle with radius congruent to the segment in Problem 1.

3. Construct a line through the point *Q* parallel to the given line.

4. Construct a triangle congruent to △*STU*.

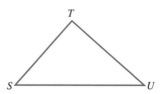

5. Give the name of each polygon.

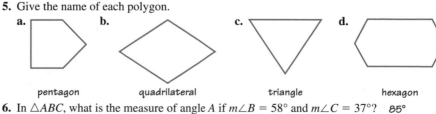

a. pentagon b. quadrilateral c. triangle d. hexagon

6. In △*ABC*, what is the measure of angle *A* if *m*∠*B* = 58° and *m*∠*C* = 37°? 85°

7. What is the test to determine whether two triangles are similar?
Two angles of one must be equal to two angles of the other.

8. Classify the angles from Figure 5.70 as acute, right, straight, or obtuse, and construct an angle congruent to each.

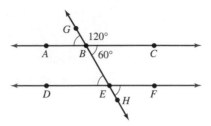

Figure 5.70 Parallel lines cut by a transversal

  a. ∠*ABC* straight **b.** ∠*GBC* obtuse **c.** ∠*FEH* acute **d.** ∠*BED* acute

9. Construct an angle congruent to ∠*DEH* from Figure 5.70.

10. Construct an angle congruent to ∠*FEH* from Figure 5.70.

11. Suppose △*ABD* ≃ △*CBD*, as shown in Figure 5.71.
 a. What angle corresponds to ∠*A*? ∠C
 b. What side corresponds to $\overline{AD}$? $\overline{CD}$
 c. What side corresponds to $\overline{BD}$? $\overline{BD}$
 d. What angle corresponds to ∠*BDC*? ∠BDA

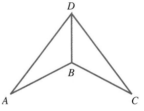

Figure 5.71 △*ABD* ≃ △*CBD*

12. If *m*∠*C* = 20° and *m*∠*CDB* = 30° in Figure 5.71, what is the measure of ∠*DBC*? 130°

13. What are the measures of the angles in Figure 5.72? 45°, 50°, 85°

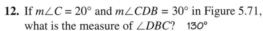

Figure 5.72

14. Find the value of *x* in each of the figures.

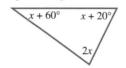

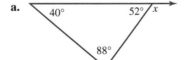

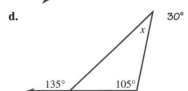

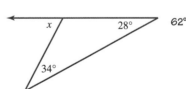

15. Is △*DEF* ~ △*HGF*? yes; similar

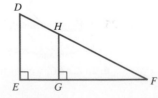

Find the unknown lengths (to the nearest tenth) in Problems 16–20 as shown in Figure 5.73.

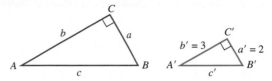

Figure 5.73 $\triangle ABC \simeq \triangle A'B'C'$

16. a. If $b = 4$, find a.   8/3 ≈ 2.7
   b. From the Pythagorean theorem, $c' \approx \sqrt{13}$. If $a = 4$, find c.   2√13 ≈ 7.2

17. a. If $a = 4$, find b.   6.0
   b. From the Pythagorean theorem, $c' \approx 3.6$. If $b = 4$, find c.   4.8

18. a. If $m\angle A = 32°$ and $b = 38$, find a.   a = 38 tan 32° = 23.7
   b. If $m\angle B = 19°$ and $b = 21$, find c.   sin 19° = 21/c; c ≈ 64.5

19. a. If $m\angle A = 35°$ and $a = 45$, find b.   tan 35° = 45/b; b ≈ 64.3
   b. If $m\angle B = 17°$ and $b = 19$, find c.   sin 17° = 19/c; c ≈ 65.0

20. a. If $m\angle B = 22°$ and $a = 38$, find b.   tan 22° = b/38; b ≈ 15.4
   b. If $m\angle A = 28°$ and $b = 128$, find c.   cos 28° = 128/c; c ≈ 145.0

21. Find the values (rounded to four decimal places) by using Table I or a calculator.
   a. $\tan 77°$ 4.3315   **b.** $\cos 83°$ 0.1219   **c.** $\cos 78°$ 0.2079   **d.** $\sin 69°$ 0.9336

22. If a tree casts a shadow of 18 ft at the same time that a yardstick (3 ft high) casts a shadow of 2 ft, find the height of the tree (to the nearest foot).   The tree is 27 ft tall.

23. Use similar triangles to find the length of the sand pit in Figure 5.74.   The pit is 45 ft long.

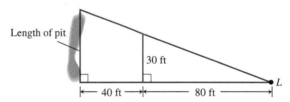

Figure 5.74 Finding the length of a sand pit

24. Find the distance $|\overline{PA}|$ (rounded to the nearest foot) across the river shown in Figure 5.75, if it is known that distance $|\overline{DA}|$ is 50 ft and that $\angle D$ is 38°.
The distance across the river is 39 ft.

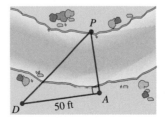

Figure 5.75 Distance across a river

25. Find the distance $|\overline{PA}|$ (rounded to the nearest foot) across the river shown in Figure 5.75, if it is known that the distance $|\overline{DA}|$ is 50 ft and that $\angle D$ is 42°.
The distance across the river is 45 ft.

Individual Projects

Learning to use sources outside your classroom and textbook is an important skill, and here are some ideas for extending some of the ideas in this chapter.

PROJECT 5.1 **Nine dots puzzle** Connect the nine dots in Figure 5.76 with four line segments, but do not lift your pencil from the paper.

Figure 5.76 Nine dots puzzle

PROJECT 5.2 The first illustration in Figure 5.77 shows a cube with the top cut off. Use solid lines and shading to depict seven other different views of a cube with one side cut off.

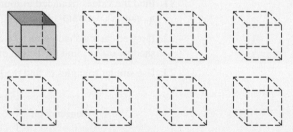

Figure 5.77 Views of a cube

PROJECT 5.3 Show that *the sum of the measures of the interior angles of any quadrilateral is* 360° by carrying out the following steps.

Step 1 Draw any quadrilateral, as illustrated in Figure 5.78 (but draw your quadrilateral so it has a different shape from the one shown).

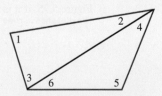

Figure 5.78 Quadrilateral

Step 2 Divide the quadrilateral into two triangles by drawing a diagonal (a line segment connecting two nonadjacent vertices). Label the angles of your triangles as shown in Figure 5.78.

What is the sum $m\angle 1 + m\angle 2 + m\angle 3$?   180°
What is the sum $m\angle 4 + m\angle 5 + m\angle 6$?   180°
What is the sum of the measures of the angles of the quadrilateral?   360°

Now, using similar reasoning, what is the sum of the measures of the interior angles of any pentagon? $180° \cdot 3 = 540°$

What is the sum of the measures of the interior angles of any octagon? $180° \cdot 6 = 1,080°$

State a formula for the sum of the measures of the interior angles of a polygon with *n* sides. $180°(n - 2)$

PROJECT 5.4 If the distance from the earth to the sun is 92.9 million miles, and the angle formed between Venus, the earth, and the sun is 47° (as shown in Figure 5.79), find the distance from the sun to Venus (to the nearest hundred thousand miles).
92,900,000 sin 47° ≈ 67,900,000 miles

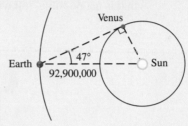

Figure 5.79 Portion of the solar system

Find the distance from the earth to Venus (to the nearest hundred thousand miles).
92,900,000 cos 47° ≈ 63,400,000 miles

PROJECT 5.5 Write a paper on the relationship between art and mathematics.

PROJECT 5.6 Prepare a portfolio of photographs of buildings with interesting architecture.
Find the architectural name for the building style, as well as the name of the mathematical solid that most closely approximates the shape of the building.

Team Projects

Working in small groups is typical of most work environments, and learning to work with others to communicate specific ideas is an important skill. Work with three or four other students to submit a single report based on each of the following questions.

T11. Suppose it were possible to count all of the individual strands of hair on your head. Also suppose that it is possible to do that for any number of people. For example, if you have 4,890 hairs on your head and I have 1,596 hairs, then the product of the number of hairs on both our heads is 7,804,440. What is the product of the number of hairs for all persons in New York City at midnight on New Year's Eve, December 31, 2007?
0; at least one person must be completely bald (0 hairs)

T12. In Figure 5.80, there are eight square rooms making up a maze. Each square room has two walls that are mirrors and two walls that are open spaces. Identify the mirrored walls, and then solve the maze by showing how you can pass through all eight rooms consecutively without going through the same room twice. If that is not possible, tell why.

Figure 5.80 Mirror maze

Measurement and Problem Solving

Mathematics may be compared to a mill of exquisite workmanship, which grinds your stuff of any degree of fineness; but, nevertheless, what you get out depends on what you put in.

Thomas Huxley, *Quarterly Journal of the Geological Society, 25, 1869*

ANTICIPATE

- *Overview; check out contents, terms, essential ideas, and learning outcomes.*
- *Numbers are used to count and to measure.*
- *In counting, the numbers are considered exact unless the result has been rounded.*
- *Measurement is never exact.*

(6.1) Precision, Accuracy, and Estimation

IN THIS WORLD THE POWER OF MATH

"Terry, did you remember to pick up the differential GPS unit so we can make our measurements of the rate of shoreline change?" asked Sherry.

"Yep, got the GPS, a pair of emery rods, a metric tape, and a hand level so that we can accurately survey the shore-line normal beach profile," answered Terry.

Measurements are essential to living in this world; we use them every day. In this section, we introduce the metric system, after making a distinction between precision and accuracy.

 See Problem 1.

Measure of Length

To measure an object is to assign a number to its size. The number representing its linear dimension, as measured from end to end, is called its **measure** or **length.**

Measurement is never exact, and you must decide how **precise** the measure should be. For example, the measurement might be to the nearest inch, nearest foot, or even nearest mile. The precision of a measurement depends not only on the instrument used, but also on the purpose of your measurement. For example, if you are measuring the size of a room to lay carpet, the precision of your measurement might be different from when you are measuring the size of an airport hangar.

The **accuracy** refers to your answer. Suppose that you use an instrument that measures to the nearest tenth of a unit. You find one measurement to be 4.6 and another measurement to be 2.1. If, in the process of your work, you need to multiply these numbers, the result you obtain is

$$4.6 \times 2.1 = 9.66$$

This product is calculated to two decimal places, using the procedures for the multiplication of decimals discussed in Chapter 1. However, it does not seem quite right that you obtain an answer that is more accurate (two decimal places) than the instrument you are using to obtain your measurements (one decimal place). In this book, we will require that the accuracy of your answers not exceed the precision of the measurement. This means that after doing your calculations, the final answer should be rounded. The principle we will use is stated in the following box.

Accuracy of Answers in This Book

All measurements are as precise as given in the text. If you are asked to make a measurement, the precision will be specified. Carry out all calculations without rounding. After obtaining a *final answer,* round this answer to be as accurate as *the least precise measurement.*

This means that, to avoid round-off error, you should round only once (at the end). This is particularly important if you are using a calculator that displays 8, 10, 12, or even more decimal places.

You will also be asked to *estimate* the size of many objects in this chapter. As we introduce different units of measurement, you should remember some reference points so that you can make intelligent estimates. Many comparisons will be mentioned in the text, but you need to remember only those that are meaningful for you to estimate other sizes or distances. You will also need to choose appropriate units of measurement. For example, you would not measure your height in yards or miles, or the distance to New York City in inches.

There have been numerous attempts to make the metric system mandatory in the United States. Figure 6.1 shows that the United States is the only major country not using the metric system.

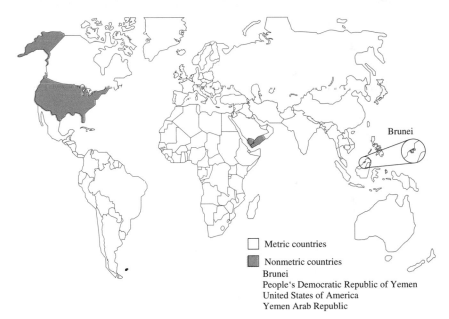

Figure 6.1 The metric world

Today, big business is supporting the drive toward metric conversion, and it appears inevitable that the metric system will eventually come into use in the United States. In the meantime, it is important that you understand how to use both the United States and metric systems.

The real advantage of using the metric system is the ease of conversion from one unit of measurement to another. Do you remember the difficulty you had in learning to change tablespoons to cups? Or pints to gallons?

In this book we will work with both the U.S. and the metric measurement systems. You should be familiar with both and be able to make estimates in both systems. The following box gives the standard units of length.

Standard Units of Length

U.S. System	Metric System
inch (in.)	**meter (m)**
foot (ft; 12 in.)	centimeter $\left(\text{cm}; \dfrac{1}{100}\, \text{m} \right)$
yard (yd; 36 in.)	kilometer (km; 1,000 m)
mile (mi; 63,360 in.)	

To understand the size of any measurement, you must see it, have experience with it, and take measurements using it as a standard unit. The basic unit of measurement for the U.S. system is the inch; it is shown in Figure 6.2. You can remember that an inch is about the distance from the joint of your thumb to the tip of your thumb. The basic unit of measurement for the metric system is the meter; it is also shown in Figure 6.2. You can remember that a meter is about the distance from your left ear to the tip of the fingers on the end of your outstretched right arm.

a. Basic unit of length in the U.S. system is the inch.

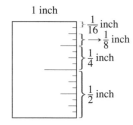

1 inch

$\frac{1}{16}$ inch
$\frac{1}{8}$ inch
$\frac{1}{4}$ inch
$\frac{1}{2}$ inch

b. In the metric system, a distance comparable to the inch is the centimeter.

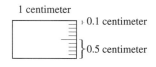

1 centimeter
0.1 centimeter
0.5 centimeter

c. Basic unit of length in the metric system is the meter. In the U.S. system, a comparable unit is the yard.

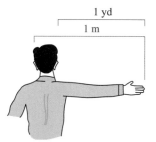

1 yd
1 m

Figure 6.2 Standard units of measurement for length

For the larger distances of a mile and a kilometer, you must look at maps or at the odometer of your car. However, you should have some idea of these distances.*

Later in the book, we will consider conversions of units within the U.S. system as well as conversions within the metric system, and we will use a variety of prefixes

*We could tell you that a mile is 5,280 ft or that a kilometer is 1,000 m, but to do so does not give you any feeling for how far these distances really are. You need to get into a car and watch the odometer to see how far you travel in going 1 mile. Most cars in the United States do not have odometers set to kilometers, and until they do it is difficult to measure in kilometers. You might, however, be familiar with a 10-kilometer race. It takes a good runner about 30 minutes to run 10 kilometers and an average runner about 45 minutes. You can walk a kilometer in about 6 minutes.

in the metric system. It might help to have a visual image of these prefixes as you progress through this chapter, even though we will not consider conversions until Section 6.6. The Greek prefixes **kilo-, hecto-,** and **deka-** are used for measurements larger than the basic metric unit, and the Latin prefixes **deci-, centi-,** and **milli-** are used for quantities smaller than the basic unit (see Figure 6.3). As you can see from Figure 6.3, a centimeter is $\frac{1}{100}$ of a meter. This means that 1 meter is equal to 100 centimeters.

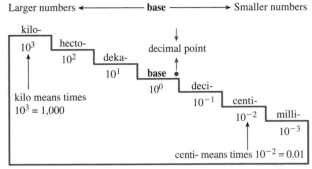

Greek prefixes for larger quantities   Latin prefixes for smaller quantities

Figure 6.3 Metric prefixes

STOP You need to learn these prefixes for the metric system.

Now we will measure given line segments with different levels of precision. We will consider two different rulers, one marked to the nearest centimeter and another marked to the nearest $\frac{1}{10}$ centimeter.

EXAMPLE 1

Measuring segments

Measure the given segment A

A ——————————————

a. to the nearest centimeter.   **b.** to nearest $\frac{1}{10}$ centimeter.

Solution

a. To measure the segment to the nearest centimeter, place a ruler showing centimeters next to the segment.

b. To measure the segment to the nearest tenth of a centimeter, place a ruler showing tenths of a centimeter next to the segment. Notice that it looks as if the length of segment A is right on 6 cm. When measuring to the nearest tenth of a centimeter, we write 6.0 cm to indicate that this measurement is correct to the nearest tenth of a unit.

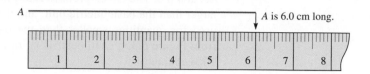

A is 6.0 cm long.

EXAMPLE 2

Measuring length; rounding down

Measure the given segment *B*

B ————————————————

a. to the nearest centimeter.   **b.** to the nearest $\frac{1}{10}$ centimeter.

Solution

a. B ———————————————— End of *B* is nearer to 5 than to 6.

b. B ————————————————

B is 5.3 cm long.

EXAMPLE 3

Measuring length; rounding up

Measure the given segment *C*

C ————————————————

a. to the nearest centimeter.   **b.** to the nearest $\frac{1}{10}$ centimeter.

Solution

a. C ———————————————— End of *C* is nearer to 5 than to 4.

b. C ————————————————

C is 4.7 cm long.

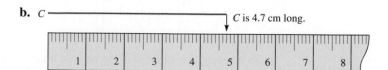

PROBLEM SET 6.1

ESSENTIAL IDEAS   LEVEL 1

Remember, you should answer the questions listed in the sections named "Essential Ideas" even if your instructor does not assign them.

1. IN YOUR OWN WORDS Discuss the differences between *precision* and *accuracy*.

2. IN YOUR OWN WORDS What is the agreement about the accuracy of the answers given in this book?

3. What is the basic unit of length in the U.S. measurement system? Name three other units and tell how they are related to the basic unit.   inch; foot (12 in.), yard (3 ft = 36 in.), and mile (5,280 ft = 63,360 in.)

4. What is the basic unit of length in the metric measurement system? Name two other units and tell how they are related to the basic unit.   meter; centimeter (1/100 m), and kilometer (1,000 m)

5. What are the three metric prefixes for units that are larger than the basic metric unit?   kilo-, hecto-, and deka-

6. What are the three metric prefixes for units that are smaller than the basic metric unit?   deci-, centi-, milli-

State the abbreviation for each unit of measurement in Problems 7–12.

7. inch   in.

8. centimeter   cm

9. yard   yd

10. mile   mi

11. kilometer   km

12. meter   m

DRILL AND PRACTICE   LEVEL 2

Pick the best choices in Problems 13–27 by estimating. Do not measure. For metric measurements, do not attempt to convert to the U.S. system. The hardest part of the transition to the metric system is the transition to thinking in metrics.

13. The length of your math textbook is about   A

A. 9 in.   B. 9 cm   C. 2 ft

14. The length of a car is about   B

A. 1 m   B. 4 m   C. 10 m

15. The length of a dollar bill is about   B

A. 3 in.   B. 6 in.   C. 9 in.

16. The width of a dollar bill is about   B

A. 1.9 cm   B. 6.5 cm   C. 0.65 m

17. The distance from your home to the nearest grocery store is most likely to be   C

A. 1 cm   B. 1 m   C. 1 km

18. Your height is closest to   A

A. 5 ft   B. 10 ft   C. 25 in.

19. An adult's height is most likely to be about   C

A. 6 m   B. 50 cm   C. 170 cm

20. The distance around your waist is closest to   B

A. 10 in.   B. 36 in.   C. 30 cm

21. The distance from floor to ceiling in a typical home is about   A

A. 2.5 m   B. 0.5 m   C. 4.5 m

22. The length of a new pencil is about   B

A. 7 cm   B. 17 cm   C. 7 m

23. The length of a 100-yard football field is   C

A. 100 m

B. more than 100 m

C. less than 100 m

24. The distance from San Francisco to New York is about 3,000 miles. This distance is   B

A. less than 3,000 km

B. more than 3,000 km

C. about 3,000 km

25. Suppose someone could run the 100-meter dash in 10 seconds flat. At the same rate, this person should be able to run the 100-yard dash in   A

A. less than 10 sec

B. more than 10 sec

C. 10 sec

26. The prefix *centi-* means   C

A. one thousand

B. one-thousandth

C. one-hundredth

27. The prefix *kilo-* means   A

A. one thousand

B. one-thousandth

C. one-hundredth

28. IN YOUR OWN WORDS What does it mean to measure the length of a segment?

29. IN YOUR OWN WORDS Write a short essay discussing your opinion about using the metric measurement system.

30. IN YOUR OWN WORDS The first section of this book was entitled "Math Anxiety" because we assumed that you had some anxiety when you began this book.

a. On a scale of 1 to 10 (with 1 low anxiety and 10 high anxiety), what was your anxiety level when you began this book?

b. This is the last chapter of the first half of the book, where we present some of the "Power of Mathematics." Hopefully as you have moved through these chapters your anxiety has gone down. On that same scale of 1 to 10, how would you rate your anxiety level today?

 31. IN YOUR OWN WORDS

a. If the second level in Problem 30 is higher than the first, consider calling the author at (707) 829-0606 or send him an e-mail:

smithkjs@mathnature.com

Report on the result of your call or e-mail.

b. If the second level is lower than the first, then you are on track! Write a report on your progress from the beginning of the course until now.

From memory, and without using any measuring devices, estimate the length of the line segments indicated in Problems 32–43. Use a ruler to measure the segments.

32. 1 in.   **33.** 2 in.   **34.** 3 in.

35. $\frac{1}{2}$ in.   **36.** $\frac{1}{4}$ in.   **37.** $\frac{3}{4}$ in.

38. 1 cm   **39.** 2 cm   **40.** 3 cm

41. 10 cm   **42.** 5 cm   **43.** 4 cm

Measure the segments given in Problems 44–55 with the indicated precision.

D ——————————
E ——————————
F ——————————

44. *D* to the nearest centimeter   3 cm

45. *D* to the nearest $\frac{1}{10}$ centimeter 2.5 cm

46. *D* to the nearest inch   1 in.

47. *D* to the nearest eighth of an inch   1 in.

48. *E* to the nearest centimeter   3 cm

49. *E* to the nearest $\frac{1}{10}$ centimeter   3.4 cm

50. *E* to the nearest inch   1 in.

51. *E* to the nearest eighth of an inch $1\frac{3}{8}$ in.

52. *F* to the nearest centimeter   4 cm

53. *F* to the nearest $\frac{1}{10}$ centimeter   4.3 cm

54. *F* to the nearest inch   2 in.

55. *F* to the nearest eighth of an inch $1\frac{3}{4}$ in.

APPLICATIONS   LEVEL 2

56. IN YOUR OWN WORDS One of the first recorded units of measurement is the *cubit*. If we define a *cubit* as the distance from your elbow to your fingertips, then we may find

that the cubit defined for a man is different than that for a woman. Figure 6.4 shows a picture of the ancient Egyptian cubit.

© Réunion des Musées Nationaux/Art Resource, NY

Figure 6.4 An ancient cubit

The actual size of this ancient cubit is 52.5 cm. How does your cubit compare with the Egyptian cubit on display at the Louvre (see Figure 6.4)?

57. IN YOUR OWN WORDS The basic subunit of the *cubit* (see Problem 56) was the digit, which was no doubt the width of a finger. If an ancient digit was 1.9 cm, how does your digit compare with the Egyptian digit?

58. The Egyptian *cubit* (see Problem 56) came in two lengths—the "common" cubit and the "royal" cubit. These two measurements were related by a ratio of 6 to 7. Thus, if your height is 2.5 common cubits, what is your height in royal cubits? Round your answer to the nearest tenth of a cubit.   2.9 royal cubits

59. The Egyptian *Khet* was 100 cubits (see Problem 56). If the standard rate of marching was 1.5 Khet per minute, what is the rate of travel in Khets per hour?   90 Khets/hour

60. IN YOUR OWN WORDS Find your own metric measurements.

	Women	Men
a.	Height	Height
b.	Bust	Chest
c.	Waist	Waist
d.	Hips	Seat
e.	Distance from waist to hemline	Neck

6.2 Perimeter

IN THIS WORLD THE POWER OF MATH

"Greg, do you have the template for the part we need to fabricate?"
asked Katlin.
   "You mean the one with the two centimeter holes in the center of
the base?" responded Greg.

In this section we will consider the idea of perimeter—that is, the distance
around an object.

 See Problem 54.

One application of both measurement and geometry involves finding the distance
around a polygon. This distance around is called the *perimeter* of the polygon.

Perimeter

The **perimeter** of a polygon is the sum of the lengths of the sides of that polygon.

EXAMPLE 1

Finding a perimeter

Find the perimeter of the polygon in Figure 6.5 by measuring each side to the near-est $\frac{1}{10}$ centimeter.

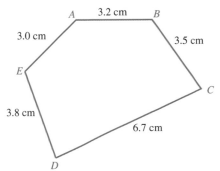

Figure 6.5 Perimeter of a polygon

Solution

Side	Length
$\overline{BA}$	3.2 cm
$\overline{BC}$	3.5 cm
$\overline{CD}$	6.7 cm
$\overline{DE}$	3.8 cm
$\overline{EA}$	3.0 cm
Total:	20.2 cm

The perimeter is 20.2 cm.

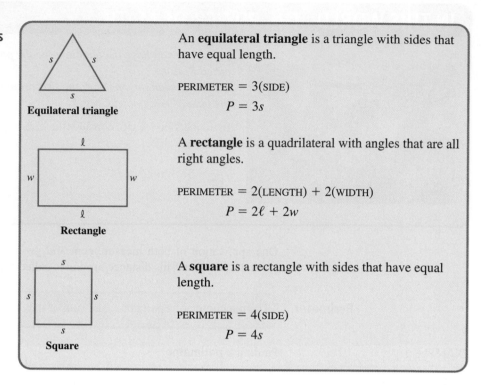

Perimeter Formulas

An **equilateral triangle** is a triangle with sides that have equal length.

PERIMETER = 3(SIDE)

$$P = 3s$$

Equilateral triangle

A **rectangle** is a quadrilateral with angles that are all right angles.

PERIMETER = 2(LENGTH) + 2(WIDTH)

$$P = 2\ell + 2w$$

Rectangle

A **square** is a rectangle with sides that have equal length.

PERIMETER = 4(SIDE)

$$P = 4s$$

Square

EXAMPLE 2

Finding perimeters

Find the perimeter of each polygon.

a.

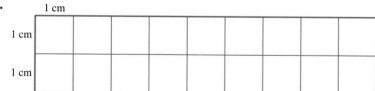

b.

c.

d.

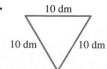

e.

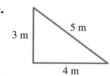

Solution

a. Rectangle is 2 cm by 9 cm, so

$$P = 2\ell + 2w$$
$$= 2(9\text{ cm}) + 2(2\text{ cm})$$
$$= 18\text{ cm} + 4\text{ cm}$$
$$= 22\text{ cm}$$

b. Rectangle is 2 ft by 4 ft, so

$$P = 2\ell + 2w$$
$$= 2(4\text{ ft}) + 2(2\text{ ft})$$
$$= 8\text{ ft} + 4\text{ ft}$$
$$= 12\text{ ft}$$

c. Square, so

$$P = 4s$$
$$= 4(5\text{ mi})$$
$$= 20\text{ mi}$$

d. Equilateral triangle, so

$$P = 3s$$
$$= 3(10\text{ dm})$$
$$= 30\text{ dm}$$

e. Triangle (add lengths of sides), so

$$P = 3\text{ m} + 4\text{ m} + 5\text{ m}$$
$$= 12\text{ m}$$

⬤

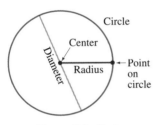

Figure 6.6 Circle

Although a **circle** (see Figure 6.6) is not a polygon, sometimes we need to find the distance around a circle. The size of a circle is determined by the length of a line segment that connects two points on a circle and also passes through the center of the circle. This distance is called the **diameter** of the circle; half this distance is the length of a segment from the center to any point on the circle, and is called the **radius** of the circle. Thus, we see that if d is the diameter of a circle and r is its radius, then

$$d = 2r$$

This distance around a circle is called the **circumference.** For *any circle,* if you divide the circumference by the diameter, you will get the *same number.* This number is given the name **pi** (pronounced "pie") and is symbolized by the Greek letter π. The number π is an irrational number and is about 3.14 or $\frac{22}{7}$. We need this number π to state a formula for the circumference C:

Circumference

> **STOP**
>
> **Formulas for the circumference of a circle:**
>
> $$C = d\pi \qquad \text{or} \qquad C = 2\pi r$$
>
> d = DIAMETER $\qquad\quad$ r = RADIUS

In a circle the radius is half the diameter. This means that, if you know the radius and want to find the diameter, you simply multiply by 2. If you know the diameter and want to find the radius, divide by 2.

EXAMPLE 3   Finding the circumference of a circle

Find the circumference of each circle (or the distance around each figure), rounded to the nearest unit.

a.

4 ft

b.
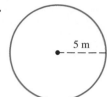
5 m

c.
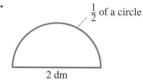
$\frac{1}{2}$ of a circle

2 dm

d.

30 cm
$\frac{1}{8}$ of a circle

Solution

a. $C = 4\pi$ ft, so we say the circumference is 4π ft, which is about 13 ft. If we use the π key on a calculator we find

$$C = 4\pi$$
$$\approx 12.56637061 \quad \text{The symbol "≈" means "approximately equal to."}$$

b. $C = 2\pi(5 \text{ m}) = 10\pi$ m; this is about 31 m.

c. This is half of a circle (called a **semicircle**); thus, the curved part is half of the circumference ($C = 2\pi$), or π, which is added to the diameter:

$$\pi \text{ dm} + 2 \text{ dm} \approx 5.141592654 \text{ dm} \quad \text{By calculator}$$

The distance around the figure is about 5 dm.

d. This is one-eighth of a circle. The circumference is $2\pi(30 \text{ cm})$, and the distance around the figure is

$$2\pi(30 \text{ cm}) \div 8 \text{ cm} + 30 \text{ cm} + 30 \text{ cm} \approx 83.5619449 \text{ cm} \quad \text{By calculator}$$

The distance around the figure is about 84 cm.   ●

The ideas involving perimeter and circumference are sometimes needed to solve certain types of problems.

EXAMPLE 4   Problem solving using a perimeter formula

Suppose you have enough material for 70 ft of fence and want to build a rectangular pen 14 ft wide. What is the length of this pen?

Solution

$$\text{PERIMETER} = 2(\text{LENGTH}) + 2(\text{WIDTH}) \quad \text{This is the formula for perimeter.}$$
$$70 \text{ ft} = 2(\text{LENGTH}) + 2(14 \text{ ft}) \quad \text{Fill in the given information.}$$
$$70 \text{ ft} = 2L + 28 \text{ ft} \quad \text{Let } L = \text{LENGTH OF PEN.}$$
$$42 \text{ ft} = 2L$$
$$21 \text{ ft} = L$$

The pen is 21 ft long.   ●

PROBLEM SET 6.2

ESSENTIAL IDEAS   LEVEL 1

1. **IN YOUR OWN WORDS** Explain the meaning of the concept of perimeter.

2. **IN YOUR OWN WORDS** Explain the meaning of the concept of circumference.

3. **IN YOUR OWN WORDS** What is π?
   (*Hint:* The correct answer is NOT 3.1416.) Explain why the calculator display for π, namely 3.141592654, does not answer this question.

4. State the following formulas:

   a. perimeter of an equilateral triangle $P = 3s$

   b. perimeter of a rectangle $P = 2(\ell + w)$

   c. perimeter of a square $P = 4s$

   d. circumference of a circle $C = \pi d$ or $C = 2\pi r$

DRILL AND PRACTICE   LEVEL 2

Pick the best choices in Problems 5–14 by estimating. Do not measure. For metric measurements, do not attempt to convert to the U.S. system.

5. The perimeter of a dollar bill is   A

   A. 18 in.   B. 6 in.   C. 44 in.

6. The perimeter of a five-dollar bill is   C

   A. 18 cm   B. 6 cm   C. 44 cm

7. The length of a new pencil is   C

   A. 4 in.   B. 18 in.   C. 7 in.

8. The circumference of a new pencil is   A

   A. 2 cm   B. 2 in.   C. 7 in.

9. The circumference of an automobile tire is   B

   A. 60 cm   B. 60 in.   C. 1 m

10. The perimeter of this textbook is   A

   A. 34 in.   B. 34 cm   C. 11 in.

11. The perimeter of a VISA credit card is   B

   A. 30 in.   B. 30 cm   C. 1 m

12. The perimeter of a sheet of notebook paper is   C

   A. 1 cm   B. 10 cm   C. 1 m

13. The perimeter of the screen of a plasma TV set is   C

   A. 30 in.   B. 100 cm   C. 5 m

14. The perimeter of a classroom is   A

   A. 100 ft   B. 100 m   C. 100 yd

Find the perimeter or circumference of the figures given in Problems 15–31 by using the appropriate formula. Round approximate answers to two decimal places.

15.

1 cm, 1 cm, 1 cm, 22 cm

16.

4 in., 5 in., 18 in.

17.
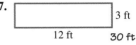
3 ft, 12 ft, 30 ft

18.

52 m, 23 m, 150 m

19.
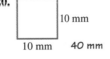
6 cm, 6 cm, 24 cm

20.
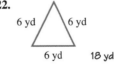
10 mm, 10 mm, 40 mm

21.
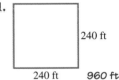
240 ft, 240 ft, 960 ft

22.
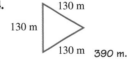
6 yd, 6 yd, 6 yd, 18 yd

23.

3 dm, 3 dm, 3 dm, 9 dm

24.

130 m, 130 m, 130 m, 390 m.

25. 5 in.
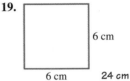
5 in., 5 in., 15 in.

26.
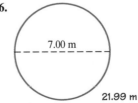
7.00 m, 21.99 m

27.
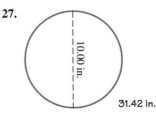
10.00 in., 31.42 in.

28.
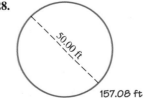
50.00 ft, 157.08 ft

29.
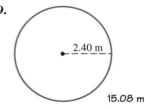
2.40 m, 15.08 m

30.

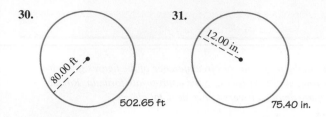

502.65 ft

31.

12.00 in.

75.40 in.

Find the distance around the exterior of the figures in Problems 32–39. Round approximate answers to one decimal place.

32.

14 ft

9 ft   9 ft

14 ft

33.

18 in.

4 in.   4 in.
4 in.   4 in.

18 in.   52 in.

46 ft

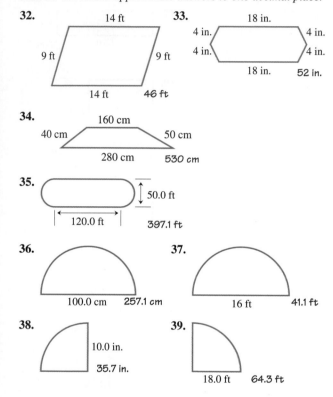

34.

160 cm

40 cm   50 cm

280 cm   530 cm

35.

50.0 ft

120.0 ft

397.1 ft

36.

100.0 cm   257.1 cm

37.

16 ft   41.1 ft

38.

10.0 in.

35.7 in.

39.

18.0 ft   64.3 ft

40. The perimeter of △*ABC* is 117 in. Find the lengths of the sides shown in Figure 6.7.

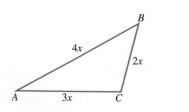

B

4*x*

2*x*

A   3*x*   *C*

Figure 6.7 △*ABC*   26 in., 39 in., 52 in.

41. The perimeter of the pentagon is 280 cm. Find the length of the sides shown in Figure 6.8.

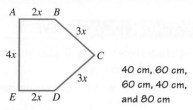

A   2*x*   *B*

3*x*

4*x*

C

3*x*

E   2*x*   *D*

40 cm, 60 cm,
60 cm, 40 cm,
and 80 cm

Figure 6.8 Pentagon

42. What is the width of a rectangular lot that has a perimeter of 410 ft and a length of 140 ft?   65 ft

43. What is the length of a rectangular lot that has a perimeter of 750 m and a width of 75 m?   300 m

44. What is the length of a rectangular room that has a perimeter of 54 ft and a length that is 3 feet more than its width?   15 ft

45. What is the length of the side of a square whose perimeter is 100 ft?   25 ft

46. What is the length of the side of a square whose perimeter is 180 cm?   45 cm

47. What is the length of the side of an equilateral triangle whose perimeter is 120 cm?   40 cm

48. Find the dimensions of an equilateral triangle that has a perimeter of 198 dm.   66 dm

49. Find the dimensions of a rectangle with a perimeter of 54 cm if the length is 5 cm less than three times the width.
8 cm by 19 cm

50. Find the dimensions of a rectangle with a perimeter of 120 in. if the length is double the width.   20 in. by 40 in.

51. The base of a box is shown in Figure 6.9, and it needs to have a bead of caulking around the perimeter. What is the length of the caulking strip?   20.0 cm

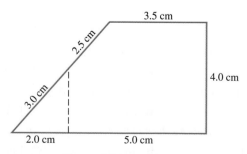

3.5 cm

2.5 cm

3.0 cm

4.0 cm

2.0 cm   5.0 cm

Figure 6.9 Base of a box

52. The side view of a sliding flange is shown in Figure 6.10. What is the perimeter of this cross section? $7\frac{1}{2}$ in.

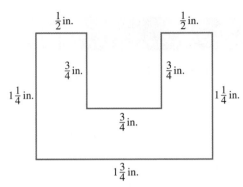

Figure 6.10 Side view of flange

53. A single piece of wood measuring 6.0 cm by 2.0 cm is to be cut into two pieces.

    a. What is the perimeter of the uncut piece of wood? 16 cm

    b. Instead of cutting the piece of wood in half with a straight line, a circular cut is made as shown in Figure 6.11. How do the perimeters of the two pieces compare? Same; perimeter of each piece is 11.1 cm.

Figure 6.11 Circular cut

54. A machine shop needs to fabricate a latch as shown in Figure 6.12. What is the distance around this object? 15.2 cm

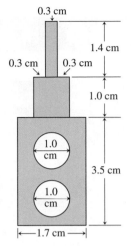

Figure 6.12 Latch assembly

RIGHT OR WRONG?   **LEVEL 3**

Explain what is wrong, if anything, with the statements in Problems 55–60. Explain your reasoning.

55. The number π is equal to 3.1416.   F; it is approximately equal.

56. The number π is 3.141592654.   F; π is an irrational number.

57. The circumference of a circle is the distance across.
F; it is the distance around the circle.

58. The radius of a circle is twice the diameter.
F; the diameter is twice the radius.

59. Perimeter is a linear measure.   T

60. The distance around a semicircle of radius r is $\pi r + 2r$.   T

6.3 Area

IN THIS WORLD   THE POWER OF MATH

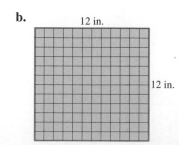

"Look at all these rugs!" said Aisha. "I can't wait to find just the right one for my living room."

"What kind of rug are you seeking?" asked the clerk.

"I want an area rug that is 13 ft by 22 ft," noted Aisha. "How much would such a rug cost, if I'm looking for a very good quality?"

"Prices really vary. You can pay up to $55/yd², " reported the clerk.

In this section we will see how size relates to a measurement called the area. We will introduce you to several important formulas for calculating area.

See Problem 48.

Suppose that you want to carpet your living room. The price of carpet is quoted as a price per square yard. A square yard is a measure of **area.** To measure the area of a plane figure, you fill it with **square units.** (See Figure 6.13.)

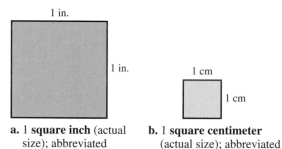

a. 1 **square inch** (actual size); abbreviated 1 sq in. or 1 in.²

b. 1 **square centimeter** (actual size); abbreviated 1 sq cm or 1 cm²

Figure 6.13 Common units of measurement for area

Square units and area are important ideas not only in mathematics, but in real-world measurements.

EXAMPLE 1   **Finding areas by counting square units**

What is the area of the shaded region?

a.

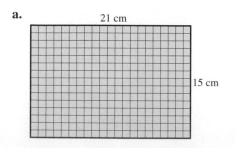

21 cm

15 cm

b.

12 in.

12 in.

Solution

a. You can count the number of square centimeters in the shaded region; there are 315 squares. Also notice:

Across   Down
$$21 \text{ cm} \times 15 \text{ cm} = 21 \times 15 \times \text{cm} \times \text{cm}$$
$$= 315 \text{ cm}^2$$

b. The shaded region is a **square foot.** You can count 144 square inches inside the region. Also notice:

Across   Down
$$12 \text{ in.} \times 12 \text{ in.} = 144 \text{ in.}^2$$

As you can see from Example 1, the area of a rectangular or square region is the product of the distance across (length) and the distance down (width).

Areas Formulas

To find the area of a rectangle or a square, use the following formulas.

Rectangles

AREA = LENGTH × WIDTH
$$= \ell w$$

Length, ℓ

Width, w

Squares

AREA = SIDE × SIDE
$$= s^2$$

Side, s

Side, s

EXAMPLE 2   **Areas by formula**

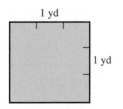

1 yd

1 yd

Figure 6.14 $1 \text{ yd}^2 = 9 \text{ ft}^2$

How many square feet are there in a square yard?

Solution   Since 1 yd = 3 ft, we see from Figure 6.14 that
$$1 \text{ yd}^2 = (3 \text{ ft})^2$$
$$= 9 \text{ ft}^2$$

A **parallelogram** is a quadrilateral with two pairs of parallel sides, as shown in Figure 6.15.

Figure 6.15 Parallelograms

To find the area of a parallelogram, we can estimate the area by counting the number of square units inside the parallelogram (which may require estimation of partial square units), or we can show that the formula for the area of a parallelogram is the same as the formula for the area of a rectangle.

Geometric Justification of the Area Formula for a Parallelogram

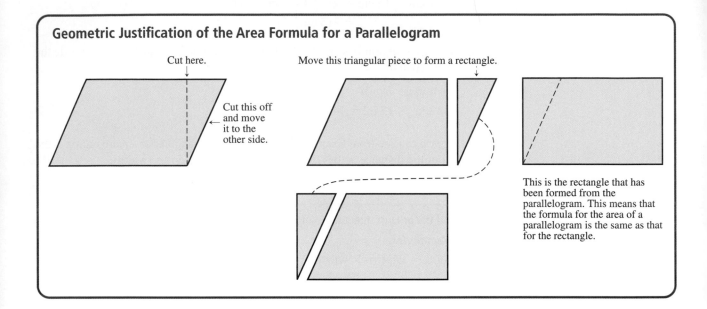

Cut here.

Move this triangular piece to form a rectangle.

Cut this off and move it to the other side.

This is the rectangle that has been formed from the parallelogram. This means that the formula for the area of a parallelogram is the same as that for the rectangle.

Area of Parallelograms

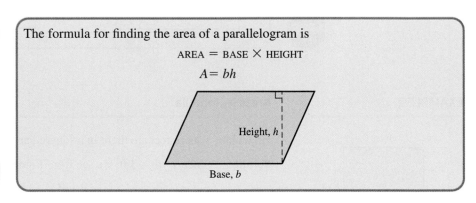

The formula for finding the area of a parallelogram is

AREA = BASE × HEIGHT

$$A = bh$$

Height, h

Base, b

STOP

EXAMPLE 3

Area of parallelograms by formula

Find the area of each shaded region.

a.

6 m

3 m

b.

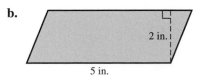

2 in.

5 in.

Note: The height is the perpendicular distance to the base.

Solution

a. $A = 3 \text{ m} \times 6 \text{ m}$
     $= 18 \text{ m}^2$

b. $A = 5 \text{ in.} \times 2 \text{ in.}$
     $= 10 \text{ in.}^2$

You can find the area of a triangle by filling in and approximating the number of square units, by rearranging the parts, or by noticing that *every* triangle has an area that is exactly half that of a corresponding parallelogram.

Geometric Justification of the Area Formula for a Triangle

These triangles have the same area.

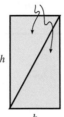

These triangles have the same area.

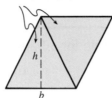

These triangles have the same area.

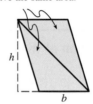

Area of Triangles

The formula for finding the area of a triangle is

$$\text{AREA} = \tfrac{1}{2} \times \text{BASE} \times \text{HEIGHT}$$
$$A = \tfrac{1}{2}bh$$

Height, h

Base, b

STOP

EXAMPLE 4   **Areas of triangles by formula**

Find the area of each shaded region.

a.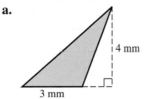

4 mm

3 mm

b.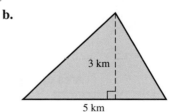

3 km

5 km

Note: The height is the perpendicular distance to the base.

Solution   a. $A = \dfrac{1}{2} \times 3 \text{ mm} \times 4 \text{ mm}$

               $= 6 \text{ mm}^2$

b. $A = \dfrac{1}{2} \times 5 \text{ km} \times 3 \text{ km}$

       $= \dfrac{15}{2} \text{ km}^2$ or $7\dfrac{1}{2} \text{ km}^2$

We can also find the area of a trapezoid by finding the area of triangles. A **trapezoid** is a quadrilateral with two sides parallel. These sides are called the *bases,* and the perpendicular distance between the bases is the *height,* as shown in Figure 6.16.

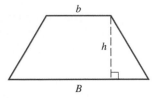

Figure 6.16 Trapezoid

The area can be found as the sum of the areas of triangle I and triangle II:

Geometric Justification of the Area Formula for a Trapezoid

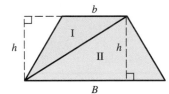

Area of triangle I: $\frac{1}{2}bh$

Area of triangle II: $\frac{1}{2}Bh$

Total area: $\frac{1}{2}bh + \frac{1}{2}Bh$

If we use the distributive property, we obtain the area formula for a trapezoid, as shown in the following box.

Area of Trapezoids

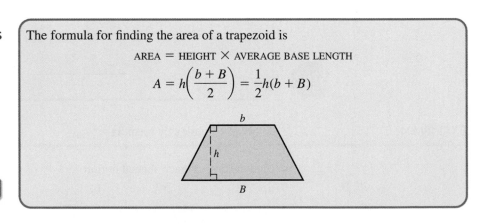

The formula for finding the area of a trapezoid is

AREA = HEIGHT × AVERAGE BASE LENGTH

$$A = h\left(\frac{b+B}{2}\right) = \frac{1}{2}h(b+B)$$

EXAMPLE 5   Area of trapezoids by formula

Find the area of each shaded region.

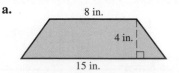

a.

8 in.

4 in.

15 in.

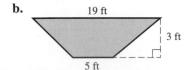

b.

19 ft

3 ft

5 ft

Solution **a.** $h = 4$ in.; $b = 8$ in.; $B = 15$ in.   **b.** $h = 3$ ft; $b = 19$ ft; $B = 5$ ft

$$A = (4 \text{ in.})\left(\frac{8 \text{ in.} + 15 \text{ in.}}{2}\right) \qquad A = (3 \text{ ft})\left(\frac{19 \text{ ft} + 5 \text{ ft}}{2}\right)$$

$$= (4 \text{ in.})(11.5 \text{ in.}) \qquad\qquad = (3 \text{ ft})(12 \text{ ft})$$

$$= 46 \text{ in.}^2 \qquad\qquad\qquad = 36 \text{ ft}^2$$

The area is 46 in.²   The area is 36 ft.² ●

The last of our area formulas is that of a circle.

Area of Circles

The formula for finding the area of a circle is

AREA = PI × SQUARE OF RADIUS

$$A = \pi r^2$$

Radius, r

STOP

Even though it is beyond the scope of this course to derive a formula for the area of a circle, we can give a geometric justification that may appeal to your intuition.

Geometric Justification of the Area Formula for a Circle

Consider a circle with radius r.   Cut the circle in half:

$C = 2\pi r$

Half of the circumference is πr.

Cut along the dashed lines so that each half lays flat when it is opened up, as shown below.

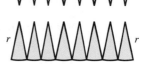

$r \times \pi$

Fit these two pieces together:

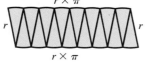

$r \times \pi$

$r \times \pi$

$r \times \pi$

Therefore, it looks as if the area of a circle of radius r is about the same as the area of a rectangle of length πr and width r— that is, πr^2.

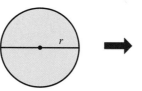
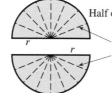

EXAMPLE 6   **Area of circles by formula**

Find the area of each shaded region to the nearest tenth unit.

a.   b.

Solution

a. $A = \pi r^2 = \pi(9 \text{ yd})^2 \approx 254.4690049 \text{ yd}^2$ By calculator
   To the nearest tenth, the area is 254.5 yd^2.

b. The shaded portion is half the area of the circle. Note that if the diameter is 10 m, then the radius is $\frac{1}{2}(10 \text{ m}) = 5$ m.

$$A = \frac{1}{2}\pi r^2 = \frac{1}{2}\pi(5 \text{ m})^2 \quad Display: \quad 39.26990817$$

To the nearest tenth, the area is 39.3 m^2.   ●

Sometimes we obtain area using one unit of measurement and then we want to convert the result to another.

EXAMPLE 7   **Problem solving with areas**

Suppose your living room is 12 ft by 15 ft and you want to know how many square yards of carpet you need to cover this area.

Solution

Method I.   **Method II.**   Change feet to yards to begin the problem:

$A = 12 \text{ ft} \times 15 \text{ ft}$ 12 ft = 4 yd   and   15 ft = 5 yd

$= 180 \text{ ft}^2$ $A = 4 \text{ yd} \times 5 \text{ yd}$

$= 180 \times 1 \text{ ft}^2$ $= 20 \text{ yd}^2$

$= 180 \times \left(\frac{1}{9} \text{ yd}^2\right)$ Since 1 yd = 3 ft

$= 20 \text{ yd}^2$ 1 yd^2 = (1 yd)(1 yd)

                                       1 yd^2 = (3 ft)(3 ft)

                                       1 yd^2 = 9 ft^2

                                       $\frac{1}{9}$ yd^2 = 1 ft^2

                                                                           ●

If the area is large, as with property, a larger unit is needed. This is called an *acre*.

Acre   An **acre** is 43,560 ft^2.
           To convert from ft^2 to acres, divide by 43,560.

Estimation Hint.   Real estate brokers estimate an acre as 200 ft by 200 ft or 40,000 ft^2. When working with acres, you usually need a calculator to convert square feet to acres, as shown in Example 8.

EXAMPLE 8   **Using acre as an area measurement**

How many acres are there in a rectangular piece of property measuring 363 ft by 180 ft?

Solution   AREA $= 363$ ft $\times 180$ ft

$= 65,340$ ft^2 ESTIMATE: $65,340 \approx 65,000$ and $65,000 \div 40,000 = 65 \div 40$
$= 13 \div 8$
$\approx 12 \div 8$
$= 1.5$

To change ft^2 to acres, divide by 43,560:

AREA $= 65,340$ ft^2

$= (65,340 \div 43,560)$ acres

$= 1.5$ acres ●

EXAMPLE 9   **Problem solving with areas**

© Richard Cummins/Corbis

You want to paint 200 ft of a four-rail fence that is made up of four boards, each 6 inches wide. You want to know:

a. the number of square feet on one side of the fence.

b. the number of square feet to be painted, if the posts and edges of the boards comprise 100 ft^2.

c. the number of gallons of paint to purchase if each gallon covers 325 ft^2.

Solution

a. First, you need to visualize a four-rail fence:

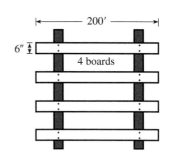

$$A = (200 \text{ ft}) \times (6 \text{ in.}) \times 4$$

$$= (200 \text{ ft}) \times \left(\frac{1}{2} \text{ ft}\right) \times 4$$

$$= 400 \text{ ft}^2$$

b. AMOUNT TO BE PAINTED $= 2(\text{AMOUNT ON ONE SIDE}) + (\text{EDGES AND POSTS})$

$$= 2(400 \text{ ft}^2) + 100 \text{ ft}^2$$

$$= 900 \text{ ft}^2$$

c. $\left(\begin{array}{c}\text{NUMBER OF SQUARE}\\ \text{FEET PAINTED}\end{array}\right) = \left(\begin{array}{c}\text{NUMBER OF SQUARE}\\ \text{FEET PER GALLON}\end{array}\right)\left(\begin{array}{c}\text{NUMBER OF}\\ \text{GALLONS}\end{array}\right)$

$$900 = 325\left(\begin{array}{c}\text{NUMBER OF}\\ \text{GALLONS}\end{array}\right)$$

$$2.77 \approx \left(\begin{array}{c}\text{NUMBER OF}\\ \text{GALLONS}\end{array}\right) \quad \text{Divide both sides by 325.}$$

If paint must be purchased by the gallon (as implied by the question), the amount to purchase is 3 gallons. ●

PROBLEM SET 6.3

ESSENTIAL IDEAS   LEVEL 1

1. **IN YOUR OWN WORDS** Describe what is meant by area.

2. **IN YOUR OWN WORDS** From memory, estimate the following areas.

   a. 1 sq in.   **b.** 1 sq cm

3. **IN YOUR OWN WORDS** Distinguish between perimeter and area.

4. **a.** What is a trapezoid?   A quadrilateral with two sides parallel

   b. What is a parallelogram?   A quadrilateral with two pairs of parallel sides

DRILL AND PRACTICE   LEVEL 2

Pick the best choices in Problems 5–16 by estimating. Do not measure. For metric measurements, do not attempt to convert to the U.S. system.

5. The area of a dollar bill is   C

   A. 18 in.   B. 6 in.^{2} C. 18 in.^{2}

6. The area of a five-dollar bill is   C

   A. 100 cm   B. 10 cm^2 C. 100 cm^2

7. The area of the front cover of this textbook is   A

   A. 70 in.^{2} B. 70 cm^2 C. 70 in.

8. The area of a VISA credit card is   B

   A. 8 in.   B. 8 in.^{2} C. 8 cm^2

9. The area of a sheet of notebook paper is   C

   A. 90 cm^2 B. 10 in.^{2} C. 600 cm^2

10. The area of a sheet of notebook paper is   A

    A. 90 in.^{2} B. 10 cm^2 C. 600 in.^{2}

11. The area of the screen of an LCD TV set is   A

    A. 4 ft^2 B. 19 in.^{2} C. 100 in.^{2}

12. The area of a classroom is   B

    A. 100 ft^2 B. 1,000 ft^2 C. 0.5 acre

13. The area of the floor space of the Superdome in New Orleans is   C

    A. 1 mi^2 B. 1,000 m^2 C. 10 acres

14. The state of California has an area of   B

    A. 5,000 acres   B. 150,000 mi^2 C. 5,000 m^2

15. The area of the bottom of your feet is   C

    A. 1 m^2 B. 400 in.^{2} C. 400 cm^2

16. It is known that your body's surface area is about 100 times the area that you will find if you trace your hand on a sheet of paper. Using this estimate, your body's surface area is   B

    A. 300 in.^{2} B. 3,000 in.^{2} C. 3,000 cm^2

Estimate the area of each shaded figure in Problems 17–24 to the nearest square centimeter.

17.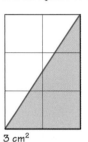

3 cm^2

18.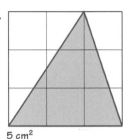

5 cm^2

19.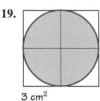

3 cm^2

20.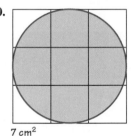

7 cm^2

21.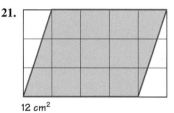

12 cm^2

22.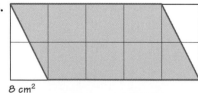

8 cm^2

23.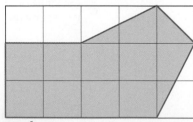

10 cm^2

24.

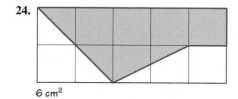

6 cm²

Find the area of each shaded region in Problems 25–42. (Assume that given measurements are exact, and round approximate answers to the nearest tenth of a square unit.)

25.

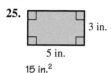

3 in.

5 in.

15 in.²

26.

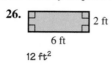

2 ft

6 ft

12 ft²

27.

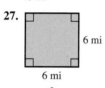

6 mi

6 mi

36 mi²

28.

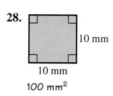

10 mm

10 mm

100 mm²

29.

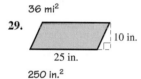

10 in.

25 in.

250 in.²

30.

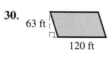

63 ft

120 ft

7,560 ft²

31.

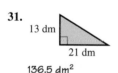

13 dm

21 dm

136.5 dm²

32.

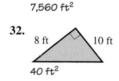

8 ft   10 ft

40 ft²

33.

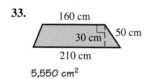

160 cm

30 cm   50 cm

210 cm

5,550 cm²

34.

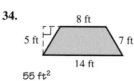

8 ft

5 ft   7 ft

14 ft

55 ft²

35.

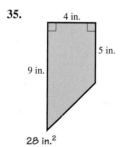

4 in.

5 in.

9 in.

28 in.²

36.

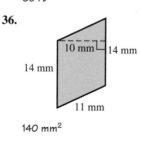

10 mm   14 mm

14 mm

11 mm

140 mm²

37.

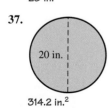

20 in.

314.2 in.²

38.

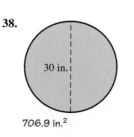

30 in.

706.9 in.²

39.

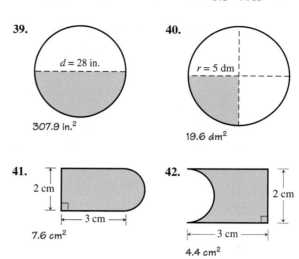

d = 28 in.

307.9 in.²

40.

r = 5 dm

19.6 dm²

41.

2 cm

3 cm

7.6 cm²

42.

2 cm

3 cm

4.4 cm²

43. What is the area of a television screen that measures 12 in. by 18 in.?   216 in.²

44. What is the area of a rectangular building lot that measures 185 ft by 75 ft?   13,875 ft²

45. What is the area of a piece of $8\frac{1}{2}$-in. by 11-in. typing paper? $93\frac{1}{2}$ in.²

46. If a certain type of fabric comes in a bolt 3 feet wide, how long a piece must be purchased to have 24 square feet?   8 ft

47. Find the cost of pouring a square concrete slab of uniform thickness with sides of 25 ft if the cost (at that uniform thickness) is $5.75 per square foot. $3,593.75

48. If a 22-ft by 13-ft living room is carpeted with carpet that costs $52 per square yard (including labor and pad), what is the total cost for carpeting the living room in this home? Assume that you cannot purchase part of a square yard. Use estimation to decide whether your answer is reasonable.   32 yd² are required; $1,664

49. If a 12-ft by 13-ft bedroom is carpeted with carpet that costs $45 per square yard (including labor and pad), what is the total cost for carpeting this room? Assume that you cannot purchase part of a square yard. Use estimation to decide whether your answer is reasonable.   18 yd² required; $810

50. What is the cost of seeding a rectangular lawn 100 ft by 30 ft if 1 pound of seed costs $5.85 and covers 150 square feet? Use estimation to decide whether your answer is reasonable.   20 pounds are necessary; $117

51. If a rectangular piece of property is 750 ft by 1,290 ft, what is the acreage? Round your answer to the nearest tenth acre.   22.2 acres

52. How many square feet are there in $4\frac{1}{2}$ acres?   196,020 ft²

53. Consider the house plan as shown in Figure 6.17. Dimensions are in feet.

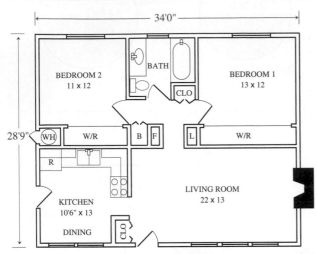

Figure 6.17 House floor plan

a. What is the area of the living room?   286 ft²

b. What is the area of bedroom 2?   132 ft²

c. The kitchen and dining area is labeled 10'6" × 13'. This means 10 ft 6 in. by 13 ft. What is the area of the kitchen and dining area?   136.5 ft²

d. The dimensions of the house are labeled 34'0" by 28'9". This means 34 ft by 28.75 ft since 9" is $\frac{3}{4}$ = 0.75 of one foot. Estimate the area of the house.   About 30 ft × 30 ft = 900 ft²; actual, 977.5 ft²

54. In the Problem of the Day for Section 6.2, a machinist calculated the perimeter of the fabrication shown in Figure 6.18. In this problem, we ask for the area (to the nearest square centimeter).   6 cm²

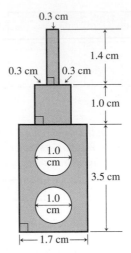

Figure 6.18 Can you find an area?

RIGHT OR WRONG?   LEVEL 3

Explain what is wrong, if anything, with the statements in Problems 55–60. Explain your reasoning.

55. The area of a square whose side is 3 ft is 9 ft.   F; it is 9 ft².

56. The area of a circle with diameter 3 ft is 9π ft.   F; it is $\frac{9}{4}\pi$ ft².

57. If the length of a rectangle is measured in km and the width is measured in km, then the unit of measurement for area is km.   F; it is km².

58. The area of a triangle with base ℓ and height h is ℓh.   F; it is $0.5\ell h$.

59. The area of a parallelogram of length ℓ and height h is ℓh.   T

60. A trapezoid is a quadrilateral with no sides parallel.   F; two sides are parallel.

6.4 Volume and Capacity

IN THIS WORLD   THE POWER OF MATH

"How much concrete did you order?" asked Rafael. "I think this is the last truck, but we still need another load."

"I ordered 35 yards," answered Alberto. "Are you saying we need the whole nine yards?"

Have you ever heard the expression "the whole nine yards"? It's related to concrete. A standard-size cement mixer has a capacity of 9 cubic yards of concrete. Thus, a job requiring the mixer's full capacity demands "the whole 9 yards."

In this section we will discuss volume and capacity in both the U.S. and metric systems.

See Problem 47.

To measure area, we covered a region with square units and then found the area by using a mathematical formula. A similar procedure is used to find the amount of space inside a solid object, which is called its **volume.** We can imagine filling the space with **cubes.** A **cubic inch** and a **cubic centimeter** are shown in Figure 6.19.

> **STOP** Cubic units and volume are important ideas not only in mathematics, but in real-world measurements.

a. 1 cubic inch
(1 cu in. or 1 in.^{3})

b. 1 cubic centimeter
(1 cu cm, cc, or 1 cm^3)

Figure 6.19 Cubic units used for measuring volume

Volume of a Cube

The formula for finding the volume of a cube is

$$\text{VOLUME} = \text{EDGE} \times \text{EDGE} \times \text{EDGE}$$

$$V = s^3$$

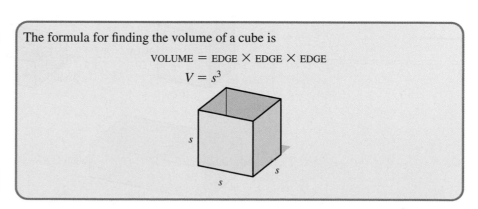

If the solid is not a cube but is a box with edges of different lengths (called a **rectangular parallelepiped**), the volume can be found similarly.

EXAMPLE 1 Finding the volume of a box

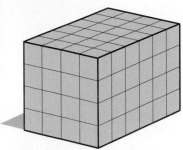

Figure 6.20 What is the volume?

Find the volume of a box that measures 4 ft by 6 ft by 4 ft (see Figure 6.20).

Solution There are 24 cubic feet on the bottom layer of cubes. Do you see how many layers of cubes will fill the solid? Since there are four layers with 24 cubes in each, the total number of cubes is

$$4 \times 24 = 96$$

The volume is 96 ft^3. ●

We use the results of Example 1 to generalize the formula for the volume of a cube to that of a box whose sides may not be the same.

Volume of a Box

The formula for finding the volume of a box (which is also called a parallelepiped) is

$$\text{VOLUME} = \text{LENGTH} \times \text{WIDTH} \times \text{HEIGHT}$$
$$V = \ell wh$$

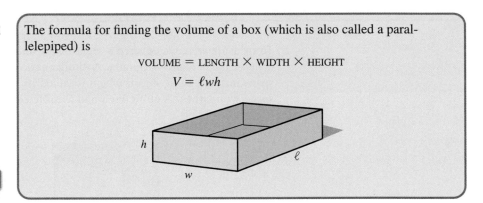

STOP

EXAMPLE 2 Finding volumes

Find the volume of each solid.

a.

10 cm
10 cm
10 cm

b.

4 cm
10 cm
25 cm

c.

3 in.
7 in.
11 in.

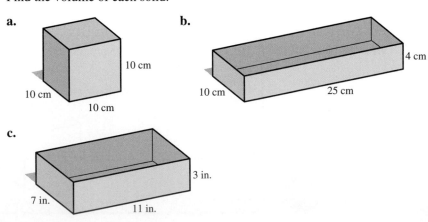

Solution

a. $V = s^3$

    $= (10 \text{ cm})^3$

    $= (10 \times 10 \times 10) \text{ cm}^3$

    $= 1{,}000 \text{ cm}^3$

b. $V = \ell w h$

    $= (25 \text{ cm})(10 \text{ cm})(4 \text{ cm})$

    $= (25 \times 10 \times 4) \text{ cm}^3$

    $= 1{,}000 \text{ cm}^3$

c. $V = \ell w h$

    $= 11 \text{ in.} \times 7 \text{ in.} \times 3 \text{ in.}$

    $= (11 \times 7 \times 3) \text{ in.}^3$

    $= 231 \text{ in.}^3$

Sometimes the dimensions for the volume we are finding are not given in the same units. In such cases, you must convert all dimensions to the same units. The common conversions are as follows:

$1 \text{ ft} = 12 \text{ in.}$	To convert feet to inches, multiply by 12.
	To convert inches to feet, divide by 12.
$1 \text{ yd} = 3 \text{ ft}$	To convert yards to feet, multiply by 3.
	To convert feet to yards, divide by 3.
$1 \text{ yd} = 36 \text{ in.}$	To convert yards to inches, multiply by 36.
	To convert inches to yards, divide by 36.

EXAMPLE 3

Problem solving with volume

Suppose you are pouring a rectangular driveway with dimensions of 24 ft by 65 ft. The depth of the driveway is 3 in., and concrete is ordered by the yard. By a "yard" of concrete, we mean a cubic yard. You cannot order part of a yard of concrete. How much concrete should you order?

Solution   There are three different units of measurement in this problem: inches, feet, and yards. Since we want the answer in cubic yards, we will convert all of the measurements to yards:

$65 \text{ ft} = (65 \div 3) \text{ yd} = \frac{65}{3} \text{ yd}$ *This is the length, ℓ.*

$24 \text{ ft} = (24 \div 3) \text{ yd} = 8 \text{ yd}$ *This is the width, w.*

$3 \text{ in.} = (3 \div 36) \text{ yd} = \frac{3}{36} \text{ yd} = \frac{1}{12} \text{ yd}$ *This is the height (depth), h.*

$V = \ell w h$

    $= \frac{65}{3}(8)\left(\frac{1}{12}\right) \text{ yd}^3$ *Think of 8 as $\frac{8}{1}$.*

    $= \frac{65 \times \overset{2}{8} \times 1}{3 \times \underset{3}{12}} \text{ yd}^3$

    $= \frac{130}{9} \text{ yd}^3$

    $= 14\frac{4}{9} \text{ yd}^3$

You must order 15 yards of concrete.*

---

*When purchasing cubic yards of material, such as concrete, everyday language often uses the term "yards" instead of the mathematically correct "cubic yards."

One of the most common applications of volume involves measuring the amount of liquid a container holds, which we refer to as its **capacity.** For example, if a container is 2 ft by 2 ft by 12 ft, it is fairly easy to calculate the volume:

$$2 \times 2 \times 12 = 48 \text{ ft}^3$$

But this still doesn't tell us how much water the container holds. The capacities of a can of cola, a bottle of milk, an aquarium tank, the gas tank in your car, and a swimming pool can all be measured by the amount of fluid they can hold.

Standard Units of Capacity

U.S. System	*Metric System*
gallon (gal)	**liter (L)**
quart $\left(\text{qt}; \frac{1}{4} \text{ gal} \right)$	kiloliter (kL; 1,000 L)
ounce $\left(\text{oz}; \frac{1}{128} \text{ gal} \right)$	milliliter $\left(\text{mL}; \frac{1}{1,000} \text{ L} \right)$
cup (c; 8 oz)	

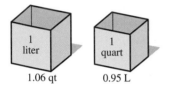

1.06 qt   0.95 L

Figure 6.21 Standard capacities

Most containers of liquid that you buy have capacities stated in both milliliters and ounces, or quarts and liters (see Figure 6.21). Some of these size statements are listed in Table 6.1. The U.S. Bureau of Alcohol, Tobacco, and Firearms has made metric bottle sizes mandatory for liquor, so the half-pint, fifth, and quart have been replaced by 200-mL, 750-mL, and 1-L sizes. A typical dose of cough medicine is 5 mL, and 1 kL is 1,000 L, or about the amount of water one person would use for all purposes in two or three days.

You should remember some of these references for purposes of estimation. For example, know that a can of Coke is 355 mL, and be able to recognize the size of a liter of milk. A cup of coffee is about 300 mL, and a spoonful of medicine is about 5 mL.

TABLE 6.1	Capacities of Common Grocery Items	
Item	**U.S. Capacity**	**Metric Capacity**
Milk	$\frac{1}{2}$ gal	1.89 L
Milk	1.06 qt	1 L
Budweiser	12 oz	355 mL
Coke	67.6 oz	2 L
Hawaiian Punch	1 qt	0.95 L
Del Monte pickles	1 pt 6 oz	651 mL

Since it is common practice to label capacities both in U.S. and in metric measuring units, it will generally not be necessary for you to make conversions from one system to another. But if you do, it is easy to remember that a liter is just a little larger than a quart, just as a meter is a little longer than a yard.

To measure capacity, you use a measuring cup.

EXAMPLE 4   **Measuring capacity**

Measure the amount of liquid in the measuring cup in Figure 6.22, both in the U.S. system and in the metric system.

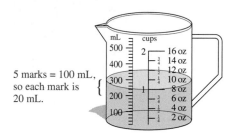

Figure 6.22 Standard measuring cup with both metric and U.S. measurements

Solution   Metric: 240 mL   U.S.:   About 1 c or 8 oz   ●

Some common relationships among volume and capacity measurements in the U.S. system are shown in Figure 6.23.

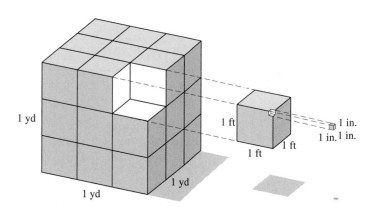

Volume: 1 yd³ = 27 ft³   1 ft³ = 1,728 in.³   1 in.³
Capacity: about 200 gallons   7.48 gallons   1 gallon = 231 in.³

Figure 6.23 U.S. measurement relationship between volume and capacity

In the U.S. system of measurement, the relationship between volume and capacity is not particularly convenient. One gallon of capacity occupies 231 in.³. This means that, since the box in part **c** of Example 2 has a volume of 231 in.³, we know that it will hold exactly 1 gallon of water.

The relationship between volume and capacity in the metric system is easier to remember. One cubic centimeter is one-thousandth of a liter. Notice that this is the same as a milliliter. For this reason, you will sometimes see cc used to mean cm³ or mL. These relationships are shown in Figure 6.24.

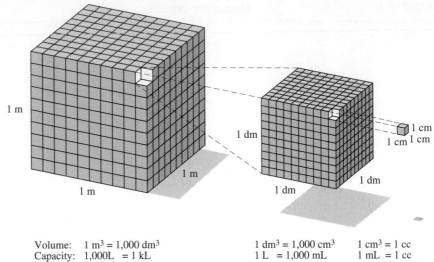

Volume: 1 m³ = 1,000 dm³   1 dm³ = 1,000 cm³   1 cm³ = 1 cc
Capacity: 1,000L = 1 kL   1 L = 1,000 mL   1 mL = 1 cc

Figure 6.24 Metric measurement relationship between volume and capacity

We summarize the relationship between volume and capacity in the following box.

Volume and Capacity

> 1 liter = 1,000 cm³   1 gallon = 231 in.³   1 ft³ ≈ 7.48 gal

To find the capacity of the 2-ft by 2-ft by 12-ft box mentioned previously, we must change 48 ft³ to cubic inches:

Estimate:
Since 1 ft³ ≈ 7.5 gal,
  48 ft³ ≈ 50 ft³
         ≈ (50 × 7.5) gal
         ≈ 375 gal

$$48 \text{ ft}^3 = 48 \times (1 \text{ ft}) \times (1 \text{ ft}) \times (1 \text{ ft})$$
$$= 48 \times 12 \text{ in.} \times 12 \text{ in.} \times 12 \text{ in.}$$
$$= 82,944 \text{ in.}^3 \quad \text{A calculator would help here.}$$

Since 1 gallon is 231 in.³, the final step is to divide 82,944 by 231 to obtain approximately 359 gallons.

EXAMPLE 5   **Calculating capacities**

How much water would each of the following containers hold?

a.   **b.**

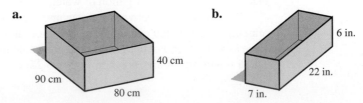

Solution

Estimate for part b:
Container is approximately

$$\frac{1}{2}\text{ft} \times 2\text{ft} \times \frac{1}{2}\text{ft} = \frac{1}{2}\text{ft}^3$$

$$\approx \left(\frac{1}{2} \times 7.5\right)\text{gal} = 3.75\text{ gal}$$

a. $V = \ell wh$
$= (90 \text{ cm})(80 \text{ cm})(40 \text{ cm})$
$= 288,000 \text{ cm}^3$

Since each $1,000 \text{ cm}^3$ is 1 liter,

$$\frac{288,000}{1,000} = 288$$

this container holds 288 liters.

b. $V = \ell wh$
$= (7 \text{ in.})(22 \text{ in.})(6 \text{ in.})$
$= 924 \text{ in.}^3$

Since each 231 in.^3 is 1 gallon,

$$\frac{924}{231} = 4$$

this container holds 4 gallons.

EXAMPLE 6

Finding the capacity of a swimming pool

An ecological swimming pool is advertised as being 20 ft × 25 ft × 5 ft. How many gallons will it hold?

Solution $V = 20 \text{ ft} \times 25 \text{ ft} \times 5 \text{ ft}$
$= 2,500 \text{ ft}^3$

Since $1 \text{ ft}^3 \approx 7.48 \text{ gal}$, the swimming pool contains

$$2,500 \times 7.48 \approx 18,700 \text{ gallons}$$

PROBLEM SET (6.4)

ESSENTIAL IDEAS   **LEVEL 1**

1. **IN YOUR OWN WORDS** Contrast area and volume.

2. **IN YOUR OWN WORDS** Compare or contrast 1 liter, 1 cm³, and 1 quart.

DRILL AND PRACTICE   **LEVEL 2**

In Problems 3–12, find the volume of each solid.

3.

60 cm³

4.

80 cm³

5.

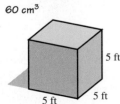

5 ft, 5 ft, 5 ft

125 ft³

6.

12 in., 12 in., 12 in.

1,728 in.³

7.

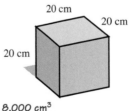

20 cm, 20 cm, 20 cm

8,000 cm³

8.

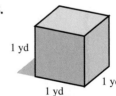

1 yd, 1 yd, 1 yd

1 yd³

9.

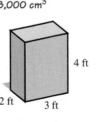

4 ft, 2 ft, 3 ft

24 ft³

10.

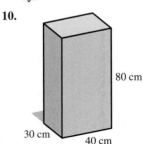

80 cm, 30 cm, 40 cm

96,000 cm³

11.

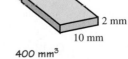

20 mm, 2 mm, 10 mm

400 mm³

12.

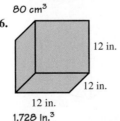

24 in., 15 in., 10 in.

3,600 in.³

Measure each amount given in Problems 13–22.

Container A

Container B

13. Container A in cups   *2 c*

14. Container A in ounces   *16 oz*

15. Container B in ounces   *11 oz*

16. Container B in milliliters   *320 mL*

Container C

Container D

17. Container C in ounces   *13 oz*

18. Container C in milliliters   *380 mL*

19. Container D in cups   *1¾ c*

20. Container D in milliliters   *420 mL*

Container E

21. Container E in milliliters   *25 mL*

22. Container G in milliliters   *75 mL*

Container G

The ability to estimate capacities is an important skill to develop. Without measuring, pick the best answer in Problems 23–35.

23. An average cup of coffee is about   *A*

   A. 250 mL   B. 750 mL   C. 1 L

24. If you want to paint some small bookshelves, how much paint would you probably need?   *C*

   A. 1 mL   B. 100 mL   C. 1 L

25. A six-pack of beer would contain about   *C*

   A. 2 mL   B. 200 mL   C. 2 L

26. The dose of a strong cough medicine might be   *A*

   A. 2 mL   B. 200 mL   C. 2 L

27. A glass of water served at a restaurant is about   *A*

   A. 200 mL   B. 2 mL   C. 2 L

28. Enough water for a bath would be about   *B*

   A. 300 mL   B. 300 L   C. 300 kL

29. Enough gas to fill your car's empty tank would be about   *C*

   A. 15 L   B. 200 mL   C. 70 L

30. 50 kL of water would be about enough for   *B*

   A. taking a bath

   B. taking a swim

   C. supplying the drinking water for a large city

31. Which measurement would be appropriate for administering some medication?   *A*

   A. mL   B. L   C. kL

32. You order some champagne for yourself and one companion. You would most likely order   *B*

   A. 2 mL   B. 700 mL   C. 20 L

33. The prefix *centi-* means   *C*

   A. one thousand

   B. one-thousandth

   C. one-hundredth

34. The prefix *milli-* means   *B*

   A. one thousand

   B. one-thousandth

   C. one-hundredth

35. The prefix *kilo-* means   *A*

   A. one thousand

   B. one-thousandth

   C. one-hundredth

What is the capacity for each of the containers in Problems 36–43? (Give answers in the U.S. system to the nearest tenth of a gallon or in metric to the nearest tenth of a liter.)

36.

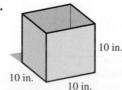

10 in.

10 in.
10 in.

4.3 gal

37.

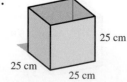

25 cm

25 cm
25 cm

15.6 L

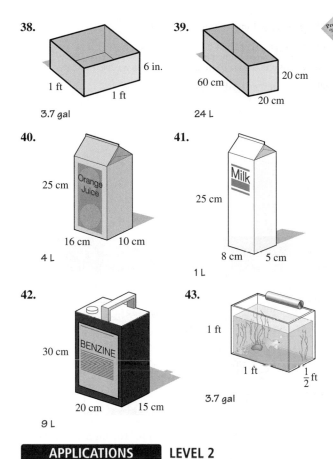

38.

6 in.

1 ft   1 ft

3.7 gal

39.

60 cm   20 cm

20 cm

24 L

40.

25 cm

Orange Juice

16 cm   10 cm

4 L

41.

Milk

25 cm

8 cm   5 cm

1 L

42.

30 cm

BENZINE

20 cm   15 cm

9 L

43.

1 ft

1 ft $\frac{1}{2}$ ft

3.7 gal

APPLICATIONS   LEVEL 2

Use the dimensions of the refrigerator shown in Figure 6.25 for your work in Problems 44–45.

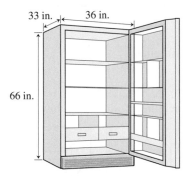

33 in.   36 in.

66 in.

Figure 6.25 Kenmore refrigerator dimensions

44. How many cubic feet are contained within the refrigerator?   45.375 ft³

45. If the refrigerator is advertised as a 19-cu-ft refrigerator, how much space is taken up by the motor, insulation, and so on?   26.375 ft³

46. The exterior dimensions of a freezer are 48 inches by 36 inches by 24 inches, and it is advertised as being 27.0 cu ft. Is the advertised volume correctly stated? no; exterior dimensions are 24 ft³, so it can't be 27 ft³ inside

47. Suppose that you must order concrete for a sidewalk 50 ft by 4 ft to a depth of 4 in. How much concrete is required? (Answer to the nearest $\frac{1}{2}$ cubic yard.)   2.5 yd³

48. How much water will a 7-m by 8-m by 2-m swimming pool contain (in kiloliters)?   112 kL

49. How much water will a 21-ft by 24-ft by 4-ft swimming pool contain (rounded to the nearest gallon)?   15,080 gal

Use the plot plan shown in Figure 6.26 to answer Problems 50–54. Answer to the nearest cubic yard.*

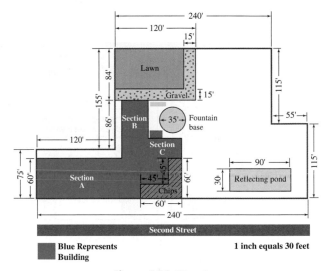

Figure 6.26 Plot plan

50. How much topsoil must be hauled in if it is to be spread to a depth of 12 inches over the lawn area?   805 yd³

51. How much water will the reflecting pond hold if the water is at a uniform depth of 1 ft?   100 yd³

52. How much concrete must be ordered if the base of the fountain is 6 inches deep? *Hint:* To find the volume, multiply the area of the circle by the depth.   18 yd³

53. How many cubic yards of chips are necessary if they are to be placed to a depth of 3 inches?   15 yd³

54. How much gravel is necessary if it is to be laid to a depth of 4 inches?   35 yd³

*In practice, you would not round to the nearest yard, but rather would round up to ensure that you had enough material. However, for consistency in this book, we will round according to the rules developed in the first chapter.

Explain what is wrong, if anything, with the statements in Problems 55–60. Explain your reasoning.

55. A cubic inch is larger than a cubic centimeter.   T

56. A quart is larger than a liter.   F; a liter is larger

57. A meter is longer than a yard.   T

58. A mL is larger than a cubic centimeter.
F; they are the same size

59. Volume is a square measure.   F; it is a cubic measure

60. $1,000 \text{ in.}^3 = 1 \text{ yd}^3$ F; $1,000 \text{ dm}^3 = 1 \text{ m}^3$

(6.5) Miscellaneous Measurements

IN THIS WORLD   THE POWER OF MATH

In this section we discuss additional measures that are important in our everyday life—volume formulas, weight (or mass), and temperature.

 See Problem 27.

In this chapter we have been discussing measurement.

Length	Area	Volume
Use linear measure:	Use square measure:	Use cubic measure:
——		
in.; ft; yd; mi; cm; m; km	in.^{2}; ft^2; yd^2; mi^2; cm^2; m^2; km^2	in.^{3}; ft^3; cm^3 (or cc); m^3; km^3

 In the previous section we found the volume and the capacity of boxes; now we can extend this to other solids. In Figure 6.27 we show some of the more common solids, along with the volume formulas. We will use *B* in each case to signify the area of the base and *h* for the height.

Right rectangular prism

$V = Bh$

Right circular cylinder

$V = Bh$

Pyramid

$V = \frac{1}{3}Bh$

Right circular cone

$V = \frac{1}{3}Bh$

Sphere

$V = \frac{4}{3}\pi r^3$

Figure 6.27 Common solids, with accompanying volume formulas

EXAMPLE 1 — Volume of a right circular cylinder

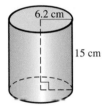

Figure 6.28 Circular cylinder

Find the volume of the solid shown in Figure 6.28 (to the nearest cubic unit).

Solution We use the formula for the volume of a right circular cylinder.

$$V = Bh$$
$$= \pi(6.2)^2(15) \quad \text{Notice that } B = \pi r^2, \text{ where } r = 6.2;$$
$$\approx 1{,}811.4423 \quad \text{the height of the cylinder is 15 } (h = 15).$$

The volume is 1,811 cm^3.

EXAMPLE 2 — Volume of a right circular cone

Figure 6.29 Circular cone

Find the volume of the solid shown in Figure 6.29 (to the nearest cubic unit).

Solution We use the formula for the volume of a right circular cone.

$$V = \frac{1}{3}Bh$$
$$= \frac{1}{3}\pi(5)^2 9 \quad \text{Notice that } B = \pi r^2 \text{ and } r = 5.$$
$$= 75\pi$$
$$\approx 235.6$$

The volume is 236 ft^3.

EXAMPLE 3 — Volume of a right triangular prism

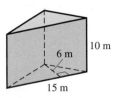

Figure 6.30 Triangular prism

Find the volume of the solid shown in Figure 6.30 (to the nearest cubic unit).

Solution We use the formula for a prism.

$$V = Bh$$
$$= \frac{1}{2}(15)(6)(10) \quad \text{Notice that } B = \frac{1}{2}ba, \text{ where } a = 6 \text{ (height of triangle)},$$
$$= 450 \quad \quad \quad \quad \quad b - 15 \text{ (base of triangle), and } h = 10 \text{ (height of prism)}.$$

The volume is 450 m^3.

EXAMPLE 4   Volume of a sphere

Figure 6.31 Sphere

Find the volume of the solid shown in Figure 6.31 (to the nearest cubic unit).

Solution We use the formula for the volume of a sphere.

$$V = \frac{4}{3}\pi r^3$$
$$= \frac{4}{3}\pi(8.2)^3$$
$$\approx 2{,}309.564878 \quad \textsf{By calculator}$$

The volume is 2,310 cm^3.

EXAMPLE 5   Volume of a pyramid

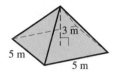

Figure 6.32 Pyramid

Find the volume of the solid in Figure 6.32 (to the nearest cubic unit).

Solution We use the formula for the volume of a pyramid.

$$V = \frac{1}{3}Bh$$
$$= \frac{1}{3}(5)^2(3) \quad \textsf{Notice that the base is a square so } B = s^2 = 5^2.$$
$$= \frac{25}{3}(3)$$
$$= 25$$

The volume is 25 m^3.

The measurements of length, area, volume, and capacity were discussed in the previous section. Two additional measurements to consider are mass and temperature.

Mass

The **mass** of an item is the amount of matter it comprises. The **weight** of an item is the heaviness of the matter.* The U.S. and metric units of measurement for mass or weight are given in the following box. Notice that, in the U.S. measurement system, ounces are used as a weight measurement; this is not the same as the capacity measurement for ounces that we used previously. The basic unit of measurement for mass in the metric system is the **gram,** which is defined as the mass of 1 cm^3 of water, as shown in Figure 6.33.

---

*Technically, weight is the force of gravity acting on a body. The mass of an object is the same on the moon or on the earth, whereas the weight of that same object would be different on the moon and on the earth, since they have different forces of gravity. For our purposes, you can use either word, *mass* or *weight,* since we are weighing things only on the earth.

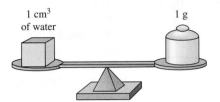

Figure 6.33 Mass of 1 gram

Standard Units of Weight

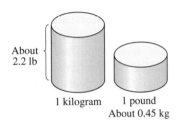

About 2.2 lb

1 kilogram   1 pound
About 0.45 kg

U.S. System	Metric System
ounce (oz)	**gram** (g)
pound (lb; 16 oz)	milligram $\left(mg; \dfrac{1}{1,000}\, g\right)$
ton (T; 2,000 lb)	kilogram (kg; 1,000 g)

A paper clip weighs about 1 g, a cube of sugar about 3 g, and a nickel about 5 g. This book weighs about 1 kg, and an average-size person weighs from 50 to 100 kg. Some common weights of grocery items are listed in Table 6.2.

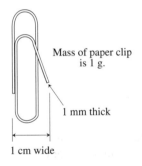

Mass of paper clip is 1 g.

1 mm thick

1 cm wide

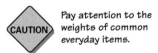

Pay attention to the weights of common everyday items.

TABLE 6.2	Weights of Common Grocery Items, as Shown on Labels	
Item	**U.S. Weight**	**Metric Weight**
Kraft cheese spread	5 oz	142 g
Del Monte tomato sauce	8 oz	227 g
Campbell cream of chicken soup	$10\frac{3}{4}$ oz	305 g
Kraft marshmallow cream	11 oz	312 g
Bag of sugar	5 lb	2.3 kg
Bag of sugar	22 lb	10 kg

We use a scale to measure weight. To weigh items, or ourselves, in metric units, we need only replace our U.S. weight scales with metric weight scales. As with other measures, we must begin to think in terms of metric units, and to estimate the weights of various items. The multiple-choice questions in Problem Set 6.5 are designed to help you do this.

Temperature

The final quantity of measure that we'll consider in this chapter is the degree of hotness or coldness, or **temperature.**

Standard Units of Temperature

U.S. System	*Metric System*
Fahrenheit (°F)	**Celsius (°C)**

To work with temperatures, it is necessary to have some reference points.

Temperature

U.S. Temperature		*Metric Temperature*	
Water freezes:	32°F	Water freezes:	0°C
Water boils:	212°F	Water boils:	100°C

We are usually interested in measuring temperature in three areas: atmospheric temperature (usually given in weather reports), body temperature (used to determine illness), and oven temperature (used in cooking). The same scales are used, of course, for measuring all of these temperatures. But notice the difference in the ranges of temperatures we're considering. The comparisons for Fahrenheit and Celsius are shown in Figure 6.34.

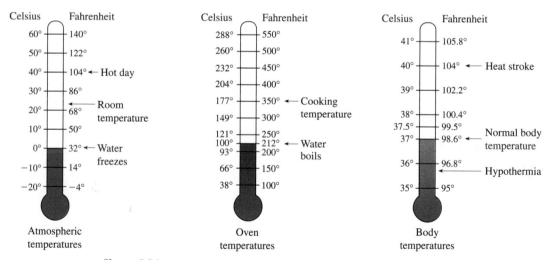

Figure 6.34 Temperature comparisons between Celsius and Fahrenheit

PROBLEM SET 6.5

ESSENTIAL IDEAS   **LEVEL 1**

1. **IN YOUR OWN WORDS** Contrast measuring length, area, and volume.

State the formula for the volume of each solid named in Problems 2–8.

2. Rectangular box $V = \ell wh$

3. Cube $V = s^3$

4. Right circular cone $V = \frac{1}{3}Bh$

5. Sphere $V = \frac{4}{3}\pi r^3$

6. Right rectangular prism $V = Bh$

7. Pyramid $V = \frac{1}{3}Bh$

8. Right circular cylinder $V = Bh$

LEVEL 2

Name the metric unit you would use to measure each of the quantities in Problems 9–20.

9. The distance from New York to Chicago   kilometer

10. The distance around your waist   centimeter

11. Your height   centimeter

12. The height of a building   meter

13. The capacity of a wine bottle   milliliter

14. The amount of gin in a martini   milliliter

15. The capacity of a car's gas tank   liter

16. The amount of water in a swimming pool   kiloliter

17. The weight of a pencil   gram

18. The weight of an automobile   kilogram

19. The outside temperature   Celsius

20. The temperature needed to bake a cake   Celsius

Answer the questions in Problems 21–28 in both the U.S. and metric systems.

21. What is the freezing point of water?   0°C; 32°F

22. What is the boiling point of water?   100°C; 212°F

23. What is a normal body temperature?   37°C; 98.6°F

24. What is a comfortable room temperature?   22°C; 70°F

25. What is a typical cooking temperature?   177°C; 350°F

26. At what temperature is heat stroke likely?   40°C; 104°F

 27. What is the temperature on a typical hot day?   40°C; 104°F

28. At what body temperature is hypothermia likely?
    35.5°C; 96°F

Find the volumes of the solids in Problems 29–40 correct to the nearest cubic unit.

29.

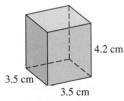

4.2 cm
3.5 cm
3.5 cm
51 cm³

30.

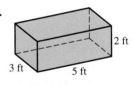

2 ft
3 ft   5 ft
30 ft³

31.

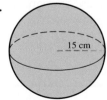

15 cm
14,137 cm³

32.

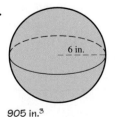

6 in.
905 in.³

33.

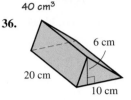

2.4 cm
1.6 cm
19 cm³

34.

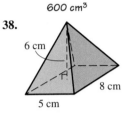

5 cm
1.6 cm
40 cm³

35.

3 in.   13 in.
5 in.   12 in.
30 in.³

36.

6 cm
20 cm
10 cm
600 cm³

37.

6 cm
8 cm
4 cm
64 cm³

38.

6 cm
8 cm
5 cm
80 cm³

39.

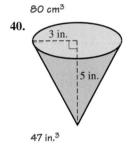

3 in.
4 in.
38 in.³

40.

3 in.
5 in.
47 in.³

LEVEL 2

Without measuring, pick the best choice in Problems 41–60 by estimating.

41. A hamburger patty would weigh about   A
    A. 170 g   B. 240 mg   C. 2 kg

42. A can of carrots at the grocery store most likely weighs about   C
    A. 40 kg   B. 4 kg   C. 0.4 kg

43. A newborn baby would weigh about   B
    A. 490 mg   B. 4 kg   C. 140 kg

44. John tells you he weighs 150 kg. If John is an adult, he is   C
    A. underweight
    B. about average
    C. overweight

45. You have invited 15 people for Thanksgiving dinner. You should buy a turkey that weighs about   C
    A. 795 mg   B. 4 kg   C. 12 kg

46. Water boils at   B
    A. 0°C   B. 100°C   C. 212°C

47. If the doctor says that your child's temperature is 37°C, your child's temperature is   B

   A. low   B. normal   C. high

48. If it is 32°C outside, you would most likely find people   B

   A. ice skating   B. water skiing

49. You would most likely broil steaks at   C

   A. 120°C   B. 500°C   C. 290°C

50. A kilogram is _____A_____ a pound.

   A. more than   B. about the same as   C. less than

51. The prefix used to mean 1,000 is   C

   A. centi-   B. milli-   C. kilo-

52. The prefix used to mean $\frac{1}{1,000}$ is   B

   A. centi-   B. milli-   C. kilo-

53. The prefix used to mean $\frac{1}{100}$ is   A

   A. centi-   B. milli-   C. kilo-

54. 15 kg is a measure of   C

   A. length   B. capacity   C. weight   D. temperature

55. 28.5 m is a measure of   A

   A. length   B. capacity
   C. weight   D. temperature

56. 6 L is a measure of   B

   A. length   B. capacity
   C. weight   D. temperature

57. 38°C is a measure of   D

   A. length   B. capacity
   C. weight   D. temperature

58. 7 mL is a measure of   B

   A. length   B. capacity
   C. weight   D. temperature

59. 68 km is a measure of   A

   A. length   B. capacity
   C. weight   D. temperature

60. 14.3 cm is a measure of   A

   A. length   B. capacity
   C. weight   D. temperature

6.6 Converting Units*

IN THIS WORLD THE POWER OF MATH

MATH CLASS
4.6 m = 46 cm
1.2 cm = ?

Cartoon from The Metrics Are Coming? The Metrics Are Coming! *by R. Cardwell. Copyright © 1975 Dorrance & Company.*

© Chattanooga Times Free Press

"*Have you seen that new sign on the turnpike?*" *asked Steve.* "*What are they thinking! Why in the world would they give us the distance in km—what does 'km' mean, anyway?*"

"*That is the metric system. Don't you know that to convert from miles to kilometers, you simply multiply by 1.6?*" *said Arnie.*

"*You've really missed the whole point of the metric system,*" *added Jim.* "*If you say it is 13 miles to Chattanooga,*" *how do you know? The odometer of a car or a road sign told you so. Won't it be just as easy to read an odometer calibrated to kilometers, or to read a metric road sign telling you that it is '21 km to Chattanooga'?*" *continued Jim.*

The most difficult problem in changing from the U.S. system to the metric system in the United States is not mathematical, but psychological. Many people fear that changing to the metric system will require complex multiplication and division and the use of confusing decimal points. Such is not the case, as we'll see in this section.

 See Problem 2.

*Optional section.

When working with either the metric or the U.S. measurement system, you sometimes need to change units of measurement within a particular system.

This section is divided into two parts so that you can work with either the U.S. system or the metric system, or with both if you prefer. The conversion between these systems is optional and is given as an appendix to this section.

Metric Measurement Conversions

One of the advantages (if not the chief advantage) of the metric system is the ease with which you can remember and convert units of measurement. As you've seen, the three basic metric units are related as shown in Figure 6.35.

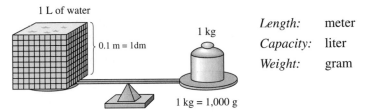

Figure 6.35 Relationship among meter, liter, and gram

These units are combined with certain prefixes:

$$milli\text{- means } \frac{1}{1,000} \qquad centi\text{- means } \frac{1}{100} \qquad kilo\text{- means } 1,000$$

Other metric units are used less frequently, but they should be mentioned:

$$deci\text{- means } \frac{1}{10} \qquad deka\text{- means } 10 \qquad hecto\text{- means } 100$$

A listing of metric units (in order of size) is given in Table 6.3.

TABLE 6.3	Metric Measurements			
Length	**Capacity**	**Weight**	**Meaning**	**Memory Aid**
kilometer (km)	**kilo**liter (kL)	**kilo**gram (kg)	1,000 units	**K**arl
hectometer (hm)	**hecto**liter (hL)	**hecto**gram (hg)	100 units	**H**as
dekameter (dkm)	**deka**liter (dkL)	**deka**gram (dkg)	10 units	**D**eveloped
meter (m)	liter (L)	gram (g)	1 unit	**M**y
decimeter (dm)	**deci**liter (dL)	**deci**gram (dg)	0.1 unit	**D**ecimal
centimeter (cm)	**centi**liter (cL)	**centi**gram (cg)	0.01 unit	**C**raving for
millimeter (mm)	**milli**liter (mL)	**milli**gram (mg)	0.001 unit	**M**etrics

Basic Unit: (points to the meter (m), liter (L), gram (g) row)

To convert from one metric unit to another, you **simply move the decimal point,** as summarized in the following box.

Converting Metrics

To convert from one metric unit to another, follow this procedure.

Step 1 Place a decimal point on the given number, if it is not shown.

Step 2 Set up a chart (patterned after Table 6.3) showing the appropriate metric prefixes.

Step 3 Write the number in the chart so the decimal point is correctly aligned, putting one digit in each column.

Step 4 Assume that there are zeros in all the other columns. To change to another unit, simply move the decimal point to the column corresponding to the unit to which you are changing.

Step 5 Find the converted number by writing the resulting number from the table.

EXAMPLE 1

Converting metric capacity

Write 5 L, using all the other prefixes.

Solution **Step 1** 5. L.

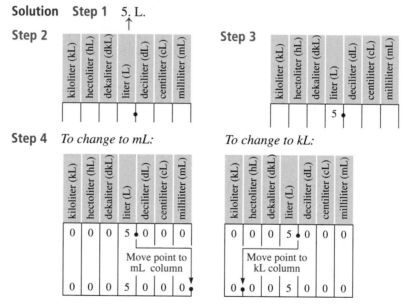

Step 5 These, as well as other possible conversions, are summarized in the following single chart:

kiloliter (kL)	hectoliter (hL)	dekaliter (dkL)	liter (L)	deciliter (dL)	centiliter (cL)	milliliter (mL)	
0	0	0	5	0	0	0	5 L This is given.
0	0	0	5	0	0	0	50 dL
0	0	0	5	0	0	0	500 cL
0	0	0	5	0	0	0	5,000 mL
0	0	0	5	0	0	0	0.5 dkL
0	0	0	5	0	0	0	0.05 hL
0	0	0	5	0	0	0	0.005 kL

In practice, only the necessary zeros are filled in, as shown in Example 2.

EXAMPLE 2   **Converting metric mass**

Write 34.71 kg, using all the other prefixes.

Solution   Follow the steps of the previous example.

To remember this chart, try to memorize a short saying with the same first letters.

Karl	Kilometer
Has	Hectometer
Developed	Dekameter
My	Meter
Decimal	Decimeter
Craving for	Centimeter
Metrics	Millimeter

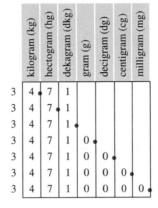

	kilogram (kg)	hectogram (hg)	dekagram (dkg)	gram (g)	decigram (dg)	centigram (cg)	milligram (mg)	
3	4•7	1						34.71 kg This is given.
3	4	7•1						347.1 hg
3	4	7	1•					3,471 dkg
3	4	7	1	0•				34,710 g
3	4	7	1	0	0•			347,100 dg
3	4	7	1	0	0	0•		3,471,000 cg
3	4	7	1	0	0	0	0•	34,710,000 mg

EXAMPLE 3   **Metric conversions**

Make the indicated conversions.

a. 46.4 cm to m   **b.** 6.32 km to m   **c.** 503 mL to L
d. 0.031 kL to L   **e.** 14 kg to dg

Solution

a. 46.4 cm = _____ m   Mentally picture a chart similar to the one shown in Example 1. Then count the number of decimal places involved in this conversion. Remember, "**K**arl **H**as **D**eveloped **M**y **D**ecimal **C**raving for **M**etrics."

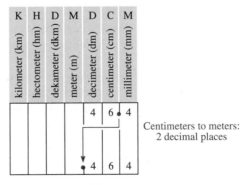

K	H	D	M	D	C	M	
kilometer (km)	hectometer (hm)	dekameter (dkm)	meter (m)	decimeter (dm)	centimeter (cm)	millimeter (mm)	
				4	6•4		Centimeters to meters: 2 decimal places
			•4	6	4		

46.4 cm = 0.464 m

b. 6.32 km = _____ m   Three decimal places on chart:

K H D M D C M
6 . 3 2

6.32 km = 6,320 m

c. 503 mL = _____ L

From memory aid change to L:

$$\text{K H D } \overset{L}{\text{M}} \text{ D C M}$$

5 0 3

Three decimal places left (←) on chart:
503 mL = 0.503 L.

d. 0.031 kL = _____ L

Three decimal places right (→) on chart:
0.031 kL = 31 L.

e. 14 kg = _____ dg

Four decimal places right (→) on chart:
14 kg = 140,000 dg

●

U.S. Measurement Conversion

Conversion within the U.S. measurement system is more difficult than in the metric system because it is not a decimal system and so involves more than moving the decimal point. First, you must remember the U.S. conversion factors, which are given in the following box.

U.S. Conversions

Length	*Capacity*	*Weight*
12 in. = 1 ft	3 tsp = 1 tbsp	16 oz = 1 lb
3 ft = 1 yd	1 oz = 2 tbsp	2,000 lb = 1 T
1,760 yd = 1 mi	16 tbsp = 1 c	
5,280 ft = 1 mi	16 oz = 1 pt	
	8 oz = 1 c	
	2 c = 1 pt	
	2 pt = 1 qt	
	4 qt = 1 gal	

To make conversions within the U.S. measurement system, you must use the following **substitution principle.**

Substitution Principle

If two quantities are equal, then one may be substituted (replaced) by an equal quantity without changing the value of the expression.

This means, for example, that

12 in. may be replaced by 1 ft;

1 ft may be replaced by 12 in.;

4 qt may be replaced by 1 gal; and so on.

It also means that if

4 qt = 1 gal   then $1 \text{ qt} = \frac{1}{4} \text{ gal}$ **Divide both sides by 4.**

EXAMPLE 4   **Converting U.S. length measurements**

Make the following conversions.

a. 8 ft to inches   **b.** 8 ft to yards   **c.** 1,500 yd to feet   **d.** 86 in. to feet

Solution

a. 8 ft = 8 × 1 ft
↓
= 8 × (12 in.)   Since 1 ft = 12 in., substitute 12 in.
= 96 in.

b. 8 ft = 8 × 1 ft
↓
$= 8 \times \left(\frac{1}{3} \text{ yd}\right)$ Since 1 ft = $\frac{1}{3}$ yd
$= 2\frac{2}{3}$ yd

c. 1,500 yd = 1,500 × 1 yd
↓
= 1,500 × (3 ft)   Since 1 yd = 3 ft
= 4,500 ft

d. 86 in. = 86 × 1 in.
↓
$= 86 \times \left(\frac{1}{12} \text{ ft}\right)$ Since 1 in. = $\frac{1}{12}$ ft
$= 7\frac{2}{12}$ ft
$= 7\frac{1}{6}$ ft

EXAMPLE 5   **Converting U.S. capacity measurements**

Make the following conversions.

a. 12 tsp to ounces   **b.** 5 c to pints   **c.** 2 qt 1 pt to ounces

Solution

a. 12 tsp = 12 × 1 tsp
↓
$= 12 \times \left(\frac{1}{3} \text{ tbsp}\right)$ Since 1 tsp = $\frac{1}{3}$ tbsp
$= 12 \times \frac{1}{3} \times 1 \text{ tbsp}$
↓
$= 12 \times \frac{1}{3} \times \left(\frac{1}{2} \text{ oz}\right)$ Since 1 tbsp = $\frac{1}{2}$ oz
$= \frac{12}{6} \text{ oz}$
$= 2 \text{ oz}$

b. $5 \text{ c} = 5 \times 1 \text{ c}$

$$= 5 \times \left(\frac{1}{2} \text{ pt}\right) \quad \text{Since 1 c} = \frac{1}{2} \text{ pt}$$

$$= 2\frac{1}{2} \text{ pt}$$

c. $2 \text{ qt } 1 \text{ pt} = 2 \times 1 \text{ qt} + 1 \text{ pt}$

$$= 2 \times (2 \text{ pt}) + 1 \text{ pt} \quad \text{Since 1 qt} = 2 \text{ pt}$$

$$= 4 \text{ pt} + 1 \text{ pt}$$

$$= 5 \times 1 \text{ pt}$$

$$= 5 \times (16 \text{ oz}) \quad \text{Since 1 pt} = 16 \text{ oz}$$

$$= 80 \text{ oz}$$

EXAMPLE 6

Converting U.S. weight measurements

Make the following conversions.

a. 48 oz to pints   **b.** 5 lb to ounces   **c.** 48 oz to pounds

d. $2\frac{1}{4}$ lb to ounces   **e.** 8.5 T to pounds

Solution

a. $48 \text{ oz} = 48 \times 1 \text{ oz}$

$$= 48 \times \left(\frac{1}{16} \text{ pt}\right) \quad \text{Since 1 oz} = \frac{1}{16} \text{ pt}$$

$$= \frac{48}{16} \text{ pt} = 3 \text{ pt}$$

b. $5 \text{ lb} = 5 \times 1 \text{ lb}$

$$= 5 \times (16 \text{ oz}) \quad \text{Since 1 lb} = 16 \text{ oz}$$

$$= 80 \text{ oz}$$

c. $48 \text{ oz} = 48 \times 1 \text{ oz}$

$$= 48 \times \left(\frac{1}{16} \text{ lb}\right) \quad \text{Since 1 oz} = \frac{1}{16} \text{ lb}$$

$$= \frac{48}{16} \text{ lb}$$

$$= 3 \text{ lb}$$

d. $2\frac{1}{4} \text{ lb} = 2\frac{1}{4} \times 1 \text{ lb}$

$$= 2\frac{1}{4} \times (16 \text{ oz}) \quad \text{Since 1 lb} = 16 \text{ oz}$$

$$= \frac{9}{4} \times \frac{16}{1} \text{ oz}$$

$$= 36 \text{ oz}$$

$$\textbf{e. } 8.5\text{ T} = 8.5 \times \underset{\downarrow}{1\text{ T}}$$

$$= 8.5 \times (2{,}000\text{ lb}) \quad \textsf{Since 1 T = 2,000 lb}$$

$$= 17{,}000\text{ lb}$$

U.S.–Metric Conversions

This section may be considered as an appendix for reference only. The emphasis in this chapter has been on everyday use of the metric system. However, certain specialized applications require more precise conversions than we've considered. On the other hand, you don't want to become bogged down with arithmetic to the point where you say "nuts to the metric system."

The most difficult obstacle in the change from the U.S. system to the metric system is not mathematical, but psychological. If you have understood the chapter to this point, you realize that this should not be the case. In fact, as you saw in the last section, *working within the metric system is much easier than working within the U.S. system.*

With these ideas firmly in mind, and realizing that your everyday work with the metric system is discussed in the other sections of this chapter, we present Table 6.4, which gives conversion factors between these measurement systems. Many calculators will make these conversions for you; check your owner's manual.

TABLE 6.4	U.S.–Metric Conversions

LENGTH CONVERSIONS

U.S. to Metric			Metric to U.S.		
When you know	Multiply by	To Find	When you know	Multiply by	To Find
in.	2.54	cm	cm	0.39370	in.
ft	30.48	cm	m	39.37	in.
ft	0.3048	m	m	3.28084	ft
yd	0.9144	m	m	1.09363	yd
mi	1.60934	km	km	0.62137	mi

CAPACITY CONVERSIONS

U.S. to Metric			Metric to U.S.		
When you know	Multiply by	To Find	When you know	Multiply by	To Find
tsp	4.9289	mL	mL	0.20288	tsp
tbsp	14.7868	mL	mL	0.06763	tbsp
oz	29.5735	mL	mL	0.03381	oz
c	236.5882	mL	mL	0.00423	c
pt	473.1765	mL	mL	0.00211	pt
qt	946.353	mL	mL	0.00106	qt
qt	0.9464	L	L	1.05672	qt
gal	3.7854	L	L	0.26418	gal

(Continued)

TABLE 6.4	U.S.–Metric Conversions (*Continued*)					

WEIGHT (MASS) CONVERSIONS

U.S. to Metric			Metric to U.S.		
When you know	**Multiply by**	**To Find**	**When you know**	**Multiply by**	**To Find**
oz	28.3495	g	g	0.0352739	oz
lb	453.59237	g	g	0.0022046	lb
lb	0.453592	kg	kg	2.2046226	lb
T	907.18474	kg			

TEMPERATURE CONVERSIONS

U.S. to Metric			Metric to U.S.		
When you know		**To Find**	**When you know**		**To Find**
°F	Subtract 32° then multiply by $\frac{5}{9}$	°C	°C	Multiply by $\frac{9}{5}$ then add 32°	°F
Formula: $C = \frac{5}{9}(F - 32°)$			Formula: $F = \frac{9}{5}C + 32°$		

PROBLEM SET 6.6

ESSENTIAL IDEAS LEVEL 1

1. IN YOUR OWN WORDS What is the relationship among meter, liter, and gram?

 2. IN YOUR OWN WORDS It has been said that "The most difficult problem in changing from the U.S. system to the metric system in the United States is not mathematical, but psychological." (See "In This World" at the beginning of this section.) Discuss this statement by registering your agreement or disagreement and explaining your position.

3. State, from memory, a useful mnemonic for making metric to metric conversions.

4. State the substitution principle.

DRILL AND PRACTICE LEVEL 2

Odd-numbered problems are U.S. measurement conversions, and *even-numbered problems* are metric conversions. Use reduced fractions for U.S. conversions, and use decimals for metric conversions.

In Problems 5–18, make the indicated conversions.

5. a. 1 in. = $\frac{1}{12}$ ft

b. 1 in. = $\frac{1}{36}$ yd

c. 1 in. = $\frac{1}{63,360}$ mi

6. a. 1 cm = 10 mm

b. 1 cm = 0.01 m

c. 1 cm = 0.00001 km

7. a. 1 ft = 12 in.

b. 1 ft = $\frac{1}{3}$ yd

c. 1 ft = $\frac{1}{5,280}$ mi

8. a. 1 mm = 0.1 cm

b. 1 mm = 0.001 m

c. 1 mm = 0.000001 km

9. a. 1 yd = 36 in.

b. 1 yd = 3 ft

c. 1 yd = $\frac{1}{1,760}$ mi

10. a. 1 m = 1,000 mm

b. 1 m = 100 cm

c. 1 m = 0.001 km

11. a. 1 tsp = $\frac{1}{3}$ tbsp

   b. 1 tsp = $\frac{1}{6}$ oz

   c. 1 tsp = $\frac{1}{48}$ c

12. a. 1 mL = 0.01 dL

   b. 1 mL = 0.001 L

   c. 1 mL = 0.000001 kL

13. a. 1 oz = $\frac{1}{8}$ c

   b. 1 oz = $\frac{1}{16}$ pt

   c. 1 c = $\frac{1}{2}$ pt

14. a. 1 L = 1,000 mL

   b. 1 L = 10 dL

   c. 1 L = 0.001 kL

15. a. 1 pt = $\frac{1}{2}$ qt

   b. 1 pt = $\frac{1}{8}$ gal

   c. 1 qt = $\frac{1}{4}$ gal

16. a. 1 kL = 1,000,000 mL

   b. 1 kL = 10,000 dL

   c. 1 kL = 1,000 L

17. a. 1 oz = $\frac{1}{16}$ lb

   b. 1 oz = $\frac{1}{32,000}$ T

   c. 1 lb = $\frac{1}{2,000}$ T

18. a. 1 g = 1,000 mg

   b. 1 g = 100 cg

   c. 1 g = 0.001 kg

In Problems 19–42, write each measurement in terms of all the other units listed in the problem. U.S. units will be changed to other U.S. units, and metric units will be changed to other metric units.   See IAS.

	mile (mi)	yard (yd)	foot (ft)	inch (in.)
19.		9		
20.				6
21.	4			
22.				150

	kilometer (km)	hectometer (hm)	dekameter (dkm)	meter (m)	decimeter (dm)	centimeter (cm)	millimeter (mm)
23.				9 •			
24.						6 •	
25.	4 •						
26.					1	5	0 •

	quart (qt)	pint (pt)	cup (c)	ounce (oz)
27.				63
28.		$3\frac{1}{2}$		
29.			8	
30.	5			

	kiloliter (kL)	hectoliter (hL)	dekaliter (dkL)	liter (L)	deciliter (dL)	centiliter (cL)	milliliter (mL)
31.						6	3 •
32.				3 • 5			
33.			8 •				
34.		3 • 1					

	ton (T)	pound (lb)	ounce (oz)
35.		4	
36.			96
37.		$5\frac{1}{4}$	
38.	$4\frac{1}{2}$		

	kilogram (kg)	hectogram (hg)	dekagram (dkg)	gram (g)	decigram (dg)	centigram (cg)	milligram (mg)
39.	6 • 5						
40.			9 • 6	•			
41.	5 • 2	5					
42.	4 • 5						

APPLICATIONS   **LEVEL 2**

Problems 43–60 require conversions between the U.S. and metric measurement systems.

43. The gas gauge on your sports car tells you that a full tank of gas is 60 L. How much is this, to the nearest gallon?   16 gal

44. If you put 48 L of gasoline in your rental car, what is this quantity, to the nearest tenth of a gallon?   12.7 gal

45. If you put 18 gallons of gasoline in your car, what is this quantity, to the nearest liter?   68 L

46. If you put 12.8 gallons of gasoline in your car, what is this quantity to the nearest liter?   48 L

47. If you are 6 ft tall, what is your height, to the nearest centimeter?   183 cm

48. If you are 5 ft 2 in. tall, what is your height, to the nearest centimeter?   157 cm

49. If the distance between two cities is 500 km, what is this distance, to the nearest mile?   311 mi

50. If the distance between two cities is 2500 km, what is this distance, to the nearest mile?   1,553 mi

51. If you purchase a 1-m salami stick, what is the length, to the nearest inch?   39 in.

52. If a wagon wheel's diameter is 1.5 m, what is the diameter, to the nearest inch?   59 in.

53. If you run a 10-km race, how many miles have you run, to the nearest tenth mile?   *6.2 mi*

54. If a road sign tells you it is 85 km to your destination, what is this distance, to the nearest mile?   *53 mi*

55. If you purchase a 750-mL bottle of wine, and you wish to pour 5-oz portions to your guests, how many guests will you be able to serve?   *750 mL ≈ 25 oz; 5 portions*

56. Suppose you are having a party with 45 guests and want to have a champagne toast. If you pour 2-oz portions to each guest, how many mL of champagne will you need to purchase?   *2,662 mL (by the way, this is about four 750-mL bottles.)*

57. The temperature gauge in your car records the temperature to be 18°C. What is that temperature, to the nearest degree Fahrenheit?   *64°F*

58. The temperature gauge in your car records the temperature to be 26°C. What is that temperature, to the nearest degree Fahrenheit?   *79°F*

59. If a prescription calls for 5 mL, what is that quantity, to the nearest teaspoon?   *1 tsp*

60. If a prescription calls for 30 mL, what is that quantity, to the nearest fluid ounce?   *1 oz*

6.7 Chapter 6 Summary and Review

Take some time getting ready to work the review problems in this section. First, look back at the definition and property boxes. You will maximize your understanding of this chapter by working the problems in this section only after you have studied the material.

IMPORTANT TERMS
Numbers refer to sections of this chapter.

Spending some time with the terms and objectives of this chapter will pay dividends in assuring your success.

Accuracy [6.1]	Inch [6.1]	Rectangle [6.2]
Acre [6.3]	Kilo- [6.1]	Rectangular parallelepiped [6.4]
Area [6.4]	Kilogram [6.5]	
Capacity [6.4]	Kiloliter [6.4]	Rectangular prism [6.5]
Celsius [6.5]	Kilometer [6.1]	Right circular cone [6.5]
Centi- [6.1]	Length [6.1]	Right circular cylinder [6.5]
Centimeter [6.1]	Liter [6.4]	Right rectangular prism [6.5]
Circle [6.2]	Mass [6.5]	
Circular cone [6.5]	Measure [6.1]	Semicircle [6.2]
Circular cylinder [6.5]	Meter [6.1]	SI system [6.1]
Circumference [6.2]	Metric system [6.1]	Sphere [6.5]
Cone [6.5]	Mile [6.1]	Square [6.2]
Cube [6.4]	Milli- [6.1]	Square centimeter [6.3]
Cubic centimeter [6.4]	Milligram [6.5]	Square foot [6.3]
Cubic inch [6.4]	Milliliter [6.4]	Square inch [6.3]
Cup [6.4]	Ounce [6.4]	Square unit [6.3]
Cylinder [6.5]	Parallelepiped [6.4]	Substitution principle [6.6]
Deci- [6.1]	Parallelogram [6.3]	Temperature [6.5]
Deka- [6.1]	Perimeter [6.2]	Ton [6.5]
Diameter [6.2]	Pi (π) [6.2]	Trapezoid [6.3]
Equilateral triangle [6.2]	Pound [6.5]	United States system [6.1]
Fahrenheit [6.5]	Precision [6.1]	Volume [6.4]
Foot [6.1]	Prism [6.5]	Weight [6.5]
Gallon [6.4]	Pyramid [6.5]	Yard [6.1]
Gram [6.5]	Quart [6.4]	
Hecto- [6.1]	Radius [6.2]	

Essential Ideas

[6.1]	Problem 1	Distinguish between *precision* and *accuracy*.
	Problem 2	Know the accuracy agreement used in this book.
	Problems 3–4; 7–12	Know the basic units of length in the U.S. and metric systems; also know their abbreviations.
	Problems 5–6	Know the metric prefixes.
[6.2]	Problems 1–2	Understand the concepts of perimeter and circumference.
	Problem 3	Be familiar with the number pi.
	Problem 4	Know the formulas for the perimeter of a triangle, equilateral triangle, square, and rectangle, as well as the formula for the circumference of a circle.
[6.3]	Problems 1–2	Understand the concept of area.
	Problem 3	Distinguish between perimeter and area.
	Problem 4	Distinguish quadrilaterals that are parallelograms and trapezoids.
[6.4]	Problem 1	Contrast area and volume.
	Problem 2	Compare or contrast liter, cubic centimeter, and quart.
[6.5]	Problem 1	Contrast length, area, and volume.
	Problems 2–8	State the formulas for the volume of a box, cube, cone, sphere, prism, pyramid, and cylinder.
[6.6]*	Problem 1	Describe the relationship among meter, liter, and gram.
	Problems 2–4	Describe conversions: metric to metric, U.S. to U.S., and metric to U.S.

LEARNING OUTCOMES

The material in this chapter is reviewed in the following list of learning outcomes. A self-test (with answers and suggestions for additional study) is given. This self-test is constructed so that each problem number corresponds to a related objective. For example, Problem 7 is testing Objective 6.7. This self-test is followed by a practice test with the questions in mixed order.

[6.1]	*Objective* 6.1	Estimate the length of segments without using any measuring device.
[6.1]	*Objective* 6.2	Measure segments with an indicated precision.
[6.1]	*Objective* 6.3	Know your own size in U.S. and metric measurements.
[6.2]	*Objective* 6.4	Find the perimeter or circumference of a simple figure.
[6.2]	*Objective* 6.5	Find the distance around a given figure.
[6.3]	*Objective* 6.6	Find the area of a given figure (rectangle, square, parallelogram, triangle, trapezoid, circle, or a combination of these).
[6.4]	*Objective* 6.7	Find the volume of a box.
[6.4]	*Objective* 6.8	Find the capacity of a given container.
[6.5]	*Objective* 6.9	Name a unit in the U.S. and metric measurement systems that you might use to measure specific everyday objects.
[6.1–6.5]	*Objective* 6.10	Estimate temperatures in both the U.S. and metric measurement systems.
[6.5]	*Objective* 6.11	State whether a given measurement measures length, capacity, mass, or temperature.
[6.5]	*Objective* 6.12	Find the volume of a solid (right prism, right circular cylinder, pyramid, right circular cone, or sphere).
[6.1–6.6]	*Objective* 6.13	Arrange the metric prefixes from largest to smallest. Know what each prefix means. Estimate measurements in both the U.S. and metric measurement systems.
[6.6]†	*Objective* 6.14	Make conversions within the metric system.
[6.6]†	*Objective* 6.15	Make conversions within the U.S. system.
[6.6]†	*Objective* 6.16	Make conversions between the metric and U.S. systems.
[6.2–6.4]	*Objective* 6.17	Solve applied problems involving perimeter, area, and volume (Problems 17–20).

*Optional section.
†Section 6.6 is an optional section.

Self-Test

Each question of this self-test is related to the corresponding objective listed above.

1. Without any measuring device, draw a segment 10 cm long.

2. Measure this segment to the nearest tenth cm. _____

3. What is the width of your index finger in both the metric and U.S. systems?

4. Find the perimeters of the given figures.

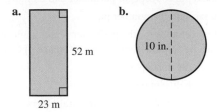

a.

52 m

23 m

b.

10 in.

5. Find the distance around the given regions (rounded to the nearest unit).

a.

2.5 cm

6.1 cm

5.0 cm

2.3 cm

10.4 cm

b.

7 in.

10 in.

8 in.

6 in.

6. Find the area of each region.

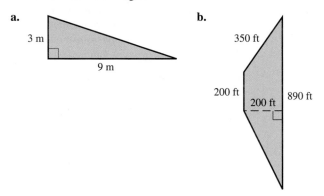

a.

3 m

9 m

b.

350 ft

200 ft

200 ft

890 ft

7. Find the volume of the box in Figure 6.36.

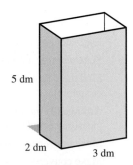

5 dm

2 dm

3 dm

Figure 6.36

8. What is the capacity of the box in Figure 6.36?

9. What are the units of measurement in both the U.S. and metric measurement systems that you would use to measure the height of a building?

10. Estimate the temperature on a hot summer day in both the U.S. and metric measurement systems.

11. a. What does the measurement 8.6 mL measure?
    b. What does the measurement 189 g measure?
    c. What does the measurement 63 miles measure?
    d. What does the measurement 4 gallons measure?
    e. What does the measurement 6 m measure?
    f. What does the measurement 6 c measure?

12. Find the volume (to the nearest tenth of a cubic foot) of a sphere with radius 1 ft.

13. What does the prefix *milli-* mean?

*14. How many centimeters are equivalent to 10 km?

*15. How many tablespoons are equivalent to 3 oz?

*16. If your automobile gas tank has a 20-gallon capacity, how much will the tank hold, to the nearest liter?

17. How many square yards of carpet are necessary to carpet an 11-ft by 16-ft room? (Assume that you cannot purchase part of a square yard.)

18. To find the price per square inch of pizza, divide the price by the number of square inches in the pizza. Refer to the pizza menu and use the price of the original style pizza.

a. What is the price per square inch for a mini pizza (6-in. diameter)?
b. What is the price per square inch for a small pizza (10-in. diameter)?
c. What is the price per square inch for a large pizza (14-in. diameter)?
d. If you order a pizza, what size should you order if you want the best price per square inch?
e. Suppose you were the owner of a pizza restaurant and were going to offer a 16-in. diameter pizza. What would you charge for the pizza if you wanted the price to be comparable with the prices of the other sizes?

19. Which property costs less per square foot?

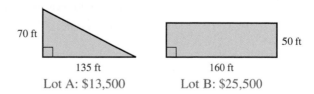

*Problems 14–16 are from the optional section.

20. Suppose you must cover 1/8 of a circle with a diameter of 60 cm with a material that costs \$0.24/cm². What is the expected cost?

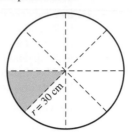

STOP

STUDY HINTS *Compare your solutions and answers to the self-test. For each problem you missed, work some additional problems in the section listed in the margin. After you have worked these problems, you can test yourself with the practice test.*

Additional Problems

[6.1] Problems 32–43

[6.1] Problems 44–55

[6.1] Problem 60

[6.2] Problems 15–31

[6.2] Problems 32–39

[6.3] Problems 25–42

Complete Solutions to the Self-Test

1. ———————————————————————————

2. 1.9 cm

3. Answers vary; $\frac{1}{2}$ in.; 1.5 cm

4. a. This is a rectangle, so the opposite sides have the same length. The perimeter is the distance around:
$$P = 2(52 \text{ m} + 23 \text{ m})$$
$$= 150 \text{ m}$$
The perimeter is 150 meters.

b. This is a circle, so the distance around is the circumference.
$$C = \pi d$$
$$= \pi(10 \text{ in.})$$
$$= 10\pi \text{ in.}$$
$$\approx 31.4159 \text{ in.}$$
The circumference is about 31 inches.

5. a. The perimeter is the distance around:
$$P = 2.5 \text{ cm} + 5.0 \text{ cm} + 10.4 \text{ cm} + 2.3 \text{ cm} + 6.1 \text{ cm}$$
$$= 26.3 \text{ cm}$$
The perimeter is 26.3 centimeters.

b. First find the distance around the semicircle:
$$\frac{1}{2}\pi d = 4\pi \approx 12.56637061$$

The distance around is
$$10 \text{ in.} + 7 \text{ in.} + 4\pi \text{ in.} + 7 \text{ in.} + 6 \text{ in.} \approx 42.5664 \text{ in.}$$
To the nearest inch, the perimeter is 43 in.

6. a. This is a triangle, so
$$A = \frac{1}{2}bh$$
$$= \frac{1}{2}(9 \text{ m})(3 \text{ m})$$
$$= 13.5 \text{ m}^2$$
The area of the triangle is 13.5 square meters.

b. This figure is a trapezoid, so

$$A = \frac{1}{2}h(b + B)$$
$$= \frac{1}{2}(200\text{ ft})(200\text{ ft} + 890\text{ ft})$$
$$= (100\text{ ft})(1{,}090\text{ ft})$$
$$= 109{,}000\text{ ft}^2$$

The area is 109,000 ft². (This is about $2\frac{1}{2}$ acres.)

7. $V = \ell wh$
    $= 2(3)(5)$
    $= 30$

The volume is 30 dm³.

8. Since 1 L = 1 dm³, we see from Problem 7 that the box holds 30 liters.

9. Feet and meters

10. Answers vary; 40°C; 100°F

11. a. Capacity   **b.** Mass (or weight)   **c.** Distance
    d. Capacity   **e.** Length   **f.** Capacity

12. $V = \frac{4}{3}\pi r^3$
    $= \frac{4}{3}\pi(1)^3$
    $= \frac{4}{3}\pi$
    ≈ 4.188790205

The volume is 4.2 ft³.

13. One-thousandth

14.

K		H	D	M	D	C	M
10	.	0	0	0	0	0	0

10 km = 1,000,000 cm

15. 3 oz $= 3 \times 1$ oz
         $= 3 \times (2\text{ tbsp})$
         $= 6$ tbsp

16. This is a conversion from the U.S. measurement system to the metric measurement system, so we must find the conversion factor in Table 6.4; this is a capacity conversion from U.S. to metric:

$$20 \times 3.7854 = 75.708$$

To the nearest liter, we see that 20 gallons is equivalent to 76 L.

Applications

17. 11 ft $\times$ 16 ft $= 3\frac{2}{3}$ yd $\times 5\frac{1}{3}$ yd
               $= \frac{11}{3} \times \frac{16}{3}$ yd²

$$= \frac{176}{9} \text{ yd}^2$$

$$= 19.6 \text{ yd}^2$$

You must purchase 20 square yards.

18. **a.** From the price list, we see that a mini pizza is $6.69 and since it is a 6-inch diameter, the area of the pizza is

$$A = \pi r^2 = \pi (3)^2 \approx 28.27 \quad \text{Radius is 3 in.}$$

The price per square inch is found by division:

$$\frac{\text{DOLLARS}}{\text{SQ. IN.}} = \frac{\$6.69}{9\pi} \approx \$0.24$$

The mini pizza is $0.24/in.^{2}.

b. The price of the small pizza is $13.29, and it has a 5-inch radius.

$$A = \pi r^2 = \pi (5)^2 \approx 78.54$$

The price per square inch is found by division:

$$\frac{\text{DOLLARS}}{\text{SQ. IN.}} = \frac{\$13.29}{25\pi} \approx \$0.17$$

The small pizza is $0.17/in.^{2}.

c. The price of the large pizza is $21.99, and it has a 7-inch radius.

$$A = \pi r^2 = \pi (7)^2 \approx 153.94$$

The price per square inch is found by division:

$$\frac{\text{DOLLARS}}{\text{SQ. IN.}} = \frac{\$21.99}{49\pi} \approx \$0.14$$

The large pizza is $0.14/in.^{2}.

d. The large pizza is the best price per square inch.

e. The radius of this new pizza is 8 inches:

$$A = \pi r^2 = \pi (8)^2 \approx 201.06$$

Based on the pricing pattern for parts **a–c**, the price would likely be $0.13/in.^{2}, so

$$\$0.13 \times 64\pi \approx \$26.14$$

The price would most likely be $25.99. (Answers vary, but any price from $24.00 to $27.00 would be acceptable. For your information, the price the company actually set for this pizza is $25.49.)

19. The area of Lot A is: $A = \frac{1}{2}(70 \text{ ft})(135 \text{ ft}) = 4{,}725 \text{ ft}^2$.

The price per square foot is

$$\frac{\$13{,}500}{4{,}725 \text{ ft}^2} \approx \$2.86/\text{ft}^2$$

The area of Lot B is: $B = (50 \text{ ft})(160 \text{ ft}) = 8{,}000 \text{ ft}^2$. The price per square foot is

$$\frac{\$25{,}500}{8{,}000 \text{ ft}^2} \approx \$3.19/\text{ft}^2$$

Lot A costs less per square foot.

20. $A = \frac{1}{8}\pi (30 \text{ cm})^2$

≈ 353.43

The cost is $353.43 \times \$0.24 \approx \$84.82$.

Chapter 6 Review Questions

*To prepare for a chapter test, first study the chapter; then, read each term from the important terms list above and make sure you know the meaning of each word; finally, review the chapter objectives. **After** these steps, take the self-test and correct all your answers. The following review questions can be used for extra practice.*

1. Without any measuring device, draw a segment with the indicated length.
   a. 2 in. **b.** 3 cm **c.** 1 cm **d.** 4 in.
   Use a ruler to check your answers to this problem.
2. Measure the segment to the specified precision. _____
   a. The nearest centimeter   2 cm
   b. The nearest tenth centimeter   1.9 cm
   c. The nearest inch   1 in.
   d. The nearest eighth of an inch $\frac{3}{4}$ in.

3. Name a unit in the U.S. and metric measurement systems that you might use to measure the named objects.
   a. Size of a notebook paper   inch and centimeter
   b. Weight of a dime   ounce and gram
   c. Capacity of a can of Pepsi   ounce and milliliter
   d. Outside temperature   degree Fahrenheit and degree Celsius

4. State whether the measurements are measuring length, capacity, mass, or temperature.
   a. 4.2 mL   capacity   **b.** 24 km   length
   c. 9.3 kg   mass (weight)   **d.** 23°C   temperature

5. Give the requested information about yourself in the U.S. and metric measurement systems.   Answers vary.
   a. height   **b.** weight   **c.** width of your hand   **d.** normal body temperature
   37°C; 98.6°F

6. a. Answers vary; 26°C to 30°C
6. b. Answers vary; 40°C to 45°C

6. **a.** What is a good temperature for the water in a swimming pool in degrees Celsius?
   b. What is a good temperature for the water when you take a bath in degrees Celsius?

7. a. Answers vary (3,000 mi or 5,000 km)

7. **a.** Estimate the distance between San Francisco and New York.
   b. Estimate the capacity of a can of 7-Up.   12 oz or 355 mL
   c. Estimate the weight (mass) of a penny. $\frac{1}{10}$ oz or 3 g
   d. Estimate a comfortable room temperature.   Answers vary (70°F or 20°C).

8. The following two articles appeared in the *New York Times*.

The *New York Times*, November 21, 1994.

Indianapolis, Nov. 20 (AP) Burglars broke into an elementary school here and passed up computer equipment, going instead for 80,000 pennies that pupils had spent months collecting.
  A maintenance worker at Greenbriar Elementary School entered the cafeteria on Friday morning and found that a see-through glass well holding the $800 in pennies, weighing 450 pounds, had been smashed and emptied.

The *New York Times*, December 22, 1994.

Ray Amoroso, collection manager for the Steel Valley Bank in Dillonvale, Ohio, sifted through some of the eight million pennies turned in by a man, now 70, who had collected pennies since he was 5 years old. The pennies, weighing an estimated 48,000 pounds, are worth about $80,000.

   a. What is the weight of a penny, according to the first article?   0.09 oz/penny
   b. What is the weight of a penny, according to the second article?   0.096 oz/penny
   c. According to which article does a penny weigh more?   the second article
   d. Suppose that 330 students in the first article saved for 6 months. If each student contributed equally, how many pennies did each student bring each school day?
   80,000 pennies/120 days = 667 pennies/day; this is 2¢ per student per day

9. Arrange from largest to smallest.
   a. mg, cg, dkg   *dkg, cg, mg*   **b.** cL, mL, kL   *kL, cL, mL*
   c. c, tsp, qt   *qt, c, tsp*   **d.** mm, hm, m   *hm, m, mm*

10. Find the perimeter and area of each figure.

   a.

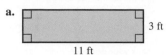

11 ft

P = 28 ft; *A* = 33 ft²

   b.

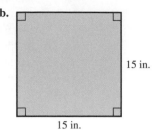

15 in.

15 in.

P = 60 in.; *A* = 225 in.²

11. Find the perimeter and area of each figure.

   a.

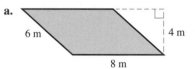

6 m   4 m

8 m

P = 28 m; *A* = 32 m²

   b.

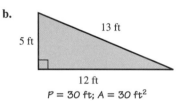

13 ft

5 ft

12 ft

P = 30 ft; *A* = 30 ft²

12. Find the area and circumference or the distance around the shaded portions (correct to two decimal places).

   a.

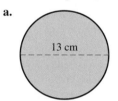

13 cm

40.84 cm; *A* = 132.73 cm²

   b.

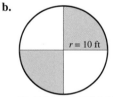

r = 10 ft

71.42 ft; *A* = 157.08 ft²

13. Find the area and circumference or the distance around the shaded portions (correct to two decimal places).

   a.

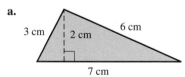

3 cm   2 cm   6 cm

7 cm

16 cm; *A* = 7 cm²

   b.

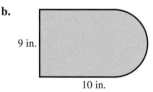

9 in.

10 in.

43.14 in.; *A* = 121.81 in.²

14. Find the volume of each solid as well as its capacity (to the nearest gallon).

   a.

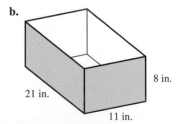

14 in.   2 in.

14 in.

392 in.³; 2 gal

   b.

21 in.   8 in.

11 in.

1,848 in.³; 8 gal

15. Find the volume of each solid as well as its capacity (to the nearest liter).

a.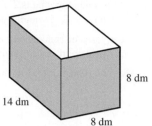

b.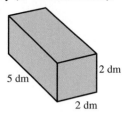

896 dm³; 896 L   *20 dm³; 20 L*

16. Find the exact volume.

a.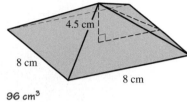

b.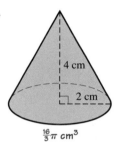

96 cm³   *16/3 π cm³*

17. Find the volume to the nearest cubic unit.

a.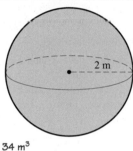

b.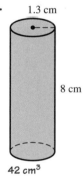

34 m³   *42 cm³*

*18. Fill in the blanks.

    a. 4.8 km = __4,800__ m   **b.** 450 mL = __0.45__ L

    c. 480 g = __0.48__ kg   **d.** 5.2 dm = __52__ cm

    e. 20 ft = __$6\frac{2}{3}$__ yd   **f.** 4 in. = __$\frac{1}{9}$__ yd

    g. 2 c = __1__ pt   **h.** $4\frac{1}{2}$ lb = __72__ oz

19. How many square yards of carpet are necessary to carpet a 13-ft by 14-ft room? (Assume that you cannot purchase part of a square yard.)   *21 yd²*

*20. a. If you ride your bike 150 miles, how far is this, to the nearest kilometer?   *241 km*

    b. If you need to consume 250 g of protein, what is the equivalent quantity, to the nearest ounce?   *9 oz*

21. How much water (to the nearest gallon) is necessary to fill to a depth of 2 ft a rectangular bathtub that measures 5 ft by 3 ft?   *224 gal*

*Optional section.

22. If you are charged $100 per square foot for custom stained glass windows, how much would you pay for a window that is 2 ft by 2 ft? How much would you pay for a circular window with a 2-ft diameter? *rectangle, $400; circular, $314*

23. How many cubic yards of concrete are necessary for a rectangular driveway that is 20 ft by 25 ft by 4 in.? Assume that you can order in units of $\frac{1}{2}$ cubic yard. *$6\frac{1}{2}$ yd³*

24. The distributive law (Chapter 1) states that

$$ab + ac = a(b + c)$$

In this chapter, we say ab and ac represent areas of two rectangles, one with sides a and b, and the other with sides a and c. Use the diagram in Figure 6.37 to give a geometric justification of the distributive law.

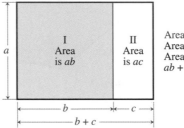

Area of rectangle I: ab
Area of rectangle II: ac
Area of large rectangle is $ab + ac$

Figure 6.37 Area of large rectangle calculated two ways illustrates the distributive property: $a(b + c) = ab + ac$

Area of large rectangle is $a(b + c)$ and this is the same as the area of I plus the area of II.

25. The Pythagorean theorem (Chapter 2) states that, for a right triangle with sides a and b and hypotenuse c, $a^2 + b^2 = c^2$. In this chapter, we saw that a^2 is the area of a square of length a. We can, therefore, illustrate the Pythagorean theorem for a triangle with sides 3, 4, and 5, as shown in Figure 6.38. Illustrate the Pythagorean theorem for a right triangle with sides 5, 12, and 13. *See IAS.*

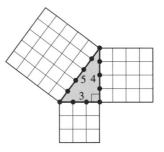

Figure 6.38 Geometric interpretation of the pythagorean theorem

Individual Projects

Learning to use sources outside your classroom and textbook is an important skill, and here are some ideas for extending some of the ideas in this chapter.

PROJECT 6.1   **IN YOUR OWN WORDS** Write a report listing the volumes or capacities of several items on your kitchen shelf, stating the amounts in both the metric and U.S. measurement systems.

PROJECT 6.2   What would happen if the *entire world population* moved to California?

California
158,600 square miles

World population about 6,600,000,000!

     a. How much space would each person have (make a guess)?

       A. 7 in.^{2} B. 7 ft^2 C. 70 ft^2 D. 700 ft^2 E. 7,000 ft^2

     b. Now, using the information in the figure, calculate the answer that you guessed in part **a**; that is, how much space would be allocated to each person?   D

PROJECT 6.3   The total human population of the earth is about 6.6×10^9.

     a. If each person has the room of a prison cell (50 sq ft), and if a square mile is about 2.8×10^7 sq ft, how many people could fit into a square mile?

a. 5.6×10^5 people per square mile

     b. How many square miles would be required to accommodate the entire human population of the earth?   *11,800 mi^2*

     c. If the total land area of the earth is about 5.2×10^7 sq mi, and if all the land area were divided equally, how many acres of land would each person be allocated (1 sq mi = 640 acres)?   *5.0 acres per person*

PROJECT 6.4   **a.** Guess what percentage of the world's population could be packed into a cubical box measuring $\frac{1}{2}$ mi on each side. [*Hint:* Assume that the world's population is 6.6 billion and that the volume of a typical person is about 2 cu ft.]

     b. Now calculate the answer to part **a.**   *72%*

Team Projects

Working in small groups is typical of most work environments, and learning to work with others to communicate specific ideas is an important skill. Work with three or four other students to submit a single report based on each of the following questions.

T13. A polyhedron is a simple closed surface in space whose boundary is composed of polygonal regions (see Figure 6.39). A rather surprising relationship exists among the numbers of vertices, edges, and sides of polyhedra. See if you can discover it by looking for patterns in the figures and filling in the blanks.

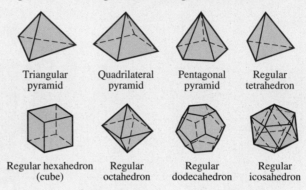

| Triangular pyramid | Quadrilateral pyramid | Pentagonal pyramid | Regular tetrahedron |
| Regular hexahedron (cube) | Regular octahedron | Regular dodecahedron | Regular icosahedron |

Figure 6.39 Some common polyhedra

Figure	Sides	Number of Vertices	Edges
a. triangular pyramid	4	4	6
b. quadrilateral pyramid	5	5	8
c. pentagonal pyramid	6	6	10
d. regular tetrahedron	4	4	6
e. cube	6	8	12
f. regular octahedron	8	6	12
g. regular dodecahedron	12	20	30
h. regular icosahedron	20	12	30

NUMBER OF SIDES + NUMBER OF VERTICES = NUMBER OF EDGES + 2

T14. Form a team of three or four others to discuss the advantages and disadvantages of the United States completely changing to the metric system. You might consider organizing a debate with another team to consider the following statement: *Resolved, the United States should convert to the metric system.*

T15. Suppose that we fit a band tightly around the earth at the equator.

Equator

We wish to raise the band so that it is uniformly supported 6 ft above the earth at the equator.

a. Guess how much extra length would have to be added to the band (not the supports) to do this.

b. Calculate the amount of extra material that would be needed. $38\ ft$

T16. Figure 6.40 illustrates a strange and interesting relationship.

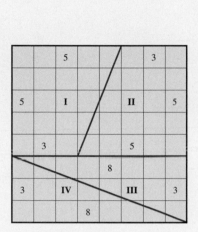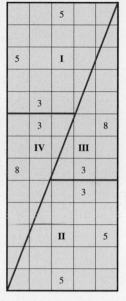

a. 8 cm x 8 cm = 64 cm² **b.** 13 cm x 5 cm = 65 cm²

Figure 6.40 Extra square centimeter?

The square in part **a** has an area of 64 cm² (8 cm by 8 cm). When *this same figure* is cut and rearranged as shown in part **b**, it appears to have an area of 65 cm². Where did this "extra" square centimeter come from? [*Hint:* Construct your own square 8 cm on a side, and then cut it into the four pieces as shown. Place the four pieces together as illustrated. Be sure to do your measuring and cutting very carefully. Satisfy yourself that this "extra" square centimeter has appeared. Can you explain this relationship?] *See IAS.*

APPLICATIONS
The Utility of Mathematics

"Knowing" mathematics is "doing" mathematics. A person gathers, discovers, or creates knowledge in the course of some activity having a purpose. This active process is different from mastering concepts and procedures. We do not assert that informational knowledge has no value, only that its value lies in the extent to which it is useful in the course of some purposeful activity. It is clear that the fundamental concepts and procedures from some branches of mathematics should be known by all students; established concepts and procedures can be relied on as fixed variables in a setting in which other variables may be unknown. But instruction should persistently emphasize "doing" rather than "knowing that."

Curriculum and Evaluation Standards for School Mathematics, p. 7. Copyright © 1989 National Council of Teachers of Mathematics.

How are you doing so far? Remember the things we talked about in the first section of this book? The first part of the book was concerned with problem solving and the mechanics of mathematics. This second part, The Utility of Mathematics, is concerned with using mathematics "In This World."

My goal is to get you thinking about how you can *use* mathematics in your own life. It is legitimate to ask, "Why should I be required to take mathematics?"

> *Mathematics, the science of the ideal, becomes the means of investigating, understanding and making known the world of the real. The complex is expressed in terms of the simple . . . .**

Many students have a particular fear and avoidance of applied problems, but I hope you do not turn away from this material without giving it an honest try. I've tried to keep each section as practical as possible without using theory, but many ideas from Part I come into play. However, without being able to *use* the mathematics you have learned, you will be like a cyclist without a cycle or a musician without an instrument. I have made special efforts in this part of the book to allay your fears and give you some insight into how mathematics can be *used* in practical ways.

*William F. White, *A Scrapbook of Elementary Mathematics* (Chicago, 1908), p. 215.

CHAPTER 7

Applications of Percent

Seventy-five percent of our planet is water—can you swim?

Author unknown

ANTICIPATE

- *Overview; check out contents, terms, essential ideas, and learning outcomes.*
- *We are now starting a new part of the book.*
- *How do you use percents outside of the classroom?*

7.1 Discount, Sale Price, and Sales Tax

IN THIS WORLD THE UTILITY OF MATH

Last-minute holiday sales often encourage purchase. As shown in the CNN photo, you sometimes see "40% OFF" sales with "Take an additional 15% OFF."

In Problem 54 we read the story of Bud and Sue, who are seeking to buy a living room set. In this problem we are asked to determine whether a sale is large enough for them to pay for their choice. In order to do this, we look at discount, sale price, and sales tax, which are calculated before finding the "out-the-door" price.

Discount

To encourage us to purchase items at one time rather than another, to introduce us to a particular store, to entice us into a store to purchase nonsale items, to sell old or damaged merchandise, or to meet or beat the competition, a retailer will often sell merchandise ON SALE at a *reduced price*. The amount an item is reduced from the regular, or original, price is called the **discount.**

Discount

> DISCOUNT = (ORIGINAL PRICE) × (PERCENT MARKDOWN)

The **percent markdown** is written as a decimal in order to calculate the discount.

EXAMPLE 1 **Amount of discount with a percent markdown given**

Find the discount, given the original price and the percent markdown.

a. Hardware, $175; 20% off   **b.** Shoes, $95; 15% discount

Solution

a. DISCOUNT = (ORIGINAL PRICE) × (PERCENT MARKDOWN)

$$= 175 \times 0.20$$
$$= 35$$

The discount is $35.

b. DISCOUNT = 95 × 0.15

$$= 14.25$$

The discount is $14.25.

Sometimes the markdown is given as a fraction.

EXAMPLE 2   **Amount of discount with a fractional markdown given**

Blouses with a regular price of \$59 are on sale marked $\frac{1}{3}$ OFF. What is the discount?

Solution   DISCOUNT $= 59 \times \frac{1}{3} \approx 19.67$ *Round money answers to the nearest cent.*
The discount is \$19.67.

Sale Price

As consumers, we are usually concerned with the sale price rather than the amount of discount. The **sale price** can be found by subtracting the discount from the original price. For example, the hardware in part **a** of Example 1 had an original price of \$175 and a discount of \$35, so the sale price is

$$\$175 - \$35 = \$140$$

However, there is an easier way to find the sale price, which involves something called the *complement.*

Complement

Two positive numbers less than 1 are called **complements** if their sum is 1.

EXAMPLE 3   **Finding complements**

Find the complements.

a. 0.7   **b.** 0.15   **c.** 40%   **d.** $\frac{1}{4}$

Solution   To find the complement, subtract the given number from 1.

a. $1 - 0.7 = 0.3$; the complement of 0.7 is 0.3.

b. $1 - 0.15 = 0.85$

c. Convert percents to decimals to carry out the arithmetic:

$$1 - 0.4 = 0.6$$

Alternatively, subtract the percent from 100%:

$$100\% - 40\% = 60\%$$

The complement is 60%.

d. $1 - \frac{1}{4} = \frac{3}{4}$

The **sale price formula** provides the sale price by multiplying the original price by the complement of the markdown.

Sale Price Formula

SALE PRICE $=$ (ORIGINAL PRICE) $\times$ (COMPLEMENT OF MARKDOWN)

EXAMPLE 4   **Finding the sale price by using the complement**

Find the sale price. (See Example 1.)   **a.** $175   **b.** $95

Solution

a. Complement of a 20% discount is 80%:

$$\text{SALE PRICE} = 175 \times 0.8 = 140$$

The sale price is $140.

b. Complement of 15% discount is 85%:

$$\text{SALE PRICE} = 95 \times 0.85 = 80.75$$

The sale price is $80.75.

    The same formula for finding the sale price of an item can be used for finding the original price or the percent markdown. Let

$$p = \text{ORIGINAL PRICE}$$
$$s = \text{SALE PRICE}$$
$$c = \text{COMPLEMENT OF THE PERCENT MARKDOWN}$$

Then, the sale price formula is $s = pc$. Also,

$$p = \frac{s}{c} \qquad \text{Divide both sides of the formula } s = pc \text{ by } c.$$

$$c = \frac{s}{p} \qquad \text{Divide both sides of the formula } s = pc \text{ by } p.$$

Furthermore, if we let

$$d = \text{AMOUNT OF DISCOUNT} \qquad \text{and} \qquad m = \text{PERCENT MARKDOWN}$$

we can summarize these **discount formulas.**

Discount Formulas

> DISCOUNT: $d = pm$
> SALE PRICE: $s = p - d$ or $s = pc$
> ORIGINAL PRICE: $p = \dfrac{s}{c}$
> COMPLEMENT: $c = \dfrac{s}{p}$

    When solving problems with discounts, markdowns, and sale prices, you can begin with the formula $s = pc$ and solve the equation for the unknown value, or you can pick the appropriate discount formula, as shown in the following examples.

EXAMPLE 5   **Finding the original price**

During a 20% OFF sale, an item is marked $52. What is the regular price?

Solution $s = pc$ This is the basic discount formula.

$$52 = p(0.80) \qquad \text{Given that } s = 52 \text{ and the percent markdown is 20\%, the}$$
$$\frac{52}{0.8} = p \qquad\qquad \text{complement of the percent markdown is 80\%.}$$
$$\qquad\qquad\qquad \text{Divide both sides by 0.8.}$$
$$65 = p$$

The regular price is $65.

EXAMPLE 6   **Finding the percent markdown**

If the sale price of an item is \$2,288 and the regular price is \$3,520, what is the percent markdown?

Solution $s = pc$ *This is the basic discount formula.*

$$2,288 = 3,520c$$ *Given that s = 2,288 and p = 3,520*

$$\frac{2,288}{3,520} = c$$ *Divide both sides by 3,520.*

$$0.65 = c$$

Since this is the complement, the percent markdown is $1 - 0.65 = 0.35$. The percent markdown is 35%.   ●

Sales Tax

Sales tax is levied by almost every state, as shown in Table 7.1.

TABLE 7.1	State Sales Tax Rate*										
Alabama	4%	Hawaii	4%	Massachusetts	5%	New Mexico	5%	South Dakota	4%
Alaska	0%	Idaho	6%	Michigan	6%	New York	4%	Tennessee	7%
Arizona	5.6%	Illinois	$6\frac{1}{4}$%	Minnesota	$6\frac{1}{2}$%	North Carolina	4.5%	Texas	6.25%
Arkansas	6%	Indiana	6%	Mississippi	7%	North Dakota	5%	Utah	$4\frac{3}{4}$%
California	6%	Iowa	5%	Missouri	4.225%	Ohio	5.5%	Vermont	6%
Colorado	2.9%	Kansas	5.3%	Montana	0%	Oklahoma	4.5%	Virginia	4%
Connecticut	6%	Kentucky	6%	Nebraska	5.5%	Oregon	0%	Washington	$6\frac{1}{2}$%
Delaware	0%	Louisiana	4%	Nevada	6.5%	Pennsylvania	6%	West Virginia	6%
Florida	6%	Maine	5%	New Hampshire	0%	Rhode Island	7%	Wisconsin	5%
Georgia	4%	Maryland	5%	New Jersey	6%	South Carolina	5%	Wyoming	4%

*Does not include local sales taxes. *Source:* Sales Tax Clearinghouse. © 1999–2006. All rights reserved. Reprinted by permission.

The procedure for finding the amount of sales tax is identical to the procedure for finding the discount; we call this the **sales tax formula.**

Sales Tax Formula | SALES TAX = (ORIGINAL PRICE) × (TAX RATE) |

EXAMPLE 7   **Finding the sales tax**

Find the Pennsylvania sales tax for building materials that cost \$84.65.

Solution   SALES TAX = (ORIGINAL PRICE) × (TAX RATE)

$$= 84.65(0.06)$$ *Find the sales tax rate in Table 7.1.*

$$= 5.079$$

The sales tax is \$5.08.   ●

To find the total price, add the sales tax to the original price; this is the way it is done on most sales slips you receive at retail stores. For Example 7 this means that the price (including tax) is

$$\$84.65 + \$5.08 = \$89.73$$

However, if you want to find the total price, you can shorten the process by making the following observation:

$$\text{TOTAL PRICE} = (\text{ORIGINAL PRICE}) + (\text{SALES TAX})$$
$$= (\text{ORIGINAL PRICE}) + (\text{ORIGINAL PRICE}) \times (\text{TAX RATE})$$
$$= (\text{ORIGINAL PRICE})(1 + \text{TAX RATE}) \quad \textit{Distributive property}$$

We summarize with the following **total price formula.**

Price (Including Tax)

> $\text{TOTAL PRICE} = (\text{ORIGINAL PRICE})(1 + \text{TAX RATE})$

EXAMPLE 8

Finding the price (including tax)

In New Jersey, a truck tire at Sears costs $159.98. What is the total cost of the tire (including tax)?

Solution In Table 7.1, we find that the New Jersey sales tax rate is 6%. Write this as a decimal and add 1: $1 + 0.06 = 1.06$. Multiply this by the original price to find the total amount:

$$\text{TOTAL AMOUNT} = (\text{ORIGINAL PRICE})(1 + \text{TAX RATE})$$
$$= 159.98(1.06)$$
$$= 169.5788$$

Round money answers to the nearest cent. The total amount (including tax) is $169.58.

PROBLEM SET 7.1

ESSENTIAL IDEAS LEVEL 1

State the formula for each idea in Problems 1–4.

1. How do you find the discount for an item for sale?
Discount = (original price)(percent markdown)
2. What is the complement of a number?
Two positive numbers are complements if their sum is 1.
3. How do you find a sale price if the original price and percent markdown are known?
sale price = (original price)(complement of markdown)
4. How do you find a price (including tax) if you know the original price and the tax rate?
total price = (original price)(1 + tax rate)

DRILL AND PRACTICE LEVEL 2

Find the discount of the items in Problems 5–8, given the original price and the percent markdown.

5. **a.** $450; 5% $22.50   **b.** $65; 20% $13.00
6. **a.** $55; 25% $13.75   **b.** $250; 35% $87.50
7. **a.** $12.49; 40% $5.00   **b.** $45.50; 50% $22.75
8. **a.** $9.95; 10% $1.00   **b.** $16.95; 15% $2.54

Find the complement of each of the numbers in Problems 9–12.

9. a. 0.1   *0.9*   **b.** 0.2   *0.8*   **c.** 0.3   *0.7*

   d. 0.4   *0.6*   **e.** 0.5   *0.5*

10. a. 90%   *10%*   **b.** 80%   *20%*   **c.** 70%   *30%*

   d. 60%   *40%*   **e.** 50%   *50%*

11. a. $\frac{1}{3}$ *$\frac{2}{3}$*   **b.** $\frac{2}{3}$ *$\frac{1}{3}$*   **c.** $\frac{3}{4}$ *$\frac{1}{4}$*

   d. $\frac{3}{5}$ *$\frac{2}{5}$*   **e.** $\frac{1}{6}$ *$\frac{5}{6}$*

12. a. 16%   *84%*   **b.** $\frac{1}{8}$ *$\frac{7}{8}$*   **c.** 83%   *17%*

   d. 39%   *61%*   **e.** 0.42   *0.58*

13. IN YOUR OWN WORDS You have now begun the second part of the book, The Utility of Mathematics, where we focus on some of the uses you can make of mathematics. In previous problems you have been asked to address your anxiety level. Hints about how to cope with that anxiety were given, with the goal of achieving success in a mathematics class. Write a paper discussing your math journey to date in this course, with particular attention given to your math anxiety levels as you traveled through the first half of this book. If you have been keeping a math journal, use your journal to help you in answering this question.

14. IN YOUR OWN WORDS List the five most important skills you've learned about developing effective math study tools. Are you willing to incorporate them into your study routine within the next month?

APPLICATIONS   **LEVEL 2**

Use estimation to select the best response in Problems 15–20. Do not calculate.

15. The discount for an item marked 20% OFF with a price of $1,256.95 is about   *C*

   A. $850   B. $25   C. $250   D. $85

16. An item costs $85.45 and the sales tax rate is 7%. The tax is about   *C*

   A. $2   B. $4   C. $6   D. $8

17. An item costs $85.45 and the sales tax rate is 7%. The total amount (including tax) is about   *B*

   A. $87   B. $90   C. $80   D. $104

18. The 5% sales tax on an automobile costing $15,850 is about   *A*

   A. $800   B. $8,000   C. $80   D. $8

19. In a 15% OFF sale, an item with an original price of $179.95 has a sale price of about   *A*

   A. $150   B. $300   C. $100   D. $30

20. The sale price of a skirt is $55, which is 30% OFF the regular price. The regular price is about   *D*

   A. $15   B. $40   C. $180   D. $80

Find the sales tax for the items in Problems 21–26. Refer to Table 7.1.

21. $230 golf clubs in Michigan   *$13.80*

22. $95 dress in Louisiana   *$3.80*

23. $85 coat in Washington state   *$5.53*

24. $35 book in Pennsylvania   *$2.10*

25. $18,350 automobile in Wisconsin   *$917.50*

26. $18,350 automobile in Texas   *$1,146.88*

Find the sales tax for the items in Problems 27–32 using the rate in your own state. If your state has no sales tax, use 7%.
Answers vary; answers given for the 7% rate.

27. Purse, $46.89   *$3.28*

28. Automobile, $21,955   *$1,536.85*

29. Shoes, $67.99   *$4.76*

30. Set of pots and pans, $109.99   *$7.70*

31. Stereo, $559.95   *$39.20*

32. Electronic game; $349.95   *$24.50*

Find the total amount, including tax, for the items whose price and tax rate are given in Problems 33–38

33. $12.50; 6%   *$13.25*

34. $1,925; 5%   *$2,021.25*

35. $4,312; $3\frac{3}{4}$%   *$4,473.70*

36. $91.60; 3%   *$94.35*

37. $25.36; $4\frac{1}{2}$%   *$26.50*

38. $365; $4\frac{1}{8}$%   *$380.06*

Find the sale price of the items in Problems 39–46, given the original price and the percent markdown. These items were all found in one issue of a local newspaper.

39.

Golf clubs, $230   *$218.50*

40.

Dress, $85   *$68.00*

41.

Men's Suit Coats
22% OFF

Coat, $95   *$74.10*

42.

STEREO COMPONENTS
36% OFF

$515.20

Stereo amplifier, $805

43.

JEANS 50% OFF

Jeans, $45   *$22.50*

44.

CALCULATORS

45% OFF

Calculator, $25   *$13.75*

45.

© Tatiana Markow/Sygma/CORBIS

HUGE SKI SALE $\frac{1}{2}$ **price**
Skis, $1,245   *$622.50*

46.

© Bob Daemmrich/PhotoEdit

REDUCED
THE PRICE MARKED IS
60% OFF

Sweater, $79   *$31.60*

47. A dealer selling an automobile for $12,830 offers a $500 rebate. What is the percent markdown (to the nearest tenth of a percent)?   *3.9%*

48. An automobile dealer offered a $1,000 rebate on a car selling for $32,100. What is the percent markdown (to the nearest tenth of a percent)?   *3.1%*

49. If an item is marked $420 during a 20% OFF sale, what is the regular price?   *$525.00*

50. If a swimming pool is marked down to $695 from $1,150, what is the percent markdown (to the nearest tenth of a percent)?   *39.6%*

51. If an item is marked $165 during a $\frac{1}{3}$ OFF sale, what is the regular price?   *$247.50*

52. You are employed at a department store that offers an employee discount of 10% that may be applied to purchases. You purchase some clothes originally marked at $155 that are on sale at 40% OFF. The sales tax is 7%. What is the total amount you must pay for this purchase?   *$89.56*

53. You are employed part-time at a department store that offers an employee discount of 10% that may be applied to purchases. You purchase a 13-in. color television set for $300 that is on sale at 25% OFF. The sales tax is 5.5%. What is the total amount you must pay for this purchase?   *$213.64*

54. Bud came home and told Sue that there was a big home improvement sale at Breuners. Perhaps now was the time they should buy that new living room set. Sue was not sure they had saved enough yet, so she wanted to know what the total cost would be. Bud showed Sue the newspaper ad: "ALL ITEMS REDUCED BY 40% (if you have the appropriate coupon)!!" The cost of the living room set was $2,550 the last time they looked, and Sue had told Bud that they had saved $1,600 for this purchase. "Great news," said Bud, "we can get it!" Is Bud correct?   *See IAS. Yes; the sale price is $1,530; however, if the sales tax is more than $70 (about 4.6% rate), then they will need a bit more.*

RIGHT OR WRONG?   LEVEL 3

Explain what is wrong, if anything, with the statements in Problems 55–60? Explain your reasoning.

55. If an item with an original price of $50 is on sale for $40, then the percent markdown is $10.   *F; the markdown is $10.*

56. If an item with an original price of $50 is on sale for 20% OFF, then the markdown is 20%.   *F; the percent markdown is 20%.*

57. In the formula $s = pc$, c represents the percent markdown.   *F; c is the complement of the percent markdown.*

58. To find the percent markdown, use the formula $s = pc$, and solve for c.   *F; after solving for c, find the percent markdown by subtracting from 1. That is, find 1 − c.*

59. The complement of 30% is 0.30.   *F; the complement is 70%.*

60. To find the price, including tax, add 1 to the tax rate and multiply this answer by the original price.   *T*

(7.2) Simple Interest

IN THIS WORLD THE UTILITY OF MATH

There is $7 billion unclaimed in treasuries across the United States. Do you have an unclaimed asset?

In this problem we see that Jerry just received an inheritance and would like to use it to help with his retirement.

"Can you help me with my retirement?" asked Jerry. "I have $25,000 and am 25 years old. How big of a part will that play in my retirement in 40 years? I will need a monthly income of $5,000/mo. What interest rate will I need to achieve this goal with no more than my $25,000 inheritance?"

 See Problem 53.

The answers to Jerry's questions are answered by working with the simple interest formula, which is introduced in this section.

Amount of Simple Interest

Certain arithmetic skills enable us to make intelligent decisions about how we spend the money we earn. One of the most fundamental mathematical concepts that consumers, as well as business people, must understand is *interest.* Simply stated, **interest** is money paid for the use of money. We receive interest when we let others use our money (when we deposit money in a savings account, for example), and we pay interest when we use the money of others (for example, when we borrow from a bank).

The amount of the deposit or loan is called the **principal** or **present value,** and the interest is stated as a percent of the principal, called the **interest rate.** The **time** is the length of time for which the money is borrowed or lent. The interest rate is usually an *annual interest rate,* and is stated in years unless otherwise indicated.

The following **simple interest formula** provides a basis for many financial formulas.

Simple Interest Formula

 This is a crucial formula to remember.

> INTEREST = PRESENT VALUE × RATE × TIME
> $I = Prt$ where I = AMOUNT OF INTEREST
> P = PRESENT VALUE (or PRINCIPAL)
> r = ANNUAL INTEREST RATE
> t = TIME (in years)

EXAMPLE 1

Finding the interest paid on a savings deposit

Suppose that you decide to save 20¢ per day, but only for a year. At the end of a year, you will have saved $73. If you then put your money into a savings account paying 8.5% interest, how much interest will the bank pay you after one year? After three years?

Solution   The present value (P) is 73, the rate (r) is 8.5% = 0.085, and the time (t, in years) is 1. Therefore,

$$I = Prt$$
$$= 73(0.085)(1)$$
$$= 6.205$$

Round money answers to the nearest cent: After one year, the interest is $6.21. For three years, $I = 73(0.085)(3) = 18.615$. After three years, the interest is $18.62. ●

Sometimes you know the amount of interest but need to find the principal, the rate, or the time. These can be easily found by solving the formula $I = Prt$ for the unknown.

These are all variations of the simple interest formula. Using algebra, you can derive them all by solving for the desired variable.

What You Want	What You Know	Formula
I, amount of interest	P, r, and t	$I = Prt$
P, present value (principal)	I, r, and t	$P = \dfrac{I}{rt}$
r, rate	I, P, and t	$r = \dfrac{I}{Pt}$
t, time	I, P, and r	$t = \dfrac{I}{Pr}$

EXAMPLE 2

Using the simple interest formula

Fill in the blanks.

	Interest (I)	Principal (P)	Rate (r)	Time (t)
a.	_____	$1,000	12%	2 yr
b.	$225	_____	9%	1 yr
c.	$112	$800	_____	2 yr
d.	$150	$500	6%	_____

Solution

a. $I = Prt$

$= 1,000(0.12)(2)$ Given $P = 1,000$, $r = 0.12$, and $t = 2$.

$= 240$

The amount of interest is $240.

b. $I = Prt$

$225 = P(0.09)(1)$ Given $I = 225$, $r = 0.09$, and $t = 1$.

$\dfrac{225}{0.09} = P$ Divide both sides by 0.09.

$2,500 = P$

The principal is $2,500.

c. $I = Prt$

$112 = 800(r)(2)$ Given $I = 112$, $P = 800$, and $t = 2$.

$$112 = 1{,}600r$$

$$\frac{112}{1{,}600} = r$$

$$0.07 = r$$

The rate is 7%.

d. $I = Prt$

$150 = 500(0.06)t$ *Given I = 150, P = 500, and r = 0.06.*

$150 = 30t$

$5 = t$

The time is 5 years.

EXAMPLE 3   **Problem solving with the simple interest formula**

How much money must be invested at a 7% annual interest rate in order to receive $100/month income?

Solution   We use the simple interest formula where $I = 100$, $r = 0.07$, and $t = \frac{1}{12}$ (one month is 1/12 of a year).

$$I = Prt \qquad \text{Simple interest formula}$$

$$100 = P(0.07)\left(\frac{1}{12}\right) \qquad \text{Substitute known values.}$$

$$1{,}200 = 0.07P \qquad \text{Multiply both sides by 12.}$$

$$17{,}142.86 = P \qquad \begin{array}{l}\text{Divide both sides by 0.07 (by calculator).}\\ \text{(Round to the nearest cent.)}\end{array}$$

The necessary amount of the investment is $17,142.86.

Future Value

There is a difference between asking for the amount of interest, as illustrated in Example 2, and asking for the **future value.** The future amount is the amount you will have after the interest is added to the principal, or present value. Let $A =$ FUTURE VALUE.

Once again, all these are algebraic variations of the same formula shown in color.

$$A = P + I \qquad \text{or} \qquad P = A - I \qquad \text{or} \qquad I = A - P$$

EXAMPLE 4   **Amount of interest if the monthly payments are known**

Suppose you see a car with a price of $12,436 that is advertised at $290 per month for 5 years. What is the amount of interest paid?

Solution   The present value is $12,436. The future value is the total amount of all the payments:

Monthly payment		Number of years	
$290	× 12	× 5	= $17,400
	Number of payments per year		

Therefore, the amount of interest is

$$I = A - P$$
$$= 17,400 - 12,436$$
$$= 4,964$$

The amount of interest is $4,964. ●

EXAMPLE 5   **Problem solving with simple interest formula**

If a business borrows $18,000 and repays $26,100 in 3 years, what is the simple interest rate?

Solution   The present value (P) is $18,000, the future value (A) is $26,100, and the time ($t$) is 3 years. We want to find r, so we use the formula

$$I = Prt$$

$$8,100 = 18,000(r)(3) \qquad P = 18,000; t = 3; \text{ we can find } I \text{ by using}$$
$$8,100 = 54,000r \qquad\qquad I = A - P = 26,100 - 18,000 = 8,100.$$

$$\frac{8,100}{54,000} = r \qquad\qquad \text{Divide both sides by 54,000.}$$

$$0.15 = r \qquad\qquad \text{Use a calculator.}$$

The rate is 15%. ●

EXAMPLE 6   **Problem solving with the simple interest formula**

Suppose you wish to save $3,720. If you have $3,000 and invest it at 8% simple interest, how long will it take you to obtain $3,720?

Solution $I = Prt$

$$720 = 3,000(0.08)t \qquad A = 3,720; P = 3,000; \text{ we can find } I \text{ by using}$$
$$720 = 240t \qquad\qquad I = A - P = 3,720 - 3,000 = 720.$$

$$\frac{720}{240} = t \qquad\qquad \text{Divide both sides by 240.}$$

$$3 = t$$

It takes you 3 years. ●

Interest for Part of a Year

The numbers in Example 6 were constructed to give a "nice" answer, but the length of time for an investment is not always a whole number of years. There are two ways to convert a number of days to a portion of a year:

Exact interest: 365 days per year

Ordinary interest: 360 days per year

Most applications and businesses use ordinary interest. So in this book, unless it is otherwise stated, assume ordinary interest; that is, use 360 for the number of days in a year.

$$t = \frac{\text{ACTUAL NUMBER OF DAYS}}{360}$$

EXAMPLE 7   **Problem solving with part of a year**

Reconsider Example 6, but this time suppose that you want to save $3,650:

$$I = Prt$$

$$650 = 3,000(0.08)t \qquad I = 3,650 - 3,000 = 650; P = 3,000; r = 0.08$$

$$650 = 240t$$

$$\frac{650}{240} = t \qquad\qquad \textit{Calculator display:} \quad 2.7083333333$$

This is 2 years plus some part of a year. To convert the fractional part to days, do not clear your calculator, but subtract 2 (the number of years); then multiply the fractional part by 360:

$$\boxed{650} \; \boxed{\div} \; \boxed{240} \; \boxed{-} \; \boxed{2} \; \boxed{=} \; \boxed{\times} \; \boxed{360} \; \boxed{=} \qquad \textit{Display:} \quad 255$$

The time is 2 years 255 days. ●

EXAMPLE 8   **Determining the sum necessary for retirement**

Suppose that you have decided that you will need $4,000 per month on which to live in retirement. If the rate of interest is 8%, how much must you have in the bank when you retire so that you can live on interest only?

Solution   We are given $I = 4,000$, $r = 0.08$, and $t = \frac{1}{12}$ (one month $= \frac{1}{12}$ year):

$$I = Prt$$

$$4,000 = P(0.08)\left(\frac{1}{12}\right) \qquad \text{Substitute.}$$

$$48,000 = (0.08)\,P \qquad \text{Multiply both sides by 12.}$$

$$600,000 = P \qquad \text{Divide both sides by 0.08.}$$

You must have $600,000 on deposit at 8% to earn $4,000 per month. ●

EXAMPLE 9   **Simple interest formula for part of a year**

Suppose that you borrow $1,200 on March 25 at 21% simple interest. How much interest accrues to September 15 (174 days later)? What is the total amount that must be repaid?

Solution   We are given $P = 1,200$, $r = 0.21$, and $t = \frac{174}{360}$ ← Actual number of days
← Assume ordinary interest.

$$I = Prt$$

$$= 1,200(0.21)\left(\frac{174}{360}\right)$$

$$= 121.8 \quad \text{By calculator}$$

The amount of interest is $121.80. To find the amount that must be repaid, find the future value:

$$A = P + I = 1,200 + 121.80 = 1,321.80$$

The amount that must be repaid is $1,321.80. ●

It is worthwhile to derive a formula for future value because sometimes we will not calculate the interest separately as we did in Example 9.

$$\text{FUTURE VALUE} = \text{PRESENT VALUE} + \text{INTEREST}$$

$$A = P + I$$
$$= P + Prt \qquad \text{Substitute } I = Prt.$$
$$= P(1 + rt) \qquad \text{Distributive property}$$

CAUTION This is a formula that will be used frequently when working with finances.

You might notice that this is the same procedure we used to find the sales tax and total price in the previous section. We call this the **future value formula.**

Future Value Formula (Simple Interest)

$$A = P(1 + rt)$$

EXAMPLE 10   **Find the future value of a savings account**

If $10,000 is deposited in an account earning $5\frac{3}{4}\%$ simple interest, what is the future value in 5 years?

Solution   We identify $P = 10,000$, $r = 0.0575$, and $t = 5$.

$$A = P(1 + rt)$$
$$= 10,000(1 + 0.0575 \times 5)$$
$$= 10,000(1 + 0.2875) \qquad \text{Don't forget order of operations: multiplication first.}$$
$$= 10,000(1.2875)$$
$$= 12,875$$

The future value in 5 years is $12,875.

PROBLEM SET 7.2

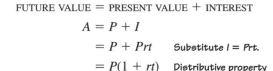

ESSENTIAL IDEAS   **LEVEL 1**

1. What is interest?   *Money paid for the use of another's money.*

2. What is the simple interest formula? Tell what each variable represents.   *$I = Prt$; I is the amount of interest; P, the present value; r, the interest rate; and t, the time (in years).*

3. How do you change a given number of days to years? *ordinary interest, divide by 360; exact interest, divide by 365*

4. What is the future value formula for simple interest? *$A = P(1 + rt)$*

DRILL AND PRACTICE   **LEVEL 2**

Use estimation to select the best response in Problems 5–14. Do not calculate.

5. If you deposit $100 in a bank account for a year, the amount of interest is likely to be *B; interest rate is not stated, but you should still recognize a reasonable answer.*

   A. $1   B. $5

   C. $105   D. impossible to estimate

6. If you deposit $100 in a bank account for a year, then the future value is likely to be *C; interest rate is not stated, but you should still recognize a reasonable answer.*

   A. $1   B. $5

   C. $105   D. impossible to estimate

7. If you purchase a new automobile and finance it for 4 years, the amount of interest you might pay is *C; price is not stated, but you should still recognize a reasonable answer.*

   A. $400   B. $100

   C. $4,000   D. impossible to estimate

8. What is a reasonable monthly income when you retire?   *B*

   A. $300   B. $10,000

   C. $500,000   D. impossible to estimate

9. To be able to retire and live on the interest only, what is a reasonable amount to have in the bank?   *C*

   A. $300   B. $10,000

   C. $500,000   D. impossible to estimate

10. If $I = Prt$ and $P = \$49,236.45$, $r = 10.5\%$, and $t = 2$ years, estimate I. **A**

   A. $10,000   B. $600

   C. $50,000   D. $120,000

11. If $I = Prt$ and $P = \$398.90$, $r = 9.85\%$, and $t = 1$ year, estimate I. **B**

   A. $400   B. $40   C. $40,000   D. $4,000

12. If $t = 3.52895$, then the time is about 3 years and how many days? **D**

   A. 30   B. 300   C. 52   D. 150

13. If a loan is held for 450 days, then t is about **C**

   A. 450   B. 3   C. $1\frac{1}{4}$ D. 5

14. If a loan is held for 180 days, then t is about **B**

   A. 180   B. $\frac{1}{2}$ C. $\frac{1}{4}$ D. 3

Fill in the blanks in Problems 15–40.

	Interest	Principal	Rate	Time	Future Value
15.	$80	$1,000	8%	1 yr	$1,080
16.	$900	$5,000	9%	2 yr	$5,900
17.	$288	$800	12%	3 yr	$1,088
18.	$9,000	$10,000	15%	6 yr	$19,000
19.	$42.50	$500	$8\frac{1}{2}\%$	1 yr	$542.50
20.	$112.50	$300	$12\frac{1}{2}\%$	3 yr	$412.50
21.	$200	$400	$12\frac{1}{2}\%$	4 yr	$600
22.	$287.50	$1,000	$5\frac{3}{4}\%$	5 yr	$1,287.50
23.	$360	$3,000	12%	1 yr	$3,360
24.	$600	$4,000	15%	1 yr	$4,600
25.	$350	$2,500	7%	2 yr	$2,850
26.	$66	$100	11%	6 yr	$166
27.	$588	$700	12%	7 yr	$1,288
28.	$432	$600	9%	8 yr	$1,032
29.	$180	$200	15%	6 yr	$380
30.	$1,260	$3,000	14%	3 yr	$4,260
31.	$960	$1,500	16%	4 yr	$2,460
32.	$432	$900	6%	8 yr	$1,332
33.	$270	$300	10%	9 yr	$570
34.	$624	$1,200	13%	4 yr	$1,824
35.	$1,800	$4,000	9%	5 yr	$5,800
36.	$5,850	$6,500	18%	5 yr	$12,350
37.	$3,240	$9,000	12%	3 yr	$12,240
38.	$320	$400	8%	10 yr	$720
39.	$25.63	$512.50	10%	180 days	$538.13
40.	$13.40	$236.50	8%	255 days	$249.90

41. Suppose you see a car advertised with a price of $32,450 and payments of $627.35 per month for 5 years. What is the amount of interest paid? **$5,191**

42. Suppose you purchase a refrigerator for $1,235 and make payments of $58.14 per month for 2 years. What is the total amount of interest paid? **$160.36**

43. If a business borrows $12,500 and repays $23,125 in 5 years, what is the simple interest rate? **17%**

44. If a business borrows $18,000 and repays $26,100 in 4 years, what is the simple interest rate? **11.25%**

45. Theron wants to save $3,900. If he has $3,000 and invests it at 5% simple interest, how long will it take him to obtain $3,900? **6 years**

46. What is the future value of $4,200 invested at 4% simple interest for 215 days? **$4,300.33**

47. What is the future value of $890 invested at 6% simple interest for 83 days? **$902.31**

48. Søren wants to save $1,000. If he has $750 and invests it at 12% simple interest, how long (to the nearest day) will it take him to obtain $1,000? **1,000 days or 2 yr. 280 days**

49. If Cole wants to retire with $1,000 per month, how much principal is necessary to generate this amount of monthly interest income if the interest rate is 6%? **$200,000**

50. If Melissa wants to retire with $50,000 per month,* how much principal is necessary to generate this amount of monthly income if the interest rate is 12%? **$5,000,000**

51. If Cole from Problem 49 has 25 years before retirement and has $25,000 to invest today, what simple interest rate does he need to achieve the amount of principal needed in Problem 49? **28%**

52. If Melissa from Problem 50 has 40 years before retirement and has $100,000 to invest today, what simple interest rate does she need to achieve the amount of principal needed in Problem 50? **$122\frac{1}{2}\%$**

53. Jerry has just received an inheritance of $25,000, and he would like to use it to help him with his retirement. Since Jerry is 25 years old, he figures that the $25,000 can be invested for 40 years before he will need to use it for retirement. If he would like to have a monthly income of $5,000, how much money will he need to have in his retirement account to provide this income from interest only? Assume that Jerry is able to invest in real estate and can earn a 15% return on his investment. **$400,000**

54. Jerry from Problem 53 wants to know what interest rate would be necessary for the $25,000 to grow to provide an

*You might say this is an exorbitant monthly income, but if you assume 10% average inflation for 40 years, a monthly income of $220 today will be equivalent to about $10,000 per month in 40 years. If we assume 2% inflation, that amount is about $500. We will discuss inflation in Section 7.5.

amount so that he can have a monthly income of $5,000 earned from the interest only. **37.5%**

RIGHT OR WRONG? **LEVEL 3**

Explain what is wrong, if anything, with the statements in Problems 55–60. Explain your reasoning.

55. Since $I = Prt$, we know that $P = Irt$. **F; $P = \frac{I}{rt}$**

56. To find the rate, use the formula $r = Prt$. **F; $r = \frac{I}{Pt}$**

57. If the time is 315 days, then in this book use $t = \frac{315}{365}$. **F; use $t = \frac{315}{360}$**

58. If the time is 5 months, then in this book use $t = \frac{5}{360}$. **F; use $t = \frac{5}{12}$**

59. If a desk is advertised at a monthly payment of $45.50 for 3 years, then the future value is $45.50 × 3 = $136.50. **F; the future value is $45.50 × 36 = $1,638.**

60. The future value formula for simple interest is $A = P(1 + rt)$. **T**

7.3 Buying on Credit

IN THIS WORLD THE UTILITY OF MATH

"Good afternoon, can I help you?" said the operator.

"Yes, I'm looking for a payday loan," answered Wayne. "Can you tell me if I can get a payday loan by phone? Our refrigerator broke and the bank would charge me 21% (APR) and Sears will give us an installment loan at 15%. What do you charge for a loan?"

In this section, Wayne will learn about installment loans, and in particular about APR (offered by the bank) and add-on interest (offered by Sears). We will also look at payday loans, which are short-term loans of small amounts until payday.

 See Problem 51.

Consumer Loans

Two types of consumer credit allow you to make installment purchases. The first, called **closed-end,** is the traditional installment loan. An **installment loan** is an agreement to pay off a loan or a purchase by making equal payments at regular intervals for some specific period of time. In this book, it is assumed that all installment payments are made monthly. The loan is said to be **amortized** if it is completely paid off by these payments; and the payments are called **installments.** If the loan is not amortized, there is a larger final payment, called a **balloon payment.** With an **interest-only loan,** there is a monthly payment equal to the interest, with a final payment equal to the amount received when the loan was obtained.

The second type of consumer credit is called **open-end, revolving credit,** or more commonly, a **credit card** loan. MasterCard, VISA, and Discover cards, as well as those from department stores and oil companies, are examples of open-ended loans. This type of loan allows for purchases or cash advances up to a specified maximum **line of credit** and has a flexible repayment schedule. We will discuss credit cards in Section 7.4.

Add-on Interest

The most common method for calculating interest on installment loans is by a method known as **add-on interest.** It is nothing more than an application of the simple interest formula. It is called *add-on interest* because the interest is *added* to the amount borrowed so that both the interest and the amount borrowed are paid for over the length of the loan. You should be familiar with the following variables:

$$P = \text{AMOUNT TO BE FINANCED (present value)}$$
$$r = \text{ADD-ON INTEREST RATE}$$
$$t = \text{TIME (in years) TO REPAY THE LOAN}$$
$$I = \text{AMOUNT OF INTEREST}$$
$$A = \text{AMOUNT TO BE REPAID (future value)}$$
$$m = \text{AMOUNT OF THE MONTHLY PAYMENT}$$
$$N = \text{NUMBER OF PAYMENTS}$$

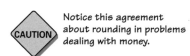

STOP *Spend some time reviewing these variables and the installment loan formulas.*

We use these variables in the following summary of **installment loan formulas.**

Installment Loans

The formulas for installment loans are:

AMOUNT OF INTEREST:	$I = Prt$
AMOUNT TO BE REPAID:	$A = P + I$ or $A = P(1 + rt)$
NUMBER OF PAYMENTS:	$N = 12t$
AMOUNT OF EACH PAYMENT:	$m = \frac{A}{N}$

CAUTION *Notice this agreement about rounding in problems dealing with money.*

When figuring monthly payments in everyday life, most businesses and banks round up for any fraction of a cent. However, for consistency in this book, we will continue to use the rounding procedures developed in Chapter 1. This means we will round money answers to the nearest cent.

EXAMPLE 1

Monthly payments for a closed-end loan

You want to purchase a computer that has a price of $1,399, and you decide to pay for it with installments over 3 years. The store tells you that the interest rate is 15%. What is the amount of each monthly payment?

Solution You ask the clerk how the interest is calculated, and you are told that the store uses add-on interest. Thus,

$$P = 1,399, \quad r = 0.15, \quad t = 3, \quad N = 36$$

Also,

$$I = Prt = 1,399(0.15)(3) = 629.55$$
$$A = P + I = 1,399 + 629.55 = 2,028.55$$

or in one step:

$$A = P(1 + rt) = 1,399[1 + (0.15)3] = 2,028.55$$

For the monthly payment, divide A by the number of payments:

$$m = \frac{2,028.55}{36} \approx 56.35$$

These calculations are best done with a calculator. You can carry out the entire calculation in one step:

$$\boxed{1399} \times \boxed{(} \boxed{1} \boxed{+} \boxed{.15} \times \boxed{3} \boxed{)} \boxed{=} \boxed{\div} \boxed{36} \boxed{=} \quad \textit{Display:} \quad 56.3486111$$

The amount of each monthly payment is $56.35.

Among the most common applications of installments loans are the purchase of a car and the purchase of a home. Interest for purchasing a car is add-on interest, but interest for purchasing a home is not. We will, therefore, delay our discussion of home loans until after we have discussed compound interest. The next example shows a calculation for a car loan.

EXAMPLE 2

Problem solving when purchasing a car

Suppose that you have decided to purchase a 2007 Honda Civic Hybrid and want to determine the monthly payment if you pay for the car in 4 years. Assume that this car will get 70 miles per gallon of gasoline, and that you will drive it for 100,000 miles. How much will it cost to drive this car for 100,000 miles if you assume that the average price of gasoline is $2.10/gal?

Courtesy Honda Motor Co.

Solution   Not enough information is given, so you need to ask some questions of the car dealer:

Sticker price of the car (as posted on the window):	$20,650
Dealer's preparation charges (as posted on the window):	$650
Tax rate (determined by the state; see Table 7.1):	7%
Add-on interest rate:	8%

You must make an offer. If you are serious about getting the best price, find out the **dealer's cost**—the price the dealer paid for the car you want to buy. In this book, we will tell you the dealer's cost, but in the real world you will need to do some research to find it (consult a reporting service, an automobile association, a credit union, or the April issue of *Consumer Reports*). Assume that the dealer's cost for this car is $18,867. You decide to offer the dealer 5% *over* this cost. We will call this a **5% offer:**

$$\$18,867(1 + 0.05) = \$19,810.35$$

You will notice that we ignored the sticker price and the dealer's preparation charges. Our offer is based only on the *dealer's cost*. Most car dealers will accept an offer that is between 3% and 10% over what they actually paid for the car. For this example, we will assume that the dealer accepted a price of $19,800. We also assume that we

have a trade-in with a value of $7,500. Here is a list of calculations shown on the sales contract:

Sales price of Honda:	$19,800.00
Destination charges:	200.00
Subtotal:	20,000.00
Tax (7%) rate:	1,400.00
Less trade-in:	7,500.00
Amount to be financed:	13,900.00

We now calculate several key amounts:

$$\text{Interest: } I = Prt = 13,900(0.08)(4) = 4,448$$

$$\text{Amount to be repaid: } A = P + I = 13,900 + 4,448 = 18,348$$

$$\text{Monthly payment: } m = \frac{18,348}{48} = 382.25$$

The monthly payment for the car is $382.25.

The cost to drive this car for 100,000 miles is found by dividing the number of miles by the miles per gallon to give the number of gallons:

$$\frac{100,000}{70} = 1,428.57$$

The cost per gallon is $2.10, so the total cost of gasoline is

$$1,428.57 \times \$2.10 = \$3,000.00$$

EXAMPLE 3

Comparing the driving cost of two cars

Refer to Example 2. Compare the cost of gasoline for driving the 2007 Honda Civic Hybrid a distance of 100,000 miles with the cost of driving a 2007 Honda Civic with a sticker price of $15,010 the same distance. Assume this car will get 25 miles per gallon, and that the cost of gasoline is $2.10/gal.

Solution Divide the miles by the number of miles per gallon:

$$\frac{100,000}{25} = 4,000$$

The total cost of gasoline is

$$4,000 \times \$2.10 = \$8,400$$

The savings by driving the Hybrid is

$$\$8,400.00 - \$3,000.00 = \$5,400.00$$

If you compare the price of this Honda Civic with that of the Hybrid, you will find the manufacturer's suggested price for the hybrid is $5,640 more expensive, so we might ask, "Do you think it is an accident that the price of the hybrid is set about $5,400 above the price of the gasoline-driven car?" If you rework this example using a more realistic $3.10/gal, you will find a savings of about $2,500 if you drive the hybrid 100,000 miles.

Annual Percentage Rate (APR)

An important aspect of add-on interest is that you are paying a rate that exceeds the quoted add-on interest rate. The reason for this is that you are not keeping the entire amount borrowed for the entire time. For the car payments calculated in Example 2, the principal used was $13,900, but you do not *owe* this entire amount for 4 years. After the first payment, you owe *less* than this amount. In fact, after you make 47 payments, you will owe only $382.25; but the calculation shown in Example 2 assumes that the principal remains constant for 4 years.

To see this a little more clearly, consider a simpler example. Suppose you borrow $2,000 for 2 years with 10% add-on interest. The amount of interest is

$$\$2,000 \times 0.10 \times 2 = \$400$$

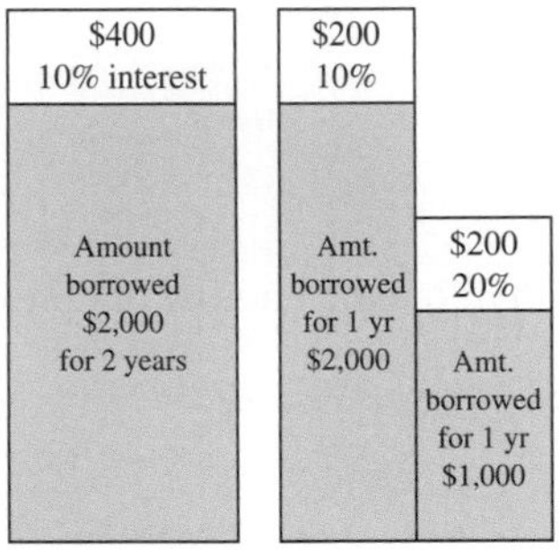

Now, if you pay back $2,000 + $400 at the end of two years, the annual interest rate is 10%. However, if you make a partial payment of $1,200 at the end of the first year and $1,200 at the end of the second year, your total paid back is still the same ($2,400), but you have now paid a higher annual interest rate. Why? Take a look at Figure 7.1.

On the left we see that the interest on $2,000 is $400. But if you make a partial payment (figure on the right), we see that $200 for the first year is the correct interest, but the remaining $200 interest piled on the remaining balance of $1,000 is 20% interest (not the stated 10%). Note that since you did not owe $2,000 for 2 years, the interest rate, r, necessary to give $400 interest can be calculated using $I = Prt$:

$$(2,000)r(1) + (1,000)r(1) = 400$$

$$3,000r = 400$$

$$r = \frac{400}{3,000} = 0.1\overline{3} \text{ or } 13.3\%$$

This number, 13.3%, is called the *annual percentage rate*. This number is too difficult to calculate, as we have just done here, if the number of months is very large. We will, instead, use the formula given in the following box.

Figure 7.1 Interest on a $2,000 two-year loan

Annual Percentage Rate

Use the formula to compare interest rates.

> The **annual percentage rate,** or **APR,** is the rate paid on a loan when that rate is based on the actual amount owed for the length of time that it is owed. It can be found for an add-on interest rate, r, with N payments made at equal time intervals by using the formula
>
> $$\text{APR} = \frac{2Nr}{N + 1}$$

In 1969, a Truth-in-Lending Act was passed by Congress; it requires all lenders to state the true annual interest rate, which is called the *annual percentage rate* (APR) and is based on the actual amount owed. Regardless of the rate quoted, when you ask a salesperson what the APR is, the law requires that you be told this rate. This regulation enables you to compare interest rates *before* you sign a contract, which must state the APR even if you haven't asked for it.

EXAMPLE 4   **Finding an APR**

In Example 1, we considered the purchase of a computer with a price of $1,399, paid for in monthly installments over 3 years at an add-on rate of 15%. What is the APR (rounded to the nearest tenth of a percent)?

Solution   Knowing the amount of the purchase is not necessary when finding the APR. We only need to know N and r. Since N is the number of payments, we have $N = 12(3) = 36$, and r is given as 0.15:

$$\text{APR} = \frac{2(36)(0.15)}{36 + 1} \approx 0.292 \quad \textit{Use a calculator.}$$

The APR is 29.2%.

●

EXAMPLE 5   **Using a calculator to find the APR for a car purchase**

Consider a 2007 Blazer with a price of $28,505 that is advertised at a monthly payment of $631.00 for 60 months. What is the APR (to the nearest tenth of a percent)?

Solution   We are given $P = 28{,}505$, $m = 631.00$, $t = 5$ (60 months is 5 years), and $N = 60$. The APR formula requires that we know the rate r. Think about the problem before using a calculator. We will use the formula $I = Prt$ to find r by first substituting the values for I, P, and t. We know P and t, but need to calculate I. The future value is the total amount to be repaid ($A = P + I$) and we know $A = 631.00(60) = 37{,}860$, so $I = A - P = 37{,}860 - 28{,}505 = 9{,}355$. Now we are ready to use the formula $I = Prt$:

$$I = Prt$$
$$9{,}355 = 28{,}505(r)(5) \quad \textit{Substitute known values.}$$
$$1{,}871 = 28{,}505r \quad \textit{Divide both sides by 5.}$$
$$0.0656376 \approx r \quad \textit{Divide both sides by 28,505.}$$

Finally, for the APR formula,

$$\text{APR} = \frac{2Nr}{N + 1} = \frac{2(60)(0.065637607437)}{61} \quad \textit{Don't round until the last step.}$$

This is a calculation for your calculator:

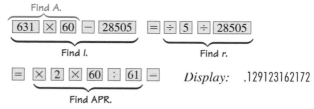

Display: .129123162172

The APR is 12.9%.

●

EXAMPLE 6   **Finding the APR for a payday loan**

A payday loan company provides short-term loans from $250 to $2,000. The cost of the loan is $1.00 per day per $100 borrowed until the loan is repaid. What is the APR for this payday loan?

Solution Begin with the formula $I = Prt$ where $t = 1$ day $= \frac{1}{365}$ year, $I = \$1.00$, and $P = \$100$.

$$I = Prt$$

$$1 = 100(r)\left(\frac{1}{365}\right) \qquad \text{Substitute known values.}$$

$$365 = 100r \qquad \text{Multiply both sides by 365.}$$

$$365\% = r \qquad \text{Divide both sides by 100.}$$

The APR formula does not apply because there are no periodic payments, just interest until the loan is repaid. For the Problem of the Day, Wayne would not want to consider a payday loan since either the Sear's rate of 21% or the installment rate of 15% would be better. See Problem 51.

CAUTION Be careful of payday loans!

PROBLEM SET 7.3

ESSENTIAL IDEAS   LEVEL 1

1. **IN YOUR OWN WORDS** What is add-on interest, and how is it calculated? How do you find the monthly payment for add-on interest?

2. What is the APR formula? $APR = \frac{2Nr}{N+1}$

DRILL AND PRACTICE   LEVEL 2

Use estimation to select the best response in Problems 3–10. Do not calculate.

3. If you purchase a $2,400 item and pay for it with monthly installments for 2 years, the monthly payment is   B

   A. $100 per month

   B. more than $100 per month

   C. less than $100 per month

4. If you purchase a $595.95 item and pay for it with monthly installments for 1 year, the monthly payment is

   A. about $50   B. more than $50   C. less than $50

   B (Don't forget interest.)

5. If you purchase an item for $1,295 at an interest rate of 9.8%, and you finance it for 1 year, then the amount of add-on interest is about   C

   A. $13.00   B. $500   C. $130

6. If you purchase an item for $1,295 at an interest rate of 9.8%, and you finance it for 4 years, then the amount of add-on interest is about   B

   A. $13.00   B. $500   C. $130

7. If you purchase a new car for $10,000 and finance it for 4 years, the amount of interest you would expect to pay is about   A

   A. $4,000   B. $400

   C. $24,000   D. Can't be estimated

8. A reasonable APR to pay for a 3-year installment loan is   B

   A. 1%   B. 12%   C. 32%

9. A reasonable APR to pay for a 3-year automobile loan is   A

   A. 6%   B. 40%   C. $2,000

10. If you wish to purchase a car with a sticker price of $10,000, a reasonable offer to make to the dealer is: B

    A. $10,000   B. $9,000   C. $11,000

APPLICATIONS   LEVEL 2

Round your answers in Problems 11–16 to the nearest dollar.

11. Make a 5% offer on a Honda Civic that has a sticker price of $16,480 and a dealer cost of $14,997. $15,747

12. Make a 5% offer on a Volkswagen New Beetle that has a sticker price of $22,120 and a dealer cost of $20,857. $21,900

13. Make a 5% offer on a Volvo S60 that has a sticker price of $35,850 and a dealer cost of $32,982. $34,631

14. Make a 7% offer on a BMW 530i that has a sticker price of $53,300 and a dealer cost of $46,904. $50,187

15. Make a 6% offer on a Chevrolet TrailBlazer that has a sticker price of $30,512 and a dealer cost of $27,460. $29,108

16. Make a 5% offer on a Porsche Boxster that has a sticker price of $54,700 and a dealer cost of $51,080. *$53,634*

Find the amount of interest and the monthly payment for each of the loans described in Problems 17–26.

17. Purchase a living room set for $3,600 at 12% add-on interest for 3 years. *$1,296 interest; $136 per month*

18. Purchase a stereo for $2,500 at 13% add-on interest for 2 years. *$650 interest; $131.25 per month*

19. A $1,500 loan at 11% add-on rate for 2 years
$330 interest; $76.25 per month
20. A $2,400 loan at 15% add-on rate for 2 years
$720 interest; $130 per month
21. A $4,500 loan at 18% add-on rate for 5 years
$4,050 interest; $142.50 per month
22. A $1,000 loan at 12% add-on rate for 2 years
$240 interest; $51.67 per month
23. Purchase an oven for $650 at 11% add-on interest for 2 years. *$143 interest; $33.04 per month*

24. Purchase a refrigerator for $2,100 at 14% add-on interest for 3 years. *$882 interest; $82.83 per month*

25. Purchase a car for $5,250 at 9.5% add-on rate for 2 years.
$997.50 interest; $260.31
26. Purchase a car for $42,700 at 2.9% add-on rate for 5 years.
$6,191.50 interest; $814.86 per month

Find the APR (rounded to the nearest percent) for each loan listed in Problems 27–36. These are for the purchases described in Problems 17–26.

27. Purchase a living room set for $3,600 at 12% add-on interest for 3 years. *23%*

28. Purchase a stereo for $2,500 at 13% add-on interest for 2 years. *25%*

29. A $1,500 loan at 11% add-on rate for 2 years *21%*

30. A $2,400 loan at 15% add-on rate for 2 years *29%*

31. A $4,500 loan at 18% add-on rate for 5 years *35%*

32. A $1,000 loan at 12% add-on rate for 2 years *23%*

33. Purchase an oven for $650 at 11% add-on interest for 2 years. *21%*

34. Purchase a refrigerator for $2,100 at 14% add-on interest for 3 years. *27%*

35. Purchase a car for $5,250 at 9.5% add-on rate for 2 years. *18%*

36. Purchase a car for $42,700 at 2.9% add-on rate for 5 years. *6%*

37. A newspaper advertisement offers a $9,000 car for nothing down and 36 easy monthly payments of $317.50. What is the total amount paid for both car and financing? *$11,430*

38. A newspaper advertisement offers a $4,000 used car for nothing down and 36 easy monthly payments of $141.62. What is the total amount paid for both car and financing? *$5,098.32*

39. A car dealer will sell you the $16,450 car of your dreams for $3,290 down and payments of $339.97 per month for 48 months. What is the total amount paid for both car and financing? *$19,608.56*

40. A car dealer will sell you a used car for $6,798 with $798 down and payments of $168.51 per month for 48 months. What is the total amount paid for both car and financing? *$8,886.48*

In Problems 41–50, round your answer to the nearest tenth of a percent.

41. A newspaper advertisement offers a $9,000 car for nothing down and 36 easy monthly payments of $317.50. What is the simple interest rate? *9.0% (0.09)*

42. A newspaper advertisement offers a $4,000 used car for nothing down and 36 easy monthly payments of $141.62. What is the simple interest rate? *9.2% (0.0915266667)*

43. A car dealer will sell you the $16,450 car of your dreams for $3,290 down and payments of $339.97 per month for 48 months. What is the simple interest rate?
6.0% (0.06000303951)
44. A car dealer will sell you a used car for $6,798 with $798 down and payments of $168.51 per month for 48 months. What is the simple interest rate? *8.7% (0.08702)*

45. A newspaper advertisement offers a $9,000 car for nothing down and 36 easy monthly payments of $317.50. What is the APR? *17.5% (0.1751351351)*

46. A newspaper advertisement offers a $4,000 used car for nothing down and 36 easy monthly payments of $141.62. What is the APR? *17.8% (0.1781059459)*

47. A car dealer will sell you the $16,450 car of your dreams for $3,290 down and payments of $339.97 per month for 48 months. What is the APR? *11.8% (0.1175569754)*

48. A car dealer will sell you a used car for $6,798 with $798 down and payments of $168.51 per month for 48 months. What is the APR? *17.0% (0.1704881633)*

49. A car dealer carries out the following calculations:

List price	$5,368.00
Options	$1,625.00
Destination charges	$ 200.00
Subtotal	$7,193.00
Tax	$ 431.58
Less trade-in	$2,932.00
Amount to be financed	$4,692.58
8% interest; 48 months	$1,501.63
MONTHLY PAYMENT	$ 129.05

What is the annual percentage rate?
8% add-on rate; APR is about 15.7%

50. A car dealer carries out the following calculations:

List price	$15,428.00
Options	$ 3,625.00
Destination charges	$ 350.00
Subtotal	$19,403.00
Tax	$ 1,164.18
Less trade-in	$ 7,950.00
Amount to be financed	$12,617.18
5% interest; 48 months	$15,771.48
MONTHLY PAYMENT	$ 262.86

What is the annual percentage rate?
5% add-on rate; APR is about 9.8%

Note: The answers for Problems 45–48 recalculate the interest rate and do not use the rounded rates stated in Problems 41–44.

51. Karen and Wayne need to buy a refrigerator because theirs just broke. Unfortunately, their savings account is depleted, and they will need to borrow money to buy a new one. The bank offers them a personal loan at 21% (APR), and Sears offers them an installment loan at 15% (add-on rate). Suppose that the refrigerator at Sears costs $1,598 plus 5% sales tax, and Karen and Wayne plan to pay for the refrigerator for 3 years. Should they finance it with the bank or with Sears?
Sears' add-on rate is 29.2% APR; bank is better.

52. Karen and Wayne must buy a refrigerator because theirs just broke. Unfortunately, their savings account is depleted, and they will need to borrow money to buy a new one. The bank offers them a personal loan at 21% (APR), and Sears offers them an installment loan at 15% (add-on rate). If the refrigerator at Sears costs $1,598 plus 5% sales tax, and Karen and Wayne plan to pay for the refrigerator for 3 years, using the Sears add-on rate, what is the monthly payment?
The monthly payment is $67.58.

53. IN YOUR OWN WORDS Karen says that she has heard something about APR rates but doesn't really know what the term means. Wayne says he thinks it has something to do with the prime rate, but he isn't sure what. Write a short paper explaining APR to Karen and Wayne.

54. IN YOUR OWN WORDS Write a short paper comparing the Problem of the Day with your own world. (That is, list similarities and/or differences.)

RIGHT OR WRONG? **LEVEL 3**

Explain what is wrong, if anything, with the statements in Problems 55–60. Explain your reasoning.

55. If you purchase a refrigerator for $895 and make monthly installments for 3 years with an add-on interest rate of 5.8%, then $N = 3$. F; $N = 12t$ and $t = 3$ so $N = 36$

56. If you purchase a refrigerator for $895 and make monthly installments for 3 years with an add-on interest rate of 5.8%, then the monthly payment (m) is found by

$$m = \$895 \div 36 \approx \$24.86$$

F; forgot to add the interest before dividing by 36

57. If you purchase a refrigerator for $895 and make monthly installments for 3 years with an add-on interest rate of 5.8%, then the amount of interest is found by

$$I = Prt = \$895(5.8)(3) = \$15,573$$

F; $r = 0.058$, not 5.8; $I = \$155.73$

58. If you purchase a sports car for $36,500 and make monthly payments for 5 years with an add-on interest rate of 9.5%, then $A = \$36,500$. F; $P = \$36,500$

59. If you purchase a sports car for $36,500 and make monthly payments for 5 years with an add-on interest rate of 9.5%, then the amount to be repaid is found by T

$$A = P(1 + rt)$$
$$= \$36,500(1 + 0.095 \times 5)$$
$$= \$53,837.50$$

60. If you purchase a sports car for $36,500 and make monthly payments for 5 years with an add-on interest rate of 9.5%, then the monthly payment is found by

$$m = \frac{A}{N} = \frac{\$53,837.50}{5} = \$10,767.50$$

F; $N = 12t$ and $t = 5$, so $N = 60$. Thus, $m = \$897.29$.

7.4 Credit Card Interest

IN THIS WORLD THE UTILITY OF MATH

© Susan Van Etten/PhotoEdit

Credit cards for students mark their passage to adulthood. We are told that 70% of college students have a credit card, and we are also told that they often fall into a credit card trap with an average balance of $2,000. What is sometimes difficult to understand is that if a person has an $1,800 balance and makes only minimum payments, it will take 14 years to pay off the balance!

However, sometimes credit cards are lifesavers. Marsha, for example, must have surgery, and she does not have the $3,000 cash necessary for the operation. Talking to an administrator at the hospital, she finds that it will accept MasterCard, VISA, and Discover credit cards. All of these credit cards have an APR of 12%, so she figures that it does not matter which card she uses, even though she plans to take a year to pay off the loan.

In this section, Marsha will learn that it does matter which credit card she uses, that not all credit cards are the same—even among credit cards with the same APR.

Open-End Credit

The most common types of open-end credit used today are through credit cards used by VISA, MasterCard, Discover, American Express, department stores, and oil companies. Because you don't have to apply for credit each time you want to charge an item, this type of credit is very convenient.

Note the agreement in this book for the number of days in a year to use when working with credit card interest.

When comparing the interest rates on loans, you should use the APR. In the previous section, we introduced a formula for add-on interest; but for credit cards, the stated interest rate *is* the APR. However, the APR on credit cards is often stated as a daily or a monthly rate. For credit cards, we use a 365-day year, rather than a 360-day year.

EXAMPLE 1

Finding the APR for credit cards

Here are some examples of different credit cards:
People's Bank, Bridgeport, CN 13.96% fixed rate; $25 fee (negotiable); average daily balance method.
NationsBank, Dallas, TX 18.15% variable rate; $0 fee; average daily balance method.
Union Bank, San Diego, CA 15.80%; $0 fee; average daily balance method

Convert the given credit card rate to APR (rounded to the nearest tenth of a percent).

a. $1\frac{1}{2}\%$ per month   **b.** Daily rate of 0.05753%

Solution

a. Since there are 12 months per year, multiply a monthly rate by 12 to get the APR:

$$1\frac{1}{2}\% \text{ monthly rate} \times 12 = 18\% \text{ APR}$$

b. Multiply the daily rate by 365 to obtain the APR:

$$0.05753\% \times 365 = 20.99845\%$$

Rounded to the nearest tenth, this is equivalent to 21.0% APR.   ●

Many credit cards charge an annual fee; some charge $1 every billing period the card is used; others are free. These charges affect the APR differently, depending on how much the credit card is used during the year and on the monthly balance. If you always pay your credit card bill in full as soon as you receive it, the card with no yearly fee would obviously be the best for you. On the other hand, if you use your credit card to stretch out your payments, the APR is more important than the flat fee. For our purposes, we won't use the yearly fee in our calculations of APR on credit cards.

Like annual fees, the interest rates or APRs for credit cards vary greatly. Because VISA and MasterCard are issued by many different banks, the terms even in one locality can vary greatly. Some common examples are shown below.

Calculating Credit Card Interest

The finance charges can vary greatly even on credit cards that show the *same* APR, depending on the way the interest is calculated. There are three generally accepted methods for calculating these charges: *previous balance*, *adjusted balance*, and *average daily balance*.

Credit Card Interest

For credit card interest, use the simple interest formula, $I = Prt$.

Previous balance method: Interest is calculated on the previous month's balance. With this method, P = previous balance, r = annual rate, and $t = \frac{1}{12}$.

Adjusted balance method: Interest is calculated on the previous month's balance *less* credits and payments. With this method, P = adjusted balance, r = annual rate, and $t = \frac{1}{12}$.

(Continued)

If you use credit cards, you should be familiar with these methods for calculating interest. They are all based on the simple interest formula.

> **Average daily balance method:** Add the outstanding balance each day in the billing period, and then divide by the number of days in the billing period to find what is called the *average daily balance*. With this method, P = average daily balance, r = annual rate, and t = number of days in the billing period divided by 365.

In Examples 2–4, we compare the finance charges on a $1,000 credit card purchase, using these three different methods. Assume that a bill for $1,000 is received on April 1 and a payment is made. Then another bill is received on May 1, and this bill shows some finance charges. This finance charge is what we are calculating in Examples 2–4.

EXAMPLE 2

Credit card interest by using the previous balance method

Calculate the interest on a $1,000 credit card bill that shows an 18% APR, using the previous balance method and assuming that $50 is sent and recorded by the due date.

Solution The payment doesn't affect the finance charge for this month unless the bill is paid in full. We have $P = \$1,000$, $r = 0.18$, and $t = \frac{1}{12}$. Thus,

$$I = Prt$$
$$= \$1,000(0.18)\left(\frac{1}{12}\right)$$
$$= \$15$$

The interest is $15 for this month.

EXAMPLE 3

Credit card interest by using the adjusted balance method

Calculate the interest on a $1,000 credit card bill that shows an 18% APR, using the adjusted balance method and assuming that $50 is sent and recorded by the due date.

Solution First, find the adjusted balance:

Previous balance:	$1,000
Less credits and payments:	50
Adjusted balance:	$ 950 ← This is P.

We have $P = \$950$, $r = 0.18$, and $t = \frac{1}{12}$. Thus,

$$I = Prt$$
$$= \$950(0.18)\left(\frac{1}{12}\right)$$
$$= \$14.25$$

The interest is $14.25 for this month.

EXAMPLE 4   **Interest by using the average daily balance**

Calculate the interest on a $1,000 credit card bill that shows an 18% APR, using the average daily balance method. Assume that you sent a payment of $50 on April 1 and that it takes 10 days for this payment to be received and recorded.

Solution   For the first 10 days the balance is $1,000, but then the balance drops to $950. Add the balance for *each day*:

10 days @ $1,000:	$10,000
20 days @ $950:	$19,000
Total:	$29,000

Divide by the number of days in the month (30 in April):

$$\$29,000 \div 30 = \$966.67 \quad \leftarrow \text{This is the average daily balance.}$$

For this problem we have $P = \$966.67$, $r = 0.18$, and $t = \frac{30}{365}$. Thus,

$$I = Prt$$

$$= \$966.67(0.18)\left(\frac{30}{365}\right)$$

$$= \$14.30$$

You can do this calculation with one calculator session, starting at the top. When using your calculator, think of what you are doing, rather than thinking in terms of individual buttons pressed:

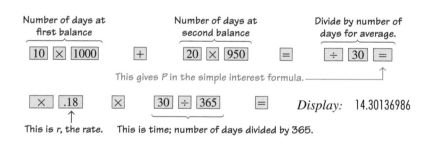

The interest is $14.30 for this month.   ●

You can sometimes make good use of credit cards by taking advantage of the period during which no finance charges are levied. Many credit cards charge no interest if you pay in full within a certain period of time (usually 20 or 30 days). This is called the **grace period.** On the other hand, if you borrow cash on your credit card, you should know that many credit cards have an additional charge for cash advances—and these can be as high as 4%. This 4% is *in addition to* the normal finance charges.

HISTORICAL NOTE

At the start of the 20th century, a few hotels began to issue credit cards, and as early as 1914, large department stores and gasoline chains were issuing credit cards. In those days, credit cards had three basic functions:

1. They were often prestige items offered only to valued customers.
2. They were more convenient to use than cash.
3. They provided some degree of safety.

During World War II, the use of credit cards virtually ceased, due to government restraint on consumer spending and credit. After wartime, restrictions were lifted, however, many plans were reinstated, and railroads and airlines began to issue their own travel cards. In 1949, the Diners Club was established, and it was followed by American Express and Carte Blanche.

PROBLEM SET (7.4)

ESSENTIAL IDEAS — LEVEL 1

1. What is the formula used to calculate credit card interest?
   $I = Prt$

2. What are the three meanings we give to P when calculating credit card interest?
   adjusted balance, previous balance, and average daily balance

3. Describe the procedure for calculating credit card interest using the previous balance method.
   Use $I = Prt$ where P is the previous balance.

4. Describe the procedure for calculating credit card interest using the adjusted balance method.
   Use $I = Prt$ where P is the adjusted balance.

5. Describe the procedure for calculating credit card interest using the average daily balance method.
   Use $I = Prt$ where P is the average daily balance.

6. Give the number of days in each of the following months.

a. January 31	**b.** February 28 or 29
c. March 31	**d.** April 30
e. May 31	**f.** June 30
g. July 31	**h.** August 31
i. September 30	**j.** October 31
k. November 30	**l.** December 31

DRILL AND PRACTICE — LEVEL 2

Estimate the answer for Problems 7–20 by picking the best choice without calculating.

7. A reasonable APR for a credit card is A
   A. 9%   B. 30%   C. 15%

8. A reasonable APR for 5-year installment loan is C
   A. 9%   B. 30%   C. 15%

9. A reasonable APR to pay for a 5-year automobile loan is A
   A. 6%   B. 40%   C. $2,000

10. A reasonable fee to pay for a credit card is A
    A. $0   B. $20   C. $200

11. If I do not pay off my credit card each month, the most important cost factor is B
    A. the annual fee   B. the APR

12. If I pay off my credit card balance each month, the most important cost factor is A
    A. the annual fee   B. the APR

13. The method of calculation most advantageous to the consumer is the B
    A. previous balance method
    B. adjusted balance method
    C. average daily balance method

14. The method of calculation most advantageous to the credit card company is the A
    A. previous balance method
    B. adjusted balance method
    C. average daily balance method

15. In an application of the average daily balance method for the month of August, t is C
    A. $\frac{1}{12}$ B. $\frac{30}{365}$ C. $\frac{31}{365}$

16. When using the average daily balance method for the month of September, t is B
    A. $\frac{1}{12}$ B. $\frac{30}{365}$ C. $\frac{31}{365}$

17. If your credit card balance is $650 and the interest rate is 12% APR, then the credit card interest charge is A
    A. $6.50   B. $65   C. $8.25

18. If your credit card balance is $952, you make a $50 payment, the APR is 12%, and the interest is calculated according to the previous balance method, then the finance charge is A
    A. $9.52   B. $9.02   C. $9.06

19. If your credit card balance is $952, you make a $50 payment, the APR is 12%, and the interest is calculated according to the adjusted balance method, then the finance charge is B
    A. $9.52   B. $9.02   C. $9.06

20. If your credit card balance is $952, you make a $50 payment, the APR is 12%, and the interest is calculated according to the average daily balance method, then the finance charge is C
    A. $9.52   B. $9.02   C. $9.06

Convert each credit card rate in Problems 21–26 to the APR. *

21. Oregon, $1\frac{1}{4}$% per month **15%**

22. Arizona, $1\frac{1}{3}$% per month **16%**

23. New York, $1\frac{1}{2}$% per month **18%**

24. Tennessee, 0.02740% daily rate **10%**

25. Ohio, 0.02192% daily rate **8%**

26. Nebraska, 0.03014% daily rate **11%**

APPLICATIONS — LEVEL 2

27. **IN YOUR OWN WORDS** Compare and contrast open-ended and closed-ended credit.

*These rates were the listed finance charges on purchases of less than $500 on a Citibank VISA statement.

28. **IN YOUR OWN WORDS** Discuss the methods for calculating credit card interest.

29. **IN YOUR OWN WORDS** If you have a credit card, describe the method of calculating interest on your card. Name the brand of card (MasterCard, VISA, etc.), as well as the bank issuing the card. If you do not have a credit card, contact a bank and obtain an application to answer this question. Name the bank.

30. **IN YOUR OWN WORDS** Discuss some advantages and disadvantages of using credit cards.

Calculate the monthly finance charge for each credit card transaction in Problems 31–48. Assume that it takes 10 days for a payment to be received and recorded and that the month is 30 days long.

	Balance	Rate	Payment	Method
31.	$300 $4.50	18%	$50	Previous balance
32.	$300 $3.75	18%	$50	Adjusted balance
33.	$300 $3.95	18%	$50	Average daily balance
34.	$300 $4.50	18%	$250	Previous balance
35.	$300 $0.75	18%	$250	Adjusted balance
36.	$300 $1.97	18%	$250	Average daily balance
37.	$500 $8.33	20%	$50	Previous balance
38.	$500 $7.50	20%	$50	Adjusted balance
39.	$500 $7.67	20%	$50	Average daily balance
40.	$500 $8.33	20%	$400	Previous balance
41.	$500 $1.67	20%	$400	Adjusted balance
42.	$500 $3.84	20%	$400	Average daily balance
43.	$3,000 $52.50	21%	$150	Previous balance
44.	$3,000 $49.88	21%	$150	Adjusted balance
45.	$3,000 $50.05	21%	$150	Average daily balance
46.	$3,000 $52.50	21%	$1,500	Previous balance
47.	$3,000 $26.25	21%	$1,500	Adjusted balance
48.	$3,000 $34.52	21%	$1,500	Average daily balance

49. Most credit cards provide for a minimum finance charge of 50¢ per month. Suppose that you buy a $30 item, make five monthly payments of $5, and then pay the remaining balance. What are the payments and the total interest for this purchase if the interest rate is 12% but you pay the minimum finance charge? **5 payments of $5 plus a last payment of $7.50; total payments of $32.50 with interest of $2.50**

50. The finance charge disclosure on a Sears Revolving Charge Card statement is shown here. Why do you suppose that the limitation on the 50¢ finance charge is from $1.00 to $33.00? **For balances over $33, the interest would be more than $0.50.**

FINANCE CHARGE is based upon account activity during the billing period preceding the current billing period, and is computed upon the "previous balance" ("new balance") outstanding at the end of the preceding billing period) before deducting payments and credits or adding purchases made during the current billing period. The FINANCE CHARGE will be the greater of 50¢ (applied to previous balances of $1.00 through $33.00) or an amount determined as follows:

PREVIOUS BALANCE	PERIODIC RATE	ANNUAL PERCENTAGE RATE
$1,000 or under Excess over **$1,000**	1.5% per month 1.0% per month	18% 12%

51. Suppose you have a $1,000 charge on a credit card charging 1.5% monthly interest using the adjusted balance method. The minimum payment due in May is $30. How much will you save in interest charges in June by paying $60 instead? **You will save $0.45.**

52. Marsha must have surgery and she does not have the $3,000 cash necessary for the operation. Talking to an administrator at the hospital, she finds that it will accept MasterCard, VISA, and Discover credit cards. All of these credit cards have an APR of 18%, so she figures that it does not matter which card she uses, even though she plans to take a year to pay off the loan. Assume that Marsha makes a payment of $300 and then receives a bill. Show the interest from credit cards of 18% APR according to the previous balance, adjusted balance, and average daily balance methods. Assume that the month has 31 days and that it takes 14 days for Marsha's payment to be mailed and recorded. **See IAS; previous balance method, $45; adjusted balance method, $40.50; average daily balance method, $43.35**

RIGHT OR WRONG? LEVEL 3

Explain what is wrong, if anything, with the statements in Problems 53–60. Explain your reasoning.

53. When calculating credit card interest, use $t = \frac{1}{12}$ because credit cards are billed monthly.
F; average daily balance method does not use $\frac{1}{12}$.

54. From the consumer's point of view, the best method of calculating interest is the average daily balance method.
F; adjusted balance method

55. From the bank's point of view, the best method of calculating interest is the average daily balance method.
F; previous balance method

56. If you owe $1,200 for 7 days in January and $1,000 for 24 days, then the average daily balance is
$$\frac{(\$1,200 \times 7) + (\$1,000 \times 24)}{30} = \$1,080$$
F; use 31 days to obtain $1,045.16.

57. If you owe $355 in February 2007 and pay $300 so that your account is credited in 10 days, the average daily balance is
$$\frac{(\$355 \times 10) + (\$55 \times 20)}{30} = \$155$$
F; use 28 days to obtain $166.07.

58. Suppose that you receive a credit card bill on December 1 for $850. You mail in a payment of $450 the same day, and

it is received in 7 days. If the interest is charged at 15% APR and is calculated according to the previous balance method, the amount of interest is

$$I = Prt$$
$$= \$450(0.15)\left(\frac{1}{12}\right) = \$5.625$$

or $5.63.   F; P = $850; I = $10.63

59. Suppose that you receive a credit card bill on December 1 for $850. You mail in a payment of $450 the same day, and it is received in 7 days. If the interest is charged at 15% APR and is calculated according to the adjusted balance method, the amount of interest is

$$I = Prt$$
$$= \$850(0.15)\left(\frac{1}{12}\right) = \$10.625$$

or $10.63.   F; P = $400; I = $5.00

60. Suppose that you receive a credit card bill on December 1 for $850. You mail in a payment of $450 the same day, and it is received in 7 days. If the interest is charged at 15% APR and is calculated according to the average daily balance method, the amount of interest is

$$I = Prt$$
$$= \$501.6129032(0.15)\left(\frac{1}{12}\right)$$
$$= \$6.27016129$$

or $6.27.   F; $t = \frac{31}{365}$; I = $6.39

(7.5) Compound Interest

IN THIS WORLD THE UTILITY OF MATH

Some time ago, Ron and Lorraine purchased a home, and they still owe $200,000. The payments are $1,950 per month, and they have 10 years left to pay. They just came into some money and want to free themselves of the monthly payments by paying off the loan. They go to the bank and are told that to pay off the home loan, they must pay $200,000 plus a "prepayment penalty" of 3%. (Older home loans often had prepayment clauses ranging from 1% to 5% of the amount to be paid off.) This means that, to own their home outright, Ron and Lorraine would need to pay

$206,000 ($200,000 + 3% of $200,000)

They want to know whether this is a wise financial move.

 See Problem 53.

 Pay attention!!! In this section, Ron and Lorraine (see Problem of the Day) will see that with their $206,000 they could not only pay off the home loan, but also end up with over a quarter of a million dollars in cash! **Who ever said math was not worthwhile?**

Annual Compounding

Most banks do not pay interest according to the simple interest formula; instead, after some period of time, they add the interest to the principal and then pay interest on this new, larger amount. When this is done, it is called **compound interest**.

EXAMPLE 1

Comparing simple and compound interest

© Chuck Savage/Corbis

Compare simple and compound interest for a $1,000 deposit at 8% interest for 3 years.

Solution   First, calculate the future value of the simple interest:

$$A = P(1 + rt)$$
$$= 1,000(1 + 0.08 \times 3)$$
$$= 1,000(1.24) \quad \text{Order of operations, multiplication first.}$$
$$= 1,240$$

Using simple interest, the future value in three years is $1,240.

Next, assume that the interest is **compounded annually.** This means that the interest is added to the principal after 1 year has passed. This new amount then becomes the principal for the following year. Since the time period for each calculation is 1 year, we let $t = 1$ for each calculation.

First year $(t = 1)$: $A = P(1 + r)$
$$= 1,000(1 + 0.08)$$
$$= 1,080$$
$$\downarrow$$

Second year $(t = 1)$: $A = P(1 + r)$ One year's principal is previous year's balance.
$$= 1,080(1 + 0.08)$$
$$= 1,166.40$$
$$\downarrow$$

Third year $(t = 1)$: $A - P(1 + r)$
$$= 1,166.40(1 + 0.08)$$
$$= 1,259.71$$

Using interest compounded annually, the future value in 3 years is $1,259.71. The earnings from compounding are $19.71 more than from simple interest.   ●

It All Adds UP

The boy that by addition grows
And suffers no subtraction
Who multiplies the thing he knows
And carries every fraction
Who well divides the precious time
The due proportion given
To sure success aloft will climb
Interest compound receiving.

The problem with compound interest relates to the difficulty of calculating it. Notice that, to simplify the calculations in Example 1, the variable representing time t was given as 1, and the process was repeated three times. Also, notice that, after the future value was found, it was used as the principal in the next step. What if we wanted to compound annually for 20 years instead of for 3 years? Look at Example 1 to discover the following pattern:

Simple interest (20 years): $A = P(1 + rt)$
$$= 1,000(1 + 0.08 \times 20)$$
$$= 1,000(1 + 1.6)$$
$$= 1,000(2.6)$$
$$= 2,600$$

Annual compounding (20 years): $A = P(1 + r)$ First year

$$= P(1 + r)(1 + r) \quad \text{Second year}$$
$$= P(1 + r)^2 \quad \text{Second year simplified}$$

$$= P(1 + r)^2(1 + r) \quad \text{Third year}$$
$$= P(1 + r)^3 \quad \text{Third year simplified}$$
$$\vdots$$
$$= P(1 + r)^{20} \quad \text{Twentieth year simplified}$$

For a period of 20 years, starting with $1,000 at 8% compounded annually, we have

$$A = 1,000(1.08)^{20}$$

CAUTION

You might wish to review exponents and how to use a calculator with exponents, which we presented in Section 1.5.

The difficulty lies in calculating this number. You will need to have a calculator with an exponent key. These are labeled in different ways, depending on the brand. It might be $\boxed{y^x}$ or $\boxed{x^y}$ or $\boxed{\frown}$. In this book we will show exponents by using $\boxed{\frown}$, but you should press the appropriate key for your own brand of calculator.

$$\boxed{1000} \quad \boxed{\times} \quad \boxed{1.08} \quad \boxed{\frown} \quad \boxed{20} \quad \boxed{=} \quad \textit{Display:} \quad 4660.957144$$

Round money answers to the nearest cent: $4,660.96 is the future value of $1,000 compounded annually at 8% for 20 years. This compares with $2,600 from simple interest. The effect of compounding yields $2,060.96 *more* than simple interest.

Compounding Periods

Most banks compound interest more frequently than once a year. For instance, a bank may pay interest as follows:

Semiannually: twice a year or every 180 days

Quarterly: 4 times a year or every 90 days

Monthly: 12 times a year or every 30 days

CAUTION

Remember these compounding period names.

Daily: 360 times a year

To write a formula for various compounding periods, we must introduce three new variables. First, let

$$n = \text{NUMBER OF TIMES INTEREST IS CALCULATED EACH YEAR}$$

That is,

$$n = 1 \text{ for } \textit{annual} \text{ compounding}$$
$$n = 2 \text{ for } \textit{semiannual} \text{ compounding}$$
$$n = 4 \text{ for } \textit{quarterly} \text{ compounding}$$
$$n = 12 \text{ for } \textit{monthly} \text{ compounding}$$
$$n = 360 \text{ for } \textit{daily} \text{ compounding}$$

Second, let

$$N = \text{NUMBER OF COMPOUNDING PERIODS}$$

That is,

$$N = nt$$

Third, let

$$i = \text{RATE PER PERIOD}$$

That is,

$$i = \frac{r}{n}$$

We can now summarize the variables we use for interest.

Interest Variables

A = FUTURE VALUE	This is the principal plus interest.	
P = PRESENT VALUE	This is the same as the principal.	
r = INTEREST RATE	This is the *annual* interest rate.	
t = TIME	This is the time *in years*.	

Calculated variables:

$N = nt$	This is the number of periods.
$i = \dfrac{r}{n}$	This is the rate per period.

It is tempting to skip past this box, but you must take some time to study what these variables represent.

EXAMPLE 2

Identifying the variables used with interest formulas

Fill in the blanks, given an annual rate of 12% and a time period of 3 years for the following compounding periods.

a. annual   **b.** semiannual   **c.** quarterly   **d.** monthly   **e.** daily

Solution

Compounding	Period n	Yearly Rate r	Time t	No. of periods $N = nt$	Rate per period $i = \dfrac{r}{n}$
a. Annual	1	12%	3 yr	3	12%
b. Semiannual	2	12%	3 yr	6	6%
c. Quarterly	4	12%	3 yr	12	3%
d. Monthly	12	12%	3 yr	36	1%
e. Daily	360	12%	3 yr	1,080	0.03%

To find the number of periods, use $N = nt$; for part e: $N = 360(3) = 1{,}080$.

To find the rate per period, use $i = \dfrac{r}{n}$; for part e: $i = \dfrac{0.12}{360} = 0.000\overline{3}$. As a percent, $i = 0.03\%$.

We are now ready to state the **future value formula** for compound interest, which is sometimes called the **compound interest formula.**

Future Value (Compound Interest)

$$A = P(1 + i)^N$$

where A is future value, P is present value, $i = r/n$, and $N = nt$.

 CAUTION To use this formula, follow the procedure described in the following box.

Future Value Formula

Follow this procedure for finding the future value for compound interest.

Step 1 Identify the present value, P.

Step 2 Identify the rate, r.

Step 3 Identify the time, t.

Step 4 Identify the number of times interest is compounded each year, n.

Step 5 Calculate $N = nt$.

Step 6 Calculate $i = \frac{r}{n}$.

Step 7 Use the future value formula using the calculated values of i and N.

EXAMPLE 3

Finding future value

Find the future value of $1,000 invested for 10 years at 8% interest compounded

a. annually   **b.** semiannually   **c.** quarterly

Solution Identify the variables: $P = 1,000$

$$r = 0.08$$
$$t = 10$$

a. $n = 1$ Calculate $N = nt = 1(10) = 10$ and $i = \frac{r}{n} = \frac{0.08}{1} = 0.08$. We use the future value formula, $A = P(1 + i)^N$ and a calculator:

Calculate: $1,000(1 + 0.08)^{10}$ *Display:* 2158.924997

The future value is $2,158.92.

b. $n = 2$ Calculate $N = nt = 2(10) = 20$ and $i = \frac{r}{n} = \frac{0.08}{2} = 0.04$.

Calculate: $1,000(1 + 0.04)^{20}$ *Display:* 2191.123143

The future value is $2,191.12.

c. $n = 4$ Calculate $N = nt = 4(10) = 40$ and $i = \frac{r}{n} = \frac{0.08}{4} = 0.02$.

Calculate: $1,000(1 + 0.02)^{40}$ *Display:* 2208.039664

The future value is $2,208.04.

EXAMPLE 4 Finding future value using a calculator

Find the future value of $815 invested for 10 years and 6 months at 8.25% interest compounded: **a.** quarterly   **b.** daily

Solution $P = \$815$; $r = 0.0825$; $t = 10.5$

a. $n = 4$ *Calculate:* $N = nt$ $i = \dfrac{r}{n}$

$$= 4(10.5) \qquad = \dfrac{0.0825}{4}$$

$$= 42 \qquad = 0.020625$$

$$A = P(1 + i)^N$$

$$= 815\left(1 + \frac{0.0825}{4}\right)^{42} \qquad Display: \quad 1921.047468$$

The future value is $1,921.05.

b. $n = 360$; $N = nt = 360(10.5) = 3{,}780$; $i = \frac{0.0825}{360}$

$$A = P(1 + i)^N$$

$$= 815\left(1 + \frac{0.0825}{360}\right)^{3{,}780} \qquad Display: \quad 1937.858683$$

The future value is $1,937.86. ●

EXAMPLE 5 Problem solving with compound interest

Consider the Problem of the Day with Ron and Lorraine described at the beginning of this section. They wish to know whether it is a wise financial move to use $206,000 to pay off their home mortgage.

Solution   The first question is, "How much principal do Ron and Lorraine need to generate $1,950 per month in income (to make their mortgage payments) if they are able to invest it at 12% interest?" "Wait! Where can you find 12% interest? My bank pays only 5% interest!" There are investments you could make (not a deposit into a savings account) that could yield a 12% return on your money. Problem solving often requires that you make certain assumptions to have sufficient information to answer a question that you might have. This first question is an application of simple interest, because the interest is withdrawn each month and is not left to accumulate:

I is the amount withdrawn each month.
↓

$$I = Prt \quad \leftarrow \quad t = \tfrac{1}{12} \text{ because it is monthly income.}$$

$$1{,}950 = P(0.12)\left(\frac{1}{12}\right)$$

$$23{,}400 = 0.12P \qquad \text{Multiply both sides by 12.}$$

$$195{,}000 = P \qquad \text{Divide both sides by 0.12.}$$

This means that a deposit of $195,000 will be sufficient to pay off their home loan, with the added advantage that, when their home is eventually paid for, they will still have the $195,000!

Now, since they have $206,000 to invest, they can also allow the remaining $11,000 to grow at 12% interest. This is an example of compound interest because the interest is not withdrawn, but instead accumulates. Since there are 10 years left on the home loan, we have $P = 11{,}000$; $r = 0.12$, $t = 10$, and $n = 12$ (assume monthly compounding). Calculate:

$$N = nt = (12)(10) = 120, \qquad i = \frac{r}{n} = \frac{0.12}{12} = 0.01$$

CAUTION

If you ever said, "When will I ever use this?" here is a real-life example that could save you a great deal of money.

Thus,

$$A = 11{,}000(1 + 0.01)^{120} \approx 36{,}304.26$$

This means that Ron and Lorraine have two options:

1. Use their $206,000 to pay off the home loan. They will have the home paid for and will not need to make any further payments.

2. Dispose of their $206,000 as follows: Deposit $195,000 into an account to make their house payments. They will not need to make any further payments. At the end of 10 years they will still have the $195,000. Deposit the excess $11,000 into an account and let it grow for 10 years. The accumulated value will be $36,304.26.
   Under Option 2 they will have

$$\$36{,}304.26 + \$195{,}000 = \$231{,}304.26$$

in 10 years in addition to all the benefits gained under Option 1. ●

Inflation

Any discussion of compound interest is incomplete without a discussion of inflation. When there is an increase in the amount of money in circulation, there is a fall in its value which, in turn, causes a rise in prices. This is called **inflation.** The same procedure we used to calculate compound interest can be used to calculate the effects of inflation. The government releases reports of monthly and annual inflation rates. In 1981, the inflation rate was nearly 9%, but in 2004 it was less than 2%. Keep in mind that inflation rates can vary tremendously, and that the best we can do in this section is to assume different constant inflation rates. For our purposes in this book, we will assume $n = 1$ (annual compounding) when working inflation problems.

EXAMPLE 6   **Effects of inflation on a salary**

Richard is earning $30,000 per year and would like to know what salary he could expect in 20 years if inflation continues at an average of 9%.

Solution $P = 30{,}000$, $r = 0.09$, and $t = 20$. In this book, assume $n = 1$ for inflation problems. This means that $N = 20$ and $i = 0.09$. Find

$$\begin{aligned} A &= P(1 + i)^N \\ &= 30{,}000(1 + 0.09)^{20} \\ &\approx 168{,}132.32 \quad \text{Use a calculator.} \end{aligned}$$

The answer means that, if inflation continues at a constant 9% rate, an annual salary of $168,000 will have about the same purchasing power in 20 years as a salary of $30,000 today. ●

Present Value

Sometimes we know the future value of an investment and wish to know its present value. Such a problem is called a **present value** problem. The **present value formula** follows directly from the future value formula (by division).

Present Value Formula

$P = \dfrac{A}{(1+i)^N}$; on a calculator this is $A \div (1+i)^N$ where P is present value, A is future value, $i = r/n$, and $N = nt$.

 STOP   This is the same as the future value formula, algebraically solved for P.

EXAMPLE 7   **Finding a present value**

Suppose that you want to take a trip to Tahiti in 5 years and you decide that you will need $5,000. To have that much money set aside in 5 years, how much money should you deposit into a bank account paying 6% compounded quarterly?

Solution   In this problem, P is unknown and A is given: $A = 5,000$. Also, $r = 0.06$; $t = 5$; and $n = 4$. Calculate:

$$N = nt = 4(5) = 20 \qquad i = \frac{r}{n} = \frac{0.06}{4}$$

We use the formula $P = \dfrac{A}{(1+i)^N}$:

Display: 3712.352091

You should deposit $3,712.35.   ●

EXAMPLE 8   **Using present value with a retirement decision**

An insurance agent wishes to sell you a policy that will pay you $100,000 in 30 years. What is the value of this policy in today's dollars, if we assume a 9% inflation rate?

Solution   This is a present value problem for which $A = 100,000$, $r = 0.09$, $n = 1$, and $t = 30$. We calculate

$$N = nt = 1(30) = 30 \qquad i = \frac{r}{n} = \frac{0.09}{1} = 0.09$$

To find the present value, calculate

$$P = \frac{100,000}{(1 + 0.09)^{30}} \approx \$7,537.11$$

This means that the agent is offering you an amount comparable to $7,537.11 in terms of today's dollars.   ●

PROBLEM SET (7.5)

ESSENTIAL IDEAS   LEVEL 1

1. What is *n* for the following compounding periods?

a. quarterly   *n* = 4

b. semiannually   *n* = 2

c. monthly   *n* = 12

d. daily   *n* = 360

2. Tell what each of the following variables represents when used in connection with interest formulas.

a. *A*   future value

b. *P*   present value

c. *r*   annual interest rate

d. *t*   time, in years

e. *n*   number of times compounded each year

f. How do you calculate *N*?   *N* = *nt*

g. How do you calculate *i*?   *i* = *r/n*

3. a. What is the future value formula for compound interest? $A = P(1 + i)^N$

b. What is the present value formula for compound interest? $P = \frac{A}{(1 + i)^N}$

4. What formula do you use to calculate inflation?   Future value

DRILL AND PRACTICE   LEVEL 2

In Problems 5–10, compare the future amounts (A) you would have if the money were invested at simple interest and if it were invested with annual compounding.

5. $1,000 at 8% for 5 years $1,400; $1,469.33; $69.33 more

6. $5,000 at 10% for 3 years $6,500; $6,655; $155 more

7. $2,000 at 12% for 3 years $2,720; $2,809.86; $89.86 more

8. $2,000 at 12% for 5 years $3,200; $3,524.68; $324.68 more

9. $5,000 at 12% for 20 years $17,000; $48,231.47; $31,231.47 more

10. $1,000 at 14% for 30 years $5,200; $50,950.16; $45,750.16 more

Find n, i (period rate), N (number of periods), and A (future value) for the information given in Problems 11–26.

	P	*r*	*t*
Compounding Period	Present Value	Annual Rate	Time
11. Annual	$1,000	9%	5 yr
n = 1; *i* = 9%; *N* = 5; *A* = $1,538.62			
12. Semiannual	$1,000	9%	5 yr
n = 2; *i* = 4.5%; *N* = 10; *A* = $1,552.97			
13. Annual	$500	8%	3 yr
n = 1; *i* = 8%; *N* = 3; *A* = $629.86			
14. Semiannual	$500	8%	3 yr
n = 2; *i* = 4%; *N* = 6; *A* = $632.66			

	P	*r*	*t*
Compounding Period	Present Value	Annual Rate	Time
15. Quarterly	$500	8%	3 yr
n = 4; *i* = 2%; *N* = 12; *A* = $634.12			
16. Semiannual	$3,000	18%	3 yr
n = 2; *i* = 9%; *N* = 6; *A* = $5,031.30			
17. Quarterly	$5,000	18%	10 yr
n = 4; *i* = 4.5%; *N* = 40; *A* = $29,081.82			
18. Quarterly	$624	16%	5 yr
n = 4; *i* = 4%; *N* = 20; *A* = $1,367.26			
19. Quarterly	$5,000	20%	10 yr
n = 4; *i* = 5%; *N* = 40; *A* = $35,199.94			
20. Monthly	$350	12%	5 yr
n = 12; *i* = 1%; *N* = 60; *A* = $635.84			
21. Monthly	$4,000	24%	5 yr
n = 12; *i* = 2%; *N* = 60; *A* = $13,124.12			
22. Quarterly	$800	12%	90 days
n = 4; *i* = 3%; *N* = 1; *A* = $824.00			
23. Quarterly	$900	12%	180 days
n = 4; *i* = 3%; *N* = 2; *A* = $954.81			
24. Quarterly	$1,900	12%	270 days
n = 4; *i* = 3%; *N* = 3; *A* = $2,076.18			
25. Quarterly	$1,250	16%	450 days
n = 4; *i* = 4%; *N* = 5; *A* = $1,520.82			
26. Quarterly	$1,000	12%	90 days
n = 4; *i* = 3%; *N* = 1; *A* = $1,030.00			

In Problems 27–40, find the future value, using the future value formula and a calculator

27. $35 at 17.65% compounded annually for 20 years $903.46

28. $155 at 21.25% compounded annually for 25 years $19,159.11

29. $835 at 3.5% compounded semiannually for 6 years $1,028.25

30. $9,450 at 7.5% compounded semiannually for 10 years $19,733.04

31. $575 at 5.5% compounded quarterly for 5 years $755.59

32. $3,450 at 4.3% compounded quarterly for 8 years $4,857.57

33. $9,730.50 at 7.6% compounded monthly for 7 years $16,536.79

34. $3,560 at 9.2% compounded monthly for 10 years $8,901.78

35. $45.67 at 3.5% compounded daily for 3 years $50.73

36. $34,500 at 6.9% compounded daily for 2 years $39,604.63

37. $89,500 at 6.2% compounded monthly for 30 years $572,177.99

38. $119,400 at 7.5% compounded monthly for 30 years $1,124,931.15

39. $225,500 at 8.65% compounded daily for 30 years $3,019,988.94

40. $355,000 at 9.5% compounded daily for 30 years $6,134,855.57

APPLICATIONS   LEVEL 2

41. Find the cost of each item in 5 years, assuming an inflation rate of 2%.

a. cup of coffee, $1.99 $2.20

b. Sunday paper, $1.50 $1.66

c. Big Mac, $1.95 $2.15

d. gallon of gas, $3.25 $3.59

42. Find the cost of each item in 10 years, assuming an inflation rate of 5%.

  a. movie admission, $12.00 $19.55

  b. CD, $16.95 $27.61

  c. textbook, $80.00 $130.31

  d. electricity bill, $165 $268.77

43. Find the cost of each item in 10 years, assuming an inflation rate of 12%.

  a. phone bill, $45 $139.76

  b. pair of shoes, $65 $201.88

  c. new suit, $370 $1,149.16

  d. monthly rent, $600 $1,863.51

44. Find the cost of each item in 20 years, assuming an inflation rate of 6%.

  a. TV, $600 $1,924.28

  b. small car, $18,000 $57,728.44

  c. car, $28,000 $89,799.79

  d. tuition, $26,000 $83,385.52

45. How much would you have in 5 years if you purchased a $1,000 5-year savings certificate that paid 4% compounded quarterly? $1,220.19

46. What is the future value after 15 years if you deposited $1,000 for your child's education and the interest was guaranteed at 16% compounded quarterly? $10,519.63

47. Find the cost of a home in 30 years, assuming an annual inflation rate of 4%, if the present value of the house is $225,000. $729,764.44

48. Find the cost of a home in 5 years, assuming an annual inflation rate of 3%, if the present value of the house is $495,000. $573,840.67

49. Find the cost of the monthly rent for a two-bedroom apartment in 30 years, assuming an annual inflation rate of 4%, if the current rent is $650. $2,108.21

50. Suppose that an insurance agent offers you a policy that will provide you with a yearly income of $50,000 in 30 years. What is the comparable annual salary today, assuming an inflation rate of 6%? $8,705.51

51. Suppose that an insurance agent offers you a policy that will provide you with a yearly income of $50,000 in 30 years. What is the comparable annual salary today, assuming an inflation rate of 4%? $15,415.93

52. Suppose an insurance agent offers you a policy that will provide you with a yearly income of $250,000 in 30 years. What is the comparable annual salary today, assuming an inflation rate of 4%? $77,079.67

53. Ron and Lorraine purchased a home some time ago and they still owe $200,000. Their payments are $1,950 per month and they have 10 years left to pay. They want to free themselves of the monthly payments by paying off the loan. They go to the bank and are told that, to pay off the home loan, they must pay $200,000 plus a "prepayment penalty" of 3%. (Older home loans often had prepayment clauses ranging from 1% to 5% of the amount to be paid off. Today, most lenders will waive this penalty, if requested.) This means that, to own their home outright, Ron and Lorraine would have to pay $206,000 ($200,000 + 3% of $200,000). They want to know whether this is a wise financial move. In Example 5, we assumed a rather high 12% investment rate. Repeat the analysis using an 8% interest rate. Deposit the money to pay off the loan.

54. Rework Problem 53, assuming a 4% interest rate. Pay off the loan.

RIGHT OR WRONG?   LEVEL 3

Explain what is wrong, if anything, with the statements in Problems 55–60. Explain your reasoning.

55. If an investment is compounded monthly, then $N = 12$. F; n = 12

56. If an investment is compounded daily, then $n = 365$.   F; in this book we use n = 360

57. If the rate of an investment is 12% compounded monthly, then $r = 1\%$.   F; i = 1%

58. If the rate of an investment is 6% compounded monthly, then $i = 0.05$.   F; i = 0.005 or 0.5%

59. To find the amount of interest I for compound interest, first find A and then subtract P.   T

60. If $500 is deposited into an account for 4 years paying 4.5% compounded daily, then $P = 500$, $N = 4$, and $i = 0.045$, so

$$A = P(1 + i)^N$$
$$= 500(1 + 0.045)^4$$

Using a calculator, we find $A \approx \$596.26$.
F; t = 4; r = 0.045; and n = 360 so N = 4(360) = 1,440; $i = \frac{r}{n} = \frac{0.045}{360}$; we find A ≈ $598.60

7.6 Buying a Home

IN THIS WORLD THE UTILITY OF MATH

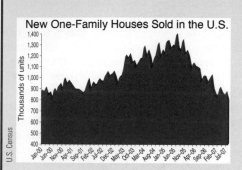

New One-Family Houses Sold in the U.S.

Dorothy and Wes, motivated by low mortgage rates, went out and found the "home of their dreams," and it costs only $525,000. They have never purchased a home before—or anything else involving so much money—and they are very excited. There seems to be so much to do, and so many new words are being used by the realtor and the banker that they are also confused. If their combined salaries are $99,500 and if the current interest rate is 7.5% APR, how much of a down payment will they need to be able to afford their "dream home," and what is the monthly payment?

In this section, Dorothy and Wes will be introduced to the terminology of buying a house, as well as the steps in negotiating a sales contract.

 See Problem 54.

Home Loans

To purchase a home, you will probably need a lender to agree to provide the money you need. You, in turn, promise to repay the money based on terms set forth in an agreement, or loan contract, called a **mortgage.** As the borrower, you pledge your home as security. It remains pledged until the loan is paid off. If you fail to meet the terms of the contract, the lender has the right to **foreclose,** which means that the lender may take possession of the property. A portion of a mortgage application is shown in Figure 7.2.

There are three types of mortgage loans: (1) conventional loans made between you and a private lender; (2) VA loans made to eligible veterans (these are guaranteed

I. TYPE OF MORTGAGE AND TERMS OF LOAN

Mortgage Applied for: ☐ V.A. ☐ FHA ☐ Conventional ☐ FmHA ☐ Other:

Agency Case Number | Lender Case Number

Amount $ | Interest Rate % | No. of Months | Amortization Type: ☐ Fixed Rate ☐ GPM ☐ Other (explain): ☐ ARM (type):

II. PROPERTY INFORMATION AND PURPOSE OF LOAN

Subject Property Address (street, city, state, ZIP) | No. of Uni

Legal Description of Subject Property (attach description if necessary) | Year Built

Purpose of Loan ☐ Purchase ☐ Refinance ☐ Construction ☐ Construction-Permanent ☐ Other (explain): | Property will be: ☐ Primary Residence ☐ Secondary Residence ☐ Investment

Complete this line if construction or construction-permanent loan.
Year Lot Acquired | Original Cost $ | Amount Existing Liens $ | (a) Present Value of Lot $ | (b) Cost of Improvements $ | Total (a + b) $

Complete this line if this is a refinance loan.
Year Acquired | Original Cost $ | Amount Existing Liens $ | Purpose of Refinance | Describe Improvements ☐ made ☐ to be mad

Cost: $

Title will be held in what Name(s) | Manner in which Title will be held | Estate will be held in: ☐ Fee Simple ☐ Leasehold (show expiration date)

Source of Down Payment, Settlement Charges and/or Subordinate Financing (explain)

Figure 7.2 Portion of a mortgage application

by the Veterans Administration, so they cost less than the other types of loans); and (3) FHA loans made by private lenders and insured by the Federal Housing Administration. Regardless of the type of loan you obtain, you will pay certain lender costs. By *lender costs,* we mean all the charges required by the lender: closing costs plus interest.

When you shop around for a loan, certain rates will be quoted:

1. **Interest rate.** This is the annual interest rate for the loan; it fluctuates on a daily basis. The APR, as stated on the loan agreement, is generally just a little higher than the quoted interest rate. This is because the quoted interest rate is usually based on ordinary interest (360-day year), whereas the APR is based on exact interest (365-day year).

2. **Down payment.** This is the amount that is paid when the loan is obtained. The purchase price minus the down payment is equal to the amount financed.

3. **Origination fee.** This is a one-time charge to cover the lender's administrative costs in processing the loan. It may be a flat $100 to $300 fee, or it may be expressed as a percentage of the loan.

4. **Points.** This refers to discount points, a one-time charge used to adjust the yield on the loan to what the market conditions demand. It offsets constraints placed on the yield by state and federal regulations. Each point is equal to 1% of the amount of the loan.

EXAMPLE 1

Finding the charge for a loan

If you are obtaining a $120,000 loan and the bank charges 8.5% plus $250 and $2\frac{1}{2}$ points, what are the one-time charges?

Solution The APR probably affects the cost of a loan the most of the three quoted rates, but it does not affect the one-time charges. The $250 origination fee is added to the fee called *points.* Since 1 point = 1%, we have

$$\text{POINTS} = \$120,000 \times 2.5\% = \$120,000 \times 0.025 = \$3,000$$

$$\text{FEE} = \$250$$

$$\text{TOTAL ONE-TIME CHARGES} = \$3,000 + \$250 = \$3,250 \qquad \bullet$$

Suppose that Lender A quotes 8.5% + 2.5 points + $250, and Lender B quotes 8.8% + 1 point + $100. Which lender should you choose? It is desirable to incorporate these three charges—interest rate, origination fee, and points—into one formula so that you can decide which lending institution is offering you the best terms on your loan. This could save you thousands of dollars over the life of your loan. The **comparison rate** formula shown in the following box can be used to calculate the combined effects of these fees. Even though it is not perfectly accurate, it is usually close enough to permit meaningful comparison among lenders.* The lower the rate, the better the offer.

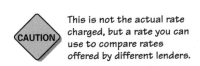
This is not the actual rate charged, but a rate you can use to compare rates offered by different lenders.

Comparison Rate

$$\text{COMPARISON RATE} = \text{APR} + 0.125 \left(\text{POINTS} + \frac{\text{ORIGINATION FEE}}{\text{AMOUNT OF LOAN}} \right)$$

*The 0.125 is a weighting factor. Since the points and origination fee are one-time factors, they should not be weighted as heavily as the interest rate. Since the decimal 0.125 is equivalent to $\frac{1}{8}$, we see that the one-time fees are weighted to be one-eighth as important as the interest rate.

EXAMPLE 2

Finding the best loan

Suppose that you wish to obtain a home loan for $120,000, and you obtain the following quotations from lenders:

Lender A: 8.5% + 2.5 points + $250
Lender B: 8.8% + 1 point + $100

Which lender is making you the better offer?

Solution Calculate the comparison rate for both lenders (a calculator is helpful for this calculation).

Lender A: $\text{COMPARISON RATE} = \text{APR} + 0.125 \left(\text{POINTS} + \dfrac{\text{FEE}}{\text{AMT OF LOAN}} \right)$

$$= \underbrace{0.085}_{\text{APR}} + 0.125 \left(\underset{\underset{\text{Write points as a decimal.}}{\uparrow}}{0.025} + \dfrac{250}{120,000} \right)$$

$$= 0.0884 \text{ or } 8.84\% \quad \text{Use a calculator.}$$

Lender B: $\text{COMPARISON RATE} = \text{APR} + 0.125 \left(\text{POINTS} + \dfrac{\text{FEE}}{\text{AMT OF LOAN}} \right)$

$$= 0.088 + 0.125 \left(0.01 + \dfrac{100}{120,000} \right)$$

$$= 0.0894 \text{ or } 8.94\%$$

Lender A is making the better offer, because its comparison rate of 8.84% is less than the comparison rate of Lender B (8.94%). ●

Monthly Payments

Now imagine that you have selected a lender; next, you need to calculate the monthly payments. Several factors influence the amount of the *monthly payment:*

1. *Length of the loan.*

Most lenders assume a 30-year period. The shorter the period, the greater the monthly payment; however, the greater the monthly payment, the less the finance charges.

2. Amount of the *down payment.*

The greater the down payment, the less the amount to finance; and the less the amount to finance, the smaller the monthly payment.

3. The *APR.*

The smaller the interest rate (APR), the smaller the finance charge and consequently the smaller the monthly payment.

The effect of some of these factors is shown in Table 7.2. Some financial counselors suggest making as large a down payment as you can afford, whereas others

TABLE 7.2	Effect of Down Payment on the Cost of a $120,000 Home with Interest at 8%					
Down Payment	**Percent**	**Monthly Payment**			**Total Payment (nearest dollar)**		
		20 Years	**25 Years**	**30 Years**	**20 Years**	**25 Years**	**30 Years**
$0	0%	$1,003.73	$926.18	$880.52	$240,895	$277,854	$316,987
$6,000	5%	$953.54	$879.87	$836.49	$228,850	$263,961	$301,136
$12,000	10%	$903.36	$833.56	$792.47	$216,806	$250,068	$285,289
$24,000	20%	$802.98	$740.94	$704.41	$192,715	$222,282	$253,588
$30,000	25%	$752.80	$694.63	$660.39	$180,672	$208,389	$237,740
$36,000	30%	$702.61	$648.33	$616.36	$168,626	$194,499	$221,890

suggest making as small a down payment as is allowed. You will have to assess many factors, such as your tax bracket and your investment potential, to determine how large a down payment you should make.

| EXAMPLE 3 | **Comparing the effect of a down payment** |

If you are obtaining a $120,000 30-year 8% loan, what would you save in monthly payment and in total payments by increasing your down payment from $12,000 to $24,000?

Solution   From Table 7.2 we see that the monthly payments for a 30-year 8% loan with a 10% ($12,000) down payment are $792.47, and with a 20% ($24,000) down payment the monthly payments are $704.41. This is a *monthly* savings of $88.06. The total savings are also found by subtracting the amounts shown in Table 7.2:

$$\$285,289 - \$253,588 = \$31,701 \qquad \bullet$$

The amount of the down payment and the monthly payments are calculated in Table 7.2. However, it is unlikely that you will buy a home with a loan of exactly $120,000 and an interest rate of exactly 8%. Let's now consider these calculations.

Since the down payment is simply a percent of the purchase price, we encountered the necessary procedures in the first part of this text.

| EXAMPLE 4 | **Finding the down payment and the amount to be financed** |

The home you select costs $145,500 and you pay 20% down. What is your down payment? How much will be financed?

Solution   DOWN PAYMENT = $145,500 × 0.20 = $29,100

AMOUNT TO BE FINANCED = TOTAL AMOUNT − DOWN PAYMENT

= $145,500 − $29,100

= $116,400

You can also find the amount to be financed by using the complement of the down payment. The complement of a 20% down payment is 0.80.

AMOUNT TO BE FINANCED = TOTAL AMOUNT × COMPLEMENT

= $145,500(0.80)

= $116,400 $\qquad \bullet$

We will use Table II in Appendix B (at the back of the book) to calculate the amount of the monthly payment for a loan. You will need to know the amount to be financed, the interest rate, and the length of time the loan is to be financed.

Monthly Payment

The formula for finding the monthly payment uses Table II in Appendix B as follows:

$$\text{MONTHLY PAYMENT} = \frac{\text{AMOUNT OF LOAN}}{1,000} \times \text{TABLE II ENTRY}$$

EXAMPLE 5   **Finding the monthly payment for a loan**

What is the monthly payment for a home loan of $54,800 if the interest rate is $7\frac{1}{2}\%$, financed for 30 years?

Solution   Notice that Table II is expressed in thousands of dollars. This means that you need to divide the amount to be financed by 1,000 (you can do this mentally). For this example, we obtain 54.8. Next, find the entry in Table II for 7.5% for 30 years: 6.99. This represents the cost to repay $1,000. Since there are 54.8 thousands, we multiply

$$6.99 \times 54.8 = 383.052$$

The monthly payments for this loan are $383.05.

Maximum House Payment

For many people, buying a home is the single most important financial decision of a lifetime. There are three steps in buying and financing a home. The first step consists of finding a home you would like to buy and then reaching an agreement with the seller on the price and the terms. For this step you will need to negotiate a *purchase-and-sale agreement* or *sales contract*. The second step involves finding a lender to finance the purchase. You will need to understand interest as you shop around to obtain the best terms. Finally, the third step involves paying certain *closing costs* in a process called *settlement* or **closing,** where the deal is finalized. The term **closing costs** refers to money exchanged at the settlement, above and beyond the down payment on the property. These costs may include an attorney's fee, the lender's administration fee, taxes, and points.

The first step in buying a home consists of finding a house you can afford and then coming to an agreement with the seller. A real estate agent can help you find the type of home you want for the money you can afford to pay. A great deal depends on the amount of down payment you can make. It is nice to look at something like Table 7.2, but in the real world the house you can afford and the down payment you can make are determined by your income. A useful rule of thumb in determining the monthly payment you can afford is given here:

1. Subtract any monthly bills (not paid off in the next 6 months) from your gross monthly income.

2. Multiply by 36%.

Your house payment should not exceed this amount. Another way of determining whether you can afford a house is to multiply your annual salary by 4; the purchase price should not exceed this amount. Today, the 36% factor is more common, and it is the one we will use in this book.

EXAMPLE 6   **Finding the maximum house payment**

Suppose that your monthly income is $3,500 and your current monthly payments on bills total $290. What is the maximum amount you should plan to spend for house payments?

Solution   Step 1 $3,500 − $290 = $3,210

               Step 2 $3,210 × 0.36 = $1,155.60

The maximum house payment should be $1,155.60 per month.

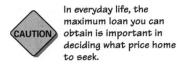

In everyday life, the maximum loan you can obtain is important in deciding what price home to seek.

You now know how much you can afford (maximum house payment), but how does this relate to the amount of the loan? Finding the answer involves using Table II "backward."

Maximum Loan

> The formula for finding the maximum loan for a home uses Table II in Appendix B as follows:
>
> $$\text{MAXIMUM LOAN} = \frac{\text{MONTHLY PAYMENT YOU CAN AFFORD}}{\text{TABLE II ENTRY}} \times 1{,}000$$

EXAMPLE 7

Finding the maximum loan

Suppose that the maximum house payment you can afford is $1,155.60 per month. What is the maximum loan you should seek if you will finance your purchase with an 8.5% 30-year loan?

Solution   We find the entry in Table II in Appendix B corresponding to 8.5% over 30 years: 7.69. Then

$$\text{MAXIMUM LOAN} = \frac{1{,}155.60}{7.69} \times 1{,}000$$

$$\approx 150{,}273.08 \qquad \textit{Display:} \quad 150273.0819$$

The maximum loan is $150,273.08.

We conclude this section with two applied examples about buying a house.

EXAMPLE 8

Financial considerations in buying a house

Suppose that you want to purchase a home for $110,000 with a 30-year mortgage at 8% interest. Suppose that you can put 20% down.

a. What is the amount of the down payment?

b. What is the amount to be financed?

c. What are the monthly payments?

d. What is the total amount of interest paid on this loan?

e. What is the necessary monthly income to be able to afford this loan?

Solution

a. DOWN PAYMENT = $110,000 × 0.20 = $22,000

b. AMOUNT TO BE FINANCED = $110,000 × 0.80 = $88,000

c. Use Table II; the entry for 8% on a 30-year loan is 7.34. Thus,

$$\text{MONTHLY PAYMENTS} = 88 \times \$7.34 = \$645.92$$

d. The total interest paid can be found by subtracting the amount financed from the total paid:

$$\text{TOTAL PAID} = (\text{NUMBER OF PAYMENTS})(\text{AMOUNT OF EACH PAYMENT})$$

$$= 360 \times \$645.92$$

$$= \$232{,}531.20$$

$$I = A - P$$
$$= \$232{,}531.20 - \$88{,}000 \quad \text{Don't forget to subtract the amount of the loan and NOT the price of the house.}$$
$$= \$144{,}531.20$$

e. Remember, the amount of the house payment should be no more than 36% of the gross monthly income less monthly bills. Consequently, you must answer the question:

36% OF WHAT NUMBER is $645.92?

$$\frac{36}{100} = \frac{645.92}{W}$$
$$36W = 64{,}592$$
$$W \approx 1{,}794.22$$

This means that the monthly salary remaining after monthly bills would need to be about $1,794.22. This is an annual salary (assuming no other monthly bills) of about $21,500.   ●

EXAMPLE 9 **Finding the necessary down payment for a home loan**

Suppose that your gross monthly salary is $2,500 and your spouse's gross salary is $2,000 per month. Your monthly bills are $800. The home you wish to purchase costs $178,000, and the loan is a 10% 30-year loan. How much down payment (rounded to the nearest hundred dollars) is necessary for you to be able to afford this home?

Solution   First, determine the monthly payment you can afford:

$$\$2{,}500 + \$2{,}000 - \$800 = \$3{,}700$$

You can afford 36% of this for the house payment:

$$0.36(\$3{,}700) = \$1{,}332 \quad \text{This is what you can afford.}$$

Next, determine the Table II entry for 10% over 30 years: 8.78. Then

$$\text{MAXIMUM AMOUNT OF LOAN} = \frac{1{,}332}{8.78} \times 1{,}000$$
$$\approx 151{,}708.43$$

Since the house costs $178,000, it would be necessary to make a down payment of $178,000 − $151,708 = $26,292. The necessary down payment is $26,300. (This is about a 15% down payment.)   ●

PROBLEM SET 7.6

1. What factors are important when looking for a home loan?
   interest rate, origination fee, and points
2. What are points on a home loan?
   Each point is a fee of 1% of the amount of the loan.
3. What factors influence the amount of monthly payment for a home loan?   length of loan, down payment, and APR

4. What is the rule of thumb for determining the monthly payment you can afford?
   Subtract monthly bills and multiply by 0.36.
5. How do you find the monthly payment for a home loan?
   Use the monthly payment formula (and Table II).
6. How do you find the maximum amount of a home loan?
   Use the maximum amount of a loan formula (and Table II).

DRILL AND PRACTICE **LEVEL 2**

Use estimation to select the best response in Problems 7–12.
Do not calculate.

7. A $98,000 30-year loan at
        10% + 0.5 point + $150
would have a fee for points of about   B

   A. $10,000   B. $500   C. $650   D. $850

8. A $98,000 30-year loan at
        10% + 0.5 point + $150
would have total fees of about   C

   A. $10,000   B. $500   C. $650   D. $850

9. A $98,000 30-year loan at
        10% + 0.5 point + $150
would have a down payment of about   A

   A. $10,000   B. $500   C. $650   D. $850

10. A $98,000 30-year loan at
        10% + 0.5 point + $150
would have a monthly payment of about   D

   A. $10,000   B. $500   C. $650   D. $850

11. A $98,000 30-year loan at
        10% + 0.5 point + $150
would have a comparison rate of   B

   A. 10%   B. more than 10%

   C. less than 10%

12. A $98,000 30-year loan at
        10% + 0.5 point + $150
would require what monthly income for the buyer?   C

   A. $8,000   B. $28,600   C. $2,500   D. $850

Determine the down payment and the amount to be financed for
each home described in Problems 13–16.

13. a. $148,500; 5% down $7,425; $141,075

   b. $169,900; 20% down $33,980; $135,920

14. a. $153,200; 10% down $15,320; $137,880

   b. $164,350; 10% down $16,435; $147,915

15. a. $250,250; 10% down $25,025; $225,225

   b. $950,000; 20% down $190,000; $760,000

16. a. $185,000; 20% down $37,000; $148,000

   b. $312,000; 30% down $93,600; $218,400

What are the bank charges for the points indicated in Prob-
lems 17–18?

17. a. $53,200; 3 points $1,596

   b. $85,000; $\frac{1}{2}$ point $425

18. a. $64,350; 5 points $3,217.50

   b. $112,000; $\frac{3}{4}$ point $840

For Problems 19–22, determine the comparable interest rate
(to two decimal places) for a $50,000 loan when the quoted
information is given.

19. 11.5% + 2 pts + $450   11.86%

20. 7.25% + 3 pts + $250   7.69%

21. 9.3% + $\frac{3}{4}$ pt + $150   9.43%

22. 10.8% + $\frac{1}{2}$ pt + $200   10.91%

Use Table II to estimate the monthly payment for each loan
described in Problems 23–28.

23. $48,500; 30 years; 6% $291.00

24. $48,500; 20 years; 8% $405.46

25. $69,900; 30 years; $6\frac{1}{2}$% $441.77

26. $112,000; 15 years; 7% $1,006.88

27. $112,000; 25 years; 7% $791.84

28. $112,000; 30 years; 7% $744.80

If you are obtaining a $120,000 30-year 8% loan, what
would you save in monthly payments and in the total
payments by increasing your down payment as given in
Problems 29–32?

29. $12,000 to $30,000 $132.08; $47,549

30. $12,000 to $36,000 $176.11; $63,399

31. $24,000 to $30,000 $44.02; $15,848

32. $30,000 to $36,000 $44.04; $15,854

Determine the maximum monthly payment for a house (to the
nearest dollar), given the information in Problems 33–38.

33. Gross monthly income of $985; current monthly payments
of $135. $306

34. Gross monthly income of $1,240; current monthly
payments of $215. $369

35. Gross monthly income of $2,800; current monthly
payments of $540. $814

36. Gross monthly income of $2,300; current monthly
payments of $350. $702

37. Gross monthly income of $1,480; current monthly
payments of $520. $346

38. Gross monthly income of $3,600; current monthly
payments of $370. $1,163

What is the maximum 30-year loan that you could obtain if you
are given the loan rate and the maximum house payment you
can afford in Problems 39–42?

39. $1,155.60; 7.5% $165,321.89

40. $2,430; 7% $365,413.53

41. $942; 8% $128,337.87

42. $1,850; 8.5% $240,572.17

APPLICATIONS **LEVEL 2**

In Problems 43–54, find the amount of the down payment (rounded to the nearest hundred dollars) necessary for the buyer to afford the monthly payments for the described home.

43. Monthly salary of $2,900, with monthly payments of $400; $125,000 home with a 30-year 10% loan **$22,500**

44. Monthly salary of $1,900, with monthly payments of $250; $89,000 home with a 30-year 9% loan **$15,200**

45. Monthly salary of $4,900, with monthly payments of $700; $195,000 home with a 30-year 11% loan **$36,200**

46. Monthly salary of $4,900, with monthly payments of $700; $195,000 home with a 30-year 9% loan **$7,200**

47. Monthly salary of $3,500, with monthly payments of $500; $148,000 home with a 30-year 12% loan **$43,000**

48. Monthly salary of $3,500, with monthly payments of $500; $225,000 home with a 30-year 10% loan **$102,000**

49. Suppose that you want to purchase a home for $375,000, with a 30-year mortgage at 7% interest. Suppose that you can put 20% down.

   a. What is the amount of the down payment? **$75,000**

   b. What is the amount to be financed? **$300,000**

   c. What are the monthly payments? **$1,995.00**

   d. What is the total amount of interest paid on the 30-year loan? **$418,200**

   e. What is the necessary monthly income for you to be able to afford this home? **$5,541.67**

© Bill Varie/Corbis

50. Suppose that you want to purchase a home for $100,000, with a 20-year mortgage at 7.5% interest. Suppose that you can put 20% down.

   a. What is the amount of the down payment? **$20,000**

   b. What is the amount to be financed? **$80,000**

   c. What are the monthly payments? **$644.80**

   d. What is the total amount of interest paid on the 20-year loan? **$74,752**

   e. What is the necessary monthly income for you to be able to afford this home? **$1,791.11**

51. Suppose that you want to purchase a home for $450,000 with a 30-year mortgage at 6% interest. Suppose that you can put 20% down.

   a. What is the amount of the down payment? **$90,000**

   b. What is the amount to be financed? **$360,000**

   c. What are the monthly payments? **$2,160**

   d. What is the total amount of interest paid on the 30-year loan? **$417,600**

   e. What is the necessary monthly income for you to be able to afford this home? **$6,000**

52. Suppose that you want to purchase a home for $225,000, with a 20-year mortgage at 11% interest. Suppose that you can put 20% down.

   a. What is the amount of the down payment? **$45,000**

   b. What is the amount to be financed? **$180,000**

   c. What are the monthly payments? **$1,857.60**

   d. What is the total amount of interest paid on the 20-year loan? **$265,824**

   e. What is the necessary monthly income for you to be able to afford this home? **$5,160**

53. In this book we use 36% as a factor of net income in calculating the amount of the maximum monthly payment for a home loan. This is not the only criterion. A booklet from the Federal National Mortgage Association ("Fannie Mae") called "A Guide to Home Ownership" computes the maximum monthly payment as follows:

   Method 1 Calculate 33% of the gross monthly income.

   Method 2 Calculate 38% of the gross monthly income. Subtract the monthly debt payments.

   Use the lesser of (1) and (2) to compute the maximum monthly house payment. Use this criterion to assess the information given in Example 6. **(1) $1,155; (2) $1,040; the maximum house payment is $1,040.**

54. Dorothy and Wes have found the "home of their dreams," and it costs only $525,000. They have never purchased a home before—or anything else involving so much money—and they are very excited. There seems to be so much to do, and so many new words are being used by the realtor and the banker that they are also confused. If their combined annual salaries are $99,500 and if the current interest rate is 7.5% APR, how much of a down payment will they need to be able to afford their "dream home," and what is the monthly payment if the loan is financed for 30 years? **Maximum loan is $427,038.63; down payment of $97,961.37**

Problem of the Day

Explain what is wrong, if anything, with the statements in Problems 55–60? Explain your reasoning.

55. For a $120,000 loan with interest rate 8% and 30% down, the total amount that can be saved by changing the term from 30 years to 25 years is $53,264, because the total amount of payments changes from $221,890 to $168,626. You can see this by looking at Table 7.2.

F; it saves $27,391 (25 years not 20 years).

56. For a $120,000 loan with interest rate 8% and 30% down, the amount that can be saved monthly by changing the term from 30 years to 25 years is $31.97, because the monthly payments change from $648.33 to $616.36. You can see this by looking at Table 7.2. *F; it costs $31.97 more (not less).*

57. If you obtain a quotation for a home costing $315,000, obtain a 30-year loan at 5.5% + $\frac{3}{4}$ point + $100, and make a 20% down payment, you can find the comparison rate as follows:

$$\text{COMPARISON RATE} = 5.5 + 0.125 \left(0.75 + \frac{100}{252,000}\right)$$

F; did not correctly change percents to decimals. It should
$$\approx 5.59\%$$
be 0.055 + 0.125(0.0075 + 100/252,000) ≈ 0.05599; 5.60%

58. If you obtain a quotation for a home costing $435,000, obtain a 20-year loan at 6% + 1.5 points + $200, and make a 20% down payment, you can find the comparison rate as follows:

$$\text{COMPARISON RATE} = 0.06 + \left(0.015 + \frac{200}{348,000}\right)$$

$$= 0.0755747126$$

The comparison rate is 7.56%.

F; forgot the 0.125 factor. The comparison rate is 6.19%.

59. If you obtain a quotation for a home costing $315,000, obtain a 30-year loan at 6.5% + $\frac{3}{4}$ point + $100, and make a 20% down payment, you can find the total amount of interest paid on this loan as follows:

$$\$315,000 \times 0.8 = \$252,000;$$

the Table II, Appendix B entry for a 6.5%, 30-year loan is 6.32, so the monthly payment is

$$\$6.32 \times 252 = \$1,592.64$$

Then,

$$I = A - P$$
$$= \$1,592.64(360) - \$315,000$$
$$= \$258,350.40$$

F; $321,350.40; should subtract the amount of the loan, not the price of the house.

60. If you obtain a quotation for a home costing $435,000, obtain a 20-year loan at 6% + 1.5 points + $200, and make a 20% down payment, you can find the monthly payment as follows:

$$\$435,000 \times 0.8 = \$348,000$$

the Table II, Appendix B entry for a 6%, 20-year loan is 6.00, so the monthly payment is

$$\$6.00 \times 348 = \$2,088$$

F; looked up the wrong number in Table II; it should be 7.16 so that the monthly payment is $2,491.68

7.7 Chapter 7 Summary and Review

Take some time getting ready to work the review problems in this section. First, look back at the definition and property boxes. You will maximize your understanding of this chapter by working the problems in this section only after you have studied the material.

IMPORTANT TERMS

Numbers refer to sections of this chapter.

Spending some time with the terms and objectives of this chapter will pay dividends in assuring your success.

Add-on interest [7.3]
Adjusted balance method [7.4]
Amortized loan [7.3]
Annual compounding [7.5]
Annual percentage rate [7.3]
APR [7.3]
Average daily balance method [7.4]
Balloon payment [7.3]
Closed-end loan [7.3]

Closing [7.6]
Closing costs [7.6]
Comparison rate for home loans [7.6]
Complement [7.1]
Compound interest [7.5]
Compound interest formula [7.5]
Credit card [7.3]
Daily compounding [7.5]
Dealer's cost [7.3]
Discount [7.1]

Discount formulas [7.1]
Down payment [7.6]
Exact interest [7.2]
Five-percent offer [7.3]
Foreclose [7.6]
Future value [7.2]
Future value formula [7.5]
Grace period [7.4]
Inflation [7.5]
Installment loan [7.3]
Installment loan formulas [7.3]

Installments [7.3]
Interest [7.2]
Interest-only loan [7.3]
Interest rate [7.2]
Line of credit [7.3]
Maximum amount of a loan
     formula [7.6]
Monthly compounding [7.5]
Monthly payment
     formula [7.6]
Mortgage [7.6]
Open-end loan [7.3]

Ordinary interest [7.2]
Origination fee [7.6]
Percent markdown [7.1]
Points [7.6]
Present value [7.5]
Present value formula [7.5]
Previous balance
     method [7.4]
Principal [7.2]
Quarterly
     compounding [7.5]
Revolving credit [7.3]

Sale price [7.1]
Sale price formula [7.1]
Sales tax formula [7.1]
Semiannual
     compounding [7.5]
Simple interest
     formula [7.2]
Sticker price [7.3]
Time (for a loan) [7.2]

Essential Ideas

[7.1]	Problem 1	Finding the discount for an item on sale.
	Problem 2	Find the complement of a number.
	Problems 3–4	Know how to find the sale price if you know the original price, percent markdown, and sales tax rate.
[7.2]	Problem 1	Know the definition of interest.
	Problems 2; 4	Know the simple interest formula and the future value formulas.
	Problem 3	Know how to change a given number of days to years.
[7.3]	Problem 1	Be able to describe add-on interest and how it is calculated.
	Problem 2	Know how to use the APR formula.
[7.4]	Problems 1–5	Know the formula for calculating credit card interest and be able to calculate it using the adjusted balance, previous balance, and average daily balance methods.
	Problem 6	Know the number of days in each month.
[7.5]	Problems 1–4	Know the formulas for calculating future value and present value of compound interest; be able to describe the meaning of each variable.
[7.6]	Problems 1; 3–4	Describe the factors that are important when looking for a home loan. Know the factors that influence the amount of monthly payment. State a rule of thumb for determining the monthly payment you can afford.
	Problem 2	Know what is meant by points in reference to home loans.
	Problem 5	Know how to find the monthly payment for a home loan.
	Problem 6	Know how to find the maximum amount of a home loan, given an income level.

LEARNING OUTCOMES

The material in this chapter is reviewed in the following list of learning outcomes. A self-test (with answers and suggestions for additional study) is given. This self-test is constructed so that each problem number corresponds to a related objective. For example, Problem 7 is testing Objective 7.7. This self-test is followed by a practice test with the questions in mixed order.

[7.1]	*Objective* 7.1	Find the discount, given the original price and the percent markdown.
[7.1]	*Objective* 7.2	Find the complement of a given number.
[7.1]	*Objective* 7.3	Find the sales tax or price including tax.

Self-Test

Each question of this self-test is related to the corresponding objective listed above.

1. If an item is priced at $286 and the discount is 35%, what is the amount of the discount?

2. Find the complement of each given number: **a.** 0.73 **b.** 38% **c.** $\frac{1}{8}$

3. What is the price, including tax, for a set of four tires that cost $89.95 each, if the sales tax is $5\frac{1}{2}\%$?

4. **a.** If a billiard table you have been wanting costs $3,500 but now is on sale for 20% OFF, what is the sale price for the billiard table?
   b. If the sale price of an item is $384 and the sale is 20% OFF the regular price, what is the regular price?
   c. The sale price of a golf cart is $1,365, and the original price is $1,950. What is the percent markdown?

5. What is the future value for a deposit of $35,500 at 8% simple interest for 6 years?

6. Fill in the blanks.

	Interest	Principal	Rate	Time
a.	$560	_____	8%	2 years
b.	$819	$1,950	_____	6 years
c.	$510	$850	15%	_____

7. Suppose that the car you wish to purchase has a sticker price of $22,730 with a dealer cost of $18,579. Make a 5% offer for this car (rounded to the nearest hundred dollars).

8. Suppose that the amount to be financed for a car purchase is $13,500 at an add-on interest rate of 2.9% for 2 years. What are the monthly installment and the amount of interest that you will pay?

9. Find the APR for the loan described in Problem 8.

10. Suppose a car with a cash price of $11,450 is offered for nothing down with 48 monthly payments of $353.04. What is the total amount paid for both car and financing?

11. Find the APR for the loan described in Problem 10.

12. If a credit card has a daily rate (365-day year) of 0.0547945%, what is the APR (rounded to the nearest tenth of a percent)?

13. From the consumer's point of view, which method of calculating interest on a credit card is most advantageous? Illustrate the three types of calculating interest for a purchase of $525 with 9% APR for a 31-day month in which it takes 7 days for your $100 payment to be received and recorded.

14. Compare the future value of $10,000 invested at 5% for 20 years simple interest with the future value compounded annually.

15. Identify the variables and then answer the following question: What is the future value of a deposit of $855 at 9% for 3 years compounded semiannually?

16. Find the future value of $25,000 invested at 5.9% interest compounded daily for 10 years.

17. If you purchase a home today for $185,000, what would you expect it to be worth in 30 years if you assume an inflation rate of 8%?

18. Suppose that you want to have $1,000,000 in 50 years. To achieve this goal, how much do you need to deposit today if you can earn 9% interest compounded monthly?

19. What is a 30% down payment for a house costing $220,000?

20. What is the amount that must be paid for $1\frac{1}{2}$ points on a home costing $462,000 with a 20% down payment?

21. What is the comparison rate (rounded to the nearest tenth of a percent) for a home loan of 6% with fees of 2 points and $350? Assume that the loan value is $154,000.

22. What is the monthly payment for a home loan of $154,000 if the rate is 6% and the time is 20 years?

23. Assume a 30-year 6.0% loan.
   a. What is the monthly payment for a home costing $320,000 with a $32,000 (10%) down payment?
   b. What is the monthly payment for the same home with a $64,000 (20%) down payment?
   c. What is the total savings over the length of the loan that is gained by making a 20% down payment (part **b**), rather than a 10% down payment (part **a**)?

24. What is the maximum monthly payment (to the nearest dollar) you can afford for a house if your gross monthly income is $3,500 and you have current monthly payments of $1,400?

25. If you have a gross monthly income of $3,500 (with no outstanding bills) and the home you wish to purchase costs $154,000, what is the necessary down payment (rounded to the nearest hundred dollars) if the loan is for 20 years at 11%?

26. Estimate the minimum amount of money necessary in a retirement account at the time of retirement. (Pick the best response.)
A. $100,000   B. $1,000,000   C. $100,000,000

27. Suppose that you expect to receive a $100,000 inheritance when you reach age 21 in 3 years and 4 months. What is the present value of your inheritance if the current interest rate is 6.4% compounded monthly?

28. Suppose that you purchase a $1,000 3-year certificate paying 4.58% simple interest. How much will you have when the certificate matures?

29. In December 2007, Sears was selling a refrigerator for $1,599.99.
  a. If the refrigerator is financed for 6 months at an add-on rate of 8%, what is the monthly payment?
  b. If the refrigerator carries 0% financing for 6 months, what is the monthly payment?
  c. The delivery charge is $50. If you are given a choice of free delivery OR 0% financing for 6 months, which would be the less expensive choice?

30. If you have a gross monthly income of $4,850 with no monthly bills and the home you wish to purchase costs $374,900, what is the necessary down payment (rounded to the nearest hundred dollars) for the indicated loans?
  a. 25 years at 8%   **b.** 25 years at 7%   **c.** 30 years at 6%

STOP

STUDY HINTS *Compare your solutions and answers to the self-test. For each problem you missed, work some additional problems in the section listed in the margin. After you have worked these problems, you can test yourself with the practice test.*

Additional Problems

[7.1] Problems 5–8

[7.1] Problems 9–12

[7.1] Problems 21–26

[7.1] Problems 27–46

Complete Solutions to the Self-Test

1. DISCOUNT = ORIGINAL PRICE × PERCENT MARKDOWN
$$= 286 \times 0.35$$
$$= 100.1$$
The discount is $100.10.

2. a. $1 - 0.73 = 0.27$
  b. $100\% - 38\% = 62\%$
  c. $1 - \frac{1}{8} = \frac{7}{8}$

3. TOTAL PRICE = ORIGINAL PRICE × (TAX RATE + 1)
$$= 4(89.95)(1 + 0.055)$$
$$= 379.589$$
The total price of the tires is $379.59.

4. a. SALE PRICE = ORIGINAL PRICE × COMPLEMENT
$$= 3,500 \times 0.80$$
$$= 2,800$$
  The sale price is $2,800.

  b. ORIGINAL PRICE = SALE PRICE ÷ COMPLEMENT
$$= 384 \div 0.80$$
$$= 480$$
  The original price is $480.

  c. COMPLEMENT = SALE PRICE ÷ ORIGINAL PRICE
$$= 1,365 \div 1,950$$
$$= 0.7$$
  The percent markdown is 30%.

[7.2] Problems 15–22

5. $A = P(1 + rt)$
   $= 35{,}500(1 + 0.08 \times 6)$
   $= 52{,}540$
The future value is $52,540.

[7.2] Problems 23–40

6. a.

$I = Prt$	Simple interest formula
$560 = P(0.08)(2)$	Substitute values.
$280 = 0.08P$	Divide both sides by 2.
$3{,}500 = P$	Divide both sides by 0.08.

The principal is $3,500.

b.

$I = Prt$	Simple interest formula
$819 = 1{,}950(r)(6)$	Substitute values.
$136.5 = 1{,}950r$	Divide both sides by 6.
$0.07 = r$	Divide both sides by 1,950.

The rate is 7%.

c.

$I = Prt$	Simple interest formula
$510 = 850(0.15)t$	Substitute values.
$510 = 127.5t$	Multiply.
$4 = t$	Divide both sides by 127.5.

The time is 4 years.

[7.3] Problems 11–16

7. $18{,}579(1 + 0.05) = \$19{,}507.95$
You should offer $19,500 for the car.

[7.3] Problems 17–26

8. $I = Prt = 13{,}500(0.029)(2) = 783$
$A = P + I = 13{,}500 + 783 = 14{,}283$
Monthly payment is $14,283 \div 24 = \$595.125$.
The total interest is $783, and the monthly payment is $595.13.

[7.3] Problems 27–36

9. $\text{APR} = \dfrac{2Nr}{N + 1}$
$\qquad = \dfrac{2(24)(0.029)}{25}$
$\qquad = 0.05568$

[7.3] Problems 37–40

10. $A = 48(\$353.04) = \$16{,}945.92$

[7.3] Problems 41–50

11. Using $A = 16{,}945.92$ from Problem 10, and $P = 11{,}450$
(given), we find
$$I = A - P = 16{,}945.92 - 11{,}450.00 = 5{,}495.92$$
Also,

$I = Prt$	48 months is 4 years, so $t = 4$.
$5{,}495.92 = 11{,}450(r)(4)$	Divide both sides by 4.
$0.12 \approx r$	Divide both sides by 11,450.

Finally,
$$\text{APR} = \frac{2Nr}{N + 1}$$
$$= \frac{2(48)r}{49}$$
$$\approx 0.235 \qquad Display: \quad .2350986187$$
The APR is about 23.5%.

[7.4] Problems 21–26

[7.4] Problems 31–48

[7.5] Problems 5–10

[7.5] Problems 11–26

[7.5] Problems 27–40

[7.5] Problems 41–44

[7.5] Problems 50–52

12. APR $= 0.0547945\% \times 365 = 19.999993\%$
The APR is about 20.0%.

13. The adjusted balance method is most advantageous to the consumer.
Previous Balance Method:
$$I = Prt = 525(0.09)\left(\tfrac{1}{12}\right) = 3.9375$$
The finance charge is $3.94.

Adjusted Balance Method:
$$I = Prt = (525 - 100)(0.09)\left(\tfrac{1}{12}\right) = 3.1875$$
The finance charge is $3.19.

Average Daily Balance Method:
Average balance: $(525 \times 7 + 425 \times 24) \div 31 \approx 447.58$
$$I = Prt = P(0.09)\left(\tfrac{31}{365}\right) \approx 3.42 \qquad Display: \quad 3.421232877$$
The finance charge is $3.42.

14. *Simple interest:*   *Compound interest:*

$$\begin{aligned} A &= P(1 + rt) & A &= P(1 + r)^N \\ &= 10{,}000(1 + 0.05 \times 20) & &= 10{,}000(1 + 0.05)^{20} \\ &= 20{,}000 & &= 26{,}532.98 \end{aligned}$$

Compound interest yields $6,532.98 more than simple interest.

15. Present value, $P = \$855$; annual rate is $r = 9\% = 0.09$; compounded semiannually, $n = 2$; and the time (in years) is $t = 3$. We calculate $N = 2(3) = 6$ and $I = \tfrac{r}{n} = \tfrac{0.09}{2}$.
By calculator:
$$\begin{aligned} A &= P(1 + i)^N \\ &= 855\left(1 + \frac{0.09}{2}\right)^6 \\ &\approx 1{,}113.432407 \end{aligned}$$
The future value is $1,113.43.

16. $A = P(1 + i)^N$
$$\begin{aligned} &= 25{,}000\left(1 + \frac{0.059}{360}\right)^{360(10)} \\ &= 25{,}000\left(1 + \frac{0.059}{360}\right)^{3{,}600} \\ &\approx 45{,}097.53. \end{aligned}$$
The future value is $45,097.53

17. For inflation, use future value where $n = 1$; for this problem, we have
$$P = 185{,}000, t = 30, \text{ and } r = 0.08.$$
$$A = 185{,}000(1 + 0.08)^{30} \approx 1{,}861{,}591.52$$
In 30 years, your home will be worth about $1.9 million.

18. $A = \$1{,}000{,}000; t = 50, r = 0.09; n = 12;$
$N = nt = 50(12) = 600; i = r/n = 0.09/12.$ Thus,
$$\begin{aligned} P &= A \div (1 + i)^N \\ &= 1{,}000{,}000 \div \left(1 + \frac{0.09}{12}\right)^{600} \\ &\approx 11{,}297.10 \qquad Display: \quad 11297.10362 \end{aligned}$$
Deposit $11,297.10 to have a million dollars in 50 years.

19. DOWN PAYMENT $= 0.30(\$220,000) = \$66,000$

20. The down payment is $0.20(462,000) = \$92,400$.
POINTS: $0.015(462,000 - 92,400) = 5,544$.
The fee for points is $5,544.

21. COMPARISON RATE $= 0.06 + 0.125\left(0.02 + \frac{350}{154,000}\right)$ *Display:* 0.0627840909
The comparison rate is 6.3%.

22. MONTHLY PAYMENT $= \dfrac{154,000}{1,000}$ (TABLE II ENTRY)

$= 154(7.16)$

$= 1,102.64$

The monthly payment is $1,102.64.

23. a. MONTHLY PAYMENT $= \dfrac{(320,000 - 32,000)}{1,000}$ (TABLE II ENTRY)

$= 288(6.00)$

$= 1,728$

The monthly payment is $1,728.00.

b. MONTHLY PAYMENT $= \dfrac{(320,000 - 64,000)}{1,000}$ (TABLE II ENTRY)

$= 256(6.00)$

$= 1,536$

The monthly payment is $1,536.00.

c. The monthly savings is $1,728 - \$1,536 = \$192$.
The total savings is
$$30 \times 12 \times \$192 = \$69,120$$

24. $0.36(3,500 - 1,400) = 756$
The maximum monthly payment is $756.

25. AMOUNT YOU CAN AFFORD $= 0.36(3,500) = 1,260$

Table II entry is 10.32. Thus,
$$\text{MAXIMUM LOAN} = \frac{1,260}{10.32} \times 1,000 \approx 122,093.02$$

The necessary down payment is
$$154,000 - 122,093 = 31,907$$
The down payment should be $31,900.

26. Estimate 10% annual interest:
A. $\$100,000(0.1) = \$10,000$; seems too little
B. $\$1,000,000(0.1) = \$100,000$; seems too high, but remember that you need to take into account inflation between now and when you retire.
Estimate B is the best choice.

Applications

27. $A = \$100,000; r = 0.064; t = 3\frac{4}{12}; n = 12$

Calculate:

$$N = nt = 12\left(\frac{40}{12}\right) = 40 \qquad i = \frac{r}{n} = \frac{0.064}{12}$$

$$P = A \div (1 + i)^N$$

$$= 100,000 \div \left(1 + \frac{0.064}{12}\right)^{40}$$

$$\approx 80,834.49 \qquad \textit{Display:} \quad 80834.48968$$

The present value of the inheritance is $80,834.49.

28. Use the future value formula:

$$A = P(1 + rt)$$
$$= 1,000(1 + 0.0458 \times 3)$$
$$= 1,137.40$$

The value of the certificate when it matures is $1,137.40.

29. a. $I = Prt = \$1,599.99 \times (0.08) \times \frac{1}{2} = \$64.00$

Since this is add-on interest, we add the interest to the loan amount:

$$\$64.00 + \$1,599.99 = \$1,663.99$$

The monthly payment is:

$$m = \frac{\$1,663.99}{6} = \$277.33$$

b. Since the refrigerator must be paid off in 6 months,

$$m = \frac{\$1,599.99}{6} = \$266.67$$

c. The difference (per month) is

$$\$277.33 - \$266.67 = \$10.66$$

For six months, this is $63.96. It is better (barely) to take the 0% financing.

30. The maximum house payment is $4,850 \times 0.36 = \$1,746$. To find the amount of loan, use Table II.

a. 25 years at 8% is 7.72.

$$\text{MAXIMUM LOAN} = \frac{1,746.00}{7.72} \times 1,000$$

$$\approx 226,165.80$$

The down payment needs to be

$$\$374,900 - \$226,165.80 = \$148,734.20$$

b. 25 years at 7% is 7.07.

$$\text{MAXIMUM LOAN} = \frac{1,746.00}{7.07} \times 1,000$$

$$\approx 246,958.98$$

The down payment needs to be

$$\$374,900 - \$246,958.98 = \$127,941.02$$

c. 30 years at 6% is 6.00.

$$\text{MAXIMUM LOAN} = \frac{1,746.00}{6.00} \times 1,000$$

$$= 291,000.00$$

The down payment needs to be

$$\$374,900 - \$291,000 = \$83,900$$

Chapter 7 Review Questions

YIELD

*To prepare for a chapter test, first study the chapter; then, read each term from the important terms list above and make sure you know the meaning of each word; finally, review the chapter objectives. **After** these steps, take the self-test and correct all your answers. The following review questions can be used for extra practice.*

1. a. Find a 5% discount on an item costing $135. $6.75
b. Find a 30% discount on an item costing $30. $9.00
c. Find a 20% discount on an item selling for $89.95. $17.99
d. Find a 45% discount on an item selling for $99. $44.55

2. Find the complement.
a. 0.18   *0.82*   **b.** $\frac{1}{7}$ $\frac{6}{7}$ **c.** 13%   *87%*   **d.** $33\frac{1}{3}\%$ $66\frac{2}{3}\%$

3. Convert the credit card rates to APR rates (rounded to the nearest percent).
a. monthly rate of $1\frac{1}{2}\%$ *18%*   **b.** monthly rate of $1\frac{1}{4}\%$ *15%*
c. daily rate of 0.05753%   *21%*   **d.** daily rate of 0.0246575%   *9%*

4. Assume that the month is 30 days long and that it takes 8 days to receive a payment. Suppose that a $1,200 purchase is made and the current billing shows this charge. What is the finance charge in the next billing period if the credit card uses 20% APR?
a. $100 payment; previous balance method   *$20.00*
b. $100 payment; adjusted balance method   *$18.33*
c. $100 payment; average daily balance method   *$18.52*
d. $1,100 payment; average daily balance method   *$6.47*

5. Assume that $2,500 is invested at 18% for five years. Find the future value.
a. simple interest   *$4,750*   **b.** compounded annually   *$5,719.39*
c. compounded monthly   *$6,108.05*   **d.** compounded semiannually   *$5,918.41*

6. Suppose that your present salary is $22,000 per year. Predict what your salary will be (to the nearest thousand dollars) when you retire in 40 years, if you assume an annual rate of inflation as specified.
a. 8%   *$478,000*   **b.** 2%   *$49,000*
c. 12%   *$2,047,000*   **d.** 7%   *$329,000*

7. Fill in the blanks.

	Interest	Principal	Rate	Time
a.	$2,565	$4,500	19%	3 years
b.	$1,650	$5,500	15%	2 years
c.	$6,210	$4,500	23%	6 years
d.	$456	$600	19%	4 years

8. What is the monthly payment for the described loans?
a. $45,800 30-year loan: 10.5% + 3 points + $500   *$419.07*
b. $45,800 20-year loan: 10.5% + 3 points + $500   *$457.08*
c. $245,000 25-year loan: 7% + 1 point + $200   *$1,732.15*
d. $245,000 30-year loan: 7% + 1 point + $200   *$1,629.25*

9. Determine the comparable interest rate (to two decimal places) for the described bank loans.
   a. $42,200 30-year loan: 10.5% + 3 points + $500   11.02%
   b. $82,000 20-year loan: 7% + 1 point + $200   7.16%
   c. $105,000 25-year loan: 13.2% + 4 points + $100   13.71%
   d. $160,000 30-year loan: 8.4% + $\frac{3}{4}$ point + $150   8.51%

10. a. If a coat you have been wanting normally costs $254, but the store now has a special 20% OFF sale, what is the sale price for this coat? $203.20
    b. If a table has a regular price of $120 but is marked $\frac{1}{3}$ OFF, what is the sale price? $80

11. a. If a dress is marked down from $145 to $87, what is the percent markdown?   40%
    b. If an item is marked $\frac{1}{4}$ OFF and is on sale for $187.50, what is its regular price? $250

12. a. What is the tax on a suit that sells for $250 if the tax rate is 6.5%? $16.25
    b. If the price for a car is $10,950 and the tax rate is 4.5%, what is the total amount, including tax? $11,442.75

13. What is the future value of $12,000 at 17% simple interest for 149 days? $12,844.33

14. How much must be deposited today to have $100,000 in 30 years if it is invested at 12%, compounded daily? $2,734.01

15. Find the amount of interest, the monthly payment, and the APR (rounded to the nearest tenth of a percent) for a bedroom set costing $2,350 with 18% add-on interest for 3 years. $1,269 interest; $100.53 monthly payment; 35.0% APR

16. If a Ford Focus has a sticker price of $17,495 and a dealer cost of $16,152.40, make a 7% offer. $17,283.07

17. If a car with a cash price of $15,450 is offered for nothing down with 60 monthly payments of $360.50, what is the APR (rounded to the nearest tenth of a percent)?   15.7%

18. Suppose a washer and dryer are advertised at a cash price of $895.95 or $39 per month for 36 months. What is the APR for the financed price (rounded to the nearest tenth of a percent)?   36.8%

19. Determine the maximum affordable monthly payment for a house (to the nearest dollar) for someone with a gross monthly income of $4,580 and current monthly payments of $1,200. $1,216.80

20. What are the fees for a $205,000 house purchased with a loan with terms of 30% down, 6% + $\frac{1}{2}$ point + $250? $967.50

21. If you decide to buy for your newborn daughter a $1,000 long-term bond that pays 18% compounded quarterly, how much will your child have on her 20th birthday? $33,830.10

22. What is the present value of an investment worth $5,000 in 3 years with an 8% rate compounded quarterly? $3,942.47

23. An insurance agent offers you a policy that will provide you with $20,000 in 30 years. What is the present value of this policy if you assume an inflation rate of 7%? $2,627.34

24. To make a $45 per month payment, you decide to deposit a lump sum into an account paying 12% interest. How much must you deposit to make the monthly payments from the interest on your deposit? $4,500

25. Compare the cost of driving a 2007 Honda Civic Hybrid (sale price $22,600; 37 miles per gallon) for 100,000 miles with the cost of driving a 2007 Honda Civic LX (sale price $17,760; 23 miles per gallon) the same distance. Also, assume that the cost of gasoline is $2.90/gallon.   The decision to drive the hybrid for 100,000 miles will cost $69.14 additional. See IAS.

Individual Projects

Learning to use sources outside your classroom and textbook is an important skill, and here are some ideas for extending some of the ideas in this chapter.

PROJECT 7.1 Conduct a survey of banks, savings and loan companies, and credit unions in your area. Prepare a report on the different types of savings accounts available and the interest rates they pay. Include methods of payment as well as interest rates.

PROJECT 7.2 Consult an almanac or some government source, and then write a report on the current inflation rate. Project some of these results to the year of your own expected retirement in order to determine what annual retirement salary you will need.

PROJECT 7.3 What is a bank debit card? Investigate and report on the advantages and disadvantages of using a bank debit card. Some aspects to consider: convenience, privacy, safety, record keeping, acceptance, and liability in case of loss or theft. Organize and submit a report.

PROJECT 7.4 Some savings and loan companies advertise that they pay interest *continuously*. Do some research to explain what this means.

PROJECT 7.5 Select a car of your choice, find the list price, and calculate 2% and 5% price offers. Check out available money sources in your community, and prepare a report showing the different costs for the same car. Back up your figures with data.

PROJECT 7.6 Look in a local newspaper and select a home to purchase. Write a report on necessary income, costs, and monthly payments for various options when buying this home.

PROJECT 7.7 Select a particular car and options. Research the cost of the car, as well as sources for purchasing the car. Decide on your best offer and then interview one of the sources to decide whether your offer would be acceptable. Prepare a report on your results.

PROJECT 7.8 **Santa Rosa street problem** On Saturday evenings, a favorite pastime of the high school students in Santa Rosa, California, is to cruise certain streets. The selected routes are shown on the map in Figure 7.3. Is it possible to choose a route so that all the permitted streets are traveled exactly once?

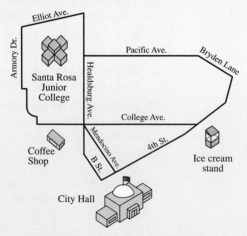

Figure 7.3 Santa Rosa street problem

Answers vary; it cannot be done.

Team Projects

Working in small groups is typical of most work environments, and learning to work with others to communicate specific ideas is an important skill. Work with three or four other students to submit a single report based on each of the following questions.

T17. A radio advertisement for a grocery store claimed, "At other stores a bagger bags your groceries, but at Food for Less you bag the groceries and save a bundle."

    a. Define what you think is meant by "save a bundle."

    b. If a bagger earns minimum wage of $12.00/hr and bags 120 bags in an hour, and you shop and take home 8 bags (the contents of each bag worth $25), how much is your savings in terms of bagger wages?
    2 bags/min is 4 min labor; the savings is 80¢; hardly "a bundle."

    c. Write your savings from part **b** as a percent of the cost of your groceries.
    0.4%; hardly a bundle

T18. Suppose you are given $1,000 to invest. With other members of your team, select an investment strategy, such as savings account, certificate of deposit, stocks, bonds (or even keep the money in a shoe box). Document your investment using your local newspaper. Track your investment for the next 60 days, and then present a report on the results.

T19. With your team, investigate the costs of obtaining a $10,000 business loan repaid in a lump sum in 18 months. List specific sources in your area for such a loan, as well as specific options. Include the rate and different methods for calculating the rate. Also include the requirements for the loan (such as a required cosigner or collateral). Each member of the team should individually obtain information from a different source, and then the team should decide on the best source.

Sets and Logic

The fact that all mathematics is symbolic logic is one of the greatest discoveries of our age.

Bertrand Russell, *Principles of Mathematics, 1903*

ANTICIPATE

- *Overview; check out contents, terms, essential ideas, and learning outcomes.*

- *A fundamental concept of mathematics—and in life, for that matter—is the sorting of objects into similar groupings.*

- *Grouping words: a herd, a flock, a school, a team, or a collection. You have been working problem sets.*

- *Do you remember sets of natural numbers, counting numbers, and whole numbers?*

8.1 Introduction to Sets

IN THIS WORLD THE UTILITY OF MATH

NASA Goddard Space Flight Center (NASA-GSFC)

"What is there in a vacuum to make one afraid?" said the flea.

"There is nothing in it," I said, *"and that is what makes one afraid to contemplate it. A person can't think of a place with nothing at all in it without going nutty, and if he tries to think that nothing is something after all, he gets nuttier."**

"But that is only part of it," retorted the flea. *"What about the infinity of the universe?"*

"Infinity!" said I. *"Infinity is an expression of your imagination!"*

This section lays the groundwork for some fundamental mathematical concepts, sets and logic.

 See Problem 55.

Denoting Sets

In mathematics, we do not define the word **set.** It is what, in mathematics, is called an **undefined term.** It is impossible to define all terms, because every definition requires other terms, so some *undefined terms* are necessary to get us started. To illustrate this idea, let's try to define the word *set* by using dictionary definitions:

"Set: a *collection* of objects."   What is a collection?

"Collection: an *accumulation."*   What is an accumulation?

"Accumulation: a *collection,* a *pile,* or a *heap."*   We see that the word *collection* gives us a **circular definition.** What is a *pile?*

"Pile: a *heap."*   What is a heap?

"Heap: a *pile."*

Do you see that a dictionary leads us in circles? In mathematics, we do not allow circular definitions, and this forces us to accept some words without definition. The term *set* is undefined. Remember, the fact that we do not define *set* does not prevent us from having an intuitive grasp of how to use the word.

Sets are usually specified in one of two ways. The first is by *description,* and the other is by the *roster* method. In the **description method,** we specify the set by describing it in such a way that we know exactly which elements belong to it. An example is the set of 50 states in the United States of America. We say that this set is **well defined,** since there is no doubt that the state of California belongs to it and that the state of Germany does not; neither does the state of confusion. Lack of confusion, in fact, is necessary in using sets. (see Figure 8.1.) The distinctive property that

---

*The first part is quoted from Don Marquis's *Archy and Mehitabel* (The Merry Flea). The second part is presented with apologies to Mr. Marquis.

Figure 8.1 Are interior and exterior areas of this building well defined?

determines the inclusion or exclusion of a particular element is called the *defining property* of the set.

Consider the example of *the set of good students in this class.* This set is not well defined, since it is a matter of opinion whether a student is a "good" student. If we agree, however, on the meaning of the words *good students,* then the set is said to be *well defined.* A better (and more precise) formulation is usually required—for example, *the set of all students in this class who received a C or better on the first examination.* This is well defined, since it can be clearly determined exactly which students received a C or better on the first test.

In the **roster method,** the set is defined by listing the members. The objects in a set are called **members** or **elements** of the set and are said to **belong to** or **be contained in** the set. For example, instead of defining a set as *the set of all students in this class who received a C or better on the first examination,* we might simply define the set by listing its members: {Howie, Mary, Larry}.

Sets are usually denoted by capital letters, and the notation used for sets is braces. Thus, the expression

$$A = \{4, 5, 6\}$$

means that A is the name for the set whose members are the numbers 4, 5, and 6.

Sometimes we use braces with a defining property, as in the following examples:

{states in the United States of America}

{all students in this class who received an A on the first test}

EXAMPLE 1

Changing a description definition to a roster definition

Specify the given sets by roster. If the set is not well defined, say so.

a. {counting numbers between 10 and 20}

b. {distinct letters in the word *happy*}

c. {counting numbers greater than 1,000}

d. {U.S. presidents arranged in chronological order}

e. {good U.S. presidents}

Solution

a. {11, 12, 13, 14, 15, 16, 17, 18, 19}
   Notice that *between* does not include the first and last numbers.

b. {h, a, p, y}

c. {1001, 1002, 1003, . . .}

Notice that it is sometimes impossible or impractical to write *all* the elements of a particular set using the roster method. We use *three dots* to indicate that some elements have been omitted. You must be careful, however, to list enough elements so that someone looking at the set can see the intended pattern.

d. {Washington, Adams, Jefferson, . . . , Clinton, Bush}

e. Not well defined ●

EXAMPLE 2

Changing a roster definition to a description definition

Specify the given sets by description.

a. {1, 2, 3, 4, 5, . . .}

b. {0, 1, 2, 3, 4, 5, . . .}

c. {. . . , −3, −2, −1, 0, 1, 2, 3, . . .}

d. {12, 14, 16, . . . , 98}

e. {4, 44, 444, 4444, . . .}

f. {m, a, t, h, e, i, c, s}

Solution   Answers may vary.

a. {Counting (or natural) numbers}   **b.** {Whole numbers}   **c.** {Integers}
d. {Even numbers between 10 and 100}   **e.** {Counting numbers whose digits consist of fours only}   **f.** {Distinct letters in the word *mathematics*} ●

   If we try to list the set of rational numbers by roster, we will find that this is a difficult task (see Problem 45 in Problem Set 8.1). A new notation called **set-builder notation** was invented to allow us to combine both the roster and the description methods. Consider:

$$\underbrace{\{x}_{\text{The set of all } x} \mid \underbrace{}_{\text{such that}} x \text{ is an even counting number}\}$$

We now use this notation for the set of rational numbers:

$$\left\{ \frac{a}{b} \;\middle|\; a \text{ is an integer and } b \text{ is a nonzero integer} \right\}$$

Read this as: "The set of all $\frac{a}{b}$ such that a is an integer and b is a nonzero integer."
   We can further shorten this notation. In Chapter 2, we gave names to the common sets of numbers:

If you did not learn the names of these sets in Chapter 2, you should do so now.

$\mathbb{N} = \{1, 2, 3, 4, . . .\}$ — Set of **natural,** or **counting, numbers**

$\mathbb{W} = \{0, 1, 2, 3, 4, . . .\}$ — Set of **whole numbers**

$\mathbb{I} = \{. . . , −2, −1, 0, 1, 2, . . .\}$ — Set of **integers**

$\mathbb{Q} = \{\frac{a}{b} \mid a \in \mathbb{I}, b \in \mathbb{I}, b \neq 0\}$ — Set of **rational numbers**

Notice that we used a new symbol in the set-builder notation for the set $\mathbb{Q}$. If S is a set, we write $a \in S$ if a is a member of the set S, and we write $b \notin S$ if b is not a member of the set S. Thus, "$a \in \mathbb{I}$" means that the variable a is an integer, and the statement "$b \in \mathbb{I}, b \neq 0$" means that the variable b is a nonzero integer.

EXAMPLE 3   **Using set inclusion notation**

Let C = cities in California; a = city of Anaheim, b = city of Berlin. Use set membership notation to describe relations among a, b, and C.

Solution $a \in C; b \notin C$ ●

Equal and Equivalent Sets

We say that two sets are **equal** if they contain exactly the same elements. Thus, if $E = \{2, 4, 6, 8, \ldots\}$, then

$$\{x \mid x \text{ is an even counting number}\} = \{x \mid x \in E\}$$

The order in which you represent elements in a set has no effect on set membership. Thus,

$$\{1, 2, 3\} = \{3, 1, 2\} = \{2, 1, 3\} = \cdots$$

Also, if an element appears in a set more than once, it is not generally listed more than a single time. For example,

$$\{1, 2, 3, 3\} = \{1, 2, 3\}$$

Another possible relationship between sets is that of *equivalence*. Two sets are **equivalent** if they have the same *number* of elements. Don't confuse this concept with equality. Equivalent sets do not need to be equal sets, but equal sets are always equivalent.

EXAMPLE 4   **Recognizing equivalent sets**

Which of the following sets are equivalent? Are any equal?

$$\{\circ, \triangle, \square\}, \{5, 8, 11\}, \{1, \lceil, \sqcap\}, \{\bullet, \odot, \star\}, \{1, 2, 3\}$$

Solution   All of the given sets are equivalent. Notice that no two of them are equal, but they all share the property of "threeness."   ●

The number of elements in a set is often called its **cardinality.** The cardinality of the sets in Example 4 is 3; that is, the common property of the sets is the **cardinal number** of the set. The cardinality of a set S is denoted by $|S|$. Equivalent sets with four elements each have in common the property of "fourness," and thus we would say that their cardinality is 4.

EXAMPLE 5   **Finding the cardinality of a given set**

Find the cardinality of:

a. $R = \{5, \triangle, Y, \pi\}$ **b.** $S = \{\ \}$ **c.** $T = \{\text{states of the United States}\}$

Solution

a. The cardinality of R is 4, so we write $|R| = 4$.

b. The set S has no elements so the cardinality of S is 0. We write $|S| = 0$.

c. The cardinality of T is 50 or $|T| = 50$. ●

Certain sets such as $\mathbb{N}$, $\mathbb{I}$, $\mathbb{W}$, or $A = \{1000, 2000, 3000, \ldots\}$ have a common property. We call these *infinite sets*. If the cardinality of a set is 0 or a counting number, we say the set is **finite.** Otherwise, we say it is **infinite.** We can also say that a set is finite if it has a cardinality less than some counting number, even though we may not know its precise cardinality. For example, we can safely assert that the set of students attending the University of Hawaii is finite even though we may not know its cardinality, because the cardinality is certainly less than a million.

You use the ideas of cardinality and of equivalent sets every time you count something, even though you don't use the term *cardinality*. For example, a set of sheep is counted by finding a set of counting numbers that has the same cardinality as the set of sheep. These equivalent sets are found by using an idea called a *one-to-one correspondence*. If the set of sheep is placed into a one-to-one correspondence with a set of pebbles, the set of pebbles can then be used to represent the set of sheep.

One-to-One Correspondence

> Two sets A and B are said to be in a **one-to-one correspondence** if we can find a pairing so that
>
> **1.** Each element of A is paired with precisely one element of B; and
>
> **2.** Each element of B is paired with precisely one element of A.

EXAMPLE 6

Showing that sets are equivalent

Show which of the following sets are equivalent.

$$M = \{3\}, N = \{\text{three}\}, P = \{\triangle, \bigstar, \circ, \triangledown\}, Q = \{t, h, r, e\}$$

Solution Notice that

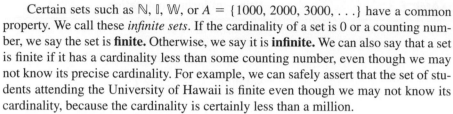

so we say "M is equivalent to N" and we write $M \leftrightarrow N$. Note $P \leftrightarrow Q$. We also see that $M = N$. ●

Since infinity is not a number, we cannot correctly say that the cardinality of the counting numbers is infinity. In the late 18th century, Georg Cantor assigned a cardinal number $\aleph_0$ (pronounced "aleph-null") to the set of counting numbers. That is, $\aleph_0$ is the cardinality of the set of counting numbers

$$\mathbb{N} = \{1, 2, 3, 4, \ldots\}$$

The set

$$\mathbb{E} = \{2, 4, 6, 8, \ldots\}$$

also has cardinality $\aleph_0$, since it can be put into a one-to-one correspondence with set $\mathbb{N}$:

$$\mathbb{N} = \{1, \ 2, \ 3, \ 4, \ldots, \ n, \ldots\}$$
$$\updownarrow \ \updownarrow \ \updownarrow \ \updownarrow \qquad \updownarrow$$
$$\mathbb{E} = \{2, \ 4, \ 6, \ 8, \ldots, 2n, \ldots\}$$

Universal and Empty Sets

We conclude this section by considering two special sets. The first is the set that contains every element under consideration, and the second is the set that contains no elements. A **universal set,** denoted by U, contains all the elements under consideration in a given discussion; and the **empty set** contains no elements, and thus has cardinality 0. The empty set is denoted by $\{\ \ \}$ or $\varnothing$. Do not confuse the notations $\varnothing$, 0, and $\{\varnothing\}$. The symbol $\varnothing$ denotes a *set* with no elements; the symbol 0 denotes a *number;* and the symbol $\{\varnothing\}$ is a set with one element (namely, the set containing $\varnothing$).

For example, if $U = \{1, 2, 3, 4, 5, 6, 7, 8, 9\}$, then all sets we would be considering would have elements only among the elements of U. No set could contain the number 10, since 10 is not in that agreed-upon universe.

For every problem, a universal set must be specified or implied, and it must remain fixed for that problem. However, when a new problem is begun, a new universal set can be specified.

Notice that we defined *a* universal set and *the* empty set; that is, a universal set may vary from problem to problem, but there is only one empty set. After all, it doesn't matter whether the empty set contains no numbers or no people—it is still empty. The following are examples of descriptions of the empty set:

{living saber-toothed tigers}   {counting numbers less than 1}

PROBLEM SET (8.1)

ESSENTIAL IDEAS   LEVEL 1

1. **IN YOUR OWN WORDS** Why do you think mathematics accepts the word *set* as an undefined term?

2. **IN YOUR OWN WORDS** Distinguish between equal and equivalent sets.

3. **IN YOUR OWN WORDS** Give an example of a set with cardinality 0.

4. **IN YOUR OWN WORDS** Give an example of a set with cardinality 2.

5. **IN YOUR OWN WORDS** Give an example of a set with cardinality 10.

6. **IN YOUR OWN WORDS** Give an example of a set with cardinality larger than one million.

7. **IN YOUR OWN WORDS** What is a universal set?

8. **IN YOUR OWN WORDS** What is the empty set?

9. **IN YOUR OWN WORDS** Give three examples of the empty set.

10. **IN YOUR OWN WORDS** Give three examples of an infinite set.

DRILL AND PRACTICE   LEVEL 2

Tell whether each set in Problems 11–18 is well defined. If it is not well defined, change it so that it is well defined.

11. The set of students attending the University of California
    well defined

12. The set of counting numbers between 3 and 4   well defined

13. The set of happy people in your country   not well defined

14. The set of people with pointed ears   not well defined

15. {Grains of sand on earth}
    well defined (assuming that a grain of sand is defined)

16. {Counting numbers less than 0}   well defined

17. {Good bets on the next race at Hialeah}   not well defined

18. {Years that will be bumper years for growing corn in Iowa}
    not well defined

Specify the sets in Problems 19–26 by roster.

19. {Distinct letters in the word *mathematics*}   {m, a, t, h, e, i, c, s}

20. {Distinct letters in the word *pipe*}   {p, i, e}

21. {Even counting numbers between 5 and 15}   {6, 8, 10, 12, 14}

22. {Odd counting numbers less than 11}   {1, 3, 5, 7, 9}

23. {Positive multiples of 3}   {3, 6, 9, ...}

24. {Positive multiples of 7}   {7, 14, 21, ...}

25. {Counting numbers greater than 150}   {151, 152, 153, ...}

26. {Counting numbers containing only 1s}   {1, 11, 111, 1111, ...}

Specify the sets in Problems 27–34 by description.

27. {1, 2, 3, 4, 5, 6, 7, 8, 9}   {counting numbers less than 10}

28. {101, 102, 103, ... , 199}
{counting numbers between 100 and 200}

29. {101, 103, 105, ... , 169}   {odd numbers between 100 and 170}

30. {1, 11, 121, 1331, 14641, ...}   {powers of 11}

31. {10, 20, 30, ... , 100}   {multiples of 10 between 0 and 105}

32. {50, 500, 5000, ...}   {numbers whose first digit is 5 and other digits are 0}

33. {b, o, k, e, p, i, n, g}   {distinct letters in the word bookkeeping}

34. {m, i, s, p}   {distinct letters in the word Mississippi}

Write out in words the description of the sets given in Problems 35–42, and then list each set in roster form.

35. {x | x is an odd counting number}   The set of all x such that x is an odd counting number; {1, 3, 5, 7, ...}

36. {x | x is a natural number between 1 and 10}   The set of all x such that x is a natural number between 1 and 10; {2, 3, 4, 5, 6, 7, 8, 9}

37. {x | x is a natural number greater than 10}   The set of all x such that x is a natural number greater than 10; {11, 12, 13, 14, ...}

38. {x | x is a negative integer}   The set of all x such that x is a negative integer; {−1, −2, −3, −4, ...}

39. {x | x ∈ ℕ, x ≠ 8}   The set of all x such that x is a natural number not equal to 8; {1, 2, 3, 4, 5, 6, 7, 9, 10, 11, ...}

40. {x | x ∈ W, x ≤ 8}   The set of all x such that x is a whole number less than or equal to 8; {0, 1, 2, 3, 4, 5, 6, 7, 8}

41. {x | x ∈ W, x < 8}   The set of all x such that x is a whole number less than 8; {0, 1, 2, 3, 4, 5, 6, 7}

42. {x | x ∈ W, x ∉ E} where E = {2, 4, 6, ...}   The set of all x such that x is a whole number that is not an even number; {0, 1, 3, 5, ...}

43. Consider the sets

    A = {distinct letters in the word *pipe*}
    B = {4}
    C = {p, i, e}
    D = {2 + 1}
    E = {three}
    F = {3}

    a. What is the cardinality of each set?
    |A| = 3; |B| = 1; |C| = 3; |D| = 1; |E| = 1; |F| = 1
    b. Which of the sets can be placed into a one-to-one correspondence?   A ↔ C; B ↔ D ↔ E ↔ F
    c. Which of the given sets are equal?
    A = C; D = E = F

44. Consider the sets

    A = {16}
    B = {10 + 6}

C = {10, 6}
D = {2⁵}
E = {2, 5}

a. What is the cardinality of each set?
|A| = 1; |B| = 1; |C| = 2; |D| = 1; |E| = 2
b. Which of the sets can be placed into a one-to-one correspondence?
A ↔ B ↔ D; C ↔ E
c. Which of the given sets are equal?
A = B

45. List the set of rational numbers between 0 and 1 by roster. List the elements systematically, and do not list elements that have been previously listed. $\{\frac{1}{2}, \frac{1}{3}, \frac{2}{3}, \frac{1}{4}, \frac{3}{4}, \frac{1}{5}, \frac{2}{5}, \frac{3}{5}, \frac{4}{5}, \frac{1}{6}, \frac{5}{6}, \frac{1}{7}, ...\}$

46. List the set of rational numbers between 10 and 11 by roster. List the elements systematically, and do not list elements that have been previously listed.
$\{10\frac{1}{2}, 10\frac{1}{3}, 10\frac{2}{3}, 10\frac{1}{4}, 10\frac{3}{4}, 10\frac{1}{5}, 10\frac{2}{5}, 10\frac{3}{5}, 10\frac{4}{5}, 10\frac{1}{6}, 10\frac{5}{6}, 10\frac{1}{7}, ...\}$

47. **IN YOUR OWN WORDS** Show that there is more than one one-to-one correspondence between the sets {m, a, t} and {1, 2, 3}.

48. **IN YOUR OWN WORDS** Show that the following sets have the same cardinality, by placing the elements into a one-to-one correspondence. {1, 2, 3, 4, ... , 999, 1000} and {7964, 7965, 7966, 7967, ... , 8962, 8963}.

49. **IN YOUR OWN WORDS** Show that the following sets do not have the same cardinality. {1, 2, 3, 4, ... , 586, 587} and {550, 551, 552, 553, ... , 902, 903}.

50. **IN YOUR OWN WORDS** Show that the following sets do not have the same cardinality. {48, 49, 50, ... , 783, 784} and {485, 487, 489, ... , 2053, 2055}.

APPLICATIONS   LEVEL 2

Classify the sets in Problems 51–54 as finite or infinite.

51. **a.** The set of shoes in my closet   finite

    b. The number of married people in the world   finite

52. **a.** The set of stars in the Milky Way   finite

    b. The set of drops of water in all the oceans on earth   finite

53. **a.** The set of all written and unwritten published novels   finite

    b. The set of grains of sand on all the beaches on earth   finite

54. **a.** The set of all possible unwritten entries in your journal   finite

    b. The set of seconds in a lifetime   finite

55. **IN YOUR OWN WORDS** "What is there in a vacuum to make one afraid?" said the flea. "There is nothing in it," I said, "and that is what makes one afraid to contemplate it. A person can't think of a place with nothing at all in it without going nutty, and if he tries to think that nothing is something after all, he gets nuttier." "But that is only part of it," retorted the flea. "What about the infinity of the universe?" "Infinity!" said I. "Infinity is an expression of your imagination." Is the infinite plausible? Write a paper on the vastness of infinity.

Explain what is wrong, if anything, with the statements in Problems 56–60. Explain your reasoning.

56. A set is defined to be a collection of objects.
F; set is undefined.

57. The empty set does not have any elements, so $\varnothing = 0$.
F; $\varnothing = \{\ \}$

58. The cardinality of $\{0\}$ is zero.   F; the cardinality is 1.

59. $\{0\} = \varnothing$ F; the cardinality of $\{0\}$ is 1, but of $\varnothing$ it is 0.

60. The number of grains of sand on all the beaches on earth can't be counted, so the set of grains of sand on beaches is infinite.   F; it is finite.

8.2 Set Relationships

IN THIS WORLD   THE UTILITY OF MATH

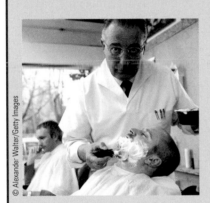

© Alexander Walter/Getty Images

"Niels, where are you going?" asked Sammy.
   "I'm going to the barber for a shave," answered Niels.
   "Frank, the barber, does a very good business. He shaves those men and only those men who do not shave themselves," said Sammy.
   "Come on, Sammy, that's impossible!" Niels responded. "Who do you think shaves him?"

The study of sets and relationships among sets can lead us to a consideration of questions such as the one asked by Niels. Consider the following Barber's Rule: **Frank shaves those men and only those men who do not shave themselves.**

   If Frank shaves himself, according to the Barber's Rule, he does not shave himself. On the other hand, if he does not shave himself, then, according to the Barber's Rule, he shaves himself!

 See Problem 57.

Subsets

To deal effectively with sets, you must understand certain relationships among sets. A set A is a **subset** of a set B, denoted by $A \subseteq B$, if every element of A is an element of B. Consider the following sets:

$$U = \{1, 2, 3, 4, 5, 6, 7, 8, 9\}$$
$$A = \{2, 4, 6, 8\}, \qquad B = \{1, 3, 5, 7\}, \qquad C = \{5, 7\}$$

Now, A, B, and C are subsets of the universal set U (*all* sets we consider are subsets of the universe, by definition of a universal set). We also note that $C \subseteq B$ since every element of C is also an element of B. However, C is not a subset of A, written $C \nsubseteq A$. In this case, we merely note that $5 \in C$ and $5 \notin A$.

   Do not confuse the notions of "element" and "subset." In the present example, 5 is an *element* of C, since it is listed in C. By the same token, $\{5\}$ is a *subset* of C, but it is not an element, since we do not find {5} contained in C; if we did, C might look like this: {5, {5}, 7}.

EXAMPLE 1   Subsets of a given set

Find all possible subsets of $C = \{5, 7\}$.

Solution

{5}, {7} are obvious subsets.

{5, 7} is also a subset, since both 5 and 7 are elements of C.

{ } is also a subset of C. It is a subset because all of its elements belong to C. Stated a different way, if it were not a subset of C, we would have to be able to find an element of { } that is not in C. Since we cannot find such an element, we say that the empty set is a subset of C (and, in fact, *the empty set is a subset of every set*). ●

We see that there are four subsets of C from Example 1, even though C has only two elements. We must therefore be careful to distinguish between a subset and an element. Remember, 5 and {5} mean different things.

The subsets of C can be classified into two categories: *proper* and *improper*. Since every set is a subset of itself, we immediately know one subset for *any* given set: the set itself. A *proper subset* is a subset that is not equal to the original set; that is, A is a **proper subset** of a subset B, written $A \subset B$, if A is a subset of B and $A \neq B$. An **improper subset** of a set A is the set A.

We see there are three proper subsets of $C = \{5, 7\}$: $\varnothing$, {5}, and {7}. There is one improper subset of C: {5, 7}.

EXAMPLE 2   Classifying proper and improper subsets

Find the proper and improper subsets of $A = \{2, 4, 6, 8\}$. What is the cardinality of A?

Solution   The cardinality of A is 4 (because there are 4 elements in A). There is one improper subset: **{2, 4, 6, 8}.** The proper subsets are:

{ },
{2}, {4}, {6}, {8},
{2, 4}, {2, 6}, {2, 8}, {4, 6}, {4, 8}, {6, 8},
{2, 4, 6}, {2, 4, 8}, {2, 6, 8}, {4, 6, 8} ●

From Example 1, we see that a set of 2 elements has four subsets, and from Example 2, we note that a set of cardinality 4 has 16 subsets. In Problems 23–27, the following property is discovered.

Number of Subsets

> The number of subsets of a set of size n is
>
> $$2^n$$

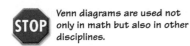

STOP Venn diagrams are used not only in math but also in other disciplines.

Venn Diagrams

A useful way to depict relationships among sets is to let the universal set be represented by a rectangle, with the proper sets in the universe represented by circular or oval regions, as shown in Figure 8.2. These figures are called **Venn diagrams,** after John Venn (1834–1923).

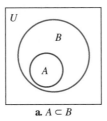 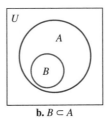 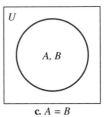

a. $A \subset B$ b. $B \subset A$ c. $A = B$

Figure 8.2 Venn diagrams for subset

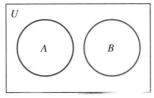

a. Disjoint sets

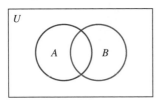

b. Overlapping sets

Figure 8.3 Set relationships

We can also illustrate other relationships between two sets: A and B may have no elements in common, in which case they are **disjoint** (as depicted by Figure 8.3a), or they may be **overlapping sets** that have some elements in common (as depicted in Figure 8.3b).

Sometimes we are given two sets X and Y, and we know nothing about how they are related. In this situation, we draw a general figure, shown in Figure 8.4. In it, there are four regions, labeled I, II, III, and IV.

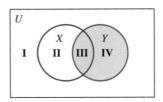

Figure 8.4 Two general sets

If $X \subseteq Y$, then region II is empty.
If $Y \subseteq X$, then region IV is empty.
If $X = Y$, then regions II and IV are empty.
If X and Y are disjoint, then region III is empty.

PROBLEM SET 8.2

ESSENTIAL IDEAS   LEVEL 1

1. **IN YOUR OWN WORDS** Explain the difference between the terms *element of a set* and *subset of a set*. Give examples.

2. **IN YOUR OWN WORDS** Explain the difference between the terms *subset* and *proper subset*. Give examples.

3. Explain the difference between *universal set* and *empty set*. Universal set is the set of all possible elements for a particular example, and the empty set is the set with no elements.

4. What is a Venn diagram?
   A diagram showing set relationships

5. Draw a Venn diagram of disjoint sets X and Y.
   See Figure 8.3a.

6. Draw a Venn diagrams of overlapping sets Y and Z.
   See Figure 8.3b.

DRILL AND PRACTICE   LEVEL 2

List all subsets of each set given in Problems 7–22. Identify any of the subsets that are improper. Improper subsets in boldface (7–14). See IAS for 15–22.

7. $\{5\}$ $\varnothing, \textbf{\{5\}}$

8. $\{x\}$ $\varnothing, \textbf{\{x\}}$

9. $\{m, y\}$ $\varnothing, \{m\}, \{y\}, \textbf{\{m, y\}}$

10. $\{b, e\}$ $\varnothing, \{b\}, \{e\}, \textbf{\{b, e\}}$

11. $\{x, y\}$ $\varnothing, \{x\}, \{y\}, \textbf{\{x, y\}}$

12. $\{4, 5\}$ $\varnothing, \{4\}, \{5\}, \textbf{\{4, 5\}}$

13. $\{3, 8\}$ $\varnothing, \{3\}, \{8\}, \textbf{\{3, 8\}}$

14. $\{2, 4\}$ $\varnothing, \{2\}, \{4\}, \textbf{\{2, 4\}}$

15. $\{y, o, u\}$

16. $\{a, r, e\}$

17. $\{b, i, g\}$

18. $\{3, 6, 9\}$

19. $\{2, 4, 6\}$

20. $\{4, 8, 9\}$

21. $\{m, a, t, h\}$

22. $\{1, 2, 3, 4\}$

23. List all possible subsets of the set $A = \emptyset$. $\emptyset$

24. List all possible subsets of the set $B = \{1\}$. $\emptyset, \{1\}$

25. List all possible subsets of the set $C = \{1, 2\}$. $\emptyset, \{1\}, \{2\}, \{1, 2\}$

26. List all possible subsets of the set $D = \{1, 2, 3\}$.
$\emptyset, \{1\}, \{2\}, \{3\}, \{1, 2\}, \{1, 3\}, \{2, 3\}, \{1, 2, 3\}$

27. List all possible subsets of the set $E = \{1, 2, 3, 4\}$.   *See IAS.*

28. List all possible subsets of the set $G = \emptyset$. $\emptyset$

29. List all possible subsets of the set $H = \{6\}$. $\emptyset, \{6\}$

30. List all possible subsets of the set $I = \{6, 7\}$.
$\emptyset, \{6\}, \{7\}, \{6, 7\}$

31. List all possible subsets of the set $J = \{6, 7, 8\}$.
$\emptyset, \{6\}, \{7\}, \{8\}, \{6, 7\}, \{6, 8\}, \{7, 8\}, \{6, 7, 8\}$

32. List all possible subsets of the set $K = \{6, 7, 8, 9\}$.   *See IAS.*

33. Look for a pattern in Problems 23–27. Can you guess how many subsets the set $F = \{1, 2, 3, 4, 5\}$ has? Does this guess match the formula?   *32 subsets; yes*

34. Look for a pattern in Problems 28–32. Can you guess how many subsets the set $L = \{1, 2, 3, 4, 5\}$ has? Does this guess match the formula?   *32 subsets; yes*

35. Using Problems 33–34, guess how many subsets there are for a set with 6 elements.   *64 subsets*

36. Using Problems 33–34, guess how many subsets there are for a set with 7 elements.   *128 subsets*

37. Using Problems 33–34, guess how many subsets there are for a set with 8 elements.   *256 subsets*

38. Using Problems 33–34, guess how many subsets there are for a set with 9 elements.   *512 subsets*

39. Using Problems 35–38, guess how many subsets there are for a set with m elements. 2^m *subsets*

40. Using Problems 35–38, guess how many subsets there are for a set with n elements. 2^n *subsets*

APPLICATIONS   **LEVEL 2**

See IAS for Venn diagrams.

41. Draw a Venn diagram showing male and female where the universe is the set of all people.

42. Draw a Venn diagram showing people under age 21 and those 21 or older.

43. Draw a Venn diagram showing hammers and drills where the universe is the set of all shop tools.

44. Draw a Venn diagram showing the relationship among cats, dogs, and animals. *Hint:* Could one of these sets be called the universal set?

45. Draw a Venn diagram showing people wearing blue and those wearing black.

46. Draw a Venn diagram showing the relationship among people who have had their wisdom teeth removed and those who have had their appendix removed.

47. Draw a Venn diagram showing that all ducks are birds.

48. Draw a Venn diagram showing that all Chevrolets are automobiles.

49. Draw a Venn diagram showing the relationship among trucks, buses, and cars.

50. Draw a Venn diagram showing the relationship among flowers, flagpoles, and fish.

51. Draw a Venn diagram showing the relationship among athletes who play soccer, basketball, and baseball.

52. Draw a Venn diagram showing people in a classroom with blue eyes, black shoes, and wedding rings.

53. Draw a Venn diagram showing people who are over 30, people who are 30 or under, and people who drive a car.

54. Draw a Venn diagram showing Olympic swimmers who have green eyes, Olympic swimmers who have won a medal, and Olympic swimmers who have not won a medal.

55. Draw a Venn diagram showing the relationship among squares, parallelograms, and quadrilaterals.

56. Draw a Venn diagram showing the relationship among the natural numbers, the integers, and the rational numbers.

57. **IN YOUR OWN WORDS**

"Niels, where are you going?" asked Sammy. "I'm going to the barber for a shave," answered Niels. "You know, Niels, Frank, the barber, does a very good business. He shaves those men and only those men who do not shave themselves." "Come on, Sammy, that's impossible! Who do you think shaves him?" Write a paper on who you think shaves the barber.

RIGHT OR WRONG?   **LEVEL 3**

Explain what is wrong, if anything, with the statements in Problems 58–60. Explain your reasoning.

58. A proper subset of the set of even counting numbers is $\{2, 4, 6, 8, 10, 12, \ldots\}$.
F; the listed set is the improper subset of E

59. A proper subset of the set of the counting numbers is $\{2, 4, 6, 8, 10, 12, \ldots\}$.   *T*

60. The list of all subsets of $\{1, 2, 3\}$ is $\{1\}, \{2\}, \{3\}, \{1, 2\}, \{2, 3\},$ and $\{1, 3\}$.   *F; {1, 2, 3} and $\emptyset$ are missing.*

8.3 Operations with Sets

IN THIS WORLD   THE UTILITY OF MATH

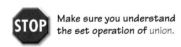

JAY E. COSSEY
2021 LARCHWOOD AVENUE
WILMETTE, ILLINOIS 60091

28 January 1974

Advertising Manager
Heublein, Inc.
Hartford, Conn. 06101

Dear Sir:

Re your recent advertisements concerning the Brass Monkey —— your conjectures are interesting, but misguided. The agent's name was Pete Yale and you could have found him sitting at table number 6 at the Brass Monkey any night.

You were right about the coaster being the tip-off, except that you went at it the wrong way. Take the name THE BRASS MONKEY and the motto SEE HEAR SPEAK NO EVIL, and cross out in order the letters that are common to both:

T͟H͟E͟ B͟R͟A͟S͟S͟ M͟O͟N͟K͟E͟Y͟
S͟E͟E͟ H͟E͟A͟R͟ S͟P͟E͟A͟K͟ N͟O͟ EVIL

This leaves T͟B͟M͟Y͟ E͟P͟E͟A͟ EVIL, which you arrange in three rows:

T B M Y   T̶ ̶B̶ M̶/Y̶
E P E A   and then draw an X through the rows: E P̶/E̶ A
E V I L   E̶/V I̶L̶

Using the letters in each section, you get PETE YALE - BM (Brass Monkey) VI (Roman numeral 6).

Pete had a sense of humor, as you might guess. The letters BM are also the term commonly used on maps for "bench mark".

Sincerely yours,

"Do you know anything about a Brass Monkey, Jay?" asked Tom.

"Do I ever!" exclaimed Jay. *"Let me show you a letter I wrote to Heublein over two decades ago. They had this advertising campaign, which was a puzzle. It received a lot of response. Anyway, I solved the puzzle by finding the intersection of two sets . . . ."*

In this section, Tom will learn, not only about a Brass Monkey, but also about three operations on sets—namely, union, intersection, and complementation.

 See Problem 41.

There are three common operations with sets: union, intersection, and complementation.

Union

Union is an operation for sets A and B in which a set is formed that consists of all the elements that are in A or B or both. The symbol for the operation of union is $\cup$, and we write $A \cup B$. The operation of *union* is sometimes translated by the English word "**or.**"

STOP Make sure you understand the set operation of *union*.

Union | The **union** of sets A and B, denoted by $A \cup B$, is the set consisting of all elements of A or B or both.

EXAMPLE 1 | **Finding the union of sets**

Let $U = \{1, 2, 3, 4, 5, 6, 7, 8, 9\}$, $A = \{2, 4, 6, 8\}$, $B = \{1, 3, 5, 7\}$, $C = \{5, 7\}$. Find the following unions of sets.

a. $A \cup C$ **b.** $B \cup C$ **c.** $A \cup B$ **d.** $(A \cup B) \cup \{9\}$

Solution

a. The union of A and C is the set consisting of all elements in A or in C or in both:

$$A \cup C = \{2, 4, 5, 6, 7, 8\}$$

b. $B \cup C = \{1, 3, 5, 7\}$

Notice that, even though the elements 5 and 7 appear in both sets, they are listed only once; that is, the sets $\{1, 3, 5, 7\}$ and $\{1, 3, 5, 5, 7, 7\}$ are equal (exactly the same). Sometimes we write $B \cup C = B$.

c. $A \cup B = \{1, 2, 3, 4, 5, 6, 7, 8\}$

d. $(A \cup B) \cup \{9\} = \{1, 2, 3, 4, 5, 6, 7, 8\} \cup \{9\}$

$$= \{1, 2, 3, 4, 5, 6, 7, 8, 9\}$$

$$= U$$

Here we are considering the union of three sets. However, the parentheses indicate the operation that should be performed first. ●

We can use Venn diagrams to illustrate union. In Figure 8.5, we first shade A (horizontal lines) and then shade B (vertical lines). *The union is all parts that have been shaded* (either horizontal or vertical) *at least once;* this region is shown as a color screen.

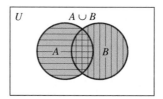

Figure 8.5 Venn diagram for union

Intersection

A second operation is called *intersection*.

Intersection	The **intersection** of sets A and B, denoted by $A \cap B$, is the set consisting of all elements common to both A and B.

 Make sure you understand the set operation of intersection.

The operation of intersection can be translated by the English word "**and.**"

EXAMPLE 2

Finding the intersection of sets

Let $U = \{a, b, c, d, e\}$, and let $A = \{a, c, e\}$, $B = \{c, d, e\}$, $C = \{a\}$, $D = \{e\}$. Find the following intersections of sets.

a. $A \cap B$ **b.** $A \cap C$ **c.** $B \cap C$ **d.** $(A \cap B) \cap D$

Solution

a. The intersection of A and B is the set consisting of elements in both A and B:

$$A \cap B = \{c, e\}$$

b. $A \cap C = C$ $A \cap C = \{a\}$, and $\{a\} = C.$

c. $B \cap C = \varnothing$ *B and C have no elements in common (they are disjoint).*

d. $(A \cap B) \cap D = \{c, e\} \cap \{e\}$ *Parentheses first*

$\qquad\qquad\qquad = \{e\}$ *Intersection*

$\qquad\qquad\qquad = D$ ●

The intersection of sets can also be easily shown using a Venn diagram as in Figure 8.6. The intersection is all parts shaded twice (both horizontal and vertical) as shown with a color screen.

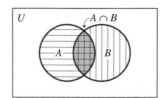

Figure 8.6 Venn diagram for intersection

Complementation

Complementation is an operation on a set that must be performed in reference to a universal set. It can be translated into English by the word "**not.**"

Complement   The **complement** of a set A, denoted by $\overline{A}$, is the set of all elements in U that are not in the set A.

EXAMPLE 3   **Finding complements**

Let $U = \{$people in California$\}$, and let
$\quad A = \{$people who are over 30$\}$;
$\quad B = \{$people who are 30 or under$\}$
$\quad C = \{$people who own a car$\}$
Find the following complements of sets.

a. $\overline{C}$ **b.** $\overline{A}$ **c.** $\overline{B}$ **d.** $\overline{U}$ **e.** $\overline{\varnothing}$

Solution

a. $\overline{C} = \{$Californians who do not own a car$\}$

b. $\overline{A} = \overline{\{$people who are over 30$\}}$

$\qquad = \{$people who are 30 or under$\}$

$\qquad = B$

c. $\overline{B} = A$ **d.** $\overline{U} = \varnothing$ **e.** $\overline{\varnothing} = U$ ●

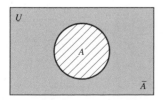

Figure 8.7 Venn diagram for complementation

Complementation, too, can be shown using a Venn diagram. The shaded part (color screen) of Figure 8.7 shows the complement of A. In a Venn diagram, *the complement is everything in U that is not in the set under consideration* (in this case, everything not in A).

EXAMPLE 4   Translating the words "and" and "or"

One question in a survey of 140 students asked the following questions:

> ☐ I'm enrolled in at least one math class.
>
> ☐ I'm enrolled in at least one English class.

a. Draw a Venn diagram showing the possible results of this survey.

b. If 50 students check the first box, what was the percent of the respondents taking math?

c. If 60 students check the second box, what was the percent of the respondents taking English?

d. If 20 checked both boxes, what is the percent of respondents taking both math **and** English?

e. If 20 checked both boxes, what is the percent of respondents taking math **or** English?

Solution

a. There are two sets, $M = $ {students enrolled in at least one math class} and $E = $ {students enrolled in at least one English class}. These sets are shown in Figure 8.8.

b. $|M| = 50$, so the percent is $\frac{50}{140} \approx 0.357$, or about 36%.

c. $|E| = 60$, so the percent is $\frac{60}{140} \approx 0.429$, or about 43%.

d. The word **and** means those in both sets, so $|M \cap E| = 20$, and the percent is $\frac{20}{140} \approx 0.143$, or about 14%.

e. The word **or** means in either of the sets, so $|M \cup E| = 30 + 20 + 40 = 90$, and the percent is $\frac{90}{140} \approx 0.643$, or about 64%.   ●

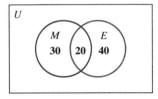

Figure 8.8 Results of survey question

PROBLEM SET 8.3

1. IN YOUR OWN WORDS Distinguish between the union and the intersection of two sets.

2. IN YOUR OWN WORDS Define *union* and illustrate with examples.

3. IN YOUR OWN WORDS Define *intersection* and illustrate with examples.

4. IN YOUR OWN WORDS Define *complement* and illustrate with examples.

5. a. Name a set operation that is translated as "and." intersection
   b. What is the English translation for the operation of "∪"? "or"

6. a. Name a set operation that is translated as "or." union
   b. What is the English translation for the operation of "∩"? "and"

7. What is the set operation that is translated as "not"? complement

8. Draw a Venn diagram for union.   See Figure 8.5.

9. Draw a Venn diagram for intersection.   See Figure 8.6.

10. Draw a Venn diagram for complement.   See Figure 8.7.

Perform the given set operations in Problems 11–20. *Let*
$$U = \{1, 2, 3, 4, 5, 6, 7, 8, 9, 10\}$$

11. $\{2, 6, 8\} \cup \{6, 8, 10\}$ {2, 6, 8, 10}

12. $\{2, 6, 8\} \cap \{6, 8, 10\}$ {6, 8}

13. $\{1, 2, 3, 4, 5\} \cap \{3, 4, 5, 6, 7\}$ {3, 4, 5}

14. $\{1, 2, 3, 4, 5\} \cup \{3, 4, 5, 6, 7\}$ {1, 2, 3, 4, 5, 6, 7}

15. $\{2, 5, 8\} \cup \{3, 6, 9\}$ {2, 3, 5, 6, 8, 9}

16. $\{2, 5, 8\} \cap \{3, 6, 9\}$ Ø

17. $\overline{\{2, 8, 9\}}$ {1, 3, 4, 5, 6, 7, 10}

18. $\overline{\{1, 2, 5, 7, 9\}}$ {3, 4, 6, 8, 10}

19. $\overline{\{8\}}$ {1, 2, 3, 4, 5, 6, 7, 9, 10}

20. $\overline{\{6, 7, 8, 9, 10\}}$ {1, 2, 3, 4, 5}

Let $U = \{1, 2, 3, 4, 5, 6, 7\}$; $A = \{1, 2, 3, 4\}$; $B = \{1, 2, 5, 6\}$; *and* $C = \{3, 5, 7\}$. *List all members of each of the sets in Problems 21–30.*

21. $A \cup B$ {1, 2, 3, 4, 5, 6}

22. $A \cup C$ {1, 2, 3, 4, 5, 7}

23. $B \cup C$ {1, 2, 3, 5, 6, 7}

24. $A \cap B$ {1, 2}

25. $A \cap C$ {3}

26. $B \cap C$ {5}

27. $\overline{A}$ {5, 6, 7}

28. $\overline{B}$ {3, 4, 7}

29. $\overline{C}$ {1, 2, 4, 6}

30. $\overline{\varnothing}$ U

Draw Venn diagrams for each of the relationships in Problems 31–36. See IAS for Venn diagrams.

31. $X \cup Y$

32. $X \cup Z$

33. $X \cap Y$

34. $X \cap Z$

35. $\overline{X}$

36. $\overline{Y}$

If $A \subseteq B$, *describe the sets shown in Problems 37–40.*

37. $A \cup B$ B

38. $A \cap B$ A

39. $\overline{A} \cup B$ U

40. $A \cap \overline{B}$ $\varnothing$

APPLICATIONS   LEVEL 2

41. "Do you know anything about a Brass Monkey, Jay?" asked Tom. "Do I ever!" exclaimed Jay. "Let me show you a letter I wrote to Heublein over two decades ago. They had this advertising campaign, which was a puzzle. It received a lot of response. Anyway, I solved the puzzle by finding the intersection of two sets:

{T, H, E, B, R, A, S, S, M, O, N, K, E, Y}
{S, E, E, H, E, A, R, S, P, E, A, K, N, O, E, V, I, L}"

Write these sets properly, without repeated letters.
{T, H, E, B, R, A, S, M, O, N, K, Y} ∩ {S, E, H, A, R, P, K, N, O, V, I, L}

42. Find the intersection of these sets listed in the Problem of the Day—that is, in Problem 41.   {H, E, R, A, S, O, N}

One question in a survey of 5,000 heads of household asked the following questions:

> ☐ This household has an Internet connection.
>
> ☐ This household has a cell phone.

Use this survey question for Problems 43–47.

43. Draw a Venn diagram illustrating the possible results of this survey.   See IAS.

44. If 1,400 of the households checked the first box, what percent of the respondents have an Internet connection?   28%

45. If 2,100 of the households checked the second box, what percent of the respondents have a cell phone?   42%

46. If 600 checked both boxes, what percent of the households have both an Internet connection and a cell phone?   12%

47. What percent of the households have an Internet connection or a cell phone?   58%

One question in a survey of 450 members of a club asked the following:

> ☐ I watched a movie at a theater in the past month.
>
> ☐ I watched a rented movie at home in the past month.

Use this survey question for Problems 48–52.

48. Draw a Venn diagram illustrating the possible results of this survey.   See IAS.

49. If 135 respondents checked the first box, what percent of the respondents watched a movie at a theater in the past month?   30%

50. If 108 respondents checked the second box, what percent of the respondents watched a rented movie at home in the past month?   24%

51. If 72 checked both boxes, what percent of the respondents watched movies both in a theater and at home?   16%

52. What percent of the households watched a movie in a theater or at home in the past month?   38%

A glazed doughnut contains 235 calories and a slice of apple pie contains 405 calories. Use the given table to list all possible sets of exercises (with no exercise combinations) that will burn off the calories in Problems 53–56.

Exercise	Calories/hr
Sitting	75
Walking	150
Golfing	300
Biking	420
Jogging	500

53. Two doughnuts and one hour of exercise   jogging

54. Two doughnuts and two hours of exercise
golfing; biking; jogging

55. One hour of exercise and a slice of apple pie
biking; jogging

56. Two hours of exercise and a slice of apple pie
golfing; biking; jogging

In Problems 57–60, let

$U = \mathbb{N}$
$A = \{1, 2, 3, 4, 5\}$
$B = \{4, 5, 6, 7, 8, 9\}$
$C = \{\text{odd numbers}\}$
$E = \{\text{even numbers}\}$

Explain what is wrong, if anything, with the given statements.
Explain your reasoning.

57. $A \cup B = \{1, 2, 3, 4, 5\} \cup \{4, 5, 6, 7, 8, 9\}$

$= \{4, 5\}$ F; union is {1, 2, 3, 4, 5, 6, 7, 8, 9}

58. $A \cap B = \{1, 2, 3, 4, 5\} \cap \{4, 5, 6, 7, 8, 9\}$

$= \{1, 2, 3, 4, 5, 4, 5, 6, 7, 8, 9\}$ F; intersection is {4, 5}

59. $\overline{A} = \overline{\{1, 2, 3, 4, 5\}}$

$= \{6, 7, 8, 9\}$ F; $\overline{A} = \{6, 7, 8, 9, 10, 11, 12, \dots\}$

60. $\overline{C} = E$ T

8.4 Venn Diagrams

Combined Operations with Sets

In the previous section, we defined union, intersection, and complementation of sets. However, the real payoff for studying these relationships comes when dealing with combined operations or with several sets at the same time.

EXAMPLE 1   **Combined operations with sets**

Draw a Venn diagram for each of the following:

a. $\overline{A \cup B}$ **b.** $\overline{A} \cup \overline{B}$

Verify your diagrams for the following particular example:

Let $U = \{1, 2, 3, 4, 5, 6, 7, 8, 9, 10\}$ and let $A = \{1, 2\}$, $B = \{4, 5, 6, 7, 8\}$.

Solution   These are combined operations; in part **a,** first find the union, and then find the complement; and in part **b,** first find the complements and then find the union.

a. For the Venn diagram, first draw the union:

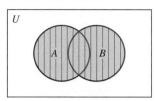

Then find the complement:

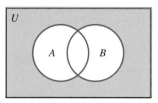

These steps are generally combined in one diagram:

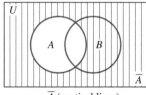

$$\overline{A \cup B}$$

The answer is shown as the shaded portion; the lines show the intermediate steps. In your own work, you will generally find it easier to show the *final answer* only in a second color (pen or a highlighter) as shown above.

For the particular example at hand, we find

$$\overline{A \cup B} = \overline{\{1, 2\} \cup \{4, 5, 6, 7, 8\}}$$

$$= \overline{\{1, 2, 4, 5, 6, 7, 8\}}$$

$$= \{3, 9, 10\}$$

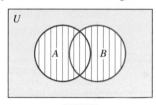

b. First find $\overline{A}$ and $\overline{B}$:

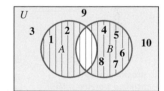

$\overline{A}$ (vertical lines) $\overline{A}$ with $\overline{B}$ (horizontal lines)

What you should show is the final step only (using a highlighter) for the union of $\overline{A}$ and $\overline{B}$, which is all parts that have horizontal or vertical lines (or both). This illustration is shown in the margin.

For the particular example, we find

$$\overline{A} \cup \overline{B} = \overline{\{1, 2\}} \cup \overline{\{4, 5, 6, 7, 8\}}$$

$$= \{3, 4, 5, 6, 7, 8, 9, 10\} \cup \{1, 2, 3, 9, 10\}$$

$$= \{1, 2, 3, 4, 5, 6, 7, 8, 9, 10\}$$

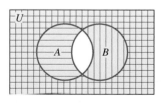

$$\overline{A} \cup \overline{B}$$

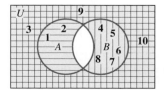

Notice from the Venn diagram that the shaded portion is not the entire universe. *For this example, $\overline{A} \cup \overline{B} = U$, but this is not true in general, since (as the Venn diagram shows) the entire region is not shaded.* ●

Cardinality of a Union

Venn diagrams can be useful in making general statements about sets. (See part **b** of Example 1, for example.) We also see for the Venn diagrams in Example 1 that $\overline{A \cup B} \neq \overline{A} \cup \overline{B}$. If they were equal, the final *shaded* portions of the Venn diagrams would be the same.

EXAMPLE 2   **Using Venn diagrams to find the cardinality of a union of sets**

Suppose that a survey indicates that 45 students are taking mathematics and that 41 are taking English. How many students are taking math or English?

Solution   At first, it might seem that all we need to do is add 41 and 45, but such is not the case, as you can see by looking at Figure 8.9.

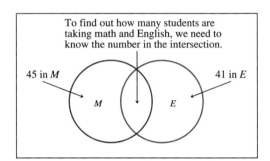
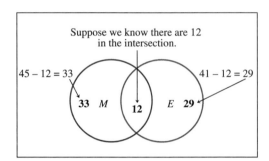

Figure 8.9 Using a Venn diagram to find the numbers in regions

We see that there are $33 + 29 + 12 = 74$ students enrolled in mathematics or in English or in both. (See Figure 8.9.) We see that the proper procedure is to fill in the number in the intersection and then to find the numbers in the other regions by subtraction. ●

STOP This property will be essential to working with survey problems, which we consider in the next section. It will also be used in the chapter on probability.

The result from Example 2 is summarized with the following property.

Cardinality of a Union

For any two sets X and Y,

$$|X \cup Y| = |X| + |Y| - |X \cap Y|$$

EXAMPLE 3   **Using Venn diagrams to establish an equality**

Show that $\overline{A \cup B} = \overline{A} \cap \overline{B}$.

Solution
The procedure is to draw a Venn diagram for the left side and a separate diagram for the right side, and then to look to see whether they are the same.

Venn diagrams: Left side of equal sign   Right side of equal sign

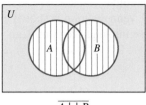   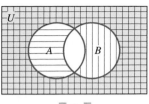

$$\overline{A \cup B}$$ $$\overline{A} \cap \overline{B}$$

Detail: See Example 1. $\overline{A}$ (vertical lines)
$\overline{B}$ (horizontal lines)
$\overline{A} \cap \overline{B}$ is the intersection of the horizontal and vertical lines; use a highlighter to show this intersection.

Compare the shaded portions of the two Venn diagrams. They are the same, so $\overline{A \cup B} = \overline{A} \cap \overline{B}$.   ●

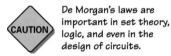

De Morgan's laws are important in set theory, logic, and even in the design of circuits.

The result proved in Example 3 is one part of a result known as **De Morgan's laws.** (In Problem 47, you are asked to verify the second part.)

De Morgan's Laws

$$\overline{X \cup Y} = \overline{X} \cap \overline{Y} \qquad \text{and} \qquad \overline{X \cap Y} = \overline{X} \cup \overline{Y}$$

The *order* of operations for sets is from left to right, unless there are parentheses. Operations within parentheses are performed first, as shown in the following example.

EXAMPLE 4   **Combined operations with Venn diagrams**

Illustrate $(A \cup C) \cap \overline{C}$ with a Venn diagram.

Solution   First, draw $A \cup C$ (vertical lines). Next, draw $\overline{C}$ (horizontal lines). The result is the intersection of the vertical and horizontal parts, and is the portion shaded in color.

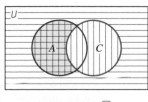

$$(A \cup C) \cap \overline{C}$$

●

Venn Diagrams with Three Sets

Sometimes you will be asked to consider the relationships among three sets. The general Venn diagram is shown in Figure 8.10. Notice that the three sets divide the universe into eight regions. Can you number each part?

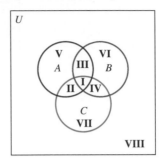

Figure 8.10 Three general sets

EXAMPLE 5

Venn diagrams for three sets

Find the results of the following operations among three sets A, B, and C:

a. $A \cup B$ **b.** $A \cap C$ **c.** $B \cap C$ **d.** $\overline{A}$ **e.** $\overline{A \cup B}$ **f.** $(A \cap B) \cap C$

Solution

a. 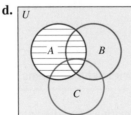 **b.** 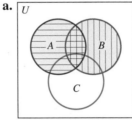 **c.**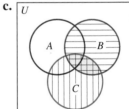

d. 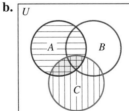 **e.** 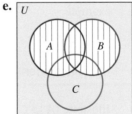 **f.**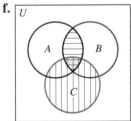

EXAMPLE 6

Venn diagrams with three sets and parentheses

Perform the following combinations of operations among three sets.

a. $A \cup (B \cap C)$ **b.** $\overline{A \cup B} \cap C$

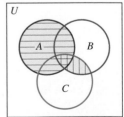

Solution

a. Do parentheses first (vertical lines); then shade A (horizontal lines). The union is all parts that show either vertical or horizontal lines (or both); the answer is the part that is shaded.

b. Overbars "act like" parentheses, so do $\overline{A \cup B}$ first (vertical); then shade C (horizontal). The intersection is all parts that show *both* vertical and horizontal lines; the answer is the part that is shaded.

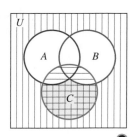

PROBLEM SET 8.4

See Instructor's Answer Section (IAS) for Venn diagrams.

ESSENTIAL IDEAS   LEVEL 1

1. Draw a Venn diagram for $A \cup B$.

2. Draw a Venn diagram for $A \cap B$.

3. Draw a Venn diagram for $\overline{A}$.

4. Use set notation to identify the shaded portion of the following Venn diagram.

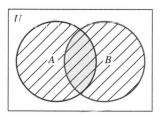

$A \cap B$

5. Use set notation to identify the shaded portion of the following Venn diagram.

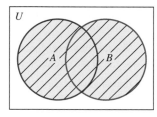

$A \cup B$

6. Use set notation to identify the shaded portion of the following Venn diagram.

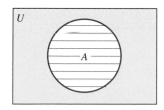

$\overline{A}$

7. Write in symbols: the complement of the union of sets A and B. Draw a Venn diagram. $\overline{A \cup B}$

8. Write in symbols: the union of the complements of sets A and B. Draw a Venn diagram. $\overline{A} \cup \overline{B}$

DRILL AND PRACTICE   LEVEL 2

Draw a Venn diagram to illustrate each relationship given in Problems 9–26.

9. $A \cup \overline{B}$

10. $\overline{A} \cup B$

11. $\overline{A} \cap C$

12. $\overline{A \cap B}$

13. $\overline{A \cap C}$

14. $\overline{A \cup B}$

15. $\overline{B \cup C}$

16. $\overline{A \cup C}$

17. $A \cap (B \cup C)$

18. $A \cup (B \cup C)$

19. $(A \cap B) \cap (A \cap C)$

20. $(A \cap B) \cup (A \cap C)$

21. $\overline{(A \cup B) \cup C}$

22. $\overline{(A \cap B) \cup C}$

23. $A \cap \overline{B \cup C}$

24. $\overline{A \cap B} \cup C$

25. $\overline{A \cup B} \cup C$

26. $A \cup \overline{B \cup C}$

Let
$U = \{1, 2, 3, 4, 5, 6, 7, 8, 9, 10\}$
$A = \{2, 4, 6, 8\}$
$B = \{5, 9\}$
$C = \{2, 5, 8, 9, 10\}$
List all the members of each set in Problems 27–39.

27. $(A \cup B) \cup C$
{2, 4, 5, 6, 8, 9, 10}

28. $(A \cap B) \cap C$ ∅

29. $A \cup (B \cap C)$ {2, 4, 5, 6, 8, 9}

30. $A \cap (\overline{B} \cup C)$
A or {2, 4, 6, 8}

31. $\overline{A} \cap (B \cup C)$ {5, 9, 10}

32. $A \cap (B \cap \overline{C})$ ∅

33. $\overline{A} \cup (B \cap C)$
A or {1, 3, 5, 7, 9, 10}

34. $A \cap \overline{B \cup C}$ {4, 6}

35. $\overline{A \cap B} \cup C$
U or {1, 2, 3, 4, 5, 6, 7, 8, 9, 10}

36. $\overline{(A \cap B) \cap C}$
U or {1, 2, 3, 4, 5, 6, 7, 8, 9, 10}

37. $\overline{(A \cup B) \cup C}$ {1, 3, 7}

38. $A \cap (B \cup C)$
{1, 3, 4, 5, 6, 7, 9, 10}

39. $\overline{A} \cup (B \cap C)$ {1, 3, 7, 10}

In Problems 40–47, draw one Venn diagram for the left side of the equation and another for the right. If the final shaded portions are the same, then you have established the equality. If the final shaded portions are not identical, then you have disproved the result.

40. $A \cup B = A \cap B$ F   **41.** $A \cup B = B \cup A$ T

42. $\overline{A} \cap \overline{B} = \overline{A \cup B}$ T   **43.** $\overline{A \cup B} = \overline{A} \cup \overline{B}$ F

44. $A \cup (B \cup C) = (A \cup B) \cup (A \cup C)$ T

45. $(A \cup B) \cup C = A \cup (B \cup C)$ T

46. $A \cap (B \cup C) = (A \cap B) \cap (A \cap C)$ F

47. De Morgan's law: $\overline{X \cap Y} = \overline{X} \cup \overline{Y}$ T

APPLICATIONS **LEVEL 2**

48. In a sample of defective tires, 72 have defects in materials, 89 have defects in workmanship, and 17 have defects of both types. How many tires are in the sample?   144

49. Santa Rosa Junior College enrolled 29,000 students in the fall. It was reported that of that number, 58% were female and 42% were male. In addition, 62% were over the age of 25. How many students were there in each category? Draw a Venn diagram showing these relationships.   males: 12,180; females: 16,820; over age 25: 17,980

50. A questionnaire of college students found that 40 students purchased a student body card, and 61 purchased their textbooks from the student union, and 20 did both. How many students were in the sample?   81

51. Montgomery College has a 50-piece band and a 36-piece orchestra. If 14 people are members of both the band and the orchestra, can the band and orchestra travel in two 40-passenger buses?

© Tom McCarthy/PhotoEdit

Yes; 72 persons can travel in 2 buses.

52. Liz knows that half the students from her school are accepted at the public university nearby. Also, half are accepted at the local private college. Liz thinks that because this adds up to 100%, she will surely be accepted at one or the other institution. Explain why Liz may be wrong. If possible, use a diagram in your explanation.*
Answers vary; need a Venn diagram to show conclusion not correct

53. **IN YOUR OWN WORDS** The Venn diagram shown in the "In This World" at the beginning of this section appears to be inconsistent with the message the advertiser wishes to convey. Draw a Venn diagram that more accurately represents what you think is intended. Interpret your Venn diagram to discuss the intended message.

RIGHT OR WRONG? **LEVEL 3**

Explain what is wrong, if anything, with the statements in Problems 54–60. Explain your reasoning.

54. For $\overline{A \cup B}$, first find the complement, then find the union.   F; first find the union, then find the complement

55. $\overline{A \cup B} = \overline{A} \cup \overline{B}$ F; complement does not distribute

56. $\overline{A \cap B} = \overline{A} \cap \overline{B}$ F; complement does not distribute

57. $\overline{A \cap B} = \overline{A} \cup \overline{B}$ T; De Morgan's law

58. $\overline{A \cup B} = \overline{A} \cap \overline{B}$ T; De Morgan's law

59. To draw the Venn diagram for $(A \cap B) \cup \overline{C}$, we would carry out (in order) the following steps:

   (1) Draw a rectangle (for the universe) containing three overlapping circles. Label the circles A, B, and C.

   (2) Shade in all parts that are in both A and B.

   (3) Shade in all parts that are not in C.

   (4) Use a highlighter to mark all parts that have been shaded in both parts (2) and (3).
F; use a highlighter to mark all parts shaded in either part (2) or part (3)

60. To draw the Venn diagram for $\overline{A \cup B} \cap C$, we would carry out (in order) the following steps:

   (1) Draw a rectangle (for the universe) containing three overlapping circles. Label the circles A, B, and C.

   (2) Shade in all parts that are not in either A or B.

   (3) Shade in C.

   (4) Use a highlighter to mark all parts that have been shaded in both parts (2) and (3).   T; there is no mistake.

*This question appeared on the 1987 Examination of the California Assessment Program as an open-ended problem.

8.5 Survey Problems Using Sets

IN THIS WORLD THE UTILITY OF MATH

"Why are you so gloomy, Matt?" asked Dave.

"Oh, I didn't get the job. The personnel manager sent me out to poll 100 people about their favorite athlete. I didn't have time to complete the survey, so I made up some responses. Everybody knows it is Tiger Woods, anyway! I don't know how she found out, but she didn't give me the job. I guess I'll need to learn more about surveys before I try that again," answered Matt.

In this section, Matt will learn how to use sets to reach conclusions about surveys.

 See Problem 58.

Venn diagrams can sometimes be used to solve survey problems. We will consider survey problems with two or three sets.

Venn Diagrams with Two Sets

If there are two sets in the survey, then we draw two overlapping sets, as shown in Figure 8.11.

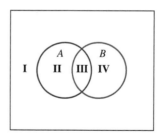

Figure 8.11 Survey problem with two sets, *A* and *B*

In Example 2 of the previous section we considered finding the number of elements in the union of two sets. We repeat that property here for convenience: For any two sets *X* and *Y*,

$$|X \cup Y| = |X| + |Y| - |X \cap Y|$$

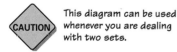

This diagram can be used whenever you are dealing with two sets.

However, when doing survey problems, it is generally easier to use Venn diagrams, as shown by the examples of this section.

EXAMPLE 1

Finding the numbers in the regions formed by two sets

Give the numbers of elements in the regions marked I, II, III, and IV in Figure 8.11 when $|U| = 100$, $|A| = 30$, $|B| = 40$, and $|A \cap B| = 12$.

Solution   Draw a Venn diagram with two overlapping sets, as shown in Figure 8.11. Begin with the intersection, and fill in the number of elements in Region III:

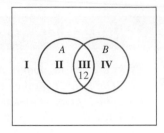

Next, find the numbers of elements in Regions II and IV. For Region II,

$$30 - 12 = 18 \qquad \text{Fill in this number in the Venn diagram in Region II.}$$

For Region IV,

$$40 - 12 = 28 \qquad \text{Fill in this number in the Venn diagram in Region IV.}$$

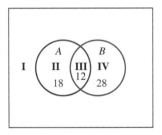

Finally, for Region I,

$$100 - (30 + 40 - 12) = 100 - 58 = 42$$

●

Venn Diagrams with Three Sets

For three sets, the situation is a little more involved. As we did with two sets, begin with a Venn diagram showing three overlapping sets, as shown in Figure 8.12.

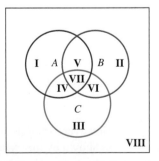

Figure 8.12 Survey problem with three sets A, B, and C

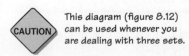

This diagram (figure 8.12) can be used whenever you are dealing with three sets.

The overall procedure is to fill in the number in the innermost set first and work your way out through the rest of the Venn diagram by using subtraction. We summarize this procedure.

Venn Diagram Problems

The procedure for finding the number of elements in each of the eight regions formed by three sets (numbered as shown in Figure 8.12) is given:

Step 1 Draw a Venn diagram with three overlapping sets.

Step 2 Fill in the number of elements in the innermost region (Region VII).

Step 3 Fill in the numbers of elements in those regions with two overlapping parts (Regions IV, V, and VI).

Step 4 Fill in the numbers of elements in those regions with one part (Regions I, II, and III).

Step 5 Finally, subtract all the numbers in the Venn diagram from $|U|$ to find the number of elements in none of the sets (Region VIII).

EXAMPLE 2

Finding the numbers in the regions formed by three sets

CAUTION This is a fairly long example, but it is an important one, so take your time and stick with it.

Give the numbers of elements in the regions marked I, II, . . . VII, and VIII in Figure 8.12 when $|U| = 100$, $|A| = 30$, $|B| = 40$, $|C| = 35$, $|A \cap B| = 12$, $|A \cap C| = 14$, $|B \cap C| = 15$, and $|A \cap B \cap C| = 3$.

Solution

Step 1 Draw a Venn diagram with three overlapping sets, as shown in Figure 8.12.

Step 2 Fill in the number of elements in Region VII, as shown in Figure 8.12.

Step 3 Fill in the numbers in Regions IV, V, and VI.

For Region IV, $|A \cap C| - |A \cap B \cap C| = 14 - 3 = 11$.

For Region V, $|A \cap B| - |A \cap B \cap C| = 12 - 3 = 9$.

For Region VI, $|B \cap C| - |A \cap B \cap C| = 15 - 3 = 12$.

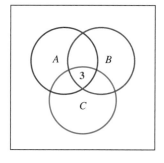

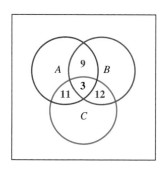

Step 4 Fill in the numbers in Regions I, II, and III.

For Region I, $|A| - (9 + 3 + 11) = 30 - (23) = 7$.

For Region II, $|B| - (9 + 3 + 12) = 40 - (24) = 16$.

For Region III, $|C| - (11 + 3 + 12) = 35 - (26) = 9$.

Step 5 Finally, for Region VIII, subtract all of the numbers in the Venn diagram from $|U|$:

$$100 - (7 + 9 + 3 + 11 + 16 + 12 + 9) = 100 - 67 = 33$$

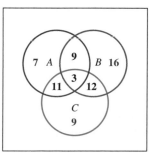

We now apply this procedure to an applied problem which we call a survey problem.

EXAMPLE 3

Survey analysis

A survey of 100 randomly selected students gave the following information:

    45 students are taking mathematics.

    41 students are taking English.

    40 students are taking history.

    15 students are taking math and English.

    18 students are taking math and history.

    17 students are taking English and history.

    7 students are taking all three.

Use Figure 8.12 (with Regions I to VIII) to answer the following questions, which are designed to follow the steps in the procedure for Venn diagram problems.

a. Name the three sets (A, B, and C) in this survey problem.

b. How many students are taking all three subjects (Region VII)?

c. How many are taking mathematics and history, but not English (Region IV)?

d. How many are taking mathematics and English, but not history (Region V)?

e. How many are taking English and history, but not mathematics (Region VI)?

f. How many are taking only mathematics (Region I)?

g. How many are taking only English (Region II)?

h. How many are taking only history (Region III)?

i. How many are taking none of the three subjects (Region VIII)?

Solution We draw a Venn diagram and fill in the various regions.

Step 1 **a.** Let the three sets be:

$$M = \{\text{students taking mathematics}\}$$
$$E = \{\text{students taking English}\}$$
$$H = \{\text{students taking history}\}$$

Notice that even though the sets in Figure 8.12 are labeled A, B, and C, we relabel those sets M, E, and H for easy reference in this survey problem.

Step 2 **b.** Start by filling in the innermost section first; there are 7 in the region $M \cap E \cap H$. Notice that we have filled in a 7 in this region. There are 7 people taking all three subjects.

Step 3 Now fill in the portions of intersection of each pair of two sets, using subtraction:

c. $|M \cap H| = 18$; but 7 have previously been accounted for, so only the *remaining* 11 are added to the Venn diagram ($18 - 7 = 11$). There are 11 students taking mathematics and history, but not English. Fill in 11 into Region IV.

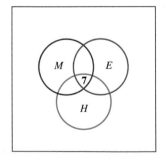

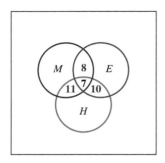

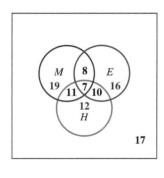

d. $|M \cap E| = 15$; so fill in 8 students $(15 - 7 = 8)$. There are 8 students taking mathematics and English, but not history. Fill in 8 into Region V.

e. $|E \cap H| = 17$; so fill in an additional 10 students $(17 - 7 = 10)$. There are 10 students taking English and history, but not mathematics. Fill 10 into Region VI.

Step 4 The next step is to fill in the regions of the Venn diagram representing single sets:

f. $|M| = 45$; but 26 (namely, $8 + 7 + 11$) have previously been accounted for, so in this case we subtract 26 from 45, leaving us with 19. Fill this number into Region I. There are 19 students taking only mathematics.

g. $|E| = 41$; but here we subtract 25 $(7 + 10 + 8)$ and fill in 16 into Region II.

h. $|H| = 40$; and we subtract 28 $(7 + 10 + 11)$ and fill in 12 into Region III.

Step 5 Finally, for Region VIII, subtract all of the numbers in the Venn diagram from $|U|$.

i. Add all the numbers in the diagram and confirm that 83 persons have been accounted for: $19 + 8 + 16 + 11 + 7 + 10 + 12 = 83$. Since 100 students were surveyed, we see that $100 - 83 = 17$ are not taking any of the three courses. We fill in 17 as the number outside the three interlocking circles.

PROBLEM SET 8.5

See IAS for Venn diagrams.

ESSENTIAL IDEAS LEVEL 1

1. How many regions are there in a Venn diagram with one set? **2**

2. How many regions are there with two overlapping sets? **4**

3. How many regions are there with three overlapping sets? **8**

4. How many regions are there with n overlapping sets? **2^n**

DRILL AND PRACTICE LEVEL 2

In Problems 5–10, give the numbers of elements in the regions marked I, II, III, and IV in Figure 8.11.

5. $|U| = 25$, $|A| = 6$, $|B| = 14$, $|A \cap B| = 2$ I: 7; II: 4; III: 2; IV: 12

6. $|U| = 21$, $|A| = 12$, $|B| = 9$, $|A \cap B| = 0$
   I: 0; II: 12; III: 0; IV: 9

7. $|U| = 74$, $|A| = 42$, $|B| = 46$, $|A \cap B| = 24$
   I: 10; II: 18; III: 24; IV: 22

8. $|U| = 1,295$, $|A| = 243$, $|B| = 582$, $|A \cap B| = 162$
   I: 632; II: 81; III: 162; IV: 420

9. $|U| = 1,000$, $|A| = 100$, $|B| = 200$, $|A \cap B| = 50$
   I: 750; II: 50; III: 50; IV: 150

10. $|U| = 1,100$, $|A| = 650$, $|B| = 425$, $|A \cap B| = 25$
    I: 50; II: 625; III: 25; IV: 400

In Problems 11–16, give the numbers of elements in the regions marked I, II, III, IV, V, VI, VII, and VIII in Figure 8.12.

11. $|U| = 25$, $|A| = 10$, $|B| = 8$, $|C| = 12$,
    $|A \cap B| = 4$, $|A \cap C| = 3$, $|B \cap C| = 2$,
    $|A \cap B \cap C| = 1$ I: 4; II: 3; III: 8; IV: 2; V: 3; VI: 1; VII: 1; VIII: 3

12. $|U| = 50$, $|A| = 30$, $|B| = 25$, $|C| = 30$,
    $|A \cap B| = 15$, $|A \cap C| = 18$, $|B \cap C| = 12$,
    $|A \cap B \cap C| = 8$ I: 5; II: 6; III: 8; IV: 10; V: 7; VI: 4; VII: 8; VIII: 2

13. $|U| = 100$, $|A| = 45$, $|B| = 20$, $|C| = 36$,
    $|A \cap B| = 2$, $|A \cap C| = 2$, $|B \cap C| = 8$,
    $|A \cap B \cap C| = 2$ I: 43; II: 12; III: 28; IV: 0; V: 0; VI: 6; VII: 2; VIII: 9

14. $|U| = 300$, $|A| = 100$, $|B| = 70$, $|C| = 50$,
    $|A \cap B| = 6$, $|A \cap C| = 6$, $|B \cap C| = 6$,
    $|A \cap B \cap C| = 0$
    I: 88; II: 58; III: 38; IV: 6; V: 6; VI: 6; VII: 0; VIII: 98

15. $|U| = 400$, $|A| = 150$, $|B| = 190$, $|C| = 65$,
    $|A \cap B| = 20$, $|A \cap C| = 60$, $|B \cap C| = 20$,
    $|A \cap B \cap C| = 20$
    I: 90; II: 170; III: 5; IV: 40; V: 0; VI: 0; VII: 20; VIII: 75

16. $|U| = 2,000$, $|A| = 143$, $|B| = 821$, $|C| = 293$,
    $|A \cap B| = 82$, $|A \cap C| = 94$, $|B \cap C| = 52$,
    $|A \cap B \cap C| = 34$
    I: 1; II: 721; III: 181; IV: 60; V: 48; VI: 18; VII: 34; VIII: 937

APPLICATIONS   LEVEL 2

17. Human blood is typed Rh$^+$ (positive blood) or Rh$^-$ (negative blood). This Rh factor is called an *antigen*. There are two other antigens known as A and B types. Blood lacking both A and B types is called type O. Sketch a Venn diagram showing the three types of antigens, A, B, and Rh, and label each of the eight regions. For example, O$^+$ is inside the Rh set (anything in Rh is positive), but outside both A and B. On the other hand, O$^-$ is that region outside all three circles.

18. There are three principal ethnic groups in the United States: whites, blacks, and Hispanics. Sketch a Venn diagram showing these groups and label each of the eight regions formed by these sets.

19. From a survey of 100 college students, a marketing research company found that 75 students owned iPhones, 45 owned cars, and 35 owned both cars and iPhones.

    a. How many students owned either a car or an iPhone (but not both)?   **50**

    b. How many students do not own either a car or an iPhone?
       15

20. In a survey of a TriDelt chapter with 50 members, 18 were taking mathematics and 35 were taking English; 6 were taking both. How many were not taking either of these subjects?
    There are 3 people who are not taking either of the courses.

21. The senior class at Rancho Cotati High School included 25 football players and 16 basketball players. If 7 persons played both sports, how many different people played in these sports?   There are 34 people playing.

22. The fire department wants to send booklets on fire hazards to all teachers and homeowners in town. How many booklets does it need, using these statistics?

    50,000 homeowners
    4,000 teachers
    3,000 teachers who own their own homes
    51,000 booklets are needed

In a recent survey of 100 *women, the following information was gathered:*

    59 use shampoo A.
    51 use shampoo B.
    35 use shampoo C.
    24 use shampoos A and B.
    19 use shampoos A and C.
    13 use shampoos B and C.
    11 use all three.

Use Figure 8.12 *(with Regions I to VIII) to answer the questions in Problems 23–31.*

23. Name the three sets (A, B, and C) in this survey problem.   A = {women who use shampoo A}; B = {women who use shampoo B}; C = {women who use shampoo C}

24. How many are using all three shampoos (Region VII)?   **11**

25. How many are using shampoos A and C, but not B (Region IV)?   **8**

26. How many are using shampoos A and B, but not C (Region V)?   **13**

27. How many are using shampoos B and C, but not A (Region VI)?   **2**

28. How many are using shampoo A only (Region I)?   **27**

29. How many are using shampoo B only (Region II)?   **25**

30. How many are using shampoo C only (Region III)?   **14**

31. How many are not using any of the three listed shampoos (Region VIII)?   **0**

A poll was taken of 100 *students at a commuter campus to find out how they got to campus. The results were:*

    42 said they drove alone.
    31 rode the bus.
    28 rode in a carpool.
    9 used both carpools and rode the bus.
    10 used both a carpool and sometimes drove alone.
    6 used buses as well as drove alone.
    4 used all three methods.

Use Figure 8.12 *(with Regions I to VIII) to answer the questions in Problems 32–40.*

32. Name the three sets (A, B, and C) in this survey problem.   A = {people who drive alone}; B = {people who ride the bus}; C = {people who carpool}

33. How many are using all three (Region VII)?   **4**

34. How many are A and C, but not B (Region IV)?   **6**

35. How many are A and B, but not C (Region V)?   **2**

36. How many are B and C, but not A (Region VI)?   **5**

37. How many are A only (Region I)?   **30**

38. How many are B only (Region II)?   **20**

39. How many are C only (Region III)?   **13**

40. How many are not using any of the three (Region VIII)?   **20**

At the time of George W. Bush's presidency, there have been 43 presidents of the United States. Draw a Venn diagram showing the following facts about where each served before assuming the presidency.

14 were vice-president.
6 were VP and served in the Senate.
15 served in the Senate.
2 were VP and held a cabinet post.
8 held a cabinet post.
4 served in the Senate and held a cabinet post.
1 was VP, in the Senate, and held a cabinet post.

© Joseph Sohm; Visions of America/Corbis

Answer the questions in Problems 41–49.

41. Name the three sets in this survey problem.   **See below.**

42. How many presidents served as vice-president, in the Senate, and held a cabinet post?   **1**

43. How many presidents served as vice-president and in the Senate, but did not serve in a cabinet post?   **5**

44. How many presidents served in the Senate and held a cabinet post, but never served as vice-president?   **3**

45. How many presidents served as vice-president and in a cabinet post, but did not serve in the Senate?   **1**

46. How many presidents served only as vice-president before becoming president?   **7**

47. How many presidents served only in the Senate before becoming president?   **6**

48. How many presidents served only in a cabinet post before becoming president?   **3**

49. How many presidents did not previously serve in the Senate, cabinet, or as vice-president?   **17**

In an interview of 50 students,

12 liked Proposition 8 and Proposition 13.
18 liked Proposition 8 but not Proposition 2.
4 liked Proposition 8, Proposition 13, and Proposition 2.
25 liked Proposition 8.
15 liked Proposition 13.
10 liked Proposition 2 but not Proposition 8 or Proposition 13.
1 liked Proposition 13 and Proposition 2 but not Proposition 8.

41. **VP = {presidents who previously served as vice-president};**
S = {presidents who previously served in the Senate};
C = {presidents who previously held a cabinet post}

Answer the questions in Problems 50–57.

Let E = {respondents who like Proposition 8}
T = {respondents who like Proposition 13}
W = {respondents who like Proposition 2}

50. How many respondents like all three propositions?   **4**

51. How many are E and W, but not T?   **3**

52. How many are E and T, but not W?   **8**

53. How many are T and W, but not E?   **1**

54. How many are E only?   **10**

55. How many are T only?   **2**

56. How many are W only?   **10**

57. How many do not like any of the propositions?   **12**

58. "Why are you so gloomy, Matt?" asked Dave. "Oh, I didn't get the job. The personnel manager sent me out to poll 100 people about their favorite athlete. I didn't have time to complete the survey, so I made up some responses. Everybody knows it is Tiger Woods, anyway! I don't know how she found out, but she didn't give me the job. I guess I'll need to learn more about surveys before I try that again." Matt's data follow:

38 picked Tiger Woods.
16 picked Michael Jordan.
9 picked Shaquille O'Neal.
7 picked Tiger Woods and Michael Jordan.
5 picked Michael Jordan and Shaquille O'Neal.
3 picked Tiger Woods and Shaquille O'Neal.
2 picked all three as their favorite athlete.
37 did not respond or picked other athletes.

If you were the personnel manager, would you hire Matt on the basis of this survey?   **See IAS. No, there were 87, not 100, polled.**

RIGHT OR WRONG?   **LEVEL 3**

Explain what is wrong, if anything, with the statements in Problems 59–60. Explain your reasoning.

59. If there are 145 elements in set A and 100 elements in set B, then there are $145 + 100 = 245$ elements in $A \cup B$.
F; we need to know how many are in the intersection

60. For any sets A and B,

$$|A \cup B| = |A| + |B|$$

F; $|A \cup B| = |A| + |B| - |A \cap B|$ because we don't want to count the elements in the intersection twice.

8.6 Inductive and Deductive Reasoning

IN THIS WORLD THE UTILITY OF MATH

"Sarah, do you remember the old song, 'Ode to Billy Joe'? I just saw the movie on my VCR and it was great! I finally figured out what Billy Joe threw off the Tallahatchee Bridge," said Bob.

"Oh yeah? I'll bet you didn't!" answered Sarah. "Anyway," continued Sarah, "the movie is not faithful to the song. From the song you cannot figure out for sure what was thrown from the bridge."

Is it possible to use deductive reasoning to answer this question?

In this section, Sarah and Bob will find out what is meant by deductive reasoning and how to use Venn diagrams to reach a valid conclusion.

 See Problem 57.

In Example 3 of Section 8.4 we used Venn diagrams to prove De Morgan's laws. In this section, we will introduce other methods of proof using what is called **logic.** Logic is a method of reasoning that accepts only those conclusions that are inescapable. We will look at two types of logical reasoning and then we conclude by using Venn diagrams to reach certain conclusions.

Inductive Reasoning

One type of logical reasoning, called *inductive reasoning,* reaches conclusions by observing patterns and then predicting other results based on those observations. It is the type of reasoning used in much of scientific investigation, and it involves reasoning from particular facts or individual cases to a general *conjecture.* A **conjecture** is a guess or generalization predicted from incomplete or uncertain evidence.

Inductive Reasoning

> **Inductive reasoning** is reasoning from the particular to the general.

The more individual occurrences you observe, the better able you are to make a correct generalization. As you reason from the particular to the general, you must keep in mind that an inductive (tentative) conclusion may have to be revised in light of new evidence. For example, consider this pattern:

$$1 \times 9 = 9$$
$$2 \times 9 = 18$$
$$3 \times 9 = 27$$
$$4 \times 9 = 36$$ *Conjecture:*   The sum of the digits of the answer
$$5 \times 9 = 45$$ of any product involving 9 is always 9.
$$6 \times 9 = 54$$ *Evidence:*   The first ten examples shown here
$$7 \times 9 = 63$$ substantiate this speculation.
$$8 \times 9 = 72$$
$$9 \times 9 = 81$$
$$10 \times 9 = 90$$

The conjecture based on this pattern is suspect because it is based on so few cases. In fact, it is shattered by the very next case, where we get $11 \times 9 = 99$. An example that contradicts a conjecture is called a **counterexample.**

EXAMPLE 1   **Finding counterexamples**

Tell whether you believe the given conjecture is true or false. If you believe it to be false, see if you can find a counterexample.

a. The sum of the digits in any product of 3 and another number is always divisible by 3.

b. All primes are odd.

c. All numbers between 1 and 2 are rational.

Solution

a. Look for a pattern:

$$1 \times 3 = 3$$
$$2 \times 3 = 6$$
$$3 \times 3 = 9$$
$$4 \times 3 = 12$$
$$5 \times 3 = 15$$ The sum of the digits in each of these
$$6 \times 3 = 18$$ answers is divisible by 3.
$$7 \times 3 = 21$$
$$8 \times 3 = 24$$
$$9 \times 3 = 27$$
$$10 \times 3 = 30$$

Try other examples:

$$8,340 \times 3 = 25,020$$

Here $2 + 5 + 0 + 2 + 0 = 9$, which is divisible by 3. The conjecture seems to be a true.

b. Try some examples:

$$3, 5, 7, 11, 13, 17, 19, 23, \ldots$$

are all odd. However, 2 is a prime and it is even, so it serves as a counterexample for the conjecture.

c. Some examples: $1\frac{1}{2}$, 1.66666, and $1.\overline{6}$ are all between 1 and 2, and they are all rational. Examples, however, do not prove the conjecture; they simply support the conjecture. We can find a counterexample: 1.6066066606666066666606 ... is not rational. ●

Sometimes you must formulate a conjecture based on inductive reasoning.

EXAMPLE 2

Formulating a conjecture

What is the 100th consecutive positive odd number? Use this information to find the sum of the first 100 consecutive positive odd numbers.

Solution Positive odd numbers are 1, 3, 5, ... What is the 100th consecutive odd number?

1 is the 1st odd number;

3 is the 2nd odd number;

5 is the 3rd odd number;

7 is the 4th odd number;

9 is the 5th odd number;

↑
This seems to be one less than twice the term number.

$$2(\mathbf{6}) - 1 = 11 \text{ is the } \mathbf{6}\text{th odd number;}$$
$$2(\mathbf{7}) - 1 = 13 \text{ is the } \mathbf{7}\text{th odd number;}$$
$$2(\mathbf{100}) - 1 = 199 \text{ is the } \mathbf{100}\text{th odd number.}$$

We now look for a pattern to find $1 + 3 + 5 + \cdots + 199$; certainly it is too large an equation to do by brute force (even with a calculator).

$$1 = 1 \qquad \text{One term}$$
$$1 + 3 = 4 \qquad \text{Two terms}$$
$$1 + 3 + 5 = 9 \qquad \text{Three terms}$$
$$1 + 3 + 5 + 7 = 16 \qquad \text{Four terms}$$
$$1 + 3 + 5 + 7 + 9 = 25 \qquad \text{Five terms}$$

It appears that the sum of 2 terms is $4 = 2^2$; of 3 terms is $9 = 3^2$; of 4 terms is $16 = 4^2$; and of 5 terms is $25 = 5^2$. Thus, the sum of the first 100 consecutive odd numbers seems to be 100^2.

Conjecture: $\quad 1 + 3 + 5 + \cdots + 199 = 100^2 = 10,000$ ●

Deductive Reasoning

Although mathematicians often proceed by inductive reasoning to formulate new ideas, they are not content to stop at the "probable" stage. Often they formulate their predictions into conjectures and then try to prove these *deductively. Deductive reasoning* is a formal structure based on a set of *unproved* statements and a set of *undefined* terms, as well as being a logical process of deriving new results. The unproved statements are called **premises** or **axioms**. For example, consider the following argument:

1. If you read the *Times,* then you are well informed.

2. You read the *Times.*

3. Therefore, you are well informed.

Statements 1 and 2 are the *premises* of the argument; statement 3 is called the **conclusion.** If you accept statements 1 and 2 as true, then you *must* accept statement 3 as true. Such reasoning is called *deductive reasoning;* and if the conclusion follows from the premises, the reasoning is said to be **valid.**

Deductive Reasoning

> **Deductive reasoning** consists of reaching a conclusion by using a formal structure based on a set of *undefined terms* and on a set of accepted unproved *axioms* or *premises.* The conclusions are said to be *proved* and are called **theorems.**

Reasoning that is not valid is called **invalid** reasoning. Logic accepts no conclusions except those that are inescapable. This is possible because of the strict way in which concepts are defined. Difficulty in simplifying arguments may arise because of their length, the vagueness of the words used, the literary style, or the possible emotional impact of the words used.

Consider the following two arguments:

If George Washington was assassinated, then he is dead.
Therefore, if he is dead, he was assassinated.

If you use heroin, then you first used marijuana.
Therefore, if you use marijuana, then you will use heroin.

Logically, these two arguments are exactly the same, and both are *invalid* forms of reasoning. Nearly everyone would agree that the first is invalid, but many people see the second as valid. The reason lies in the emotional appeal of the words used.

To avoid these difficulties, we look at the *form* of the arguments and not at the independent truth or falsity of the statements. One type of logic problem is called a **syllogism.** A syllogism has three parts: two *premises,* or hypotheses, and a *conclusion.* The premises give us information from which we form a conclusion. With the syllogism, we are interested in knowing whether the conclusion *necessarily follows* from the premises. If it does, it is called a *valid syllogism;* if not, it is called *invalid.* Consider the following examples:

Valid Forms of Reasoning		*Invalid Forms of Reasoning*
All Chevrolets are automobiles.	Premise	Some people are nice.
All automobiles have four wheels.	Premise	Some people are broke.
Therefore, all Chevrolets have four wheels.	Conclusion	Therefore there are some nice broke people.
All teachers are crazy.	Premise	All dodos are extinct.
Karl Smith is a teacher.	Premise	No dinosaurs are dodos.
Therefore, Karl Smith is crazy.	Conclusion	Therefore, all dinosaurs are extinct.

To analyze such arguments, we need to have a systematic method of approach. We will use Venn diagrams.* For two sets *p* and *q,* we make the interpretations shown in Figure 8.13.

*In logic, Venn diagrams are often called *Euler circles,* after the famous mathematician Leonhard Euler, who used circles and ovals to analyze this type of argument. However, Venn used these circles in a more general way.

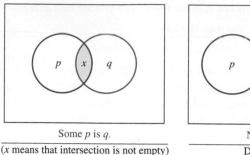 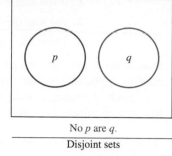 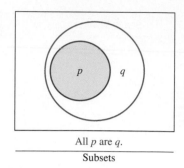

Some p is q.

(x means that intersection is not empty)

No p are q.

Disjoint sets

All p are q.

Subsets

Figure 8.13 Venn diagrams for syllogisms

EXAMPLE 3   **Using Venn diagrams in a syllogism**

Test the validity of the following arguments.

a. All dictionaries are books.
This is a dictionary.
Therefore, this is a book.

b. If you like potato chips, then you will like Krinkles.
You do not like potato chips.
Therefore, you do not like Krinkles.

Solution

a. Begin with a Venn diagram showing the first premise: *All dictionaries are books.*
   Let p: dictionaries; draw a circle and label it p.
          q: books; draw a circle and label it q. Since
          all dictionaries are books, draw circle q
          so that it includes circle p as a subset.

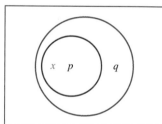

For the second premise, we place x (this object) inside the circle labeled set p (set of dictionaries). The conclusion, "This object is a book," cannot be avoided (since x *must* be inside the circle labeled q) so it is valid.

b. Again, begin with a Venn diagram: *If you like potato chips, then you will like Krinkles.* The first premise is the same as: *All people who like potato chips like Krinkles.*
   Let p: people who like potato chips;
          draw a circle and label it p.
          q: people who like Krinkles;
          draw a circle and label it q. Since
          all people who like potato chips also like
          Krinkles, draw circle q so that it includes
          circle p as a subset.

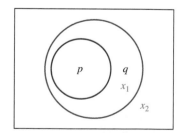

For the second premise, you will place the x (you) outside the circle labeled p. Notice that you are not forced to place x into a single region; it could be placed in either of two places—those labeled x_1 and x_2. Since the stated conclusion is not forced, the argument is not valid.   ●

PROBLEM SET 8.6

ESSENTIAL IDEAS LEVEL 1

1. **IN YOUR OWN WORDS** Explain inductive reasoning. Give an original example of an occasion when you have used inductive reasoning or heard it being used.

2. **IN YOUR OWN WORDS** In your own words, explain deductive reasoning. Give an original example of an occasion when you have used deductive reasoning or heard it being used.

3. Distinguish a *premise* from a *theorem*.
A premise is accepted without proof, and a theorem is proved.

4. What is a syllogism?
An argument with two premises and a conclusion

DRILL AND PRACTICE LEVEL 2

In Problems 5–12, answer the question and tell whether it illustrates inductive or deductive reasoning.
They are all inductive reasoning.

5. Consider the successive products of 8 (1×8, 2×8, 3×8, 4×8, . . .). If the product has more than 1 digit, add the digits successively to obtain a single digit. What is the pattern that you observe?   8, 7, 6, 5, 4, 3, 2, 1, 9, 8, 7, 6, 5, 4, 3, . . .

6. Consider the successive products of 3 (1×3, 2×3, 3×3, 4×3, . . .). If the product has more than 1 digit, add the digits successively to obtain a single digit. What pattern do you observe?   3, 6, 9, 3, 6, 9, . . .

7. What is the 100th consecutive even number?   200

8. Give the 100th number in the pattern: 1, 4, 9, 16, 25, . . .
$100^2 = 10,000$

9. What is the sum of the first 25 consecutive odd numbers?
$25^2 = 625$

10. What is the sum of the first 1,000 consecutive odd numbers?
$1,000^2 = 1,000,000$

11. Compute the following.

   a. 11^2 121   **b.** 111^2 12,321   **c.** $1,111^2$ 1,234,321

   d. Describe a pattern from parts **a–c.**

12. Compute the following.

   a. $9 \times 1 - 1$ 8

   b. $9 \times 21 - 1$ 188

   c. $9 \times 321 - 1$ 2,888

   d. Describe a pattern from parts **a–c.**

Tell whether you believe that the conjecture in Problems 13–22 is true or false. If you believe it to be false, see if you can find a counterexample.   Counterexamples vary.

13. The sum of two even numbers is even.   T

14. The sum of two odd numbers is odd.   F; 3 + 5 = 8

15. The sum of two primes is prime.   F; 3 + 5 = 8

16. The product of two even numbers is even.   T

17. The product of two odd numbers is odd.   T

18. The product of two primes is prime.   F; 3 × 5 = 15

19. The area of a rectangle (number of square units) is larger than its perimeter (number of units).
F; 3 by 4 rectangle has A = 12 and P = 14

20. The basic metric units for length, capacity, and weight are larger than their U.S. counterparts.   F; gram is smaller than a lb.

21. All of the subsets of $S = \{a, b, c, d, e\}$ have cardinality less than the cardinality of S.
F; S ⊆ S but the cardinality is not less.

22. Every equilateral triangle has one angle of 60°.   T

Use Venn diagrams to check the validity of the arguments in Problems 23–35.   See IAS for Venn diagrams.

23. All mathematicians are eccentrics.
All eccentrics are rich.
Therefore, all mathematicians are rich.   valid

24. All snarks are fribbles.
All fribbles are ugly.
Therefore, all snarks are ugly.   valid

25. All cats are animals.
This is not an animal.
Therefore, this is not a cat.   valid

26. All bachelors are handsome.
Some bachelors do not drink lemonade.
Therefore, some handsome men do not drink lemonade.   valid

27. Some beautiful women are blond.
Blonds have more fun.
Therefore, some beautiful women have more fun.   valid

28. No students are enthusiastic.
You are enthusiastic.
Therefore, you are not a student.   valid

29. Some women are tall.
No men are strong.
Therefore, some tall people are not strong.
Set of men is the complement of the set of women; not valid

30. No politicians are honest.
Some dishonest people are found out.
Therefore, some politicians are found out.   not valid

31. All candy is fattening.
All candy is delicious.
Therefore, all fattening food is delicious.   not valid

32. No professors are ignorant
All ignorant people are vain.
Therefore, no professors are vain.   not valid

33. No monkeys are soldiers.
All monkeys are mischievous.
Therefore, this mischievous creature is not a soldier.   not valid

34. All lions are fierce.

Some lions do not drink coffee.

Therefore, some creatures that drink coffee are not fierce.
not valid

35. All red hair is pretty.

No pretty things are valuable.

Therefore, no red hair is valuable.   *valid*

APPLICATIONS   LEVEL 2

36. Does the following *B.C.* cartoon illustrate inductive or deductive reasoning? Explain your answer.
Inductive reasoning; explanations vary.

B.C. By permission of Johnny Hart and Creator's Syndicate, Inc.

Publishers-Hall Syndicate, 1968

37. Does the news story illustrate inductive or deductive reasoning? Explain your answer.
Deductive reasoning; explanations vary.

> The young man in charge of the checkroom in a fancy restaurant was known for his memory. He never used the usual markers to identify the hats and coats. One day a guest decided to put him to a test, and said to the clerk, "How do you know this is my hat?" "I don't," was the response. "But why did you return it to me?" asked the guest. "Because," said the clerk, "it's the one you gave to me."

Problems 38–41 refer to the lyrics of "By the Time I Get to Phoenix." Tell whether each answer you give is arrived at inductively or deductively.

By the Time I Get to Phoenix

By the time I get to Phoenix she'll be risin'.
She'll find the note I left hangin' on her door.
She'll laugh when she reads the part that says I'm leavin',
'Cause I've left that girl so many times before.

By the time I make Albuquerque she'll be workin'.
She'll probably stop at lunch and give me a call.
But she'll just hear that phone keep on ringin'
Off the wall, that's all.

By the time I make Oklahoma she'll be sleepin'.
She'll turn softly and call my name out low.
And she'll cry just to think I'd really leave her,
'tho' time and time I've tried to tell her so,
She just didn't know
I would really go.

38. In what basic direction (north, south, east, or west) is the person traveling?   *east; deductive reasoning*

39. What method of transportation or travel is the person using?
car; deductive reasoning

40. What is the probable starting point of this journey?
probably Las Vegas; inductive reasoning

41. List five facts you know about each person involved.
Answers vary.

Problems 42–45 refer to the lyrics of "Ode to Billy Joe." Tell whether each answer you give is arrived at inductively or deductively.

Ode to Billy Joe

It was the third of June, another sleepy, dusty, delta day.
I was choppin' cotton and my brother was balin' hay.
And at dinnertime we stopped and walked back to the house to eat,
And Mama hollered at the back door, "Y'all remember to wipe your feet."
Then she said, "I got some news this mornin' from Choctaw Ridge,
Today Billy Joe McAllister jumped off the Tallahatchee Bridge."

Papa said to Mama, as he passed around the black-eyed peas,
"Well, Billy Joe never had a lick o' sense, pass the biscuits please,
There's five more acres in the lower forty I've got to plow,"
And Mama said it was a shame about Billy Joe anyhow.
Seems like nothin' ever comes to no good up on Choctaw Ridge,
And now Billy Joe McAllister's jumped off the Tallahatchee Bridge.

Brother said he recollected when he and Tom and Billy Joe,
Put a frog down my back at the Carroll County picture show,
And wasn't I talkin' to him after church last Sunday night,
"I'll have another piece of apple pie, you know, it don't seem right,
I saw him at the sawmill yesterday on Choctaw Ridge,
And now you tell me Billy Joe's jumped off the Tallahatchee Bridge."

Mama said to me, "Child, what's happened to your appetite?
I been cookin' all mornin' and you haven't touched a single bite,
That nice young preacher Brother Taylor dropped by today,
Said he'd be pleased to have dinner on Sunday, Oh, by the way,
He said he saw a girl that looked a lot like you up on Choctaw Ridge
And she an' Billy Joe was throwin' somethin' off the Tallahatchee Bridge."

A year has come and gone since we heard the news 'bout Billy Joe,
Brother married Becky Thompson, they bought a store in Tupelo,
There was a virus goin' round, Papa caught it and he died last spring,
And now Mama doesn't seem to want to do much of anything.
And me I spend a lot of time pickin' flowers up on Choctaw Ridge,
And drop them into the muddy water off the Tallahatchee Bridge.

42. How many people are involved in this story? List them by name and/or description.   *At least eight persons*

43. Who "saw him at the sawmill yesterday"?
brother; deductive reasoning
44. In which state is the Tallahatchee Bridge located?
Answers vary; probably Alabama
45. On what day or days of the week could the death not have taken place? On what day of the week was the death most probable?   *Answers vary; probably Wednesday*

Problems 46–56 are included to develop critical thinking and are not directly related to the material in the text. Some will seem very easy, whereas others will seem very difficult. You are not expected to be able to answer them all, but you are expected to try.

46. How many 3-cent stamps are there in a dozen?   *12*

47. Two U.S. coins total $0.30, yet one of these coins is not a nickel. What are the coins?
One is a nickel and one is a quarter.
48. Oak Park Cemetery in Oak Park, New Jersey, will not bury anyone living west of the Mississippi. Why?
They only bury dead people.
49. What weighs more—a ton of coal or a ton of feathers?
Neither; they are the same.
50. If you had only one match and entered a room in which there was a kerosene lamp, an oil burner, and a wood-burning stove, which would you light first?   *the match*

51. Do they have a 4th of July in England?   *yes*

52. Some months have 30 days and some have 31 days. How many have 28 days?   *12 (All months have 28 days.)*

53. A man built a house that has four sides and it is rectangular. Each side has a southern exposure. A big bear came wandering by. What color is the bear?
white (It must be at the North Pole).
54. If a doctor gave you three pills and told you to take one every half-hour, how long would they last you?   *1 hour*

55. Two girls were born on the same day of the same month of the same year to the same parents, but they are not twins. Explain how this is possible.   *They are triplets.*

56. A woman gives a beggar 50¢. The woman is the beggar's sister, but the beggar is not the woman's brother. How can this be?   *They are sisters; the beggar is a woman.*

57. **IN YOUR OWN WORDS** "Sarah, do you remember the old song 'Ode to Billy Joe'? I just saw the movie on my VCR and it was great. I finally figured out what Billy Joe threw off the Tallahatchee Bridge," said Bob. "Oh, yeah? I'll bet you didn't!" answered Sarah. "Anyway," continued Sarah, "the movie is not faithful to the song. From the song you cannot figure out for sure what was thrown from the bridge." Is it possible to use deductive reasoning to answer this question?   *Answers vary; flower, deductive reasoning.*

58. **IN YOUR OWN WORDS** Write a short paper comparing the Problem of the Day with your own situation. (That is, find some examples from your life in which you have used inductive or deductive reasoning. Give examples, sources, and classifications as inductive or deductive.)

59. **IN YOUR OWN WORDS** By now, you have had a chance to deal with this book and math class for some time, and it might be a good time to assess your progress. We offered some suggestions for success at the beginning, and here you are asked to comment on each in light of your experience so far.

   a. Stay current with your reading and classwork.

   b. Attend all classes.

   c. Be bold: sit near the front. If you sat near the front, did it make a difference? If not, do you wish you had? Why or why not?

   d. Take full class notes.

   e. Doing all the assigned homework problems is important.

60. **IN YOUR OWN WORDS** Write a letter to a friend who is contemplating taking this class. Offer advice after reading Problem 59.

8.7 Chapter 8 Summary and Review

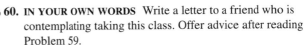

Take some time getting ready to work the review problems in this section. First, look back at the definition and property boxes. You will maximize your understanding of this chapter by working the problems in this section only after you have studied the material.

IMPORTANT TERMS
Numbers refer to sections of this chapter

And [8.3]
Axiom [8.6]
Belong to a set [8.1]
Cardinal number [8.1]
Cardinality [8.1]
Circular definition [8.1]

Complement [8.3]
Conclusion [8.6]
Conjecture [8.6]
Contained in a set [8.1]
Counterexample [8.6]
Deductive reasoning [8.6]

De Morgan's laws [8.4]
Description method [8.1]
Disjoint sets [8.2]
Element [8.1]
Empty set [8.1]
Equal sets [8.1]

Spending some time with the terms and objectives of this chapter will pay dividends in assuring your success.

Equivalent sets [8.1]
Finite set [8.1]
Improper subset [8.2]
Inductive reasoning [8.6]
Infinite set [8.1]
Intersection [8.3]
Invalid [8.6]
Logic [8.6]
Member [8.1]
Not [8.3]

One-to-one
  correspondence [8.1]
Or [8.3]
Overlapping sets [8.2]
Premise [8.6]
Proper subset [8.2]
Roster method [8.1]
Set [8.1]
Set-builder notation [8.1]
Subset [8.2]

Syllogism [8.6]
Theorem [8.6]
Undefined term [8.1]
Union [8.3]
Universal set [8.1]
Valid [8.6]
Venn diagram [8.2]
Well-defined set [8.1]

Essential Ideas

[8.1] Problem 1	Know why it is necessary to have some terms that are undefined.
Problem 2	Distinguish between equal and equivalent sets.
Problems 3–6	Give examples of sets of varying cardinality.
Problems 7–10	Distinguish among universal, empty, infinite, and finite sets.
[8.2] Problems 1–3	Distinguish among element, subset, and proper subset.
Problems 4–6	Draw Venn diagrams of disjoint and overlapping sets.
[8.3] Problems 1–7	Distinguish among union, intersection, and complement of sets, their English translations, and symbols for denoting.
Problems 8–10	Draw Venn diagrams for union, intersection, and complement.
[8.4] Problems 1–8	Draw Venn diagrams for unions, intersections, complements, and combinations of these operations.
Problems 4–6	Recognize union, intersection, and complement by looking at a Venn diagram.
[8.5] Problems 1–4	Know the number of Venn diagram regions defined by varying numbers of sets.
[8.6] Problems 1–2	Distinguish between inductive and deductive reasoning.
Problem 3	Distinguish between a premise and a theorem.
Problem 4	Know what is meant by a syllogism.

LEARNING OUTCOMES

The material in this chapter is reviewed in the following list of learning outcomes. A self-test (with answers and suggestions for additional study) is given. This self-test is constructed so that each problem number corresponds to a related objective. For example, Problem 7 is testing Objective 8.7. This self-test is followed by a practice test with the questions in mixed order.

[8.1] *Objective* 8.1	Decide whether a given set is well defined.
[8.1] *Objective* 8.2	Specify a set in roster form, given a description or set-builder notation.
[8.1] *Objective* 8.3	Specify a set given by roster in description form.
[8.1] *Objective* 8.4	State the cardinality of a given set.
[8.1] *Objective* 8.5	Decide whether two sets can be placed into a one-to-one correspondence; if so, show at least one such correspondence.
[8.1] *Objective* 8.6	Classify a given set as finite or infinite.
[8.2] *Objective* 8.7	List all the subsets of a given set. Know the number of subsets of a set of arbitrary size n.
[8.2] *Objective* 8.8	Draw a Venn diagram for given sets.
[8.3] *Objective* 8.9	Find the intersection, union, or complement of given sets.
[8.3] *Objective* 8.10	Draw Venn diagrams for union, intersection, and complement.

Self-Test

Each question of this self-test is related to the corresponding objective listed above.

1. Is the following set well defined? The set of persons in this classroom who are under 20 years of age.

2. Write the following set in roster form: $T = \{x \mid 2 < x \le 5; x \in \mathbb{N}\}$

3. Write the following set in description form: $S = \{101, 103, 105, \ldots, 197, 199\}$

4. Give the cardinality of T (Problem 2) and S (Problem 3).

5. Can the following sets be placed in a one-to-one correspondence?
   $\mathbb{N} = \{1, 2, 3, 4, \ldots\}$ and $E = \{2, 4, 6, 8, \ldots\}$
   If so, show one such correspondence; if not, explain.

6. Is the number of reruns of *I Love Lucy* finite or infinite? Explain your answer.

7. **a.** List all subsets of the set $\{0, 1\}$.
   b. How many subsets are there of the letters $\{a, b, c, d, \ldots, y, z\}$?

In Problems 8–10, let $A = \{$multiples of $2\}$ and $B = \{$multiples of $3\}$.

8. Draw a Venn diagram showing the sets A and B.

9. **a.** Find $A \cap B$.
   b. Find $\{1, 2, 3, 4, \ldots\} \cup \{2, 4, 6, 8, \ldots\}$.
   c. If the universe is $\mathbb{W}$ (whole numbers), find $\overline{\mathbb{N}}$, where $\mathbb{N}$ is the set of natural numbers.

10. Draw a Venn diagram for: **a.** $A \cap C$ **b.** $A \cup B$ **c.** $\overline{A \cup C}$

11. One section in a survey of 800 households asked the respondents to check the boxes that apply:

> ☐ This household uses a liquid detergent.
>
> ☐ This household uses a powder detergent.

   a. Draw a Venn diagram illustrating the possible results of this survey.
   b. If 344 of the households checked the first box, what percent of the respondents use liquid detergent?
   c. If 432 of the households checked the second box, what percent of the respondents use powder detergents?
   d. If 200 checked both boxes, what percent of the households use both liquid and powder detergents?
   e. If 200 checked both boxes, what percent of the households use either a liquid or a powder detergent?

12. Draw a Venn diagram for $\overline{A \cup \overline{B}}$.

13. Let $U = \{m, a, t, h, i, s, f, u, n\}, A = \{m, a\}, B = \{t, h, i, s\}, C = \{i, s\}, and D = \{n, u, t, s\};$ find $\overline{A} \cup B \cup (D \cap C)$.

14. Does $\overline{A \cup B} = \overline{A} \cup \overline{B}$?

15. Draw a Venn diagram showing people who read *MAD* magazine or *Rolling Stone*. Also, suppose 19 people like to read *MAD* and 25 read *Rolling Stone,* but 8 like to read both. How many like to read either one or the other or both?

16. For overlapping sets A and B, if $|U| = 100$, $|A| = 20$, $|B| = 65$, $|A \cap B| = 15$, tell how many elements are in each region of the universe.

17. For overlapping sets A, B, and C, if $|U| = 150$, $|A| = 55$, $|B| = 83$, $|C| = 49$, $|A \cap B| = 12$, $|B \cap C| = 14$, $|A \cap C| = 16$, and $|A \cap B \cap C| = 4$, tell how many elements are in each region of the universe.

18. A survey of 70 college students showed the following data: 42 had a car; 50 had a TV; 30 had a bicycle; 17 had a car and a bicycle; 35 had a car and a TV; 25 had a TV and a bicycle; and 15 had all three. How many students have none of the items?

19. Your brother watches *Saturday Night Live* every Saturday evening, and tonight is Saturday evening, so you conclude that he must be watching *Saturday Night Live.* What type of reasoning are you using?

20. What is the sum of the first 99 counting numbers?

21. Use a Venn diagram to check the validity of the following argument:

All squares are rectangles.

All rectangles are polygons.

Therefore, all squares are polygons.

22. A survey of 100 women finds that 40 jog, 25 swim, 16 cycle, 15 swim and jog, 10 swim and cycle, 8 jog and cycle, and 3 jog, swim, and cycle. Let $J = \{$people who jog$\}$, $S = \{$people who swim$\}$, and $C = \{$people who cycle$\}$. Use a Venn diagram to show how many are in each of the eight possible categories.

23. Listed below are five female and five male Wimbledon tennis champions, along with their country of citizenship and handedness.

Female	*Male*
Steffi Graf, Germany, right	Michael Stich, Germany, right
Martina Navratilova, U.S., left	Stefan Edberg, Sweden, right
Chris Evert Lloyd, U.S., right	Boris Becker, Germany, right
Evonne Goolagong, Australia, right	Pat Cash, Australia, right
Virginia Wade, Britain, right	John McEnroe, U.S., left

Using Figure 8.14, indicate in which region each of these individuals would be placed.

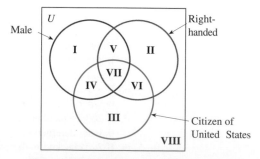

Figure 8.14 Wimbledon tennis champions

24. Use the results of the following survey, which included 500 motorists.

> 140 had received a ticket for speeding.
>
> 120 had received a ticket for failure to yield the right-of-way.
>
> 98 had received a ticket for failure to stop at a stop sign.
>
> 41 had received tickets for speeding and failure to yield.
>
> 35 had received tickets for speeding and failure to stop at a stop sign.
>
> 47 had received tickets for failure to yield and failure to stop at a stop sign.
>
> 24 had received tickets for all three violations.

   a. How many motorists did not receive any tickets?
   b. How many motorists received only one ticket?
   c. How many motorists received exactly two tickets?
   d. How many motorists received only a ticket for speeding?

25. Does the following story illustrate inductive or deductive reasoning?

> Q: What has 18 legs and catches flies?
> A: I don't know, what?
> Q: A baseball team. What has 36 legs and catches flies?
> A: I don't know that either.
> Q: Two baseball teams. If the United States has 100 senators and 50 states, what does . . .
> A: I know this one!
> Q: Good. What does each state have?
> A: Three baseball teams!

STUDY HINTS   *Compare your solutions and answers to the self-test. For each problem you missed, work some additional problems in the section listed in the margin. After you have worked these problems, you can test yourself with the practice test.*

Additional Problems

[8.1] Problems 11–18

[8.1] Problems 19–26; 35–42

[8.1] Problems 27–34

[8.2] Problems 43–46

[8.1] Problems 47–50

[8.1] Problems 7–22

[8.2] Problems 23–40

Complete Solutions to the Self-Test

1. Yes, it is well defined because it is clear what it means to be under 20 years of age.

2. The set of all natural numbers (or counting numbers) greater than 2 and smaller than or equal to 5; in other words, by roster the set is:

$$\{3, 4, 5\}$$

3. Answers vary; the set of odd counting numbers between 100 and 200.

4. $|T| = 3$; for the cardinality of S notice that the number of odd numbers less than 200 is 100, so from 101 to 199 must be half of that number; thus, $|S| = 50$.

5. Yes; answers vary.

$$\mathbb{N} = \{1, 2, 3, 4, \ldots\}$$
$$\uparrow \uparrow \uparrow \uparrow$$
$$\downarrow \downarrow \downarrow \downarrow$$
$$E = \{2, 4, 6, 8, \ldots\}$$

6. Finite; answers vary.

7. a. $\varnothing$, $\{0\}$, $\{1\}$, $\{0, 1\}$

   b. Since the number of subsets of a set with cardinality n is 2^n, and since the set is the letters of the alphabet (26 letters), the number of subsets is 2^{26}.

[8.2] Problems 41–56

8.

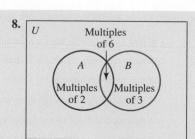

[8.3] Problems 11–30

9. a. $A \cap B = \{$numbers that are multiples of both 2 and 3$\}$

   $= \{$multiples of 6$\}$

b. $\mathbb{N} \cup E = \{1, 2, 3, 4, \ldots\} = \mathbb{N}$, where E is the set of even numbers.

c. $\mathbb{W} = \{0, 1, 2, 3, \ldots\}$ and $\mathbb{N} = \{1, 2, 3, \ldots\}$; $\overline{\mathbb{N}}$ is the set of all elements of $\mathbb{W}$ that are not in $\mathbb{N}$. We see this is only one number, namely, 0. Thus, $\overline{\mathbb{N}} = \{0\}$.

[8.3] Problems 31–36

10. a.

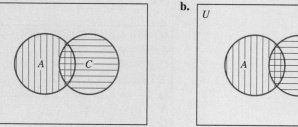

c.

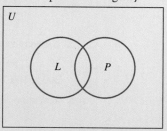

[8.3] Problems 37–52

11. a. Let $U = \{$households that were surveyed$\}$

   $L = \{$households that use a liquid detergent$\}$

   $P = \{$households that use a powder detergent$\}$

b. Calculate $\frac{344}{800} = 43\%$.   **c.** Calculate $\frac{432}{800} = 54\%$.

d. Calculate $\frac{200}{800} = 25\%$.   **e.** Calculate $\dfrac{144 + 200 + 232}{800} = 72\%$.

[8.4] Problems 9–26

12. First shade A (see vertical line segments); then shade $\overline{B}$ (see horizontal line segments). The union of these sets is that part of the universe which consists of all shaded parts. Finally, the complement is everything not shaded, which is shown as the shaded region inside of *B*, but outside *A*.

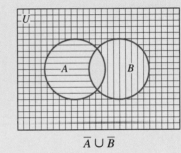

[8.4] Problems 27–39

13. $\overline{A \cup B} \cup (D \cap C) = \overline{\{m, a, t, h, i, s\}} \cup \{s\}$
$= \{f, u, n\} \cup \{s\}$
$= \{f, u, n, s\}$

[8.4] Problems 40–47

14.

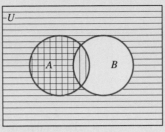

$\overline{A \cup B}$ $\overline{A} \cup \overline{B}$

They are not equal.

[8.4] Problems 48–52

15.

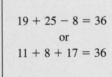

$19 + 25 - 8 = 36$
or
$11 + 8 + 17 = 36$

There are 36 who like to read one or the other, or both.

[8.5] Problems 5–10

16. Use a Venn diagram with two overlapping sets:

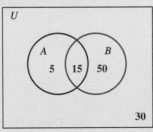

First, fill in the intersection, then fill in the part of *A* not in the intersection: $20 - 15 = 5$. Next, fill in the part of *B* not in the intersection: $65 - 15 = 50$. Finally, subtract the numbers within *A* and *B* from the number in the universe:

$$100 - (5 + 15 + 50) = 30.$$

17. Use a Venn diagram with three overlapping sets:

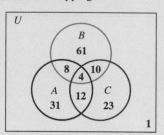

First, fill in the intersection (4). Next, fill in the parts in the intersections of two circles: 8, 10, and 12. Third, fill in the parts in each of the sets not accounted for: 31, 61, 23. Finally, subtract the numbers within the sets from the number in the universe to complete the Venn diagram.

18. Draw a Venn diagram; begin with the innermost part first.

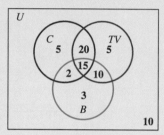

15 have all three. Next, use the information for two overlapping sets to fill in 2, 20, and 10. Fill in the regions in each circle not yet completed to fill in 5, 5, and 3. Finally, total all the numbers to see that 10 of the students have none of these items.

19. If you base your conclusion on observing your brother's behavior, then your conclusion is based on inductive reasoning. If you accept the following premises:
(1) Your brother watches *SNL* every Saturday evening,
(2) Tonight is Saturday night, then the conclusion,

"Your brother is watching *SNL* this evening" is arrived at deductively.

20. Look for a pattern:
$1 + 2 + 3 + \cdots + 49 + 50 + 51 + \cdots + 97 + 98 + 99$
Pair up first and last on list $(1 + 99 = 100)$
next pair $(2 + 98 = 100)$
next pair $(3 + 97 = 100)$
$$\vdots$$
There are 49 pairs with middle number of 50 not paired.
Thus,
$$49 \times 100 + 50 = 4{,}950$$

21. Draw a Venn diagram. Inside the universe rectangle, *U*, draw a circle labeled *S* (squares) inside a circle labeled *R* (rectangles). Next, since all rectangles are polygons, draw a circle labeled *P* so that it contains the circle labeled *R*.

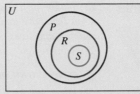

The conclusion, "all squares are polygons" is valid because the circle labeled S *must* be inside the circle labeled P.

22. Draw a Venn diagram

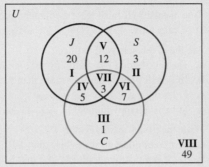

Step 1 Draw circles
Step 2 Region VII first
Step 3 Regions IV, V, and VI
Step 4 Regions I, II, and III
Step 5 Finally, Region VIII

I: 20; II: 3; III: 1; IV: 5; V: 12; VI: 7; VII: 3; and VIII: 49

23. Use Figure 8.14.

Female	Region	Male	Region
Graf	II	Stich	V
Navratilova	III	Edberg	V
Lloyd	VI	Becker	V
Goolagong	II	Cash	V
Wade	II	McEnroe	IV

24. We use a Venn diagram to answer the questions.
Let S = {received a ticket for speeding}
F = {failure to stop at a stop sign}
Y = {failure to yield}
Step 1 Draw Venn diagram.
Step 2 Region VII: 24
Step 3 Region IV: $41 - 24 = 17$
Region V: $35 - 24 = 11$
Region VI: $47 - 24 = 23$
Step 4 Region I:
$140 - (17 + 11 + 24) = 88$
Region II:
$98 - (11 + 24 + 23) = 40$
Region III:
$120 - (17 + 24 + 23) = 56$
Step 5 Region VIII: $500 - (88 + 11 + 17 + 24 + 40 + 23 + 56) = 241$

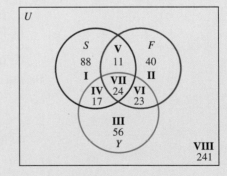

a. 241
b. Regions I, II, and III: $88 + 40 + 56 = 184$
c. Regions IV, V, and VI: $17 + 11 + 23 = 51$
d. Region I: 88
25. It is an example of inductive reasoning.

Chapter 8 Review Questions

*To prepare for a chapter test, first study the chapter; then, read each term from the important terms list above and make sure you know the meaning of each word; finally, review the chapter objectives. **After** these steps, take the self-test and correct all your answers. The following review questions can be used for extra practice.*

1. **IN YOUR OWN WORDS** Compare and contrast inductive and deductive reasoning.

2. If you make a conjecture based on a series of observations, what type of reasoning are you using?   *inductive reasoning*

3. True or false? (If false, give a counterexample.)
   There are no irrational numbers between 0 and 1. F; 0.121121112 . . .

4. True or false? (If false, give a counterexample.)
   $x^2 > x$ for all x *F; $x = \frac{1}{2}$; $\left(\frac{1}{2}\right)^2 = \frac{1}{4}$ is not greater than $\frac{1}{2}$*

5. Are the given sets well defined?
   a. The set of good baseball players   *not well defined*
   b. {baseball players earning more than $1 million per year}   *well defined*
   c. $\{x \mid x < 0, x \in \mathbb{N}\}$ *well defined*
   d. $\{x \mid x$ is a happy number$\}$ *not well defined*

6. Write the given sets by roster.
   a. {even counting numbers less than 10}   *{2, 4, 6, 8}*
   b. $\{x \mid x$ is a positive multiple of 3 that is less than 30$\}$ *{3, 6, 9, 12, 15, 18, 21, 24, 27}*
   c. $\{x \mid x$ is a counting number between 453 and 490$\}$ *{454, 455, 456, . . . , 489}*
   d. {distinct letters in the word *happy*}   *{h, a, p, y}*

7. Write the given sets by description.
   a. {10, 12, 14, 16, 18}   *{even numbers between 9 and 20}*
   b. {2001, 2003, 2005, . . . , 2999}   *{odd numbers between 2,000 and 3,000}*
   c. {1, 2, 3, 4, . . .}   *{counting or natural numbers}*
   d. {1, 4, 9, 16, 25, 36, . . . , 100, 121, 144}   *{perfect squares less than 150}*

8. Do the given pairs of sets have the same cardinality? If so, show a possible one-to-one correspondence.   *Actual correspondence may vary.*
   a. $A = \{3, 5, 7, 9\}$; $B = \{a, b, c, d\}$ *{yes}*
   b. $C = \{1, 2, 3, . . . , 588\}$; $D = \{185, 187, 189, . . . , 1361\}$ *no*
   c. $E = \{1, 2, 3, . . . , 40\}$; $F = \{988, 978, . . . , 508\}$ *no*
   d. $G = \{1, 2, 3, . . . ,\}$; $H = \{2, 4, 6, . . .\}$ *yes*

9. Tell whether the given sets are finite or infinite.
   a. The set of counting numbers greater than 5 million   *infinite*
   b. The set of counting numbers less than 5 million   *finite*
   c. The set of cells in your body at a particular time   *finite*
   d. The set of all possible books that have been written or could ever be written   *finite*

10. List the subsets of the given sets.
    a. $\{H, I\}$ *Ø, {H}, {I}, {H, I}*
    b. $\{m, a, d\}$ *Ø, {m}, {a}, {d}, { m, a}, {m, d}, {a, d}, {m, a, d}*
    c. $\{4, 5, 6, 7\}$ *Ø, {4}, {5}, {6}, {7}, {4, 5}, {4, 6}, {4, 7}, {5, 6}, {5, 7}, {6, 7}, {4, 5, 6}, {4, 5, 7}, {4, 6, 7}, {5, 6, 7}, {4, 5, 6, 7}*
    d. $\{0\}$ *Ø, {0}*

For Problems 11–13, let $U = \mathbb{N}$ (counting numbers); and let
$$A = \{1, 2, 3, 4, 5, 6, 7, 8, 9, 10\}$$
$$B = \{x \mid x \text{ is a multiple of 3 that is less than 31}\}$$
$$E = \{x \mid x \text{ is an even counting number}\}$$

11. Find the union as requested.
    a. $\{1, 3, 5, 7, 9\} \cup \{2, 4, 5, 9, 10\}$ *{1, 2, 3, 4, 5, 7, 9, 10}*
    b. $\{10, 11, . . . , 24, 25\} \cup B$ *{3, 6, 9, 10, 11 . . . , 25, 27, 30}*
    c. $A \cup B$ *{1, 2, 3, . . . , 10, 12, 15, 18, 21, 24, 27, 30}*
    d. $\varnothing \cup U$ *U*

12. Find the intersection as requested.
   a. $\{1, 3, 5, 7, 9\} \cap \{2, 4, 5, 9, 10\}$ {5, 9}
   b. $\{10, 11, \ldots, 24, 25\} \cap B$ {12, 15, 18, 21, 24}
   c. $A \cap B$ {3, 6, 9}
   d. $\varnothing \cup U$ U

13. Find the complements.
   a. $\overline{\{1, 3, 5, 7, 9\}}$ {2, 4, 6, 8, 10, 11, 12, . . .}
   b. $\overline{E}$ {x | x is an odd counting number}
   c. $\overline{A}$ {11, 12, 13, 14, . . .}
   d. $\overline{\varnothing}$ U

14. Draw Venn diagrams for the given sets.   See IAS.
   a. $\overline{A \cap B}$ **b.** $A \cup B$ **c.** $\overline{A}$ **d.** $\overline{B}$

15. Draw Venn diagrams for the given sets.   See IAS.
   a. $A \cup \overline{B}$ **b.** $\overline{A} \cup \overline{B}$ **c.** $(A \cup B) \cap \overline{C}$ **d.** $\overline{(A \cup B) \cup C}$

Prove or disprove each statement in Problems 16–18.

16. $(A \cup B) \cup C = A \cup (B \cup C)$ valid

17. $A \cap (B \cup C) = (A \cap B) \cup (A \cap C)$ valid

18. $A \cap (B \cup C) = (A \cap B) \cup C$ not valid

19. Prove one of De Morgan's laws.   See IAS.

20. Consider the successive products of 6. If the product has more than one digit, add the digits successively to obtain a single digit. What is the pattern you observe?
   6, 3, 9, 6, 3, 9, . . .

21. What is the 100th number in the pattern 2, 5, 10, 17, 26, . . .? $100^2 + 1 = 10{,}001$

Use a Venn diagram to check the validity of each of the arguments given in Problems 22–25.
   See IAS for Venn diagrams.

22. All birds have wings.
   All flies have wings.
   Therefore, some flies are birds.   not valid

23. No apples are bananas.
   All apples are fruit.
   Therefore, no bananas are fruit.   not valid

24. All artists are creative.
   Some musicians are artists.
   Therefore, some musicians are creative.   valid

25. All rectangles are polygons.
   All squares are rectangles.
   Therefore, all squares are polygons.   valid

Individual Projects

*Learning to use sources outside your classroom and textbook is an important skill, and
here are some ideas for extending some of the ideas in this chapter.*

PROJECT 8.1 In 1995 the United States population was approximately 263 million. It was reported that of that number, 72% have two white parents, 11.5% have two black
parents, and 9% have two Hispanic parents. If $\frac{1}{2}$% have one black and one white
parent, 2% have one black and one Hispanic parent, and 1% have one white and
one Hispanic parent, how many people (rounded to the nearest million) are there
in each category? Draw a Venn diagram showing these relationships.
in millions; I: 189, II: 30, III: 24, IV: 3, V: 1, VI: 5, VII: empty, VIII: 11

PROJECT 8.2 Each of the circles in Figure 8.15 is identified by a letter, each having a number
value from 1 to 9. Where the circles overlap, the number is the sum of the values of
the letters in the overlapping circles. What is the number value for each letter?*
A = 3, B = 6, C = 1, D = 5, E = 8, F = 4, G = 9, H = 2, I = 7

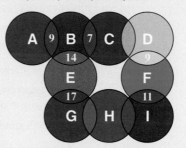

Figure 8.15 Circle intersection puzzle

PROJECT 8.3 On the *NBC Nightly News* on Thursday, May 25, 1995, Tom Brokaw read a brief
report on computer use in the United States. The story compared computer users by
ethnic background, and Brokaw reported that 14% of blacks and 13% of Hispanics
use computers, but 27% of whites use computers. Brokaw then commented that
computer use by whites was equal to that of blacks and Hispanics combined. Use
the Venn diagram and percents from Project 8.1 to show that percentages cannot be
added as was done by Brokaw.   Region I (white): 51.13 million; Region II (black): 4.23 million;
Region III (Hispanic) 3.08 million; cannot add percents

PROJECT 8.4 Can you place ten lumps of sugar in three empty cups so that there is an odd number of lumps in each cup?   Yes; see IAS.

PROJECT 8.5 Six glasses are standing in a row. The first three are empty, and the last three are
full of water. By handling and moving only one glass, it is possible to change this
arrangement so that no empty glass is next to another empty one and no full glass is
next to another full glass. How can this be done?   Pour the contents of glass 5 into glass 2.

* From "Perception Puzzles," by Jean Moyer, *Sky*, January 1995, p. 120.

Team Projects

Working in small groups is typical of most work environments, and learning to work with others to communicate specific ideas is an important skill. Work with three or four other students to submit a single report based on each of the following questions.

T20. A famous mathematician, Bertrand Russell, created a whole series of paradoxes by considering situations such as the following *barber's rule*: "Suppose in the small California town of Ferndale it is the practice of many of the men to be shaved by the barber. Now, the barber has a rule that has come to be known as the barber's rule: *He shaves those men and only those men who do not shave themselves.* The question is: Does the barber shave himself?" If he does shave himself, then according to the barber's rule, he does not shave himself. On the other hand, if he does not shave himself, then, according to the barber's rule, he shaves himself. We can only conclude that there can be no such barber's rule. But why not? Write a paper explaining what is meant by a *paradox*. Use the information in Project T21 for some suggestions about mathematicians who have done work in this area. You might begin with this Internet site: http://plato.stanford.edu/entries/russell-paradox

T21. About the time that Cantor's work began to gain acceptance, certain inconsistencies began to appear. One of these inconsistencies, called Russell's paradox, is what Project T20 is about. Other famous paradoxes in set theory have been studied by many famous mathematicians, including Zermelo, Frenkel, von Neumann, Bernays, and Poincaré. Divide the work among your team members and together write a 500-word paper about a famous paradox.

T22. With your team, draw Venn diagrams showing all possible regions for the following numbers of intersecting sets:

a. one set **b.** two sets **c.** three sets **d.** four sets **e.** five sets *See IAS.*

T23. What is the millionth counting number that is not a perfect square or a perfect cube? *1,001,090; see IAS for solution.*

CHAPTER 9

Probability

Life is a school of probability.

Walter, Bagehot, *The World of Mathematics*
by J. R. Newman (ed.), p. 1360.

ANTICIPATE

- *Overview; check out contents, terms, essential ideas, and learning outcomes.*
- *Have you used the idea of probability outside of class? How about weather forecasts, stock market analyses, contests, children's games, political polls, game shows, and gambling?*
- *Probability is the mathematics of uncertainty.*

9.1 Introduction to Probability

Terminology

An **experiment** is an observation of any physical occurrence. The **sample space** of an experiment is the set of all its possible outcomes. An **event** is a subset of the sample space. If an event is the empty set, it is called the **impossible event;** and if it has only one element, it is called a **simple event.**

EXAMPLE 1   Listing a sample space

Figure 9.1 Sample space for tossing a coin and rolling a die

a. What is the sample space for the experiment of tossing a coin and then rolling a die?

b. List the following events for the sample space in part **a:**

$$E = \{\text{rolling an even number of the die}\}$$
$$H = \{\text{tossing a head}\}$$
$$X = \{\text{rolling a six and tossing a tail}\}$$

Which (if any) of these are simple events?

Solution   A coin is considered **fair** if the outcomes of head and tail are **equally likely.** We also note that a fair die is one for which the outcomes from rolling it are *equally likely*. A die for which one outcome is more likely than the others is called a **loaded die.** In this book, we will assume fair dice and fair coins unless otherwise noted.

a. You can visualize the sample space as shown in Figure 9.1. If the sample space is not very large, it is sometimes worthwhile to make a direct listing, as shown in Figure 9.1. For this reason, it is sometimes helpful to build sample spaces by using what is called a **tree diagram.**

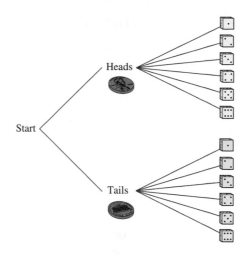

We see that S (the sample space) is

$$S = \{H1, H2, H3, H4, H5, H6, T1, T2, T3, T4, T5, T6\}$$

b. An event must be a *subset* of the sample space. Notice that E, H, and X are all subsets of S. Therefore,

$$E - \{H2, H4, H6, T2, T4, T6\}$$
$$H = \{H1, H2, H3, H4, H5, H6\}$$
$$X = \{T6\}$$

X is a simple event, because it has only one element.

Two events E and F are said to be **mutually exclusive** (that is, the sets E and F are disjoint) if $E \cap F = \varnothing$.

EXAMPLE 2   **Mutually exclusive events**

Suppose that you perform an experiment of rolling a die. Find the sample space, and then let $E = \{1, 3, 5\}$, $F = \{2, 4, 6\}$, $G = \{1, 3, 6\}$, and $H = \{2, 4\}$. Which of these are mutually exclusive?

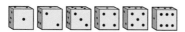

Figure 9.2 Sample space for a single die

Solution   The **sample space for a single die,** as shown in Figure 9.2, is

$$S = \{1, 2, 3, 4, 5, 6\}   \text{We look only at the number of spots on top.}$$

Evidently,

E and F are mutually exclusive, since $E \cap F = \varnothing$.

G and H are mutually exclusive, since $G \cap H = \varnothing$.

E and H are mutually exclusive, since $E \cap H = \varnothing$.

But

F and H are *not* mutually exclusive (elements 2 and 4 in common).

E and G are *not* mutually exclusive (elements 1 and 3 in common).

F and G are *not* mutually exclusive (element 6 in common).

Probability

If the sample space can be divided into *mutually exclusive* and *equally likely* outcomes, we can define the probability of an event. Let's consider the experiment of tossing a single coin. A suitable sample space is

$$S = \{\text{heads, tails}\}$$

Suppose we wish to consider the event of obtaining heads; we'll call this event A. Then,

$$A = \{\text{heads}\}$$

and this is a simple event.

We wish to define the probability of event A, which we denote by $P(A)$. Notice that the outcomes in the sample space are mutually exclusive; that is, if one occurs, the other cannot occur. If we flip a coin, there are two possible outcomes, and *one and only one* outcome can occur on a toss. If each outcome in the sample space is equally likely, we define the probability of A as

$$P(A) = \frac{\text{NUMBER OF SUCCESSFUL RESULTS}}{\text{NUMBER OF POSSIBLE RESULTS}}$$

A "successful" result is a result that corresponds to the event whose probability we are seeking—in this case, {heads}. Since we can obtain a head (success) in only one way, and the total number of possible outcomes is two, the probability of heads is given by this definition as

$$P(\text{heads}) = P(A) = \frac{1}{2}$$

This must correspond to the empirical results you would obtain if you repeated the experiment a large number of times. In Problem 26 of Problem Set 9.1, you are asked to repeat this experiment 100 times.

Probability

STOP

This is the foundational definition for this chapter. Does that sound important enough?

> If an experiment can occur in any of n mutually exclusive and equally likely ways, and if s of these ways are considered favorable, then the **probability** of an event E, denoted by $P(E)$, is
>
> $$P(E) = \frac{s}{n} = \frac{\text{NUMBER OF OUTCOMES FAVORABLE TO } E}{\text{NUMBER OF ALL POSSIBLE OUTCOMES}}$$

EXAMPLE 3

Using the definition of probability

Figure 9.3 A spinner; a randomizing device

Use the definition of probability to find, first, the probability of white, and second, the probability of black, using the spinner shown in Figure 9.3 and assuming that the arrow will never lie on a border line.

Solution   Looking at the spinner, we note that it is divided into three areas of the same size. We assume that the spinner is equally likely to land in any of these three areas.

$P(\text{white}) = \dfrac{2}{3}$ ← Two sections are white.
← Three sections altogether

$P(\text{black}) = \dfrac{1}{3}$ ← One section is black.
← Three sections altogether   ●

EXAMPLE 4   **Probability of a simple event**

Figure 9.4 A jar of marbles

Consider a jar that contains marbles as shown in Figure 9.4. Suppose that each marble has an equal chance of being picked from the jar. Find:

a. $P(\text{blue})$ **b.** $P(\text{green})$ **c.** $P(\text{yellow})$

Solution

a. $P(\text{blue}) = \dfrac{4}{12}$ ← 4 blue marbles in jar
← 12 marbles in jar

$= \dfrac{1}{3}$ Reduce fractions.

b. $P(\text{green}) = \dfrac{7}{12}$ **c.** $P(\text{yellow}) = \dfrac{1}{12}$ ●

Reduced fractions are used to state probabilities when the fractions are fairly simple. If, however, the fractions are not simple, and you have a calculator, it is acceptable to state the probabilities as decimals, as shown in Example 5.

EXAMPLE 5   **Using the definition of probabilities with decimals**

Suppose that, in a certain study, 46 out of 155 people showed a certain kind of behavior. Assign a probability to this behavior.

Solution $P(\text{behavior shown}) = \frac{46}{155} \approx 0.3$ *Display:*   0.2967741935   ●

EXAMPLE 6   **Using probabilities in playing a game**

Consider two spinners as shown in Figure 9.5. You and an opponent are to spin your spinners simultaneously, and the one with the higher number wins. Which spinner should you choose, and why?

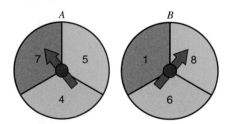

Figure 9.5 Spinner game

Solution   We begin by listing the sample space:

B	1	6	8
A			
4	(4, 1)	(4, 6)	(4, 8)
5	(5, 1)	(5, 6)	(5, 8)
7	(7, 1)	(7, 6)	(7, 8)

The times that A wins are highlighted.

$P(A \text{ wins}) = \frac{4}{9}$; $P(B \text{ wins}) = \frac{5}{9}$

We would choose spinner B because it has a greater probability of winning.   ●

EXAMPLE 7   Probabilities with a deck of cards

Suppose that a single card is selected from an ordinary deck of 52 cards. Find:

a. $P(\text{ace})$ **b.** $P(\text{heart})$ **c.** $P(\text{face card})$

Solution   The **sample space for a deck of cards** is shown in Figure 9.6.

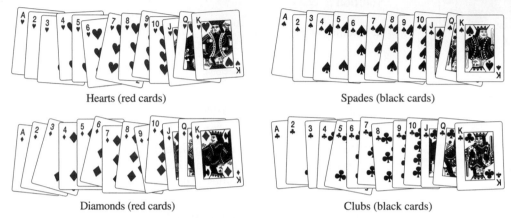

Hearts (red cards)   Spades (black cards)

Diamonds (red cards)   Clubs (black cards)

Figure 9.6 Sample space for a deck of cards

You will need to be familiar with a deck of cards for many examples in this chapter.

a. An ace is a card with one spot. $P(\text{ace}) = \frac{4}{52} = \frac{1}{13}$ **b.** $P(\text{heart}) = \frac{13}{52} = \frac{1}{4}$

c. $P(\text{face card}) = \dfrac{12}{52}$ ← A face card is a jack, queen, or king.

$\phantom{P(\text{face card})} $ ← Number of cards in the sample space

$\phantom{P(\text{face card}) } = \dfrac{3}{13}$

EXAMPLE 8   Probabilities with a pair of dice

Suppose you are just beginning a game of Monopoly® (see Figure 9.7). You roll a pair of dice. What is the probability that you land on a railroad on the first roll of the dice?

© Michael Newman/PhotoEdit

Figure 9.7 Monopoly playing board

Solution There are four railroads on a Monopoly playing board (see Figure 9.7), and these are positioned so that only one can be reached on one roll of a pair of dice. The required number to roll is a 5. We begin by listing the sample space. You might try

$$\{2, 3, 4, 5, 6, 7, 8, 9, 10, 11, 12\},$$

but these possible outcomes are not equally likely, which you can see by considering a tree diagram. The roll of the first die has 6 possibilities, and then *each* of these in turn can combine with any of 6 possibilities for a total of 36 possibilities. The **sample space for a pair of dice** is summarized in Figure 9.8.

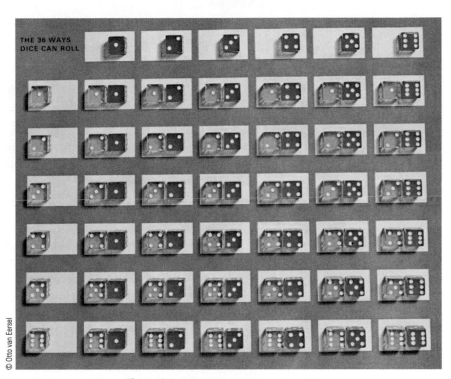

THE 36 WAYS
DICE CAN ROLL

© Otto van Eersel

Figure 9.8 Sample space for a pair of dice

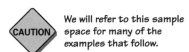

CAUTION We will refer to this sample space for many of the examples that follow.

Thus, $n = 36$ for the definition of probability. We need to look at Figure 9.8 to see how many possibilities there are for obtaining a 5. We find $(1, 4)$, $(2, 3)$, $(3, 2)$, and $(4, 1)$, so $s = 4$. Then

$$P(\text{five}) = \frac{4}{36} \quad \leftarrow \text{4 ways to obtain a 5}$$
$$\phantom{P(\text{five}) = \frac{4}{36}} \quad \leftarrow \text{36 ways to roll a pair of dice}$$
$$= \frac{1}{9}$$

You should use Figure 9.8 when working probability problems that deal with rolling a pair of dice. You will be asked to perform an experiment (Problem 27 in Problem Set 9.1) in which you roll a pair of dice 100 times and then compare the results you obtain with the probabilities you calculate by using Figure 9.8.

Probabilities of Unions and Intersections

The word *or* is translated as $\cup$ (union), and the word *and* is translated as $\cap$ (intersection). We will find the probabilities of combinations of events involving the words *or* and *and* by finding unions and intersections of events.

EXAMPLE 9   **Finding probabilities of unions and intersections**

Suppose that a single card is selected from an ordinary deck of cards.

a. What is the probability that it is a two or a king?

b. What is the probability that it is a two and a heart?

c. What is the probability that it is a two or a heart?

d. What is the probability that it is a two and a king?

Solution

a. P(two or a king) $= P$(two $\cup$ king)

Look at Figure 9.6 on page 452.

> two = {two of hearts, two of spades, two of diamonds, two of clubs}
> king = {king of hearts, king of spades, king of diamonds, king of clubs}
> two $\cup$ king = {two of hearts, two of spades, two of diamonds, two of clubs,
>   king of hearts, king of spades, king of diamonds, king of clubs}

There are 8 possibilities for success. It is usually not necessary to list all of these to know that there are 8 possibilities—simply look at Figure 9.6.

$$P(\text{two} \cup \text{king}) = \frac{8}{52} = \frac{2}{13}$$

b. Look at Figure 9.6.

> two = {**two of hearts,** two of spades, two of diamonds, two of clubs}
> heart = {ace of hearts, **two of hearts,** three of hearts, . . . , king of hearts}
> two $\cap$ heart = {**two of hearts**}

There is one element in common (as shown in boldface), so

$$P(\text{two} \cap \text{heart}) = \frac{1}{52}$$

c. This is very similar to parts **a** and **b,** but there is one important difference. Look at the sample space and notice that although there are 4 twos and 13 hearts, the total number of successes is *not* $4 + 13 = 17$, *but rather* 16.

> two = {**two of hearts,** two of spades, two of diamonds, two of clubs}
> heart = {ace of hearts, **two of hearts,** three of hearts, . . . , king of hearts}
> two $\cup$ heart = {**two of hearts,** two of spades, two of diamonds, two of clubs,
>   ace of hearts, three of hearts, four of hearts, five of hearts, six of
>   hearts, seven of hearts, eight of hearts, nine of hearts, ten
>   of hearts, jack of hearts, queen of hearts, king of hearts}

It is not necessary to list these possibilities. The purpose of doing so in this case was to reinforce the fact that there are *actually* 16 (not 17) possibilities. The reason for this is that there is one common element (as found in part **b**):

$$P(\text{two} \cup \text{heart}) = \frac{16}{52} = \frac{4}{13}$$

d. two $\cap$ king $= \varnothing$, so there are no elements in the intersection.

$$P(\text{two} \cap \text{king}) = \frac{0}{52} = 0$$

The probability of the empty set is 0, which means that the event *cannot* occur. In Problem Set 9.1 (Problem 50), you will be asked to show that the probability of an event that *must* occur is 1. These are the two extremes. All other probabilities fall somewhere in between. The closer a probability is to 1, the more likely the event is to occur; the closer a probability is to 0, the less likely the event is to occur.

Now let's summarize the procedure for finding the probability of an event E when all simple events in the sample space are equally likely:

1. Describe and identify the sample space, S. The number of elements in S is n.
2. Count the number of occurrences that interest us; call this the number of successes and denote it by s.
3. Compute the probability of the event using the formula

$$P(E) = \frac{s}{n}$$

The procedure just outlined will work only when the simple events in S are equally likely. If the equally likely model does not apply to your experiments, you need a more complicated model, or else you must proceed experimentally. This model will, however, be sufficient for the problems you will find in this book.

PROBLEM SET 9.1

ESSENTIAL IDEAS — LEVEL 1

1. What is a sample space? *set of all possible outcomes*
2. What is an event? *a subset of the sample space*
3. What is the formula for finding probability? What are the necessary conditions for using this formula?
   $P(E) = \frac{s}{n}$; *equally likely and mutually exclusive.*
4. How is the probability of a union translated? *"or"*
5. How is the probability of an intersection translated? *"and"*

DRILL AND PRACTICE — LEVEL 2

For the spinners in Problems 6–8, assume that the pointer can never lie on a border line.

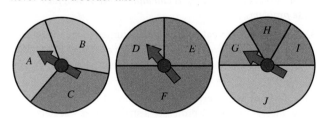

6. **a.** $P(A)$ $\frac{1}{3}$ **b.** $P(B)$ $\frac{1}{3}$ **c.** $P(C)$ $\frac{1}{3}$
7. **a.** $P(D)$ $\frac{1}{4}$ **b.** $P(E)$ $\frac{1}{4}$ **c.** $P(F)$ $\frac{1}{2}$
8. **a.** $P(G)$ $\frac{1}{6}$ **b.** $P(H)$ $\frac{1}{6}$ **c.** $P(I)$ $\frac{1}{6}$

Consider the jar containing marbles shown in Figure 9.9.

Figure 9.9 Count the marbles

In Problems 9–10, find the probabilities of picking each color; assume that each marble has an equal chance of being picked from the jar.

9. **a.** $P(\text{yellow})$ $\frac{5}{18}$ **b.** $P(\text{blue})$ $\frac{2}{9}$
10. **a.** $P(\text{green})$ $\frac{1}{2}$ **b.** $P(\text{black})$ 0

Suppose that you toss a coin and roll a die in Problems 11–14. The sample space is shown in Figure 9.1.

11. What is the probability of obtaining:
    a. Tails *and* a five? $\frac{1}{12}$ **b.** Tails *or* a five? $\frac{7}{12}$
    c. Heads *and* a two? $\frac{1}{12}$

12. What is the probability of obtaining:
    a. Tails? $\frac{1}{2}$ **b.** One, two, three, *or* four? $\frac{2}{3}$
    c. Heads *or* a two? $\frac{7}{12}$

13. What is the probability of obtaining:

a. Heads *and* an odd number? $\frac{1}{4}$

b. Heads *or* an odd number? $\frac{3}{4}$

14. What is the probability of obtaining:

a. Heads *and* a five? $\frac{1}{12}$ **b.** Heads *or* a five? $\frac{7}{12}$

15. Simultaneously toss a coin and roll a die 100 times, and note the results. The possible outcomes are H1, H2, H3, H4, H5, H6, T1, T2, T3, T4, T5, and T6. Do these appear to be equally likely outcomes? yes

16. Flip three coins simultaneously 100 times, and note the results. The possible outcomes (rounded to the nearest hundredth) are: Answers vary.

a. three heads 0.13

b. two heads and one tail 0.38

c. two tails and one head 0.38

d. three tails 0.13

Based on your experiment, find the probabilities of each of these events. Do these appear to be equally likely? no

A single card is selected from an ordinary deck of cards. The sample space is shown in Figure 9.6. Find the probabilities in Problems 17–20.

17. a. P(five of hearts) $\frac{1}{52}$ **b.** P(five) $\frac{1}{13}$

18. a. P(heart) $\frac{1}{4}$ **b.** P(jack) $\frac{1}{13}$

19. a. P(diamond) $\frac{1}{4}$ **b.** P(even number) $\frac{5}{13}$

20. a. P(heart and a jack) $\frac{1}{52}$ **b.** P(heart or a jack) $\frac{4}{13}$

Use the sample space shown in Figure 9.8 to find the probabilities in Problems 21–25 for the experiment of rolling a pair of dice.

21. a. P(five) $\frac{1}{9}$ **b.** P(six) $\frac{5}{36}$

22. a. P(seven) $\frac{1}{6}$ **b.** P(eight) $\frac{5}{36}$

23. a. P(nine) $\frac{1}{9}$ **b.** P(two) $\frac{1}{36}$

24. a. P(four *or* five) $\frac{7}{36}$ **b.** P(even number) $\frac{1}{2}$

25. a. P(eight *or* ten) $\frac{2}{9}$ **b.** P(odd number) $\frac{1}{2}$

Perform the experiments in Problems 26–27, tally your results, and calculate the probabilities (to the nearest hundredth).

26. Toss a coin 100 times. Make sure that, each time the coin is flipped, it rotates several times in the air and lands on a table or on the floor. Keep a record of the results of this experiment. Based on your experiment, what is P(heads)?
Answers vary; $P(H) = \frac{1}{2}$

27. Roll a pair of dice 100 times.

Keep a record of the results. Based on your experiment, find:
Answers vary.

a. P(two) 0.03   **b.** P(three) 0.06

c. P(four) 0.08   **d.** P(five) 0.11

e. P(six) 0.14   **f.** P(seven) 0.17

g. P(eight) 0.14   **h.** P(nine) 0.11

i. P(ten) 0.08   **j.** P(eleven) 0.06

k. P(twelve) 0.03

If you do not have any dice, you can use the pattern in Figure 9.10 to construct your own.

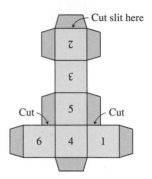

Figure 9.10 Pattern for making a die

In Problems 28–31, consider a die with only four sides, marked 1, 2, 3, and 4. Toss a pair of these dice and assume that the outcomes are equally likely.

28. Write out a sample space similar to the one in Figure 9.8 for rolling a pair of these dice. See IAS.

29. Find the probability that the sum of the dice is the given number.

a. P(two) $\frac{1}{16}$ **b.** P(three) $\frac{1}{8}$

30. Find the probability that the sum of the dice is the given number.

a. P(four) $\frac{3}{16}$ **b.** P(five) $\frac{1}{4}$

31. Find the probability that the sum of the dice is the given number.

a. P(six) $\frac{3}{16}$ **b.** P(seven) $\frac{1}{8}$

APPLICATIONS   LEVEL 2

Give the probabilities in Problems 32–35 in decimal form (correct to two decimal places). A calculator may be helpful with these problems.

32. Last year, 1,485 calculators were returned to the manufacturer. If 85,000 were produced, assign a number to specify the probability that a particular calculator would be returned. about 0.02

33. Last semester, a certain professor gave 13 A's out of 285 grades. If one of the professor's students was selected randomly, what is the probability of the student receiving an A? about 0.05

34. Last year in Ferndale, CA, it rained on 75 days. What is the probability of rain on a day selected at random? about 0.21

35. The campus vets club is having a raffle and is selling 1,500 tickets. If the people on your floor of the dorm bought 285 of those tickets, what is the probability that someone on your floor will hold the winning ticket? *0.19*

Poker is a common game in which players are dealt five cards from a deck of cards. It can be shown that there are 2,598,960 different possible poker hands. The winning hands (from highest to lowest) are shown in Table 9.1.

TABLE 9.1	Poker Hands
Royal flush 4 hands	
Other straight flush 36 hands	
Four of a kind 624 hands	
Full house 3,744 hands	
Flush 5,108 hands	
Straight 10,200 hands	
Three of a kind 54,912 hands	
Two pair 123,552 hands	
One pair 1,098,240 hands	
Other hands 1,302,540 hands	

Find the requested probabilities in Problems 36–39. Use a calculator, and show your answers to whatever accuracy possible on your calculator.

36. a. *P*(royal flush) *0.000001539077169*

   b. *P*(straight flush) *0.00001385169452*

37. a. *P*(four of a kind) *0.0002400960384*

   b. *P*(full house) *0.00144057623*

38. a. *P*(flush) **b.** *P*(straight)
   0.00196540155 *0.003924646782*
39. a. *P*(three of a kind) **b.** *P*(two pair)
   0.02112845138 *0.04753901561*

Dice is a popular game in gambling casinos. Two dice are tossed, and various amounts are paid according to the outcome. Find the requested probabilities in Problems 40–42.

40. If a seven or eleven occurs on the first roll, the player wins. What is the probability of winning on the first roll? $\frac{2}{9}$

41. The player loses if the outcome of the first roll is a two, three, or twelve. What is the probability of losing on the first roll? $\frac{1}{9}$

42. A pair of ones is called *snake eyes.*

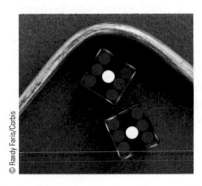

© Randy Faris/Corbis

What is the probability of losing a dice game by rolling snake eyes? $\frac{1}{36}$

43. The game of Dungeons and Dragons uses nonstandard dice. Consider a die with eight sides marked 1, 2, 3, 4, 5, 6, 7, and 8. Write a sample space similar to the one in Figure 9.8 for rolling a pair of these dice. *See IAS.*

Suppose you and an opponent each pick one of the spinners shown in Figure 9.11.

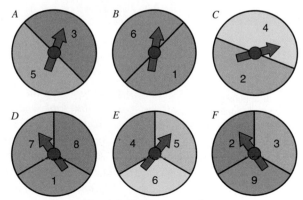

Figure 9.11 Six game spinners

A "win" means spinning a higher number. Construct a sample space to answer each question, and tell which of the two spinners given in Problems 44–49 you would choose in each case. *Also show sample spaces for these problems.*

44. *A* plays *C*
pick A; *P*(A winning) = $\frac{3}{4}$

45. *A* plays *B*
pick either; fair game; *P*(A) = *P*(B) = $\frac{1}{2}$

46. B plays C **47.** D plays E
pick either; fair game; $P(B) = P(C) = \frac{1}{2}$ pick D; $P(D$ winning$) = \frac{2}{3}$
48. E plays F pick E; $P(E$ winning$) = \frac{2}{3}$

49. D plays F pick F; $P(F$ winning$) = \frac{5}{9}$

50. IN YOUR OWN WORDS Show that the probability of some event E falls between 0 and 1. Show that $P(E) = 0$ if the event cannot occur and $P(E) = 1$ if the event must occur.

51. We see examples of probability every day. Weather forecasts, stock market analyses, contests, children's games, television game shows, and gambling all involve ideas of probability. Probability is the mathematics of uncertainty. "Wait a minute," interrupts Sammy. "I thought that mathematics was absolute and that there was no uncertainty about it!" Well, Sammy, suppose you are playing a game of Monopoly®. Do you know what you'll land on in your next turn? "No, but neither do you!" Suppose you are just beginning a Monopoly game. What space are you most likely to land on with your first roll of the dice?
Chance, since the most likely number to roll is 7

52. IN YOUR OWN WORDS Probability is a way of describing uncertainty. For example, what is the probability of tossing a coin and obtaining heads? "That's easy, it's one-half," answers Sammy. Right, but *why* do you say it is one-half? What should Sammy say?

RIGHT OR WRONG?   LEVEL 3

Explain what is wrong, if anything, with the statements in Problems 53–60. Explain your reasoning.

53. The sample space for rolling a single die is   T

$$S = \{1, 2, 3, 4, 5, 6\}, \quad \text{so} \quad P(\text{two}) = \frac{1}{6}$$

54. The sample space for rolling a pair of dice is

$$S = \{2, 3, 4, 5, 6, 7, 8, 9, 10, 11, 12\}$$

so $P(\text{two}) = \frac{1}{11}$.   F; there are 36 events in the sample space; $P(\text{two}) = \frac{1}{36}$

55. The sample space for drawing a card from a deck of cards has 52 elements, so $P(\text{two}) = \frac{1}{52}$.   F; $P(\text{two}) = \frac{4}{52} = \frac{1}{13}$

56. The definition of the probability of an event E is

$$P(E) = \frac{\text{NUMBER OF OUTCOMES FAVORABLE TO } E}{\text{NUMBER OF ALL POSSIBLE OUTCOMES}}$$

F; the outcomes must be mutually exclusive and equally likely.

57. $P(A$ or $B)$ means $P(A \cap B)$.   F; $P(A$ or $B) = P(A \cup B)$

58. $P(A$ and $B)$ means $P(A \cup B)$.   F; $P(A$ and $B) = P(A \cap B)$

59. $P(A \cup B) = P(A) + P(B)$ F

60. $P(A \cap B) = P(A) \cdot P(B)$ F

For Problems 59 and 60, toss 1 die and let $A = \{2, 4, 6\}$ and $B = \{2\}$, so $P(A) = \frac{3}{6} = \frac{1}{2}$ and $P(B) = \frac{1}{6}$,
$P(A \cup B) = \frac{1}{2}$; $P(A \cap B) = \frac{1}{6}$, so
$P(A \cup B) \neq P(A) + P(B)$ and
$P(A \cap B) \neq P(A) \cdot P(B)$.

9.2 Probability Models

IN THIS WORLD   THE UTILITY OF MATH

DEAR ABBY: My husband and I just had our eighth child. Another girl, and I am really one disappointed woman. I suppose I should thank God she was healthy, but, Abby, this one was supposed to have been a boy. Even the doctor told me the law of averages was in our favor 100 to one. What is the probability of our next child being a boy?

"We need to talk, Ben," said Melissa. "I know we have eight children, but I want a boy!"

"I know, dear, so do I, but I'm not sure we can afford another child. The doctor told us that the law of averages for having a boy is in our favor if we try again, but look what happened last time."

Melissa quickly cut in, "My dad is a math teacher, and he said that the chances of having nine girls in a row is 1 out of 512."

A worried look swept over Ben's face and he said, "Right, and the doctor said 1 out of 100 last time, too. I'll tell you what, write to Ann Landers or Dear Abby and see what advice the experts can give, then . . ."

See Problem 51.

Complementary Probabilities

In Section 9.1, we looked at the probability of an event E. Now we wish to expand our discussion. Let

$$s = \text{NUMBER OF GOOD OUTCOMES (successes)}$$
$$f = \text{NUMBER OF BAD OUTCOMES (failures)}$$
$$n = \text{TOTAL NUMBER OF POSSIBLE OUTCOMES } (s + f = n)$$

Then the probability that event E occurs is

$$P(E) = \frac{s}{n}$$

The probability that event E does not occur is

$$P(\overline{E}) = \frac{f}{n}$$

STOP This says that some event either happens or does not.

An important property of probability is found by adding these probabilities:

$$P(E) + P(\overline{E}) = \frac{s}{n} + \frac{f}{n} = \frac{s+f}{n} = \frac{n}{n} = 1$$

Probabilities whose sum is 1 are called **complementary probabilities,** and the following box shows what is known as the **property of complements.**

Complements

> The **property of complements** can be stated in two ways:
> $$P(E) = 1 - P(\overline{E}) \qquad \text{or} \qquad P(\overline{E}) = 1 - P(E)$$

EXAMPLE 1

Using the property of complements

Use Table 9.1 (on page 457) to find the probability of not obtaining one pair with a poker hand.

Solution   From Table 9.1 we see that $P(\text{pair}) = \frac{1,098,240}{2,598,960} \approx 0.42$, so that

$$P(\text{no pair}) = P(\overline{\text{pair}}) = 1 - P(\text{pair}) \approx 1 - 0.42 = 0.58 \qquad \bullet$$

EXAMPLE 2

Finding a probability

What is the probability of obtaining at least one head when a coin is flipped three times?

Solution   Let $F = \{\text{receive at least one head when a coin is flipped three times}\}$

Method I. Work directly; use a tree diagram to find the possibilities.

	FIRST	SECOND	THIRD	FIRST	SECOND	THIRD	SUCCESS
				H	H	H	yes
				H	H	T	yes
				H	T	H	yes
Start				H	T	T	yes
				T	H	H	yes
				T	H	T	yes
				T	T	H	yes
				T	T	T	no

$P(F) = \frac{7}{8}$

Method II. For one coin there are 2 outcomes (head and tail); for two coins there are 4 outcomes (HH, HT, TH, TT); and for three coins there are 8 outcomes. We answer the question by finding the complement; $\overline{F}$ is the event of receiving no heads (that is, of obtaining all tails). *Without* drawing the tree diagram, we note that there is only one way of obtaining all tails (TTT). Thus

$$P(F) = 1 - P(\overline{F}) = 1 - \frac{1}{8} = \frac{7}{8}$$ ●

Fundamental Counting Principle

For one coin there are 2 possible outcomes, and for 2 coins there are 4 possible outcomes. In Example 2, we considered flipping a coin three times, and by drawing a tree diagram we found 8 possibilities. These are applications of a counting technique called the **fundamental counting principle,** which can be understood by looking at tree diagrams.

Fundamental Counting Principle

> If task A can be performed in m ways, and if, after task A is performed, a second task B can be performed in n ways, then task A followed by task B can be performed in
> $$m \times n$$
> ways.

EXAMPLE 3   **Verifying the fundamental counting principle**

What is the probability that, in a family with two children, the children are of opposite sex?

Solution   The fundamental counting principle tells us that, since there are 2 ways of having a child (B or G), for 2 children there are

$$2 \cdot 2 = 4 \text{ ways}$$

We verify this by looking at a tree diagram:

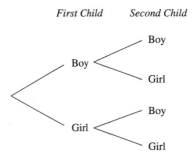

There are 4 equally likely outcomes: BB, BG, GB, and GG. Thus, the probability of having a boy and a girl in a family of two children is

$$\frac{\text{NUMBER OF SUCCESSFUL OUTCOMES}}{\text{TOTAL NUMBER OF POSSIBLE OUTCOMES}} = \frac{2}{4} = \frac{1}{2}$$

●

EXAMPLE 4   **Probability using the fundamental counting principle**

What is a family's probability of having two boys and two girls, if it has four children?

Solution   The fundamental counting principle tells us the number of possibilities is

$$2 \times 2 \times 2 \times 2 = 16$$

Thus, $n = 16$. To find s we list the event (by using a tree diagram for four children) that brings success:

{BBGG, BGBG, BGGB, GBGB, GBBG, GGBB}

Since there are 6 elements in this set, we see that $s = 6$. Thus, the desired probability is

$$\frac{6}{16} = \frac{3}{8}$$

●

License Plate Problem

States issue license plates, and as the number of vehicles increases, it is often necessary to design plates with more numerals and letters. For example, the state of California has some plates consisting of three letters followed by three digits. When all such possibilities were used, the state began making license plates with three digits followed by three letters. Many states issue personalized plates. Figure 9.12 shows a work by Stephen Underwood, who not only assembled the plates to spell out the preamble of the U.S. Constitution, but also did it by using all 50 states in *alphabetical order*!

Figure 9.12 U.S. Preamble using license plates

EXAMPLE 5

License plate problem

What is the probability (rounded to the nearest percent) of getting a license plate that has a repeated letter or digit if you live in a state (such as Texas) where the scheme is three numerals followed by three letters?

Solution   A license plate bears three numerals followed by three letters. We begin by using the fundamental counting principle to find *n* (the total number of possibilities):

Number of digits   Letters in the alphabet
↓   ↓
$$\underbrace{10}_{} \times 10 \times 10 \times \underbrace{26}_{} \times 26 \times 26 = 17,576,000$$
$\underbrace{\qquad\qquad}_{\text{Three digits}}$ $\underbrace{\qquad\qquad}_{\text{Three letters}}$

To count the number of successes, you must understand the problem. To confirm this, which of the following plates would be considered a success?

123ABC	*Failure*
122ABC	*Success; repeated digit*
456MMA	*Success; repeated letter*
111TTT	*Success; repeated letter and repeated numeral*
890XYZ	*Failure*

Success is one repetition or two repetitions or three repetitions ... . Let R be the event that a repetition is received. It is difficult to count all possible repetitions, but we can use the fundamental counting principle to count the number of license plates that *do not* have a repetition:

Number of digits   Letters in the alphabet

$$10 \quad \times 9 \quad \times 8 \times 26 \quad \times 25 \quad \times 24 = 11,232,000$$

Digits left   Letters left after the first one (no repetitions)

$$P(R) = 1 - P(\overline{R}) = 1 - \frac{11,232,000}{17,576,000} \approx 0.36 \quad \textit{Display:} \quad 0.3609467456$$

This means that about 36% of all license plates in the state have at least one repeated letter or digit. ●

PROBLEM SET 9.2

ESSENTIAL IDEAS — LEVEL 1

1. Explain what we mean by "complementary probabilities." *probabilities whose sum is 1*
2. What is the fundamental counting principle? *See p. 460.*

DRILL AND PRACTICE — LEVEL 2

Use estimation to select the best response in Problems 3–8. Do not calculate.

3. According to the National Safety Council, which of these three means of travel is the safest? B

   A. car (1.12 deaths per 100 billion passenger miles)

   B. plane (0.04 death per 100 billion passenger miles)

   C. train (0.06 death per 100 billion passenger miles)

4. Which of the following is most probable? C

   A. Winning the grand prize in a state lottery (1 chance in 5,000,000)

   B. Being struck by lightning (1 chance in 600,000)

   C. Appearing on the *Tonight Show* (1 chance in 490,000)

5. Which of the following is more probable? B

   A. Obtaining at least 2 heads in 3 flips of a coin

   B. Obtaining at least 2 heads in 4 flips of a coin

6. Which of the following is more probable? B

   A. Obtaining a six 2 times in 3 rolls of a die

   B. Obtaining a six at least 2 times in 3 rolls of a die

7. Which of the following is more probable? *They are the same.*

   A. Guessing all the correct answers on a 20-question true–false examination

   B. Obtaining all heads in 20 tosses of a coin

8. Which of the following is more probable? B

   A. Guessing all the correct answers on a 10-question 5-part multiple-choice test *about 1 chance in 10,000,000*

   B. Your living room is filled with white ping pong balls. There is also one red ping pong ball in the room. You reach in and select a ping pong ball at random and select the red ping pong ball. *about 1 chance in 2,000,000*

Find the requested probabilities in Problems 9–14.

9. $P(\overline{A})$ if $P(A) = 0.6$ *0.4*

10. $P(\overline{B})$ if $P(B) = \frac{4}{5}$ *$\frac{1}{5}$*

11. $P(C)$ if $P(\overline{C}) = \frac{9}{13}$ *$\frac{4}{13}$*

12. $P(D)$ if $P(\overline{D}) = 0.005$ *0.995*

13. $P(E)$ if $P(\overline{E}) = 0.02$ *0.98*

14. $P(F)$ if $P(\overline{F}) = \frac{18}{31}$ *$\frac{13}{31}$*

List the outcomes considered a failure, as well as the probability of failure, for the experiments named in Problems 15–20.

	Experiment	Success	P(success)
15.	Tossing a coin	head *tails*	$\frac{1}{2}$ *$\frac{1}{2}$*
16.	Rolling a die	four or six *1, 2, 3, or 5*	$\frac{1}{3}$ *$\frac{2}{3}$*
17.	Guessing an answer on a 5-choice multiple-choice test	correct guess *incorrect guess*	$\frac{1}{5}$ *$\frac{4}{5}$*
18.	Card game	drawing a heart *drawing a spade, club, or diamond*	0.18 *0.82*
19.	Baseball game	White Sox win *White Sox lose*	0.57 *0.43*
20.	Football game	your school wins *your school loses*	0.83 *0.17*

21. Three fair coins are tossed. What is the probability that at least one is a head? *$\frac{7}{8}$*

22. Three fair coins are tossed. What is the probability that at least two are heads? $\frac{1}{2}$

23. What is the probability of obtaining at least one head in 4 flips of a coin? $\frac{15}{16}$

24. What is the probability of obtaining at least two heads in 4 flips of a coin? $\frac{11}{16}$

25. What is the probability of obtaining a sum of at least 4 when rolling a pair of dice? $\frac{33}{36} = \frac{11}{12}$

26. What is the probability of obtaining a sum of at least 5 when rolling a pair of pair of dice? $\frac{30}{36} = \frac{5}{6}$

27. What is the probability of obtaining a sum that is at least 7 when rolling a pair of dice? $\frac{21}{36} = \frac{7}{12}$

28. Choose a natural number between 1 and 20, inclusive. What is the probability that the number is a multiple of 3? $\frac{6}{20} = \frac{3}{10}$

29. Choose a natural number between 1 and 100, inclusive. What is the probability that the number chosen is not a multiple of 5? $\frac{4}{5}$

30. IN YOUR OWN WORDS In Problem 59, Section 8.6, we reminded you that we offered some suggestions for success at the beginning of this text, and asked you to comment on each in light of your experience so far. We continue with that list in this question by asking you to comment on each suggestion listed here.

a. Read each section of the book before and after class.

b. Use more than one math book.

c. Some things must simply be memorized.

APPLICATIONS   **LEVEL 2**

31. How many skirt-blouse outfits can a woman wear if she has three skirts and five blouses? **15**

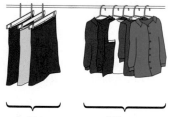

3 skirts   5 blouses

32. A certain lock has four tumblers, and each tumbler can assume six positions. How many different possibilities are there? **1,296**

33. Suppose a restaurant offers the following prix fixe menu:

Main Course:	prime rib, steak, chicken, filet of sole, shrimp
Side Dish:	soup, salad, crab cakes
Dessert:	cheesecake, chocolate chip delight, ice cream
Beverage:	coffee, tea, milk

How many different dinners can this restaurant serve? **135**

34. If a state issued license plates using the scheme of one letter followed by five digits, how many plates could it issue? **2,600,000**

35. New York license plates consist of three letters followed by three numerals, and 245 letter arrangements are not allowed. How many plates can New York issue? **17,331,000**

36. Some California license plates consist of one digit followed by three letters followed by three digits. How many such plates can California issue? **175,760,000**

37. Many states offer personalized license plates.

The state of California, for example, allows personalized plates with seven positions for numerals, letters, spaces, or one of the following four symbols:

What is the total number of license plates possible using this scheme? **194,754,273,881**

38. For traveling from their home in Sebastopol, CA, to San Francisco, the navigation system in the Normans' car offers three different routes, and from San Francisco to Napa, CA, offers two different routes. Finally, from Napa back to Sebastopol the system offers four routes. Using the suggestions from the navigational system, how many round-trip routes can they take for this trip? **24 routes**

39. In getting dressed, you reach into your dresser and choose one sock and then another. (Unfortunately, the socks are loose and are not tied together in pairs.) If you have 6 black socks, 4 blue socks, and 8 brown socks, in how many ways can you reach in and pick out two socks? *See bottom of the column.*

40. The advertisement shown in Figure 9.13 claims the following 12 mix-and-match items give 122 outfits.

Figure 9.13 Mix-and-match advertisement

39. 306   Note: Don't read more into this problem than is there; we don't care if the socks match or if they are distinguishable. We are simply asking how many ways of drawing 2 socks.

The wardrobe consists of 4 blouses, 2 slacks, 2 skirts, 1 sweater, 2 jackets, and 1 scarf. Assume that the model must choose one top and one bottom item of clothing. She may or may not choose a sweater or jacket and finally may choose to wear or not wear a scarf. How many different outfits are possible?   **128**

41. A history teacher gives a 20-question true–false exam. In how many different ways can the test be answered? 2^{20}

42. A history teacher gives a 20-question T–F exam. In how many different ways can the test be answered if the possible answers are T or F, or possibly to leave the answer blank? 3^{20}

43. A typical Social Security number is

$$555\text{-}47\text{-}5593$$

How many Social Security numbers are possible if the first two digits cannot be zeros?   **810,000,000**

44. A typical phone number (with area code) is

$$(707)\ 555\text{-}1234$$

How many phone numbers are possible if the first two digits of the phone number cannot be 1 or 0?   **6,400,000,000**

45. What is the probability of a family with four children having one boy and three girls? $\frac{4}{16} = \frac{1}{4}$

46. What is the probability of a family with six children having three boys and three girls. $\frac{20}{64} = \frac{5}{16}$

47. What is the probability of flipping a coin 7 times and receiving all heads? $\frac{1}{128}$

48. What is the probability of flipping a coin 7 times and receiving at least one tail? $\frac{127}{128}$

49. *One roulette system is to bet $1 on black. If black comes up on the first spin of the wheel, you win $1 and the game is over. If black does not come up, double your bet ($2). If you win, the game is over and your net winnings for two spins is still $1 (show this). If black does not come up, double your bet again ($4). If you win, the game is over and your net winnings for three spins is still $1 (show this). Continue this doubling procedure until you eventually win; in every case your net winnings amount to $1 (show this). What is the fallacy with this betting system?   **The betting limit imposed on the game**

50. †Suppose you like to bet on a silly card game. If you and a friend each select a card, the card with the higher value wins. If you bet 25¢ and win, you stop playing. On the other hand, if you lose, you raise your bet to 50¢. If you win, you stop playing with winnings of 25¢ (−$0.25 + $0.50 = $0.25). If you lose, you raise your bet to $1.00. If you continue with this process, eventually you will stop with a net gain of 25¢. What is the fallacy with the betting system?   **At some point, your friend will decide to stop and at that point you will have a net loss.**

*You do not need to know anything about roulette to answer this question.

†You do not need to know anything about cards to answer this question.

51. "We need to talk, Ben," said Melissa. "I know we have eight children, but I want a boy!" "I know, dear, so do I, but I'm not sure we can afford another child. The doctor told us that the law of averages for having a boy is in our favor if we try again, but look what happened last time." Melissa quickly cut in, "My dad is a math teacher, and he said that the chances of having nine boys in a row is 1 out of 512." A worried look swept over Ben's face as he said, "Right, and the doctor said 1 out of 100 last time, too. I'll tell you what, write to Ann Landers or Dear Abby and see what advice the experts can give, then . . . ." What is the probability that the next child for Melissa and Ben is a boy?   **The probability of a boy for the 9th child is $\frac{1}{2}$.**

52. IN YOUR OWN WORDS   Write a short paper comparing the Problem of the Day with your own situation. (That is, list similarities and/or differences.) Answer the question: "Can probability help us decide on the gender of an unborn child or children?"

53. What is the probability (rounded to the nearest percent) of getting a license plate that has a repeated letter or digit if you live in a state where the scheme is two letters followed by four numerals?   **52%**

54. What is the probability (rounded to the nearest percent) of getting a license plate that has a repeated letter or digit if you live in a state where the scheme is one numeral followed by three letters followed by three numerals?   **55%**

RIGHT OR WRONG?   **LEVEL 3**

Explain what is wrong, if anything, with the statements in Problems 55–60. Explain your reasoning.

55. If $P(E) = \frac{3}{7}$, then $P(\overline{E}) = \frac{3}{5}$.   **F; $P(\overline{E}) = \frac{4}{7}$**

56. $P(E)$ and $P(\overline{E})$ are reciprocals.   **F; they are complements.**

57. The probability of obtaining a head in one toss of a coin is $\frac{1}{2}$, and the probability of obtaining two heads in two tosses of a coin is $\frac{1}{4}$. It then follows that the probability of obtaining five heads in five tosses is $\frac{1}{32}$. Suppose I flip a coin four times and obtain four heads. Then it is better to bet on tails for the fifth flip because the probability of five heads in a row is very small.   **F; the probability of heads on the next flip is $\frac{1}{2}$.**

58. This example is from the book *How to Take a Chance* by Darrell Huff. "On August 18, 1913 at a casino in Monte Carlo, black came up 26 times in a row on a roulette wheel. If you had bet $1 on black and continued to let your bet ride for the entire run of blacks, you would have won $67,108,863.00." If you were to bet on the next spin of the wheel, you should bet on red because the chances of black on the 27th spin are very, very, small.   **See bottom of the column.**

59. Roll a die twice, and suppose that a six is obtained on the first roll, so the probability that a six will be obtained again is 1/36.   **F; it is $\frac{1}{6}$.**

60. Draw five cards from a deck of cards. The probability of drawing a heart on the fifth card is 13/48.   **F; it is $\frac{13}{52} = \frac{1}{4}$**

58. F; the probability of black on the next spin is not changed by past spins of the wheel; the wheel does not "remember" previous spins.

9.3 Odds and Conditional Probability

IN THIS WORLD   THE UTILITY OF MATH

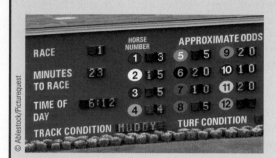

RACE ▪ 1

MINUTES TO RACE 23

TIME OF DAY 5:12

TRACK CONDITION MUDDY   TURF CONDITION

HORSE NUMBER   APPROXIMATE ODDS

1 ▪ 3   5 ▪ 5   9 ▪ 20
2 ▪ 15   6 ▪ 20   10 ▪ 10
3 ▪ 5   7 ▪ 10   11 ▪ 20
4 ▪ 4   8 ▪ 5   12 ▪

"Last week I won a free Big Mac at McDonald's. I sure was lucky!" exclaimed Charlie.

"Do you go there often?" asked Pat.

"Only twenty or thirty times a month. And the odds of winning a Big Mac were only 20 to 1."

"Don't you mean 1 to 20?" queried Pat.

"Don't confuse me with details," said Charlie. "I don't even understand odds at the racetrack, and I go all the time. Why do I need to know anything about odds, anyway?"

In this section, Charlie will learn about odds, the calculation of odds, and their relationship to probability.

 See Problems 34 and 54.

> The odds are in on the Academy Awards
> LAS VEGAS, Nevada
> The Odds Are Against You...
> Your chances of becoming ___ are only 1 out of ___ the book

Odds

Related to probability is the notion of odds. Instead of forming ratios

$$P(E) = \frac{s}{n} \quad \text{and} \quad P(\overline{E}) = \frac{f}{n}$$

we form the following ratios:

Odds in favor of an event E: $\dfrac{s}{f}$ (ratio of successes to failures);

Odds against an event E: $\dfrac{f}{s}$ (ratio of failures to success);

where

$$s = \text{NUMBER OF SUCCESSES}$$
$$f = \text{NUMBER OF FAILURES}$$
$$n = \text{NUMBER OF POSSIBILITIES}$$

EXAMPLE 1

Finding the odds of an event

If a jar has 2 quarters, 200 dimes, and 800 pennies, what are the odds against picking a quarter if a coin is chosen at random?

Solution   We are interested in picking a quarter, so let $s = 2$; a failure is not obtaining a quarter, so $f = 1{,}000$. (Find f by adding 200 and 800.)

Odds in favor of obtaining a quarter: $\dfrac{s}{f} = \dfrac{2}{1{,}000} = \dfrac{1}{500}$

Odds against obtaining a quarter: $\dfrac{f}{s} = \dfrac{1{,}000}{2} = \dfrac{500}{1}$ *Do not write $\dfrac{500}{1}$ as 500.*

The odds against choosing a quarter at random are 500 to 1.

EXAMPLE 2   **Visualizing odds**

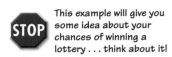

This example will give you some idea about your chances of winning a lottery . . . think about it!

The odds against winning a lottery are 50,000,000 to 1. Make up an example to help visualize these odds.

Solution   Imagine one red ping pong ball and 50,000,000 white ping pong balls. Winning a lottery is equivalent to reaching into a container containing these 50,000,001 ping pong balls and obtaining the red one. To visualize this, consider the size container you would need. Assume that a ping pong ball takes up a volume of 1 in.^{3}. A home of 1,200 ft^2 with an 8-ft ceiling has a volume of

$$1,200 \text{ ft}^2 \times 8 \text{ ft} = 9,600 \text{ ft}^3$$
$$= 9,600 \times (12 \text{ in.} \times 12 \text{ in.} \times 12 \text{ in.})$$
$$= 16,588,800 \text{ in.}^3$$

This means that we would need to *fill* about 3 homes with ping pong balls and then choose one ball out of *one* of the houses. If the red one is chosen, we win the lottery!

●

Sometimes you know the probability and want to find the odds, or you may know the odds and want to find the probability. These relationships are easy if you remember:

$$s + f = n$$

First, we show

$$\frac{P(E)}{P(\overline{E})} = \frac{\frac{s}{n}}{\frac{f}{n}} = \frac{s}{n} \cdot \frac{n}{f} = \frac{s}{f} = \text{odds in favor}$$

Similarly, it can be shown (Problem 27) that $\frac{P(\overline{E})}{P(E)} = $ odds against. This leads to the following procedure for finding odds when we know the probability.

Probability to Odds

Suppose you know the probability of an event, $P(E)$, and wish to find the odds.

Step 1   Use $P(\overline{E}) = 1 - P(E)$ to find the probability of the complementary event.

Step 2   To find the odds in favor, divide the probability by its complementary probability: $\dfrac{P(E)}{P(\overline{E})}$

Step 3   To find the odds against, divide the complementary probability by the probability: $\dfrac{P(\overline{E})}{P(E)}$

EXAMPLE 3   **Finding the odds when the probability is known**

Suppose the probability of an event is 0.45.

a. What are the odds in favor of the event?

b. What are the odds against the event?

Solution   Begin by finding $P(E)$ and $P(\overline{E})$ in fractional form.

$$P(E) = 0.45 = \frac{45}{100} = \frac{9}{20} \quad \text{This is given.}$$

$$P(\overline{E}) = 1 - \frac{9}{20} = \frac{11}{20}$$

a. The odds in favor of E are $\dfrac{P(E)}{P(\overline{E})} = \dfrac{\frac{9}{20}}{\frac{11}{20}} = \frac{9}{20} \cdot \frac{20}{11} = \frac{9}{11}$

b. The odds against E are $\dfrac{P(\overline{E})}{P(E)} = \dfrac{\frac{11}{20}}{\frac{9}{20}} = \frac{11}{20} \cdot \frac{20}{9} = \frac{11}{9}$

On the other hand, if we know the odds and wish to find the probability, use the following procedure:

Odds to Probability

Suppose you know the odds in favor (s to f) of event E, or the odds against (f to s), and wish to find $P(E)$ and $P(\overline{E})$.

Step 1 Calculate $s + f$

Step 2 $P(E) = \dfrac{s}{s + f}$

Step 3 $P(\overline{E}) = \dfrac{f}{s + f}$

EXAMPLE 4

Finding the probability when the odds against are known

If the odds against you are 20 to 1, what is the probability of the event (rounded to three decimal places)?

Solution Odds against are f to s, so $f = 20$ and $s = 1$; thus,

$$P(E) = \frac{s}{s + f} = \frac{1}{1 + 20} = \frac{1}{21} \approx 0.048$$

EXAMPLE 5

Finding the probability of the complement of an event

If the odds against you finding a lost ring are 1,000 to 1, what is the probability that you will not find the ring?

Solution Odds against are f to s, so $f = 1{,}000$ and $s = 1$; thus,

$$P(\overline{E}) = \frac{f}{s + f} = \frac{1{,}000}{1 + 1{,}000} = \frac{1{,}000}{1{,}001} \approx 0.999$$

EXAMPLE 6

Finding the probability when the odds in favor are known

If the odds in favor of some event are 2 to 5, what is the probability of the event (rounded to three decimal places)?

Solution Odds in favor are s to f, so $s = 2$ and $f = 5$; thus,

$$P(E) = \frac{s}{s + f} = \frac{2}{2 + 5} = \frac{2}{7} \approx 0.286$$

HISTORICAL NOTE

Le Trente-et-un, ou la maison de pret sur natissement, by Darcis

The engraving depicts gambling in 18th-century France. The mathematical theory of probability arose in France in the 17th century when a gambler, Chevalier de Méré, became interested in adjusting the stakes so that he could win more often than he lost. In 1654, he wrote to Blaise Pascal, who in turn sent his questions to Pierre de Fermat. Together they developed the first theory of probability. The first treatise on probability was written by Girolamo Cardano (1501–1576) who was also led to probability because at one time in his life he made his living from gambling. In fact, it is said that gambling was an addiction for him. He died on the day he predicted that he would die—cause of death: suicide!

Conditional Probability

Frequently, we wish to compute the probability of an event but we have additional information that will alter the sample space. For example, suppose that a family has two children. What is the probability that the family has two boys?

$$P(2 \text{ boys}) = \frac{1}{4} \quad \text{Sample space: BB, BG, GB, GG; 1 success out of 4 possibilities}$$

Now, let's complicate the problem a little. Suppose that we know that the older child is a boy. We have *altered* the sample space as follows:

Original sample space: BB, BG, GB, GG; but we need to cross out the last two possibilities because we *know* that the older child is a boy.

$$\underset{\text{Altered sample space has two elements.}}{\text{\emph{Altered sample space:}} \quad \underbrace{\overset{\overset{\text{Success}}{\downarrow}}{\text{BB}}, \text{BG}}} \quad , \quad \overset{\text{These are crossed out.}}{\overbrace{\cancel{\text{GB}}, \cancel{\text{GG}}}}$$

Therefore,

$$P(2 \text{ boys given the older is a boy}) = \frac{1}{2}$$

This is a problem involving a **conditional probability**—namely, the *probability of an event E, **given** that another event F has occurred.* We denote this by

$$P(E \mid F) \quad \text{Read this as "probability of E given F."}$$

EXAMPLE 7

Finding a conditional probability with coins

Suppose that you toss two coins (or a single coin twice). What is the probability that two heads are obtained if you know that at least one head is obtained?

Solution   Consider an altered sample space: HH, HT, TH, ~~TT~~. The probability is $\frac{1}{3}$.

●

EXAMPLE 8

Finding a conditional probability with cards

Suppose that you draw two cards from a deck of cards. The first card selected is not returned to the deck before the second card is drawn. Let $H = \{$the second card drawn is a heart$\}$. Find the following probabilities (correct to three decimal places).

a. $P(H\,|\,$a heart is drawn on the first draw$)$
b. $P(H\,|\,$a heart is not drawn on the first draw$)$
c. $P(H)$

Solution

a. Since the first card is a heart, the number of remaining cards is $n = 51$, and $s = 12$ (because a heart was drawn on the first draw):

$$P(H \,|\, \text{a heart is drawn on the first draw}) = \frac{12}{51} \approx 0.235$$

b. We still have $n = 51$, but this time $s = 13$:

$$P(H \,|\, \text{a heart is not drawn on the first draw}) = \frac{13}{51} \approx 0.255$$

c. This time we do not know the first card drawn, so it is as if it is still in the deck of cards, so $n = 52$ this time, and $s = 13$, so

$$P(H) = \frac{13}{52} = \frac{1}{4} = 0.250$$

Remember, it does not matter what happened on the first draw because we do not know what happened on that draw. The second card "does not remember" what is drawn on the first draw.

●

EXAMPLE 9

Conditional probability with a life-science experiment

In a life-science experiment, it is necessary to examine fruit flies and to determine their sex and whether they have mutated after exposure to a certain dose of radiation. The experiment examined 1,000 fruit flies and found that there were 643 females and 357 males. Also, 403 of the females were normal and 240 were mutated; of the males, 190 were normal and 167 were mutated. Suppose a single fruit fly is selected at random from the radiated fruit flies. Find the following probabilities (correct to the nearest hundredth).

a. It is male.
b. It is a normal male.
c. It is normal, given that it is a male.
d. It is male, given that it is normal.

Solution We display the data in table form to make it easier to calculate the desired probabilities.

	Mutated	Normal	Total
Male	167	190	357
Female	240	403	643
Total	407	593	1,000

a. $P(\text{male}) = \frac{357}{1,000} = 0.36$ *Round answers to the nearest hundredth.*

b. $P(\text{normal male}) = \frac{190}{1,000} = 0.19$

c. $P(\text{normal} \mid \text{male}) = \frac{190}{357} \approx 0.53$ *Note the altered sample space.*

d. $P(\text{male} \mid \text{normal}) = \frac{190}{593} \approx 0.32$ *Yet another altered sample space.*

●

PROBLEM SET 9.3

ESSENTIAL IDEAS LEVEL 1

1. **IN YOUR OWN WORDS** Explain what we mean by "conditional probability."

2. **IN YOUR OWN WORDS** Contrast probability and odds.

3. What is the formula for finding odds in favor if you know $P(E)$? $P(E)/P(\bar{E})$

4. What is the formula for finding $P(E)$ if the odds in favor of E is known? $P(E) = \frac{s}{s+f}$

DRILL AND PRACTICE LEVEL 2

Find the odds in favor of the events whose probabilities are given in Problems 5–12.

5. $P(E) = \frac{1}{2}$ 1 to 1

6. $P(E) = \frac{1}{10}$ 1 to 9

7. $P(E) = \frac{3}{4}$ 3 to 1

8. $P(E) = \frac{7}{10}$ 7 to 3

9. $P(E) = 0.3$ 3 to 7

10. $P(E) = 0.8$ 4 to 1

11. $P(E) = 0.04$ 1 to 24

12. $P(E) = 0.99$ 99 to 1

Find the probabilities whose odds against are given in Problems 13–16.

13. Odds against are 100 to 1 $\frac{1}{101}$

14. Odds against are 10,000 to 1 $\frac{1}{10,001}$

15. Odds against are 5 to 1 $\frac{1}{6}$

16. Odds against are 1 to 5 $\frac{5}{6}$

Find the probabilities whose odds in favor are given in Problems 17–20.

17. Odds in favor are 3 to 2 $\frac{3}{5}$

18. Odds in favor are 10,000 to 1 $\frac{10,000}{10,001}$

19. Odds in favor are 1 to 9 $\frac{1}{10}$

20. Odds in favor are 1 to 5 $\frac{1}{6}$

Use the results of the fruit fly experiment (Example 9) to find the probabilities (rounded to the nearest hundredth) in Problems 21–26.

21. P (mutated male) $\frac{167}{1,000} \approx 0.17$

22. P (mutated | male) $\frac{167}{357} \approx 0.47$

23. P (mutated female) $\frac{240}{1,000} \approx 0.24$

24. P (mutated | female) $\frac{240}{643} = 0.37$

25. P (male | mutated) $\frac{167}{407} \approx 0.41$

26. P (female | mutated) $\frac{240}{407} \approx 0.59$

27. Show that the odds against an event E can be found by computing $\frac{P(\bar{E})}{P(E)}$. $\frac{P(\bar{E})}{P(E)} = \frac{\frac{f}{n}}{\frac{s}{n}} = \frac{f}{n} \cdot \frac{n}{s} = \frac{f}{s} = \text{odds against}$

APPLICATIONS LEVEL 2

28. What are the odds in favor of drawing an ace from an ordinary deck of cards?   1 to 12

29. What are the odds in favor of drawing a heart from an ordinary deck of cards?   1 to 3

30. What are a family's odds against having four boys, if it has four children?   15 to 1

31. What are the odds against flipping a coin three times and obtaining heads all three times?   7 to 1

32. Suppose that the odds in favor that a man will be bald by the time he is 60 are 9 to 1. State this as a probability. $\frac{9}{10}$

33. Suppose the odds in favor are 33 to 1 in favor that someone will lie to you at least once in the next seven days. State this as a probability. $\frac{33}{34}$

34. Racetracks quote the approximate odds for each race on a large display board called a *tote board*.

© PhotoDisc/Getty Images

Here's what it might say for a particular race:

Horse Number	Odds	
#1	18 to 1	$P(\#1) = \frac{1}{19}$
#2	3 to 2	$P(\#2) = \frac{2}{5}$
#3	15 to 1	$P(\#3) = \frac{1}{16}$
#4	7 to 5	$P(\#4) = \frac{5}{12}$
#5	1 to 1	$P(\#5) = \frac{1}{2}$

What would be the probability of winning for each of these horses? [*Note:* The odds stated are for the horse's *losing*.] Thus,

$$P(\text{horse 1 losing}) = \frac{18}{18 + 1} = \frac{18}{19}$$

so

$$P(\text{horse 1 winning}) = 1 - \frac{18}{19} = \frac{1}{19}$$

35. Consider the following table showing the results of a survey of TV network executives asking their opinion of current programming.

	Satisfied, S	Not satisfied, $\overline{S}$	Total
NBC, N	18	7	25
CBS, C	21	9	30
ABC, A	15	10	25
Total	54	26	80

Suppose one network executive is selected at random. Find the indicated probabilities (rounded to the nearest hundredth).

a. What is the probability that it is an NBC executive? $P(N) = \frac{25}{80} \approx 0.31$

b. What is the probability that the selected person is satisfied? $P(S) = \frac{54}{80} \approx 0.68$

c. What is the probability the selected person is from CBS if we know the person is satisfied with current programming? $P(C \mid S) = \frac{21}{54} \approx 0.39$

d. What is the probability the selected person is satisfied, if we know the person is from CBS? $P(S \mid C) = \frac{21}{30} = 0.70$

36. What is the probability of obtaining exactly three heads in four flips of a coin, given that at least one is a head? $\frac{4}{15}$

37. What is the probability of obtaining exactly three heads in four flips of a coin, given that at least two are heads? $\frac{4}{11}$

38. What is a family's probability of having exactly two boys, given that at least one of their three children is a boy? $\frac{3}{7}$

39. Suppose that a family wants to have four children.

a. What is the sample space? BBBB; BBBG; BBGB; BBGG; BGBB; BGBG; BGGB; BGGG; GBBB; GBBG; GBGB; GBGG; GGBB; GGBG; GGGB; GGGG

b. What is the probability of 4 girls? 4 boys? $\frac{1}{16}$; $\frac{1}{16}$

c. What is the probability of 1 girl and 3 boys? 1 boy and 3 girls? $\frac{1}{4}$; $\frac{1}{4}$

d. What is the probability of 2 boys and 2 girls? $\frac{3}{8}$

e. What is the sum of your answers in parts **b–d**? The sum is 1.

A single card is drawn from a standard deck of cards. (A deck of cards is shown in Figure 9.6 on page 452.) In Problems 40–45, find the probabilities if the given information is known about the chosen card. A face card is a jack, queen, or king.

40. $P(\text{face card} \mid \text{jack})$ 1

41. $P(\text{jack} \mid \text{face card})$ $\frac{1}{3}$

42. $P(\text{heart} \mid \text{not a spade})$ $\frac{1}{3}$

43. $P(\text{two} \mid \text{not a face card})$ $\frac{1}{10}$

44. $P(\text{black} \mid \text{jack})$ $\frac{1}{2}$

45. $P(\text{jack} \mid \text{black})$ $\frac{1}{13}$

Two cards are drawn from a standard deck of cards. (The first card selected is not returned to the deck before the second card is drawn.) A characteristic of the first card is noted. Find the probabilities of the second card, given the information about the first card provided in Problems 46–51.

46. $P(\text{ace} \mid \text{two})$ $\frac{4}{51}$

47. $P(\text{king} \mid \text{king})$ $\frac{1}{17}$

48. $P(\text{heart} \mid \text{heart})$ $\frac{4}{17}$

49. $P(\text{heart} \mid \text{spade})$ $\frac{13}{51}$

50. $P(\text{black} \mid \text{red})$ $\frac{26}{51}$

51. $P(\text{black} \mid \text{black})$ $\frac{25}{51}$

For Problems 52–53, use the sample space for a pair of dice (see Figure 9.8 on page 453).

52. On a single roll of a pair of dice, what is the probability that the sum is seven, given that at least one die came up two? $P(7 \mid 2) = \frac{2}{11}$

53. What are the odds in favor of rolling a seven or eleven on a single roll of a pair of dice? 2 to 7

54. "Last week I won a free Big Mac at McDonald's. I sure was lucky!" exclaimed Charlie. "Do you go there often?" asked Pat. "Only twenty or thirty times a month. And the odds of winning a Big Mac were only 20 to 1." "Don't you mean 1 to 20?" queried Pat. Is Charlie or Pat correct? Pat is correct.

55. **IN YOUR OWN WORDS** Write a short paper comparing the Problem of the Day with your own situation. (That is, list similarities and/or differences.) Answer the question, "Why do I need to know anything about odds anyway?"

56. **IN YOUR OWN WORDS** Suppose the odds against winning the lottery are a million to one. Make up an example to help visualize these odds.

Explain what is wrong, if anything, with the statements in Problems 57–60. Explain your reasoning.

57. If $P(E) = \frac{2}{3}$, then the odds in favor of E are 2 to 3.
        F; odds in favor are 2 to 1

58. If the odds of winning are 3 to 2, that is better than if the odds of winning are 2 to 3.
        T; $P(\text{win}) = \frac{3}{5}$ is better than $P(\text{win}) = \frac{2}{5}$.

59. If the odds in favor of an event are 3 to 5, then the odds against the event are 2 to 5.   F; odds against are 5 to 3

60. The odds in favor of an event and the odds against an event are complements.   F; they are reciprocals

9.4 Mathematical Expectation

IN THIS WORLD THE UTILITY OF MATH

Black on both sides

Black on one side, white on the other

White on both sides

Suppose that your friend George shows you three cards. One card is white on both sides, one is black on both sides, and the last one is black on one side and white on the other. He mixes the cards and tells you to select one at random and place it on a table. Suppose that the upper side turns out to be black. It is not the white/white card; it must be either the black/black or the black/white card. "Thus," says George, "I'll bet you $1 that the other side is black." Would you play? Perhaps you hesitate. Now, George says he feels generous. You need to pay him only 75¢ if you lose, and he will pay you $1 if he loses. Would you play now?

 See Problem 54.

In this section, you'll learn how to analyze a variety of gambling situations. Whether you enjoy gambling and games of chance or are opposed to them and would never play a gambling game, you should find some valuable information in this section. Gambling situations range from dice, cards, and slot machines, to buying insurance and selling a home. By analyzing these games, you can show that without proper analysis, a person could be destined for financial ruin, given enough time and limited resources. You can also find situations that should not be considered gambling—situations in which you can't lose.

Expectation

Smiles toothpaste is giving away $10,000. All you must do to have a chance to win is send a postcard with your name on it (the fine print says you do not need to buy a tube of toothpaste). Is it worthwhile to enter?

Suppose the contest receives 1 million postcards (a conservative estimate). We wish to compute the **expected value** (or your **expectation**) of entering this contest. The expected value of this contest is obtained by multiplying the amount to win by the probability of winning:

$$E = (\text{AMOUNT TO WIN}) \times (\text{PROBABILITY OF WINNING})$$
$$= \$10,000 \times \frac{1}{1,000,000}$$
$$= \$0.01$$

What does this expected value mean? It means if you were to play this "game" a large number of times, you would expect your *average winnings per game* to be $0.01. A game is said to be **fair** if the expected value equals the cost of playing the game. If the expected value is positive, then the game is in your favor; if the expected value is negative, then the game is not in your favor. Is this game fair? If the toothpaste company charges you 1¢ to play the game, then it is fair. But how much does the postcard cost? We see that this is not a fair game.

EXAMPLE 1

Finding the expected value

Suppose that you draw a card from a deck of cards and are paid $10 if the card is an ace. What is the expected value?

Solution $E = \$10 \times \dfrac{4}{52}$

$\approx \$0.77$ Round to the nearest cent.

Sometimes there is more than one possible payoff, and we define the expected value (or expectation) as the sum of the expected values from each separate payoff.

EXAMPLE 2

Finding the expected value

A recent contest offered one grand prize worth $10,000, two second prizes worth $5,000 each, and ten third prizes worth $1,000 each. What is the expected value if you assume that there are 1 million entries and that the winners' names are replaced after being drawn?

Solution

$$P(\text{1st prize}) = \frac{1}{1,000,000}; P(\text{2nd prize}) = \frac{2}{1,000,000}; P(\text{3rd prize}) = \frac{10}{1,000,000}$$

$$E = \overbrace{\$10,000}^{\text{amount of 1st prize}} \times \underbrace{\frac{1}{1,000,000}}_{P(\text{1st prize})} + \$5,000 \times \overbrace{\frac{2}{1,000,000}}^{\text{2nd prize}} + \$1,000 \times \underbrace{\frac{10}{1,000,000}}_{\text{3rd prize}}$$

$= \$0.01 + \$0.01 + \$0.01$

$= \$0.03$

EXAMPLE 3

Using expected value to make a decision

You are offered two games:

Game A: Two dice are rolled. You will be paid $3.60 if you roll two ones, and you will not receive anything for any other outcome.

Game B: Two dice are rolled. You will be paid $36.00 if you roll any pair, but you must pay $3.60 for any other outcome.

Which game should you play?

Solution You might say, "I'll play the first game because, if I play that game, I cannot lose anything." This strategy involves *minimizing your losses*. On the other hand, you can use a strategy that *maximizes your winnings*. In this book, we will base our decisions on maximizing the winnings—that is, we wish to select the game that provides the larger expectation.

Game A: $E = \$3.60 \times \frac{1}{36} = \$0.10$

Game B: When calculating the expected value with a charge (a loss), write that charge as a negative number (a negative payoff is a loss).

$$E = \$36.00 \times \frac{6}{36} + (-\$3.60) \times \frac{30}{36}$$
$$= \$6.00 + (-\$3.00)$$
$$= \$3.00$$

This means that, if you were to play each game 100 times, you would expect your winnings for Game A to be about 100($0.10) or $10 and those from playing Game B to be about 100($3.00) or $300. You should choose to play Game B. ●

Now we give a formal definition of expectation.

Mathematical Expectation

Use this definition to help you decide whether to place a bet, play a game, or enter a business venture.

> If an event E has several possible outcomes with probabilities $p_1, p_2, p_3, \ldots$, and if for each of these outcomes, the amount that can be won is $a_1, a_2, a_3, \ldots$, respectively, then the **mathematical expectation** (or expected value) of E is
>
> $$E = a_1p_1 + a_2p_2 + a_3p_3 + \cdots$$

EXAMPLE 4

Mathematical expectation for a contest

A contest offered the prizes shown in Figure 9.14. What is the expected value for this contest?

Solution We note the following values:

$$a_1 = \$15,000; \quad p_1 = 0.000008$$
$$a_2 = \$1,000; \quad p_2 = 0.000016$$
$$a_3 = \$625; \quad p_3 = 0.000016$$
$$a_4 = \$525; \quad p_4 = 0.000016$$
$$a_5 = \$390; \quad p_5 = 0.000032$$
$$a_6 = \$250; \quad p_6 = 0.000032$$

$$E = \$15,000(0.000008) + \$1,000(0.000016) + \$625(0.000016)$$
$$+ \$525(0.000016) + \$390(0.000032) + \$250(0.000032)$$
$$\approx \$0.17$$ ●

$ WIN   WIN   WIN $

PRIZE	VALUE	PROBABILITY
Grand Prize Trip	$15,000	0.000008
Samsonite Luggage	$1,000	0.000016
Magic Chef Range	$625.00	0.000016
Murray Bicycle	$525.00	0.000016
Lawn Boy Mower	$390.00	0.000032
Weber Kettle	$250.00	0.000032

Figure 9.14 Contest prize statement

Life insurance is also a form of gambling. When you purchase a policy, you are betting that you will die during the term of the policy, and the company is betting that you will live. The probability that you will die in any particular year of your life is an empirical probability and is listed in what is called a **mortality table,** such as Table III, Appendix B, at the back of this book.

EXAMPLE 5   **Expected value of buying an insurance policy**

Suppose that you turned 21 years old today, and you wish to take out a $100,000 insurance policy for 1 year. How much should you be willing to pay for this policy?

Solution   To answer this question, we need to know the probability that a 21-year-old person will die during his or her next year. By consulting Table III, we can see that, out of 96,478 persons of age 21, we could expect 177 to die within a year. Thus,

$$E = \text{AMOUNT TO WIN} \times \text{PROBABILITY OF WINNING}$$
$$= \$100,000 \times \frac{177}{96,478}$$
$$\approx \$183.46$$

This means that you should be willing to pay $183.46. However, if the company charged $183.46 for such a policy, its gain (in the long run) would be zero. The actual premium, then, should be fixed at $183.46 plus a set amount for administrative costs and profit.

Expectation with a Cost of Playing

Many games charge you a fee to play. If you must pay to play, this cost of playing should be taken into consideration when you calculate the expected value. Remember, if the expected value is 0, it is a fair game; if the expected value is positive, you should play; but if it is negative, you should not.

Finding Expectation

In order to find the mathematical expectation with a cost of playing use the following procedure.

Step 1   Decide whether there is a cost, c, for playing the game. If not, then let $c = 0$.

Step 2   Determine the amount to win, a, and the probability of winning, p.

Step 3   Use this formula:
$$\text{EXPECTATION} = ap - c$$

EXAMPLE 6   **Expected value with a cost of playing**

Consider a game consisting of drawing a card from a deck of cards. If it is a face card, you win $20. Should you play the game if it costs $5 to play?

Amount to win   Cost of playing

Solution $E = \quad \$20 \quad \left(\frac{12}{52}\right) \quad - \quad \$5 \quad \approx -\$0.38$

Probability of winning

You should not play this game, because it has a negative expectation. ●

EXAMPLE 7   **Expected value for selling a house**

Walt, who is a realtor, knows that if he takes a listing to sell a house, it will cost him $1,000. However, if he sells the house, he will receive 6% of the selling price. If another realtor sells the house, Walt will receive 3% of the selling price. If the house remains unsold after 3 months, he will lose the listing and receive nothing. Suppose that the probabilities for selling a particular $200,000 house are as follows: the probability that Walt will sell the house is 0.4; the probability that another agent will sell the house is 0.2; and the probability that the house will remain unsold is 0.4. What is Walt's expectation if he takes this listing?

Solution   First, we must decide whether there is a "cost for playing" for this problem. Is Walt required to pay the $1,000 before the "game" of selling the house is played? The answer is yes, so the $1,000 must be subtracted from the payoffs. Now let's calculate those payoffs:

$$6\% \text{ of } \$200,000 = 0.06(\$200,000) = \$12,000$$
$$3\% \text{ of } \$200,000 = 0.03(\$200,000) = \$6,000$$

Now we can use the procedure for calculating the expectation with a cost of playing, $c = \$1,000$.

$$
\underbrace{(\$12,000)(0.4)}_{\text{Walt sells the house.}} + \underbrace{(\$6,000)(0.2)}_{\text{Another agent sells.}} - \underbrace{(\$1,000)}_{\text{House doesn't sell.}} = \$5,000
$$

Walt's expectation is $5,000.   ●

You must understand the nature of the game to know whether the cost of playing, c, is 0 or whether it is not. If you surrender your money to play, then c is nonzero, but if you "leave it on the table," then $c = 0$. Consider the following example of a U.S. roulette game. In this game, your bet is placed on the table but is not collected until after the play of the game and it is determined that you lost. A U.S. roulette wheel has 38 numbered slots (1–36, 0, and 00), as shown in Figure 9.15.

Here is how bets are placed on the roulette table

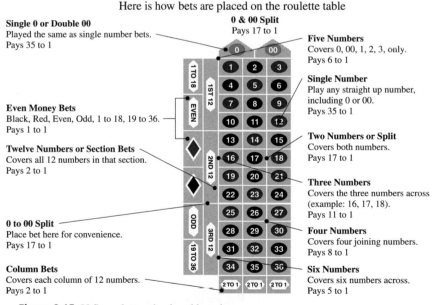

Single 0 or Double 00
Played the same as single number bets.
Pays 35 to 1

0 & 00 Split
Pays 17 to 1

Five Numbers
Covers 0, 00, 1, 2, 3, only.
Pays 6 to 1

Single Number
Play any straight up number, including 0 or 00.
Pays 35 to 1

Even Money Bets
Black, Red, Even, Odd, 1 to 18, 19 to 36.
Pays 1 to 1

Two Numbers or Split
Covers both numbers.
Pays 17 to 1

Twelve Numbers or Section Bets
Covers all 12 numbers in that section.
Pays 2 to 1

Three Numbers
Covers the three numbers across
(example: 16, 17, 18).
Pays 11 to 1

0 to 00 Split
Place bet here for convenience.
Pays 17 to 1

Four Numbers
Covers four joining numbers.
Pays 8 to 1

Column Bets
Covers each column of 12 numbers.
Pays 2 to 1

Six Numbers
Covers six numbers across.
Pays 5 to 1

Figure 9.15 U.S. roulette wheel and board

Some of the more common bets and payoffs are shown. If the payoff is listed as 6 to 1, you would receive $6 for each $1 bet. In addition, you would keep the $1 you originally wagered. One play consists of having the dealer spin the wheel and a little ball in opposite directions. As the ball slows to a stop, it lands in one of the 38 numbered slots, which are colored black, red, or green. A single-number bet has a payoff of 35 to 1. The $1 you bet is collected only if you lose.

EXAMPLE 8

Expected value when playing roulette

What is the expectation for playing roulette if you bet $1 on number 5?

Solution Calculate the expected value:

$$E = \overbrace{35\left(\frac{1}{38}\right)}^{\text{win}} + \overbrace{(-1)\left(\frac{37}{38}\right)}^{\text{lose}} \overset{\text{cost of playing}}{\underset{\downarrow}{-\ 0}}$$

$$\approx -\$0.05$$

The expected loss is about 5¢ per play. ●

EXAMPLE 9

Using the expected value in making a decision

Black on both sides

Black on one side, white on the other

White on both sides

Remember the Problem of the Day? Your friend George shows you three cards. One is white on both sides, one is black on both sides, and the last is black on one side and white on the other. He mixes the cards and lets you select one at random and place it on the table. George then calls out the color on the underside. If he selects the right color, you lose $1; if he does not select the correct color on the underside, you win $1. Should you play?

Solution First, decide whether there is an "entry fee to play." Since you and George are each putting up $1, there is no entry fee, so $c = 0$. However, suppose that you are not sure you want to play, so George explains:

> *Suppose you select a card, and we see that it's black on top. We know it's not the white–white card, so it must be either the black–black card or the black–white card. This gives you a 50–50 chance of winning, so it's a fair game. Come on, let's play!*

Before you agree to play, consider the sample space. Let's start by distinguishing between the front (side 1) and the back (side 2) of each card. The sample space of *equally likely* events is as follows:

Result	Card 1		Card 2		Card 3	
Side showing (side 1)	B_1	B_2	B	W	W_1	W_2
Side not showing (side 2)	B_2	B_1	W	B	W_2	W_1

Let's also assume that, after we select the card, we see that a black side is face up. (If it is a white side that we see, we can repeat the same argument, with colors reversed.) We also see that

$$P(\text{black is face down}) = \frac{3}{6} = \frac{1}{2} \quad \textbf{(This is George's incorrect argument.)}$$

But we have additional information. We wish to compute the *conditional probability* of black on the underside, given that a black card is face up. Alter the sample space to take into account the additional information:

Result	Card 1		Card 2		Card 3	
Side showing (side 1)	B_1	B_2	B	$W\!\!\!/$	$W\!\!\!/_1$	$W\!\!\!/_2$
Side not showing (side 2)	B_2	B_1	W	$B\!\!\!/$	$W\!\!\!/_2$	$W\!\!\!/_1$

Cross these out since black must be on top.

$$P(\text{black is face down} \,|\, \text{black on top}) = \frac{2}{3}$$

This means that, if George picks the color on the bottom to match the color on top, he will have a probability of winning of 2/3, so the probability that we will win is 1/3. We now calculate the expectation:

$$E = (\$1)\left(\frac{1}{3}\right) + (-\$1)\left(\frac{2}{3}\right)$$
$$\approx -\$0.33$$

Since the expectation is negative, you should not play.

PROBLEM SET ⑨.4

ESSENTIAL IDEAS   **LEVEL 1**

1. What is the definition of mathematical expectation?
See p. 475.

2. What is the formula for finding mathematical expectation?
$E = ap - c$

Decide whether each statement in Problems 3–6 is true or false. In addition, explain your reasoning.

3. In roulette, if you bet on black, the probability of winning is $\frac{1}{2}$ because there are the same number of black and red spots.   *F; there are also green spots; $P(\text{black}) = \frac{18}{38} = \frac{9}{19}$.*

4. An expected value of $5 means that you should expect to win $5 each time you play the game.   *F; if you play the game a number of times, the average winnings per game should be $5.*

5. If the expected value of a game is positive, then it is a game you should play.   *T*

6. If you were asked to choose between a sure $10,000, or an 80% chance of winning $15,000 and a 20% chance of winning nothing, which would you take?

Game A:
$E = \$10,000(1) = \$10,000$ *This is a sure thing.*

Game B:
$E = \$15,000(0.8) + \$0(0.2) = \$12,000$

The better choice, according to expected value, is to take the 80% chance of winning $15,000.   *T*

DRILL AND PRACTICE   **LEVEL 2**

Use estimation to select the best response in Problems 7–12. Do not calculate.

7. The expectation from playing a game in which you win $950 by correctly calling heads or tails when you flip a coin is about   *A*
A. $500   B. $50   C. $950

8. The expectation from playing a game in which you win $950 by correctly calling heads or tails on each of five flips of a coin is about   *B*
A. $500   B. $50   C. $950

9. If the expected value of playing a $1 game of blackjack is $0.04, then after playing the game 100 times you should have netted about   *C*
A. $104   B. −$4   C. $4

10. If your expected value when playing a $1 game of roulette is −$0.05, then after playing the game 100 times you should have netted about   *B*
A. −$105   B. −$5   C. $5

11. The probability of correctly guessing a telephone number is about   *C*
A. 1 out of 100
B. 1 out of 1,000
C. 1 out of 10,000,000

© Reuters/Corbis

12. Winning the grand prize in a state lottery is about as probable as   *B*
A. having a car accident
B. having an item fall out of the sky into your yard

Use the mortality table (Table III, Appendix B) to answer the questions in Problems 13–18.

13. What is the expected value of a 1-year, $10,000 policy issued at age 10? **$12.14**

14. What is the expected value of a 1-year, $10,000 policy issued at age 38? **$30.11**

15. What is the expected value of a 1-year, $10,000 policy issued at age 65? **$317.47**

16. What is the expected value of a 1-year, $20,000 policy issued at age 18? **$33.82**

17. What is the expected value of a 1-year, $25,000 policy issued at age 19? **$43.38**

18. What is the expected value of a 1-year, $50,000 policy issued at age 23? **$94.67**

What is the expectation for the $1 bets in Problems 19–28 on a U.S. roulette wheel?

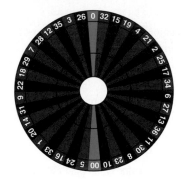

See Figure 9.15 on page 477.

19. Black   −$0.05

20. Odd   −$0.05

21. Single-number bet   −$0.05

22. Double-number bet   −$0.05

23. Three-number bet   −$0.05

24. Four-number bet   −$0.05

25. Five-number bet   −$0.08

26. Six-number bet   −$0.05

27. Twelve-number bet   −$0.05

28. Column bet   −$0.05

APPLICATIONS   **LEVEL 2**

29. Suppose that you roll two dice. You will be paid $5 if you roll a double. You will not receive anything for any other outcome. How much should you be willing to pay for the privilege of rolling the dice? **$0.83**

30. A magazine subscription service is having a contest in which the prize is $80,000. If the company receives 1 million entries, what is the expectation of the contest? **$0.08**

31. A game involves tossing two coins and receiving 50¢ if they are both heads. What is a fair price to pay for the privilege of playing? *A fair price would be to pay $0.25 for two plays of the game.*

32. Suppose that you have 5 quarters, 5 dimes, 10 nickels, and 5 pennies in your pocket. You reach in and choose a coin at random. What is the expectation? What type of coin is most likely to be picked? *This expectation is $0.092, but a nickel is most likely to be picked.*

33. A punch-out card contains 100 spaces. One space pays $100, five spaces pay $10, and the others pay nothing. How much should you pay to punch out one space? **$1.50**

34. A box contains one each of $1, $5, $10, $20, and $100 bills. You reach in and withdraw one bill. What is the expected value? **$27.20**

35. A box contains one each of $1, $5, $10, $20, and $100 bills. It costs $20 to reach in and withdraw one bill. What is the expected value? **$7.20**

36. Krinkles potato chips is having a "Lucky Seven Sweepstakes." The one grand prize is $70,000; 7 second prizes each pay $7,000; 77 third prizes each pay $700; and 777 fourth prizes each pay $70. What is the expectation of this contest (rounded to the nearest cent), if there are 10 million entries? **$0.02**

37. A game involves drawing a single card from an ordinary deck. If an ace is drawn, you receive 50¢; if a heart is drawn, you receive 25¢; if the queen of spades is drawn, you receive $1. If the cost of playing is 10¢, should you play? *E ≈ $0.02; yes, you should play the game.*

38. Consider the following game in which a player rolls a single die. If a prime (2, 3, or 5) is rolled, the player wins $2. If a square (1 or 4) is rolled, the player wins $1. However, if the player rolls a perfect number (6), it costs the player $11. Is this a good deal for the player or not? *The expectation is a loss of $0.50 per play. It is not a good deal.*

39. Suppose that you roll one die. You are paid $5 if you roll a one, and you pay $1 otherwise. What is the expectation? *E = $0*

40. A realtor who takes the listing on a house to be sold knows that she will spend $800 trying to sell the house. If she sells it herself, she will earn 6% of the selling price. If another realtor sells a house from her list, the first realtor will earn only 3% of the price. If the house remains unsold after 6 months, she will lose the listing. Suppose the probabilities are as follows:

Event	Probability
Sell by herself	0.50
Sell by another realtor	0.30
Not sell in 6 months	0.20

What is the expected profit from listing a $185,000 house? **$6,415**

41. An oil-drilling company knows that it costs $25,000 to sink a test well. If oil is hit, the income for the drilling company will be $425,000. If only natural gas is hit, the income will be $125,000. If nothing is hit, there will be no income. If the probability of hitting oil is $\frac{1}{40}$ and if the probability of hitting gas is $\frac{1}{20}$, what is the expectation for the drilling company? Should the company sink the test well?

$E = -\$8,125$; they should not dig since the expectation is negative.

42. In Problem 41, suppose that the income for hitting oil is changed to $825,000 and the income for gas to $225,000. Now what is the expectation for the drilling company? Should the company sink the test well? $E = \$6,875$; They should dig the well since the expectation is positive.

Consider the spinners in Problems 43–46. Determine which represent fair games. Assume that the cost to spin the wheel once is $5.00 and that you will receive the amount shown on the spinner after it stops.

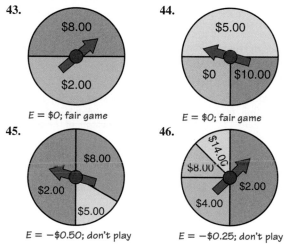

43. $8.00 / $2.00
$E = \$0$; fair game

44. $5.00 / $0 / $10.00
$E = \$0$; fair game

45. $8.00 / $2.00 / $5.00
$E = -\$0.50$; don't play

46. $14.00 / $8.00 / $2.00 / $4.00
$E = -\$0.25$; don't play

47. Assume that a dart is randomly thrown at the following dart board and strikes the board every time. The payoffs are listed on the board. How much should you be willing to pay for the opportunity to play this game?

$1.00	$6.00
	$8.00 $10.00
	$4.00

Since $E = \$4$, pay any amount up to $4.00.

48. Assume that a dart is randomly thrown at the following dart board and strikes the board every time. The payoffs are listed on the board. How much should you be willing to pay for the opportunity to play this game?

$16	−$5
$8 $2 $1	
$4	

Since $E \approx \$2.84$, pay any amount up to $2.84.

49. A company held a contest, and the following information was included in the fine print:

$ WIN $ WIN $

PRIZE	NUMBER OF PRIZES	PROBABILITY OF WINNING INDICATED PRIZE
$10,000	13	0.000005
$1,000	52	0.00002
$100	520	0.0002
$10	28,900	0.010886
TOTAL	**29,485**	**0.011111**

$E \approx 0.19886$ or about $0.20

Read this information carefully, and calculate the expectation (to the nearest cent) for this contest.

50. A company held a bingo contest for which the following chances of winning were given:

PLAY *ONE* CARD *AND WIN*
YOUR CHANCES OF WINNING ARE AT LEAST:

	1 TIME	7 TIMES	13 TIMES
$25 prize	1 in 21,252	1 in 3,036	1 in 1,630
$3 prize	1 in 2,125	1 in 304	1 in 163
$1 prize	1 in 886	1 in 127	1 in 68
Any prize	1 in 609	1 in 87	1 in 47

$E \approx 0.0484482136$ or about $0.05

What is the expectation (to the nearest cent) from playing one card 13 times?

51. Calculate the expectation (to the nearest cent) for the *Reader's Digest* sweepstakes described below. Assume there are 197,000,000 entries.

$10,500,000.00
SWEEPSTAKES ENTRY DOCUMENT

Official Disclosure of Dates
To be eligible to win the FIVE MILLION DOLLAR Grand Prize, you must return the attached Sweepstakes Entry Document by August 19, 1991. Failure to respond by that date will result in the forfeiture of Grand Prize eligibility. To be eligible to win any of 58,567 other prizes (but not the Grand Prize) return your Sweepstakes Entry Document by March 2, 1992.

Grand Prize Distribution Information
If you are chosen Grand Prize winner, you will receive FIVE MILLION DOLLARS in your choice of payment options: Either 30 equal yearly payments of $167,000.00 each OR 360 equal monthly payments of $14,000.00 each. You must specify your choice of payment option now by detaching the appropriate card at left and affixing it to the box provided on your Sweepstakes Entry Document.

OFFICIAL PRIZE LIST

1 First Prize $100,000.00
2 Second Prizes.....................$50,000.00
3 Third Prizes $20,000.00
4 Fourth Prizes $5,000.00
10 Fifth Prizes $500.00
400 Sixth Prizes $100.00
58,147 Seventh Prizes.....Winner's choice of a "Special Edition" Men's or Women's wristwatch, at an $89.00 approximate retail value.

Sponsor *D. P. Burr*
SWEEPSTAKES DIRECTOR

$E \approx 0.0532999137$ or about $0.05

In a card game called blackjack, each player is dealt two cards. One of the dealer's cards is exposed so that it can be seen by all players. The object is to have cards totaling 21. Face cards are worth 10 points, aces are worth 1 or 11 points, and all other cards are worth their face value Suppose you have bet $12 and are dealt a five and a six with the dealer showing an ace. The dealer asks if you want insurance. *If you say "yes" you are betting $6 that the dealer has a face card or a 10 as the second card. If so, you win $12 on this bet. In Problems 52–53, decide whether you should take "insurance."*

52. You are playing with a single deck of 52 cards.
See bottom of the column.
53. You are playing with four decks, a total of 208 cards.
See bottom of the column.

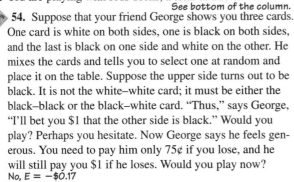

54. Suppose that your friend George shows you three cards. One card is white on both sides, one is black on both sides, and the last is black on one side and white on the other. He mixes the cards and tells you to select one at random and place it on the table. Suppose the upper side turns out to be black. It is not the white–white card; it must be either the black–black or the black–white card. "Thus," says George, "I'll bet you $1 that the other side is black." Would you play? Perhaps you hesitate. Now George says he feels generous. You need to pay him only 75¢ if you lose, and he will still pay you $1 if he loses. Would you play now? No, $E = -\$0.17$

RIGHT OR WRONG?   LEVEL 3

Explain what is wrong, if anything, with the statements in Problems 55–60. Explain your reasoning.

55. According to an article written for *Futures* magazine, the developer of the AIM trading system, Bill A. Sadek, gives the mathematical expectation for trading in certain foreign currencies as shown in the following table.

Currencies	Mathematical Expectation
Australian dollar	14.0
British pound	45.0
Canadian dollar	10.0
American dollar	43.0
Euro	84.0

According to this table, the best investing choice would be to trade currencies in the American dollar.
F; the highest expectation is the Euro.

52. There are 49 unseen cards. $E = \frac{16}{49}(\$12) + \frac{33}{49}(-\$6) \approx -\$0.12$. Since the expectation is negative, the player should not take insurance.

53. There are 205 unseen cards. $E = \frac{64}{205}(\$12) + \frac{141}{205}(-\$6) \approx -\$0.38$. Since the expectation is negative, the player should not take insurance.

56. According to an article written for *Futures* magazine, the developer of the AIM trading system, Bill A. Sadek, gives the mathematical expectation for trading in commodities as shown in the following table.

Commodities	Mathematical Expectation
Butter	129.0
Feeder cattle	21.0
Lean hogs	11.0
Live cattle	−5.0
Pork bellies	−15.0

According to this table, the best investing choice would be pork bellies because that commodity has the best chance of increasing in the future.   F; the worst choice is the smallest expectation, which is pork bellies.

57. If you were asked to choose between a sure $10 or a 1% chance of winning $10,000, you should take $10 because it is a sure thing, and the thousand dollars will happen only one time out of a hundred.   *See bottom of the column.*

58. The probability to win $1,000,000 in a sweepstakes is one in a million. It is reasonable to buy a $1 ticket because
See bottom of the column.
$$E = \$1,000,000\left(\frac{1}{1,000,000}\right) = \$1$$

59. Suppose that you buy a lottery ticket for $1. The payoff is $50,000 with a probability of winning 1/1,000,000. Therefore, the expected value is
$$E = \$50,000\left(\frac{1}{1,000,000}\right) = \$0.05$$
F; the $1 cost of the ticket is not taken into account.

60. Suppose you pay $1. The payoff is $50 with odds against winning 99 to 1. Then the expected value is
$$E = (\$50 - \$1)\left(\frac{1}{99}\right) + (-\$1)\left(\frac{98}{99}\right) = -\$0.49$$

F; change odds to a probability; $\$50(\frac{1}{100}) - \$1 = -\$0.50$

57. F; consider Game #1: $E = \$10(1) = \$10$; Game #2: $E = \$10,000(0.01) = \$100$; Game #2 is better, since it has the higher expectation.
58. F; there is a cost of playing; $\$999,999(\frac{1}{1,000,000}) - \$1 = -\$0.95$

9.5 Chapter 9 Summary and Review

Take some time getting ready to work the review problems in this section. First, look back at the definition and property boxes. You will maximize your understanding of this chapter by working the problems in this section only after you have studied the material.

IMPORTANT TERMS

Numbers refer to sections of this chapter.

Spending some time with the terms and objectives of this chapter will pay dividends in assuring your success.

Cards (sample space) [9.1]
Complementary probabilities [9.2]
Conditional probability [9.3]
Dice (sample space) [9.1]
Die (sample space) [9.1]
Equally likely outcomes [9.1]
Event [9.1]
Expectation [9.4]
Expected value [9.4]

Experiment [9.1]
Fair coin [9.1]
Fair game [9.4]
Fundamental counting principle [9.2]
Impossible event [9.1]
Loaded die [9.1]
Mathematical expectation [9.4]
Mortality table [9.4]
Mutually exclusive [9.1]

Odds against [9.3]
Odds in favor [9.3]
Poker hands [9.1]
Probability [9.4]
Property of complements [9.2]
Roulette wheel [9.4]
Sample space [9.1]
Simple event [9.1]
Tree diagram [9.1]

Essential Ideas

[9.1]	Problems 1–3	Know the formula for finding probability and the conditions for using that formula, as well as the terms *event* and *sample space*.
	Problems 4–5	Know how to translate the probability of a union and the probability of an intersection.
[9.2]	Problem 1	Find complementary probabilities.
	Problem 2	Know the fundamental counting principle.
[9.3]	Problem 1	Distinguish probability and conditional probability.
	Problems 2–4	Distinguish probability and odds, including numerically converting one to the other.
[9.4]	Problems 1–2	Define mathematical expectation and know the formula for finding it.
	Problems 3–6	Apply the basic concept of mathematical expectation.

LEARNING OUTCOMES

The material in this chapter is reviewed in the following list of learning outcomes. A self-test (with answers and suggestions for additional study) is given. This self-test is constructed so that each problem number corresponds to a related objective. For example, Problem 7 is testing Objective 9.7. This self-test is followed by a practice test with the questions in mixed order.

[9.1]	*Objective* 9.1	Understand and apply the definition of probability.
[9.1]	*Objective* 9.2	Find probabilities by looking at the sample space.
[9.1]	*Objective* 9.3	Find an empirical probability using the definition of probability.
[9.1]	*Objective* 9.4	Find probabilities using a deck of cards. (See Figure 9.6.)
[9.1]	*Objective* 9.5	Find probabilities involving the union and intersection of events by looking at the sample space.

Self-Test

Each question of this self-test is related to the corresponding objective listed above.

1. a. What is the formula for finding probability?
  b. What are the conditions for using this formula?
  c. Discuss how you might use probability outside the classroom.

2. What is the probability of rolling a single die and obtaining a prime?

3. Roll a pair of dice. Find the following.
  a. $P(5$ on one of the dice)
  b. $P(5$ on one die or 4 on the other)
  c. $P(5$ on one die and 4 on the other)

4. If a sample of 1,000 items from an assembly line reveals four defective items, what is the probability that any one item is defective?

5. A card is selected from an ordinary deck of cards. What is the probability that it is a jack or better? (A jack or better is a jack, queen, king, or ace.)

6. A pair of dice is rolled. What is the probability that the resulting sum is eight?

7. Rank the following events from least likely to most likely:
  An event A has odds in favor of winning of 10 to 1.
  An event B has odds against winning of 10 to 1.
  An event C has a probability of one-half.

8. If the probability of dropping an egg is 0.01, what is the probability of not dropping the egg?

9. How many license plates can be issued by a state using a scheme of two letters followed by four numerals?

10. If $P(E) = 0.9$, what are the odds in favor of E?

11. If the odds against an event are 1,000 to 1, what is the probability of the event?

12. Two cards are drawn from a standard deck of cards. (The first card is selected and is not returned to the deck before the second card is drawn.) What is the probability that the second card is an ace, if you know that the first card drawn was an ace?

13. What are the odds against obtaining a pair when rolling a pair of dice?

14. A game consists of rolling a die and receiving $12 if a one is rolled and nothing otherwise. What is the mathematical expectation?

15. What is the expected value for a $100,000 life insurance policy issued at age 24?

16. What is the mathematical expectation for betting $100 on black in a roulette game?

17. In a TV game show, four prizes are hidden on a game board with 20 spaces. One prize is worth $10,000, two prizes are each worth $5,000, and the other prize is worth $1,000. The remaining spaces contain no prizes. The game show host offers a sure prize of $1,000 not to play this game. Should the contestant choose the sure prize or play the game?

18. Consider a game in which you roll a pair of dice. Suppose you are paid $7.20 if you roll a pair, and nothing otherwise. If you are asked to pay $1 to play this game, is it a fair game? If it is not fair, is it unfair to your benefit or to your detriment?

19. In old gangster movies on TV, you often hear of "numbers runners" or the "numbers racket." This numbers game, which is still played today, involves betting $1 on the last three digits of the number of stocks sold on a particular day in the future as reported in *The Wall Street Journal*. If the payoff is $500, what is the expectation for this numbers game?

20. Which one of the following events has odds against of about a million to one?
    A. Selecting a particular Social Security number by picking the digits at random
    B. Selecting a particular phone number at random if the first digit is known
    C. Winning first prize in a state lottery

STUDY HINTS *Compare your solutions and answers to the self-test. For each problem you missed, work some additional problems in the section listed in the margin. After you have worked these problems, you can test yourself with the practice test.*

Additional Problems

[9.1] Problem 3

[9.1] Problems 6–10

[9.2] Problems 11–14

[9.1] Problems 15–16; 26–27; 32–35

[9.1] Problems 17–20; 36–39

[9.1] Problems 21–25; 40–42

[9.2] Problems 3–8

[9.4] Problems 7–12

[9.2] Problems 9–29

Complete Solutions to the Self-Test

1. **a.** $P(E) = \frac{s}{n}$, where s is the number of successes with n possible outcomes.

   b. The outcomes must be mutually exclusive and equally likely.

   c. Answers vary; you can use probability in making business decisions (real estate broker example), deciding on a life insurance policy (mortality table), or critically reading news articles (understanding the likelihood of rain).

2. The possible primes are 2, 3, and 5 so $P(\text{prime}) = \frac{3}{6} = \frac{1}{2}$.

3. Look at Figure 9.8.

   a. $P(5 \text{ on one of the dice}) = \frac{11}{36}$

   b. $P(5 \text{ on one die or 4 on the other}) = \frac{20}{36} = \frac{5}{9}$

   c. $P(5 \text{ on one die and 4 on the other}) = \frac{2}{36} = \frac{1}{18}$

4. $P(\text{defective}) = \frac{4}{1,000} = 0.004$

5. Look at Figure 9.6. $P(\text{jack or better}) = \frac{16}{52} = \frac{4}{13}$

6. Look at Figure 9.8. $P(\text{eight}) = \frac{5}{36}$

7. Event A is very likely, event B is not very likely, and event C is in the middle. Thus, the correct order is B, C, A.

8. $P(E) = 0.01; P(\overline{E}) = 1 - P(E)$

$$= 1 - 0.01$$

$$= 0.99$$

9. Use the fundamental counting principle:

$$26 \times 26 \times 10 \times 10 \times 10 \times 10 = 6{,}760{,}000$$

10. We are given the probability; $P(E) = \frac{9}{10}$;

$$P(\overline{E}) = 1 - \frac{9}{10}$$
$$= \frac{1}{10}$$

Now, find the odds:

$$\text{Odds in favor} = \frac{P(E)}{P(\overline{E})}$$
$$= \frac{\frac{9}{10}}{\frac{1}{10}}$$
$$= \frac{9}{10} \cdot \frac{10}{1}$$
$$= \frac{9}{1}$$

The odds are 9 to 1.

11. Let E be the event. Given $f = 1{,}000$ and $s = 1$,

$$P(E) = \frac{s}{s+f}$$
$$= \frac{1}{1{,}000 + 1}$$
$$= \frac{1}{1{,}001}$$

12. The altered sample space (after removing the card) has 51 cards, 3 of which should be considered success.

$$P(\text{ace}) = \frac{3}{51} = \frac{1}{17}$$

13. Using Figure 9.8, we see that $n = 36$, $s = 6$, and $f = 30$. Odds against are f to s or 30 to 6. This can be reduced to odds against as 5 to 1.

14. $E = P(\text{one}) \cdot \$12$

$$= \frac{1}{6}(12)$$
$$= 2$$

The expected value is $2.

15. $E = \$100{,}000 \left(\dfrac{183}{95{,}940} \right)$ **From Table III in Appendix B.**

$$\approx \$190.74$$

The expected value is $190.74.

16. Use Figure 9.15, and note that a bet on black is an even-money bet.

$$E = \$100 \left(\frac{18}{38} \right) - \$100 \left(\frac{20}{38} \right) = -\$5.26$$

The mathematical expectation is a loss of about $5.26.

17. There are 20 equally likely choices (spaces). We calculate the mathematical expectation.

$$E = \$10,000\left(\frac{1}{20}\right) + \$5,000\left(\frac{2}{20}\right) + \$1,000\left(\frac{1}{20}\right)$$

$$= \$1,050$$

If we compare this expectation with the offer from the game show host, we see that the correct decision is to refuse the host and play the game.

18. A game is fair if the mathematical expectation is $0. If necessary, you can look at the sample space for rolling a pair of dice in Figure 9.8.

$$E = \$7.20\left(\frac{1}{6}\right) - \$1.00 = \$0.20$$

This is not a fair game, and it is unfair to the player's benefit.

19. $E = 500(0.001) - 1 = -0.5$ or $-\$0.50$

20. A typical Social Security number is 555-55-5555, so by the fundamental counting principle, the odds are about 1 in 10^9. A typical phone number is 555-1234; if the first digit is known, the odds are about 1 in 10^6. A state lottery almost always has more than a million entries; the best choice is B.

Chapter 9 Review Questions

*To prepare for a chapter test, first study the chapter; then, read each term from the important terms list above and make sure you know the meaning of each word; finally, review the chapter objectives. **After** these steps, take the self-test and correct all your answers. The following review questions can be used for extra practice.*

1. IN YOUR OWN WORDS Define probability; explain the words "equally likely and mutually exclusive."

2. If a spinner has 18 red, 18 black, and 2 green compartments, what is the probability of landing on a green in one spin of the wheel? $\frac{1}{19}$

3. If a jar contains 25 blue marbles, 55 cat-eye marbles, and 20 clear marbles, what is the probability of obtaining a clear marble when one marble is chosen from the jar? Assume that all marbles have an equal chance of being drawn. $\frac{1}{5}$

4. A die is rolled. What is the probability that it comes up:
   a. a three? $\frac{1}{6}$ **b.** a four? $\frac{1}{6}$ **c.** a three and a four? 0
   d. even? $\frac{1}{2}$ **e.** odd? $\frac{1}{2}$ **f.** an even or an odd? 1

5. A pair of dice is tossed. What is the probability that the sum is:
   a. six? $\frac{5}{36}$ **b.** seven? $\frac{1}{6}$

6. A card is selected from an ordinary deck of cards. What is the probability that it comes up
   a. a diamond? $\frac{1}{4}$ **b.** a two? $\frac{1}{13}$ **c.** a diamond and a two? $\frac{1}{52}$

7. A card is selected from an ordinary deck of cards. What is the probability that it comes up
   a. a king? $\frac{1}{13}$ **b.** a heart? $\frac{1}{4}$ **c.** a king or a heart? $\frac{4}{13}$

8. Consider a pair of dice in which each die has three green faces, two red faces, and one yellow face. Roll the pair of dice. Write out the sample space and find the probability of obtaining two faces of the same color with one roll of the pair of dice.
   See IAS for sample space; P(same color faces) = $\frac{7}{18}$

9. Using the sample space from Problem 8, find the following.
   a. P(both green) $\frac{1}{4}$ b. P(both red) $\frac{1}{9}$ c. P(both yellow) $\frac{1}{36}$

10. If $P(A) = \frac{5}{11}$, what is $P(\overline{A})$? $\frac{6}{11}$

11. If the probability of drawing a defective item from an assembly line is 0.09, what is the probability of not drawing a defective item? 0.91

12. What is the probability of having a phone number with at least one repeated digit? (Assume the phone numbers are assigned randomly and also that the first digit cannot be a 0 or a 1.) See bottom of the page.

13. A coin is tossed four times. What is the probability of obtaining at least one tail? $\frac{15}{16}$

14. What are the odds in favor of drawing a heart from an ordinary deck of cards? 1 to 3

15. If the odds in favor of a particular event are 20 to 1, what is the probability of that event? $\frac{20}{21}$

16. According to the Internal Revenue Service, the odds against having a corporate tax return being audited are 15 to 1. What is the probability that a corporate tax return will be audited? $\frac{1}{16}$

17. If Ferdinand the Frog has twice as good a chance of winning the jumping contest as either one of the other two champion frogs, what is the probability of Ferdinand winning (stated as a percent)? What are the odds in favor of Ferdinand winning? 50%; 1 to 1

18. A jar contains three orange balls and two purple balls. Two balls are chosen at random. What is the probability of obtaining two orange balls if we know that the first ball drawn was orange and if we draw the second ball without replacing the first ball? $\frac{1}{2}$

19. Repeat Problem 18, except replace the first ball before drawing the second ball. $\frac{3}{5}$

20. What is the probability that a family of four children will contain two boys and two girls, given that the first child was a boy? $\frac{3}{8}$

21. A single card is drawn from a standard deck of cards. What is the probability that it is a king, if you know that it is a face card? $\frac{1}{3}$

22. A game consists of cutting a standard deck of cards. You win $2 if a face card turns up, but you lose $1 otherwise. Should you play? No, the expectation is about −$0.31 per game.

23. What is the expected value of a $50,000 life insurance policy issued at age 25? $96.60

24. A lottery offers a prize of a color TV set (value $500), and 800 tickets are sold.
    a. What is the expectation if you buy three tickets? E = $1.88
    b. If the tickets cost $1 each, should you buy them? no
    c. How much should you be willing to pay for the three tickets? $1.87

25. **IN YOUR OWN WORDS** Explain mathematical expectation using your own words. Tell why it is a useful concept, and give some examples of when you might use mathematical expectation.

12. $P(\text{repeated digit}) = 1 - P(\text{no repeated digit}) = 1 - \frac{8 \cdot 9 \cdot 8 \cdot 7 \cdot 6 \cdot 5 \cdot 4}{8 \cdot 10 \cdot 10 \cdot 10 \cdot 10 \cdot 10 \cdot 10} = 0.93952$

Individual Projects

Learning to use sources outside your classroom and textbook is an important skill, and here are some ideas for extending some of the ideas in this chapter.

PROJECT 9.1   The old lady jumping rope in the following cartoon is counting one at a time.

Cartoon by Doug. Reprinted by permission from *The Saturday Evening Post* © 1976.

"Five trillion, four hundred eighty billion, five hundred twenty-three million, two hundred ninety-seven thousand, one hundred and sixty-two. . ."

Assume that she jumps rope 50 times per minute, and that she jumps 8 hours per day, 5 days a week, 50 weeks a year. Estimate the length of time necessary for her to jump the rope the number of times indicated in the cartoon.   *over 9,000 centuries*

PROJECT 9.2   The following news clip describes the longest paper-link chain.

> According to the *Guinness Book of World Records*, the longest recorded paper-link chain was 6,077 ft long and was made by the first- and second-grade children at Rose City Elementary School, Indiana.

If there are 12 paper links per foot, and it takes 1 minute to construct each link, estimate the length of time necessary to build this paper-link chain if the class takes 30 minutes per day, five times per week. Assume there are 20 students working on this project.   *1/2 year*

PROJECT 9.3   The following news clip presents an argument proving that at least two New Yorkers must have *exactly* the same number of hairs on their heads.

> An example about reaching a conclusion about the number of objects in a set is given by M. Cohen and E. Nagel in *An Introduction to Logic*. They conclude that there are at least two people in New York City who have the same number of hairs on their heads. This conclusion was reached not through counting the hairs on the heads of 8 million inhabitants of the city, but through studies revealing that: (1) the maximum number of hairs on the human scalp could never be as many as 5,000 per square centimeter, and (2) the maximum area of the human scalp could never reach 1,000 square centimeters. We can now conclude that no human head could contain even
>
> $$5,000 \times 1,000 = 5,000,000$$
>
> hairs. Since this number is less than the population of New York City, it follows that at least two New Yorkers must have the same number of hairs on their heads!

For this problem, just *suppose* you knew the number of hairs on your head, as well as the *exact* number of hairs on everyone else's head. Now multiply the number of hairs on your head by the number of hairs on your neighbor's head. Take this result and multiply by the number of hairs on the heads of each person in your town or city. Continue this process until you have done this for everyone in the entire world! Make a guess (you can use scientific notation, if you like) about the size of this answer. *Hint:* The author has worked this out and claims to know the *exact* answer.   o

PROJECT 9.4   We see examples of probability every day. Weather forecasts, stock market analyses, contests, children's games, television game shows, and gambling all involve ideas of probability. Search current newspapers and magazines to provide examples of probability. After looking for at least a week, collate your material to present a portfolio of the examples you have found.

Team Projects

Working in small groups is typical of most work environments, and learning to work with others to communicate specific ideas is an important skill. Work with three or four other students to submit a single report based on each of the following questions.

T24. **Experiment**   Consider the following birth dates of some famous mathematicians:

Mathematician	Birthday
Niels Abel	August 5, 1802
Girolamo Cardano	September 24, 1501
René Descartes	March 31, 1596
Leonhard Euler	April 15, 1707
Pierre de Fermat	August 17, 1601
Evariste Galois	October 25, 1811
Karl Gauss	April 30, 1777
Isaac Newton	December 25, 1642
Blaise Pascal	June 19, 1623
Georg Riemann	September 17, 1826
Andrew Wiles	April 11, 1953

Add to this list the birth dates of the members of your class. *But before you compile this list, guess the probability that at least two people in this group will have exactly the same birthday (not counting the year).* Be sure to make your guess *before* finding out the birth dates of your classmates. The answer, of course, depends on the number of people on the list. Eleven mathematicians are listed and you may have 20 people in your class, giving 31 names on the list.

T25. **Birthday problem**   Suppose that you select 23 people out of a crowd.

© Herb Watson/Corbis

The probability that two or more of them will have the same birthday is greater than 50%! This seemingly paradoxical situation will fool most people. Figure 9.16 is a chart showing these probabilities.

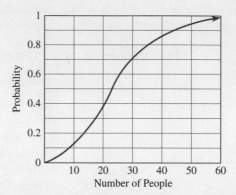

Figure 9.16 Probabilities for the birthday problem

a. Pick 23 names at random from a biographical dictionary or a *Who's Who*, and verify some of the probabilities of the table. The further you go past 23, the greater the probability of finding two people with the same birthday.

b. The graph (Figure 9.16) is approaching a probability of 1 as the number of people increases. How many people are necessary for the probability actually to reach 1?   **367**

T26. **a.** Suppose your instructor makes the following offer. Each member of the team is given a piece of paper as shown here and asked to check one of the boxes, *without* communication with other members of the team.

> ☐ I share the wealth and will receive $1,000 if *everyone* in the class checks this box.
>
> ☐ I will not share the wealth and want a certain $100.

If *everyone* on your team checks the first box, then all will receive $1,000. If at least *one* person on your team checks the second box, then only those who check the second box will receive $100. Which box would you check, and why?

b. Repeat except change the stakes to $110 and $100, respectively.

c. Repeat except change the stakes to $10,000 and $10, respectively.

d. Repeat except change the stakes to be an A grade if *everyone* on your team checks the first box, but if anyone checks the second box, the following will occur: Those who check it will have a 50% chance of an A and a 50% chance of a F, but those who do not check the second box will be given an F in this course.

T27. Repeat the steps in Project T26, but instead of asking the questions of your teammates, do the same for your entire class.

T28. **The game of WIN** Construct a set of nonstandard dice as shown in Figure 9.17.

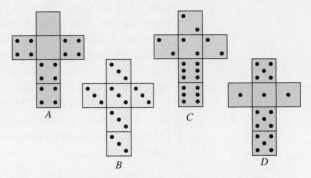

Figure 9.17 Faces on the dice for a game of WIN

Suppose that your opponent picks die *A* and that you pick die *B*. Then we can enumerate the sample space as shown here.

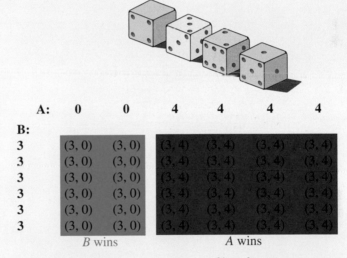

A:	0	0	4	4	4	4
B:						
3	(3, 0)	(3, 0)	(3, 4)	(3, 4)	(3, 4)	(3, 4)
3	(3, 0)	(3, 0)	(3, 4)	(3, 4)	(3, 4)	(3, 4)
3	(3, 0)	(3, 0)	(3, 4)	(3, 4)	(3, 4)	(3, 4)
3	(3, 0)	(3, 0)	(3, 4)	(3, 4)	(3, 4)	(3, 4)
3	(3, 0)	(3, 0)	(3, 4)	(3, 4)	(3, 4)	(3, 4)
3	(3, 0)	(3, 0)	(3, 4)	(3, 4)	(3, 4)	(3, 4)

B wins   *A* wins

We see that the probability of *A* winning is $\frac{24}{36}$, or $\frac{2}{3}$. If you were to play the game of WIN, would you choose your die first or second? *Choose second; A beats B, B beats C, C beats D, but D beats A! See IAS.*

T29. **St. Petersburg paradox**

a. $E = \$1\left(\frac{1}{2}\right) + \$2\left(\frac{1}{4}\right) + \$4\left(\frac{1}{8}\right) = \$1.50$

b. $E = \$1\left(\frac{1}{2}\right) + \$2\left(\frac{1}{4}\right) + \$4\left(\frac{1}{8}\right) + \cdots = \$5.00$

a. Suppose that you toss a coin and will win $1 if it comes up heads. If it comes up tails, you toss again. This time you will receive $2 if it comes up heads. If it comes up tails, toss again. This time you will receive $4 if it is heads and nothing if it comes up tails. What is the mathematical expectation for this game?

b. Suppose that you toss a coin and will win $1 if it comes up heads. If it comes up tails, you toss again. This time you will receive $2 if it comes up heads. If it comes up tails, toss again. This time you will receive $4 if it is heads. Continue in this fashion for a total of 10 flips of the coin, after which you receive nothing if it comes up tails. What is the mathematical expectation for this game?

$E = \$1\left(\frac{1}{2}\right) + \$2\left(\frac{1}{4}\right) + \$4\left(\frac{1}{8}\right) + \cdots$
$= \$500.00$

c. Suppose that you toss a coin and will win \$1 if it comes up heads. If it comes up tails, you toss again. This time you will receive \$2 if it comes up heads. If it comes up tails, toss again. This time you will receive \$4 if it is heads. Continue in this fashion for a total of 1,000 flips of the coin, after which you receive nothing if it comes up tails. What is the mathematical expectation for this game?

d. Suppose that you toss a coin and will win \$1 if it comes up heads. If it comes up tails, you toss again. This time you will receive \$2 if it comes up heads. If it comes up tails, toss again. This time you will receive \$4 if it is heads. You continue in this fashion until you finally toss a head. Would you pay \$100 for the privilege of playing this game? What is the mathematical expectation for this game? *Note:*

$$E = \$1\left(\frac{1}{2}\right) + \$2\left(\frac{1}{4}\right) + \$4\left(\frac{1}{8}\right) + \$8\left(\frac{1}{16}\right) + \cdots$$

$$= \$0.50 + \$0.50 + \$0.50 + \cdots \qquad \text{yes; pay any amount; } E \text{ is infinite.}$$

Statistics

Say you were standing with one foot in the oven and one foot in an ice bucket. According to the law of averages, you should be perfectly comfortable.

Bobby Bragan, 1963

ANTICIPATE

- *Overview; check out contents, terms, essential ideas, and learning outcomes.*

-

- *What do you know of statistics already?*

- *Statistics on population growth or cost of living*

- *Information about the depletion of the rain forests or global warming*

- *The Gallup Poll's use of statistics to predict election outcomes*

- *The Nielsen ratings, which indicate that one show has 30% more viewers than another*

- *Baseball or sports statistics*

- *Two uses of **statistics**; refers to data and the methodology of collecting, analyzing, and interpreting them. This is called descriptive statistics.*

10.1 Frequency Distributions and Graphs

IN THIS WORLD THE UTILITY OF MATH

Caffeine . . . What is caffeine addiction? Nine out of ten Americans use caffeine.*

© Tony Freeman/PhotoEdit

We see graphs on television in the form of advertising and we remember slogans such as "Kids Prefer Del Monte fruit cups," "Nine out of ten dentists recommend Trident for their patients who chew gum," "Crest has been shown to be . . . ," "You can clearly see that Bufferin is the most effective . . . ," "Penzoil is better suited . . . ," "Sylvania was preferred by . . . ."

"How can anyone analyze the claims of the commercials we see and hear on a daily basis?" asked Betty. "I even subscribe to Consumer Reports, *but so many of the claims seem to be unreasonable. I don't like to buy items by trial and error, and I really don't believe all the claims in advertisements."*

 See Problem 55.

Frequency Distributions

The first step in dealing with and understanding statistics is to think critically and understand some of the ways in which data can be organized. Computers, spreadsheets, and simulation programs have done a lot to help us deal with hundreds or thousands of pieces of information at the same time.

We can deal with large batches of data by organizing them into groups, or **classes.** The difference between the lower limit of one class and the lower limit of the next class is called the **interval** of the class. After determining the number of values within a class, termed the **frequency,** you can use this information to summarize the data. The end result of this classification and tabulation is called a **frequency distribution.** For example, suppose that you roll a pair of dice 50 times and obtain these outcomes:

3, 2, 6, 5, 3, 8, 8, 7, 10, 9, 7, 5, 12, 9, 6, 11, 8, 11, 11, 8, 7, 7, 7, 10, 11,
6, 4, 8, 8, 7, 6, 4, 10, 7, 9, 7, 9, 6, 6, 9, 4, 4, 6, 3, 4, 10, 6, 9, 6, 11

We can organize these data in a convenient way by using a frequency distribution, as shown in Table 10.1.

*Brave News World, Fall 2005, Journalism JRN 410 led by Professor Anthony Curtis, Department of Mass Communications, University of North Carolina at Pembroke.

TABLE 10.1	**Frequency Distribution for 50 Rolls of a Pair of Dice**					
Outcome	**Tally**	**Frequency**		**Outcome**	**Tally**	**Frequency**
2	I	1		8	ЖИ I	6
3	III	3		9	ЖИ I	6
4	ЖИ	5		10	IIII	4
5	II	2		11	ЖИ	5
6	ЖИ IIII	9		12	I	1
7	ЖИ III	8				

We will use the sales tax rates for each of the 50 states as a source of data for several examples and applications. This information is summarized in Table 10.2.

TABLE 10.2	**State Sales Tax Rates***								
Alabama	4%	Hawaii	4%	Massachusetts	5%	New Mexico	5%	South Dakota	4%
Alaska	0%	Idaho	6%	Michigan	6%	New York	4%	Tennessee	7%
Arizona	5.6%	Illinois	$6\frac{1}{4}$%	Minnesota	$6\frac{1}{2}$%	North Carolina	4.5%	Texas	6.25%
Arkansas	6%	Indiana	6%	Mississippi	7%	North Dakota	5%	Utah	$4\frac{3}{4}$%
California	6%	Iowa	5%	Missouri	4.225%	Ohio	5.5%	Vermont	6%
Colorado	2.9%	Kansas	5.3%	Montana	0%	Oklahoma	4.5%	Virginia	4%
Connecticut	6%	Kentucky	6%	Nebraska	5.5%	Oregon	0%	Washington	$6\frac{1}{2}$%
Delaware	0%	Louisiana	4%	Nevada	6.5%	Pennsylvania	6%	West Virginia	6%
Florida	6%	Maine	5%	New Hampshire	0%	Rhode Island	7%	Wisconsin	5%
Georgia	4%	Maryland	5%	New Jersey	6%	South Carolina	5%	Wyoming	4%

*Does not include local sales taxes. *Source:* Sales Tax Clearinghouse. © 1999–2006. All rights reserved. Reprinted by permission.

EXAMPLE 1   **Making a frequency distribution**

Make a frequency distribution for the information in Table 10.2.

Solution   Make three columns. First, list the sales tax categories; next, tally; and finally, count the tallies to determine the frequency of each. To account for irregularities (such as $4\frac{3}{4}$%), the categories are often grouped. For this example, the data are divided into 8 categories (or groups) in the **grouped frequency distribution** as shown here. The number of categories is usually arbitrary and chosen for convenience.

Sales Tax, t	Tally	Frequency
$0\% \leq t < 1\%$	ЖИ	5
$1\% \leq t < 2\%$		0
$2\% \leq t < 3\%$	I	1
$3\% \leq t < 4\%$		0
$4\% \leq t < 5\%$	ЖИ ЖИ II	12
$5\% \leq t < 6\%$	ЖИ ЖИ II	12
$6\% \leq t < 7\%$	ЖИ ЖИ ЖИ II	17
$t \geq 7\%$	III	3

Bar Graphs

A **bar graph** compares several related pieces of data using horizontal or vertical bars of uniform width. There must be some type of scale of measurement on both the horizontal and vertical axes. An example of a bar graph is shown in Figure 10.1, which shows the data from Table 10.1.

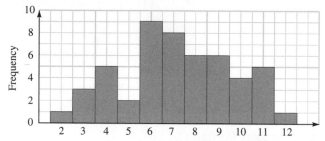

Figure 10.1 Outcomes of experiment of rolling a pair of dice

EXAMPLE 2

Constructing a bar graph

Construct a bar graph for the sales tax data given in Table 10.2. Use the grouped categories.

Solution To construct a bar graph, draw and label the horizontal and vertical axes, as shown in Figure 10.2**a.** It is helpful (although not necessary) to use graph paper. Next, draw marks indicating the frequencies as shown in Figure 10.2**b.** Finally, complete the bars and shade them as shown in Figure 10.2**c.**

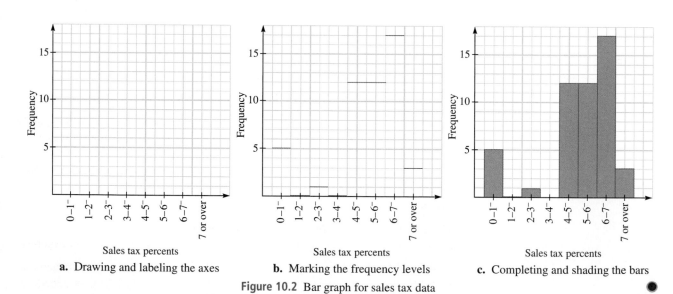

a. Drawing and labeling the axes   **b.** Marking the frequency levels   **c.** Completing and shading the bars

Figure 10.2 Bar graph for sales tax data

If a bar graph represents a frequency distribution (as in Figure 10.1), it is called a **histogram.** A histogram consists of a series of equal-width bars drawn on a horizontal axis; the height of the bar for a given category is drawn in proportion to the frequency of values that occur in that category.

You will frequently need to look at and interpret bar graphs in which bars of different lengths are used for comparison.

| EXAMPLE 3 | **Reading a bar graph** |

Refer to Figure 10.3 to answer the following questions.

a. Who is the favorite in the election poll?

b. What percent of the voters favored Becker in July 2008?

c. In which month was the undecided vote the greatest?

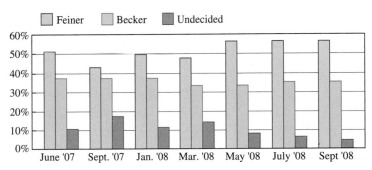

Figure 10.3 Example of a bar graph from an election

Solution

a. Feiner was the favorite, since the largest percentage of voters preferred her throughout the polling period.

b. The bar for Becker for July 2008 appears to come midway between the lines marking 30% and 40%, so we estimate 35%.

c. The undecided vote is shown by the darkest bars, and the darkest bar is the tallest for the month of September 2007. ●

Line Graphs

A graph that uses a broken line to illustrate how one quantity changes with respect to another is called a **line graph.** A line graph is one of the most widely used kinds of graph.

| EXAMPLE 4 | **Drawing a line graph** |

Draw a line graph for the sales tax data given in Table 10.2. Use the grouped categories.

Solution   The line graph uses points instead of bars to designate the locations of the frequencies. These points are then connected by line segments, as shown in Figure 10.4. Note that we are now designating the categories on the x-axis at the gridlines instead of between the gridlines as we did when drawing a bar graph. To plot the points, use the frequency distribution (from Example 1) to find the category $(0\% \leq t < 1\%$, for example); then plot a point showing the frequency (5, in this example). This step is shown in Figure 10.4**a.** The last step is to connect the dots with line segments as shown in Figure 10.4**b.**

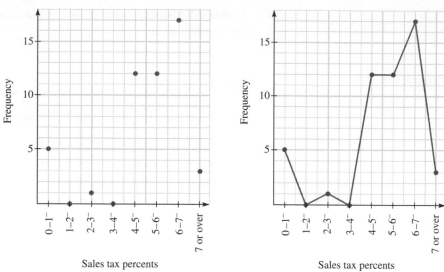

a. Plotting the points to represent frequency levels   **b.** Connecting the dots with line segments

Figure 10.4 Constructing a line graph for sales tax data

Just as with bar graphs, you must be able to read and interpret line graphs.

EXAMPLE 5   **Reading a line graph**

The monthly rainfalls for Honolulu and New Orleans are shown in Figure 10.5.

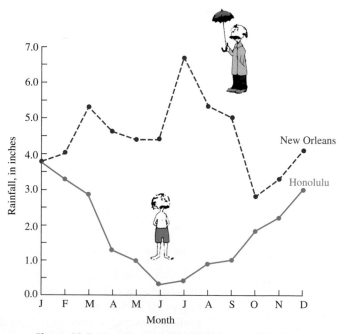

Figure 10.5 Monthly normal rainfall for two U.S. cities

a. During which month does it rain the most in New Orleans? In Honolulu?

b. During which month does it rain the least in New Orleans? In Honolulu?

Solution

a. It rains the most in New Orleans (dashed line graph) in July, and in Honolulu (solid line graph) in January.

b. The least rain falls in New Orleans in October, and in Honolulu in June. ●

Circle Graphs

Another type of commonly used graph is the **circle graph,** also known as a **pie chart.** This graph is particularly useful in illustrating how a whole quantity is divided into parts—for example, income or expenses in a budget.

To create a circle graph, first write the number in each category as a percent of the total. Then convert this percent to an angle in a circle. Remember that a circle is divided into 360°, so we multiply the percent by 360 to find the number of degrees for each category. You can use a protractor to construct a circle graph, as shown in Example 6.

EXAMPLE 6   **Constructing a circle graph**

The 2007 expenses for Karlin Enterprises are shown in Figure 10.6.

KE KARLIN ENTERPRISES | EXPENSE REPORT FY 2007

Salaries	$ 72,000
Rents, taxes, insurance	$ 24,000
Utilities	$ 6,000
Advertising	$ 12,000
Shrinkage	$ 1,200
Materials and supplies	$ 1,200
Depreciation	$ 3,600
TOTAL	**$120,000**

Figure 10.6 Expenses for Karlin Enterprises

Construct a circle graph showing the expenses for Karlin Enterprises.

Solution   The first step in constructing a circle graph is to write the ratio of each entry to the total of the entries, as a percent. This is done by finding the total expenses ($120,000) and then dividing each entry by that total.

Salaries: $\dfrac{72,000}{120,000} = 60\%$ Rents: $\dfrac{24,000}{120,000} = 20\%$ Utilities: $\dfrac{6,000}{120,000} = 5\%$

Advertising: $\dfrac{12,000}{120,000} = 10\%$ Shrinkage: $\dfrac{1,200}{120,000} = 1\%$ Depreciation: $\dfrac{3,600}{120,000} = 3\%$

Materials/supplies: $\dfrac{1,200}{120,000} = 1\%$

A circle has 360°, so the next step is to multiply each percent by 360°:

Salaries: $360° \times 0.60 = 216°$ Rents: $360° \times 0.20 = 72°$ Utilities: $360° \times 0.05 = 18°$

Advertising: $360° \times 0.10 = 36°$ Shrinkage: $360° \times 0.01 = 3.6°$ Depreciation: $360° \times 0.03 = 10.8°$

Materials/supplies: $360° \times 0.01 = 3.6°$

Finally, use a protractor to construct the circle graph, as shown in Figure 10.7.

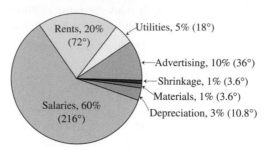

Figure 10.7 Circle graph showing the expenses for Karlin Enterprises

Pictographs

Consider the raw data shown in Table 10.3.

TABLE 10.3	Marital Status of Persons Age 65 and Older*			
	Married	**Widowed**	**Divorced**	**Never Married**
Women	5.5	7.2	0.5	0.8
Men	7.5	1.4	0.5	0.6

*Figures are in millions, rounded to the nearest 100,000.

We could represent these data as a bar graph or a line graph, but a graphical representation often used in popular publications (rather than scientific applications) represents the data using pictures to show quantity in a graph called a **pictograph.** For the data in Table 10.3, suppose that we draw pictures of a woman and a man so that each picture represents 1 million persons, as shown in Figure 10.8.

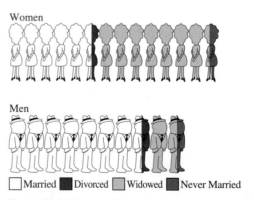

Figure 10.8 Pictograph for the data in Table 10.3

Misuses of Graphs

The scales on the axes of bar or line graphs are frequently chosen so as to exaggerate or diminish real differences. Even worse, graphs are often presented with no scale whatsoever. For example, Figure 10.9 shows a graphical "comparison" between rates paid by banks clipped from a newspaper advertisement; only the name of the bank has been changed.

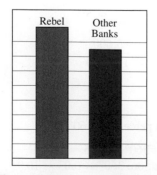

Figure 10.9 Misuse of a bar graph

The most misused type of graph is the pictograph. Consider the data from Table 10.3. Such data can be used to determine the height of a three-dimensional object, as in Figure 10.10**a.** When an object (such as a person) is viewed as three-dimensional, differences seem much larger than they actually are. Look at Figure 10.10**b,** and notice that, as the height and width are doubled, the volume is increased eightfold.

a. Pictograph showing the number of widowed persons of age 65 and older

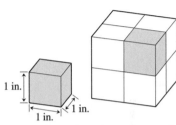

b. Change in volume as a result of changes in length and width

Figure 10.10 Examples of misuses in pictographs

PROBLEM SET 10.1

ESSENTIAL IDEAS   LEVEL 1   *See IAS for graphs.*

1. **IN YOUR OWN WORDS** What is the meaning of the word "statistics"?

2. **IN YOUR OWN WORDS** What is a bar graph?

3. **IN YOUR OWN WORDS** What is a histogram?

4. **IN YOUR OWN WORDS** What is a line graph?

5. **IN YOUR OWN WORDS** What is a circle graph?

6. **IN YOUR OWN WORDS** What is a pictograph?

DRILL AND PRACTICE   LEVEL 2

Consider the following data sets:

Data set A: The annual wages of employees at a small accounting firm are given in thousands of dollars.

25	25	25	30	30	35	50	60
16	14	18	18	20

Data set B: The numbers of cars registered to homes in a certain neighborhood are given.

1	2	1	1	0	3	4	1
2	2	2	3	2	2	2	2

Data set C: The heights (rounded to the nearest inch) of 30 students are given.

66	68	65	70	67	67	68	64	64	66
64	70	72	71	69	64	63	70	71	63
68	67	67	65	69	65	67	66	69	69

Data set D: The temperatures (°F) at a particular location for 30 days are given.

57	50	58	45	49	50	53	52	43	55
39	53	50	49	57	45	49	40	47	55
52	58	50	44	59	54	51	49	43	54

Prepare a frequency distribution for each data set in Problems 7–10.   *See IAS.*

7. Data set A   8. Data set B

9. Data set C   10. Data set D

Draw a bar graph for each data set in Problems 11–14.

11. Data set A   12. Data set B

13. Data set C   14. Data set D

Draw a line graph for each data set in Problems 15–18.

15. Data set A   16. Data set B

17. Data set C   18. Data set D

19. Rearrange the salaries from Data set A into the following groupings:

$0–$20,000
$20,001–$30,000
$30,001–$40,000 |
$40,001–$50,000 |
Over $50,000 |

Show the grouped frequency distribution.

20. Draw a bar graph using the grouped frequency distribution constructed in Problem 19.

APPLICATIONS   LEVEL 2

Use the information in Figure 10.11 in Problems 21–23.

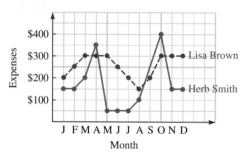

Figure 10.11 Expenses for two salespeople of the Leadwell Pencil Company

21. During which month did Herb incur the most expenses?
October
22. Which salesperson has more variability in his or her expenses?   Herb Smith

23. During which month did Lisa incur the least expenses?
August

Use the bar graph in Figure 10.12 for Problems 24–27.

"If the election for U.S. Senate were being held today, for whom would you vote?"

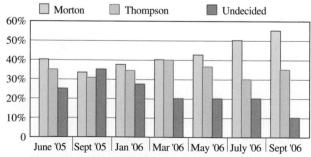

Figure 10.12 Political bar graph from the 2006 election

24. a. How many candidates were running for office?   two
   b. Who was the favorite in the election poll?   Morton

25. a. What percent of the voters favored Thompson in July 2006?   30%

   b. What percent of the voters favored Morton in September 2005?   33%

26. In which month was the undecided vote the greatest?
Sept. 2005
27. In which month was Morton's lead the greatest?
July 2006 and Sept. 2006

Use the bar graph in Figure 10.13 for Problems 28–31.

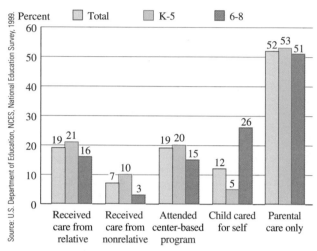

Figure 10.13 Before- and after-school care: Percentage of children in grades K–8 who received various types of care before and after school

28. Among children in grades K–8, what is the preferred method of child care before or after school?
parental care only (52%)
29. Among children in grades K–8 who received care on a regular basis from someone other than a parent before or after school, what was the least preferred method of child care?
received care from a nonrelative (7%)
30. Among children in grades K–5 who received care on a regular basis from someone other than a parent before or after school, what was the preferred method of child care?
received care from a relative (21%)
31. Among children in grades 6–8 who received care on a regular basis from someone other than a parent before or after school, what was the preferred method of child care?
child cared for self (26%)

When a person in California renews the registration for an automobile, the bar graph shown in Figure 10.14 is included with the bill. Use this bar graph to answer the questions in Problems 32–37. The following statement is included with the graph:

There is no safe way to drive after drinking. These charts show that a few drinks can make you an unsafe driver. They show that drinking affects your BLOOD ALCOHOL CONCENTRATION (BAC). The BAC zones for various numbers of drinks and time periods are printed in white, gray, and red. HOW TO USE THESE CHARTS: First, find the chart that includes your weight. For example, if you weigh 160 lbs., use the "150 to 169" chart. Then look under "Total Drinks" at the "2" on this "150 to 169" chart. Now look below the "2" drinks, in the row for 1 hour. You'll see your BAC is in the gray shaded zone. This means that if you drive after 2 drinks in 1 hour, you could be arrested. In the gray zone, your chances of having an accident are 5 times higher than if you had no drinks. But if you had 4 drinks in 1 hour, your BAC would be in the red shaded area . . . and your chances of having an accident 25 times higher.

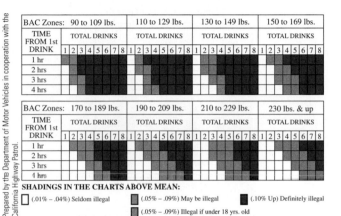

SHADINGS IN THE CHARTS ABOVE MEAN:

□ (.01% – .04%) Seldom illegal ▨ (.05% – .09%) May be illegal ■ (.10% Up) Definitely illegal
▨ (.05% – .09%) Illegal if under 18 yrs. old

Figure 10.14 Blood Alcohol Concentration (BAC) charts

Prepared by the Department of Motor Vehicles in cooperation with the California Highway Patrol.

32. Suppose that you weigh 115 pounds and that you have two drinks in two hours. If you then drive, how much more likely are you to have an accident than if you had refrained from drinking? *5 times*

33. Suppose that you weigh 115 pounds and that you have four drinks in three hours. If you then drive, how much more likely are you to have an accident than if you had refrained from drinking? *25 times*

34. Suppose that you weigh 195 pounds and have two drinks in two hours. According to Figure 10.14, are you seldom illegal, maybe illegal, or definitely illegal? *seldom illegal*

35. Suppose that you weigh 195 pounds and that you have four drinks in three hours. According to Figure 10.14, are you seldom illegal, maybe illegal, or definitely illegal?
maybe illegal

36. If you weigh 135 pounds, how many drinks in three hours would you need to be definitely illegal? *5*

37. If you weigh 185 pounds and drink a six-pack of beer during a 3-hour baseball game, can you legally drive home? *no*

Use the following information in Problems 38–42. The amount of electricity used in a typical all-electric home is shown in the circle graph in Figure 10.15. If, in a certain month, a home used 1,100 kwh (kilowatt-hours), find the amounts of electricity used from the graph.

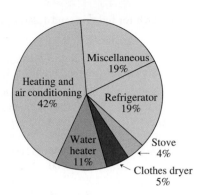

Figure 10.15 Home electricity usage

38. The amount of electricity used by heating and air conditioning *462 kwh*

39. The amount of electricity used by the water heater *121 kwh*

40. The amount of electricity used by the stove *44 kwh*

41. The amount of electricity used by the refrigerator *209 kwh*

42. The amount of electricity used by the clothes dryer *55 kwh*

Use the following information in Problems 43–45. The gross profits for January at Tower Center for the five departments were:

  Appliance Department, $20,000
  Automotive Department, $10,000
  Clothing Department, $55,000
  Grocery Department, $260,000
  Nursery Department, $15,000

43. Change each of the profit amounts to the nearest tenth of a percent. *appliance, 5.6%; automotive, 2.8%; clothing, 15.3%; grocery, 72.2%; nursery, 4.2%*

44. Change each of the percents in Problem 43 to degrees.
appliance, 20°; automotive, 10°; clothing, 55°; grocery, 260°; nursery, 15°

45. Draw a circle graph of these data.

In Problems 46-49, draw a circle graph to represent the given information.

46. The breakdown for the cost of serving a meal in a restaurant is 12.5% for food, 22.0% for rent, 10.0% for marketing and administrative costs, 15.0% for dishes and equipment, 30.0% for labor, and 10.5% for profit.

47. The amount of electricity used in a typical all-electric home includes: 48% for heating and air conditioning, 9% for water heater, 15% for refrigerator, 4% for stove, 5% for clothes dryer, and 19% miscellaneous.

48. According to the Specialty Coffee Association, the cost of a $1.75 latte includes $0.26 for the coffee bean and milk, $0.20 for dishes and equipment, $0.44 for rent, $0.18 for marketing and administrative costs, $0.58 for labor, and $0.09 profit.

49. The breakdown for the electricity consumption of a home using 8,000 kwh of electricity is 3,840 kwh for heating, 960 kwh for hot water, 800 kwh for refrigerator, 560 kwh for freezer, 560 kwh for lighting, and 1,280 kwh for other uses.

Use the following history of the cost to mail a 1-oz first-class letter in the United States since 1900 for Problems 50–51.

1900–1918	3 cents	1981–1984	20 cents
1919–1931	2 cents	1985–1987	22 cents
1932–1957	3 cents	1988–1990	25 cents
1958–1962	4 cents	1991–1994	29 cents
1963–1967	5 cents	1995–1998	32 cents
1968–1970	6 cents	1999–2000	33 cents
1971–1973	8 cents	2001	34 cents
1974	10 cents	2002–2005	37 cents
1975–1977	13 cents	2006	39 cents
1978–1980	15 cents	2007	41 cents

50. Summarize this information, using a line graph.

51. Summarize this information, using a bar graph.

The time required for three leading pain relievers to reach your bloodstream is as follows:

Brand A, 480 seconds
Brand B, 500 seconds
Brand C, 490 seconds

Use this information for Problems 52–54.

52. Draw a bar graph for the three brands using a vertical scale from 0 to 500 with each unit representing 100 seconds.

53. Draw a bar graph for the three brands using a vertical scale from 450 to 500 with each unit representing 10 seconds.

54. If you were an advertiser working on a promotion campaign for Brand A, construct a graph using a scale that would seem to give your product a more distinct advantage. *Hint:* See Problems 52 and 53.   the graph in Problem 53

55. IN YOUR OWN WORDS "Nine out of ten dentists recommend Trident for their patients who chew gum." "Crest has been shown to be . . . ." "You can clearly see that Bufferin is the most effective . . . ." "Penzoil is better suited . . . ." "Sylvania was preferred by . . . ." "How can anyone analyze the claims of the commercials we see and hear on a daily basis?" asked Betty. "I even subscribe to *Consumer Reports,* but so many of the claims seem to be unreasonable. I don't like to buy items by trial and error, and I really don't believe all the claims in advertisements." Collect examples

of good statistical graphs and examples of misleading graphs. Use some of the leading newspapers and national magazines.

RIGHT OR WRONG?   **LEVEL 3**

Explain what is wrong, if anything, with the statements in Problems 56–60. Explain your reasoning.

56. Consider the graph shown in Figure 10.16. The potential commercial forest growth, as compared with the current commercial forest growth, is almost double (44.9 to 74.2). Two dimensions should not be used for one-dimensional data.

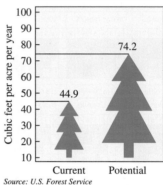

Figure 10.16 Commercial forest growth

57. Consider the graph shown in Figure 10.17. Clearly, Brand B is better.   Graph is meaningless without a scale.

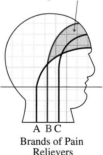

Figure 10.17 From an advertisement for a pain reliever

58. Consider the graph shown in Figure 10.18. *The graph is appropriate and accurate.*

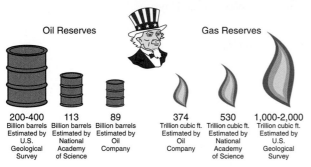

How much is "in the bank"?
Conflicting estimates of undiscovered oil and gas reserves—which can be recovered and produced.

Oil Reserves   Gas Reserves

200-400	113	89	374	530	1,000-2,000
Billion barrels	Billion barrels	Billion barrels	Trillion cubic ft.	Trillion cubic ft.	Trillion cubic ft.
Estimated by U.S. Geological Survey	Estimated by National Academy of Science	Estimated by Oil Company	Estimated by Oil Company	Estimated by National Academy of Science	Estimated by U.S. Geological Survey

Figure 10.18 Pictograph showing reserves

59. In 1998 it was reported on the evening news that the number of deaths since the lifting of the 55 mph speed limit was up by 350, representing a 22% increase. From this study, the conclusion reached was that there was a connection between the rise in the death rate and the raising of the speed limit. *false*

60. Consider the Saab advertisement.

The advertisement says that the car is 57 in. wide on the outside, but a full 5 ft wide across the inside.

There are two cars built in Sweden. Before you buy theirs, drive ours.

When people who know cars think about Swedish cars, they think of them as being strong and durable. And conquering some of the toughest driving conditions in the world.

But, unfortunately, when most people think about buying a Swedish car, the one they think about usually isn't ours. (Even though ours doesn't cost any more.)

Ours is the SAAB 99E. It's strong and durable. But it's a lot different from their car.

Our car has Front-Wheel Drive for better traction, stability and handling.

It has a 1.85 liter, fuel-injected, 4 cylinder, overhead cam engine as standard in every car. 4-speed transmission is standard too. Or you can get a 3-speed automatic (optional).

Our car has four-wheel disc brakes and dual-diagonal braking system so you can stop straight and fast every time.

It has a wide stance. (About 55 inches.) So it rides and handles like a sports car.

Outside, our car is smaller than a lot of "small" cars. 172" overall length, 57" overall width.

Inside, our car has bucket seats up front and a full five feet across in the back so you can easily accommodate five adults.

It has more headroom than a Rolls Royce and more room from the brake pedal to the back seat than a Mercedes 280. And it has factory air conditioning as an option.

There are a lot of other things that make our car different from their car. Like roll cage construction and a special "hot seat" for cold winter days.

So before you buy their car, stop by your nearest SAAB dealer and drive our car. The SAAB 99E. We think you'll buy it instead of theirs. **SAAB 99E**

10.2 Measures of Central Tendency

IN THIS WORLD THE UTILITY OF MATH

"My dad is better than your dad!" teased Violet. "Na, na, na-na!" Do you suppose that Violet's dad bowled better on Monday nights (185 avg.) than on Thursday nights (170 avg.)? Don't be too hasty to say yes!

See Problem 54.

In Section 10.1, we organized data into a frequency distribution and then discussed their presentation in graphical form. However, some properties of data can help us interpret masses of information. We will use the situation to introduce the notion of *average*.

 Let's begin by looking at the Problem of the Day.

	Monday Night	Thursday Night
Game 1	175	180
Game 2	150	130
Game 3	160	161
Game 4	180	185
Game 5	160	163
Game 6	183	185
Game 7	287	186
Totals	1,295	1,190

To find the averages used by Violet in the *Peanuts* cartoon, we divide these totals by the number of games:

$$\underset{\text{Monday Night}}{\frac{1{,}295}{7} = 185} \qquad \underset{\text{Thursday Night}}{\frac{1{,}190}{7} = 170}$$

If we consider the averages, Violet's dad did better on Mondays; but if we consider the games separately, we see that Violet's dad typically did better on Thursday (five out of seven games). Would any other properties of the bowling scores tell us this fact?

The average used by Violet is only one kind of statistical measure that can be used. It is the measure that most of us think of when we hear someone use the word *average*. It is called the *mean*. Other statistical measures, called **averages** or **measures of central tendency,** are defined in the following box.

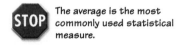 The average is the most commonly used statistical measure.

Measures of Central Tendency

1. **Mean.** The number found by adding the data and then dividing by the number of values in the data set.
2. **Median.** The middle number when the numbers in the data set are arranged in order of size. If there are two middle numbers (in the case of an even number of values in the data set), the median is the mean of these two middle numbers.
3. **Mode.** The value that occurs most frequently. If no number occurs more than once, there is no mode. It is possible to have more than one mode.

The **mean** is the most sensitive average. It reflects the entire distribution and is the most common average. The **median** gives the middle value. It is useful when there are a few extraordinary values to distort the mean. The **mode** is the average that measures "popularity." It is possible to have no mode or more than one mode.

Consider these other measures of central tendency for Violet's dad's bowling scores.

Median Rearrange the data from smallest to largest when finding the median:

Monday Night		Thursday Night
150		130
160		161
160		163
175	← Middle number is the median. →	180
180		185
183		185
287		186

STOP Be sure you can distinguish among mean, median, and mode.

Mode Look for the number that occurs most frequently:

Monday Night		Thursday Night
150		130
160 ⎫		161
160 ⎭ Most frequent is the mode.		163
175		180
180 ⎧		⎰ **185**
183 ⎭ Most frequent is the mode.		⎱ **185**
287		186

If we compare the three measures of central tendency for the bowling scores, we find the following:

	Monday Night	Thursday Night
Mean	185	170
Median	175	180
Mode	160	185

We are no longer convinced that Violet's dad did better on Monday nights than on Thursday nights.

EXAMPLE 1

Finding measures of central tendency

Find the mean, median, and mode for the following sets of numbers.

a. 3, 5, 5, 8, 9   **b.** 4, 10, 9, 8, 9, 4, 5   **c.** 6, 5, 4, 7, 1, 9

Solution

a. *Mean:* $\dfrac{\text{SUM OF TERMS}}{\text{NUMBER OF TERMS}} = \dfrac{3+5+5+8+9}{5} = \dfrac{30}{5} = 6$

Median: Arrange in order: 3, 5, **5**, 8, 9. The middle term is the median: 5.

Mode: The most frequently occurring term is the mode: 5.

b. *Mean:* $\dfrac{4+10+9+8+9+4+5}{7} = \dfrac{49}{7} = 7$

Median: 4, 4, 5, 8, 9, 9, 10; the median 8.

Mode: The data set has two modes: 4 and 9. If a data set has two modes, we say it is **bimodal.**

c. *Mean* : $\dfrac{6 + 5 + 4 + 7 + 1 + 9}{6} = \dfrac{32}{6} \approx 5.33$

Median: 1, 4, 5, 6, 7, 9; the median is $\frac{11}{2} = 5.5$.
$$\underbrace{5 + 6}{2} = \frac{11}{2}$$

Mode: There is no mode because no term appears more than once. ●

A rather nice physical model illustrates the idea of the mean. Consider a seesaw that consists of a plank and a movable support (called a *fulcrum*). We assume that the plank has no weight and is marked off into units as shown in Figure 10.19.

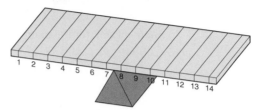

Figure 10.19 Fulcrum and plank model for mean

Now let's place some 1-lb weights in the positions of the numbers in some given distribution. The balance point for the plank is the mean. For example, consider the data from part **a** of Example 1: 3, 5, 5, 8, 9. If these weights are placed on the plank, the balance point is 6, as shown in Figure 10.20.

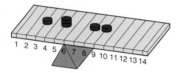

Figure 10.20 The balance point for the data set 3, 5, 5, 8, 9 is 6.

EXAMPLE 2

Measures of central tendency from a frequency distribution

Consider the number of days one must wait for a marriage license in the various states in the United States.

Days' Wait	Frequency
0	25
1	1
2	1
3	19
4	1
5	3
Total	50

What are the mean, the median, and the mode for these data?

Solution

Mean: To find the mean, we could, of course, add all 50 individual numbers, but instead, notice that

0 occurs 25 times, so we write	0×25
1 occurs 1 time, so write	1×1
2 occurs 1 time, so write	2×1
3 occurs 19 times, so write	3×19
4 occurs 1 time, so write	4×1
5 occurs 3 times, so write	5×3

Thus, the mean is

$$\dfrac{0 \times 25 + 1 \times 1 + 2 \times 1 + 3 \times 19 + 4 \times 1 + 5 \times 3}{50} = \dfrac{79}{50} = 1.58$$

Median: Since the median is the middle number, and since there are 50 values, the median is the mean of the 25th and 26th numbers (when they are arranged in order).

$$\left.\begin{array}{l} \text{25th term is 0} \\ \text{26th term is 1} \end{array}\right\} \quad \frac{0 + 1}{2} = 0.5$$

Mode: The mode is the value that occurs most frequently, which is 0.   ●

PROBLEM SET 10.2

ESSENTIAL IDEAS   LEVEL 1

1. **IN YOUR OWN WORDS** What is the mean?

2. **IN YOUR OWN WORDS** What is the median?

3. **IN YOUR OWN WORDS** What is the mode?

4. **IN YOUR OWN WORDS** Compare and contrast measures of central tendency.

DRILL AND PRACTICE   LEVEL 2

In Problems 5–15, find the three measures of central tendency (the mean, median, and mode).

5. 1, 2, 3, 4, 5
mean = 3; median = 3; no mode
7. 765, 766, 767, 768, 769
mean = 767; median = 767; no mode
9. 4, 7, 10, 7, 5, 2, 7
mean = 6; median = 7; mode = 7
11. 3, 5, 8, 13, 21
mean = 10; median = 8; no mode
13. 79, 90, 95, 95, 96
mean = 91; median = 95; mode = 95
15. 1, 2, 3, 3, 3, 4, 5
mean = 3; median = 3; mode = 3

6. 17, 18, 19, 20, 21
mean = 19; median = 19; no mode
8. 15, 13, 10, 7, 6, 9, 10
mean = 10; median = 10; mode = 10
10. 1, 4, 9, 16, 25
mean = 11; median = 9; no mode
12. 70, 81, 95, 79, 85
mean = 82; median = 81; no mode
14. 0, 1, 1, 2, 3, 4, 16, 21
mean = 6; median = 2.5; mode = 1

16. **IN YOUR OWN WORDS** Roll a single die until all six numbers occur at least once. Repeat the experiment 20 times. Find the mean, the median, and the mode of the number of tosses.

17. **IN YOUR OWN WORDS** Roll a pair of dice until all 11 possible sums occur at least once. Repeat the experiment 20 times. Find the mean, the median, and the mode of the number of tosses.

APPLICATIONS   LEVEL 2

For Problems 18–21, use the salaries of employees of the Moe D. Lawn Landscaping Company:

Salary	Frequency
$25,000	4
$28,000	3
$30,000	2
$45,000	1

18. What is the mean? $28,900

19. What is the median? $28,000

20. What is the mode? $25,000

21. Which measure seems to best describe the average salary for the company?   *The median is most descriptive.*

© PhotoDisc/Getty Images

For Problems 22–25, consider G. Thumb, the leading salesperson for the Moe D. Lawn Landscaping Company. Thumb turned in the following summary of clients contacted for the week of October 23–28:

Date	No. of Clients
Oct. 23	12
Oct. 24	9
Oct. 25	10
Oct. 26	16
Oct. 27	10
Oct. 28	21

22. What is the mean?   13

23. What is the median?   11

24. What is the mode?   10

25. Which measure seems to best describe the average number of contacted clients?   *The mean is most descriptive.*

In Problems 26–29, suppose a class obtained the following scores on a test:

Score	Frequency
90	1
80	3
70	10
60	5
50	2

26. What is the mean?   *68.1*   **27.** What is the median?   *70*

28. What is the mode?   *70*

29. Which measure seems to best describe the average class score?   *The mean is most descriptive.*

In Problems 30–33, suppose a class obtained the following scores on a test:

Score	Frequency
90	1
80	6
70	10
60	4
50	3
40	1

30. What is the mean?   *68*   **31.** What is the median?   *70*

32. What is the mode?   *70*

33. Which measure seems to best describe the average class score?   *The mean is most descriptive.*

In Problems 34–37, suppose a class obtained the following test scores:

Score	Frequency
90	2
80	4
70	9
60	5
50	3
40	1
30	2
0	4

34. What is the mean?   *56*   **35.** What is the median?   *65*

36. What is the mode?   *70*

37. Which measure seems to best describe the average class score?   *The mean is most descriptive.*

In Problems 38–41, consider the following salaries for the executives of a certain company:

Position	Salary
President	$170,000
1st VP	$140,000
2nd VP	$120,000
Supervising manager	$54,000
Accounting manager	$40,000
Personnel manager	$40,000
Department manager	$30,000
Department manager	$30,000

38. What is the mean?   *$78,000*

39. What is the median?   *$47,000*

40. What is the mode?   *$40,000 and $30,000*

41. Which measure seems to best describe the average executive salary for the company?   *The median is most descriptive.*

In Problems 42–45, suppose the 2006 prices, per ton, of wine grapes for different kinds of wine are given in the following table.

Variety	Price
Cabernet Sauvignon	$1,650
Merlot	$1,800
Zinfandel	$1,600
Pinot Noir	$1,500
Chardonnay	$1,600
Sauvignon Blanc	$1,100

42. What is the mean?   *$1,541.67*

43. What is the median?   *$1,600.00*

44. What is the mode?   *$1,600.00*

45. Which measure seems to best describe the average price?   *The median is most descriptive.*

In Problems 46–49, suppose that the 1999 monthly cost for health care for an employee and two dependents is given in the following table.

Provider	Cost
Maxicare	$415.24
Cigna	$424.77
Health Net	$427.48
Pacific Care	$428.05
Health Plan of the Redwoods	$431.52
Kaiser	$433.50
Aetna U.S. Healthcare	$436.11
Blue Shield HMO	$442.28
Omni Healthcare	$457.86
Lifeguard	$457.94

46. What is the mean?   *$435.48*   **47.** What is the median?   *$432.51*

48. What is the mode?   *no mode*

49. Which measure seems to best describe the average cost?   *The median is most descriptive.*

In Problems 50–53, consider the California counties with population more than one million, as given in the following table. *

County	2005 Population
Alameda	1,448,905
Contra Costa	1,017,878
Los Angeles	9,935,475
Orange	2,988,072
Riverside	1,946,419
Sacramento	1,363,482
San Bernardino	1,963,535
San Diego	2,933,462
Santa Clara	1,699,052

*Source: U.S. Bureau of Census.

50. What is the mean?
2,810,698

51. What is the median?
1,946,419

52. What is the mode?   no mode

53. Which measure seems to best describe the average population?   The mean is most descriptive.

54. **IN YOUR OWN WORDS** Jerry and John have the same mean bowling score, although Jerry bowled better on each game except one. Give an example of such scores.

	Andy			Dave		
	Hits	*AB*	*Avg.*	*Hits*	*AB*	*Avg.*
1989	113	476	0.236	12	51	0.235
1990	140	493	0.284	124	439	0.282

Therefore, it follows that Andy's combined 1989–1990 batting average is better than Dave's.   See bottom of the column.

57. For the data 6, 7, 10, 10, and 15, the median is

$$\frac{6 + 7 + 10 + 10 + 15}{5} = \frac{48}{5}$$

F; the middle number is 10

58. For the data 6, 7, 10, and 15, the median is

$$\frac{7 + 10}{2} = \frac{17}{2} \text{ T}$$

59. For the data 6, 7, 10, 10, and 15, the mean is

$$\frac{6 + 7 + 10 + 10 + 15}{5} = 9.6$$

the median is $\frac{7 + 10}{2} = \frac{17}{2}$, and the mode is 10.
F; the median is 10

60. For the data 6, 7, 10, 10, 15, and 15, the mode is 10.
F; the data set is bimodal with modes 10 and 15.

56. F; can't average averages. Combined, Dave had 136 hits for 490 at bats (0.278 avg). Combined, Andy had 253 hits for 969 at bats (0.261 avg).

RIGHT OR WRONG?   LEVEL 3

Explain what is wrong, if anything, with the statements in Problems 55–60. Explain your reasoning.

55. The average of the numbers 11, 50, 50, and 9 is found as follows:

$$\frac{11 + 50 + 50 + 9}{4} = \frac{120}{4} = 30$$

F; the type of average was not specified. Do not assume "average" is the mean.

56. In 1989, Andy Van Slyke's batting average was better than Dave Justice's; and in 1990 Andy once again beat Dave.

(10.3) Measures of Position

IN THIS WORLD   THE UTILITY OF MATH

Transcript Records

Be hereby notified that

Gustavo G. Rivas

graduated 10th in his class of 50 graduates.

It is also hereby confirmed that

Shannon J. Sovndal

graduated 25th in his class of 625 graduates.

These notices are confirmed without prejudice and acknowledge the good work of both candidates.

"I can't make up my mind which candidate to hire," sighed Cole. "Both Gustavo and Shannon have stunning recommendations, which are equal in all respects."
    "How will you decide—flip a coin?" asked Hannah.
    "No, since they both came from equally prestigious schools, I think I will use their standing in their graduating classes," responded Cole.

Which candidate should Cole hire?

 See Problem 60.

In the last section, we considered measures of central tendency, and we noted that the median divides the data into two equal parts; half the values are above the median and half are below the median. Sometimes we use benchmark positions, often called **measures of position,** that divide the data into more than two parts. **Quartiles,**

denoted by Q_1 (first quartile), Q_2 (second quartile), and Q_3 (third quartile), divide the data into four equal parts.

EXAMPLE 1

Finding quartiles

On a recent examination the following scores were obtained:

98, 95, 92, 90, 88, 83, 82, 80, 77, 77, 74, 69, 65, 60, 59, 37

Divide these data into quartiles.

Solution The median is the measure that determines the middle of a given data set. This data set has 16 scores (an even number), so we must find the mean of the 8th and 9th scores:

$$\frac{80 + 77}{2} = 78.5$$

The median is 78.5.

The first quartile is the value that has 25% of the scores below it, and since there are 16 scores, 25% (one-fourth) of 16 is 4. The value of the first quartile is the mean of the fourth and fifth scores from the bottom:

$$\frac{65 + 69}{2} = 67$$

The third quartile is the value that has 75% of the scores below it (or 25% above), so that it is the mean of the fourth and fifth scores from the top, namely,

$$\frac{90 + 88}{2} = 89$$

We see that

$$Q_1 = 67, \quad Q_2 = 78.5, \quad \text{and} \quad Q_3 = 89$$

are the quartiles. These scores divide the data into four parts, by position. ●

It is often desirable to divide the data into more than four parts. For example, if John tells you he received a test score of 83, this does not really tell you how well he did on the exam. If John says his score is one of the scores listed in Example 1, then we have a bit more information and we can say he scored between the second and third quartiles. Recall, $Q_1 = 67$, $Q_2 = 78.5$, and $Q_3 = 89$, so these numbers divide the data into four parts:

lowest quarter of the scores:	0–65	$Q_1 = 67$
second quarter of the scores:	69–77	$Q_2 = 78.5$
third quarter of the scores:	80–88	$Q_3 = 89$
highest quarter of the scores:	90–98	

We could also say that John's score is the sixth highest score in the class, but unless we know the number of scores, we do not have a meaningful measure of position. In other words, to know position we would need to know that John scored sixth out of 16 taking the test.

Deciles are nine values that divide the data into ten equal parts, and **percentiles** are 99 values that divide the data into 100 equal parts. For example, when you take the Scholastic Assessment Test (SAT), your score is recorded as a percentile score. If you scored in the 92nd percentile, it means that you scored better than approximately 92% of those who took the test.

EXAMPLE 2

Finding percentile rank

Lisa says her score was 23, and that score was the 85th score from the top in a class of 240 scores. Calculate Lisa's percentile rank.

Solution   In Lisa's class, there are $240 - 85 = 155$ scores ranked below her. Thus,

$$\frac{155}{240} \approx 0.65$$

This means that approximately 65% of Lisa's classmates were ranked lower than she, so we would say Lisa is at the 65th percentile.   ●

EXAMPLE 3

Finding the class rank

Lee has received a percentile rank of 85% in a class of 50 students. What is Lee's rank in the class?

Solution   Lee's percentile rank means that 85% of the students have scores less than his, so

$$0.85 \text{ of } 50 = 42.5$$

This means that 42 students scored lower than Lee, so Lee's rank in the class is

$$50 - 42 = 8$$

or eighth in a class of 50.   ●

EXAMPLE 4

Finding decile rank

The 1999 monthly cost for health care for an employee and two dependents is given in the following table.

Provider	Cost
Maxicare	$415.24
Cigna	$424.77
Health Net	$427.48
Pacific Care	$428.05
Health Plan of the Redwoods	$431.52
Kaiser	$433.50
Aetna U.S. Healthcare	$436.11
Blue Shield HMO	$442.28
Omni Healthcare	$457.86
Lifeguard	$457.94

What is the decile rank for Kaiser?

Solution   Since the data are arranged from lowest to highest, we see that there are five below Kaiser, and there are ten providers. Kaiser is at the 5th decile. You say, "How convenient it was that there were ten health care providers." Suppose that Omni and Lifeguard are eliminated from the list. Now, in which percentile is Kaiser? There are still five ranked below Kaiser out of a total of eight providers, so

$$\frac{5}{8} \approx 0.625 \quad \text{or} \quad 62.5\%$$

We would say that Kaiser is at the 62nd percentile.   ●

HISTORICAL NOTE

Karl Smith library

Florence Nightingale
(1820–1910)

Even though the origins of statistics are ancient, the development of modern statistical techniques began in the 19th century. Adolph Quetelet (1796–1874) was the first person to apply statistical methods to accumulated data. He correctly predicted (to his own surprise) the crime and mortality rates from year to year. Florence Nightingale was an early proponent of the use of statistics in her work. Since the advent of the computer, statistical methods have come within the reach of almost everyone. Today, statistical methods strongly influence agriculture, biology, business, chemistry, economics, education, electronics, medicine, physics, psychology, and sociology. If you decide to enter one of these disciplines for a career, you will, no doubt, be required to take at least one statistics course.

PROBLEM SET 10.3

ESSENTIAL IDEAS LEVEL 1

1. **IN YOUR OWN WORDS** Distinguish measures of central tendency from measures of position.

2. What are quartiles? three values that divide the data into four parts

3. What are deciles? nine values that divide the data into ten parts

4. What are percentiles? ninety-nine values that divide the data into one hundred parts

DRILL AND PRACTICE LEVEL 2

Find the percentile rank in Problems 5–16.

5. 10th in a class of 100
   90th percentile
6. 10th in a class of 50
   80th percentile
7. 12th in a class of 200
   94th percentile
8. 12th in a class of 100
   88th percentile
9. 14th out of 150
   91st percentile
10. 14th out of 75
    81st percentile
11. 58th out of 450
    87th percentile
12. 385 out of 450
    14th percentile
13. 83rd out of 690
    88th percentile
14. 500 out of 690
    28th percentile
15. 106th out of 17,500
    99th percentile
16. 2,134 out of 10,000
    79th percentile

Find the class ranking in Problems 17–28.

17. 90th percentile out of 20   2

18. 80th percentile out of 30   6

19. 50th percentile out of 80   40

20. 99th percentile out of 5,000   50

21. 98th percentile out of 400   8

22. 60th percentile out of 120   48

23. 97th percentile out of 53   2

24. 55th percentile out of 140   63

25. 99th percentile out of 825   8

26. 70th percentile out of 35   11

27. 73rd percentile out of 38   10

28. 73rd percentile out of 40   11

In Problems 29–33, consider a class of examination scores:

{93, 86, 83, 75, 71, 67, 65, 63, 60, 53}

29. What is the percentile rank of a score of 93?   90th percentile

30. What is the median?   69

31. What score is the first quartile?   63

32. What score is the fourth decile?   65

33. What score is at the 70th percentile?   75

In Problems 34–38, consider a class of examination scores.

{93, 86, 83, 75, 71, 67, 65, 63, 60, 53, 45, 38}

34. What is the percentile rank of a score of 93? 92nd percentile

35. What is the median?   66

36. What score is the first quartile?   56.5

37. What score is the fourth decile?   63

38. What score is at the 70th percentile?   71

APPLICATIONS LEVEL 2

The numbers of cars imported into the United States during a certain time period were as listed in the following table:

Country	Number	Country	Number
Canada	1,589,980	South Korea	140,572
Japan	1,012,785	Sweden	86,593
Mexico	550,620	United Kingdom	43,890
Germany	234,381	Italy	1,125

Use these data to answer the questions in Problems 39–42.

© Lexus, a Division of Toyota Motor Sales, U.S.A., Inc.

39. What is the rank of Mexico?   3rd

40. What is the percentile rank of United Kingdom?
13th percentile

41. What is the decile rank of Germany?   5th decile

42. What is the quartile rank of Sweden?   2nd quartile

43. California ranks 39th (out of 50) in graduation rate for public high schools. What is California's quartile rank?   1st quartile

44. Columbia University ranks as the 13th most expensive out of 50 listed universities. What is Columbia's quartile rank?   3rd quartile

45. According to the 2004 *U.S. News and World Report* of college rankings, St. Olaf was 61 out of 110 schools. What is St. Olaf's decile rank?   4th decile

46. New Jersey ranks 8th (out of 50) in graduation rate for public high schools. What is New Jersey's decile rank?   8th decile

47. Florida ranks 48th (out of 50) in graduation rate for public high schools. What is Florida's percentile rank?   4th percentile

48. According to the 2004 *U.S. News and World Report* of college rankings, Vassar College was 14 out of 110 schools. What is Vassar's percentile rank?   about the 87th percentile

49. If there are 36 students in a class and Amy's score is at the third quartile, how many students scored lower than Amy?   27

50. Jerry is ranked at the first quartile of his graduating class of 1,400 students. What is his rank in the class?   1,050

51. James is ranked at the median of his math class of 45 students. What is his rank in the class?   23

52. James is ranked 80th in his class of 450, and John, who is in the same class, has a percentile rank of 80. Who has a higher standing in the class?   James

53. In 1997, in terms of population, Contra Costa County ranked 9th out of 58 counties. What was its percentile rank?   84th percentile

54. In 1997, in terms of population, Modoc County ranked 55th out of 58 counties. What was its decile rank?   1st decile

The top 18 *American Kennel Club* 2000 *registrations are given:*

Breed	Number	Breed	Number
Labrador Retriever	172,841	Shih Tzu	37,599
Golden Retriever	66,300	Rottweiler	37,355
German Shepherd	57,660	Pomeranian	33,568
Dachshund	52,026	Mini Schnauzer	30,472
Beagle	52,026	Cocker Spaniel	29,393
Poodle	45,868	Pug	24,373
Yorkshire Terrier	43,574	Shet Sheepdog	23,866
Chihuahua	43,096	Mini Pinscher	22,020
Boxer	38,803	Boston Terrier	19,922

Use these data to answer the questions in Problems 55–59.

© Daniel Dempster Photography/Alamy

55. What is the rank of the Poodle?   The Poodle is 6th.

56. What is the rank of the Golden Retriever?
The Golden Retriever is 2nd.

57. What is the percentile rank of the Dachshund?
78th percentile

58. What is the decile rank of the Pomeranian?   4th decile

59. What is the quartile rank of the Chihuahua?   3rd quartile

60. "I can't make up my mind which candidate to hire," sighed Cole. "Both Gustavo and Shannon have stunning recommendations, which are equal in all respects." "How will you decide, flip a coin?" asked Hannah. "No, since they both came from equally prestigious schools, I think I will use their standing in their graduating classes," responded Cole. Which candidate should Cole hire? Assume that Gustavo G. Rivas graduated 10th in his class of 50 graduates, and Shannon J. Sovndal graduated 25th in his class of 625 graduates.   Shannon

(10.4) Measures of Dispersion

IN THIS WORLD THE UTILITY OF MATH

"We need privacy and a consistent wind," said Wilbur. "Did you write to the Weather Bureau to find a suitable location?"

"Well," replied Orville, "I received this list of possible locations and Kitty Hawk, North Carolina, looks like just what we want. Look at this . . . ."

However, Orville and Wilbur spent many days waiting in frustration after they arrived at Kitty Hawk, because the winds weren't suitable. The Weather Bureau's information gave the averages, but the Wright brothers didn't realize that an acceptable average can be produced by unacceptable extremes.

 See Problem 58.

We have considered measures of central tendency and measures of position, but these measures do not give the entire story. For example, consider these sets of data:

Set A: $\{8, 9, 9, 9, 10\}$ *Mean:* $\dfrac{8 + 9 + 9 + 9 + 10}{5} = 9$ *Median:* 9   *Mode:* 9

Set B: $\{2, 9, 9, 12, 13\}$ *Mean:* $\dfrac{2 + 9 + 9 + 12 + 13}{5} = 9$ *Median:* 9   *Mode:* 9

Notice that, for sets A and B, the measures of central tendency do not distinguish the data. However, if you look at the data placed on planks, as shown in Figure 10.21, you will see that the data in Set B are relatively widely dispersed along the plank, whereas the data in Set A are clumped around the mean.

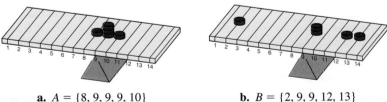

a. $A = \{8, 9, 9, 9, 10\}$ **b.** $B = \{2, 9, 9, 12, 13\}$

Figure 10.21 Visualization of dispersion of sets of data with mean, median, and mode of 9

In statistics, a **population** is the total set of items defined by some characteristic. Thus, we might refer to sets A and B as *populations*. We'll consider three **measures of dispersion:** the *range,* the *standard deviation,* and the *variance.*

Range

> The **range** of a set of data is the difference between the largest and the smallest numbers in the set.

EXAMPLE 1   Finding the range

Find the ranges for the following populations:

a. Set $A = \{8, 9, 9, 9, 10\}$ **b.** Set $B = \{2, 9, 9, 12, 13\}$

Solution   Notice from Figure 10.21 that the means, medians, and modes for these sets of data are the same. The range is found by computing the difference between the largest and smallest values in the set.   **a.** $10 - 8 = 2$ **b.** $13 - 2 = 11$ ●

The range is used, along with quartiles, to construct a statistical tool called a *box plot*. For a given set of data, a **box plot** consists of a rectangular box positioned above a numerical scale, drawn from Q_1 (the first quartile) to Q_3 (the third quartile). The median (Q_2, or second quartile) is shown as a dashed line, and a segment is extended to the left to show the distance to the minimum value; another segment is extended to the right for the maximum value.

EXAMPLE 2   Drawing a box plot

The 1999 monthly cost for health care for an employee and two dependents is given in the following table.

Provider	Cost
Maxicare	$415.24
Cigna	$424.77
Health Net	$427.48
Pacific Care	$428.05
Health Plan of the Redwoods	$431.52
Kaiser	$433.50
Aetna U.S. Healthcare	$436.11
Blue Shield HMO	$442.28
Omni Healthcare	$457.86
Lifeguard	$457.94

Draw a box plot for the monthly costs of health care.

Solution   We find the quartiles by first finding Q_2, the median. Since there are 10 entries, the median is the mean of the two middle items:

$$Q_2 = \frac{431.52 + 433.50}{2} = 432.51$$

Next, we find Q_1 (first quartile), which is the median of all items below Q_2:

$$Q_1 = 427.48$$

Finally, find Q_3 (third quartile), which is the median of all items above Q_2:

$$Q_3 = 442.28$$

The minimum cost is $415.24 and the maximum cost is $457.94, so we have a box plot, as shown in Figure 10.22.

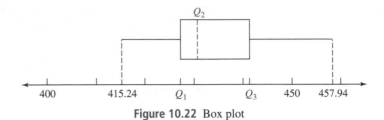

Figure 10.22 Box plot

Sometimes a box plot is called a *box-and-whisker plot*. Its usefulness should be clear when you look at Figure 10.22. It shows:

1. the median (labeled Q_2, a measure of central tendency);

2. the location of the middle half of the data (represented by the extent of the box; the endpoints are Q_1 and Q_3);

3. the range (a measure of dispersion, the ends of the whiskers sticking out of the box);

4. the skewness (the nonsymmetry of both the box and the whiskers).

Notice that the range is determined by only the largest and the smallest numbers in the set; it does not give us any information about the other numbers. It thus seems reasonable to invent another measure of dispersion that takes into account all the numbers in the data. We will consider the *deviations from the mean* and then the *standard deviation*. We proceed here as we did with the range, but instead of finding the difference between the largest and smallest values, we find the difference between *each number* and the mean.

Again, let's use the data set we worked with in Example 1.

Set $A = \{8, 9, 9, 9, 10\}$ Set $B = \{2, 9, 9, 12, 13\}$
Mean is 9.   Mean is 9.

Find the deviation of each term from the mean by subtracting the mean from each member in the set:

$$
\begin{array}{ll}
8 - 9 = -1 & \quad 2 - 9 = -7 \\
9 - 9 = 0 & \quad 9 - 9 = 0 \\
9 - 9 = 0 & \quad 9 - 9 = 0 \\
9 - 9 = 0 & \quad 12 - 9 = 3 \\
10 - 9 = 1 & \quad 13 - 9 = 4 \\
\quad\uparrow & \qquad\uparrow \\
\text{mean} & \quad\text{mean}
\end{array}
$$

If we total these deviations (to obtain a measure of the total deviation), in each case we obtain 0. To find a measure of total dispersion of a population, we calculate the mean of the *square of each of these deviations:*

Set $A = \{8, 9, 9, 9, 10\}$ Set $B = \{2, 9, 9, 12, 13\}$

$$
\begin{array}{ll}
(8 - 9)^2 = (-1)^2 = 1 & \quad (2 - 9)^2 = (-7)^2 = 49 \\
(9 - 9)^2 = (0)^2 = 0 & \quad (9 - 9)^2 = (0)^2 = 0 \\
(9 - 9)^2 = (0)^2 = 0 & \quad (9 - 9)^2 = (0)^2 = 0 \\
(9 - 9)^2 = (0)^2 = 0 & \quad (12 - 9)^2 = (3)^2 = 9 \\
(10 - 9)^2 = (1)^2 = 1 & \quad (13 - 9)^2 = (4)^2 = 16
\end{array}
$$

Mean: $\dfrac{1 + 0 + 0 + 0 + 1}{5} = \dfrac{2}{5} = 0.4$ Mean: $\dfrac{49 + 0 + 0 + 9 + 16}{5} = \dfrac{74}{5} = 14.8$

We sometimes must refer to this mean of the squares of the deviations, so we give it a name: the **variance.** Still, we need to continue to develop a true picture of the dispersion. Since we squared each difference it seems reasonable that (since we are working with positive numbers) we should find the square root of the variance as a more meaningful measure of dispersion. This number, called the *standard deviation*, is denoted by the lowercase Greek letter sigma (σ). You will need a calculator to find square roots:

$$\text{Set } A: \quad \sigma = \sqrt{0.4} \qquad\qquad \text{Set } B: \quad \sigma = \sqrt{14.8}$$
$$\approx 0.632 \qquad\qquad\qquad\qquad \approx 3.85$$

Display: .632455532 *Display:* 3.847076812

Standard Deviation

> The **standard deviation** of a population, denoted by σ, is the square root of the variance.

The procedure for finding the standard deviation is to first find the variance and then take the square root. This procedure is summarized here:

Standard Deviation

> The procedure for finding the standard deviation involves six steps:
>
> **Step 1** Determine the mean of the set of numbers.
>
> **Step 2** Subtract the mean from each number in the set.
>
> **Step 3** Square each of these differences?
>
> **Step 4** Find the sum of the squares of these differences.
>
> **Step 5** Divide this sum by the number of pieces of data.
> *The result here is the variance of a population: the mean of the squares of the deviations from the mean*
>
> **Step 6** Take the square root of the variance.

 You might want to spend some time reading the steps in this procedure.

EXAMPLE 3

Finding the standard deviation of a population

Suppose that Missy received the following test scores in a math class: 92, 85, 65, 89, 96, and 71. What is the standard deviation for her test scores?

Solution First, we calculate the mean:

Step 1: $\dfrac{92 + 85 + 65 + 89 + 96 + 71}{6} = 83$ This is the mean.

Steps 2 and 3: We summarize steps 2 and 3 by using a table format:

Score	(Deviation from the mean)²
92	$(92 - 83)^2 = 9^2 = 81$
85	$(85 - 83)^2 = 2^2 = 4$
65	$(65 - 83)^2 = (-18)^2 = 324$
89	$(89 - 83)^2 = 6^2 = 36$
96	$(96 - 83)^2 = 13^2 = 169$
71	$(71 - 83)^2 = (-12)^2 = 144$

Steps 4 and 5: Mean of squares of deviations:

$$\frac{81 + 4 + 324 + 36 + 169 + 144}{6} = \frac{758}{6} = 126\frac{1}{3}$$

We note that this number, $126\frac{1}{3}$, is called the variance. If you do not have access to a calculator, you can use the variance as a measure of dispersion. However, we assume that you have a calculator and can find the standard deviation:*

Step 6: $\sigma = \sqrt{\frac{758}{6}} \approx 11.24$ *Display:*   11.2398102   ●

How can we use the standard deviation? We will begin the discussion in Section 10.5 with this question. For now, however, we will give one example. Suppose that Missy obtained 65 on an examination for which the mean was 50 and the standard deviation was 15, whereas in another class Theron scored 74 on an examination for which the mean was 80 and the standard deviation was 3. Did Theron or Missy do better in her respective class? We see that Missy scored one standard deviation above the mean $(50 + 15 = 65)$, whereas Theron scored two standard deviations *below* the mean $(80 - 2 \times 3 = 74)$; so Missy did better compared to her classmates than did Theron.

*What we are finding here is the *population variance* (step 5), but there is another variance called the *sample variance*, which divides the sum in step 5 by $(n - 1)$ instead of n. Some calculators are programmed to find the sample variance rather than the population variance, so take care if you use a calculator to find the standard deviation for the problems in this book. If you are using a calculator, you should test the answer you obtain with your calculator against the results shown in this example.

PROBLEM SET (10.4)

ESSENTIAL IDEAS | **LEVEL 1**

See IAS for box-and-whisker plots.

1. What is the range?
   the difference between the largest and smallest values
2. What is the variance?
   the mean of the squares of the deviations
3. What is the standard deviation?
   the square root of the variance
4. **IN YOUR OWN WORDS** Compare and contrast measures of dispersion.

5. Suppose that a variance is zero. What can you say about the data?   All data are the same.

DRILL AND PRACTICE | **LEVEL 2**

In Problems 6–17, find the range and mean for each data set.

6. 1, 2, 3, 4, 5   4, 3
7. 17, 18, 19, 20, 21   4, 19
8. 103, 104, 105, 106, 107   4, 105
9. 765, 766, 767, 768, 769   4, 767
10. 4, 7, 10, 7, 5, 2, 7   8, 6
11. 15, 13, 10, 7, 6, 9, 10   9, 10
12. 3, 5, 8, 13, 21   18, 10
13. 1, 4, 9, 16, 25   24, 11
14. 79, 90, 95, 95, 96   17, 91
15. 70, 81, 95, 79, 85   25, 82

16. 1, 2, 3, 3, 3, 4, 5   4, 3   17. 0, 1, 1, 2, 3, 4, 16, 21   21, 6

In Problems 18–29, find the variance and the standard deviation (correct to two decimal places). If you do not have a calculator, you may give the variance only.

18. 1, 2, 3, 4, 5   2, 1.41
19. 17, 18, 19, 20, 21   2, 1.41
20. 103, 104, 105, 106, 107   2, 1.41
21. 765, 766, 767, 768, 769   2, 1.41
22. 4, 7, 10, 7, 5, 2, 7   5.71, 2.39
23. 15, 13, 10, 7, 6, 9, 10   8.57, 2.93
24. 3, 5, 8, 13, 21   41.6, 6.45
25. 1, 4, 9, 16, 25   74.8, 8.65
26. 79, 90, 95, 95, 96   40.4, 6.36
27. 70, 81, 95, 79, 85   66.4, 8.15
28. 1, 2, 3, 3, 3, 4, 5   1.43, 1.20
29. 0, 1, 1, 2, 3, 4, 16, 21   55, 7.42

30. By looking for a pattern, find the mean and variance of the numbers 217,849, 217,850, 217,851, 217,852, and 217,853.
Mean is the middle number, namely 217,851; variance is 2.

31. IN YOUR OWN WORDS A professor gives six exams. Two students' scores have the same mean, although one student's scores have a small standard deviation and the other student's scores have a large standard deviation. Give an example of such scores.

32. IN YOUR OWN WORDS Roll a single die until all six numbers occur at least once. Repeat the experiment 20 times. Find the mean, the median, the mode, and the range of the number of tosses.

33. IN YOUR OWN WORDS Roll a pair of dice until all 11 possible sums occur at least once. Repeat the experiment 20 times. Find the mean, the median, the mode, and the range of the number of tosses.

If you roll a pair of dice 36 times, the expected number of times for rolling each of the possible sums is as given in the accompanying table.

Outcome	Expected Frequency
2	1
3	2
4	3
5	4
6	5
7	6
8	5
9	4
10	3
11	2
12	1

A graph of these data is shown in Figure 10.23.

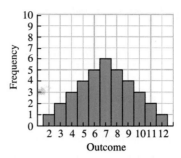

Figure 10.23 Distribution for rolling a pair of dice

Use this information to answer the questions in Problems 34–38.

34. What is the mean? mean = 7

35. What is the variance? var = 5.8$\overline{3}$

36. What is the standard deviation? $\sigma \approx 2.42$

37. IN YOUR OWN WORDS Roll a pair of dice 36 times. Construct a table and a graph similar to the ones shown here. What is the mean for your results? How do your results compare with those shown in Figure 10.23?

38. IN YOUR OWN WORDS What is the standard deviation for your results from Problem 37? How do your results compare with those shown in Figure 10.23?

APPLICATIONS   LEVEL 2

In Problems 39–42, consider the following test scores obtained by a class:

Test score	90	80	70	60	50
Frequency	1	3	10	5	2

39. Find the range and mean (rounded to the nearest unit).
40, 68

40. Draw a box-and-whisker plot for these data.

41. Find the variance (rounded to the nearest hundredth). 91.61

42. Find the standard deviation (rounded to the nearest hundredth). 9.57

In Problems 43–46, consider the following test scores obtained by a class:

Test score	90	80	70	60	50	40
Frequency	1	6	10	4	3	1

43. Find the range and mean (rounded to the nearest unit).
50, 68

44. Draw a box-and-whisker plot for these data.

45. Find the variance. 136

46. Find the standard deviation (rounded to the nearest hundredth). 11.66

In Problems 47–50, consider the following test scores obtained by a class:

Test score	90	80	70	60	50	40	30	0
Frequency	2	4	9	5	3	1	2	4

47. Find the range and mean.   *90, 56*

48. Draw a box-and-whisker plot for these data.

49. Find the variance (rounded to the nearest hundredth). *690.67*

50. Find the standard deviation (rounded to the nearest unit). *26*

For Problems 51–54, use the salaries of employees of the Moe D. Lawn Landscaping Company:

Salary	$25,000	$28,000	$30,000	$45,000
Frequency	4	3	2	1

51. Find the range and mean.   *$20,000; $28,900*

52. Draw a box-and-whisker plot for these data.

53. Find the variance.   *32,490,000*

54. Find the standard deviation (rounded to the nearest dollar).   *$5,700*

For Problems 55–56, consider G. Thumb, the leading salesperson for the Moe D. Lawn Landscaping Company. Thumb turned in the following summary of clients contacted for the week of October 23–28:

Date	No. of Clients
Oct. 23	12
Oct. 24	9
Oct. 25	10
Oct. 26	16
Oct. 27	10
Oct. 28	21

55. Find the variance.   *18*

56. Find the standard deviation (rounded to the nearest hundredth). $\sigma \approx 4.24$

57. IN YOUR OWN WORDS Comment on the following ten commandments of work checking:

> **Ten Commandments of Work Checking**
> 1. Does your answer make sense?
> 2. Does your answer fit your estimate?
> 3. Recalculate.
> 4. Do your problem twice.
> 5. Check your use of signs.
> 6. Check your decimal points.
> 7. Recheck your writing.
> 8. Check your exponents.
> 9. Reread visuals.
> 10. Substitute your answer.

58. IN YOUR OWN WORDS

"We need privacy and a consistent wind," said Wilbur. "Did you write to the Weather Bureau to find a suitable location?" "Well," replied Orville, "I received this list of possible locations and Kitty Hawk, North Carolina, looks like just what we want. Look at this . . . ." However, Orville and Wilbur spent many days waiting in frustration after they arrived in Kitty Hawk, because the winds weren't suitable. The Weather Bureau's information gave the averages, but the Wright brothers didn't realize that an acceptable average can be produced by unacceptable extremes. Write a paper explaining how it is possible to have an acceptable average produced by unacceptable extremes.

Wright Brothers' first flight at Kitty Hawk,
North Carolina

RIGHT OR WRONG?   LEVEL 3

Explain what is wrong, if anything, with the statements in Problems 59–60. Explain your reasoning.

59. The standard deviation is always smaller than the variance, because the standard deviation is the square root of the variance.   *F; if the variance is between 0 and 1, the standard deviation will be larger than the variance.*

60. For the data 70, 80, and 90, the standard deviation is found as follows: The mean is

$$\frac{70 + 80 + 90}{3} = \frac{240}{3} = 80$$

$$(70 - 80)^2 = (-10)^2 = 100$$

$$(80 - 80)^2 = 0^2 = 0$$

$$(90 - 80)^2 = 10^2 = 100$$

The mean of the deviations is

$$\frac{100 + 0 + 100}{3} = \frac{200}{3} = 66\frac{2}{3}$$

The standard deviation is

$$\sqrt{66\frac{2}{3}} \approx 8.16 \quad \text{T}$$

10.5 The Normal Curve and Sampling

"I signed up for Hunter in History 17," said Ben.
   "Why did you sign up for her?" asked Ted. "Don't you know she has given only three A's in the last 14 years?!"
   "That's just a rumor. Hunter grades on a curve," Ben replied.
   "Don't give me that 'on a curve' stuff," continued Ted. "I'll bet you don't even know what that means. Anyway, my sister-in-law had her last year and said it was so bad that . . . ."

 See Problem 50.

Normal Curve

The cartoon in the margin suggests that most people do not like to think of themselves or their children as having "normal intelligence." But what do we mean by *normal* or *normal intelligence?*

   Suppose we survey the results of 20 children's scores on an IQ test. The scores (rounded to the nearest 5 points) are 115, 90, 100, 95, 105, 95, 105, 105, 95, 125, 120, 110, 100, 100, 90, 110, 100, 115, 105, and 80. A frequency graph of these data is shown in Figure 10.24**a.** If we consider 10,000 scores instead of only 20, we might obtain the frequency distribution shown in Figure 10.24**b.**

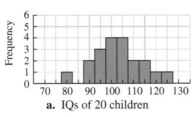

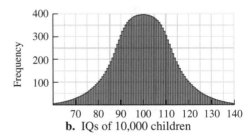

a. IQs of 20 children

b. IQs of 10,000 children

Figure 10.24 Frequency distributions for IQ scores

CAUTION This curve is important in many different applications and when observing many natural phenomena.

   The data illustrated in Figure 10.24 approximate a commonly used curve called a *normal frequency curve,* or simply a **normal curve.** (See Figure 10.25.)

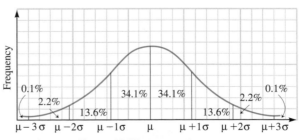

Figure 10.25 A normal curve

If we obtain the frequency distribution of a large number of measurements (as with IQ), the corresponding graph tends to look normal, or **bell-shaped.** The normal curve has some interesting properties. In it, the mean, the median, and the mode all have the same value, and all occur exactly at the center of the distribution; we denote this value by the Greek letter mu (μ). The standard deviation for this distribution is σ (sigma). Roughly 68% of all values lie within the region from one standard deviation below to one standard deviation above the mean. About 95% lie within two standard deviations on either side of the mean, and virtually all (99.8%) values lie within three standard deviations on either side. These percentages are the same regardless of the particular mean or standard deviation.

EXAMPLE 1

Using a normal curve to predict occurrence of IQ score

Predict the distribution of IQ scores of 1,000 people if we assume that IQ scores are normally distributed, and if we know that the mean is 100 and the standard deviation is 15.

Solution First, find the breaking points around the mean for a normal distribution with $\mu = 100$ and $\sigma = 15$.

$$\mu + \sigma = 100 + 15 = 115 \qquad \mu - \sigma = 100 - 15 = 85$$
$$\mu + 2\sigma = 100 + 2 \cdot 15 = 130 \qquad \mu - 2\sigma = 100 - 2 \cdot 15 = 70$$
$$\mu + 3\sigma = 100 + 3 \cdot 15 = 145 \qquad \mu - 3\sigma = 100 - 3 \cdot 15 = 55$$

We use Figure 10.25 to find that 34.1% of the scores will be between 100 and 115 (i.e., between μ and $\mu + \sigma$):

$$0.341 \times 1,000 = 341$$

About 13.6% will be between 115 and 130 (i.e., between $\mu + \sigma$ and $\mu + 2\sigma$):

$$0.136 \times 1,000 = 136$$

About 2.2% will be between 130 and 145 (i.e., between $\mu + 2\sigma$ and $\mu + 3\sigma$):

$$0.022 \times 1,000 = 22$$

About 0.1% will be above 145 (more than $\mu + 3\sigma$):

$$0.001 \times 1,000 = 1$$

The intervals for standard deviations below the mean repeat these expected numbers, since the normal curve is symmetric to the left and to the right of the mean. The distribution is shown in the margin. ●

Scores	Percent	Expected Number
Below 55	0.1	1
55–69	2.2	22
70–84	13.6	136
85–99	34.1	341
100–114	34.1	341
115–129	13.6	136
130–144	2.2	22
Above 144	0.1	1
Totals	100.0	1,000

EXAMPLE 2

Grading on a curve

Suppose that an instructor "grades on a curve." Show the grading distribution on an examination of 45 students, if the scores are normally distributed with a mean of 73 and a standard deviation of 9.

Solution Grading on a curve means determining students' grades according to the percentages shown in Figure 10.26.

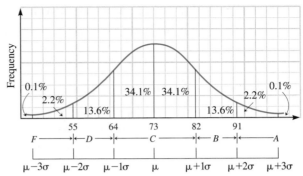

Figure 10.26 Grade distribution for a class "graded on a curve"

We calculate these numbers as shown:

	Calculation	Scores	Grade	Calculation	Number
Two or more standard deviations above the mean	$\mu + 2\sigma = 73 + 2 \cdot 9 = 91$	91–100	A	$0.023 \times 45 = 1.035$	1
	$\mu + 1\sigma = 73 + 1 \cdot 9 = 82$	82–90	B	$0.136 \times 45 = 6.12$	6
Mean:	$\mu = 73$	64–81	C	$0.682 \times 45 = 30.69$	31
	$\mu - 1\sigma = 73 - 1 \cdot 9 = 64$	55–63	D	Same as grade B	6
Two or more standard deviations below the mean	$\mu - 2\sigma = 73 - 2 \cdot 9 = 55$	0–54	F	Same as grade A	1

Grading on a curve means that the person with the top score in the class receives an A; the next 6 ranked persons (from the top) receive B grades; the bottom score in the class receives an F; the next 6 ranked persons (from the bottom) receive D grades; and finally, the remaining 31 persons receive C grades. Notice the majority of the class $(34.1\% + 34.1\% = 68.2\%)$ will receive an "average" C grade.   ●

EXAMPLE 3

Problem solving with a normal distribution

The Eureka Lightbulb Company tested a new line of lightbulbs and found their lifetimes to be normally distributed, with a mean life of 98 hours and a standard deviation of 13 hours.

a. What percentage of bulbs will last less than 72 hours?

b. What is the probability that a bulb selected at random will last longer than 111 hours?

Solution Draw a normal curve with mean 98 and standard deviation 13, as shown in Figure 10.27.

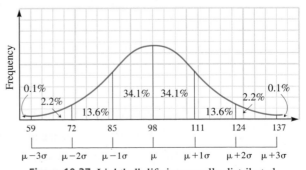

Figure 10.27 Lightbulb life is normally distributed

a. About 2.3% (2.2% + 0.1% = 2.3%) will last less than 72 hours.

b. We know that about 15.9% (13.6% + 2.2% + 0.1% = 15.9%) of the bulbs will last longer than 111 hours, so *P*(bulb life > 111 hours) ≈ 0.159. ●

Sampling

The previous sections of this chapter dealt with the accumulation of data, measures of central tendency, and dispersion. However, a more important part of statistics is its ability to help us make predictions about a population based on a sample from that population. A **sample** is a smaller group of items chosen to represent a larger group, or population. Thus, a sample is a proper subset of the population. The sample is analyzed; then based on this analysis, some conclusion about the entire population is made. Sampling necessarily involves some error, because the sample and the population are not identical.

The inference drawn from a poll can, of course, be wrong, so statistics is also concerned with estimating the error involved in predictions based on samples. In 1936, the *Literary Digest* predicted that Alfred Landon would defeat Franklin D. Roosevelt—who was subsequently reelected president by a landslide. (The magazine ceased publication the following year.) In 1948, the *Chicago Daily Tribune* drew an incorrect conclusion from its polls and declared in a headline that Thomas Dewey had just been elected president over Harry S. Truman. A more recent example of an erroneous prediction based on polling is the famous Bush/Gore 2000 election controversy.

In an attempt to minimize error in their predictions, statisticians follow a very careful **sampling procedure,** as outlined in the following box.

Sampling

The proper steps in the sampling procedure are:

Step 1 Propose some hypothesis about a population.

Step 2 Gather a sample from the population.

Step 3 Analyze the data.

Step 4 Accept or reject the hypothesis.

Suppose that you want to decide whether a certain coin is a "fair" coin. You decide to test the hypothesis, "This is a fair coin," by flipping the coin 100 times. This provides a *sample*. Suppose the result is

Heads: 55   Tails: 45

Do you accept or reject the hypothesis that "This coin is fair"? The expected number of heads is 50, but certainly a fair coin might well produce the results obtained.

As you can readily see, two types of error are possible when we make a decision in a *hypothesis-testing* situation; they are summarized in the following box:

Decision Errors

These types of error are essential for the ideas of hypothesis testing.

There are two possible types of decision errors in hypothesis testing:

Type I: Rejection of the hypothesis when it is true.

Type II: Acceptance of the hypothesis when it is false.

How can we minimize the possibility of making either error? Let's carry this example further, and repeat the experiment of flipping the coin 100 times:

Trial number: 1   2   3   4   5   6 ⋯
Number of heads: 55   52   54   57   59   55 ⋯

If the coin is fair and we repeat the experiment a large number of times, the distribution of the number of heads should be normal, with a mean of 50 and a standard deviation of 5, as shown in Figure 10.28. The question is whether or not to accept the *unknown* test coin as fair.

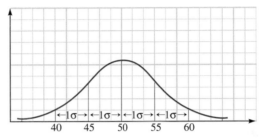

Figure 10.28 Given normal distribution for the number of heads upon flipping a fair coin 100 times

Suppose that you are willing to accept the coin as fair only if the number of heads falls between 45 and 55 (that is, within one standard deviation on either side of the expected number). If you adopt this standard, you know you will be correct 68% of the time, if the coin is fair. How do you know this? Look at Figure 10.28, and note that 34.1% of the results will be within $+1\sigma$ and 34.1% will be within -1σ; the total is $34.1\% + 34.1\% = 68.2\%$.

But a friend says, "Yes, you will be correct 68% of the time, but you will also be rejecting a lot of fair coins!" You respond, "But suppose that a coin really is a bad coin (it really favors heads), with a mean number of heads of 60 and a standard deviation of 5. If I adopted the same standard ($\pm 1\sigma$), I'd be accepting all the coins in the shaded region of Figure 10.29."

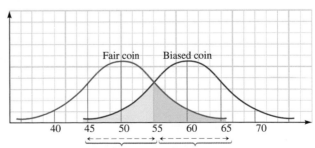

Accept $\pm 1\sigma$:   Type II error;   Type I error;
                       accept hypothesis   reject hypothesis
                       when it is false.   when it is true.

Figure 10.29 Comparison of Type I and Type II errors

Poll-taker to boss: "Our latest opinion poll showed that 90% of the people aren't interested in the opinions of others."

As you can see, a decrease in the probability of a Type I error increases the probability of a Type II error, and vice versa. Deciding which type of error to minimize depends on the stakes involved and on some statistical calculations that go beyond the scope of this course.

Consider a company that produces two types of valves. The first type is used in jet aircraft, and the failure of this valve might cause many deaths. A sample of the valves is taken and tested, and the company must accept or reject the entire shipment on the basis of these test results. Under these circumstances, the company would rather reject many good valves than accept a bad one. On the other hand, the second valve is used in toy airplanes; the failure of this valve would merely cause the crash of the model. In this case, the company wouldn't want to reject too many good valves, so it would minimize the probability of rejecting the good valves.

Many times we read of a poll in the newspaper or hear of it on the evening news, and a percent is given. For example, "The candidate was favored by 48% of those sampled." What is not often stated (or is stated only in small print) is that there is a margin of error and a confidence level. For example, "The margin of error is 4 percent at a confidence level of 95%." This means that we are 95% confident that the actual percentage of people who favor the candidate is between 44% and 52%.

PROBLEM SET (10.5)

ESSENTIAL IDEAS   LEVEL 1

1. Draw a normal curve, label the mean, and label the standard deviations on each side of the mean. Fill in the frequency percents for each standard deviation.
   See Figure 10.25.
2. What is the sampling procedure?   See p. 528.

3. **IN YOUR OWN WORDS** Discuss the two types of decision error in hypothesis testing. How are they related to each other?

DRILL AND PRACTICE   LEVEL 2

In Problems 4–8, suppose that people's heights (in centimeters) are normally distributed, with a mean of 170 and a standard deviation of 5. We find the heights of 50 people.

4. How many would you expect to be between 165 and 175 cm tall?   34

5. How many would you expect to be taller than 160 cm?   49

6. How many would you expect to be taller than 175 cm?   8

7. What is the probability that a person selected at random is taller than 165 cm?   0.841

8. What is the variance for this experiment?   25

In Problems 9–13 suppose that, for a certain exam, a teacher grades on a curve. It is known that the grades follow a normal distribution with a mean of 50 and a standard deviation of 5. There are 45 students in the class.

9. How many students should receive a C?   31

10. How many students should receive an A?   1

11. What score would be necessary to obtain an A?   60 or above

12. If an exam paper is selected at random, what is the probability that it will be a failing paper?   0.023

13. What is the variance for this exam?   25

In Problems 14–23, suppose the neck size of men is normally distributed, with a mean of 15.5 inches and a standard deviation of 0.5 inch. A shirt manufacturer is going to introduce a new line of shirts, and plans on making 1,000 shirts.

14. How many shirts should have a neck size 14?   1

15. How many shirts should have a neck size 14.5?   22

16. How many shirts should have a neck size 15?   136

17. How many shirts should have a neck size 15.5?   341

18. How many shirts should have a neck size 16?   341

19. How many shirts should have a neck size 16.5?   136

20. How many shirts should have a neck size 17?   22

21. How many shirts should have a neck size 17.5?   1

22. What is the probability that a person will have a neck size between 15 and 16?   68.2%

23. What is the probability that the person will have a neck size between 14.5 and 15?   13.6%

APPLICATIONS   **LEVEL 2**

In Problems 24–27, consider two teams in a tug-of-war.

Suppose that the breaking strength of a rope (in pounds) is normally distributed, with a mean of 100 *pounds and a standard deviation of* 16.

24. What is the probability that the rope will break when subjected to a force of 100 pounds?   *0.50*

25. What is the probability that the rope will break when subjected to a force of 116 pounds or less?   *0.841*

26. What is the probability that the rope will break when subjected to a force of 132 pounds or less?   *0.977*

27. Predict the distribution of the breaking points of a sample of 1,000 ropes assuming that the breaking strength is normally distributed.   Below 52, 1; 52–67, 22; 68–83, 136; 84–99, 341; 100–115, 341; 116–131, 136; 132–147; 22; above 147, 1

In Problems 28–31, suppose that the diameter of an electric cable is normally distributed, with a mean of 0.90 *inch and a standard deviation of* 0.01 *inch. Suppose that a sample of the cable is randomly selected.*

28. What is the probability that the diameter will be less than 0.9 inch?   *0.50*

29. What is the probability that the diameter will be greater than 0.9 inch?   *0.50*

30. What is the probability that the diameter will exceed 0.91 inch?   *0.159*

31. Predict the distribution of the diameters of a sample of 1,000 cables assuming that the diameter is normally distributed.   See bottom of the column.

In Problems 32–35, suppose that the annual rainfall in Ferndale, California, is known to be normally distributed, with a mean of 35.5 *inches and a standard deviation of* 2.5 *inches.*

The Victorian Village of Ferndale, CA

31. Below 0.87, 1; 0.87–0.88, 22; 0.88–0.89, 136; 0.89–0.90, 341; 0.90–0.91, 341; 0.91–0.92, 136; 0.92–0.93; 22; above 0.93, 1

32. What is the probability that the annual rainfall in Ferndale in a randomly selected year will be between 33 inches and 38 inches?   *0.682*

33. What is the probability that the rainfall in a given year will exceed 30.5 inches in Ferndale?   *0.977*

34. About 0.1% of the time, the annual rainfall will be less than how many inches?   *28 inches*

35. About 2.3% of the time, the annual rainfall will exceed how many inches?   *40.5 inches*

In Problems 36–39, the diameter of a pipe is normally distributed, with a mean of 0.40 *inch and a variance of* 0.0004. *Suppose one pipe is randomly selected.*

36. What is the probability that the diameter will be less than 0.38 inch?   *0.159*

37. What is the probability that the diameter will be less than 0.36?   *0.023*

38. What is the probability that the diameter will be between 0.4 and 0.42?   *0.341*

39. What is the probability that the diameter will exceed 0.44 inch?   *0.023*

In Problems 40–43, the breaking strength (in pounds) of a certain new synthetic is normally distributed, with a mean of 165 *pounds and a variance of* 9. *The material is considered defective if the breaking strength is less than* 159 *pounds.*

40. What is the probability a randomly selected sample will have a breaking strength greater than 165 pounds?   *0.50*

41. What is the probability a randomly selected sample will have a breaking strength greater than 168 pounds?   *0.159*

42. What is the probability a randomly selected sample will have a breaking strength greater than 171 pounds?   *0.023*

43. What is the probability that a randomly selected piece of material will be defective?   *0.023*

In Problems 44–47, a package of Toys Galore cereal is marked "Net Wt. 12 oz." The actual weight is normally distributed, with a mean of 12 *oz and a variance of* 0.04.

44. What percent of the packages will weigh less than 12 oz?   50%

45. What percent of the packages will weigh more than 12.4 oz?   2.3%

46. What percent of the packages will weigh between 12 oz and 12.4 oz?   47.7%

47. What weight will be exceeded by 2.3% of the packages?   12.4 oz

48. Instant Dinner comes in packages with weights that are normally distributed, with a standard deviation of 0.3 oz. If 2.3% of the dinners weigh more than 13.5 oz, what is the mean weight?   12.9 oz

49. Vitavegi dog food comes in cartons with weights that are normally distributed, with a standard deviation of

2 lb. If 2.3% of the cartons weigh more than 102 lb, what is the mean weight?   **98 lb**

 50. "I signed up for Hunter in History 17," said Ben. "Why did you sign up for her?" asked Ted. "Don't you know she has given only three A's in the last fourteen years?!" "That's just a rumor. Hunter grades on a curve," Ben replied. "Don't give me that 'on a curve' stuff," continued Ted, "I'll bet you don't even know what that means. Anyway, my sister-in-law had her last year and said it was so bad that . . . ." Assume that Hunter does, indeed, grade on a curve. Show the grading distribution if 200 students take an examination, with a mean of 73 and a standard deviation of 9. What are the grades Hunter would give?   **See bottom of the column.**

IN YOUR OWN WORDS   *In Problems* 51–60 *decide on a reasonable means for conducting the survey to obtain the desired information.*

51. A newsstand wishes to use a survey to determine which out-of-town newspapers it should regularly stock.

52. Sprint would like to take customers from AT&T, one of its competitors in a certain geographical area. Sprint would like to survey AT&T's customers in order to find out which elements of its service are least satisfactory.

53. A pet store would like to use a survey to determine which factors are most important to cat owners in determining the brand of cat food that they purchase.

50. *Grade A (91 or above), 5 or 2.3%; Grade B (82–90), 27 or 13.6%; C (64–81), 136 or 68.2%; D (55–63), 27 or 13.6%; F (below 55), 5 or 2.3%*

54. A local political party would like to use a survey to determine the level of support among party members for the party's candidates in the upcoming primary election.

55. A health and fitness club would like to survey its members in order to determine which new equipment they would prefer.

56. A union wants to use a survey to determine the extent to which its members approve of a newly negotiated collective bargaining agreement.

57. The city council wants to use a survey to determine the extent of public approval for a project to construct a new playground in a certain residential neighborhood.

58. The college student government will use a survey to determine the level of support among students for a proposal to lower the student fees.

59. A retailer is considering offering extended warranty policies on video cameras. It will use a survey to determine the extent of interest among owners of the video cameras.

60. A supermarket is considering expanding its services by adding a florist, but prior to doing so, it will use a survey to determine the extent to which its customers are interested in such a service.

(10.6) Chapter 10 Summary and Review

 Take some time getting ready to work the review problems in this section. First, look back at the definition and property boxes. You will maximize your understanding of this chapter by working the problems in this section only after you have studied the material.

IMPORTANT TERMS
Numbers refer to sections of this chapter.

Spending some time with the terms and objectives of this chapter will pay dividends in assuring your success.

Average [10.2]	Histogram [10.1]	Pictograph [10.1]
Bar graph [10.1]	Interval [10.1]	Pie chart [10.1]
Bell-shaped curve [10.5]	Line graph [10.1]	Population [10.4]
Bimodal [10.2]	Mean [10.2]	Quartile [10.3]
Box plot [10.4]	Measure of central tendency [10.2]	Range [10.4]
Circle graph [10.1]		Sample [10.5]
Classes [10.1]	Measure of dispersion [10.4]	Standard deviation [10.4]
Decile [10.3]	Measure of position [10.3]	Statistics [10.1]
Frequency [10.1]	Median [10.2]	Type I error [10.5]
Frequency distribution [10.1]	Mode [10.2]	Type II error [10.5]
Grouped frequency distribution [10.1]	Normal curve [10.5]	Variance [10.4]
	Percentile [10.3]	

Essential Ideas

[10.1] Problem 1	Know the meaning of the word *statistics*.
Problems 2–6	Be able to use and read various graphs, including bar graphs, histograms, line graphs, circle graphs, and pictographs.
[10.2] Problems 1–4	Compare and contrast measures of central tendency, and in particular, be able to describe mean, median, and mode.
[10.3] Problem 1	Distinguish measures of central tendency with measures of position.
Problems 2–4	Be able to use quartiles, deciles, and percentiles.
[10.4] Problems 1–4	Distinguish measures of dispersion, in particular, range, variance, and standard deviation.
Problem 5	Understand the meaning of variance and standard deviation.
[10.5] Problem 1	Draw a normal curve with the mean and standard deviation, including the frequency percents.
Problems 2–3	Be able to discuss a sampling procedure, including the two types of decision error in hypothesis testing.

LEARNING OUTCOMES

The material in this chapter is reviewed in the following list of learning outcomes. A self-test (with answers and suggestions for additional study) is given. This self-test is constructed so that each problem number corresponds to a related objective. For example, Problem 7 is testing Objective 10.7. This self-test is followed by a practice test with the questions in mixed order.

[10.1]	*Objective* 10.1	Make a frequency distribution, as well as a grouped frequency distribution.
[10.1]	*Objective* 10.2	Draw a histogram or a bar graph to represent data.
[10.1]	*Objective* 10.3	Draw a line graph to represent data.
[10.1]	*Objective* 10.4	Be able to read and interpret graphs.
[10.1]	*Objective* 10.5	Draw a circle graph to represent data.
[10.1]	*Objective* 10.6	Be able to recognize misuses of statistics.
[10.2]	*Objective* 10.7	Find the mean, median, and mode.
[10.2]	*Objective* 10.8	Decide on the most appropriate measure of central tendency.
[10.3]	*Objective* 10.9	Find the percentile, given a data position.
[10.3]	*Objective* 10.10	Find the decile, given a data position.
[10.3]	*Objective* 10.11	Find the quartile rank, given a data position.
[10.3]	*Objective* 10.12	Find a class ranking, given the percentile and number of data points.
[10.4]	*Objective* 10.13	Find the range and mean for a set of data.
[10.4]	*Objective* 10.14	Find the variance and standard deviation for a set of data.
[10.4]	*Objective* 10.15	Draw a box-and-whisker plot.
[10.5]	*Objective* 10.16	Understand and use a normal distribution.
[10.5]	*Objective* 10.17	Understand the basic ideas of sampling.
[10.1–10.5]	*Objective* 10.18	Work applied problems dealing with statistics (Problems 18–20).

Self-Test

Each question of this self-test is related to the corresponding objective listed above.

1. Make a frequency table for the following results of tossing a coin:

HTTTT HHTHH TTHHT THTHT HHTTH THHTH HHTHT TTTTT

2. Draw a bar graph for the number of heads and tails given in Problem 1.

3. Three coins are tossed onto a table, and the following frequencies are noted:

Number of heads	3	2	1	0
Frequency	18	56	59	17

Draw a line graph to represent these data.

4. Consider the graph shown in Figure 10.30, which shows the salary and sex data from a survey of United States companies.

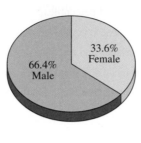

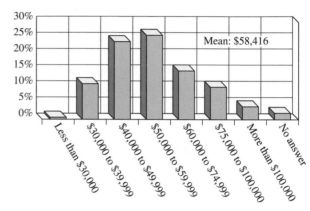

Figure 10.30 Salary survey

a. Which salary category had the greatest percent of respondents? What percent of respondents received salaries in that class?

b. What fraction of respondents are female? (Choose the best response.)

   A. $\frac{1}{3}$ B. $\frac{2}{3}$ C. $\frac{4}{5}$ D. $\frac{1}{2}$ E. Information not available

c. If there were 2,000 respondents to this survey, what would be the approximate number of males?

5. Suppose that a student's college expenses are as follows:

Registration fee	$1,800
Education fee	$1,000
Books and supplies	$ 600
Room and board	$6,400
Miscellaneous	$ 200

Make a circle graph showing these data.

6. Consider the graph of an Anacin advertisement, as shown in Figure 10.31. Does it tell you anything at all about the effectiveness of the three pain relievers? Explain your answer.

In Problems 7–9, use the following test scores:

96, 92, 92, 89, 88, 88, 87, 87, 87, 87, 80, 79, 79, 78, 76, 76, 76, 74, 73, 72, 72, 71, 71, 70, 70, 66, 66, 60, 53, 20

7. a. Find the mean (rounded to the nearest unit).   **b.** Find the median.
   c. Find the mode.

8. Which measure of central tendency is most appropriate for these test scores?

9. If Frank's score is 87, what is his percentile rank?

10. a. If there is a list of 263 mutual funds, then how many funds would be in the top decile?
   b. Is the top decile called the first decile or the 10th decile?

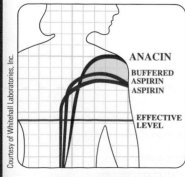

Figure 10.31 Anacin advertisement

11. Sharon is ranked in the second quartile in her senior class of 65 students. Rico is in the same class and is ranked 23rd. Who ranks higher and why?

12. If Jane's score is one of the test scores listed in Problems 7–9, and is in the 87th percentile, what is her class rank?

13. Table 10.2 on page 497 gives the state sales tax rates for the 50 states. What is the range of the sales taxes, and what is the mean sales tax?

14. **a.** Find the variance for the scores 90, 85, 70, 70, and 65.
    b. Find the standard deviation (rounded to the nearest tenth) for the scores in part **a.**

15. Draw a box-and-whisker plot for the test scores listed in Problems 7–9 (ranked lowest to highest).

16. If grades are assigned to a class of 30 students and the instructor "grades on a curve," how many students each will receive A's, B's, C's, D's, and F's?

17. Explain how you would obtain a sample of people in your community to ask how they feel about a recent crime.

18. The number of miles driven on each of five tires was 17,000, 19,000, 19,000, 20,000, and 21,000. Find the mean, the range, and the standard deviation (rounded to the nearest unit) for these mileages.

19. A powerbar is produced in three sizes, 20 g, 25 g, and 50 g, and is sold to wholesalers in case lots. The sales figures for Region IV are shown in Table 10.4. Find the mean, the median, and the mode of the sizes of the powerbars sold in Region IV. If the wholesaler decides to cut back the variety and stock only one size, which measure of central tendency will be most useful in making this decision?

20. **IN YOUR OWN WORDS** A professor gives five exams. Two students' scores have the same mean, although one student did better on all the tests except one. Give an example of such scores.

TABLE 10.4	Sales of Powerbar
Size	Number of Cases Sold
20 g	5 cases
25 g	10 cases
50 g	35 cases

STUDY HINTS *Compare your solutions and answers to the self-test. For each problem you missed, work some additional problems in the section listed in the margin. After you have worked these problems, you can test yourself with the practice test.*

Additional Problems

[10.1] Problems 7–10; 19

[10.1] Problems 11–14; 20

[10.1] Problems 15–18

[10.1] Problems 21–37

Complete Solutions to the Self-Test

1. Heads: 卌 卌 卌 ⦀ (18); Tails 卌 卌 卌 卌 ‖ (22)

2.

3.

4. **a.** $50,000 to $59,999; 27%

   b. A

   c. 0.664(2,000) = 1,328

5. The sum of the expenses is $10,000, so the percents and degrees are as follows:

Registration: $0.18(360°) = 64.8°$

Education: $0.10(360°) = 36°$

Books/supplies $(0.06)(360°) = 21.6°$

Room: $0.64(360°) = 230.4°$

Misc.: $0.02(360°) = 7.2°$

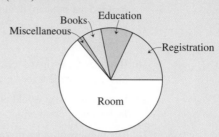

6. No, it does not. No scale is shown.

7. a. Add the numbers and divide by 30: $2{,}275 \div 30 = 75.8\overline{3}$. The mean is 76.

    b. The median is the mean of the 15th and 16th entries (arranged by magnitude). Since they are both the same, we see the median is 76.

    c. The mode is the most frequently occurring value, 87.

8. The mean is the most appropriate measure.

9. A score of 87 is higher than 20 of the 30 scores, so 87 is in the 67th percentile.

10. a. Deciles divide the data into 10 parts, so there would be $(10\%)(263) = 26.3$, or 26 funds in the top decile.

    b. Neither; the top decile is the 9th decile. Remember, deciles divide the data into 10 parts, so there are only nine deciles.

11. Since quartiles divide the data into four parts, we find the median score is the 33rd score, with the third quartile consisting of rankings 17–32. Thus, a rank of 23rd is in the third quartile, so Rico is higher than Sharon.

12. $30 \times 0.87 = 26.1$; the 87th percentile is the score 89, which means that Jane's rank is 4th.

13. The range is from 0% to 7%. To find the mean, we find the sum of the entries in Table 10.2, and divide by the number of entries (50):

$$\text{Mean} = \frac{2.39775}{50} = 0.047955$$

The mean sales tax in the U.S. is about 4.8%.

14. a. The variance is found as follows:

$$\text{Mean} = \frac{90 + 85 + 70 + 70 + 65}{5} = 76$$

Data	90	85	70	70	65
Deviation from the mean	14	9	−6	−6	−11
Square of the deviation	196	81	36	36	121

Mean of the squares: $\dfrac{196 + 81 + 36 + 36 + 121}{5} = 94$

The variance is 94.

    b. The standard deviation is $\sqrt{94} \approx 9.7$.

15. Since there are 30 scores, the median (Q_2) is the mean of the 15th and 16th scores; this is 76. The 8th score from the bottom (Q_1) is 71 and the 8th score from the top (Q_3) is 87. The range is $96 - 20 = 76$.

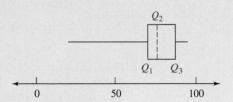

16. 2.3% should be A's: $0.023(30) = 0.69$; 1 A
13.6% should be B's: $0.136(30) = 4.08$; 4 B's
68.2% should be C's: $0.682(30) = 20.46$; 20 C's
Same number of D's as B's: 4 D's
Same number of F's as A's: 1F

17. Answers vary.

18. Mean $= \dfrac{17{,}000 + 19{,}000 + 19{,}000 + 20{,}000 + 21{,}000}{5}$

$\qquad = \dfrac{96{,}000}{5}$

$\qquad = 19{,}200$

Range $= 21{,}000 - 17{,}000$

$\qquad\ = 4{,}000$

(Deviation from the mean)^2

$(17{,}000 - 19{,}200)^2 = (-2{,}200)^2 = 4{,}840{,}000$
$(19{,}000 - 19{,}200)^2 = (-200)^2 = 40{,}000$
$(19{,}000 - 19{,}200)^2 = (-200)^2 = 40{,}000$
$(20{,}000 - 19{,}200)^2 = (800)^2 = 640{,}000$
$(21{,}000 - 19{,}200)^2 = (1{,}800)^2 = 3{,}240{,}000$

Mean $= \dfrac{4{,}840{,}000 + 2(40{,}000) + 640{,}000 + 3{,}240{,}000}{5}$

$\qquad = 1{,}760{,}000$

$\sigma = \sqrt{1{,}760{,}000} \approx 1{,}326.65$ or $1{,}327$ (rounded to the nearest unit)

19. Mean $= \dfrac{5(20) + 10(25) + 35(50)}{5 + 10 + 35}$

$\qquad = 42$

The mean size is 42 g. (Note that powerbars are not produced at this size. This is the *mean* size of all powerbars sold in the region.) The median is the middle value, and since there are a total of 50 cases, the median is the size of the mean of the 25th and 26th cases, which is 50 g. The mode is the most frequently occurring size, which is 50 g.

The most useful measure is 50 g (the mode).

20. Examples vary. Suppose the first student's scores were all 90 points, and the second student's scores were 91, 91, 91, 91, and 86. Then both students would have a mean score of 90, but the second student had a higher score on four of the five exams.

Chapter 10 Review Questions

To prepare for a chapter test, first study the chapter; then, read each term from the important terms list above and make sure you know the meaning of each word; finally, review the chapter objectives. **After** *these steps, take the self-test and correct all your answers. The following review questions can be used for extra practice.* See IAS for graphs and frequency distributions.

1. Make a frequency table for the following data:

$$7, 8, 8, 7, 8, 9, 6, 9, 8, 6, 8, 9, 10, 7, 7$$

2. Make a frequency table identifying the political party of the U.S. Speaker of the House for the 110 Congresses. The parties are designated by Democrat (D), Republican (R), Federalist (F), Dem.-Rep. (DR), Whig (W), and American (A):*

F, F, F, F, F, F, DR, DR, DR, DR, DR, DR, DR, DR, DR, DR, DR, DR, DR, DR,
D, D, D, D, D, D, D, W, D, D, W, D, D, D, A, D, R, R, R, R, R, R, R, R, R, D, D, D,
D, R, D, D, D, R, D, D, R, R, R, R, R, R, R, R, R, D, D, D, D, D, R, R, R, R, R, R, D, D, D,
D, D, D, D, D, D, D, R, D, D, R, R, D, D, D, D, D, D, D, D, D, D, D, D, D, D, D, D, D, D,
D, D, D, D, D, R, R, R, R, R, R, R, D

3. Make a bar graph for the data in Problem 2.

4. Make a line graph for the data in Problem 2.

5. Consider the data listed in the margin. The table shows the U.S. government's expenditures for social welfare.
   a. Draw a bar graph to represent these data.
   b. Suppose that you had the following viewpoint:

   Social welfare expenditures rose only $0.5 trillion from 1989 to 1995.

   Draw a graph that seems to show very little increase in the expenditures.
   c. Suppose you had the following viewpoint:

   Social welfare expenditures rose $548,000,000,000 from 1989 to 1995.

   Draw a graph that seems to shows a tremendous increase in the expenditures.
   d. In view of parts **a–c,** discuss the possibilities of using statistics to mislead or support different views.   Answers vary.

6. Find the mean, the median, and the mode for the following data: 23, 24, 25, 26, 27.
   mean = 25; median = 25; no mode

7. A small grocery store stocked several sizes of Copycat cola last year. The sales figures are shown below. Find the mean, the median, and the mode for size.
   mean = 13.5; median = 14; mode = 16

Size	Number of cases sold
6 oz	5 cases
10 oz	10 cases
12 oz	35 cases
16 oz	50 cases

8. A student's scores in a certain math class are 72, 73, 74, 85, and 91. Find the mean, the median, and the mode.   mean = 79; median = 74; no mode

9. The earnings of the part-time employees of a small real estate company for the past year were (in thousands of dollars): 12, 22, 18, 15, 9, 11, 18, 57, 17, and 10. Find the mean, median, and mode.   mean = 18.9; median = 16; mode = 18

10. **IN YOUR OWN WORDS** Discuss the differences and similarities among the mean, the median, and the mode. Amplify with your own examples.

11. The manager of the store described in Problem 7 decides to cut back on variety and stock only one size of cola. Which of the measures of central tendency will be most useful in making this decision?   mode

Year	Expenditure (billions)
1989	$ 957
1990	$1,150
1991	$1,162
1992	$1,265
1993	$1,367
1994	$1,436
1995	$1,505

*There are more than 110 entries because some Congresses had more than one speaker.

12. Which measure of central tendency would be most appropriate for the situation in Problem 8?   *mean*

13. Which measure of central tendency is most representative of the employees' earnings as described in Problem 9?   *median*

Find the range and the standard deviation (to two decimal places) for the data from Problems 14–17. Find the variance if you do not have a calculator.

14. Problem 6   *range = 4; $\sigma \approx 1.41$; $\sigma^2 = 2$*

15. Problem 7   *range = 10; $\sigma \approx 2.82$; $\sigma^2 = 7.95$*

16. Problem 8   *range = 19; $\sigma \approx 7.62$; $\sigma^2 = 58$*

17. Problem 9   *range = 48; $\sigma = 13.3$; $\sigma^2 = 176.89$*

18. The heights of 10,000 women students at Eastern College are known to be normally distributed, with a mean of 67 inches and a standard deviation of 3 inches. How many women would you expect to be between 64 and 70 inches tall?   *6,820*

19. How many women in Problem 18 would you expect to be shorter than 5 ft 1 in.?   *230*

20. Determine the upper and lower scores for the middle 68% of scores on a test on which the scores are normally distributed with mean 73 and standard deviation 8.   *65 and 81*

21. **IN YOUR OWN WORDS** Two instructors gave the same Math 1A test in their classes. Both classes had the same mean score, but one class had a standard deviation twice as large as that of the other class. Which class do you think would be easier to teach, and why?   *smaller standard deviation; less variance*

22. **IN YOUR OWN WORDS** What do we mean by Type I error?
   Answers vary; reject true hypothesis.

23. **IN YOUR OWN WORDS** What do we mean by Type II error?
   Answers vary; accept false hypothesis.

24. **IN YOUR OWN WORDS** What is the difference between a sample and a population?
   Answers vary; population includes everything under study; sample is a proper subset of the population.

25. How would you obtain a sample of one-syllable words used in this text? How would you apply those results to the whole book?   *Answers vary; take a sample of representative pages.*

Individual Projects

Learning to use sources outside your classroom and textbook is an important skill, and here are some ideas for extending some of the ideas in this chapter.

PROJECT 10.1   Suppose you are interested in knowing the number and ages of children (0–18 years) in a part (or all) of your community. You will need to sample 50 families, finding the number of children in each family and the age of each child. It is important that you select the 50 families at random. How to do this is a subject of a course in statistics. For this problem, however, follow these steps:

Step 1   Determine the geographic boundaries of the area with which you are concerned.

Step 2   Consider various methods for selecting the families at random. For example, could you: (i) select the first 50 homes at which someone is at home when you call? (ii) select 50 numbers from the phone book? Using (i) or (ii) could result in a biased sample. Can you guess why this might be true? In a statistics course, you might explore other ways of selecting the homes. For this problem, use one of these methods.

Step 3 Consider different ways of asking the question. Can the way the family is approached affect the response?

Step 4 Gather your data.

Step 5 Organize your data. Construct a frequency distribution for the number of children per family. Also construct a frequency distribution for the ages of the children, with integral values from 0 to 18.

Step 6 Find out the number of families who actually live in the area you've selected. If you can't do this, assume that the area has 1,000 families.

a. What is the average number of children per family?

b. What percent of the children are in the first grade (age 6)?

c. If all the children age 12–15 are in junior high, how many are in junior high for the geographic area you are considering?

d. See if you can actually find out the answers to parts **b** and **c**, and compare these answers with your projections.

e. What other inferences can you make from your data?

PROJECT 10.2 Prepare five identical containers (shoe boxes, paper cups, etc.) each containing red and white items (such as marbles, poker chips, or colored slips of paper).

Box	Contents
#1	15 red and 15 white
#2	30 red and 0 white
#3	25 red and 5 white
#4	20 red and 10 white
#5	10 red and 20 white

Select one of the boxes at random so that you don't know its contents.

Step 1 Shake the box.

Step 2 Select one marker, note the result, and return it to the box.

Step 3 Repeat the first two steps 20 times with the same box.

a. What do you think is inside the box you have sampled?

b. Could you have guessed the contents by repeating the experiment five times? Ten times? Do you think you should have more than 20 observations per experiment? Discuss.

PROJECT 10.3 Suppose someone hands you a coin to flip and wants to bet on the outcome. Now, John has tried this sort of thing before, and you suspect that the coin is "rigged." You decide to test this hypothesis by taking a sample. You flip the coin twice, and it is heads both times. You say, "Aha, I knew it was rigged!" John replies, "Don't be silly. Any coin can come up heads twice in a row." The following scheme was devised by mathematician John von Neumann to allow fair results even if the coin is somewhat biased. The coin is flipped twice. If it comes up heads both times or tails both times, it is flipped twice again. If it comes up heads–tails, this will decide the outcome in favor of the first party; and if it comes up tails–heads, this will decide the outcome in favor of the second party. Show that this will result in a fair toss even if the coins are biased. *Suppose the coin lands heads 60% of the time. This means tails is 40%. Heads–tails is 0.6 × 0.4 = 0.24 and tails–heads is 0.4 × 0.6 = 0.24.*

PROJECT 10.4   Select something that you think might be normally distributed (for example, the ring size of students at your college). Next, select 100 people and make the appropriate measurements (in this example, ring size). Calculate the mean and standard deviation. Illustrate your findings using a bar graph. Do your data appear to be normally distributed?

PROJECT 10.5   Prepare a report or exhibit showing how statistics are used in baseball.

PROJECT 10.6   Prepare a report or exhibit showing how statistics are used in educational testing.

PROJECT 10.7   Prepare a report or exhibit showing how statistics are used in psychology.

PROJECT 10.8   Investigate the work of Adolph Quetelet, François Galton, Karl Pearson, R. A. Fisher, and Florence Nightingale. Prepare a report or an exhibit of their work in statistics.

PROJECT 10.9   Write a short book report on *Innumeracy* by John Allen Paulos (New York: Hill & Wang, 1988). In particular, comment on the contents of Chapter 5, "Statistics, Trade-Offs, and Society."

Team Projects

Working in small groups is typical of most work environments, and learning to work with others to communicate specific ideas is an important skill. Work with three or four other students to submit a single report based on each of the following questions.

T30.   Your team has been hired to conduct a survey and to prepare a report of your findings. Begin by determining a suitable multiple-choice question, for example, "Do you watch any soap opera, and if so, which one is your favorite?" Identify five to ten possible responses for your question, including "None of the above." Determine your team's survey methods; for example, specify the number of responses and where you will obtain your data. Discuss how location and time of day can affect the results. Conduct the survey, tabulate the results, and construct bar, line, and circle graphs to display the results. Your report should include your methods, results, and conclusions, as well as tabulated responses and summary graphs.

Graphs

The analytical geometry, as Descartes' method was called, soon led to an abundance of new theorems and principles, which far transcended everything that ever could have been reached upon the path pursued by the ancients.

H. Hankel

ANTICIPATE

- *Overview; check out contents, terms, essential ideas, and learning outcomes.*
- *A major change in thinking about algebra and geometry occurs in this chapter.*

11.1 Cartesian Coordinate System

IN THIS WORLD THE UTILITY OF MATH

Jack has not been to San Francisco before, and he was looking forward to seeing Fisherman's Wharf, North Beach, Nob Hill, Chinatown, and the Civic Center. However, the first thing he wanted to do was to look up his old friend Charlie, who lives on Main Street in San Francisco. He bought a map and looked up Charlie's street in the index. It was listed as (7, B). What does (7, B) mean?

In mathematics, such a representation is called an *ordered pair* and has many useful applications. The first one we'll consider in this section is called a *Cartesian coordinate system* and sets the stage for the remainder of this chapter.

Problem of the Day See Problem 55.

Can you connect the dots?

Ordered Pairs

Have you ever drawn a picture by connecting the dots or found a city or street on a map? If you have, then you've used the ideas we'll be discussing in this section.

Problem of the Day Let's consider the Problem of the Day. How can you find Fisherman's Wharf by looking at the map shown in Figure 11.1?

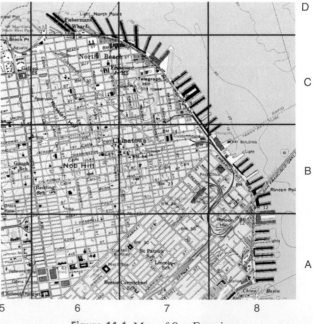

Figure 11.1 Map of San Francisco

Look at the index for the map and you find Fisherman's Wharf listed as (6, D). Can you locate section (6, D) in Figure 11.1? Did you find it? Next, see if you can find Main Street—located at (7, B). Hard to find, right? How could we improve the map to make our task easier?

Let's create a smaller grid, as shown in Figure 11.2.

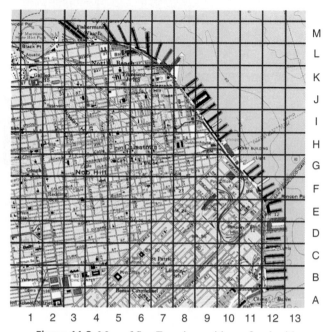

Figure 11.2 Map of San Francisco with a refined grid

Now, Main Street is located at (9, G) and is easier to find because of the smaller grid. However, a smaller grid means that a lot of letters are needed for the vertical scale, and we might need more letters than there are in the alphabet. So let's use a notation that will allow us to represent points on the map with pairs of numbers. A pair of numbers written as (2, 3) is called an **ordered pair** to remind you that the order in which the numbers 2 and 3 are listed is important. That is, (2, 3) specifies a different location than does (3, 2). For the ordered pair (2, 3), 2 is the **first component** and 3 is the **second component.** The ordered pair is referred to as the **coordinates** for location on a map or a graph.

first component
↓
(x, y)
↑
second component

Don't forget the meaning of this notation.

For our map, suppose that we relabel the vertical scale with numbers and change both scales so that we label the *lines instead of the spaces,* as shown in Figure 11.3. (By the way, most technical maps number lines instead of spaces.)

Now we can fix the location of any street on the map quite precisely. Notice that, if we use an ordered pair of numbers (instead of a number and a letter), it is important to know which component of the ordered pair represents the horizontal distance and which component represents the vertical distance. If we use Figure 11.3, we see

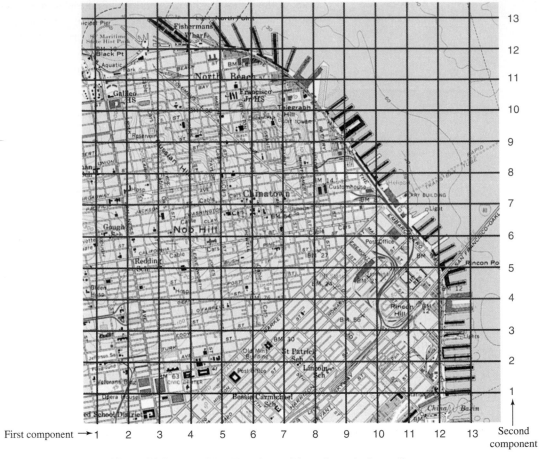

Figure 11.3 Map of San Francisco with mathematical coordinates

that the coordinates of Main Street are about (9.5, 6.3); we can even say that Main Street runs from about (9.5, 6.3) to (11.2, 4.5). Notice that, by using ordered pairs and numbering the lines instead of the spaces, we have refined our grid. We've refined it even more with decimal components.

When using ordered pairs of numbers, remember that the first component is on the horizontal axis and the second component is on the vertical axis.

EXAMPLE 1

Using ordered pairs to find map locations

Find the major landmarks with the following coordinates in Figure 11.3.

a. (3.5, 1.5)   **b.** (3.5, 12.5)   **c.** (5, 11)   **d.** (4, 6)   **e.** (6, 7.3)

Solution

a. Civic Center   **b.** Fisherman's Wharf   **c.** North Beach
d. Nob Hill   **e.** Chinatown

There are many ways to use ordered pairs to find particular locations. For example, a teacher may make a seating chart like the one shown in Figure 11.4.

5	Hannah Becker	Susan Reiland		Jeff Clark	Søren Sovndal
4	Sharon Boschen	Linda Smith	Bob Anderson	Josephine Lee	Milt Hoehn
3	Jeff Atz	Laurie Pederson	Tim Selbo	Todd Humann	Brian Claasen
2	Terry Shell	Arnie Norman	Clint Stevenson	Steve Switzer	
1	Theron Sovndal	Beverly Schaap	Niels Pedersen	Cole Becker	Eva Mikalson
	1	2	3	4	5

Figure 11.4 Classroom seating chart

In the grade book, the teacher records

Anderson (3, 4) *Remember, first component is horizontal direction;*

Atz (1, 3) *second component is vertical direction.*

Anderson's seat is in column 3, row 4. Can you think of some other ways in which ordered pairs could be used to locate a position?

Cartesian Coordinate System

The idea of using an ordered pair to locate a certain position requires particular terminology. **Axes** are two perpendicular real number lines, such as those shown in Figure 11.5. The point of intersection of the axes is called the **origin.** In Chapter 2, we associated direction to the right or up with positive numbers. The upward and rightward arrows in Figure 11.5 are pointing in the positive directions. These perpendicular lines are usually drawn so that one is horizontal and the other is vertical. The horizontal axis is called the **x-axis,** and the vertical axis is called the **y-axis.**

HISTORICAL NOTE

René Descartes
(1596–1650)

René Descartes, the person after whom we name the coordinate system, was a person of frail health. He had a lifelong habit of lying in bed until late in the morning or even the early afternoon. It is said that these hours in bed were probably his most productive. During one of these periods, it is presumed, Descartes made the discovery of the coordinate system. This discovery led to a branch of modern mathematics called **analytic geometry,** which can be described as an algebraic way of looking at geometry, or a geometric way of looking at algebra; simply put, it is the blending of algebra and geometry. His own writings tell us that he viewed analytic geometry as an applied science, and not theoretical. In fact, he considered mathematics for its own sake to be an idle searching or vain play of the mind.

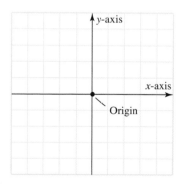

Figure 11.5 Cartesian coordinate system

QUADRANT II	QUADRANT I
x is negative	x is positive
y is positive	y is positive
QUADRANT III	QUADRANT IV
x is negative	x is positive
y is negative	y is negative

Figure 11.6 Quadrants

Notice that the axes of a Cartesian coordinate system divide the plane into four parts. These parts are called **quadrants** and are labeled as shown in Figure 11.6.

We can now label points in the plane by using ordered pairs. The first component of the pair gives the horizontal distance, and the second component gives the vertical distance, as shown in Figure 11.7.

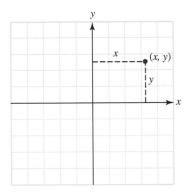

Figure 11.7 (x, y) are coordinates of a point

If x and y are components of a point, representation of the point (x, y) is called the **rectangular** or **Cartesian coordinates** of the point. To **plot** (or **graph**) a point means to show the coordinates of the ordered pair by drawing a dot at the specified location.

EXAMPLE 2   **Plotting points**

Plot (graph) the given points.

a. $(5, 2)$ **b.** $(3, 5)$ **c.** $(-2, 1)$ **d.** $(0, 5)$

e. $(-6, -4)$ **f.** $(3, -2)$ **g.** $(\frac{1}{2}, 0)$ **h.** $(0, 0)$

Solution   The points are shown in Figure 11.8.

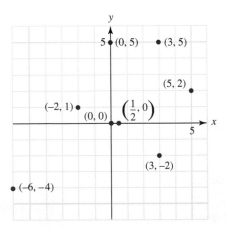

Figure 11.8 Plotting points

PROBLEM SET (11.1)

See IAS for graphs.

ESSENTIAL IDEAS | **LEVEL 1**

1. **IN YOUR OWN WORDS** When plotting a point with coordinates (x, y), is the x-value horizontal or vertical? horizontal

2. Draw a correctly labeled coordinate system. See Figure 11.7. Be sure to show the positive direction and label axes and scale.

3. Draw a coordinate system and label the origin and each of the four quadrants. See Figure 11.6.

4. Name x and y as positive or negative for each of the given quadrants.

   a. Quadrant I   x is positive; y is positive

   b. Quadrant II   x is negative; y is positive

   c. Quadrant III   x is negative; y is negative

   d. Quadrant IV   x is positive; y is negative

DRILL AND PRACTICE | **LEVEL 2**

Use the map of Venus shown in Figure 11.9 to name the landmarks specified in Problems 5–14.

5. $(90, 0)$ Aphrodite

6. $(0, 65)$ Maxwell Montes

7. $(165, 65)$ Atalanta Planitia

8. $(-80, 32)$ Rhea Mons

9. $(-80, 25)$ Theia Mons

10. $(-30, -50)$ Lavina Planitia

11. $(-30, 45)$ Sedna Planitia

12. $(60, 45)$ Leda Planitia

13. $(60, 70)$ Terra

14. $(160, -25)$ Dali Chasma

Find the landmarks given by the coordinates in Problems 15–24. Use the map in Figure 11.3.

15. $(7, 10)$ Telegraph Hill

16. $(1, 2)$
    Jefferson Square Playground

17. $(11, 6)$ Embarcadero

18. $(12, 0.5)$ China Basin

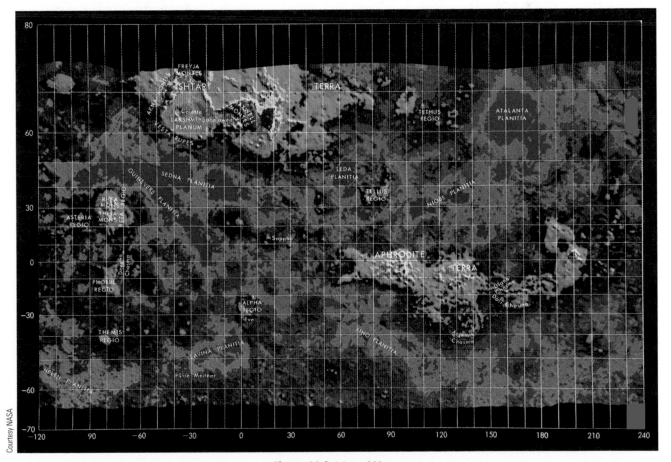

Figure 11.9 Map of Venus

Courtesy NASA

19. $(11, 7.3)$ Ferry Building   **20.** $(1.5, 11.3)$ Aquatic Park

21. $(6.5, 2.5)$ Old Mint Building   **22.** $(6.5, 4.5)$ Union Square

23. $(6.9, 9.8)$ Coit Tower   **24.** $(5.5, 1.5)$ Post office

Using the seating chart in Figure 11.4, name the occupant of the seat given by the coordinates in Problems 25–34.

25. $(5, 1)$ Eva Mikalson   **26.** $(4, 1)$ Cole Becker

27. $(1, 2)$ Terry Shell   **28.** $(4, 2)$ Steve Switzer

29. $(2, 3)$ Laurie Pederson   **30.** $(3, 1)$ Niels Pederson

31. $(1, 5)$ Hannah Becker   **32.** $(4, 5)$ Jeff Clark

33. $(2, 1)$ Beverly Schaap   **34.** $(2, 4)$ Linda Smith

Plot the points given in Problems 35–42. Use the indicated scale.

35. Scale: 1 square on your paper = 1 unit

  a. $(1, 2)$ **b.** $(3, -3)$ **c.** $(-4, 3)$

  d. $(-2, -3)$ **e.** $(0, 4)$

36. Scale: 1 square on your paper = 1 unit

  a. $(1, 4)$ **b.** $(3, 1)$ **c.** $(4, -5)$

  d. $(2, 5)$ **e.** $(-2, -1)$

37. Scale: 1 square on your paper = 1 unit

  a. $(-3, 3)$ **b.** $(3, -2)$ **c.** $(2, -4)$

  d. $(3, 4)$ **e.** $(-4, -2)$

38. Scale: 1 square on your paper = 1 unit

  a. $(-1, 4)$ **b.** $(6, 2)$ **c.** $(1, -5)$

  d. $(3, 0)$ **e.** $(-1, -2)$

39. Scale: 1 square on your paper = 5 units

  a. $(10, 25)$ **b.** $(-5, 15)$ **c.** $(0, 0)$

  d. $(-50, -35)$ **e.** $(-30, -40)$

40. Scale: 1 square on your paper = 50 units

  a. $(0, 175)$ **b.** $(50, 300)$ **c.** $(-200, 125)$

  d. $(100, -225)$ **e.** $(-50, -75)$

41. Scale, *x*-axis: 1 square on your paper = 1 unit;
Scale, *y*-axis: 1 square on your paper = 5 units

  a. $(4, 40)$ **b.** $(-3, 0)$ **c.** $(2, -40)$

  d. $(-5, -10)$ **e.** $(0, 0)$

42. Scale, *x*-axis: 1 square on your paper = 10 units;
Scale, *y*-axis: 1 square on your paper = 1 unit

  a. $(50, 4)$ **b.** $(-75, 0)$ **c.** $(25, -4)$

  d. $(-50, -10)$ **e.** $(100, 10)$

APPLICATIONS   LEVEL 2

43. Plot the following coordinates on graph paper, and connect each point with the preceding one: $(-2, 2)$, $(-2, 9)$,

$(-7, 2)$, $(-2, 2)$. Start again: $(-6, -6)$, $(-6, -8)$, $(6, -8)$, $(10, -8)$, $(10, -6)$, $(6, -6)$, $(6, 0)$, $(10, 0)$, $(10, 2)$, $(6, 2)$, $(6, 16)$, $(-2, 14)$, $(-11, 2)$, $(-9, -1)$, $(-2, -1)$, $(-2, -6)$, $(-6, -6)$.

44. Plot the following coordinates on graph paper, and connect each point with the preceding one: $(9, 0)$, $(7, -1)$, $(6, -2)$, $(7, -5)$, $(5, -8)$, $(-8, -10)$, $(-2, -5)$, $(0, -2)$, $(-2, -1)$, $(-6, -5)$, $(-5, -3)$, $(-6, -2)$, $(-5, -1)$, $(-6, 0)$, $(-5, 1)$, $(-6, 2)$, $(-5, 3)$, $(-6, 4)$, $(-5, 5)$, $(-6, 7)$, $(-2, 3)$, $(0, 4)$, $(-1, 10)$, $(-6, 15)$, $(0, 14.5)$, $(3, 14)$, $(6, 5)$, $(4, 3)$, $(5, 2)$, $(7, 2)$, $(9, 0)$. Finally, plot a point at $(7, 1)$.

45. Suppose that we place coordinate axes on the connect-the-dots figure shown at the beginning of the section. Let *A* be $(2, 9)$ and *Z* be $(1, 5)$. Write directions similar to those of Problems 43 and 44 about how to sketch the dog shown in Figure 11.10. See IAS.

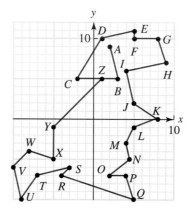

Figure 11.10 Connect-the-dots picture

46. IN YOUR OWN WORDS Draw a picture similar to the ones in Problems 43 and 44, and then describe the picture using ordered pairs.

47. Connect the points $(0, 2)$, $(1, 5)$, $(2, 8)$, $(-1, -1)$, $(-2, -4)$. What do you observe? They all lie on the same line.

48. Connect the points $(0, 1)$, $(1, -2)$, $(-1, 4)$, $(2, -5)$, $(-2, 7)$. What do you observe?   They all lie on the same line.

49. a. How many points lie on a line?   infinitely many

  b. How many points do you need to plot in order to determine a line?   2

50. Plot any two (distinct) points. What is the path that represents the shortest distance between those points? How many points are along this path? a line; infinitely many

51. Plot five points, each of which has 2 as the first component. Connect the plotted points.

52. Plot five points, each of which has 3 as the second component. Connect the plotted points.

53. Plot five points in each of which the second component is twice the first component. Connect the plotted points.

54. Plot five points in each of which the second component is 2 less than the first component. Connect the plotted points.

55. IN YOUR OWN WORDS Jack had not been to San Francisco before, and he was looking forward to seeing Fisherman's Wharf, North Beach, Nob Hill, Chinatown, and the Civic Center. However, the first thing he wanted to do was to look up his old friend, Charlie, who lives on Main Street in San Francisco. He bought a map and looked up Charlie's street in the index. It was listed as (7, B). What does (7, B) mean?

56. IN YOUR OWN WORDS Congratulations! If you are at this place of this book, you have probably taken significant steps in conquering your math anxiety. Now, it is time to open the doors to your future. List five action steps you are willing to take in the next six months to reinforce your success. Make sure to write down your target date for each step taken.

Explain what is wrong, if anything, with the statements in Problems 57–60. Explain your reasoning.

57. In plotting a point (x, y), the x is called the x-value. F; it is called the x-component.

58. In plotting a point (x, y), the y-component is the distance the point is from the y-axis. F; it is the distance from the x-axis.

59. In Quadrant IV, both components are negative. F; $x > 0$ and $y < 0$.

60. Quadrant I is the region of the plane where $x > 0$ and $y > 0$. The other quadrants are numbered clockwise from Quadrant I. F; they are numbered counterclockwise.

11.2 Functions

IN THIS WORLD THE UTILITY OF MATH

Courtesy National Park Service

"Look out! That old abandoned well is very dangerous, Huck. I think that it should be capped so that nobody could fall in and kill his self."

"Ah, shucks, Tom, let's climb down and see how deep it is. I'll bet it is a mile down to the bottom."

If we assume that it is not possible for Tom or Huck to climb down into the well, how can they determine the depth of the well?

 See Problem 54.

The idea of looking at two sets of variables at the same time was introduced in the previous section. Sets of ordered pairs provide a very compact and useful way to represent relationships between various sets of numbers. To consider this idea, let's look at the following cartoon.

The distance an object will fall depends on (among other things) the length of time it falls. If we let the variable d be the distance the object has fallen and the variable t be the time it has fallen (in seconds), and if we disregard air resistance, the formula is

$$d = 16t^2$$

Therefore, in the *B.C.* cartoon, if the well is 16 seconds deep (and we neglect the time it takes for the sound to come back up), we know that the depth of the well (in feet) is

$$d = 16(16)^2$$
$$= 16(256)$$
$$= 4{,}096$$

The formula $d = 16t^2$ gives rise to a set of data:

Time (in seconds)	0	1	2	3	4	...	15	16
Distance (in ft)	0	16	64	144	256	...	3,600	4,096

For every nonnegative value of t, there is a corresponding value for d.

first component (values for t)
↓
(x, y)
↑
second component (values for d)

We can represent the data in the table as a set of ordered pairs in which the first component represents a value for t and the second component represents a corresponding value for d. For this example, we have (0, 0), (1, 16), (2, 64), (3, 144), (4, 256), . . . , (15, 3600), (16, 4096).

Whenever we have a situation comparable to the one illustrated by this example—namely, whenever the first component of an ordered pair is associated with exactly one second component—we call the set of ordered pairs a *function*.

Function

A **function** is a set of ordered pairs in which the first component is associated with exactly one second component.

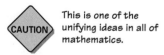

This is one of the unifying ideas in all of mathematics.

Not all sets of ordered pairs are functions, as we can see from the following examples.

EXAMPLE 1

Distinguishing functions from nonfunctions

Which of the following sets of ordered pairs are functions?

a. $\{(0, 0), (1, 2), (2, 4), (3, 9), (4, 16)\}$

b. $\{(0, 0), (1, 1), (1, -1), (4, 2), (3, -2)\}$

c. $\{(1, 3), (2, 3), (3, 3), (4, 3)\}$

d. $\{(3, 1), (3, 2), (3, 3), (3, 4)\}$

Solution

a. We see that

$$
\begin{array}{rcl}
0 & \to & 0 \\
1 & \to & 2 \\
2 & \to & 4 \\
3 & \to & 9 \\
4 & \to & 16
\end{array}
$$

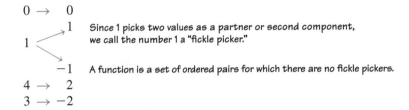

Sometimes it is helpful to think of the first component as the "picker" and the second component as the "pickee." Given an ordered pair (x, y), we find that each replacement for x "picks" a partner, or a second value. We can symbolize this by x → y.

Since each first component is associated with exactly one second component, the set is a function.

b. For this set,

$$
\begin{array}{rcl}
0 & \to & 0 \\
1 & & 1 \\
& & -1 \\
4 & \to & 2 \\
3 & \to & -2
\end{array}
$$

Since 1 picks two values as a partner or second component, we call the number 1 a "fickle picker."

A function is a set of ordered pairs for which there are no fickle pickers.

Since the first component can be associated with more than one second component, the set is not a function.

c. For this set,

$$
\begin{array}{c}
1 \\
2 \\
\quad\ 3 \\
3 \\
4
\end{array}
$$

There are no fickle pickers, so it is a function.

This is an example of a function.

d. Finally,

$$
3
\begin{array}{c}
1 \\
2 \\
3 \\
4
\end{array}
$$

The number 3 is a fickle picker, so this set is not a function.

Since the first component is associated with several second components, the set is not a function.

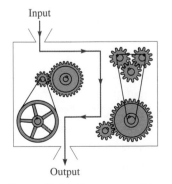

Input

Output

Figure 11.11 Function machine

Another way to consider functions is with the idea of a function machine. Think of a function machine as shown in Figure 11.11.

Think of this machine as having an input where items are entered and an output where results are obtained, much like a vending machine. If the number 2 is dropped into the input, a function machine will output a single value. If the name of the function machine is f, then the output value is called "f of 2" and is written as $f(2)$. This is called **functional notation.**

EXAMPLE 2   **Finding output values for a function**

If you input each of the given values into a function machine named g, what is the resulting output value?

a. 4   **b.** –3   **c.** π **d.** x

Solution

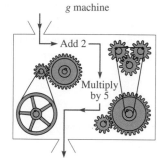

g machine

Add 2

Multiply by 5

a. Input is 4; output is $g(4)$, pronounced "gee of four." To calculate $g(4)$, first add 2, then multiply by 5:

input value

output value

$$(4 + 2) \times 5 = 6 \times 5 = 30$$

We write $g(4) = 30$.

b. Input is -3; output is $g(-3)$, pronounced "gee of negative three."

$$g(-3) = (-3 + 2) \times 5 = -1 \times 5 = -5$$

c. Input is π; output is $g(\pi)$, pronounced "gee of pi."

$$g(\pi) = (\pi + 2) \times 5 = 5(\pi + 2)$$

d. Input is x; output is $g(x)$, pronounced "gee of ex."

$$g(x) = (x + 2) \times 5 = 5(x + 2)$$

●

EXAMPLE 3   **Using functional notation**

If a function machine f squares the input value, we write $f(x) = x^2$, where x represents the input value. We usually define functions by simply saying "Let $f(x) = x^2$." Identify the value of f for the given value.

a. $f(2)$ **b.** $f(8)$ **c.** $f(-3)$ **d.** $f(t)$

Solution

a. $f(2) = 2^2 = 4$ **b.** $f(8) = 8^2 = 64$

c. $f(-3) = (-3)^2 = 9$ **d.** $f(t) = t^2$

●

PROBLEM SET 11.2

ESSENTIAL IDEAS   **LEVEL 1**

1. IN YOUR OWN WORDS What is a function?

2. IN YOUR OWN WORDS What does it mean to evaluate a function, and what is the notation for this process?

DRILL AND PRACTICE   **LEVEL 2**

Which of the sets in Problems 3–14 are functions?

3. $\{(1, 4), (2, 5), (4, 7), (9, 12)\}$ function

4. $\{(4, 1), (5, 2), (7, 4), (12, 9)\}$ function

5. $\{(1, 1), (2, 1), (3, 4), (4, 4), (5, 9), (6, 9)\}$ function

6. $\{(1, 1), (1, 2), (4, 3), (4, 4), (9, 5), (9, 6)\}$ not a function

7. $\{(4, 3), (17, 29), (18, 52), (4, 19)\}$ not a function

8. $\{(13, 4), (29, 4), (5, 4), (9, 4)\}$ function

9. $\{(19, 4), (52, 18), (29, 17), (3, 4)\}$ function

10. $\{(4, 9), (4, 4), (4, 29), (4, 19)\}$ not a function

11. $\{(5, 0)\}$ function   **12.** $\{(0, 0)\}$ function

13. $\{1, 2, 3, 4, 5\}$ not a function

14. $\{69, 82, 44, 37\}$ not a function

Tell what the output value is for each of the function machines in Problems 15–22 for

(a) 4   **(b)** 6   **(c)** −8   **(d)** $\frac{1}{2}$ **(e)** t

15. f machine

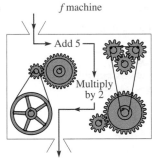

$f(4) = 18,$
$f(6) = 22,$
$f(-8) = -6,$
$f(\frac{1}{2}) = 11,$
$f(t) = 2(t + 5)$

16. g machine

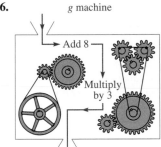

$g(4) = 36,$
$g(6) = 42,$
$g(-8) = 0,$
$g(\frac{1}{2}) = 25\frac{1}{2},$
$g(t) = 3(t + 8)$

17.

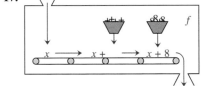

$f(4) = 12,$
$f(6) = 14,$
$f(-8) = 0,$
$f(\frac{1}{2}) = 8\frac{1}{2},$
$f(t) = t + 8$

18.

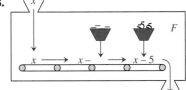

$F(4) = -1,$
$F(6) = 1,$
$F(-8) = -13,$
$F(\frac{1}{2}) = -4\frac{1}{2},$
$F(t) = t - 5$

19.

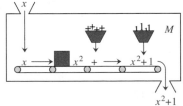

$M(4) = 17,$
$M(6) = 37,$
$M(-8) = 65,$
$M(\frac{1}{2}) = 1\frac{1}{4},$
$M(t) = t^2 + 1$

20.

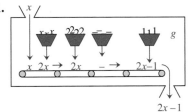

$S(4) = 12,$
$S(6) = 18,$
$S(-8) = -24,$
$S(\frac{1}{2}) = \frac{3}{2},$
$S(t) = 3t$

21.

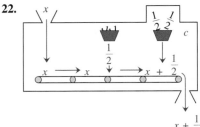

$g(4) = 7,$
$g(6) = 11,$
$g(-8) = -17,$
$g(\frac{1}{2}) = 0,$
$g(t) = 2t - 1$

22.

$c(4) = 4\frac{1}{2},$
$c(6) = 6\frac{1}{2},$
$c(-8) = -7\frac{1}{2},$
$c(\frac{1}{2}) = 1,$
$c(t) = t + \frac{1}{2}$

Find the functional values requested in Problems 23–46.

23. $f(x) = x - 7$
   a. $f(15)$ 8
   b. $f(-9)$ −16

24. $f(x) = x - 7$
   a. $f(7)$ 0
   b. $f(p)$ $p - 7$

25. $g(x) = 2x$
   a. $g(100)$ 200
   b. $g(-25)$ −50

26. $g(x) = 2x$
   a. $g(-3)$ −6
   b. $g(m)$ $2m$

27. $h(x) = 3x - 1$
   a. $h(0)$ −1
   b. $h(-10)$ −31

28. $h(x) = 3x - 1$
   a. $h(10)$ 29
   b. $h(a)$ $3a - 1$

29. $F(x) = 2x - 8$
   a. $F(7)$ 6
   b. $F(m)$ $2m - 8$

30. $F(x) = 2x - 8$
   a. $F(-3)$ −14
   b. $F(s)$ $2s - 8$

31. $G(x) = 3x$
   a. $G(10)$ 30
   b. $G(-20)$ −60

32. $G(x) = 3x$
   a. $G(-8)$ −24
   b. $G(t)$ $3t$

33. $H(x) = 8x + 4$

   a. $H(-1)$ −4   **b.** $H(u)$ $8u + 4$

34. $H(x) = 3x - \pi$

   a. $H(0)$ $-\pi$ **b.** $H(\pi)$ 2π

35. $f(x) = x^2 + 1$

   a. $f(-3)$ 10   **b.** $f(\pi)$ $\pi^2 + 1$

36. $f(x) = x^2 + 1$

   a. $f(\tfrac{1}{2})$ $1\tfrac{1}{4}$ **b.** $f(b)$ $b^2 + 1$

37. If $g(x) = \tfrac{x}{2}$

   a. $g(10)$ 5   **b.** $g(\pi)$ $\tfrac{\pi}{2}$

38. If $g(x) = \tfrac{x}{2}$

   a. $g(-4)$ −2   **b.** $g(3)$ $\tfrac{3}{2}$

39. $h(x) = 0.6x$

   a. $h(4.1)$ 2.46   **b.** $h(\pi)$ 0.6π

40. $h(x) = 0.6x$

   a. $h(2.3)$ 1.38   **b.** $h(\tfrac{5}{2})$ 1.5

41. $F(x) = x^2 - t^2$

   a. $F(0)$ $-t^2$ **b.** $F(m)$ $m^2 - t^2$

42. $F(x) = x^2 - t^2$

   a. $F(t)$ 0   **b.** $F(2t)$ $3t^2$

43. $G(x) = 3x^2$

   a. $G(10)$ 300   **b.** $G(\pi)$ $3\pi^2$

44. $G(x) = 3x^2$

   a. $G(-4)$ 48   **b.** $G(p)$ $3p^2$

45. $H(t) = 6t + 4m$

   a. $H(m)$ 10m   **b.** $H(u)$ $6u + 4m$

46. $H(m) = 6t + 4m$

   a. $H(t)$ 10t   **b.** $H(u)$ $6t + 4u$

APPLICATIONS   **LEVEL 2**

The velocity v (in feet per second) of the rock dropped into the well in the B.C. *cartoon at the beginning of this section is also related to time t (in seconds) by the formula*

$$v = 32t$$

Use the formula for Problems 47–49.

47. Complete the table showing the time and velocity of the rock.

Time (in sec)	0	1	2	3	4	⋯	8	⋯	16
Velocity (in feet per sec)			**a.** 64	**b.** 96	**c.** 128		**d.** 256		**e.** 512

48. What is the velocity of the rock at the indicated instant? Write your answer in the form (t, v).

   a. When the rock is released $(0, 0)$

   b. After 6 seconds $(6, 192)$

49. Look at the last frame of the cartoon.

What is the velocity when the rock hits the bottom of the well?   512 ft/s

An independent distributor bought a new vending machine for $2,000. It had a probable scrap value of $100 at the end of its expected 10-year life. The value V at the end of n years is given by

$$V = 2,000 - 190n$$

Use this information for Problems 50–51.

50. Complete the table showing the year and the value of the machine.

Year	0	1	3	5	7	9	10
Value	2,000	1,810	**a.** 1,430	**b.** 1,050	**c.** 670	**d.** 290	**e.** 100

51. What is the value of the machine at the indicated time? Write your answers in the form (n, V).

   a. When it is purchased $(0, 2000)$

   b. When it is 6 years old $(6, 860)$

   c. When it is scrapped $(10, 100)$

Let A be the set of the following cities: A = {Arm, MI; Bone, ID; Cheek, TX; Doublehead, AL; Elbow Lake, MN}, which we abbreviate as {a, b, c, d, e}. Suppose that these cities are connected by direct service as shown in Figure 11.12.

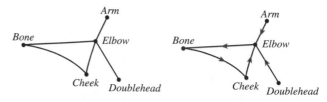

  a. City network   **b. Directed network**

Figure 11.12 Networks

We define a set of ordered pairs (x, y) if and only if x and y are connected by direct service. Use this information for Problems 52–53.

52. a. Find the elements of this set of ordered pairs, as shown in Figure 11.12**a**.

$\{(a, e), (e, a), (b, e), (e, b), (b, c), (c, b), (c, e), (e, c), (e, d), (d, e)\}$

   b. Is this set a function?   *Not a function.*

53. a. Suppose that we make the connections one-way, as shown by the arrows in Figure 11.12**b**. Find the elements of this set of ordered pairs.

$\{(a, e), (e, b), (b, c), (c, e), (d, e)\}$

   b. Is this set a function?   *It is a function.*

54. "Look out! That old abandoned well is very dangerous, Huck. I think that it should be capped so that nobody could fall in and kill his self." "Ah, shucks, Tom, let's climb down and see how deep it is. I'll bet it is a mile down to the bottom." If we assume that it is not possible for Tom or Huck to climb down into the well, how can

they find out the depth of the well? Assume that the well is a mile deep. How long before the rock hits the bottom? *See IAS for complete solution.* 1 mi = 5,280 ft so $5{,}280 = 16t^2$; $330 = t^2$; $t = \sqrt{330} \approx 18.2$; It would be about 18 seconds to the bottom.

RIGHT OR WRONG?   **LEVEL 3**

Explain what is wrong, if anything, with the statements in Problems 55–60. Explain your reasoning.

55. The set $\{(1, 1), (2, 1), (3, 1)\}$ is not a function because 1, 2, and 3 all are associated with the same number, namely, 1.
   F; each value 1, 2, and 3 is associated with one value, so it is a function.

56. If $f(5) = 6$, then the input value is 6.   F; input value is 5

57. If $f(5) = 6$, then the output value is $f(5)$.   T

58. If $f(x) = x + 10$, then $f(10) = 10$.   F; $f(10) = 10 + 10 = 20$

59. If $g(x) = 10x$, then $g(10) = 10$.   F; $g(10) = 10(10) = 100$

60. If $h(x) = 2x$, then $h(\pi) = 6.28$.   F; $h(\pi) = 2\pi$

(11.3) Lines

IN THIS WORLD   THE UTILITY OF MATH

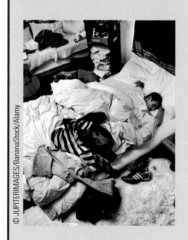

"René, would you please get out of bed! This is the third time I've called you to come down for breakfast."

"But, Mama, I don't feel well today. Must I get up?" said René. "If I can lie here just a bit longer, Mama, I can finish my meditation. I was watching this fly on my ceiling and I have this great idea about representing its position in the room. Can't you let me stay just a few minutes more? Please!"

In this section, we will learn how to represent a point on a flat surface, such as a piece of paper. In more advanced work, the representation of a point in a room (space) is discussed. René Descartes, the person after whom we name the coordinate system, was a person of frail health. He had a lifelong habit of lying in bed until late in the morning or even early afternoon. It is said that these hours were probably his most productive.

See Problem 54.

Solving Equations with Two Variables

Let's consider an equation with two variables, say x and y. If there are two values x and y that make an equation true, then we say that the ordered pair (x, y) **satisfies** the equation and that it is a **solution** of the equation.

EXAMPLE 1 Finding a solution for a given equation

Tell whether each point satisfies the equation $3x - 2y = 7$.

a. $(1, -2)$ **b.** $(-2, 1)$ **c.** $(-1, -5)$

Solution You should substitute each pair of values of x and y into the given equation to see whether the resulting equation is true or false. If it is true, the ordered pair is a solution; if it is false, the ordered pair is not a solution. If it is a solution, we say that it satisfies the equation.

a. $(1, -2)$ means $x = \mathbf{1}$ and $y = -\mathbf{2}$:

$$3x - 2y = 3(\mathbf{1}) - 2(-\mathbf{2})$$
$$= 3 + 4$$
$$= 7$$

Since $7 = 7$, we see that $(1, -2)$ is a solution.

b. $(-2, 1)$ means $x = -\mathbf{2}$ and $y = \mathbf{1}$ (compare with part **a** and notice that the order is important in determining which variable takes which value).

$$3x - 2y = 3(-\mathbf{2}) - 2(\mathbf{1})$$
$$= -6 - 2$$
$$= -8$$

Since $-8 \neq 7$, we see that $(-2, 1)$ is not a solution.

c. $(-1, -5)$: $3x - 2y = 3(-\mathbf{1}) - 2(-\mathbf{5})$
$$= -3 + 10$$
$$= 7$$

The ordered pair $(-1, -5)$ is a solution.   ●

Graphing a Line

The process of graphing a line requires that you find ordered pairs that make an equation true. To do this, *you,* the student, must choose convenient values for x and then solve the resulting equation to find a corresponding value for y.

EXAMPLE 2 Finding ordered pairs that satisfy an equation

Find three ordered pairs that satisfy the equation $y = -2x + 3$.

Solution *You* choose any x value—say, $x = \mathbf{1}$. Substitute this value into the given equation to find a corresponding value of y:

$$y = -2x + 3 \qquad \textit{Given equation}$$
$$= -2(1) + 3 \qquad \textit{Substitute chosen value.}$$
$$= -2 + 3$$
$$= 1$$

You choose this value.
$$\downarrow$$
The first ordered pair is $(\mathbf{1}, \mathbf{1})$.
$$\uparrow$$

You find this value by substitution into the equation.

Choose a second value—say, $x = 2$. Then

$$y = -2x + 3 \qquad \text{Start with given equation.}$$
$$= -2(2) + 3 \qquad \text{Substitute.}$$
$$= -4 + 3$$
$$= -1$$

The second ordered pair is $(2, -1)$.

Choose a third value—say, $x = -1$. Then

$$y = -2x + 3$$
$$= -2(-1) + 3$$
$$= 2 + 3$$
$$= 5$$

The third ordered pair is $(-1, 5)$.

We plot these points (shown in blue) in Figure 11.13.

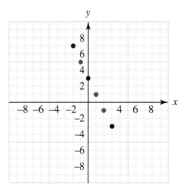

Figure 11.13 Some points that satisfy $y = -2x + 3$

Have we found *all* the ordered pairs that satisfy the equation $y = -2x + 3$? Can you find others? Three more are shown in black in Figure 11.13. Do you notice anything about the arrangement of these points in the plane? Suppose that we draw a line passing through these points in Figure 11.13, as shown in Figure 11.14. This line represents the set of *all* ordered pairs that satisfy the equation.

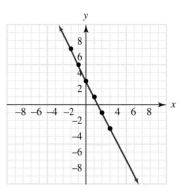

Figure 11.14 Representation of all points satisfying $y = -2x + 3$

If we carry out the process of finding three ordered pairs that satisfy an equation with two first-degree variables, and then we draw a line through those points to find the representation of all ordered pairs satisfying the equation, we say that we are *graphing the line,* and the final set of points we have drawn represents the **graph** of the line.

Graphing a Line

STOP — If three points don't lie on a straight line, then you have made an error.

In order to graph a line by plotting points, follow these steps.

Step 1 First find two ordered pairs that lie on the line.

Step 2 Two points determine a line. As a check, find a third ordered pair.

Step 3 Draw the line (using a straightedge) passing through these three points.

EXAMPLE 3   Graphing a line

Figure 11.15 Graph of $y = 2x + 2$

Graph $y = 2x + 2$.

Solution It is generally easier to pick x and find y.

If $x = 0$: $y = 2x + 2$ Given equation.
$= 2(0) + 2$ Substitute.
$= 2$ Plot the point $(0, 2)$.

If $x = 1$: $y = 2x + 2$
$= 2(1) + 2$
$= 4$ Plot the point $(1, 4)$.

If $x = 2$: $y = 2x + 2$
$= 2(2) + 2$
$= 6$ Plot the point $(2, 6)$.

Draw the line through the plotted points, as shown in Figure 11.15. ●

EXAMPLE 4   Graphing a line given in standard form

Graph the line $x + 2y = 6$.

Solution It is generally easier if you solve for y before you substitute in values for x.

$x + 2y = 6$ Given equation.
$2y = -x + 6$ Subtract x from both sides.
$y = -\frac{1}{2}x + 3$ Divide both sides (all terms) by 2.

If $x = 0$: $y = -\frac{1}{2}x + 3$ Given equation.
$= -\frac{1}{2}(0) + 3$ Substitute.
$= 3$ Simplify.   Plot the point $(0, 3)$.

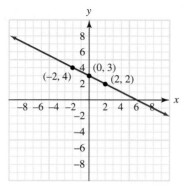

Figure 11.16 Graph of $x + 2y = 6$

We could choose $x = 1$ next, but then we would need to calculate with a fraction, so instead we pick values of x to make the calculation easier.

$$\text{If } x = 2: \quad \begin{aligned} y &= -\tfrac{1}{2}x + 3 \\ &= -\tfrac{1}{2}(2) + 3 \\ &= 2 \end{aligned} \qquad \text{Plot the point } (2, 2).$$

And finally, a third (check) point.

$$\text{If } x = -2: \quad \begin{aligned} y &= -\tfrac{1}{2}x + 3 \\ &= -\tfrac{1}{2}(-2) + 3 \\ &= 4 \end{aligned} \qquad \text{Plot the point } (-2, 4).$$

Draw the line through the plotted points, as shown in Figure 11.16. ●

EXAMPLE 5   Graphing a horizontal line

Graph $y = 4$.

Solution Since the only requirement is that y (the second component) equal 4, we see that there is no restriction on the choice for x. Thus, $(0, 4)$, $(1, 4)$, and $(-2, 4)$ all satisfy the equation

$$y = 4$$

If you plot and connect these points, you will see that the line formed is shown in Figure 11.17. This line, described as parallel to the x-axis, is called a **horizontal line.** ●

Figure 11.17 Graph of $y = 4$

EXAMPLE 6   Graphing a vertical line

Graph $x = 3$.

Solution Since the only requirement is that x (the first component) equal 3, we see that there is no restriction on the choice for y. Thus, $(3, 2)$, $(3, -1)$, and $(3, 0)$ all satisfy the equation

$$x = 3$$

If you plot and connect these points, you will see that the line formed is shown in Figure 11.18. This line, described as parallel to the y-axis, is called a **vertical line.** ●

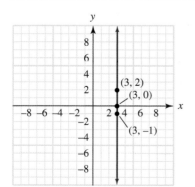

Figure 11.18 Graph of $x = 3$

PROBLEM SET 11.3

Answers that are graphs are shown in the IAS.

ESSENTIAL IDEAS   LEVEL 1

1. **IN YOUR OWN WORDS** What does it mean to be a solution to an equation with two variables?

2. **IN YOUR OWN WORDS** Describe a process for graphing a line.

3. **a.** What is a horizontal line?   A line parallel to the x-axis

   b. Is the graph of a line with equation $x = 5$ a horizontal or a vertical line?   A vertical line

DRILL AND PRACTICE   LEVEL 2

Find three ordered pairs that satisfy each equation in Problems 4–15.   Ordered pair choices vary.

4. $y = x + 5$

5. $y = 2x - 1$

6. $y = 2x + 5$

7. $y = x - 4$

8. $y = x - 1$

9. $y = x + 1$

10. $y = -2x + 1$

11. $y = -3x + 1$

12. $y = 2x + 1$

13. $y - 3x = 1$

14. $3x + 4y = 8$

15. $x + 2y = 4$

Graph the lines in Problems 16–27. These are the same equations as those in Problems 4–15.

16. $y = x + 5$

17. $y = 2x - 1$

18. $y = 2x + 5$

19. $y = x - 4$

20. $y = x - 1$

21. $y = x + 1$

22. $y = -2x + 1$

23. $y = -3x + 1$

24. $y = 2x + 1$

25. $y - 3x = 1$

26. $3x + 4y = 8$

27. $x + 2y = 4$

Graph the lines in Problems 28–47.

28. $y = x + 3$

29. $y = 1 - x$

30. $y = 4 - x$

31. $y = 3x - 2$

32. $y = 5x - 2$

33. $y = 2x + 3$

34. $x + y = 0$

35. $x - y = 0$

36. $2x + y = 3$

37. $3x + y = 10$

38. $2x + 4y = 16$

39. $x + 3y = 6$

40. $x = 5$

41. $x = -4$

42. $x = -1$

43. $y = -2$

44. $y = 6$

45. $y = 4$

46. $x + y + 100 = 0$

47. $5x - 3y = 27$

APPLICATIONS   LEVEL 2

48. The cost, y, in dollars, for renting a car from a leasing firm is given by $y = 0.2x + 25$, where x is the distance driven, in miles. Graph this equation.

49. The water pressure, y, beneath the surface of the ocean is related to the depth, x, by the formula $y = 0.5x + 15$. Graph this equation.

50. If an amount of money A results from investing a sum of P at a simple interest rate of 7% for 10 years, then $A = 1.7P$. Graph this equation for ordered pairs (P, A).

51. A retailer bought a vending machine for $2,000 with a probable scrap value of $100 at the end of its expected 10-year life. The value V at the end of n years is given by the formula $V = 2,000 - 190n$. Graph this equation for ordered pairs (n, V).

52. The temperature, F, in degrees Fahrenheit, is related to the corresponding Celsius temperature, C, by $F = \frac{9}{5}C + 32$. Graph this equation, for ordered pairs (C, F).

53. The temperature, F, in degrees Fahrenheit, can be approximated by $F = \frac{1}{4}n + 40$ where n is the number of cricket chirps in a minute. Graph this equation for ordered pairs (n, F).

"What do you mean, I can't predict the weather!"

 54. **IN YOUR OWN WORDS** "René, would you please get out of bed! This is the third time I've called you to come down for breakfast." "But, Mama, I don't feel well today. Must I get up?" said René. "If I can lie here just a bit longer, Mama, I can finish my meditation. I was watching this fly on my ceiling, and I have this great idea about representing its position in the room. Can't you let me stay just a few minutes more? Please!" Use patterns or do some outside research to explain a three-dimensional coordinate system for describing the fly's position in René's room.

RIGHT OR WRONG?   LEVEL 3

Explain what is wrong, if anything, with the statements in Problems 55–60. Explain your reasoning.

55. The point $(5, 4)$ satisfies the equation $3x - 5y = -13$ because

$$3x - 5y = 3(4) - 5(5)$$
$$= 12 - 25$$
$$= -13$$

F; it should be $3x - 5y = 3(5) - 5(4) = -5$. Order is important.

56. To graph $2x - 3y = 12$, we first find three ordered pairs satisfying the equation:

$$2x - 3y = 12$$
$$-3y = -2x + 12$$

F; $y = \frac{2}{3}x - 4$.
If $x = 0$, $y = -4$;
$x = 3$, $y = -2$;
$x = -3$, $y = -6$.

$$y = \frac{2}{3}x + 4$$

If $x = 0$, then $y = 4$; if $x = 3$, then $y = 6$; and if $x = -3$, then $y = 2$.

57. The graph of $y = 5$ does not exist because there is no x-value in the equation.   F; the graph is a horizontal line.

58. The graph of $x = 15$ passes through the points $(15, 0)$, $(15, 15)$, and $(15, -3.5)$.   T

59. The graph of $x = 5$ is a horizontal line.   F; it is a vertical line.

60. The graph of $y = 15$ is a vertical line.   F; it is a horizontal line.

11.4 Systems and Inequalities

IN THIS WORLD   THE UTILITY OF MATH

Linda is on a business trip and needs to rent a car for the day. The car rental agency has the following options on the car she wants to rent:

> *Option A: $40/day plus 50¢ per mile*
>
> *Option B: Flat rate of $60/day with unlimited mileage*

Which car should she rent?

In this section, Linda will learn how to use lines to solve *systems of equations* to help her with problems like the Problem of the Day.

See Problem 47.

Solving Systems of Equations by Graphing

Many situations involve two variables or unknowns that are related in some specific fashion. The Problem of the Day relates the cost c of a car rental to the number of miles driven, in the following way:

Option A   COST = BASIC CHARGE + MILEAGE CHARGE

50¢ per mile
↓

COST = 40 + 0.5   (NUMBER OF MILES)
↓   ↓
Let COST = c NUMBER OF MILES = m
↓   ↓
$c = 40 + 0.5m$

Option B   COST = FLAT FEE
↓   ↓
$c = 60$

Suppose that we represent these relationships in a graph, as described by a Cartesian coordinate system. We will find ordered pairs (m, c) that make these equations true.

Option A	$c = 40 + 0.5m$	This means that, if Linda drives 20 miles, the cost of the rental is $50; plot (20, 50).
Let $m = 20$:	$c = 40 + 0.5(20) = 40 + 10 = 50$	
Let $m = 50$:	$c = 40 + 0.5(50) = 40 + 25 = 65$	Plot (50, 65).
Let $m = 100$:	$c = 40 + 0.5(100) = 40 + 50 = 90$	Plot (100, 90).

We now have three ordered pairs, so we plot those three points as shown in Figure 11.19.

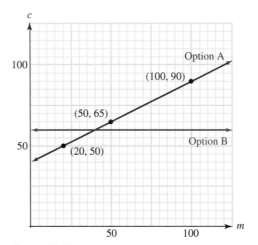

Figure 11.19 Graphs for the Problem of the Day

Next, notice that these points all lie on the same line. Draw a line through these points. This line is shown in color in Figure 11.19.

Next, we consider Option B:

$$\text{Option B} \quad c = 60$$

The second component of the ordered pair (m, c) is always 60 regardless of the number of miles, m. This is shown as a blue horizontal line in Figure 11.19. We complete the Problem of the Day with the following example.

EXAMPLE 1 **Problem solving using lines**

As a continuation of the Problem of the Day, Linda is offered two options when renting a car:*

Option A $40 plus 50¢ per mile; equation is $c = 40 + 0.5m$ for a cost of c dollars and m miles.

Option B Flat $60 with unlimited miles; equation is $c = 60$.

Estimate the mileage for which both rates are the same.

*Problem 47 asks you to answer the question in the Problem of the Day using a flat fee of $50 and a variable fee of $30 plus 25¢/mi.

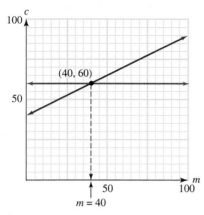

Figure 11.20 Comparing car rental rates

Solution The solution is the point of intersection of the graphs shown in Figure 11.19. We estimate the coordinates to be (40, 60), as shown in Figure 11.20.

This point of intersection means that, if Linda drives 40 miles, the rates are the same. It also means that, if Linda expects to drive more than 40 miles, she should take the fixed rate (Option B). She should choose Option A if she expects to drive less than 40 miles. ●

In Example 1, we looked at the intersection point of the graphs of two lines. When two or more equations are considered together, we call them a **system of equations.** The intersection point on the graph is called the **simultaneous solution** of a system of equations.

EXAMPLE 2

Finding the simultaneous solution of a system of equations

Solve the following system of equations by graphing:

$$\begin{cases} x + 2y = 5 \\ 3x - y = 8 \end{cases}$$

The brace is used to signify that we want to find the simultaneous solution of the system of equations. The method of graphing involves looking for the point of intersection for the two lines.

Solution Graph both lines on the same coordinate axes.

Line $x + 2y = 5$		Line $3x - y = 8$	
x	y	x	y
1	2	0	-8
3	1	1	-5
5	0	2	-2

Remember, to find these points, you choose the x-value and then calculate the corresponding y-value.

Plot these points and draw each line passing through them, as shown in Figure 11. 21.

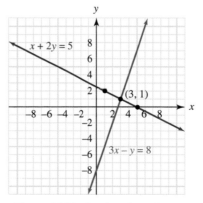

Figure 11.21 Graphs of $x + 2y = 5$ and $3x - y = 8$

The solution to the system of equations is the point of intersection; it looks like the point (**3**, **1**). We can check this point to see whether it satisfies *both* equations:

$$x + 2y = 5 \qquad\qquad 3x - y = 8$$
$$(3) + 2(\mathbf{1}) = 5 \qquad\quad 3(3) - (\mathbf{1}) = 8$$
$$5 = 5 \text{ is true} \qquad\qquad 8 = 8 \text{ is true}$$

The point (3, 1) satisfies both of the given equations, so we say that (3, 1) checks.

●

An interesting application of graphing systems of equations has to do with **supply and demand.** If supply greatly exceeds demand, money will be lost because of unsold items. On the other hand, if demand greatly exceeds supply, money will be lost because of insufficient inventory. The most desirable situation is when supply and demand are equal. If we assume that supply and demand are linear, then the solution of the system is called the **equilibrium point** and represents the point at which supply and demand are equal. In more advanced courses, it is shown that the price that maximizes the profit occurs at this equilibrium point.

EXAMPLE 3

Finding an equilibrium point

Suppose that you have a small product that is marketable to the students on your campus. A little research shows that only 200 people would buy it at $10, but 2,000 would buy it at $1. This information represents the demand. You also find that a local shop can make the product during slack time and can supply 100 items at a price that allows you to sell the product for $1 each. To supply more, the shop must use overtime. If the shop supplies 1,500 items, you would have to charge $6. This information represents the supply. What price should you charge for this item to maximize your profit?

Solution   First, find the demand points. Let p = PRICE and n = NUMBER OF ITEMS. Because the demand n is determined by the price p, let the price be the independent variable; that is, let the ordered pair be (p, n). From the demand, we have

$$(10, \qquad 200) \qquad \text{and} \qquad (1, \qquad 2000)$$

Price   Number   Price   Number

We call these points the *demand points* because they determine the demand line. Draw a line through these points, and label the line "Demand" (see Figure 11.22).

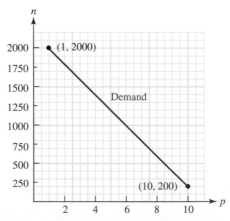

Figure 11.22 Demand curve

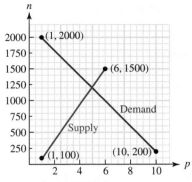

Figure 11.23 Supply curve

Next, find the supply points:

(1,   100)   and   (6,   1500)
 ↑   ↑   ↑   ↑
Price   Number   Price   Number

Draw a line passing through these points, and label the line "Supply" (see Figure 11.23).
  The profit is maximized at the equilibrium point, which is the intersection of the supply and demand lines, as shown in Figure 11.24.

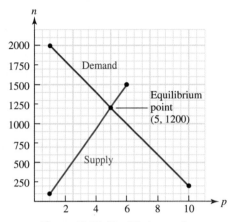

Figure 11.24 Equilibrium point

The price charged should be $5. At this price, you should expect to sell 1,200 items. ●

Graphing Linear Inequalities*

A second application of graphing lines involves extending the concept to graphing linear inequalities. We begin by noting that every line divides a plane into three parts, as shown in Figure 11.25.

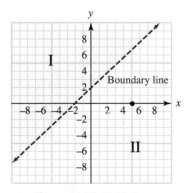

Figure 11.25 Half-planes

---

*This topic requires Section 3.7.

Two parts are labeled I and II; these are called **half-planes.** The third part is called the **boundary** and is the line separating the half-planes. The solution of a first-degree inequality in two unknowns is the set of all ordered pairs that satisfy the given inequality. A half-plane is **closed** if it includes its boundary line and is **open** if it does not. This solution set is a half-plane.

The following table offers some examples of first-degree inequalities with two unknowns, along with associated terminology.

Example	*Inequality Symbol*	*Boundary Included*	*Term*
$3x - y > 5$	$>$	no	**open half-plane**
$3x - y < 5$	$<$	no	open half-plane
$3x - y \geq 5$	$\geq$	yes	**closed half-plane**
$3x - y \leq 5$	$\leq$	yes	closed half-plane

We can now summarize the procedure for graphing a first-degree inequality in two unknowns.

Graphing Inequalities

The procedure for graphing an equality can be summarized in two steps.

Step 1 **Graph the boundary.**

Replace the inequality symbol with an equality symbol and draw the resulting line. This is the boundary line. Use a solid line when the boundary is included ($\leq$ or $\geq$). Use a dashed line when the boundary is not included ($<$ or $>$).

Step 2 **Test a point.**

Choose any point in the plane that is not on the boundary line; the point $(0, 0)$ is usually the simplest choice. If this point, called a **test point,** makes the *inequality* true, shade in that half-plane for the solution.*

If the test point makes the *inequality* false, shade in the other half-plane for the solution.

This process sounds complicated, but if you know how to draw lines from equations, you will not find it difficult.

EXAMPLE 4

Graphing a linear inequality

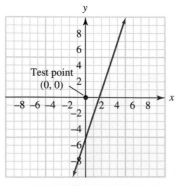

Figure 11.26 Graph of $3x - y \geq 5$

Graph $3x - y \geq 5$.

Solution Note that the inequality symbol is $\geq$, so the boundary is included.

Step 1 Graph the boundary; draw the (solid) line corresponding to

$3x - y = 5$ *Replace the inequality symbol with an equality symbol.*

Let $x = 0$; then $3(0) - y = 5$ or $y = -5$.   Plot the point $(0, -5)$.
Let $x = 1$; then $3(1) - y = 5$ or $y = -2$.   Plot the point $(1, -2)$.
Let $x = 2$; then $3(2) - y = 5$ or $y = 1$.   Plot the point $(2, 1)$.

The boundary line is shown in Figure 11.26.

Step 2 Choose a test point; we choose $(0, 0)$.

*A highlighter pen does a nice job of shading your work.

Plot $(0, 0)$ in Figure 11.26 and note that it lies in one of the half-planes determined by the boundary line. We now check this test point with the given *inequality*.

$$3(0) - (0) \geq 5 \quad \text{You can usually test this in your head.}$$
$$0 \geq 5 \quad \text{This is false.}$$

Therefore, shade the half-plane that does *not* contain $(0, 0)$, as shown in Figure 11.26. ●

EXAMPLE 5　　　　　　　　**Graphing a linear inequality that passes through (0, 0)**

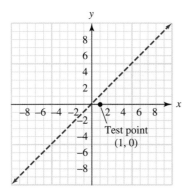

Figure 11.27 Graph of $y < x$

Graph $y < x$.

Solution　Note that the inequality is $<$, so the boundary line is not included.

Step 1　Draw the (dashed) boundary line, $y = x$, as shown in Figure 11.27.

Step 2　Choose a test point. We can't pick $(0, 0)$, because $(0, 0)$ is on the boundary line. Since we must choose some point *not* on the boundary, we choose $(1, 0)$.

$$y < x$$
$$0 < 1 \quad \text{Substitute coordinates for given point.}$$

The inequality $0 < 1$ is true, so we shade the half-plane that contains the test point, as shown in Figure 11.27. ●

PROBLEM SET (11.4)

Graphs are shown in the IAS.

DRILL AND PRACTICE **LEVEL 2**

Solve the systems in Problems 1–16.

1. $\begin{cases} x + y = 5 \\ x - y = 1 \end{cases}$ (3, 2)

2. $\begin{cases} 2x + y = 5 \\ x - y = 4 \end{cases}$ (3, −1)

3. $\begin{cases} 2x + y = 1 \\ x - y = 5 \end{cases}$ (2, −3)

4. $\begin{cases} 2x - y = -2 \\ 3x + y = 7 \end{cases}$ (1, 4)

5. $\begin{cases} 2x - y = 6 \\ 4x + y = 6 \end{cases}$ (2, −2)

6. $\begin{cases} y = 4x + 5 \\ y = x + 2 \end{cases}$ (−1, 1)

7. $\begin{cases} y = 2x + 1 \\ y = 3x + 3 \end{cases}$ (−2, −3)

8. $\begin{cases} y = x + 1 \\ y = -2x + 4 \end{cases}$ (1, 2)

9. $\begin{cases} 4x + y = -3 \\ 2x + y = 1 \end{cases}$ (−2, 5)

10. $\begin{cases} 3x + 2y = 4 \\ x + y = 1 \end{cases}$ (2, −1)

11. $\begin{cases} x + 2y = 2 \\ 3x + y = -4 \end{cases}$ (−2, 2)

12. $\begin{cases} 4x + y = -3 \\ 3x + 2y = 4 \end{cases}$ (−2, 5)

13. $\begin{cases} 2x - 3y = 6 \\ x + 2y = 10 \end{cases}$ (6, 2)

14. $\begin{cases} x - 2y = -2 \\ 3x - y = 4 \end{cases}$ (2, 2)

15. $\begin{cases} x + y = 1 \\ 3x + 2y = -4 \end{cases}$ (−6, 7)

16. $\begin{cases} x + 3y = -5 \\ 2x - y = 11 \end{cases}$ (4, −3)

Graph the first-degree inequalities in two unknowns in Problems 17–34.

17. $y \leq 2x + 1$

18. $y \geq 5x - 3$

19. $y > 5x - 3$

20. $y \geq -2x + 3$

21. $y > 3x - 3$

22. $y < -2x + 5$

23. $x \geq y$

24. $y > x$

25. $x \leq 2y$

26. $2x < y$

27. $3x \leq 2y$

28. $2x < 3y$

29. $y \geq 0$

30. $x \leq 0$

31. $x - 3y \geq 9$

32. $6x - 2y < 1$

33. $3x + 2y > 1$

34. $2x - 3y < 1$

APPLICATIONS **LEVEL 2**

In Problems 35–37, suppose that a car rental agency gave you the following choices:

Option A　*$30 per day plus 40¢ per mile*
Option B　*Flat $50 per day*

35.　Write equations for options A and B.
　　Option A: $c = 30 + 0.4m$; Option B: $c = 50$

36. Graph the equations for options A and B.

37. Estimate the mileage for which both rates are the same.
They are the same for 50 miles.

In Problems 38–40, suppose you can rent a paint sprayer for $4 per hour or for $24 per day.

38. Write equations for the given options, assuming that you need the sprayer for one day or less. *A: c = 4h; B: c = 24*

© Stockbyte/Getty Images

39. Graph the equations for the two options.

40. Estimate the number of hours for which both rates are the same. *They are the same for 6 hours.*

Find the price that maximizes the profit in Problems 41–46. Assume that supply and demand are linear.

41. The demand for a product varies from 200 at a price of $6 each to 800 at a price of $2 each. Also, 800 could be supplied at a price of $7 each, whereas only 200 could be supplied for $1 each. *$4.00*

42. The demand for a product varies from 1,000 at a price of $9 each to 7,000 at a price of $3 each. Also, 6,000 could be supplied at a price of $10 each, whereas only 2,000 could be supplied for $2 each. *$6.00*

43. The demand for a commodity is 5,000 at a one-dollar price, down to 1,000 at a seven-dollar price. It is possible to obtain 2,000 at a two-dollar price, but 5,000 can be had at a price of eight dollars each. *$4.00*

44. The demand for a commodity is twenty at $2,000 each, but only five at $8,000 each. It is possible to obtain nine at $2,000 each, but eleven can be available at $10,000 each. *$6,000*

45. By test marketing its T-shirts at UCLA, California Beach-wear finds that it can sell 180 shirts when they are priced at $10, but only 20 when they are priced at $40. On the other hand, it finds that 20 shirts can be supplied at $10 each. If they were supplied at $40 each, overtime shifts could be used to raise the supply to 180 shirts. What is the optimum price for the T-shirts? *$25*

46. A manufacturer of class rings test-marketed a new item at the University of Texas. It found that it could sell 900 items when they are priced at $1, but it can sell only 300 items if the price is raised to $7. On the other hand, it found that 600 items can be supplied at $1 each. If they were supplied at $9 each, overtime shifts could be used to raise the supply to 1,000 items. What is the optimum price for the items? *$3.00*

47. Linda is on a business trip and must rent a car for the day. The car rental agency has the following options on the car she wants to rent: **Option A:** $30 plus 25¢ per mile (instead of $40 and 50¢/mi); **Option B:** Flat $50 (instead of $60) with unlimited mileage. Which option should she choose? *Option A if she drives less than 80 miles*

RIGHT OR WRONG?　　**LEVEL 3**

Explain what is wrong, if anything, with the statements in Problems 48–60. Explain your reasoning.

48. (3, 2) is a solution to the system

$$\begin{cases} 2x - y = 1 \\ x + 2y = 8 \end{cases}$$

because $2(2) - 3 = 1$ is true and $2 + 2(3) = 8$ is true.
F; x = 3 and y = 2 so 2(3) −2 = 4, not 1.

49. (3, 2) is a solution to the system

$$\begin{cases} x - y = 1 \\ 5 - y = x \end{cases}$$

because $3 - 2 = 1$ is true and $5 - 2 = 3$ is true. *T*

50. Nothing seems to work in the system

$$\begin{cases} x = 1 - y \\ y = 3 - x \end{cases}$$

so the solution is (0, 0). *F; 0 = 1 − 0 is not true.*

51. The linear inequality $2x + 5y < 2$ does not have a boundary line, because the inequality is $<$. *F; the boundary is 2x + 5y = 2.*

52. A good test point for the linear inequality $y \geq x$ is (0, 0).
F; can't choose a test point on the boundary line.

53. A good test point for the linear inequality $x + 2y \leq 0$ is $(-2, 1)$ *F; can't choose a test point on the boundary line.*

54. To graph the linear inequality $x - y \leq 2$, we write

$$x - y \leq 2$$
$$-y \leq -x + 2$$
$$y \geq x - 2$$

The half-plane to be shaded is the upper half-plane because the inequality is $\geq$. *See bottom of the column.*

55. The test point (0, 0) satisfies the inequality $2y - 3x < 2$. *T*

56. The test point (0, 0) satisfies the inequality $3x - 2y \geq -1$. *T*

57. The test point (0, 0) satisfies the inequality $3x > 2y$.
F; (0, 0) is not a test point because it lies on the boundary.

58. The test point $(-2, 4)$ satisfies the inequality $y > 2x - 1$. *T*

59. The test point $(-2, 4)$ satisfies the inequality $5x + 2y \leq 9$. *T*

60. The test point $(-2, 4)$ satisfies the inequality $4x < 3y$. *T*

---

54. F; the graph is not only the upper half-plane, but also the graph of the boundary, which is the equation x − y = 2.

11.5 Graphing Curves

IN THIS WORLD THE UTILITY OF MATH

"Well, Billy, can I make it?" asked Evel.

"If you can accelerate to the proper speed, and if the wind is not blowing too much, I think you can," answered Billy.

"It will be one huge moneymaker, but I want some assurance that it can be done!" retorted Evel.

About 30 years ago, a daredevil named Evel Knievel attempted a Skycycle ride across the Snake River. In this section, Evel will learn how to plot points to draw curves that are not lines. He will learn about a curve called a *parabola* that traces the path of his Skycycle.

 See Problem 57.

Graphing Curves by Plotting Points

When cannons were introduced in the 13th century, their primary use was to demoralize the enemy. It was much later that they were used for strategic purposes. In fact, cannons existed nearly three centuries before enough was known about the behavior of projectiles to use them with any accuracy. The cannonball does not travel in a straight line, it was discovered, because of an unseen force that today we know as *gravity*. Consider Figure 11.28. It is a scale drawing (graph) of the path of a cannonball fired in a particular way.

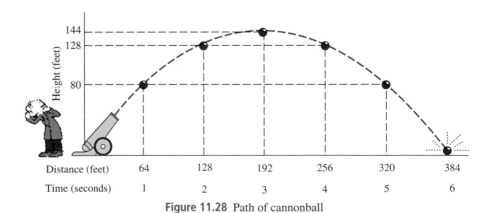

Figure 11.28 Path of cannonball

The path described by a projectile is called a **parabola.** Any projectile—a ball, an arrow, a bullet, a rock from a slingshot, even water from the nozzle of a hose or sprinkler—will travel a parabolic path. Note that this parabolic curve has a maximum height and is symmetric about a vertical line through that height. In other words, the ascent and descent paths are symmetric.

EXAMPLE 1   Graphing a nonlinear curve

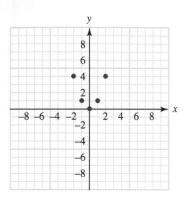

Figure 11.29 Points that satisfy the equation $y = x^2$

Graph $y = x^2$.

Solution We will choose x-values and find corresponding y-values.

Let $x = 0$:   Let $x = 1$:   Let $x = -1$:
$\quad y = 0^2 = 0$; plot $(0, 0)$ $\quad y = 1^2 = 1$; plot $(1, 1)$ $\quad y = (-1)^2 = 1$;
$\qquad\qquad\qquad\qquad\qquad\qquad\qquad\qquad\qquad\qquad\qquad\qquad\qquad$ plot $(-1, 1)$

Notice in Figure 11.29 that these points do not fall in a straight line. If we find two more points, we can see the shape of the graph.

$\quad$ Let $x = 2$:$\quad y = 2^2 = 4$; plot $(2, 4)$
$\quad$ Let $x = -2$:$\quad y = (-2)^2 = 4$; plot $(-2, 4)$

These two additional points are also shown in Figure 11.29. We can now connect the points to form a smooth curve, as shown in Figure 11.30.

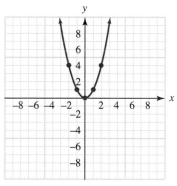

Figure 11.30 Graph of $y = x^2$ ⬤

The curve shown in Figure 11.30 is a parabola that is said to *open upward.* The lowest point, $(0, 0)$ in Example 1, is called the **vertex.** The following example is a parabola that *opens downward.*

EXAMPLE 2   Graphing a parabola

Sketch $y = -\frac{1}{2}x^2$.

Solution

$\quad$ Let $x = 0$; then $y = -\frac{1}{2}(0)^2 = 0$ or $y = 0$; plot the point $(0, 0)$.
$\quad$ Let $x = 1$; then $y = -\frac{1}{2}(1)^2 = -\frac{1}{2}$; plot the point $(1, -\frac{1}{2})$.

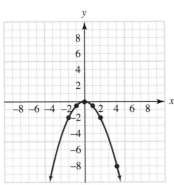

Figure 11.31 Graph of $y = -\frac{1}{2}x^2$

Let $x = -1$; then $y = -\frac{1}{2}(-1)^2 = -\frac{1}{2}$; plot the point $(-1, -\frac{1}{2})$.

Let $x = 2$; then $y = -\frac{1}{2}(2)^2 = -2$; plot the point $(2, -2)$.

Let $x = -2$; then $y = -\frac{1}{2}(-2)^2 = -2$; plot the point $(-2, -2)$.

Let $x = 4$; then $y = -\frac{1}{2}(4)^2 = -8$; plot the point $(4, -8)$.

First, plot the points. Next, connect these points to form a smooth curve, as shown in Figure 11.31. ●

You can sketch many different curves by plotting points. The procedure is to decide whether you should pick x-values and find the corresponding y-values, or pick y-values and find the corresponding x-values. Find enough ordered pairs to that you can connect the points with a smooth graph. Many graphs in mathematics are not smooth, but we will not consider those in this course.

EXAMPLE 3

Curve sketching by choosing y-values

Sketch the graph of the curve $x = y^2 - 6y + 4$.

Solution We use the same procedure to find points on the graph, except that in this equation we see that it will be easier to choose y-values and find corresponding x-values.

Let $y = 0$; then $x = (0)^2 - 6 \cdot 0 + 4 = 4$; plot the point $(4, 0)$. (See Figure 11.32.)

Let $y = 1$; then $x = (1)^2 - 6 \cdot 1 + 4 = -1$; plot the point $(-1, 1)$.

Let $y = 2$; then $x = (2)^2 - 6 \cdot 2 + 4 = -4$; plot the point $(-4, 2)$.

Let $y = 3$; then $x = (3)^2 - 6 \cdot 3 + 4 = -5$; plot the point $(-5, 3)$.

Let $y = 4$; then $x = (4)^2 - 6 \cdot 4 + 4 = -4$; plot the point $(-4, 4)$.

Let $y = 5$; then $x = (5)^2 - 6 \cdot 5 + 4 = -1$; plot the point $(-1, 5)$.

Let $y = 6$; then $x = (6)^2 - 6 \cdot 6 + 4 = 4$; plot the point $(4, 6)$.

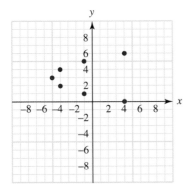

Figure 11.32 Points that satisfy the equation $x = y^2 - 6y + 4$

How many points should we find? For lines, we had to find only two points, with a third point as a check. For curves that are not lines, we must plot as many points as are needed to enable us to draw a smooth curve. We connect the points we have plotted to draw the curve shown in Figure 11.33.

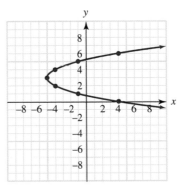

Figure 11.33 Graph of $x = y^2 - 6y + 4$ ●

Exponential Curves

An **exponential equation** is one in which a variable appears as an exponent. Consider the equation $y = 2^x$. This equation represents a doubling process. The graph of such an equation is called an *exponential curve* and is graphed by plotting points. In particular, the graph of $y = b^x$ is an **exponential curve** if $b > 0$ and $b \neq 1$.

EXAMPLE 4 **Graphing an exponential curve by plotting points**

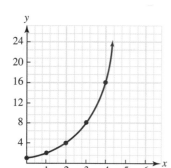

Figure 11.34 Graph of $y = 2^x$

Sketch the graph of $y = 2^x$ for nonnegative values of x.

Solution Choose x-values and find corresponding y-values. These values form ordered pairs (x, y). Plot enough ordered pairs so that you can see the general shape of the curve, and then connect the points with a smooth curve.

Let $x = 0$; then $y = 2^0 = 1$; plot the point $(0, 1)$.
Let $x = 1$; then $y = 2^1 = 2$; plot the point $(1, 2)$.
Let $x = 2$; then $y = 2^2 = 4$; plot the point $(2, 4)$.
Let $x = 3$; then $y = 2^3 = 8$; plot the point $(3, 8)$.
Let $x = 4$; then $y = 2^4 = 16$; plot the point $(4, 16)$.

Connect the points with a smooth curve, as shown in Figure 11.34. ●

Population growth is described by an exponential equation. The population P at some future date can be predicted if you know the present population, P_0, and the growth rate, r. In more advanced courses, it is shown that the predicted population in t time periods is approximated by the equation $P = P_0(2.72)^{rt}$.

EXAMPLE 5 **Problem solving with an exponential equation**

Tony calls his local Chamber of Commerce and finds that the population growth rate of his town is now 5%. Also, according to the 1990 census, the population is 2,500. Find the growth equation, and draw a graph showing the population between the years 1990 and 2010.

Solution

$P_0 = 2{,}500$ and $r = 5\% = 0.05$ Remember, to change a percent to a decimal, move the decimal point two places to the left.

The equation of the graph is $P = \mathbf{2{,}500(2.72)^{0.05t}}$.

If $t = 0$: $P = 2{,}500(2.72)^0 = 2{,}500$; plot the point $(0, 2500)$.   This is the 1990 population; 1990 is called the base year. It is called the "present time" (even though it is not now 1990). Thus, if $t = 5$, then the population corresponds to the year 1995. If $t = 10$, the population is for the year 2000.

If $t = 10$: $P = 2{,}500(2.72)^{0.05(10)} \approx 4{,}123$ *Display:* 4123.105626

This means that the predicted population in the year 2000 is 4,123. Plot the point $(10, 4123)$.

If $t = 20$: $P = 2{,}500(2.72)^{0.05(20)} = 6800$ *Display:* 6800. Plot the point $(20, 6800)$.

We have plotted these points in Figure 11.35.

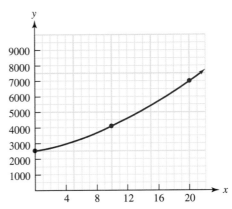

Figure 11.35 Graph showing population P from 1990 to 2010 (base year, $t = 0$, is 1990)

One of the first applications in Part II of this book and one of the most important concepts for intelligent functioning in today's world is interest. We can now return to this idea and look at graphs showing the growth of money as the result of interest accumulation. Simple interest is represented by a line, whereas compound interest requires an exponential graph. This means that, for short periods of time, there is very little difference between simple and compound interest, but as time increases, the differences become significant.

EXAMPLE 6

Graphs comparing simple and compound interest

Suppose that you deposit $100 at 10% interest. Graph the total amounts you will have if you invest your money at simple interest and if you invest your money at interest compounded annually. Here are the appropriate formulas:

Simple interest: $A = P(1 + rt)$
Compound interest: $A = P(1 + r)^t$

Solution   For this example, $P = 100$ and $r = 0.10$; the variables are t and A. We begin by finding some ordered pairs. A calculator is necessary for calculating compound interest.

Year	Simple Interest	Point	Compound Interest	Point
$t = 0$	$A = 100(1 + 0.1 \cdot 0) = 100$	$(0, 100)$	$A = 100(1 + 0.1)^0 = 100$	$(0, 100)$
$t = 1$	$A = 100(1 + 0.1 \cdot 1) = 110$	$(1, 110)$	$A = 100(1 + 0.1)^1 = 110$	$(1, 110)$
$t = 10$	$A = 100(1 + 0.1 \cdot 10) = 200$	$(10, 200)$	$A = 100(1 + 0.1)^{10} \approx 259$	$(10, 259)$
$t = 20$	$A = 100(1 + 0.1 \cdot 20) = 300$	$(20, 300)$	$A = 100(1 + 0.1)^{20} \approx 673$	$(20, 673)$

The graphs through these points are shown in Figure 11.36.

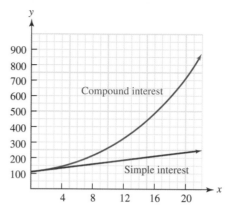

Figure 11.36 Comparison of simple interest and compound interest

---

PROBLEM SET 11.5

Graphs are shown in the IAS.

ESSENTIAL IDEAS | LEVEL 1

1. **IN YOUR OWN WORDS** What is a parabola?

2. **IN YOUR OWN WORDS** What is an exponential graph?

DRILL AND PRACTICE | LEVEL 2

Sketch the graph of each equation in Problems 3–28.

3. $y = 3x^2$ 4. $y = 2x^2$ 5. $y = 10x^2$

6. $y = -x^2$ 7. $y = -2x^2$ 8. $y = -3x^2$

9. $y = -5x^2$ 10. $y = 5x^2$ 11. $y = \frac{1}{2}x^2$

12. $x = 2y^2$ 13. $x = -3y^2$ 14. $x = \frac{1}{2}y^2$

15. $y = 2x^3$ 16. $y = -x^3$ 17. $x = -y^3$

18. $y = \frac{1}{3}x^2$ 19. $y = -\frac{2}{3}x^2$ 20. $y = \frac{1}{10}x^2$

21. $y = -\frac{1}{10}x^2$ 22. $y = \frac{1}{1,000}x^2$

23. $y = x^2 - 4$ 24. $y = x^2 + 4$

25. $y = 9 - x^2$ 26. $y = -3x^2 + 4$

27. $y = 2x^2 - 3$ 28. $y = x^2 - 2x + 1$

Sketch the graphs of the equations in Problems 29–40 for nonnegative values of x.

29. $y = 3^x$ 30. $y = 4^x$ 31. $y = 5^x$

32. $y = -2^x$ 33. $y = -6^x$ 34. $y = -7^x$

35. $y = 10^x$ 36. $y = 100 - 2^x$

37. $y = (\frac{1}{2})^x$ 38. $y = (\frac{1}{3})^x$

39. $y = (\frac{1}{10})^x$ 40. $y = -(\frac{1}{10})^x$

Draw the graphs in Problems 41–46.

41. $y = -2x^2 + 4x - 2$ 42. $y = \frac{1}{4}x^2 - \frac{1}{2}x + \frac{1}{4}$

43. $y = \frac{1}{2}x^2 + x + \frac{1}{2}$ 44. $y = x^2 - 2x + 3$

45. $x = 3y^2 + 12y + 14$ 46. $x = 4y - y^2 - 4$

APPLICATIONS | LEVEL 2

47. Change the growth rate in Example 5 to 6%, and graph the population curve.

48. Change the growth rate in Example 5 to 3.5%, and graph the population curve.

49. Change the growth rate in Example 5 to 1.5%, and graph the population curve.

50. Rework Example 6 for a 12% interest rate.

51. Rework Example 6 for an 8% interest rate.

52. Rework Example 6 for an 18% interest rate.

53. **a.** Graph $h = -\frac{144}{9}(t - 3)^2 + 144$.

    b. Does the parabola in part **a** open upward or downward? *downward*

    c. If we relate the graph in part **a** to the cannonball in Figure 11.28, can t be negative? *no*

    d. Draw the graph of the parabola in part **a** for $0 \le t \le 6$.

54. **a.** Graph $d = 16t^2$.

    b. Does the parabola in part **a** open upward or downward? *upward*

    c. If we relate the graph in part **a** to the falling object in the B.C. cartoon in Section 11.2, can t be negative? *no*

    d. Draw the graph of the parabola in part **a** for $0 \le t \le 16$.

55. In archeology, carbon-14 dating is a standard method of determining the age of certain artifacts. Decay rate can be measured by half-life, which is the time required for one-half of a substance to decompose. Carbon-14 has a half-life of approximately 5,600 years. If 100 grams of carbon were present originally, then the amount A of carbon present today is given by the formula

$$A = 100\left(\frac{1}{2}\right)^{t/5,600}$$

where t is the time since the artifact was alive until today. Graph this relationship by letting $t = 5,600$, $t = 11,200, \ldots$, and adjust the scale accordingly.

56. IN YOUR OWN WORDS Predict the population of your city or state for the year 2010.

57. "Well, Billy, can I make it?" asked Evel. "If you can accelerate to the proper speed, and if the wind is not blowing too much, I think you can," answered Billy. "It will be one huge moneymaker, but I want some assurance that it can be done!" retorted Evel. About 30 years ago a daredevil named Evel Knievel attempted a Skycycle ride across the Snake River (see Figure 11.37).

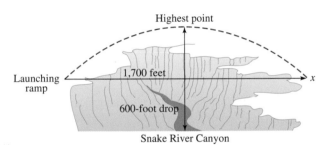

Figure 11.37 Snake River Canyon

Suppose that the path of Evel Knievel's Skycycle is

$$y = -0.0005x^2 + 2.39x$$

Assuming that the ramp is at the origin and x is the horizontal distance traveled, graph this relationship. Using your graph, answer Evel's question: Will he make it? Assume that the actual distance the Skycycle must travel is 4,700 ft.   **Yes; he will make it.**

RIGHT OR WRONG?   **LEVEL 3**

Explain what is wrong, if anything, with the statements in Problems 58–60. Explain your reasoning.

58. In graphing $y = 2x^2$, we need to plot three points:

 If $x = 0$, then $y = 2(0)^2 = 0$; plot $(0, 0)$.

 If $x = 1$, then $y = 2(1)^2 = 2$; plot $(1, 2)$.

 If $x = -2$, then $y = 2(-2)^2 = 8$; plot $(-2, 8)$.

Complete the graph by drawing the line passing through these three points.   **F; the points satisfying this equation do not form a line.**

59. In graphing $x = y^2$, it is easier to pick y-values and to find the corresponding x-values.

 If $y = 0$, then $x = 0^2 = 0$; plot $(0, 0)$.

 If $y = 1$, then $x = 1^2 = 1$; plot $(1, 1)$.

 If $y = -1$, then $x = (-1)^2 = 1$; plot $(1, -1)$.

 If $y = 2$, then $x = 2^2 = 4$; plot $(4, 2)$.

 If $y = 3$, then $x = 3^2 = 9$; plot $(9, 3)$.

Complete the graph by drawing the curve passing through these points. This curve is a parabola.   **T**

60. In graphing $y = x^3$, plot points to draw the graph shown in Figure 11.38.   **F**

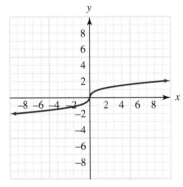

Figure 11.38 Graph of $y = x^3$

11.6 Chapter 11 Summary and Review

Take some time getting ready to work the review problems in this section. First, look back at the definition and property boxes. You will maximize your understanding of this chapter by working the problems in this section only after you have studied the material.

IMPORTANT TERMS

Numbers refer to sections of this chapter.

Spending some time with the terms and objectives of this chapter will pay dividends in assuring your success.

Axes [11.1]
Boundary [11.4]
Cartesian coordinates [11.1]
Closed half-plane [11.4]
Coordinates [11.1]
Demand [11.4]
Equilibrium point [11.4]
Exponential curve [11.5]
Exponential equation [11.5]
First component [11.1]
Function [11.2]
Functional notation [11.2]

Graph [11.1; 11.3]
Half-plane [11.4]
Horizontal line [11.3]
Inequality [11.4]
Open half-plane [11.4]
Ordered pair [11.1]
Origin [11.1]
Parabola [11.5]
Plot a point [11.1]
Quadrants [11.1]
Rectangular coordinates [11.1]

Satisfy [11.3]
Second component [11.1]
Simultaneous solution [11.4]
Solution [11.3]
Supply [11.4]
System of equations [11.4]
Test point [11.4]
Vertex [11.5]
Vertical line [11.3]
x-axis [11.1]
y-axis [11.1]

Essential Ideas

[11.1] Problems 1–3	Plot points on a Cartesian coordinate system.
Problem 4	Know the signs of *x* and *y* in each of the four quadrants.
[11.2] Problem 1	Know the definition of a function.
Problem 2	Distinguish a function from the evaluation of a function, along with the notation for each.
[11.3] Problem 1	Solve linear equations with two variables.
Problem 2	Describe the process for graphing a line.
Problem 3	Distinguish horizontal and vertical lines.
[11.5] Problem 1	Describe a parabola.
Problem 2	Describe an exponential graph.

LEARNING OUTCOMES

The material in this chapter is reviewed in the following list of learning outcomes. A self-test (with answers and suggestions for additional study) is given. This self-test is constructed so that each problem number corresponds to a related objective. For example, Problem 7 is testing Objective 11.7. This self-test is followed by a practice test with the questions in mixed order.

[11.1]	*Objective* 11.1	Look at a map or seating chart and locate positions using an ordered pair.
[11.1]	*Objective* 11.2	Plot points on a coordinate system.
[11.2]	*Objective* 11.3	Decide whether a given set is a function.
[11.2]	*Objective* 11.4	Use a function machine to find output values for given input numbers.
[11.2]	*Objective* 11.5	Find the values of a function.
[11.3]	*Objective* 11.6	Find ordered pairs satisfying a given equation.
[11.3]	*Objective* 11.7	Graph a first-degree equation in two unknowns.
[11.4]	*Objective* 11.8	Solve a system of equations graphically.

[11.4]   *Objective* 11.9   Graph a first-degree inequality in two unknowns.
[11.5]   *Objective* 11.10   Sketch the graph of an equation with two variables that is not linear.
[11.5]   *Objective* 11.11   Sketch the graph of an exponential equation.
[11.1–11.5] *Objective* 11.12   Solve applied problems. (Problems 12–15)

Self-Test

Each question of this self-test is related to the corresponding objective listed above.

1. There are two empty seats in the seating chart in Figure 11.4 on page 547. Name these seats using ordered pairs.

2. Plot the points $(2, 100)$, $(-5, 50)$, and $(3, -70)$.

3. Is $\{(4, 3), (5, -2), (6, 3)\}$ a function? Why or why not?

4. Suppose you drop the number 1,000 into the function machine shown in Figure 11.39. What is the output value?

5. If $f(x) = 10 - 3x$, find
   a. $f(0)$ **b.** $f(10)$ **c.** $f(-4)$

6. Find three ordered pairs that satisfy the equation
$$3x + 2y = 12$$

7. Graph $5x - y = 15$.

8. Find the simultaneous solution for the system $\begin{cases} 2x - y = -1 \\ x - 3y = 7 \end{cases}$

9. Graph $x < 3y$.

10. Graph $y = 1 - x^2$.

11. Graph $y = -2^x$ for nonnegative values of x.

12. Suppose the *profit* (in dollars) of a certain item is given by the equation
$$P = 1.25x - 850$$
where x is the number of items sold.
   a. Interpret the value of P when $x = 0$.
   b. Graph this profit relationship.

13. If a cannonball is fired upward with an initial velocity of 128 feet per second, its height, h, can be calculated according to the formula
$$h = 128t - 16t^2$$
where t is the length of time (in seconds) after the cannonball is fired. Sketch this equation by letting $t = 0, 1, 2, \ldots, 7, 8$. Connect these points with part of a parabola.

14. An amount of money, A, results from investing a sum of P at a simple interest rate of 7% for 10 years, and is specified by the formula
$$A = 1.7P$$
   a. Is this a linear equation?
   b. Graph this equation, where P is plotted along the x-axis and A is plotted along the y-axis.

15. Graph the earnings for the next 50 years of $50 invested at a simple interest rate of 10%. Use the formula $A = P(1 + rt)$.

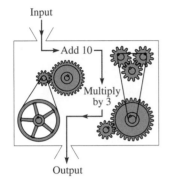

Input

Add 10

Multiply by 3

Output

Figure 11.39 Function machine

STUDY HINTS   *Compare your solutions and answers to the self-test. For each problem you missed, work some additional problems in the section listed in the margin. After you have worked these problems, you can test yourself with the practice test.*

Additional Problems

Complete Solutions to the Self-Test

1. The empty seats are (3, 5) and (5, 2).

2. First, decide on appropriate scales. It looks as if the scales for the x- and y-axes should be different. On the x-axis we let one square = 1 unit, and on the y-axis, we let one square = 10 units.

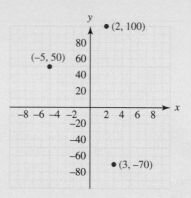

3. Yes, each x-value is associated with exactly one y-value.

4. If we drop in the number 1,000, the first direction inside the machine is to "add 10," so now the machine is holding 1,010. Next, this number drops down to the direction that says to "multiply by 3," which gives the output value 3,030.

5. **a.** $f(0) = 10 - 3(0) = 10$
   b. $f(10) = 10 - 3(10) = 10 - 30 = -20$
   c. $f(-4) = 10 - 3(-4) = 10 + 12 = 22$

6. Consider the equation $3x + 2y = 12$; the actual values chosen for the three ordered pairs, of course, vary. Suppose we select

$y = 0$; then $3x + 2(0) = 12$ $x = 2$; then $3(2) + 2y = 12$
$\qquad\qquad 3x = 12$ $\qquad\qquad 6 + 2y = 12$
$\qquad\qquad\; x = 4$ $\qquad\qquad\quad 2y = 6$
Ordered pair is (4, 0). $\qquad\qquad\qquad y = 3$

$x = 0$; then $3(0) + 2y = 12$ Ordered pair is (2, 3).
$\qquad\qquad 2y = 12$
$\qquad\qquad\; y = 6$
Ordered pair is (0, 6).

7.

x	y
0	-15
1	-10
3	0

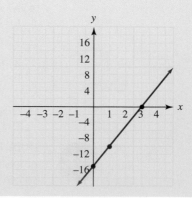

[11.4] Problems 1–16

8. First line:

x	y
−1	−1
0	1
1	3

Second line:

x	y
−2	−3
7	0
4	−1

The point of intersection is $(-2, -3)$.

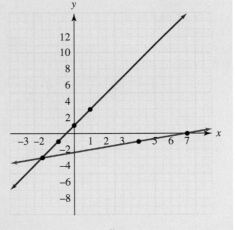

[11.4] Problems 17–34

9.

x	y
0	0
3	1
6	2

Test point: $(0, 3)$
  $x < 3y$
  $0 < 3(3)$
This is true; shade the same side, as shown in yellow.

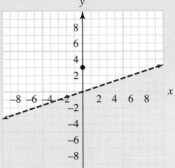

[11.5] Problems 3–28; 41–46

10. This is not linear.

x	y
0	1
1	0
−1	0
2	−3
3	−8

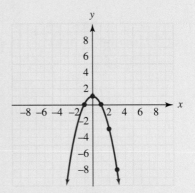

[11.5] Problems 29–40

11. This is not linear.

x	y
0	−1
1	−2
2	−4
3	−8

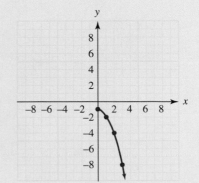

12. a. The value of P when $x = 0$ is the profit when no items are sold. Thus, if no items are sold, the profit is

$$P = 1.25(0) - 850 = -850$$

We call this the *loss*. Sometimes, this is called the *fixed cost*.

b. To graph this line, begin with a table of values.

x	P
0	−850
1000	400
5000	5400

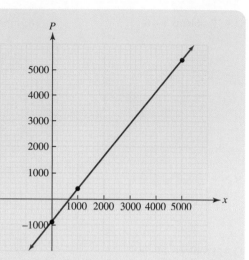

13. This is not linear.

t	h
0	0
1	112
2	192
3	240
4	256
5	240
6	192
7	112
8	0

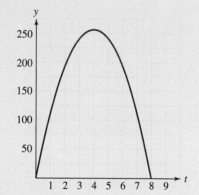

14. a. This is a first-degree equation, so yes, it is a linear equation.

b. To graph this line, begin with a table of values.

P	A
0	0
6	10.2
10	17

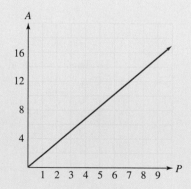

15. $A = P(1 + rt)$
$= 50(1 + 0.1t)$

t	A
0	50
10	100
30	200
50	300

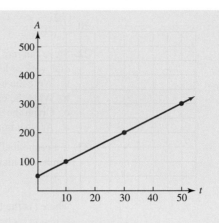

Chapter 11 Review Questions

*To prepare for a chapter test, first study the chapter; then, read each term from the important terms list above and make sure you know the meaning of each word; finally, review the chapter objectives. **After** these steps, take the self-test and correct all your answers. The following review questions can be used for extra practice.*

1. a. Plot five points so that the first and second components are the same. Draw the line passing through the plotted points.   Plotted points vary.

    b. Plot five points so that the first component is 5. Draw the line passing through the plotted points.   Plotted points vary.

2. Decide whether each set is a function.
    a. $\{(4, 19), (19, 4), (18, 19)\}$ function
    b. $\{(12, 6), (12, 8), (12, 10)\}$ not a function
    c. $\{(1, 2), (2, 4), (3, 9), (4, 16), (5, 25)\}$ function
    d. $\{1, 5, 9, 10\}$ not a function

3. Find the value of each function.
    a. $f(x) = 3x + 2$; find $f(6)$.   20
    b. $g(x) = x^2 - 3$; find $g(0)$.   −3
    c. $F(x) = 5x + 25$; find $F(10)$.   75
    d. $m(x) = 5$; find $m(10)$.   5

Graph the equations in Problems 4–9.   See IAS for graphs.

    4. $y = 3x - 2$ **5.** $x + 2y + 10 = 0$ **6.** $y = 25$

    7. $y = 5 - x^2$ **8.** $3y^2 + x = 0$ **9.** $y = x^2 + 6x + 11$

Graph the equations in Problems 10–13 for nonnegative values of x.

    10. $y = -3^x$ **11.** $y = \left(\frac{1}{4}\right)^x$ **12.** $y = 2^x - 10$ **13.** $y = 10 - 2^x$

Graph the inequalities in Problems 14–17.

    14. $y > 2x - 1$ **15.** $y > 3x + 2$ **16.** $y \geq 2x - 3$ **17.** $y \leq 3x + 4$

Solve the systems of equations in Problems 18–21.

    18. $\begin{cases} x + y = 5 \\ 2x - y = 1 \end{cases}$ (2, 3)   **19.** $\begin{cases} 2x + y = 5 \\ x - y = 4 \end{cases}$ (3, −1)

20. $\begin{cases} 2x + y = 1 \\ x - y = 5 \end{cases}$ (2, −3)   21. $\begin{cases} x + y = 1 \\ 2x - y = 5 \end{cases}$ (2, −1)

22. Steve can rent a rototiller for $8 per day or $40 per week. He wants to rent the tiller for one week or less.
   a. Write the equation for the cost if he rents it by the day. $c = 8d$
   b. Write the equation for the cost if he rents it by the week. $c = 40$
   c. Graph the equations for parts **a** and **b** on the same axes.   See IAS.
   d. At what number of days are both rates the same?   5 days

23. If a cannonball is fired upward with an initial velocity of 144 feet per second, its height can be calculated according to the formula   See IAS.

$$y = 144t - 16t^2$$

where t is the length of time (in seconds) after the cannonball is fired. Sketch this equation by letting $t = 0, 1, 2, \ldots, 8, 9$. Connect these points with part of a parabola.

24. Consider the earnings for the next 40 years of $100 invested at 12%.   See IAS.
   a. Graph $A = P(1 + rt)$.
   b. Graph $A = P(1 + r)^t$.
   c. Compare the graphs. What is the difference in the amount of money you will have after 40 years?   The difference is over $8,725.

25. Draw a population curve for a city whose growth rate is $r = 1.3\%$ and whose present population, P_0, is 53,000. The appropriate equation is $P = P_0(2.72)^{rt}$. Let $t = 0, 10,$ and 20 to help you find points for graphing this curve.

Absolute value   The absolute value of a number is the distance of that number from the origin. Symbolically,

$$|n| = \begin{cases} n & \text{if } n \geq 0 \\ -n & \text{if } n < 0 \end{cases}$$

Accuracy   One speaks of an *accurate statement* in the sense that it is true and correct, or of an *accurate computation* in the sense that it contains no numerical error. *Accurate to a certain decimal* place means that all digits preceding and including the given one are correct.

Acre   A unit commonly used in the United States system for measuring land. It contains $43{,}560$ ft^2.

Acute angle   An angle whose measure is smaller than a right angle

Addition of integers   If the integers to be added have the same sign, the answer will also have that same sign and will have a magnitude equal to the sum of the absolute values of the given integers. If the integers to be added have opposite signs, the answer will have the sign of the integer with the larger absolute value, and will have a magnitude equal to the difference of the absolute values. Finally, if one or both of the given integers is 0, use the property $n + 0 = n$ for any integer n.

Addition law of exponents   To multiply two numbers with like bases, add the exponents. That is, $b^m \cdot b^n = b^{m+n}$.

Addition property of equations   The solution of an equation is unchanged by adding the same number to both sides of the equation.

Addition property of inequality   The solution of an inequality is unchanged if you add the same number to both sides of the inequality.

Add-on interest   It is a method of calculating interest and installments on a loan. The amount of interest is calculated according to the formula $I = Prt$ and is then added to the amount of the loan. This sum divided by the number of payments is the amount of monthly payment.

Adjacent side   In a right triangle, an acute angle is made up of two sides, one called the *hypotenuse* (the side opposite the right angle) and the other side called the adjacent side.

Adjusted balance method   A method of calculating credit card interest using the formula $I = Prt$ in which

P is the balance owed after the current payment is subtracted

Algebra   A generalization of arithmetic that uses letters, or variables, to denote numbers

Algebraic expression   Any meaningful combination of numbers, variables, and signs of operation

Amortization   The process of paying off a debt by systematically making partial payments until the debt (principal) and interest are repaid

Amortization schedule   A table showing the schedule of payments of a loan detailing the amount of each payment that goes to repay the principal and how much goes to pay interest

Amortized loan   A loan that is fully paid off with the last periodic payment

And   A word that indicates the set consisting of elements in both the given sets

Angle   Two rays or segments with a common endpoint

Annual compounding   In the compound interest formula, it is when $n = 1$.

Annual percentage rate   The percentage rate charged on a loan based on the actual amount owed and the actual time it is owed. The approximation formula for annual percentage rate (APR) is APR $= 2Nr/(N + 1)$.

Approximately equal symbol   The symbol "$\approx$" is used when numbers are "almost equal," as in $2.834 \approx 2.9$ or $\pi \approx 3.1416$.

APR   Abbreviation for annual percentage rate. See *Compound interest.*

Area   A number describing the two-dimensional content of a set. Specifically, it is the number of square units enclosed in a plane figure.

Area formulas   Square, s^2; rectangle, ℓw; circle, πr^2; trapezoid, $\frac{1}{2}h(b_1 + b_2)$

Associative property   A property of grouping that applies to addition and multiplication, but not to subtraction or division: If a, b, and c are real numbers, then

$$(a + b) + c = a + (b + c) \quad \text{and} \quad (ab)c = a(bc)$$

Average   A single number that is used to typify or represent a set of numbers. In this book, it refers to the *mean, median,* or *mode.*

Average daily balance method   A method of calculating credit card interest using the formula $I = Prt$ in which P is the average daily balance owed for a current month, and t is the number of days in the month divided by 365

Axes   The intersecting lines of a Cartesian coordinate system. The horizontal axis is called the x-axis, and the vertical axis is called the y-axis. The axes divide the plane into four parts called *quadrants*.

Axiom   A statement that is accepted without proof

Balloon payment   A single larger payment made at the end of the time period of an installment loan that is not amortized

Bar graph   See *Graph*.

Base   The whole quantity in a percent problem

Base of an exponential   In $y = b^x$, the *base* is b ($b \neq 1$).

Bell-shaped curve   See *Normal curve*.

Belong to a set   To be an element of a set

Bimodal   A data set that contains two modes

Binary numeration system   A numeration system with two symbols, 0 and 1. It is the internal numeration system used in computer programming.

Binomial   A polynomial with exactly two terms

Bisect   To divide into two equal or congruent parts

Bond   An interest-bearing certificate issued by a government or business, promising to pay the holder a specified amount (usually $1,000) on a certain date

Boundary   See *Half-plane*.

Box plot   A rectangular box positioned above a numerical scale, drawn from Q_1 (the first quartile) to Q_3 (the third quartile). The median (Q_2) is shown as a dashed line and a segment is extended to show both the maximum and minimum values.

Braces   See *Grouping symbols*.

Brackets   See *Grouping symbols*.

Canceling   The process of reducing a fraction by dividing the same number into both the numerator and the denominator

Capacity   A measurement for the amount of liquid a container holds

Cardinal number   A number that designates the many-ness of a set; the number of units, but not the order in which they are arranged

Cardinality   The number of elements in a set

Cards   A set of fifty-two thin rectangular pieces of cardboard or plastic marked on one side to show its magnitude and suit (hearts, spades, diamonds, or clubs), and used for playing any number of games. A standard set, or deck, of cards is shown on page 452.

Cartesian coordinate system   Two intersecting lines, called *axes*, used to locate points in a plane. Ordered pairs used to locate points in this coordinate system are called *Cartesian coordinates*. If the intersecting lines are perpendicular, the system is called a *rectangular coordinate system*.

Cartesian plane   See *Cartesian coordinate system*.

Celsius   A metric measurement for temperature for which the freezing point of water is 0° and the boiling point of water is 100°

Center   See *Circle*.

Centi-   A prefix that means 1/100

Centimeter   One hundredth of a meter

Circle   The set of points in a plane that are a given distance from a given point. The given point is called the *center*, and the given distance is called the *radius* . The diameter is twice the radius. The *unit circle* is the circle with center at (0, 0) and $r = 1$.

Circle graph   See *Graph*.

Circular cone   A cone with a circular base

Circular cylinder   A cylinder with a circular base

Circular definition   A definition that relies on the use of the word being defined, or other words that rely on the word being defined

Circumference   The distance around a circle

Class   One of the groupings when organizing data. The difference between the lower limit of one class and the lower limit of the next class is called the *interval* of the class. The number of values within a class is called the *frequency*.

Closed-end loan   An installment loan

Closed half-plane   See *Half-plane*.

Closing   The process of settlement on a real estate loan

Closing costs   Costs paid at the closing of a real estate loan

Coefficient   Any factor of a term is said to be the coefficient of the remaining factors. Generally, the word *coefficient* is taken to be the numerical coefficient of the variable factors.

Common denominator   For two or more fractions, a common multiple of the denominators

Common factor   A factor that two or more terms of a polynomial have in common

Common fraction   Fractions written in the form of one integer divided by a whole number are common fractions. For example, 1/10 is common fraction representation and 0.1 is the decimal representation of the same number.

Commutative property   A property of order that applies to addition and multiplication, but not to subtraction and division. If a and b are real numbers, then

$$a + b = b + a \quad \text{and} \quad ab = ba$$

Comparison property   For any two numbers x and y, exactly one of the following is true:
1. $x = y$; x is equal to y (the same as)

2. $x > y$; x is greater than y (bigger than)

3. $x < y$; x is less than y (smaller than).

This is sometimes known as the *trichotomy* property.

Comparison rate for home loans A formula for comparing terms of a home loan. The formula is

$$\text{APR} + 0.125\left(\text{POINTS} + \frac{\text{ORIGINATION FEE}}{\text{AMOUNT OF LOAN}}\right)$$

Compass An instrument for constructing circles or for measuring distances between two points

Complement (1) Two numbers less than 1 are called complements if their sum is 1. (2) The complement of a set is everything not in the set relative to a given universe.

Complementary probabilities $P(E) = 1 - P(\overline{E})$

Completely reduced See *Reduced fraction.*

Complex decimal A form that mixes decimal and fractional form, such as $0.12\frac{1}{2}$

Complex fraction A rational expression a/b where a or b (or both) have fractional form

Components See *Ordered pair.*

Composite A number that has two or more prime factors

Compound interest A method of calculating interest by adding the interest to the principal at the end of the compounding period so that this sum is used in the interest calculation for the next period

Compound interest formula $A = P(1 + i)^N$, where A = future value; P = present value (or principal); r = annual interest rate (APR); t = number of years; n = number of times compounded per year; $i = \frac{r}{n}$; and $N = nt$.

Compounded See *Interest.*

Compounded annually $n = 1$ in the compound interest formula

Conclusion The statement that follows (or is to be proved to follow) as a consequence of the hypothesis of the theorem

Conditional equation See *Equation.*

Conditional inequality See *Inequality.*

Conditional probability A probability that is found on the condition that a certain event has occurred. The notation $P(E|F)$ is the probability of event E *on the condition* that event F has occurred.

Cone A solid bounded by a region for its base in a plane and a surface formed by the line segments that join points on the base to a fixed point (called the *vertex*) not in the plane of the base.

Congruent Of the same size and shape; if one is placed on top of the other, the two figures will coincide exactly in all their parts.

Congruent triangles Two triangles with the same size and shape

Conjecture A guess or prediction based on incomplete or uncertain evidence

Consecutive numbers Counting numbers that differ by 1

Consistent system If a system of equations has at least one solution, it is consistent; otherwise it is said to be *inconsistent.*

Constant Symbol with exactly one possible value

Construction The process of drawing a figure that will satisfy certain given conditions

Contained in a set An element is contained in a set if it is a member of the set.

Contradiction An equation for which the solution set is empty

Coordinate A numerical description for a point. Also see *Ordered pair.*

Coordinate plane See *Cartesian coordinate system.*

Corresponding angles Angles in different triangles that are similarly related to the rest of the triangle

Corresponding parts Points, angles, lines, etc., in different figures, similarly related to the rest of the figures

Corresponding sides Sides of different triangles that are similarly related to the rest of the triangle

Cosine In a right triangle ABC with right angle C,

$$\cos A = (\text{adjacent side of } A)/\text{hypotenuse}$$

Counterclockwise In the direction of rotation opposite to that in which the hands move around the dial of a clock

Counterexample An example used to disprove a proposition

Counting numbers See *Natural numbers.*

Credit card A card signifying that the person or business issued the card has been approved open-ended credit. It can be used at certain restaurants, airlines, and stores accepting that card.

Cube A solid with six equal square sides

Cube root See *Root of a number.*

Cubed In an expression such as x^3, which is pronounced "x cubed," it means xxx.

Cubic centimeter A cube with all sides of length 1 cm

Cubic inch A cube with all sides of length 1 in.

Cup A standard unit of capacity equal to 8 oz; abbreviated as c

Cursor A mark indicating the location on a computer screen or a calculator display

Cylinder A closed surface consisting of two congruent simple closed curves in parallel planes and a *lateral surface* that is the union of all line segments joining corresponding points on the given closed curves.

Daily compounding In the compound interest formula, it is when $n = 365$ (exact interest) or when $n = 360$ (ordinary interest). In this book, use ordinary interest unless otherwise indicated.

Dealer's cost The actual amount that a dealer pays for the goods sold

Decagon A polygon having ten sides

Deci- A prefix that means $1/10$

Deciles Nine values that divide the data into ten parts

Decimal Any number written in decimal notation; sometimes called a Hindu–Arabic numeral

Decimal fraction A number in decimal notation that has fractional parts, such as 23.25. If a common fraction p/q is written as a decimal fraction, the result will be either a *terminating decimal* as with $\frac{1}{4} = 0.25$ or a *repeating decimal* as with $\frac{2}{3} = 0.6666\ldots$.

Decimal numeration system A numeration system with ten symbols

Decimal point A period used in the decimal numeration system. It separates the portion greater than one from the fractional part.

Deductive reasoning A formal structure based on a set of axioms and a set of undefined terms. New terms are defined in terms of the given undefined terms and new statements, or *theorems*, are derived from the axioms by proof.

Degree (1) The degree of a term in one variable is the exponent of the variable, or it is the sum of the exponents of the variables if there are more than one. The degree of a polynomial is the degree of its highest-degree term. (2) A unit of measurement of an angle that is equal to $1/360$ of a revolution

Deka- A prefix that means 10

Deleted point A single point that is excluded from the domain

Demand The number of items that can be sold at a given price

De Morgan's laws For sets X and Y,

$$\overline{X \cup Y} = \overline{X} \cap \overline{Y} \quad \text{and} \quad \overline{X \cap Y} = \overline{X} \cup \overline{Y}$$

Denominator See *Rational number*.

Dependent system If *every* ordered pair satisfying one equation in a system of equations also satisfies every other equation of the given system, then we describe the system as dependent.

Dependent variable The variable associated with the second component of an ordered pair

Derived equation See *Equation*.

Description method A method of defining a set by describing the set (as opposed to listing its elements)

Diameter See *Circle*.

Dice Plural of *die*, which is a cube with the sides marked with from one to six dots. A sample space for a die is shown on page 450, and for a pair of dice, on page 453.

Difference The result of a subtraction

Dimension A configuration having length only is said to be of one dimension; area and not volume, two dimensions; volume, three dimensions.

Discount A reduction from a usual or list price

Discount formulas Let $p = $ ORIGINAL PRICE, $s = $ SALE PRICE, $c = $ COMPLEMENT OF THE PERCENT MARKDOWN, $d = $ AMOUNT OF DISCOUNT, and $m = $ PERCENT MARKDOWN. Then
Discount formula: $d = pm$
Sale price formula: $s = p - d$ or $s = pc$
Original price formula: $p = s/c$
Complement formula: $c = s/p$

Disjoint sets Sets that have no elements in common

Distributive law (for multiplication over addition) If a, b, and c are real numbers, then $a(b + c) = ab + ac$ and $(a + b)c = ac + bc$ for the basic operations. That is, the number outside the parentheses indicating a sum or difference is distributed to each of the numbers inside the parentheses.

Dividend The number or quantity to be divided. In a/b, the dividend is a.

Division $a/b = x$ is $a \div b = x$ and means $a = bx$.

Division by zero With $a \div b$ we insist $b \neq 0$ because if $b = 0$, then $bx = 0$, regardless of the value of x, and therefore could not equal a nonzero number a. On the other hand, if $a = 0$, then $0/0 = 1$ checks from the definition, and so also does $0/0 = 2$, which means that $1 = 2$, another contradiction. Thus, division by 0 is not ever possible.

Division of integers The quotient of two integers is the quotient of the absolute values, and is positive if the given integers have the same sign, and negative if the given integers have opposite signs. Furthermore, division by zero is not possible and division into 0 gives the answer 0.

Division property of equations The solution of an equation is unchanged by dividing both sides of the equation by the same nonzero number.

Division property of inequality See *Multiplication property of inequality*.

Divisor The quantity by which the dividend is to be divided. In a/b, b is the divisor.

Dodecagon A polygon with 12 sides

Domain The *domain* of a variable is the set of replacements for the variable. The *domain* of a graph of an equation with two variables x and y is the set of permissible real-number replacements for x.

Double negative $-(-a) = a$

Down payment An amount paid at the time a product is financed. The purchase price minus the down payment is equal to the amount financed.

Element   One of the individual objects that belong to a set

Elementary operations   Refers to the operations of addition, subtraction, multiplication, and division

Empty set   See *Set.*

Equal   Two numbers are equal if they represent the same quantity or are identical. In mathematics, this refers to a relationship that satisfies the axioms of equality.

Equal angles   Two angles that have the same measure

Equal sets   Sets that contain the same elements

Equality, axioms of   For real numbers a, b, c:
   reflexive: $a = a$
   substitution: If $a = b$, then a may be replaced throughout by b (or b by a) in any statement without changing the truth or falsity of the statement.
   symmetric: If $a = b$, then $b = a$.
   transitive: If $a = b$ and $b = c$, then $a = c$.

Equally likely outcomes   Outcomes whose probabilities of occurring are the same

Equation   A statement of equality. If always true, an equation is called an *identity;* if always false, it is called a *contradiction.* If it is sometimes true and sometimes false, it is called a *conditional equation.* Values that make an equation true are said to *satisfy* the equation and are called *solutions* or *roots* of the equation. Equations with the same solutions are called *equivalent equations.*

Equation of a graph   Every point on the graph has coordinates that satisfy the equation, and every ordered pair that satisfies the equation has coordinates that lie on the graph.

Equation-solving procedure

1. Simplify the left and right sides.
2. Use equation properties to isolate the variable on one side.
   a. First, use the addition or subtraction property.
   b. Next, use the multiplication or division property.

Equilateral triangle   A triangle whose three sides all have the same length

Equilibrium point   A point for which the supply and demand are equal

Equivalent equations   See *Equation.*

Equivalent sets   Sets that have the same cardinality

Equivalent systems   Systems that have the same solution set

Estimation   An approximation (usually mental) of size or value used to form an opinion

Euclidean geometry   The study of geometry based on the assumptions of Euclid. These basic assumptions are called Euclid's postulates.

Euclid's postulates   The five postulates are: 1. A straight line can be drawn from any point to any other point. 2. A straight line extends infinitely far in either direction. 3. A circle can be described with any point as center and with a radius equal to any finite straight line drawn from the center. 4. All right angles are equal to each other. 5. Given a straight line and any point not on this line, there is one and only one line through that point that is parallel to the given line.

Evaluate   To *evaluate* an expression means to replace the variables by given numerical values and then simplify the resulting numerical expression. To *evaluate* an absolute value means to write the expression without using the absolute value symbols. To *evaluate* a trigonometric ratio means to find its approximate numerical value.

Event   A subset of a sample space

Exact interest   The calculation of interest assuming that there are 365 days in a year

Expanded notation   The representation of a number showing its meaning. It shows the number of units, the number of tens, the number of hundreds, ...

Expectation   See *Mathematical expectation.*

Expected value   See *Mathematical expectation.*

Experiment   An observation of any physical occurrence

Exponent   Where b is any nonzero real number and n is any natural number, exponent is defined as follows:

$$b^n = \underbrace{b \cdot b \cdot \cdots \cdot b}_{n \text{ factors}} \qquad b^0 = 1 \qquad b^{-n} = \frac{1}{b^n}$$

b is called the *base,* n is called the *exponent,* and b^n is called a *power.*

Exponential curve   The graph of an exponential equation. It indicates an increasingly steep rise, and passes through the point $(0, 1)$.

Exponential equation   An equation of the form $y = b^x$ where b is positive and not equal to 1

Exponential notation   A notation involving exponents

Expression   Numbers, variables, and operations involving numbers and variables

Extended order of operations   1. Perform any operations enclosed in parentheses. 2. Perform any operations that involve raising to a power. 3. Perform multiplication and division, reading from left to right. 4. Do addition and subtraction, reading from left to right.

Exterior angle   An exterior angle of a triangle is the angle on the other side of an extension of one side of the triangle.

Exterior angle formula The measure of the exterior angle of a triangle equals the sum of the measures of the two opposite interior angles.

Extraneous root A number obtained in the process of solving an equation that is not a root of the equation to be solved

Extremes See *Proportion.*

Factor Each of the numbers multiplied to form a product is called a factor of the product.

Factoring The process of determining the factors of a product

Factorization The result of factoring a number or an expression

Fahrenheit A unit of measurement in the United States system for measuring temperature where the freezing point of water is 32° and the boiling point of water is 212°

Fair coin A coin for which heads and tails are equally likely

Fair game A game for which the mathematical expectation is zero

False equation An equation without a variable in which the number on the left side of the equal sign is not the same number as the number on the right side of the equal sign.

Finite set See *Set.*

First component See *Ordered pair.*

Five-percent offer An offer made that is 105% of the price paid by the dealer. That is, it is an offer that is 5% over the cost.

Foot A unit of linear measure in the United States system that is equal to 12 inches

Foreclose If the scheduled payments are not made, the lender takes the right to redeem the mortgage and keeps the collateral property.

Formula A general answer, rule, or principle stated in mathematical notation

Fraction See *Rational number.*

Frequency See *Class.*

Frequency distribution For a collection of data, the tabulation of the number of elements in each class

Function A rule that assigns to each element in the domain a single (unique) element

Functional notation The representation of a function f using the notation $f(x)$ to denote the output for f when x is the input value.

Fundamental counting principle If one task can be performed in m ways and a second task can be performed in n ways, then the number of ways that the tasks can be performed one after the other is mn.

Fundamental property of equations If P and Q are algebraic expressions, and k is a real number,

then each of the following is equivalent to $P = Q$:

Addition	$P + k = Q + k$
Subtraction	$P - k = Q - k$
Nonzero multiplication	$kP = kQ, k \neq 0$
Nonzero division	$\frac{P}{k} = \frac{Q}{k}, k \neq 0$

Fundamental property of fractions If both the numerator and denominator are multiplied or divided by the same nonzero number, the resulting fraction will be the same.

Fundamental property of inequalities If P and Q are algebraic expressions, and k is a real number, then each of the following is equivalent to $P < Q$:

Addition	$P + k < Q + k$
Subtraction	$P - k < Q - k$
Positive multiplication	$kP < kQ, k > 0$
Positive division	$\frac{P}{k} < \frac{Q}{k}, k > 0$
Negative multiplication	$kP > kQ, k < 0$
Negative division	$\frac{P}{k} > \frac{Q}{k}, k < 0$

This property also applies for $\leq$, $>$, and $\geq$.

Fundamental property of rational expressions

$$\frac{PK}{QK} = \frac{P}{Q}, \ Q, K \neq 0$$

Future value See *Compound interest.*

Future value formula For simple interest: $A = P(1 + rt)$; for compound interest: $A = P(1 + i)^N$.

Gallon A measure of capacity in the United States system that is equal to 4 quarts or 231 cubic inches

Googol The number with 1 followed by 100 zeros—that is,
10,000,000,000,000,000,000,000,000,000,000,
000,000,000,000,000,000,000,000,000,000,000,
000,000,000,000,000,000,000,000,000

Grace period A period of time between when an item is purchased and when it is paid for during which no interest is charged

Gram A unit of weight in the metric system. It is equal to the weight of one cubic centimeter of water at 4°C.

Graph (1) In statistics, it is a drawing that shows the relation between certain sets of numbers. Common forms are *bar graphs, line graphs, pictographs*, and *pie charts (circle graphs).* (2) A drawing that shows the relation between certain sets of numbers. It may be one-dimensional ($\mathbb{R}$), two-dimensional ($\mathbb{R}^2$), or three-dimensional ($\mathbb{R}^3$).

Graph of an equation See *Equation of a graph.*

Greater than If a lies to the right of b on a number line, then a is greater than b, $a > b$. Formally, $a > b$ if and only if $a - b$ is positive.

Greater than or equal to Written $a \geq b$, means $a > b$ or $a = b$

Grouped frequency distribution If the data are grouped before they are tallied, then the resulting distribution is called a *grouped frequency distribution.*

Grouping symbols Parentheses ( ), brackets [ ], and braces { } indicate the order of operations and are also sometimes used to indicate multiplication, as in $(2)(3) = 6$. Also called *symbols of inclusion.*

Growth formula $A = A_0 e^{rt}$ or $A = A_0 (2.72)^{rt}$

Half-plane The part of a plane that lies on one side of a line in the plane. It is a *closed* half-plane if the line is included. It is an *open* half-plane if the line is not included. The line is the *boundary* of the half-plane in either case.

Hecto- A prefix meaning 100

Heptagon A polygon having seven sides

Hexadecimal numeration system A numeration system with sixteen symbols

Hexagon A polygon having six sides

Hindu–Arabic numeration system A numeration system with ten symbols. It is the same as the decimal numeration system in everyday use.

Histogram A bar graph that represents a frequency diagram

Horizontal line A line with zero slope; that is, a line that is level, usually drawn so that it is parallel to the top edge of your paper. It is a line parallel to the horizon. Its equation has the form $y = $ constant.

Hundred A group consisting of ten groups of ten

Hypotenuse The longest side in a right triangle

Hypothesis An assumed proposition used as a premise in proving something else

Identity for addition The number 0 has the property
$$0 + n = n + 0$$
for any real number n, and is called the *identity for addition.*

Identity for multiplication The number 1 has the property
$$1 \cdot n = n \cdot 1$$
for any real number n, and is called the *identity for multiplication.*

Implication A statement that follows from other statements. It is also a proposition formed from two given propositions by connecting them with an "if . . . , then . . . " form. It is symbolized by $p \rightarrow q$.

Impossible event An event for which the probability is zero—that is, an event that cannot happen

Improper fraction A fraction for which the numerator is greater than the denominator

Improper subset See *Subset.*

Inch A linear measurement in the United States system equal in length to the following segment:

——————————

Inconsistent system See *Consistent system.*

Independent variable The variable associated with the first component of an ordered pair

Inductive reasoning A type of reasoning accomplished by first observing patterns and then predicting answers for more complicated similar problems

Inequality A statement of order. If always true, an inequality is called an *absolute inequality;* if always false, an inequality is called a *contradiction.* If sometimes true and sometimes false, it is called a *conditional inequality.* Values that make the statement true are said to *satisfy* the inequality. A *string of inequalities* may be used to show the order of three or more quantities.

Inequality symbols The symbols $>$, $\geq$, $<$, and $\leq$

Infinite set See *Set.*

Inflation An increase in the amount of money in circulation, resulting in a fall in its value and a rise in prices. In this book, we assume annual compounding with the future value formula; that is, use $A = P(1 + r)^n$, where r is the projected annual inflation rate, n is the number of years, and P is the present value.

Installment loan A financial problem in which an item is paid for over a period of time. It is calculated using add-on or compound interest.

Installment loan formula Let
$P = $ AMOUNT TO BE FINANCED (present value),
$A = $ AMOUNT TO BE REPAID (future value),
$r = $ ADD-ON INTEREST RATE,
$t = $ TIME (in years) TO REPAY THE LOAN,
$I = $ AMOUNT OF INTEREST,
$m = $ AMOUNT OF THE MONTHLY PAYMENT,
$N = $ NUMBER OF PAYMENTS; then
AMOUNT OF INTEREST: $I = Prt$
AMOUNT TO BE REPAID: $A = P + I$
  or $A = P(1 + rt)$
NUMBER OF PAYMENTS: $N = 12t$
AMOUNT OF EACH PAYMENT: $m = A/N$

Installments Part of a debt paid at regular intervals over a period of time

Integers $\mathbb{Z} = \{\ldots, -3, -2, -1, 0, 1, 2, 3, \ldots\}$, composed of the natural numbers, their opposites, and zero.

Intercepts The point or points where a line or a curve crosses a coordinate axis. The x-intercepts are sometimes called the *zeros* of the equation.

Interest An amount of money paid for the use of another's money. See *Compound interest.*

Interest-only loan A loan in which periodic payments are for interest only so that the principal amount of the loan remains the same

Interest rate The percentage rate paid on financial problems. In this book it is denoted by r and is assumed to be an annual rate unless otherwise stated.

Intersection The *intersection* of sets A and B, denoted by $A \cap B$, is the set consisting of elements in *both* A and B.

Interval See *Class*.

Invalid Reasoning that is not valid

Invert In relation to the fraction a/b, it means to interchange the numerator and the denominator to obtain the fraction b/a.

Irrational number A number that can be expressed as a nonrepeating, nonterminating decimal; the set of irrational numbers is denoted by $\mathbb{Q}'$.

Juxtaposition When two variables, a number and a variable, or a symbol and a parenthesis are written next to each other with no operation symbol, as in xy, $2x$, or $3(x + y)$. Juxtaposition is used to indicate multiplication.

Kilo- A prefix that means 1,000

Kilogram 1,000 grams

Kiloliter 1,000 liters

Kilometer 1,000 meters

LCD An abbreviation for least common denominator

Least common denominator (LCD) The smallest number that is exactly divisible by each of the given numbers

Length A measurement of an object from end to end

Less than If a is to the left of b on a number line, then a is less than b, $a < b$. Formally, $a < b$ if and only if $b > a$.

Less than or equal to Written $a \le b$, means $a < b$ or $a = b$

Like terms Terms that differ only in their numerical coefficients. Also called *similar terms*.

Line In mathematics, it is an undefined term. It is a curve that is straight, so it is sometimes referred to as a *straight line* . It extends in both directions, and is considered one-dimensional, so it has no thickness.

Line graph See *Graph*.

Line of credit The maximum amount of credit to be extended to a borrower. That is, it is a promise by a lender to extend credit up to some predetermined amount.

Line of symmetry A line with the property that for a given curve, any point P on the curve has a corresponding point Q (called the reflection point of P) so that the perpendicular bisector of $\overline{PQ}$ is on the line of symmetry.

Line segment A part of a line between two points on the line

Linear equation A first-degree equation with one or two variables. For example, $x + 5 = 0$ and $x + y + 5 = 0$ are linear equations. An equation is linear in a certain variable if it is first degree in that variable. For example, $x + y^2 = 0$ is linear in x, but not y.

Linear function A function whose equation can be written in the form $f(x) = mx + b$

Linear inequality A first-degree inequality with one or two variables

Linear polynomial A first-degree polynomial

Linear system A system of equations, each of which is first degree

Liter The basic unit of capacity in the metric system. It is the capacity of 1 cubic decimeter.

Literal equation An equation with more than one variable

Loaded die A die in which the faces do not have an equal chance of occurring

Logic The science of correct reasoning

Logical conclusion The statement that follows logically as a consequence of the hypotheses of a theorem

Lowest common denominator For two or more fractions, the smallest common multiple of the denominators

Mass In this course, it is the amount of matter an object comprises. Formally, it is a measure of the tendency of a body to oppose changes in its velocity.

Mathematical expectation A calculation defined as the product of an amount to be won and the probability that it is won. If there is more than one amount to be won, it is the sum of the expectations of all the prizes. It is also called the *expected value*.

Mathematical modeling An iterative procedure that makes assumptions about real-world problems to formulate the problem in mathematical terms. After the mathematical problem is solved, it is tested for accuracy in the real world and revised for the next step in the iterative process.

Mathematical system A set with at least one defined operation and some developed properties

Maximum loan In this book, it refers to the maximum amount of loan that can be obtained for a home with a given amount of income and a given amount of debt

Maximum loan formula

$$\text{MAXIMUM AMOUNT OF A LOAN} = \frac{\text{MONTHLY PAYMENT YOU CAN AFFORD}}{\text{TABLE II ENTRY}} \times 1,000$$

Mean The number found by adding the data and dividing by the number of values in the data set

Means See *Proportion*.

Measure Comparison to some unit recognized as standard

Measure of central tendency Refers to the averages of mean, median, and mode

Measure of dispersion Refers to the measures of range, standard deviation, and variance

Measure of position The use of benchmark positions to describe data sets, such as quartiles, deciles, or percentiles

Median The middle number when the numbers in the data are arranged in order of size. If there are two middle numbers (in the case of an even number of data values), the median is the mean of these two middle numbers.

Members See *Set*.

Meter The basic unit for measuring length in the metric system

Metric system A decimal system of weights and measures in which the gram, the meter, and the liter are the basic units of mass, length, and capacity, respectively. One gram is the mass of one cm^3 of water and one liter is the same as 1,000 cm^3. In this book, the metric system refers to the SI metric system as revised in 1960.

Mile A unit of linear measurement in the United States system that is equal to 5,280 ft

Milli- A prefix that means 1/1,000

Milligram 1/1,000 of a gram

Milliliter 1/1,000 of a liter

Minus Refers to the operation of subtraction. The symbol "$-$" means minus only when it appears between two numbers, between two variables, or between numbers and variables.

Mixed number A number that has both a counting number part and a proper fraction part; for example, $3\frac{1}{2}$

Mode The value in a data set that occurs most frequently. If no number occurs more than once, there is no mode. It is possible to have more than one mode.

Monomial A polynomial with one and only one term

Monthly compounding In the compound interest formula, it is when $n = 12$.

Monthly payment In an installment loan, it is a periodic payment that is made once every month.

Monthly payment formula [7.6]

MONTHLY PAYMENT
$$= \frac{\text{AMOUNT OF LOAN}}{1,000} \times \text{TABLE II ENTRY}$$

Mortality table A table showing the probability of a person living or dying during a particular year of his or her life

Mortgage An agreement, or loan contract, in which a borrower pledges a home or other real estate as security

Multiplication of integers If the integers to be multiplied both have the same sign, the result is positive and the magnitude of the answer is the product of the absolute values of the integers. If the integers to be

multiplied have opposite signs, the product is negative and has magnitude equal to the product of the absolute values of the given integers. Finally, if one or both of the given integers is 0, the product is 0.

Multiplication principle See *Fundamental counting principle.*

Multiplication property of equations Both sides of an equation may be multiplied or divided by any nonzero number to obtain an equivalent equation.

Multiplication property of inequality Both sides of an inequality may be multiplied or divided by a positive number, and the order of the inequality will remain unchanged. The order is reversed if both sides are multiplied or divided by a negative number.

Multiplicative identity The number 1, with the property that $1 \cdot a = a$ for any real number a

Multiplicative inverse See *Reciprocal.*

Multiplicative law of inequality If $a < b$ then $ac < bc$ if $c > 0$, and $ac > bc$ if $c < 0$. This also applies to $\leq$, $>$, and $\geq$.

Mutually exclusive Events are *mutually exclusive* if their intersection is empty.

Natural numbers $\mathbb{N} = \{1, 2, 3, 4, 5, \ldots\}$, the positive integers, also called the *counting numbers*

Negative number A number less than zero

Negative sign The symbol "$-$" when used in front of a number, as in -5. Do not confuse with the same symbol used for subtraction as in $8 - 5$ or with the symbol for opposite.

***n*-gon** A polygon with n sides

Nonagon A polygon with nine sides

Normal curve A graphical representation of a normal distribution. Its high point occurs at the mean, and it is symmetric with respect to this mean. On each side of the mean, it has an area that includes 34.1% of the population within one standard deviation, 13.6% from one to two standard deviations, and about 2.3% of the population more than two standard deviations from the mean.

Null set See *Set*.

Number A *number* represents a given quantity, as opposed to *numeral*, which is the symbol for the number. In mathematics, it generally refers to a specific set of numbers—for example, counting numbers, whole numbers, integers, rationals, or real numbers. If the set is not specified, the assumed usage is to the set of real numbers.

Number line A line used to display a set of numbers graphically (the axis for a one-dimensional graph)

Numeral A symbol used to represent a number

Numeration system A system of symbols with rules of combination for representing all numbers

Numerator   See *Rational number.*

Numerical coefficient   See *Coefficient.*

Numerical expression   A number or a group of numbers connected by valid or defined mathematical operations

Obtuse angle   An angle that is greater than a right angle and smaller than a straight angle

Octagon   A polygon with eight sides

Octal numeration system   A numeration system with eight symbols

Odds   If $s + f = n$, where s is considered favorable to an event E and n is the total number of possibilities, then the *odds in favor* of E are s/f and the *odds against* E are f/s.

One-dimensional coordinate system   A real number line

One-to-one correspondence   Between two sets A and B, this means each element of A can be matched with exactly one element of B and also each element of B can be matched with exactly one element of A.

Open equation   An equation that has at least one variable

Open-end loan   A preapproved line of credit that the borrower can access as long as timely payments are made and the credit line is not exceeded. It is usually known as a credit card loan.

Open half-plane   See *Half-plane.*

Opposite   Opposites x and $-x$ are the same distance from 0 on the number line but in opposite directions; $-x$ is also called the *additive inverse* of x. Do not confuse the symbol " $-$ " meaning opposite with the same symbol as used to mean subtraction or negative.

Opposite property   The opposite of a number is the same as the product of that number and negative one. That is,

$$-n = (-1)n$$

Opposite side   In a right triangle, an acute angle is made up of two sides. The opposite side of the angle refers to the third side that is not used to make up the sides of the angle.

Or   A word that indicates the set consisting of elements in either of two given sets.

Order of an inequality   Refers to a $>$, $\geq$, $<$, or $\leq$ relationship

Order of operations   If no grouping symbols are used in a numerical expression, first perform all multiplication and division from left to right, and then perform all addition and subtraction from left to right.

Order symbols   Refers to $>$, $\geq$, $<$, $\leq$ in an inequality

Ordered pair   A pair of numbers, written (x, y), in which the order of naming is important. The numbers x and y are sometimes called the *first* and *second components* of the pair and are called the *coordinates* of the point designated by (x, y).

Ordinary interest   The calculation of interest assuming a year has 360 days. In this book, we assume ordinary interest unless otherwise stated.

Origin   The point designating 0 on a number line. In two dimensions, the point of intersection of the coordinate axes; the coordinates are $(0, 0)$.

Origination fee   A fee paid to obtain a real estate loan

Ounce   (1) A unit of capacity in the United States system equal to 1/128 of a gallon. (2) A unit of mass in the United States system equal to 1/16 of a pound.

Overlapping sets   Sets whose intersection is not empty

Parabola   A set of points in the plane equidistant from a given point (called the *focus*) and a given line (called the *directrix*). It is the path of a projectile. The *axis of symmetry* is the axis of the parabola. The point where the axis cuts the parabola is the *vertex.*

Parallel lines   Two nonintersecting straight lines in the same plane

Parallelepiped   A polyhedron, all of whose faces are parallelograms

Parallelogram   A quadrilateral with its opposite sides parallel

Parentheses   See *Grouping symbols.*

Pentagon   A polygon with five sides

Percent   The ratio of a given number to 100; hundredths; denoted by %; that is, 5% means 5/100.

Percentage   The total amount in a percentage problem

Percentiles   Ninety-nine values that divide the data into one hundred parts

Percent markdown   The percent of an original price used to find the amount of discount

Percent problem   The percent problem is one that can be restated as "A is $P\%$ of W," and is formulated as a proportion

$$\frac{P}{100} = \frac{A}{W}$$

Perfect square   Since $1^2 = 1$, $2^2 = 4$, $3^2 = 9$, . . . , the perfect squares are 1, 4, 9, 16, 25, 36, 49, ...

Perimeter   The distance around a polygon

Perpendicular   Two lines or line segments are perpendicular if their intersection forms right angles.

Pi (π)   A number that is defined as the ratio of the circumference to the diameter of a circle. It cannot be represented exactly as a decimal, but it is a number between 3.1415 and 3.1416.

Pictograph   See *Graph.*

Pie chart   See *Graph.*

Place-value names   From large to small, the place value names are: trillions, hundred billions, ten billions, billions, hundred millions, ten millions, millions, hundred thousands, ten thousands, thousands, hundreds, tens, units, tenths, hundredths, thousandths, ten-thousandths, hundred-thousandths, and millionths.

Plane In mathematics, it is an undefined term. It is flat and level and extends infinitely in horizontal and vertical directions. It is considered two-dimensional.

Plot a point To mark the position of a point

Point (1) In the decimal representation of a number, it is a mark that divides the whole number part of a number from its fractional part. (2) In geometry, it is an undefined word that signifies a position, but that has no dimension or size. (3) In relation to a home loan, it represents 1% of the value of a loan, so that 3 points would be a fee paid to a lender equal to 3% of the amount of the loan.

Polygon A geometric figure that has three or more straight sides that all lie in a plane so that the starting point and the ending point are the same

Polynomial An algebraic expression that may be written as a sum (or difference) of terms. Each *term* of a polynomial contains multiplication only.

Population The total set of items (actual or potential) defined by some characteristic of the items

Positive number A number greater than 0

Positive sign The symbol "+" when used in front of a number or an expression

Postulate A statement that is accepted without proof

Pound A unit of measurement for mass in the United States system. It is equal to 16 oz.

Power See *Exponent*.

Precision The accuracy of the measurement; for example, a measurement is taken to the nearest inch, nearest foot, or nearest mile. It is not to be confused with accuracy that applies to the calculation.

Premise A previous statement or assertion that serves as the basis for an argument

Present value See *Compound interest*.

Present value formula $P = \dfrac{A}{(1 + i)^N}$

where P is present value, A is future value, $i = r/n$, and $N = nt$.

Previous balance method A method of calculating credit card interest using the formula $I = Prt$ in which P is the balance owed before the current payment is subtracted

Prime factorization The factorization of a number so that all of the factors are primes and so that their product is equal to the given number

Prime numbers A number with exactly two factors: 1 and the number itself. That is, $P = \{2, 3, 5, 7, 11, 13, 17, 19, 23, \ldots\}$.

Principal See *Compound interest*.

Prism A solid with two congruent faces, the *bases*, whose other faces are parallelograms formed by joining corresponding vertices of the bases. A box, or parallelepiped, is the most common prism.

Probability If an experiment can result in any of n ($n \geq 1$) mutually exclusive and equally likely outcomes, and if s of these are considered favorable to event E, then $P(E) = s/n$.

Problem solving procedure 1. *Read the problem*. Note what it is all about. Focus on processes rather than numbers. You can't work a problem you don't understand. 2. *Restate the problem*. Write a verbal description of the problem using operation signs and an equal sign. Look for equality. If you can't find equal quantities, you will never formulate an equation. 3. *Choose a variable*. If there is a single unknown, choose a variable. 4. *Substitute*. Replace the verbal phrases by known numbers and by the variable. 5. *Solve the equation* . This is the easy step. Be sure your answer makes sense by checking it with the original question in the problem. Use estimation to eliminate unreasonable answers. 6. *State the answer*. There were no variables defined when you started, so $x = 3$ is not an answer. Pay attention to units of measure and other details of the problem. Remember to answer the question that was asked.

Product The result of a multiplication

Profit formula $P = S - C$ where P represents the profit, S represents the selling price (or revenue), and C represents the cost (or overhead)

Proof A logical argument that establishes the truth of a statement

Proper fraction A fraction for which the numerator is less than the denominator

Proper subset See *Subset*.

Properties of rational expressions Let $P, Q, R, S,$ and K be any polynomials such that all values of the variable that cause division by zero are excluded from the domain.

Equality $\frac{P}{Q} = \frac{R}{S}$ if and only if $PS = QR$

Fundamental property $\frac{PK}{QK} = \frac{P}{Q}$

Addition $\frac{P}{Q} + \frac{R}{S} = \frac{PS + QR}{QS}$

Subtraction $\frac{P}{Q} - \frac{R}{S} = \frac{PS - QR}{QS}$

Multiplication $\frac{P}{Q} \cdot \frac{R}{S} = \frac{PR}{QS}$

Division $\frac{P}{Q} \div \frac{R}{S} = \frac{PS}{QR}$

Property of complements For any event E, $P(E) + P(\overline{E}) = 1$.

Property of proportions If the product of the means equals the product of the extremes, then the ratios form a proportion. Also, if the ratios form a proportion, then the product of the means equals the product of the extremes.

Property of zero $AB = 0$ if and only if $A = 0$ or $B = 0$ (or both).

Proportion A statement of equality between two ratios. For example,

$$\frac{a}{b} = \frac{c}{d}$$

For this proportion, a and d are called the *extremes*; b and c are called the *means*.

Protractor A device used to measure angles

Pyramid A solid figure having a polygon as a base, the sides of which form the bases of triangular surfaces that meet at a common vertex

Pythagorean theorem If a triangle with legs a and b and hypotenuse c is a right triangle, then $a^2 + b^2 = c^2$. Also, if $a^2 + b^2 = c^2$, then the triangle is a right triangle.

Quadrant See *Axes.*

Quadratic A second-degree polynomial

Quadratic equation An equation of the form

$$ax^2 + bx + c = 0, a \neq 0$$

Quadratic formula If $ax^2 + bx + c = 0$ and

$$a \neq 0, \text{ then } x = \frac{-b \pm \sqrt{b^2 - 4ac}}{2a}$$

The number $b^2 - 4ac$ is called the *discriminant* of the quadratic.

Quadrilateral A polygon having four sides

Quart A measure of capacity in the United States system equal to $1/4$ of a gallon

Quarterly compounding In the compound interest formula, it is when $n = 4$.

Quartiles Three values that divide the data into four parts

Quotient The result of a division

Radical The $\sqrt{}$ symbol in an expression such as $\sqrt{2}$. The number 2 is called the *radicand,* and an expression involving a radical is called a radical expression.

Radius The distance of a point on a circle from the center of the same circle

Range In statistics, it is the difference between the largest and the smallest numbers in the data set.

Rate (1) In percent problems, it is the percent. (2) In tax problems, it is the level of taxation, written as a percent. (3) In financial problems, it refers to the APR.

Ratio The quotient of two numbers or expressions

Rational equation An equation that has at least one variable in the denominator

Rational number A number belonging to the set $\mathbb{Q}$ defined by

$$\mathbb{Q} = \{\tfrac{a}{b} \mid a \text{ is an integer, } b \text{ is a nonzero integer}\}$$

Ray If P is a point on a line, then a ray from the point P is all points on the line on one side of P.

Real number line A line on which points are associated with real numbers in a one-to-one fashion

Real numbers The set of all rational and irrational numbers, denoted by $\mathbb{R}$

Reciprocal The reciprocal of n is $\frac{1}{n}$, also called the *multiplicative inverse of n.*

Rectangle A quadrilateral whose angles are all right angles

Rectangular coordinate system See *Cartesian coordinate system.*

Rectangular coordinates See *Ordered pair.*

Rectangular parallelepiped In this book, it refers to a box all of whose angles are right angles.

Reduced fraction A fraction in which the numerator and denominator have no common divisors (other than 1 or -1)

Reducing fractions The process by which we make sure that there are no common factors (other than 1) for the numerator and denominator of a fraction

Reflection Given a line L and a point P, we call the point P' the *reflection* about the line L if PP' is perpendicular to L and is also bisected by L.

Relation A set of ordered pairs

Remainder When an integer m is divided by a positive integer n, and a quotient q is obtained for which $m = nq + r$ with $0 \leq r < n$, then r is the remainder.

Repeating decimal See *Decimal fraction.*

Revolving credit It is the same as open-end or credit-card credit.

Right angle An angle of 90°

Right circular cone A cone with a circular base for which the base is perpendicular to its axis

Right circular cylinder A cylinder with a circular base for which the base is perpendicular to its axis

Right rectangular prism A prism whose rectangular base is perpendicular to the lateral edges, and each lateral edge is a rectangle

Root of an equation See *Solution.*

Root of a number An nth root (n is a natural number) of a number b is a only if $a^n = b$. If $n = 2$, then the root is called a *square root;* if $n = 3$, it is called a *cube root.*

Roster method A method of defining a set by listing the elements in the set

Rounding a number Dropping decimals after a certain significant place. The procedure for rounding is: 1. *Locate the rounding place digit.* 2. *Determine the rounding place digit:* It stays the same if the first digit to its right is a 0, 1, 2, 3, or 4; it increases by 1 if the digit to the right is a 5, 6, 7, 8, or 9. 3. *Change digits:* All digits to the left of the rounding digit remain the same (unless there is a carry), and all digits to the right of the rounding digit are changed to zeros. 4. *Drop zeros:* If the rounding place digit is to the left of the decimal point, drop all trailing zeros; if the rounding place digit is to the right of the decimal point, drop all trailing zeros to the right of the rounding place digit.

Sale price A reduced price usually offered to stimulate sales

Sale price formula It can be found by subtracting the discount from the original price, or by multiplying the original price by the complement of the markdown.

Sales tax A tax levied by government bodies that is based on the selling price of an item

Sales tax formula
SALES TAX = (ORIGINAL PRICE) × (TAX RATE)

Sample A finite part taken from a population

Sample space The set of possible outcomes for an experiment

Satisfy See *Equation* or *Inequality.*

Scientific notation Writing a number as the product of a number between 1 and 10 and a power of 10: For any real number n, $n = m \cdot 10^c$, $1 \le m < 10$, and c is an integer. Calculators often switch to scientific notation to represent large or small numbers. The usual notation is 8.234 05 where the space separates the number from the power; thus 8.234 05 means 8.234×10^5.

Second component See *Ordered pair.*

Semiannual compounding In the compound interest formula, it is when $n = 2$.

Semicircle Half a circle

Set A collection of particular things, called the *members* or *elements* of the set. A set with no elements is called the *null set* or *empty set* and is denoted by the symbol $\varnothing$. All elements of a *finite set* may be listed, whereas the elements of an *infinite set* continue without end.

Set-builder notation The notation $\{x \mid x$ has some specific property$\}$ which is pronounced as "the set of all x such that x has some specific property."

SI system See *Metric system.*

Signed number An integer

Similar figures Two geometric figures are similar if they have the same shape, but not necessarily the same size.

Similar terms Terms that differ only in their numerical coefficients

Similar triangle property Two triangles are similar if two angles of one triangle are equal to two angles of the other triangle. If the triangles are similar, then their corresponding sides are proportional.

Similar triangles Triangles that have the same shape

Simple event An event for which the sample space has only one element

Simple interest formula $I = Prt$

Simplify (1) A *numerical expression*: Carry out all the operations, according to the order-of-operations agreement, and write the answer as a single number. (2) A *polynomial*: Carry out all the operations, according to the order of operations, combine similar terms, and write terms in order of descending degree. (3) A *fraction* (a *rational expression*): Carry out all the operations, according to the order of operations, simplify numerator and denominator, factor if possible, and eliminate all common factors (except for 1 or -1).

Simultaneous solution The solution of a simultaneous system of equations

Sine In a right triangle ABC with right angle C, $\sin A = $ (opposite side of A)/hypotenuse.

Solution The values or ordered pairs of values for which an equation, a system of equations, inequality, or system of inequalities is true. Also called *roots.*

Solution set The set of all solutions to an equation

Solve To find the values of the variable that satisfy the equation

Solve a proportion Find the missing term of a proportion. *Procedure*: First, find the product of the means or the product of the extremes, whichever does not contain the unknown term; next, divide this product by the number that is opposite the unknown term.

Sphere The set of all points in space that are a given distance from a given point

Spreadsheet A rectangular grid used to collect and perform calculations on data. *Rows* are horizontal and labeled with numbers and *columns* are vertical and labeled with letters to designate *cells* such as A4, P604. Each cell can contain text, numbers, or formulas.

Square A rectangle with sides that are equal

Square centimeter A square with sides of length 1 centimeter

Square foot A square with sides of length 1 foot

Square inch A square with sides of length 1 inch

Square root See *Root of a number.*

Square root symbol The $\sqrt{}$ symbol over a number or variable

Square unit A square with side length 1 unit by 1 unit. A *square centimeter* is a square 1 cm by1 cm; a *square foot* is a square 1 ft by1 ft; and a *square inch* is 1 in. by1 in.

Squared In an expression such as x^2, pronounced "x squared," means xx.

Standard deviation It is a measure of the variation from a trend. In particular, it is the square root of the mean of the squares of the deviations from the mean.

Standard form of a fraction   If p and q are positive integers, then $\frac{p}{q}$ and $\frac{-p}{q}$ are called the **standard forms** of a fraction.

Statistics   Methods of obtaining and analyzing data

Sticker price   In this book, it refers to the manufacturer's total price of a new automobile as listed on the window of the car.

Straight angle   An angle whose rays point in opposite directions; an angle whose measure is 180°

Straightedge   A device used as an aid in drawing a straight line segment

Subset   A set contained within a set. There are 2^n subsets of a set with n distinct elements. A subset is *improper* if it is equivalent to the given set; otherwise, it is *proper*.

Substitution   The process of replacing one quantity or unknown by another equal quantity

Subtraction of integers $a - b = a + (-b)$

Subtraction property of equations   The solution of an equation is unchanged by subtracting the same number from both sides of the equation.

Subtraction property of inequality   See *Addition property of inequality*.

Sum   The result of an addition

Sum of the measures of the angles in a triangle property   The sum of the measures of the angles in any triangle is 180°.

Supply   The number of items that are available at a given price

Surface   In mathematics, it is an undefined term. It is the outer face or exterior of an object; it has an extent or magnitude with length and breadth, but no thickness.

Syllogism   A logical argument that involves three propositions, usually two premises and a conclusion, the conclusion necessarily being true if the premises are true

Symbols of inclusion   See *Grouping symbols*.

Symmetric property   If $a = b$, then $b = a$.

System of equations   A set of equations that are to be solved *simultaneously*. A brace symbol is used to show the equations belonging to the system.

Tangent   In a right triangle ABC with right angle C, $\tan A = $ (opposite side of A)/(adjacent side of A).

Temperature   The degree of hotness or coldness

Term   A number, a variable, or a product of numbers and variables. See *Polynomial*.

Test point   A point that is chosen to find the appropriate half-plane when graphing a linear inequality in two variables

Theorem   A statement that has been proved. See *Deductive reasoning*.

Time   In a financial problem, the length of time (in years) from the present value to the future value

Ton   A measurement of mass in the United States system; it is equal to 2,000 lb.

Trailing zeros   Sometimes zeros are placed after the decimal point or after the last digit to the right of the decimal point, and if these zeros do not change the value of the number, they are called *trailing zeros*.

Transformation   A passage from one figure or expression to another, such as a reflection, translation, rotation, contraction, or dilation

Transitive law   If $a = b$ and $b = c$, then $a = c$.

Translating   The process of writing an English sentence in mathematical symbols

Translation   The process of changing a verbal expression into a symbolic expression

Trapezoid   A quadrilateral that has two parallel sides

Tree diagram   A device used to list all the possibilities for an experiment

Triangle   A polygon with three sides

Trichotomy   Exactly one of the following is true, for any real numbers a and b: $a < b$, $a > b$, or $a = b$.

Trigonometric ratios   The sine, cosine, and tangent ratios are known as the *trigonometric* ratios.

Trinomial   A polynomial with exactly three terms

True equation   An equation without variables in which the number on the left side of the equal sign is the same as the number on the right side of the equal sign.

Type I error   Rejection of a hypothesis based on sampling when, in fact, the hypothesis is true

Type II error   Acceptance of a hypothesis based on sampling when, in fact, it is false

Undefined terms   To avoid circular definitions, it is necessary to include certain terms without specific mathematical definitions.

Union   The union of sets A and B, denoted by $A \cup B$, is the set consisting of elements in A or in B or in both A and B.

Unit circle   A circle with radius 1 centered at the origin

Unit scale   The distance between the points marked 0 and 1 on a number line

United States system   The measurement system used in the United States

Universal set   The largest set under consideration for a particular discussion

Valid   In logic, refers to a correctly inferred logical argument

Variable   A symbol that represents unspecified elements of a given set. On a calculator, it refers to the name given to a location in the memory that can be assigned a value.

Variable expression   An expression that contains at least one variable

Variance The square of the standard deviation

Venn diagram A diagram used to illustrate relationships among sets

Vertex (1) A *vertex* of a polygon is a corner point, or a point of intersection of two sides. (2) A *vertex* of a parabola is the lowest point for a parabola that opens upward, the highest point for one that opens downward, the leftmost point for one that opens to the right, and the rightmost point for one that opens to the left.

Vertical angles Opposite angles formed by two intersecting lines. That is, two angles such that each side of one is a prolongation through the vertex of a side of the other.

Vertical line A line that is perpendicular to a horizontal line. Its equation has the form $x = $ constant.

Volume A number describing the three-dimensional content of a set. Specifically, it is the number of cubic units enclosed in a solid figure.

Weight In everyday usage, the heaviness of an object; in scientific usage, the gravitational pull on a body

Well-defined set A set for which there is no doubt about whether a particular element is included in the given set

Whole numbers The positive integers and zero; $\mathbb{W} = \{0, 1, 2, 3, \ldots\}$

x-axis The horizontal axis in a Cartesian coordinate system

x-intercept The place where a graph passes through the x-axis

Yard A linear measure in the United States system; it has the same length as 3 ft.

y-axis The vertical axis in a Cartesian coordinate system

y-intercept The place where a graph passes through the y-axis. For a line $y = mx + b$, it is the point $(0, b)$.

Zero The number that separates the positive and negative numbers; it is also called the *identity element* for addition; that is, it satisfies the property that
$$x + 0 = 0 + x = x$$
for all numbers x.

Zero property If a is any real number, then $a \cdot 0 = 0 \cdot a = 0$.

Zero multiplication theorem If $a \cdot b = 0$, then either $a = 0$ or $b = 0$.

APPENDIX B TABLES

TABLE I	Trigonometric Ratios						
Degrees	sin x	cos x	tan x	Degrees	sin x	cos x	tan x
1	0.0175	0.9998	0.0175	46	07193	0.6947	1.0355
2	0.0349	0.9994	0.0349	47	0.7314	0.6820	1.0724
3	0.0523	0.9986	0.0524	48	0.7431	0.6691	1.1106
4	0.0698	0.9976	0.0699	49	0.7547	0.6561	1.1504
5	0.0872	0.9962	0.0875	50	0.7660	0.6428	1.1918
6	0.1045	0.9945	0.1051	51	0.7771	0.6293	1.2349
7	0.1219	0.9925	0.1228	52	0.7880	0.6157	1.2799
8	0.1392	0.9903	0.1405	53	0.7986	0.6018	1.3270
9	0.1564	0.9877	0.1584	54	0.8090	0.5878	1.3764
10	0.1736	0.9848	0.1763	55	0.8192	0.5736	1.4281
11	0.1908	0.9816	0.1944	56	0.8290	0.5592	1.4826
12	0.2079	0.9781	0.2126	57	0.8387	0.5446	1.5399
13	0.2250	0.9744	0.2309	58	0.8480	0.5299	1.6003
14	0.2419	0.9703	0.2493	59	0.8572	0.5150	1.6643
15	0.2588	0.9659	0.2679	60	0.8660	0.5000	1.7321
16	0.2756	0.9613	0.2867	61	0.8746	0.4848	1.8040
17	0.2924	0.9563	0.3057	62	0.8829	0.4695	1.8807
18	0.3090	0.9511	0.3249	63	0.8910	0.4540	1.9626
19	0.3256	0.9455	0.3443	64	0.8988	0.4384	2.0503
20	0.3420	0.9397	0.3640	65	0.9063	0.4226	2.1445
21	0.3584	0.9336	0.3839	66	0.9135	0.4067	2.2460
22	0.3746	0.9272	0.4040	67	0.9205	0.3907	2.3559
23	0.3907	0.9205	0.4245	68	0.9272	0.3746	2.4751
24	0.4067	0.9135	0.4452	69	0.9336	0.3584	2.6051
25	0.4226	0.9063	0.4663	70	0.9397	0.3420	2.7475
26	0.4384	0.8988	0.4877	71	0.9455	0.3256	2.9042
27	0.4540	0.8910	0.5095	72	0.9511	0.3090	3.0777
28	0.4695	0.8829	0.5317	73	0.9563	0.2924	3.2709
29	0.4848	0.8746	0.5543	74	0.9613	0.2756	3.4874
30	0.5000	0.8660	0.5774	75	0.9659	0.2588	3.7321
31	0.5150	0.8572	0.6009	76	0.9703	0.2419	4.0108
32	0.5299	0.8480	0.6249	77	0.9744	0.2250	4.3315
33	0.5446	0.8387	0.6494	78	0.9781	0.2079	4.7046
34	0.5592	0.8290	0.6745	79	0.9816	0.1908	5.1446
35	0.5736	0.8192	0.7002	80	0.9848	0.1736	5.6713
36	0.5878	0.8090	0.7265	81	0.9877	0.1564	6.3138
37	0.6018	0.7986	0.7536	82	0.9903	0.1392	7.1154
38	0.6157	0.7880	0.7813	83	0.9925	0.1219	8.1444
39	0.6293	0.7771	0.8098	84	0.9945	0.1045	9.5144
40	0.6428	0.7660	0.8391	85	0.9962	0.0872	11.4300
41	0.6561	0.7547	0.8693	86	0.9976	0.0698	14.3007
42	0.6691	0.7431	0.9004	87	0.9986	0.0523	19.0812
43	0.6820	0.7314	0.9325	88	0.9994	0.0349	28.6362
44	0.6947	0.7193	0.9657	89	0.9998	0.0175	57.2898
45	0.7071	0.7071	1.0000	90	1.0000	0.0000	undefined

TABLE II	Monthly Cost to Finance $1,000					
	Number of Years Financed					
Rate of Interest	**5 Years** $N = 60$	**10 Years** $N = 120$	**15 Years** $N = 180$	**20 Years** $N = 240$	**25 Years** $N = 300$	**30 Years** $N = 360$
6.0%	19.33	11.10	8.44	7.16	6.44	6.00
6.5%	19.57	11.35	8.71	7.46	6.75	6.32
7.0%	19.80	11.61	8.99	7.75	7.07	6.65
7.5%	20.04	11.87	9.27	8.06	7.39	6.99
8.0%	20.28	12.13	9.56	8.36	7.72	7.34
8.5%	20.52	12.40	9.85	8.68	8.05	7.69
9.0%	20.76	12.67	10.14	9.00	8.39	8.05
9.5%	21.00	12.94	10.44	9.32	8.74	8.41
10.0%	21.25	13.22	10.75	9.65	9.09	8.78
10.5%	21.49	13.49	11.05	9.98	9.44	9.15
11.0%	21.74	13.77	11.37	10.32	9.80	9.52
11.5%	21.99	14.06	11.68	10.66	10.16	9.90
12.0%	22.24	14.35	12.00	11.01	10.53	10.29
12.5%	22.50	14.64	12.33	11.36	10.90	10.67
13.0%	22.75	14.93	12.65	11.72	11.28	11.06
13.5%	23.01	15.23	12.98	12.07	11.66	11.45
14.0%	23.27	15.53	13.32	12.44	12.04	11.85
14.5%	23.53	15.83	13.66	12.80	12.42	12.25
15.0%	23.79	16.13	14.00	13.17	12.81	12.64
15.5%	24.05	16.44	14.34	13.54	13.20	13.05
16.0%	24.32	16.75	14.69	13.91	13.59	13.45
16.5%	24.58	17.06	15.04	14.29	13.98	13.85
17.0%	24.85	17.38	15.39	14.67	14.38	14.26
17.5%	25.12	17.70	15.75	15.05	14.78	14.66
18.0%	25.39	18.02	16.10	15.43	15.17	15.07
18.5%	25.67	18.34	16.47	15.82	15.57	15.48
19.0%	25.94	18.67	16.83	16.21	15.98	15.89
19.5%	26.22	19.00	17.19	16.60	16.38	16.30
20.0%	26.49	19.33	17.56	16.99	16.78	16.71

TABLE III	Mortality Table

n = age; ℓ_n = number living at the beginning of year n (based on 100,000 births);
d_n = number dying in year n; p_n = probability of living through year n;
q_n = probability of dying in year n

n	ℓ_n	d_n	p_n	q_n	n	ℓ_n	d_n	p_n	q_n
0	100000	708	.9929	.0071	50	87624	729	.9917	.0083
1	99292	175	.9982	.0018	51	86895	792	.9909	.0091
2	99117	151	.9985	.0015	52	86103	858	.9900	.0100
3	98966	144	.9986	.0015	53	85245	928	.9891	.0109
4	98822	138	.9986	.0014	54	84317	1003	.9881	.0119
5	98684	133	.9987	.0014	55	83314	1083	.9870	.0130
6	98551	128	.9987	.0013	56	82231	1168	.9858	.0142
7	98423	124	.9987	.0013	57	81063	1260	.9845	.0156
8	98299	121	.9988	.0012	58	79803	1357	.9830	.0170
9	98178	119	.9988	.0012	59	78446	1458	.9814	.0186
10	98059	119	.9988	.0012	60	76988	1566	.9797	.0204
11	97940	120	.9988	.0012	61	75422	1677	.9778	.0222
12	97820	123	.9988	.0013	62	73745	1793	.9757	.0243
13	97697	129	.9987	.0013	63	71952	1912	.9734	.0266
14	97568	136	.9986	.0014	64	70040	2034	.9710	.0291
15	97432	142	.9986	.0015	65	68006	2159	.9683	.0318
16	97290	150	.9985	.0016	66	65847	2287	.9653	.0347
17	97140	157	.9984	.0016	67	63560	2418	.9620	.0381
18	96983	164	.9983	.0017	68	61142	2548	.9583	.0417
19	96819	168	.9983	.0017	69	58594	2672	.9544	.0456
20	96651	173	.9982	.0018	70	55922	2784	.9502	.0498
21	96478	177	.9982	.0018	71	53138	2877	.9459	.0542
22	96301	179	.9982	.0019	72	50261	2948	.9414	.0587
23	96122	182	.9981	.0019	73	47313	2993	.9368	.0633
24	95940	183	.9981	.0019	74	44320	3019	.9319	.0681
25	95757	185	.9981	.0019	75	41301	3030	.9266	.0734
26	95572	187	.9981	.0020	76	38271	3030	.9208	.0792
27	95385	190	.9980	.0020	77	35241	3020	.9143	.0857
28	95195	193	.9980	.0020	78	32221	2998	.9070	.0931
29	95002	198	.9979	.0021	79	29223	2957	.8988	.1012
30	94804	202	.9979	.0021	80	26266	2888	.8901	.1100
31	94602	207	.9978	.0022	81	23378	2790	.8807	.1194
32	94395	212	.9978	.0023	82	20588	2659	.8709	.1292
33	94183	218	.9977	.0023	83	17929	2499	.8606	.1394
34	93965	226	.9976	.0024	84	15430	2314	.8500	.1500
35	93739	235	.9975	.0025	85	13116	2113	.8389	.1611
36	93504	247	.9974	.0027	86	11003	1901	.8272	.1728
37	93257	261	.9972	.0028	87	9102	1685	.8149	.1851
38	92996	280	.9970	.0030	88	7417	1470	.8018	.1982
39	92716	301	.9968	.0033	89	5947	1263	.7876	.2124
40	92415	326	.9965	.0035	90	4684	1068	.7720	.2280
41	92089	354	.9962	.0039	91	3616	888	.7544	.2456
42	91735	383	.9958	.0042	92	2728	725	.7342	.2658
43	91352	414	.9955	.0045	93	2003	579	.7109	.2891
44	90938	447	.9951	.0049	94	1424	450	.6840	.3160
45	90491	484	.9947	.0054	95	974	341	.6499	.3501
46	90007	525	.9942	.0058	96	633	253	.6003	.3997
47	89482	569	.9937	.0064	97	380	185	.5132	.4869
48	88913	618	.9931	.0070	98	195	129	.3385	.6615
49	88295	671	.9924	.0076	99	66	66	.0000	1.0000

Courtesy of the Society of Actuaries, Chicago, Illinois.

CHAPTER 1

1.1 Math Anxiety, p. 9

Throughout this book you will find problems that are designated **IN YOUR OWN WORDS.** Since these are opinion questions, the answers are not right or wrong, so we do not show answers to these questions in the answer section. However, that does not mean that any answer is correct. You need to honestly attempt to answer each of these questions, and you need to back up your arguments with examples and facts. One-word (and usually one-sentence) answers will not receive full credit.
1. This *stop sign* designates important material, and you should stop, understand, and study the highlighted concept.   **3.** The *yield sign* is used throughout the book to tell you to move slowly and remember the result.   **41.** This sign is used to designate the location of a women's rest room.   **43.** This sign is used to designate the location of a restaurant.   **45.** This sign is used to designate a location as a kangaroo crossing.   **47.** B, employment   **49.** A, announcements   **51.** E, recreation

1.2 Formulating the Problem, p. 18

1. Parentheses first; then multiplication and division, reading from left to right; and, finally, addition and subtraction, reading from left to right   **3. a.** 17; sum   **b.** 14; sum   **5. a.** 5; sum   **b.** 5; quotient   **7. a.** 17; sum   **b.** 14; difference   **9. a.** 32; sum   **b.** 56; sum
11. a. 27; sum   **b.** 13; sum   **13. a.** 9; sum   **b.** 19; sum   **15. a.** 29; difference   **b.** 8; difference   **17. a.** $3 \times 4 + 3 \times 8$
b. $7 \times 9 + 7 \times 4$ **19. a.** $4 \times 300 + 4 \times 20 + 4 \times 7$ **b.** $6 \times 500 + 6 \times 30 + 6 \times 3$ **21.** $3 + 2 \times 4$ **23.** $10(5 + 6)$
25. $8 \times 5 + 10$ **27.** $8(11 - 9)$ **29.** 261; difference   **31.** 800; sum   **33.** 1,080; sum   **35.** 1,600; product   **37.** 59; difference
39. 2,700; difference   **41.** 285,197; sum   **43.** 2,323; sum   **45.** 8,640 hours   **47.** \$10,600   **49.** \$18,516   **51.** \$37,440   **53.** 345 miles
55. F   **57.** F   **59.** F

1.3 Fractions and Decimals, p. 27

5. The place-value names (in decreasing order) are: trillions, hundred billions, ten billions, billions, hundred millions, ten millions, millions, hundred thousands, ten thousands, thousands, hundreds, tens, units, decimal point, tenths, hundredths, thousandths, ten-thousandths, hundred-thousandths, and millionths.   **7. a.** proper; $\boxed{8} \div \boxed{13} \boxed{=}$ **b.** proper; $\boxed{17} \div \boxed{21} \boxed{=}$
9. a. $\boxed{4} \boxed{+} \boxed{3} \div \boxed{7} \boxed{=}$ **b.** $\boxed{2} \boxed{+} \boxed{1} \div \boxed{2} \boxed{=}$ **11. a.** $5\frac{1}{3}$ **b.** $6\frac{1}{4}$ **c.** $14\frac{1}{10}$ **d.** $16\frac{3}{10}$ **13. a.** $1\frac{11}{16}$ **b.** $17\frac{7}{10}$ **c.** $2\frac{1}{16}$ **d.** $3\frac{6}{7}$
15. a. $16\frac{3}{5}$ **b.** 14   **c.** 6   **d.** $31\frac{1}{4}$ **17. a.** $\frac{7}{4}$ **b.** $\frac{18}{5}$ **19. a.** $\frac{11}{3}$ **b.** $\frac{26}{5}$ **21. a.** $\frac{13}{10}$ **b.** $\frac{22}{3}$ **23. a.** $\frac{53}{3}$ **b.** $\frac{64}{5}$ **25. a.** $\frac{29}{15}$ **b.** $\frac{47}{17}$ **27. a.** $\frac{151}{8}$
b. $\frac{47}{12}$ **29. a.** $0.8\overline{3}$ **b.** $1.1\overline{6}$ **31. a.** 2.5   **b.** $5.\overline{3}$ **33. a.** $6.08\overline{3}$ **b.** $6.\overline{6}$ **35. a.** $7.8\overline{3}$ **b.** $4.0\overline{6}$ **37. a.** $2.\overline{6}$ **b.** $4.1\overline{6}$ **39. a.** 4.375
b. $3.\overline{1}$ **41. a.** $\frac{41}{50}$ **b.** $\frac{5}{8}$ **43. a.** 0.63   **b.** 0.82   **45. a.** $0.4\overline{6}$ **b.** $0.3\overline{18}$ **47.** \$5,250   **49.** \$8,450   **51.** \$6,312.50   **53.** T   **55.** T
57. F   **59.** T

1.4 Rounding and Estimation, p. 33

3. 2.3   **5.** 6,287.45   **7.** 5.3   **9.** 6,300   **11.** 12.82   **13.** 4.818   **15.** 5   **17.** \$12.99   **19.** \$15.00   **21.** 690   **23.** \$86,000   **25.** 0.667
27. 0.118   **29.** 0.137   **31.** 0.333   **33.** 0.417   **35.** 0.318   **37.** B   **39.** C   **41.** B   **43.** \$1,250   **45.** \$12.13   **47.** \$70.83   **49.** \$112.33
51. almost 3 hours   **55.** F   **57.** F   **59.** T

1.5 Exponents and Prime Factorization, p. 40

5. a. one million   **b.** 10   **c.** 6   **d.** $10 \times 10 \times 10 \times 10 \times 10 \times 10$ **7. a.** one-tenth   **b.** 10   **c.** -1 **d.** 0.1   **9. a.** 3.2×10^3
b. 2.5×10^4 **c.** 1.8×10^7 **d.** 6.4×10^2 **11. a.** 5.624×10^3 **b.** 1.5824×10^4 **c.** 2.379×10 **d.** 8.17×10^{-4}
13. a. 4.21×10^{-6} **b.** 9.2×10^7 **c.** 1 or 10^0 **d.** 1.5×10^0 **15. a.** 6.34×10^9 **b.** 5.2019×10^{11} **c.** 4.093745×10^8
d. $8.291029292 \times 10^{12}$ **17. a.** 72,000,000,000   **b.** 4,500   **19. a.** 0.0021   **b.** 0.00000 046   **21. a.** 3.2   **b.** 0.00080 3   **23. a.** 49
b. 25   **25. a.** 256   **b.** 64   **27. a.** 10,000   **b.** 81   **29. a.** 21,892,827,100   **b.** 329   **31. a.** $2^2 \times 3$ **b.** $2^2 \times 5$ **33. a.** 2^8 **b.** 2×3^2
35. a. $2^4 \times 5^2$ **b.** $2^3 \times 5^3$ **37. a.** $7^3 \times 13$ **b.** $13^2 \times 23 \times 59$ **39. a.** $19 \times 29 \times 83$ **b.** 31^3 **41.** A   **43.** C   **45.** A   **47.** 4.184×10^7
49. 333,000   **51. a.** 886,000,000   **b.** 9.5 times farther   **53. a.** 5.8697136×10^9 **b.** 71,321   **c.** 8 years   **55.** \$150 (Estimate, do not use a calculator.)   **57.** F   **59.** F

1.6 Common Fractions, p. 50

7. a. $\frac{1}{2}$ **b.** $\frac{1}{3}$ **c.** $\frac{1}{4}$ **d.** $\frac{1}{5}$ **9. a.** $\frac{1}{4}$ **b.** $\frac{1}{3}$ **c.** $\frac{1}{2}$ **d.** $\frac{2}{3}$ **11. a.** $\frac{24}{5}$ **b.** 3   **c.** $\frac{2}{3}$ **d.** $\frac{1}{2}$ **13. a.** $\frac{1}{3}$ **b.** $\frac{3}{2}$ **c.** $\frac{5}{14}$ **d.** $\frac{7}{15}$ **15.** Shade 6 of the
20 squares.   **17.** Shade 4 of the 15 squares.   **19.** Shade 2 of the 18 squares.   **21. a.** divisor, 5; 3; 3   **b.** divisor, 3; 2; 2
23. a. divisor, 4; 5; 5   **b.** divisor, 16; 15; 15   **25. a.** $\frac{1}{24}$ **b.** $\frac{8}{15}$ **c.** $\frac{1}{8}$ **d.** $\frac{5}{2}$ **e.** $\frac{2}{5}$ **f.** $\frac{1}{4}$ **27. a.** $\frac{3}{2}$ **b.** $\frac{2}{3}$ **c.** $\frac{4}{3}$ **d.** $\frac{9}{8}$ **e.** $\frac{3}{4}$ **f.** 1

29. a. 1 **b.** 1 **c.** 1 **d.** 4 **e.** $\frac{7}{5}$ **f.** $\frac{9}{7}$ **31. a.** $\frac{2}{15}$ **b.** $\frac{1}{8}$ **c.** $\frac{3}{25}$ **d.** 18 **e.** $\frac{5}{6}$ **f.** $\frac{13}{6}$ **33. a.** $\frac{108}{25}$ **b.** $\frac{121}{6}$ **c.** $\frac{225}{16}$ **d.** $\frac{49}{18}$ **e.** $\frac{65}{9}$ **f.** $\frac{19}{10}$ **35. a.** $\frac{1}{12}$ **b.** $\frac{1}{15}$ **c.** $\frac{1}{2}$ **d.** $\frac{19}{2}$ **e.** 4 **f.** $\frac{3}{8}$ **37. a.** $\frac{1}{4}$ **b.** $\frac{87}{100}$ **c.** $\frac{3}{8}$ **39. a.** $\frac{39}{50}$ **b.** $\frac{17}{20}$ **c.** $\frac{123}{500}$ **41. a.** $\frac{2}{3}$ **b.** $\frac{7}{8}$ **c.** $\frac{1}{6}$ **43. a.** $\frac{1}{9}$ **b.** $\frac{5}{9}$ **c.** $\frac{1}{12}$ **45.** \$138,000 **47.** \$625,000 **49.** \$2,346 **51.** \$11.35 **53.** \$10,000 **55.** F **57.** F **59.** T

1.7 Adding and Subtracting Fractions, p. 59

5. A **7.** D **9.** B **11.** A **13. a.** $\frac{3}{5}$ **b.** $\frac{8}{7}$ **c.** $\frac{8}{11}$ **d.** 4 **e.** 1 **f.** $\frac{2}{3}$ **15. a.** 4 **b.** 9 **c.** 13 **d.** $1\frac{2}{3}$ **e.** $5\frac{1}{2}$ **f.** $\frac{1}{2}$ **17. a.** 12 **b.** 180 **c.** 336 **d.** 630 **19. a.** 55,125 **b.** 2,205 **c.** 6,300 **d.** 1,800 **21. a.** $\frac{1}{2}$ **b.** $\frac{35}{24}$ **c.** $\frac{7}{24}$ **d.** $\frac{1}{3}$ **e.** $\frac{23}{30}$ **f.** $\frac{5}{6}$ **23. a.** $7\frac{1}{4}$ **b.** $7\frac{1}{6}$ **c.** $8\frac{7}{8}$ **25. a.** $2\frac{23}{24}$ **b.** $1\frac{37}{70}$ **27. a.** $25\frac{1}{3}$ **b.** 20 **29. a.** $\frac{8}{15}$ **b.** $\frac{12}{5}$ **31. a.** $\frac{19}{15}$ **b.** $\frac{43}{35}$ **33.** 0.8 **35.** $9.\overline{3}$ **37.** 0.4487116145 (approx.) **39.** $\frac{7}{24}$ **41.** $\frac{7}{12}$ **43.** $\frac{17}{24}$ **45.** $\frac{1}{6}$ **47.** $\frac{5}{18}$ **49.** $\frac{5}{6}$ **51.** $7\frac{5}{12}$ pounds **53.** $18\frac{1}{16}$ in. **55.** F **57.** T **59.** T

1.8 Hindu–Arabic Numeration System, p. 64

5. a. 100 **b.** 400

7.

9. Let $X =$ . Then 1,234 can be represented as

11. 5 units **13.** 5 thousandths **15.** 5 ten thousands **17. a.** 100,000 **b.** 1,000 **19. a.** 0.0001 **b.** 0.001 **21. a.** 5,000 **b.** 500 **23. a.** 0.06 **b.** 0.00009 **25. a.** 10,234 **b.** 65.089 **27. a.** 7,000,000.03 **b.** 6,000,000,000.002 **29.** 3,028.5402 **31. a.** $7 \times 10^2 + 4 \times 10 + 1$ **b.** $7 \times 10^5 + 2 \times 10^4 + 8 \times 10^3 + 4 \times 10^2 + 7$ **33. a.** $4 \times 10^1 + 7 + 2 \times 10^{-3} + 1 \times 10^{-4} + 5 \times 10^{-5}$ **b.** $5 \times 10^2 + 2 \times 10 + 1$ **35. a.** $4 \times 10^2 + 2 \times 10^1 + 8 + 3 \times 10^{-1} + 1 \times 10^{-2}$ **b.** $5 \times 10^3 + 2 \times 10^2 + 4 \times 10^1 + 5 + 5 \times 10^{-1}$ **37. a.** $8 \times 10^2 + 9 \times 10^1 + 3 + 1 \times 10^{-4}$ **b.** $8 + 5 \times 10^{-5}$ **39.** 31 **41.** 10,905 **43.** 1,051,004

45. 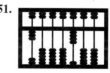   **47.**    **49.** 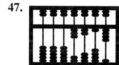   **51.**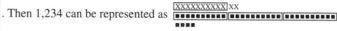

53. 12 years, 3 months **55.** 18 ft, 5 in. **57.** 8 gross, 1 dozen, 2 units **59.** 3 years, 2 months, 7 days

1.9 Different Numeration Systems, p. 70

5. a. 9 **b.** 14_{five} **c.** 100_{three} **d.** 11_{eight} **e.** 1001_{two} **f.** 10_{nine} **7.** $6 \times 8^2 + 4 \times 8^1 + 3 \times 8^0$ **9.** $1 \times 2^5 + 1 \times 2^4 + 1 \times 2^2 + 1 \times 2^1 + 1 \times 2^0 + 1 \times 2^{-1} + 1 \times 2^{-4}$ **11.** $6 \times 8^7 + 4 \times 8^6 + 2 \times 8^5 + 5 \times 8^1 + 1 \times 8^0$ **13.** $3 \times 4^5 + 2 \times 4^4 + 3 \times 4^3 + 2 \times 4^{-1}$ **15.** $3 \times 5^0 + 4 \times 5^{-1} + 2 \times 5^{-3} + 3 \times 5^{-4} + 1 \times 5^{-5}$ **17.** 343 **19.** 4,307 **21.** 116 **23.** 11.625 **25.** 807 **27.** 66 **29.** 351.125 **31.** 10344_{five} **33.** 100000000_{two} **35.** 3122_{five} **37.** $2E79_{twelve}$ **39.** 1000000000_{two} **41.** 1221_{three} **43.** 1132_{eight} **45.** 6 days, 14 hours **47.** 2 lb, 7 oz **49.** 18 quarters, 1 nickel, 4 pennies **51.** 242_{five}; financial status is \$0.72 **53.** 33 quarters, 1 nickel, 4 pennies **55.** $54 = 46_{twelve}$; 4 years, 6 months **57.** $49 = 21_{twenty-four}$; 2 days, 1 hour

Chapter 1 Review Questions, p. 78

3. a. $5 \times 8 + 5 \times 2$ **b.** $2 \times 25 + 2 \times 35$ **c.** $3 \times 200 + 3 \times 50 + 3 \times 6$ **d.** $5 \times 400 + 5 \times 50 + 5 \times 9$ **5. a.** $16\frac{2}{7}$ **b.** $8\frac{1}{3}$ **c.** $16\frac{7}{10}$ **d.** $1\frac{53}{100}$ **7. a.** 0.875 **b.** $0.8\overline{3}$ **c.** $8.\overline{6}$ **d.** 2.8 **9. a.** 3.4×10^{-3} **b.** 4.0003×10^6 **c.** 1.74×10^4 **d.** 5 **11. a.** 2×43 **b.** $2^3 \times 3^2$ **c.** 2×3^5 **d.** $2^2 \times 7^3$ **13. a.** $\frac{333}{1,000}$ **b.** $\frac{2}{9}$ **c.** $\frac{19}{20}$ **d.** $\frac{1}{200}$ **15. a.** 22; sum **b.** 16; quotient **c.** 17; sum **d.** 8; difference **17. a.** $\frac{5}{4}$ **b.** $\frac{2}{5}$ **c.** 2 **d.** $\frac{26}{15}$ **19. a.** $\frac{13}{24}$ **b.** $\frac{9}{20}$ **c.** $3\frac{11}{20}$ **d.** $\frac{1}{30}$ **21. a.** 2.266666667; sum **b.** 1.291666667; quotient **c.** 0.347826087; difference **d.** 0.347826087; product **23. a.** 4,063.02 **b.** 2,099.03125 **c.** 9.5 **d.** 483 **25.** Your favorite digit is repeated six times.

CHAPTER 2

2.1 Symbol Shock, p. 89

1. terms **3. a.** plus, sum, added to, will be **b.** minus, difference, subtracted from **c.** times, product, multiplied by **d.** divided by, quotient, per **e.** equals, same as, results in **5.** To evaluate an expression, replace a variable by a given numerical value and then simplify the numerical expression. **7.** 1, 3, 7, 15 **9.** 50, 49, 41, 1 **11.** 100, 144, 169, 400 **13.** 13 **15.** 8 **17.** 21

19. 19   **21.** 2   **23.** 4   **25.** 9   **27.** 20   **29.** 11   **31.** 17   **33.** 48   **35.** 100   **37.** 4   **39.** $n + 5$ **41.** $5 - n$ **43.** $x + \frac{3}{2}$ **45.** $1 - n$
47. $7n$ **49.** $\frac{5}{n}$ **51.** $x, x + 6, 2x + 12, 2x + 4, x + 2, 2$; thus, the answer must be 2.   **53.** Pick a number; add 7; double it; subtract 4; divide by 2; subtract the original number. The answer is 5.   **57.** F   **59.** T

2.2 Addition of Integers, p. 96
7. opposite   **9.** minus   **11.** opposite   **13. a.** <   **b.** >   **c.** <   **d.** <   **15. a.** =   **b.** <   **c.** >   **d.** <   **17. a.** 7   **b.** 10   **c.** 0   **d.** -10
19. a. 3   **b.** 3   **c.** -3 **d.** 3   **21. a. i.** 9; **ii.** 9   **b. i.** -6; **ii.** 9   **c. i.** 6; **ii.** 9   **d. i.** 9; **ii.** 9   *Show Problems 23–28 on number lines.*
23. -1 **25.** 1   **27.** -6 **29. a.** 4   **b.** -4 **c.** 4   **d.** -14 **31. a.** -13 **b.** -5 **c.** 13   **d.** 5   **33. a.** 17   **b.** 39   **c.** 6   **d.** -123
35. a. 0   **b.** 0   **c.** -19 **d.** -19 **37. a.** The point N is seven units to the right of H.   **b.** $+6$ **c.** -8 **d.** $+8$ *Show Problems 39–44*
on number lines.   **39.** 8   **41.** -3 **43.** 2   **45. a.** 108   **b.** $-4{,}700$ **47. a.** -799 **b.** -199 **49.** 0   **51.** $-9°C$ **53.** 16-yard line
55. F   **57.** T   **59.** T

2.3 Subtraction of Integers, p. 101
3. a. $8 - 5 = 8 + (-5) = 3$ **b.** $12 - 7 = 12 + (-7) = 5$ **c.** $15 - (-15) = 15 + 15 = 30$ **d.** $15 - 15 = 15 + (-15) = 0$
5. a. $-7 - (-18) = -7 + 18 = 11$ **b.** $-7 - 18 = -7 + (-18) = -25$ **c.** $7 - 18 = 7 + (-18) = -11$
d. $7 - (-18) = 7 + 18 = 25$ **7. a.** $17 - (-8) = 17 + 8 = 25$ **b.** $-17 - 8 = -17 + (-8) = -25$ **c.** $17 - 8 = 17 + (-8) = 9$
d. $-17 - (-8) = -17 + 8 = -9$ **9. a.** $-13 - (-6) = -13 + 6 = -7$ **b.** $13 - 6 = 13 + (-6) = 7$ **c.** $13 - (-6) = 13 + 6 = 19$
d. $-13 - 6 = -13 + (-6) = -19$ **11. a.** 9   **b.** 8   **c.** 7   **d.** 6   **13. a.** -21 **b.** -9 **c.** 7   **d.** -7 **15. a.** -15 **b.** -17 **c.** 13
d. -21 **17. a.** five minus three   **b.** five minus negative three   **19. a.** the opposite of three   **b.** the opposite of negative three
21. a. x plus the opposite of y **b.** opposite of x minus y **23. a.** opposite of six times negative one minus one   **b.** six minus the
opposite of negative one   **25.** -3 **27.** -2 **29.** -1 **31.** 2   **33.** -6 **35.** -2 **37.** 0   **39.** -356 **41.** $-2{,}255$ **43.** $-8{,}000$
45. $-5{,}744$ **47.** $159°$ **49.** $25{,}850$ ft   **51.** $3°$ **53.** $25°$ **55.** T   **57.** F   **59.** F

2.4 Multiplication of Integers, p. 107
1. m addends of n; that is, $\underbrace{n + n + n + \cdots + n}_{m \text{ addends}}$ **3.** $n \cdot 0 = 0 \cdot n = 0$ **7. a.** -54 **b.** -15 **c.** -8 **d.** -8 **9. a.** -48 **b.** 28

c. 35   **d.** 27   **11. a.** 54   **b.** -42 **c.** 50   **d.** -75 **13. a.** 40   **b.** 6   **c.** -84 **d.** 8   **15. a.** 25   **b.** -25 **c.** 0   **d.** 0   **17. a.** 49
b. -49 **c.** 0   **d.** -98 **19. a.** -32 **b.** -128 **c.** -30 **d.** -16 **21. a.** -75 **b.** -32 **c.** 11   **d.** -25 **23.** -6 **25.** -2
27. 13   **29.** 25   **31.** -9 **33.** -8 **35.** 25   **37.** 16   **39.** 5 or 5 steps to the right   **41.** -92 **43.** 750 calories   **45.** moving to the
right 15 units   **47.** losing a total of \$450 or $-\$450$ **49.** T   **51.** T   **53.** T   **55.** F   **57.** F   **59.** T

2.5 Division of Integers, p. 111
5. a. 6   **b.** 7   **c.** 7   **d.** 11   **7. a.** -7 **b.** 11   **c.** -6 **d.** -4 **9. a.** 7   **b.** 5   **c.** -30 **d.** -17 **11. a.** impossible   **b.** 0   **c.** impossible
d. impossible   **13. a.** 4; $\boxed{(}\ \boxed{12}\ \boxed{-}\ \boxed{4}\ \boxed{)}\ \boxed{\div}\ \boxed{2}\ \boxed{=}$ **b.** 10; $\boxed{12}\ \boxed{-}\ \boxed{4}\ \boxed{\div}\ \boxed{2}\ \boxed{=}$ **15. a.** -9; $\boxed{(}\ \boxed{6}\ \boxed{+}\ \boxed{21}\ \boxed{)}\ \boxed{\div}\ \boxed{(-)}\ \boxed{3}\ \boxed{=}$
b. -1; $\boxed{6}\ \boxed{+}\ \boxed{21}\ \boxed{\div}\ \boxed{(-)}\ \boxed{3}\ \boxed{=}$ **17.** 4   **19.** 12   **21.** -5 **23.** -3 **25.** 4   **27.** -2 **29.** 3   **31.** -13 **33.** 2   **35.** 1   **37.** 2
39. -2 **41.** -4 **43.** -5 **45.** -1 **47.** 5   **49.** -2 **51.** 1   **53.** F   **55.** F   **57.** F   **59.** F

2.6 Rational and Irrational Numbers, p. 122
5. $\sqrt{4}$ is the positive number that when squared is equal to 4.   **7.** $\sqrt{2}$ is the positive number that when squared is equal to 2.
9. a. $\frac{-7}{8}$ **b.** $\frac{-5}{8}$ **c.** $\frac{-7}{9}$ **d.** $\frac{a}{b}$ **11. a.** $\frac{x}{y}$ **b.** $\frac{y}{3}$ **c.** $\frac{-1}{x}$ **d.** $\frac{a}{b}$ **13. a.** $\frac{-1}{2}$ **b.** $\frac{5}{2}$ **c.** $\frac{-23}{35}$ **d.** $\frac{7}{9}$ **15. a.** $\frac{-1}{6}$ **b.** $\frac{-3}{10}$ **c.** $\frac{-3}{8}$ **d.** $\frac{-3}{8}$
17. a. 3   **b.** 1   **c.** 0   **d.** impossible   **19. a.** 9   **b.** impossible   **c.** 13   **d.** 14   **21. a.** 35   **b.** 45   **c.** 98   **d.** 78   **23. a.** 3.87
b. 4.12   **c.** 4.47   **d.** 7.07   **25. a.** 13.78   **b.** 31.62   **c.** 44.72   **d.** 54.77   **27. a.** rational; 5   **b.** irrational; $2 < \sqrt{5} < 3$
c. rational; 5   **d.** rational; 0.25   **29. a.** irrational, $3 < \sqrt{10} < 4$ **b.** irrational; $3 < \sqrt{15} < 4$ **c.** rational; 4   **d.** irrational;
$4 < \sqrt{17} < 5$ **31. a.** irrational; $48 < \sqrt{2{,}400} < 49$ **b.** rational; 49   **c.** irrational; $49 < \sqrt{2{,}402} < 50$ **d.** irrational;
$0 < \sqrt{\frac{1}{10}} < 1$ **33.** 10 ft   **35.** 24 ft   **37.** $\sqrt{8}$ (or $2\sqrt{2}$) in.   **39.** 200 ft   **41.** Length is 25 ft each; would need to purchase 100 ft
43. Exact length is $\sqrt{325}$; this is approximately 18 ft; $4\sqrt{325} \approx 72.11$, so would need to purchase 73 ft.   **45.** T   **47.** F   **49.** F
51. F   **53.** F   **55.** F   **57.** T   **59.** T

Chapter 2 Review Questions, p. 129
3. a. Carry out all operations according to the order-of-operations agreement and write your answer as a single number.   **b.** Carry out all operations according to the order-of-operations agreement and write your answer as a reduced standard-form fraction.   **5. a.** 128
b. 31   **c.** 48   **d.** -61 **e.** 22   **f.** 2   **g.** 27   **h.** -10 **i.** -1 **j.** 61   **7. a.** -14 **b.** 69   **c.** -47 **d.** 50   **e.** 12   **f.** 39   **g.** -8
h. -38 **i.** -28 **j.** 30   **9. a.** 5   **b.** -25 **c.** 12   **d.** -4 **e.** 2   **f.** -11 **g.** 1   **h.** 77   **i.** -7 **j.** 0   **11. a.** -9 **b.** 48   **c.** 8   **d.** 0
13. a. $\frac{-3}{n}$ **b.** -14 **c.** 3   **d.** -5 **15. a.** rational; 23   **b.** irrational; $31 < \sqrt{1{,}000} < 32$ **c.** rational; $0.\overline{6}$ **d.** rational; 2.6
17. $\frac{n}{n+1}$ **19.** $50 - n$ **21.** It is 200 ft shorter.   **23.** $\sqrt{52}$ or $2\sqrt{13}$; 7 ft   **25.** 150 ft

CHAPTER 3

3.1 Polynomials, p. 138

5. a. degree 4; coefficient 3 **b.** degree 2; coefficient 5 **7. a.** degree 1; coefficient 1 **b.** degree 1; coefficient 8 **9. a.** degree 3; coefficient 1 **b.** degree 4; coefficient -2 **11. a.** second-degree binomial **b.** third-degree binomial **13. a.** zero-degree monomial **b.** third-degree binomial **15. a.** second-degree trinomial **b.** second-degree trinomial **17. a.** y^6 **b.** x^7y^5 **19. a.** x^2y^4 **b.** x^3y^4 **21. a.** $8xy$ **b.** $-18xy$ **23. a.** $30x^2$ **b.** $-30xy$ **25. a.** $4x^2$ **b.** $9y^2$ **27. a.** $-25x^2$ **b.** $50xy^2$ **29. a.** $16x^3$ **b.** $-12x^3$ **31. a.** $20y^6$ **b.** $20y^6$ **33. a.** $-12x^3$ **b.** $18x^3$ *Examples for Problems 35–40 vary.* **35. a.** $x + y + z$ **b.** $x^2 + 2x + 1$ **37. a.** x^2 **b.** $x^2y^2 + x^2 + y^2$ **39. a.** xyz **b.** $x^3 + y^2$ **41. a.** $2^2 + 3^2 = 13$ **b.** $(2 + 3)^2 = 25$ **43. a.** $3x^3$ **b.** $(3x)^3$ **45. a.** $x^2 - y^2$ **b.** $(x - y)^2$ **47. a.** 41 minutes **b.** 33 minutes **c.** $(x + 3)$ minutes **d.** $(y - 1)$ minutes **49. a.** $425 **b.** $(450 - x)$ **c.** $(438 - y)$ **d.** $(450 + d)$ **51.** F **53.** F **55.** F **57.** F

3.2 Similar Terms, p. 142

1. $a(b + c) = ab + ac$ **3.** $3x$ and $10x$ **5.** $2x^2y$ and $6x^2y$ **7.** $6x^2y$ and $12x^2y$ **9. a.** $7x$ **b.** $8y$ **11. a.** y **b.** $6z$ **13. a.** $-2z$ **b.** $-5x$ **15. a.** $-14x$ **b.** $-3x$ **17. a.** 0 **b.** 0 **19. a.** $13x$ **b.** $13x$ **21. a.** $3y$ **b.** $2x$ **23. a.** $5x$ **b.** x **25. a.** 8 **b.** -7 **27.** $-3x + 4y$ **29.** $-b$ **31.** $-4a + 2b$ **33.** $x + 8$ **35.** $2x - 7$ **37.** $-4y + 2$ **39.** $-7x + 8y + 18$ **41.** $4x - 7y$ **43.** $4x - 4y$ **45.** $4x + 4y$ **47.** $4x^2 - 3x - 1$ **49.** 21 apples and 20 oranges **51.** $11x$'s and $17y$'s **53.** 63 b's and 64 n's **55.** $H =$ weight of hippo; $p =$ weight of professor **57.** F **59.** F

3.3 Simplification, p. 147

1. $a(b + c) = ab + ac$ **3.** $9x + 12$ **5.** $7x + 23$ **7.** $5x - 13$ **9.** $10x - 20$ **11.** $7x - 3y$ **13.** $3x - 4y$ **15.** $3x - 3$ **17.** $3x - 1$ **19.** $x - 17$ **21.** $-2x + 4$ **23.** $-3x + 9y$ **25.** $-x + 2y$ **27.** $-2x + 3y$ **29.** $x + 1$ **31.** $-x - 7$ **33.** $x - 8$ **35. a.** $x^2 + 3x + 2$ **b.** $x^2 + 6x + 9$ **37. a.** $x^2 + x - 6$ **b.** $x^2 - 3x - 10$ **39. a.** $x^2 - 4$ **b.** $x^2 - x - 6$ **41. a.** $x^2 - 6x + 9$ **b.** $x^2 + 4x + 4$ **43.** $2x^2 - 4x + 3$ **45.** $-2x^2 + 9x$ **47.** $6x^2 - 6x + 10$ **49.** $11x^3 - 4x^2 + 4x + 1$ **51. a.** $x + y$ **b.** $2(x + y)$ **c.** $2x + 2y$ **53.** F **55.** T **57.** F **59.** F

3.4 Equations, p. 154

1. To solve an equation means to find the replacement(s) for the variable(s) that makes the equation true. **3.** A solution of an equation is the replacement(s) for the variable(s) that makes the equation true. **5. a.** 15 **b.** 22 **7. a.** 8 **b.** 112 **9. a.** 5 **b.** 4 **11. a.** -4 **b.** 3 **13.** -3 **15.** -9 **17.** 6 **19.** -22 **21.** 21 **23.** -60 **25.** -44 **27.** 39 **29.** 40 **31.** 0 **33.** 11 **35.** 12 **37.** -14 **39.** -14 **41.** -45 **43.** 0 **47. a.** $2x$ carbon atoms and $6x$ hydrogen atoms **b.** $2x + 6x = 8x$ atoms **c.** 8 **d.** $8y$ **49.** F **51.** F **53.** F **55.** F **57.** F **59.** F

3.5 Solving Equations, p. 158

1. a. $5x$ **b.** $7y$ **3. a.** y **b.** $3x$ **5. a.** $-y$ **b.** -5 **7. a.** $4x$ **b.** $7x$ **11. a.** 4 **b.** 5 **13. a.** 5 **b.** -3 **15. a.** -19 **b.** -17 **17. a.** -4 **b.** -13 **19. a.** 14 **b.** 30 **c.** 41 **d.** 31 **21. a.** 21 **b.** -12 **c.** 70 **d.** -84 **23. a.** 3 **b.** -5 **c.** 15 **d.** -2 **25.** 128 **27. a.** 2 **b.** 9 **29. a.** 13 **b.** 7 **31. a.** 2 **b.** 3 **33. a.** 5 **b.** -1 **35. a.** -7 **b.** -4 **37. a.** -3 **b.** 20 **39. a.** 1 **b.** -5 **45.** $13.34 **47.** $48.16 **49.** $547.69 **51.** $30.22 **53.** F **55.** F **57.** F **59.** F

3.6 Problem Solving with Algebra, p. 167

3. A **5.** B **7.** B **9.** B **11.** C **13.** $B = c - a$ **15.** $X = y + 5$ **17.** $X = 2y + 7$ **19.** $P = \frac{i}{n}$ **21.** $Y = 3x + 2$ **23.** $Y = -6x + 5$ **25.** $Y = \frac{-3}{2}x - 2$ **27.** $Y = \frac{3}{2}x + 2$ **29.** $W = \frac{1}{2}p - \ell$ **31.** 9 **33.** 3 **35.** -1 **37.** 3 **39.** 6 **41.** 46, 48 **43.** 26 gallons **45.** 200 mi/15 gal $\approx$ 13 mpg; 13.6 mpg **47.** 350 mi/10 gal $\approx$ 35 mpg; 31.4 mpg **49.** 200 mi/20 gal $\approx$ 10 mpg; 9.5 mpg **51.** 2,000 mi/50 gal $\approx$ 40 mpg; 39.5 mpg **53.** Green Giant asparagus spears are about 0.8¢/oz less expensive. **55.** The 4-pack is the better buy, and is about $0.06/battery less expensive. **57.** The 1-lb 2-oz = 18-oz box is $0.008/oz less expensive. **59.** The value of the lot is $36,000.

3.7 Inequalities, p. 174

1. a. Nineteen is greater than four. **b.** x is less than eight. **3. a.** Negative five is less than or equal to negative two. **b.** The opposite of x is greater than two. **5. a.** x is positive **b.** y is not positive. **7. a.** $P > 0$ **b.** $N < 0$ **9. a.** $x > 0$ **b.** $x \le 0$ **11. a.** $M \le 4$ **b.** $Q \ge 4$

13. a.

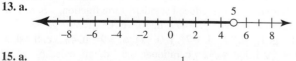

b.

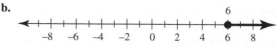

15. a.

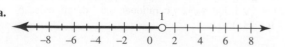

b.

17. a.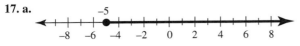

b.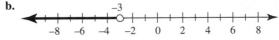

19. a.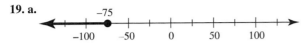

b.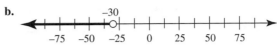

21. a.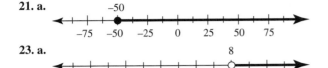

b.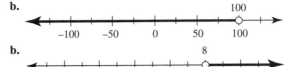

23. a.

b.

25. $x \geq -4$ **27.** $x \geq -2$ **29.** $y > -6$ **31.** $s > -2$ **33.** $m < 5$ **35.** $x > -1$ **37.** $x \leq 1$ **39.** $s < -6$ **41.** $a \geq 2$
43. any number greater than -5 **45.** any number less than -4 **47.** any number less than 4 **49.** All values in the domain satisfy the inequality. **51.** The number is 2. **53.** The number is less than 2. **55.** F **57.** F **59.** F

Chapter 3 Review Questions, p. 180
1. a. 3; 5 **b.** 1; 2 **c.** 4; 1 **d.** 5; -3 **3. a.** x^9y^{11} **b.** $36x^2y$ **c.** $48x^2y^2$ **d.** x^3y **5. a.** $6x - 14$ **b.** $-4x - 1$ **c.** $3x - 9y$
d. $-2x - 1$ **7. a.** $9x^2 - 16$ **b.** $2a^2b^2 + abc - 3c^2$ **9. a.** -3 **b.** -31 **c.** 21 **d.** -10 **11. a.** 23 **b.** -5 **13. a.** 2 **b.** -20
15. a. $x > -3$ **b.** $x > 3$ **17.** $t = \frac{I}{Pr}$ **19.** $y = 2x$ **21.** The first number is 24; estimate by $75/3 = 25$. **23.** The estimated cruising range is about $10 \times 25 = 250$; by direct calculation it is 285.6 miles. **25.** The trip's MPG is 35.

CHAPTER 4
4.1 Ratio and Proportion, p. 187
1. A ratio is a quotient of two numbers; a proportion is a statement of equality between ratios. **3. a.** $3/2$ **b.** $5/4$ **5. a.** $4/7$
b. $7/4$ **7. a.** $23/1$ **b.** $5/6$ **9. a.** $3/1$ **b.** $5/1$ **11. a.** $2/5$ **b.** $10/3$ **13. a.** $17/7$ **b.** $19/13$ **15.** means: 47, 2; extremes: 94, 1; 94 is to 47 as 2 is to 1. **17.** means: x, 1; extremes: 5, 2; 5 is to x as 1 is to 2. **19.** means: b, c; extremes: 8, 2; 8 is to b as c is to 2.
21. means: x, y; extremes: w, z; w is to x as y is to z. **23.** yes **25.** no **27.** yes **29.** yes **31.** yes **33.** no **35.** no **37.** yes
39. 39 to 100 **41.** 8 to 25 **43.** 183 to 500 **45. a.** 53 to 50 **b.** 50 to 53 **47. a.** 3 to 2 **b.** 3 to 19 **49.** 14 to 1 **51.** 18 to 1
53. 37 to 2 **55.** F; ratios involve two numbers **57.** T **59.** F

4.2 Problem Solving with Proportions, p. 192
1. $\frac{9}{10} = \frac{x}{20}$; $x = 18$ **3.** $\frac{4}{9} = \frac{y}{18}$; $y = 8$ **5.** $\frac{3}{t} = \frac{15}{20}$; $t = 4$ **7.** $\frac{12}{s} = \frac{8}{5}$; $s = 12$ **9.** $\frac{u}{18} = \frac{1}{2}$; $u = 9$ **11.** 18 **13.** 12 **15.** 6 **17.** 8
19. 30 **21.** 10 **23.** 8 **25.** 21 **27.** 16 **29.** $\frac{15}{2}$ or 7.5 **31.** 4 **33.** 3 **35.** 9 **37.** $\frac{1}{4}$ or 0.25 **39.** $\frac{5}{2}$ or 2.5 **41.** $\frac{4}{5}$ **43.** $\frac{5}{6}$ **45.** $4.90
47. 10 gallons **49.** 9 minutes **51.** 2 gallons **53.** 27 minutes **55.** 2,475 calories **57.** $8\frac{1}{3}$ in. **59.** F

4.3 Percent, p. 197
1. Percent is the ratio of a number to 100. **9.** $5\frac{1}{2}$ or $\frac{11}{2}$ **11.** $\frac{37}{1,000}$ **13.** $\frac{3}{50}$ **15.** 0.50; 50% **17.** 0.125; 12.5% or $12\frac{1}{2}$% **19.** $0.\overline{3}$; $33\frac{1}{3}$%
21. 0.4; 40% **23.** $0.\overline{6}$; $66\frac{2}{3}$% **25.** $0.08\overline{3}$; $8\frac{1}{3}$% **27.** $0.\overline{5}$; $55\frac{5}{9}$% **29.** $\frac{3}{4}$; 75% **31.** $\frac{17}{20}$; 85% **33.** $\frac{9}{10}$; 90% **35.** $\frac{3}{20}$; 15% **37.** $\frac{13}{20}$; 65%
39. $\frac{3}{8}$; $37\frac{1}{2}$% **41.** $\frac{7}{8}$; $87\frac{1}{2}$% **43.** $\frac{2}{5}$; 0.4 **45.** 1; 1 **47.** $\frac{3}{5}$; 0.6 **49.** $\frac{9}{20}$; 0.45 **51.** $\frac{2}{25}$; 0.08 **53.** $\frac{5}{8}$; 0.625 **55.** $\frac{1}{9}$; $0.\overline{1}$ **57. a.** 75%; C
b. 92%; A **c.** 38%; F **d.** 67%; C **59. a.** 75%; C **b.** 65%; C **c.** 68%; C **d.** 83%; B

4.4 Problem Solving with Percents, p. 205
Estimates for Problems 3–14 may vary. **3.** 1,000 **5.** 9,000 **7.** 5,000 **9.** 200 **11.** 750 **13.** 6,000 **15.** $\frac{15}{100} = \frac{A}{64}$; 9.6

17. $\frac{14}{100} = \frac{21}{W}$; 150 **19.** $\frac{P}{100} = \frac{10}{5}$; 200% **21.** $\frac{P}{100} = \frac{4}{5}$; 80% **23.** $\frac{P}{100} = \frac{25}{5}$; 500% **25.** $\frac{12}{100} = \frac{3}{W}$; 25 **27.** $\frac{33\frac{1}{3}}{100} = \frac{12}{W}$; 36

29. $\frac{6}{100} = \frac{A}{8,150}$; $489 *Estimates for Problems 31–38 may vary.* **31.** 90 million **33.** 45 million **35.** 162 million **37.** 5.4 million
39. 19.8 million **41.** $10.86 **43.** 5% **45.** 59 **47.** The tax withheld is $2,624. **49.** $66\frac{2}{3}$% **51.** 20 questions **53.** 29.3 MPG
55. 1% **57.** T **59.** T

Chapter 4 Review Questions, p. 210
1. a. 20 to 1 **b.** 2 to 1 **c.** 31 to 15 **d.** 18 to 1 **3. a.** 0.6; 60% **b.** 1.5; 150% **c.** $1.\overline{3}$; $133\frac{1}{3}$% **d.** $0.1\overline{6}$; $16\frac{2}{3}$% **5. a.** $\frac{7}{20}$; 0.35
b. $\frac{12}{5}$; 2.4 **c.** $\frac{3}{50}$; 0.06 **d.** $\frac{3}{8}$; 0.375 **7.** $\frac{15}{4}$ **9.** 15 **11.** $\frac{82}{100} = \frac{A}{85}$; 69.7 **13.** $\frac{P}{100} = \frac{1,450}{3,000}$; $48\frac{1}{3}$ **15.** $\frac{250}{100} = \frac{603}{W}$; 241.2 **17.** $\frac{45}{100} = \frac{A}{490}$; 220.5
19. 5 gallons **21.** 7.5 gallons **23.** 17 **25.** $62.54

CHAPTER 5

5.1 Euclidean Geometry, p. 221

9.

11.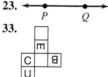

13.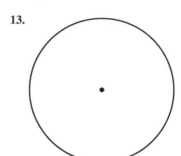

15.

17.

19.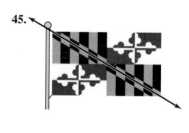

21.

23.

25. ●———●
P   Q

27. ◄——●——●——►
P   Q

29. ◄——●———●
R   S

31.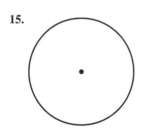

33.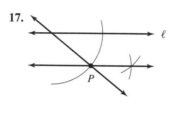

35.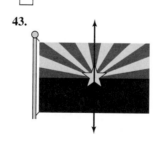

37. rotation

39.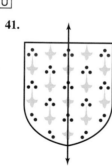

41.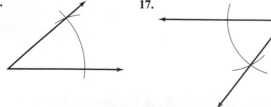

43.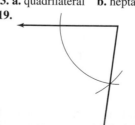

45.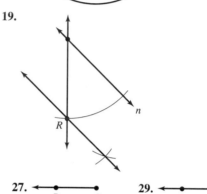

47. symmetric   **49.** not symmetric   **51.** symmetric   **53.** symmetric   **57.** F   **59.** F

5.2 Polygons and Angles, p. 230

9. a. quadrilateral   **b.** pentagon   **11. a.** triangle   **b.** hexagon   **13. a.** quadrilateral   **b.** heptagon

15.

17.

19.

21. a. obtuse   **b.** obtuse   **c.** acute   **d.** acute   **e.** straight angle   **f.** right angle   **g.** acute   **h.** straight angle   **i.** acute
j. $m\angle COB = m\angle DOA$ **k.** $\angle AOC$ **23. a.** acute   **b.** right angle   **25. a.** right angle   **b.** obtuse angle   **27. a.** acute   **b.** acute

29. a. adjacent angles and supplementary angles   **b.** adjacent angles and supplementary angles   **31. a.** alternate interior angles
b. alternate interior angles   **33. a.** $m\angle 2 = m\angle 4 = m\angle 6 = m\angle 8 = 19°$; $m\angle 1 = m\angle 3 = m\angle 5 = m\angle 7 = 161°$ **b.** $m\angle 1 = m\angle 3 =$
$m\angle 5 = m\angle 7 = 153°$; $m\angle 2 = m\angle 4 = m\angle 6 = m\angle 8 = 27°$ **35.** $m\angle 2 = m\angle 4 = m\angle 6 = m\angle 8 = 42°$; $m\angle 1 = m\angle 3 = m\angle 5 = m\angle 7 = 138°$
b. $m\angle 2 = m\angle 4 = m\angle 6 = m\angle 8 = 48°$; $m\angle 1 = m\angle 3 = m\angle 5 = m\angle 7 = 132°$ **37.** F   **39.** T   **41.** F   **43. a.** T   **b.** F   **45. a.** T
b. T   **47.** all yes   **49.** yes, yes, yes, no, no   **51.** yes, yes, yes, no, no   **53.** acute   **55.** two obtuse angles and one right angle
57. F   **59.** T

5.3 Triangles, p. 238

5. $\overline{AB} \simeq \overline{ED}$; $\overline{AC} \simeq \overline{EF}$; $\overline{CB} \simeq \overline{FD}$; $\angle A \simeq \angle E$; $\angle B \simeq \angle D$; $\angle C \simeq \angle F$ **7.** $\overline{RS} \simeq \overline{TU}$; $\overline{RT} \simeq \overline{TR}$; $\overline{ST} \simeq \overline{UR}$; $\angle SRT \simeq \angle UTR$;
$\angle S \simeq \angle U$; $\angle STR \simeq \angle URT$ **9.** $\overline{KL} \simeq \overline{MN}$; $\overline{KJ} \simeq \overline{MP}$; $\overline{JL} \simeq \overline{PN}$; $\angle J \simeq \angle P$; $\angle K \simeq \angle M$; $\angle L \simeq \angle N$ **11.** 88°   **13.** 145°
15. 56°   **17.** 75°   **19.** 80°   **21.** 100°   *Constructions in Problems 23–28 can be verified by comparison with the art in the text.*
29. 20°   **31.** 21°   **33.** 6°   *Triangles for Problems 35–42 may vary.*   **43.** 30°; 60°; 90°   **45.** 50°; 60°; 70°   **47.** 13°; 53°; 114°
53. 50°   **55.** 120°   **57.** 42°   **59.** $x = 135°$; $y = 45°$

5.4 Similar Triangles, p. 247

1. Similar triangles are triangles that have the same shape.   **3.** For any right triangle with sides a and b and hypotenuse c, $a^2 + b^2 = c^2$.
Furthermore, if $a^2 + b^2 = c^2$ for three sides of a triangle, then the triangle is a right triangle.   **5.** a **7.** b **9.** c **11.** $\frac{b}{c}$ **13.** $\frac{a}{c}$
15. $\frac{b}{a}$ **17. a.** 0.2588   **b.** 0.8290   **c.** 1.2799   **19. a.** 0.9903   **b.** 0.9903   **c.** 5.1446   **21. a.** 0.3090   **b.** 0.9511   **c.** 57.2900
23. not possible to tell   **25.** similar; $\overline{GH} \simeq \overline{JK}$; $\overline{GI} \simeq \overline{JL}$; $\overline{IH} \simeq \overline{LK}$; $\angle G \simeq \angle J$; $\angle H \simeq \angle K$; $\angle I \simeq \angle L$ **27.** similar;
$\overline{TV} \simeq \overline{WY}$; $\overline{TU} \simeq \overline{WX}$; $\overline{VU} \simeq \overline{YX}$; $\angle T \simeq \angle W$; $\angle U \simeq \angle X$; $\angle V \simeq \angle Y$ **29.** $\sqrt{58}$ **31.** $\sqrt{189}$ **33.** 9   **35.** $\frac{15}{7}$ **37.** $\frac{10}{9}$
39. a. $\sin A = \frac{\sqrt{35}}{6} \approx 0.9860$; $\cos A = \frac{1}{6} \approx 0.1667$; $\tan A = \frac{\sqrt{35}}{1} \approx 5.9161$ **b.** $\sin A = \frac{1}{6} \approx 0.1667$; $\cos A = \frac{\sqrt{35}}{6} \approx 0.9860$;
$\tan A = \frac{1}{\sqrt{35}} \approx 0.1690$ **41. a.** $\sin A = \frac{3}{5}$; $\cos A = \frac{4}{5}$; $\tan A = \frac{3}{4}$ **b.** $\sin A = \frac{1}{\sqrt{5}} \approx 0.4472$; $\cos A = \frac{2}{\sqrt{5}} \approx 0.8944$; $\tan A = \frac{1}{2} = 0.5000$
43. a. yes   **b.** no   **45.** 45 ft   **47.** 24 ft   **49.** 19 ft   **51.** 10 ft   **53.** 70 ft   **55.** F   **57.** T   **59.** F

Chapter 5 Review Questions, p. 259

Verify constructions by looking at the given parts.   **5. a.** pentagon   **b.** quadrilateral   **c.** triangle   **d.** hexagon   **7.** Two angles of one must
be equal to two angles of the other.   **11. a.** $\angle C$ **b.** $\overline{CD}$ **c.** $\overline{BD}$ **d.** $\angle BDA$ **13.** 45°, 50°, 85°   **15.** yes; similar   **17. a.** 6.0   **b.** 4.8
19. a. 64.3   **b.** 65.0   **21. a.** 4.3315   **b.** 0.1219   **c.** 0.2079   **d.** 0.9336   **23.** The pit is 45 ft long.   **25.** The distance across the river
is 45 ft.

CHAPTER 6

6.1 Precision, Accuracy, and Estimation, p. 271

3. inch (basic unit); foot (12 in.), yard (3 ft or 36 in.), and mile (63,360 in. or 5,280 ft or 1,760 yd)   **5.** kilo-, hecto-, and deka-
7. in.   **9.** yd   **11.** km   **13.** A   **15.** B   **17.** C   **19.** C   **21.** A   **23.** C   **25.** A   **27.** A   **33.** ——————
35. ——   **37.** ————   **39.** ————
41. ————————————   **43.** ————————
45. 2.5 cm   **47.** 1 in.   **49.** 3.4 cm   **51.** $1\frac{3}{8}$ in.   **53.** 4.3 cm   **55.** $1\frac{3}{4}$ in.   **59.** 90 Khets/hour

6.2 Perimeter, p. 277

5. A   **7.** C   **9.** B   **11.** B   **13.** C   **15.** 22 cm   **17.** 30 ft   **19.** 24 cm   **21.** 960 ft   **23.** 9 dm   **25.** 15 in.   **27.** 31.42 in.   **29.** 15.08 m
31. 75.40 in.   **33.** 52 in.   **35.** 397.1 ft   **37.** 41.1 ft   **39.** 64.3 ft   **41.** The sides are 40 cm, 60 cm, 60 cm, 40 cm, and 80 cm.
43. 300 m   **45.** 25 ft   **47.** 40 cm   **49.** 8 cm by 19 cm   **51.** 20.0 cm   **53. a.** 16 cm   **b.** same   **55.** F   **57.** F   **59.** T

6.3 Area, p. 288

5. C   **7.** A   **9.** C   **11.** A   **13.** C   **15.** C   **17.** 3 cm^2 **19.** 3 cm^2 **21.** 12 cm^2 **23.** 10 cm^2 **25.** 15 in.^{2} **27.** 36 mi^2 **29.** 250 in.^{2}
31. 136.5 dm^2 **33.** 5,550 cm^2 **35.** 28 in.^{2} **37.** 314.2 in.^{2} **39.** 307.9 in.^{2} **41.** 7.6 cm^2 **43.** 216 in.^{2} **45.** $93\frac{1}{2}$ in.^{2} **46.** $3,593.75
49. 18 yd^2 required; $810   **51.** 22.2 acres   **53. a.** 286 ft^2 **b.** 132 ft^2 **c.** 136.5 ft^2 **d.** about 30 ft $\times$ 30 ft = 900 ft^2 (actual, 977.5 ft^2)
55. F   **57.** F   **59.** T

6.4 Volume and Capacity, p. 297

3. 60 cm^3 **5.** 125 ft^3 **7.** 8,000 cm^3 **9.** 24 ft^3 **11.** 400 mm^3 **13.** 2 c   **15.** 11 oz   **17.** 13 oz   **19.** $1\frac{3}{4}$ c   **21.** 25 mL   **23.** A
25. C   **27.** A   **29.** C   **31.** A   **33.** C   **35.** A   **37.** 15.6 L   **39.** 24 L   **41.** 1 L   **43.** 3.7 gal   **45.** 26.375 ft^3 **47.** 2.5 yd^3
49. 15,080 gal   **51.** 100 yd^3 **53.** 15 yd^3 **55.** T   **57.** T   **59.** F

6.5 Miscellaneous Measurements, p. 304

3. $V = s^3$ **5.** $V = \frac{4}{3}\pi r^3$ **7.** $V = \frac{1}{3}Bh$ **9.** kilometer   **11.** centimeter   **13.** milliliter   **15.** liter   **17.** gram   **19.** Celsius
21. 0°C; 32°F   **23.** 37°C; 98.6°F   **25.** 177°C; 350°F   **27.** 40°C; 104°F   **29.** 51 cm^3 **31.** 14,137 cm^3 **33.** 19 cm^3 **35.** 30 in.^{3}
37. 64 cm^3 **39.** 38 in.^{3} **41.** A   **43.** B   **45.** C   **47.** B   **49.** C   **51.** C   **53.** A   **55.** A   **57.** D   **59.** A

6.6 Converting Units, p. 314

5. a. $\frac{1}{12}$ **b.** $\frac{1}{36}$ **c.** $\frac{1}{63,360}$ **7. a.** 12   **b.** $\frac{1}{3}$ **c.** $\frac{1}{5,280}$ **9. a.** 36   **b.** 3   **c.** $\frac{1}{1,760}$ **11. a.** $\frac{1}{3}$ **b.** $\frac{1}{6}$ **c.** $\frac{1}{48}$ **13. a.** $\frac{1}{8}$ **b.** $\frac{1}{16}$ **c.** $\frac{1}{2}$
15. a. $\frac{1}{2}$ **b.** $\frac{1}{8}$ **c.** $\frac{1}{4}$ **17. a.** $\frac{1}{16}$ **b.** $\frac{1}{32,000}$ **c.** $\frac{1}{2,000}$ **19.** $\frac{9}{1,760}$ mi; 27 ft; 324 in.   **21.** 7,040 yd; 21,120 ft; 253,440 in.   **23.** 0.009 km;
0.09 hm; 0.9 dkm; 90 dm; 900 cm; 9,000 mm   **25.** 40 hm; 400 dkm; 4,000 m; 40,000 dm; 400,000 cm; 4,000,000 mm
27. $1\frac{31}{32}$ qt; $3\frac{15}{16}$ pt; $7\frac{7}{8}$ c   **29.** 2 qt; 4 pt; 64 oz   **31.** 0.000063 kL; 0.00063 hL; 0.0063 dkL; 0.063 L; 0.63 dL; 6.3 cL   **33.** 0.08 kL;
0.8 hL; 80 L; 800 dL; 8,000 cL; 80,000 mL   **35.** $\frac{1}{500}$ T; 64 oz   **37.** $\frac{21}{8,000}$ T; 84 oz   **39.** 65 hg; 650 dkg; 6,500 g; 65,000 dg; 650,000 cg;
6,500,000 mg   **41.** 52.5 hg; 525 dkg; 5,250 g; 52,500 dg; 525,000 cg; 5,250,000 mg   **43.** 16 gal   **45.** 68 L   **47.** 183 cm
49. 311 mi   **51.** 39 in.   **53.** 6.2 mi   **55.** 5 portions   **57.** 64°F   **59.** 1 tsp

Chapter 6 Review Questions, p. 323

1. a. ——————————————   **b.** ————————————   **c.** ———
d. ——————————————————————————   **3. a.** inch and centimeter   **b.** ounce and gram
c. ounce and milliliter   **d.** degree Fahrenheit and degree Celsius   **5.** Answers vary.   **d.** 37°C; 98.6°F   **7. a.** 3,000 mi or 5,000 km
b. 12 oz or 355 mL   **c.** $\frac{1}{10}$ oz or 3 g   **d.** Answers vary; 70°F or 20°C   **9. a.** dkg, cg, mg   **b.** kL, cL, mL   **c.** qt, c, tsp   **d.** hm, m, mm
11. a. $P = 28$ m; $A = 32$ m^2 **b.** $P = 30$ ft; $A = 30$ ft^2 **13. a.** $P = 16$ cm; $A = 7$ cm^2 **b.** $P = 43.14$ in.; $A = 121.81$ in.^{2}
15. a. 896 dm^3; 896 L   **b.** 20 dm^3; 20 L   **17. a.** 34 m^3 **b.** 42 cm^3 **19.** 21 yd^2 **21.** 224 gal   **23.** $6\frac{1}{2}$ yd^3
25.

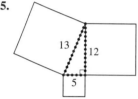

CHAPTER 7

7.1 Discount, Sale Price, and Sales Tax, p. 338

5. a. $22.50   **b.** $13.00   **7. a.** $5.00   **b.** $22.75   **9. a.** 0.9   **b.** 0.8   **c.** 0.7   **d.** 0.6   **e.** 0.5   **11. a.** $\frac{2}{3}$ **b.** $\frac{1}{3}$ **c.** $\frac{1}{4}$ **d.** $\frac{2}{5}$ **e.** $\frac{5}{6}$ **15.** C
17. B   **19.** A   **21.** $13.80   **23.** $5.53   **25.** $917.50   *Answers to Problems 27–32 vary by state.*   **33.** $13.25   **35.** $4,473.70
37. $26.50   **39.** $218.50   **41.** $74.10   **43.** $22.50   **45.** $622.50   **47.** 3.9%   **49.** $525.00   **51.** $247.50   **53.** $213.64   **55.** F
57. F   **59.** F

7.2 Simple Interest, p. 346

5. B   **7.** C   **9.** C   **11.** B   **13.** C   **15.** $80; $1,080   **17.** $288; $1,088   **19.** $42.50; $542.50   **21.** $200; $600   **23.** $3,000; $3,360
25. 2 yr; $2,850   **27.** 12%; $1,288   **29.** $200; $380   **31.** 4 yr; $2,460   **33.** 10%; $570   **35.** $4,000; $5,800   **37.** $9,000; $12,240
39. $25.63; $538.13   **41.** $5,191   **43.** 17%   **45.** 6 years   **47.** $902.31   **49.** $200,000   **51.** 28%   **53.** $400,000   **55.** F   **57.** F
59. F

7.3 Buying on Credit, p. 354

3. B   **5.** C   **7.** A   **9.** A   **11.** $15,747   **13.** $34,631   **15.** $29,108   **17.** $1,296 interest; $136 per month   **19.** $330 interest; $76.25
per month   **21.** $4,050 interest; $142.50 per month   **23.** $143 interest; $33.04 per month   **25.** $997.50 interest; $260.31   **27.** 23%
29. 21%   **31.** 35%   **33.** 21%   **35.** 18%   **37.** $11,430   **39.** $19,608.56   **41.** 9.0% (0.09)   **43.** 6.0% (0.06000303951)   *The answers
for Problems 45–48 recalculate the interest rate and do not use the rounded rates stated in Problems 41–44.*   **45.** 17.5% (0.1751351351)
47. 11.8% (0.1175569754)   **49.** 8% add-on rate; APR is about 15.7%   **51.** Sears' add-on rate is 29.2% APR; bank rate is better.
55. F   **57.** F   **59.** T

7.4 Credit Card Interest, p. 360

1. $I = Prt$ **3.** Use $I = Prt$, where P is the previous balance, r is annual interest rate, and $t = \frac{1}{12}$.   **5.** Use $I = Prt$, where P is the
average daily balance, r is annual interest rate, and t is the time, in years.   **7.** A   **9.** A   **11.** B   **13.** B   **15.** C   **17.** A   **19.** B
21. 15%   **23.** 18%   **25.** 8%   **31.** $4.50   **33.** $3.95   **35.** $0.75   **37.** $8.33   **39.** $7.67   **41.** $1.67   **43.** $52.50   **45.** $50.05
47. $26.25   **49.** $32.50; $2.50   **51.** Will save $0.45   **53.** F   **55.** F   **57.** F   **59.** F

7.5 Compound Interest, p. 370

1. a. $n = 4$ **b.** $n = 2$ **c.** $n = 12$ **d.** $n = 360$ **3. a.** $A = P(1 + i)^N$ **b.** $P = \frac{A}{(1 + i)^N}$ **5.** $1,400; $1,469.33; $69.33 more
7. $2,720; $2,809.86; $89.86 more **9.** $17,000; $48,231.47; $31,231.47 more **11.** $n = 1$; $i = 9\%$; $N = 5$; $A = \$1,538.62$
13. $n = 1$; $i = 8\%$; $N = 3$; $A = \$629.86$ **15.** $n = 4$; $i = 2\%$; $N = 12$; $A = \$634.12$ **17.** $n = 4$; $i = 4.5\%$; $N = 40$; $A = \$29,081.82$
19. $n = 4$; $i = 5\%$; $N = 40$; $A = \$35,199.94$ **21.** $n = 12$; $i = 2\%$; $N = 60$; $A = \$13,124.12$ **23.** $n = 4$; $i = 3\%$; $N = 2$; $A = \$954.81$
25. $n = 4$; $i = 4\%$; $N = 5$; $A = \$1,520.82$ **27.** $903.46 **29.** $1,028.25 **31.** $755.59 **33.** $16,536.79 **35.** $50.73 **37.** $572,177.99
39. $3,019,988.94 **41. a.** $2.20 **b.** $1.66 **c.** $2.15 **d.** $3.59 **43. a.** $139.76 **b.** $201.88 **c.** $1,149.16 **d.** $1,863.51
45. $1,220.19 **47.** $729,764.44 **49.** $2,108.21 **51.** $15,415.93 **53.** Deposit the money to pay off the loan. **55.** F **57.** F **59.** T

7.6 Buying a Home, p. 378

1. interest rate, origination fee, and points **3.** length of loan, down payment, and APR **5.** Use the monthly payment formula and
Table II. **7.** B **9.** A **11.** B **13. a.** $7,425; $141,075 **b.** $33,980; $135,920 **15. a.** $25,025; $225,225 **b.** $190,000; $760,000
17. a. $1,596 **b.** $425 **19.** 11.86% **21.** 9.43% **23.** $291.00 **25.** $441.77 **27.** $791.84 **29.** $132.08; $47,549 **31.** $44.02;
$15,848 **33.** $306 **35.** $814 **37.** $346 **39.** $165,321.89 **41.** $128,337.87 **43.** $22,500 **45.** $36,200 **47.** $43,000
49. a. $75,000 **b.** $300,000 **c.** $1,995.00 **d.** $418,200 **e.** $5,541.67 **51. a.** $90,000 **b.** $360,000 **c.** $2,160.00
d. $417,600 **e.** $6,000 **53.** (1) $1,155; (2) $1,040; the maximum house payment is $1,040. **55.** F **57.** F **59.** F

Chapter 7 Review Questions, p. 390

1. a. $6.75 **b.** $9.00 **c.** $17.99 **d.** $44.55 **3. a.** 18% **b.** 15% **c.** 21% **d.** 9% **5. a.** $4,750 **b.** $5,719.39 **c.** $6,108.05
d. $5,918.41 **7. a.** $2,565 **b.** $5,500 **c.** 23% **d.** 4 years **9. a.** 11.02% **b.** 7.16% **c.** 13.71% **d.** 8.51% **11. a.** 40%
b. $250 **13.** $12,844.33 **15.** $1,269 interest; $100.53 monthly payment; 35.0% APR **17.** 15.7% **19.** $1,216.80
21. $33,830.10 **23.** $2,627.34 **25.** It costs $69.14 more to drive the hybrid.

CHAPTER 8

8.1 Introduction to Sets, p. 401

11. well defined **13.** not well defined **15.** well defined **17.** not well defined **19.** $\{m, a, t, h, e, i, c, s\}$ **21.** $\{6, 8, 10, 12, 14\}$
23. $\{3, 6, 9, \ldots\}$ **25.** $\{151, 152, 153, \ldots\}$ **27.** {counting numbers less than 10} **29.** {odd numbers between 100 and 170}
31. {multiples of 10 between 0 and 105} **33.** {distinct letters in the word *bookkeeping*} **35.** The set of all x such that x is an
odd counting number; $\{1, 3, 5, 7, \ldots\}$ **37.** The set of all x such that x is a natural number greater than 10; $\{11, 12, 13, 14, \ldots\}$
39. The set of all x such that x is a natural number not equal to 8; $\{1, 2, 3, 4, 5, 6, 7, 9, 10, 11, \ldots\}$ **41.** The set of all
x such that x is a whole number less than 8; $\{0, 1, 2, 3, 4, 5, 6, 7\}$ **43. a.** $|A| = 3$; $|B| = 1$; $|C| = 3$; $|D| = 1$; $|E| = 1$; $|F| = 1$
b. $A \leftrightarrow C$; $B \leftrightarrow D \leftrightarrow E \leftrightarrow F$ **c.** $A = C$; $D = E = F$ **45.** $\{\frac{1}{2}, \frac{1}{3}, \frac{2}{3}, \frac{1}{4}, \frac{3}{4}, \frac{1}{5}, \frac{2}{5}, \frac{3}{5}, \frac{4}{5}, \frac{1}{6}, \frac{5}{6}, \frac{1}{7}, \ldots\}$
47. Answers vary. $\{1, 2, 3\}, \{1, 2, 3\}, \ldots$

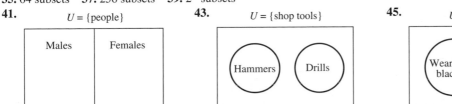

49. $\{1, \quad 2, \quad 3, \ldots, \quad n, \ldots, \quad 353, \quad 354, \ldots, \quad 586, \quad 587\}$
    550 551 552 $n + 549$ 902 903   ?   ?
Not 1-to-1, so they do not have the same cardinality

51. a. finite **b.** finite **53. a.** finite **b.** finite **57.** F **59.** F

8.2 Set Relationships, p. 405

7. $\varnothing$; improper subset is $\{5\}$ **9.** $\varnothing$, $\{m\}$, $\{y\}$; improper subset is $\{m, y\}$ **11.** $\varnothing$, $\{x\}$, $\{y\}$; improper subset is $\{x, y\}$ **13.** $\varnothing$, $\{3\}$,
$\{8\}$; improper subset is $\{3, 8\}$ **15.** $\varnothing$, $\{y\}$, $\{o\}$, $\{u\}$, $\{y, o\}$, $\{y, u\}$, $\{o, u\}$; improper subset is $\{y, o, u\}$ **17.** $\varnothing$, $\{b\}$, $\{i\}$, $\{g\}$, $\{b, i\}$,
$\{b, g\}$, $\{i, g\}$; improper subset is $\{b, i, g\}$ **19.** $\varnothing$, $\{2\}$, $\{4\}$, $\{6\}$, $\{2, 4\}$, $\{2, 6\}$, $\{4, 6\}$; improper subset is $\{2, 4, 6\}$ **21.** $\varnothing$, $\{m\}$,
$\{a\}$, $\{t\}$, $\{h\}$, $\{m, a\}$, $\{m, t\}$, $\{m, h\}$, $\{a, t\}$, $\{a, h\}$, $\{t, h\}$, $\{m, a, t\}$, $\{m, a, h\}$, $\{m, t, h\}$, $\{a, t, h\}$; improper subset is $\{m, a, t, h\}$
23. $\varnothing$ **25.** $\varnothing$, $\{1\}$, $\{2\}$, $\{1, 2\}$ **27.** $\varnothing$, $\{1\}$, $\{2\}$, $\{3\}$, $\{4\}$, $\{1, 2\}$, $\{1, 3\}$, $\{1, 4\}$, $\{2, 3\}$, $\{2, 4\}$, $\{3, 4\}$, $\{1, 2, 3\}$, $\{1, 2, 4\}$,
$\{1, 3, 4\}$, $\{2, 3, 4\}$, $\{1, 2, 3, 4\}$ **29.** $\varnothing$, $\{6\}$ **31.** $\varnothing$, $\{6\}$, $\{7\}$, $\{8\}$, $\{6, 7\}$, $\{6, 8\}$, $\{7, 8\}$, $\{6, 7, 8\}$ **33.** 32 subsets; yes
35. 64 subsets **37.** 256 subsets **39.** 2^m subsets
41.

$U = \{\text{people}\}$

Males	Females

43.

$U = \{\text{shop tools}\}$

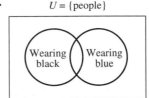

Hammers   Drills

45.

$U = \{\text{people}\}$

Wearing black   Wearing blue

47.

$U = \{\text{animals}\}$

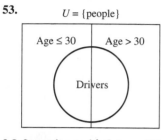

49.

$U = \{\text{vehicles}\}$

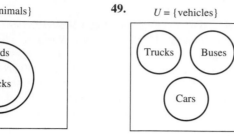

51.

$U = \{\text{athletes}\}$

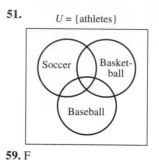

53.

$U = \{\text{people}\}$

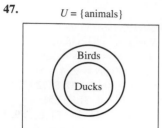

55.

$U = \{\text{quadrilaterals}\}$

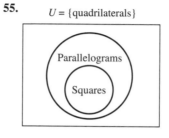

59. F

8.3 Operations with Sets, p. 410

5. a. intersection **b.** or **7.** complement **9.** See Figure 8.6. **11.** {2, 6, 8, 10} **13.** {3, 4, 5} **15.** {2, 3, 5, 6, 8, 9} **17.** {1, 3, 4, 5, 6, 7, 10} **19.** {1, 2, 3, 4, 5, 6, 7, 9, 10} **21.** {1, 2, 3, 4, 5, 6} **23.** {1, 2, 3, 5, 6, 7} **25.** {3} **27.** {5, 6, 7} **29.** {1, 2, 4, 6}

31. 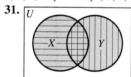 **33.** 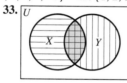 **35.** 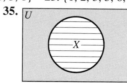 **37.** B **39.** U

41. {T, H, E, B, R, A, S, M, O, N, K, Y} ∩ {S, E, H, A, R, P, K, N, O, V, I, L}

43. 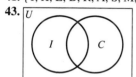 **45.** 42% **47.** 58% **49.** 30% **51.** 16% **53.** jogging **55.** biking; jogging **57.** F **59.** F

8.4 Venn Diagrams, p. 417

1. 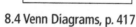 **3.** 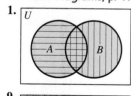 **5.** $A \cup B$ **7.** 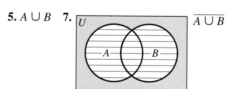 $\overline{A \cup B}$

9. 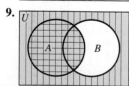 **11.** 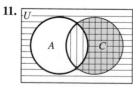 **13.**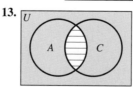

15. 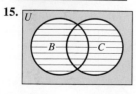 **17.** 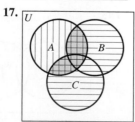 **19.**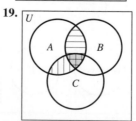

21. 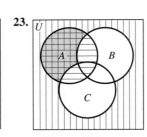 **23.** 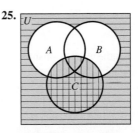 **25.**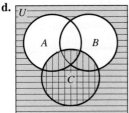

27. {2, 4, 5, 6, 8, 9, 10} **29.** {2, 4, 5, 6, 8, 9} **31.** {5, 9, 10} **33.** $\overline{A}$ or {1, 3, 5, 7, 9, 10} **35.** U or {1, 2, 3, 4, 5, 6, 7, 8, 9, 10}
37. {1, 3, 7} **39.** {1, 3, 7, 10} **41.** T **43.** F **45.** T **47.** T **49.** Males: 12,180; females: 16,820; over age 25: 17,980
51. Yes; 72 persons can travel in 2 buses. **55.** F **57.** T **59.** F

8.5 Survey Problems Using Sets, p. 423

1. 2 **3.** 8 **5.** I: 7; II: 4; III: 2; IV: 12 **7.** I: 10; II: 18; III: 24; IV: 22 **9.** I: 750; II: 50; III: 50; IV: 150
11. I: 4; II: 3; III: 8; IV: 2; V: 3; VI: 1; VII: 1; VIII: 3 **13.** I: 43; II: 12; III: 28; IV: 0; V: 0; VI: 6; VII: 2; VIII: 9
15. I: 90; II: 170; III: 5; IV: 40; V: 0; VI: 0; VII: 20; VIII: 75

17.

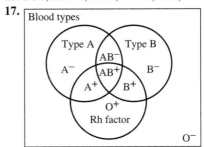

19. a. 50 **b.** 15 **21.** There are 34 people playing.
23. A = {women who use shampoo A}; B = {women who use shampoo B};
C = {women who use shampoo C} **25.** 8 **27.** 2 **29.** 25 **31.** 0 **33.** 4 **35.** 2
37. 30 **39.** 13 **41.** VP = {presidents who previously served as vice-president};
S = {presidents who previously served in the Senate}; C = {presidents who previously
held a cabinet post} **43.** 5 **45.** 1 **47.** 6 **49.** 17 **51.** 3 **53.** 1 **55.** 2 **57.** 12
59. F

8.6 Inductive and Deductive Reasoning, p. 431

3. A *premise* is accepted without proof, and a *theorem* is proved. **5.** 8, 7, 6, 5, 4, 3, 2, 1, 9, 8, 7, 6, 5, 4, 3, . . . ; inductive reasoning
7. 200; inductive reasoning **9.** $25^2 = 625$; inductive reasoning **11.** inductive reasoning **a.** 121 **b.** 12,321 **c.** 1,234,321
d. Count up to the number of ones squared, and then count down. **13.** T **15.** F; $3 + 5 = 8$ **17.** T **19.** F; 3 by 4 rectangle has
$A = 12$ and $P = 14$ **21.** F; $S \subseteq S$, but the cardinality is not less. **23.** valid **25.** valid **27.** valid **29.** not valid **31.** not valid
33. not valid **35.** valid **37.** deductive reasoning **39.** car; deductive reasoning **41.** Answers vary; deductive reasoning
43. brother; deductive reasoning **45.** Answers vary; probably Wednesday; inductive reasoning. **47.** One is a nickel and one is a
quarter. **49.** Neither; they are the same. **51.** yes **53.** white **55.** They are triplets.

Chapter 8 Review Questions, p. 442

3. F; examples vary: 0.121121112 . . . **5. a.** not well defined **b.** well defined **c.** well defined **d.** not well defined **7. a.** {even
numbers between 9 and 20} **b.** {odd numbers between 2,000 and 3,000} **c.** {counting or natural numbers} **d.** {perfect squares
less than 150} **9. a.** infinite **b.** finite **c.** finite **d.** finite **11. a.** {1, 2, 3, 4, 5, 7, 9, 10} **b.** {3, 6, 9, 10, 11, . . . , 25, 27, 30}
c. {1, 2, 3, . . . , 10, 12, 15, 18, 21, 24, 27, 30} **d.** U or $\mathbb{N}$ **13. a.** {2, 4, 6, 8, 10, 11, 12, . . .} **b.** {$x \mid x$ is an odd counting number}
c. {11, 12, 13, 14, . . .} **d.** U

15. a. 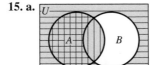 **b.** 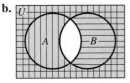 **c.** 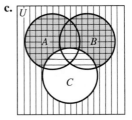 **d.**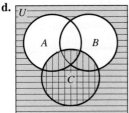

17. valid **19.** See Example 3 in Section 8.4. **21.** 10,001 **23.** not valid **25.** valid

CHAPTER 9

9.1 Introduction to Probability, p. 455

1. Set of all possible outcomes   **3.** $P(E) = \frac{s}{n}$; s is the number of successes out of n mutually exclusive and equally likely possibilities.   **5.** The operation of intersection is translated by the word *and*.   **7. a.** $\frac{1}{4}$ **b.** $\frac{1}{4}$ **c.** $\frac{1}{2}$ **9. a.** $\frac{5}{18}$ **b.** $\frac{2}{9}$ **11. a.** $\frac{1}{12}$ **b.** $\frac{7}{12}$ **c.** $\frac{1}{12}$ **13. a.** $\frac{1}{4}$ **b.** $\frac{3}{4}$ **15.** yes   **17. a.** $\frac{1}{52}$ **b.** $\frac{1}{13}$ **19. a.** $\frac{1}{4}$ **b.** $\frac{5}{13}$ **21. a.** $\frac{1}{9}$ **b.** $\frac{5}{36}$ **23. a.** $\frac{1}{9}$ **b.** $\frac{1}{36}$ **25. a.** $\frac{2}{9}$ **b.** $\frac{1}{2}$ **27. a.** 0.03   **b.** 0.06   **c.** 0.08   **d.** 0.11   **e.** 0.14   **f.** 0.17   **g.** 0.14   **h.** 0.11   **i.** 0.08   **j.** 0.06   **k.** 0.03   **29. a.** $\frac{1}{16}$ **b.** $\frac{1}{8}$ **31. a.** $\frac{3}{16}$ **b.** $\frac{1}{8}$ **33.** about 0.05   **35.** 0.19   **37. a.** 0.0002400960384   **b.** 0.00144057623   **39. a.** 0.02112845138   **b.** 0.04753901561   **41.** $\frac{1}{9}$

43.

	1	2	3	4	5	6	7	8
1	(1, 1) or 2	(1, 2) or 3	(1, 3) or 4	(1, 4) or 5	(1, 5) or 6	(1, 6) or 7	(1, 7) or 8	(1, 8) or 9
2	(2, 1) or 3	(2, 2) or 4	(2, 3) or 5	(2, 4) or 6	(2, 5) or 7	(2, 6) or 8	(2, 7) or 9	(2, 8) or 10
3	(3, 1) or 4	(3, 2) or 5	(3, 3) or 6	(3, 4) or 7	(3, 5) or 8	(3, 6) or 9	(3, 7) or 10	(3, 8) or 11
4	(4, 1) or 5	(4, 2) or 6	(4, 3) or 7	(4, 4) or 8	(4, 5) or 9	(4, 6) or 10	(4, 7) or 11	(4, 8) or 12
5	(5, 1) or 6	(5, 2) or 7	(5, 3) or 8	(5, 4) or 9	(5, 5) or 10	(5, 6) or 11	(5, 7) or 12	(5, 8) or 13
6	(6, 1) or 7	(6, 2) or 8	(6, 3) or 9	(6, 4) or 10	(6, 5) or 11	(6, 6) or 12	(6, 7) or 13	(6, 8) or 14
7	(7, 1) or 8	(7, 2) or 9	(7, 3) or 10	(7, 4) or 11	(7, 5) or 12	(7, 6) or 13	(7, 7) or 14	(7, 8) or 15
8	(8, 1) or 9	(8, 2) or 10	(8, 3) or 11	(8, 4) or 12	(8, 5) or 13	(8, 6) or 14	(8, 7) or 15	(8, 8) or 16

45. Pick either   **47.** Pick D **49.** Pick F **51.** The property called *Chance*.   **53.** T   **55.** F   **57.** F   **59.** F

9.2 Probability Models, p. 463

1. probabilities whose sum is 1   **3.** B   **5.** B   **7.** They are the same.   **9.** 0.4   **11.** $\frac{4}{13}$ **13.** 0.98   **15.** tails; $\frac{1}{2}$ **17.** incorrect guess; $\frac{4}{5}$ **19.** White Sox lose; 0.43   **21.** $\frac{7}{8}$ **23.** $\frac{15}{16}$ **25.** $\frac{11}{12}$ **27.** $\frac{7}{12}$ **29.** $\frac{4}{5}$ **31.** 15   **33.** 135   **35.** 17,331,000   **37.** 194,754,273,881   **39.** 306   **41.** 2^{20} **43.** 810,000,000   **45.** $\frac{1}{4}$ **47.** $\frac{1}{128}$ **49.** The betting limit imposed on the game   **51.** $\frac{1}{2}$ **53.** 52%   **55.** F   **57.** F   **59.** F

9.3 Odds and Conditional Probability, p. 471

3. $P(E)/P(\overline{E})$ **5.** 1 to 1   **7.** 3 to 1   **9.** 3 to 7   **11.** 1 to 24   **13.** $\frac{1}{101}$ **15.** $\frac{1}{6}$ **17.** $\frac{3}{5}$ **19.** $\frac{1}{10}$ **21.** 0.17   **23.** 0.24   **25.** 0.41   **27.** $\dfrac{P(\overline{E})}{P(E)} = \dfrac{\frac{f}{n}}{\frac{s}{n}} = \dfrac{f}{n} \cdot \dfrac{n}{s} = \dfrac{f}{s}$ = odds against   **29.** 1 to 3   **31.** 7 to 1   **33.** $\frac{33}{34}$ **35. a.** 0.31   **b.** 0.68   **c.** 0.39   **d.** 0.70   **37.** $\frac{4}{11}$ **39. a.** BBBB; BBBG; BBGB; BBGG; BGBB; BGBG; BGGB; BGGG; GBBB; GBBG; GBGB; GBGG; GGBB; GGBG; GGGB; GGGG   **b.** $\frac{1}{16}; \frac{1}{16}$ **c.** $\frac{4}{4}; \frac{1}{4}$ **d.** $\frac{3}{8}$ **e.** 1   **41.** $\frac{1}{3}$ **43.** $\frac{1}{10}$ **45.** $\frac{1}{13}$ **47.** $\frac{1}{17}$ **49.** $\frac{13}{51}$ **51.** $\frac{25}{51}$ **53.** 2 to 7   **57.** F   **59.** F

9.4 Mathematical Expectation, p. 479

1. See page 475.   **3.** F   **5.** T   **7.** A   **9.** C   **11.** C   **13.** $12.14   **15.** $317.47   **17.** $43.38   **19.** −$0.05   **21.** −$0.05   **23.** −$0.05   **25.** −$0.08   **27.** −$0.05   **29.** $0.83   **31.** A fair price would be to pay $0.25 for two plays of the game.   **33.** $1.50   **35.** $7.20   **37.** yes   **39.** $0   **41.** −$8,125; no   **43.** fair   **45.** not fair   **47.** $4   **49.** $0.20   **51.** $0.05   **53.** no   **55.** F   **57.** F   **59.** F

Chapter 9 Review Questions, p. 487

3. $\frac{1}{5}$ **5. a.** $\frac{5}{36}$ **b.** $\frac{1}{6}$ **7. a.** $\frac{1}{13}$ **b.** $\frac{1}{4}$ **c.** $\frac{4}{13}$ **9. a.** $\frac{1}{4}$ **b.** $\frac{1}{9}$ **c.** $\frac{1}{36}$ **11.** 0.91   **13.** $\frac{15}{16}$ **15.** $\frac{20}{21}$ **17.** 50%; 1 to 1   **19.** $\frac{3}{5}$ **21.** $\frac{1}{3}$ **23.** $96.60

CHAPTER 10

10.1 Frequency Distributions and Graphs, p. 503

7.

Wages	Tally	Frequency
14	I	1
16	I	1
18	II	2
20	I	1
25	III	3
30	II	2
35	I	1
50	I	1
60	I	1

9.

Height	Tally	Frequency
63	II	2
64	IIII	4
65	III	3
66	III	3
67	IIII I	5
68	III	3
69	IIII	4
70	III	3
71	II	2
72	I	1

11.

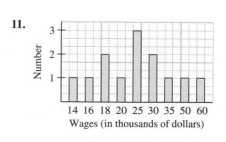

Wages (in thousands of dollars)

13.
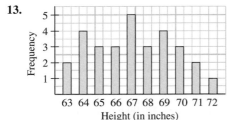

15.
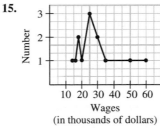

17.
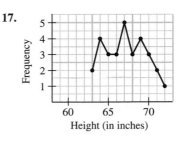

19.

Wages	Tally	Frequency
$0–$20,000	IIII I	5
$20,001–$30,000	IIII I	5
$30,001–$40,000	I	1
$40,001–$50,000	I	1
Over $50,000	I	1

21. October **23.** August **25. a.** 30% **b.** 33% **27.** July 2006 and Sept. 2006 **29.** received care from a nonrelative (7%) **31.** child cared for self (26%) **33.** 25 times **35.** maybe illegal **37.** no **39.** 121 kwh **41.** 209 kwh **43.** appliance, 5.6%; automotive, 2.8%; clothing, 15.3%; grocery, 72.2%; nursery, 4.2%

45.
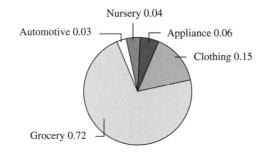

47.
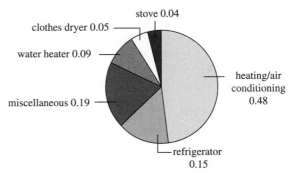

49.
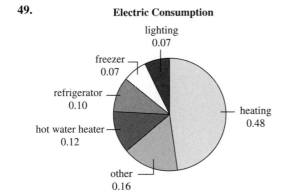

51.
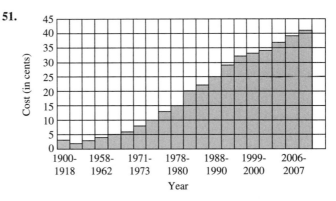

53.
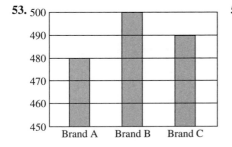

57. Graph is meaningless without a scale. **59.** F

10.2 Measures of Central Tendency, p. 511

5. mean = 3; median = 3; no mode **7.** mean = 767; median = 767; no mode **9.** mean = 6; median = 7; mode = 7
11. mean = 10; median = 8; no mode **13.** mean = 91; median = 95; mode = 95 **15.** mean = 3; median = 3; mode = 3
19. $28,000 **21.** median **23.** 11 **25.** mean **27.** 70 **29.** mean **31.** 70 **33.** mean **35.** 65 **37.** mean **39.** $47,000
41. median **43.** $1,600.00 **45.** median **47.** $432.51 **49.** median **51.** 1,946,419 **53.** mean **55.** F **57.** F **59.** F

10.3 Measures of Position, p. 516

5. 90th percentile **7.** 94th percentile **9.** 91st percentile **11.** 87th percentile **13.** 88th percentile **15.** 99th percentile **17.** 2
19. 40 **21.** 8 **23.** 2 **25.** 8 **27.** 10 **29.** 90th percentile **31.** 63 **33.** 75 **35.** 66 **37.** 63 **39.** 3rd **41.** 5th decile
43. 1st quartile **45.** between the 4th and 5th deciles **47.** 4th percentile **49.** 27 **51.** 23 **53.** 84th percentile **55.** The Poodle is 6th.
57. 78th percentile **59.** 3rd quartile

10.4 Measures of Dispersion, p. 522

7. range = 4; mean = 19 **9.** range = 4; mean = 767 **11.** range = 9; mean = 10 **13.** range = 24; mean = 11 **15.** range = 25;
mean = 82 **17.** range = 21; mean = 6 **19.** var = 2; $\sigma \approx 1.41$ **21.** var = 2; $\sigma \approx 1.41$ **23.** var ≈ 8.57; $\sigma \approx 2.93$ **25.** var ≈ 74.8;
$\sigma \approx 8.65$ **27.** var = 66.4; $\sigma \approx 8.15$ **29.** var = 55; $\sigma \approx 7.42$ **35.** var $= 5.8\overline{3}$ **39.** range = 40; mean = 68 **41.** 91.61
43. range = 50; mean = 68 **45.** 136 **47.** range = 90; mean = 56 **49.** 690.67 **51.** range = $20,000; mean = $28,900
53. 32,490,000 **55.** 18 **59.** F

10.5 The Normal Curve and Sampling, p. 530

1. See Figure 10.25. **5.** 49 **7.** 0.841 **9.** 31 **11.** 60 or above **13.** 25 **15.** 22 **17.** 341 **19.** 136 **21.** 1 **23.** 13.6% **25.** 0.841
27. Below 52, 1; 52–67, 22; 68–83, 136; 84–99, 341; 100–115, 341; 116–131, 136; 132–147, 22; above 147, 1
29. 0.50 **31.** Below 0.87, 1; 0.87–0.88, 22; 0.88–0.89, 136; 0.89–0.90, 341; 0.90–0.91, 341; 0.91–0.92, 136; 0.92–0.93, 22; above
0.93, 1 **33.** 0.977 **35.** 40.5 inches **37.** 0.023 **39.** 0.023 **41.** 0.159 **43.** 0.023 **45.** 2.3% **47.** 12.4 oz **49.** 98 lb

Chapter 10 Review Questions, p. 538

1.

No.	Tally	Frequency
6	II	2
7	IIII	4
8	IHII	5
9	III	3
10	I	1

3.

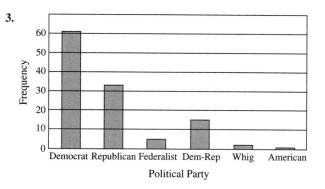

5. a.

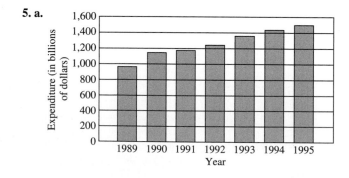

b.

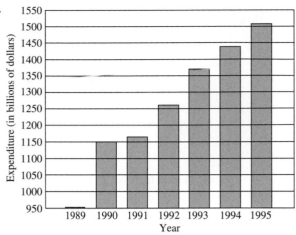

c.

d. Answers vary. **7.** mean = 13.5; median = 14; mode = 16 **9.** mean = 18.9; median = 16; mode = 18 **11.** mode **13.** median **15.** range =10; $\sigma \approx$ 2.82; σ^2 = 7.95 **17.** range = 48; σ =13.3; σ^2 = 176.89 **19.** 230 **21.** smaller standard deviation; less variance **23.** Accept false hypothesis. **25.** Take a sample of representative pages.

CHAPTER 11

11.1 Cartesian Coordinate System, p. 549

1. horizontal **3.**

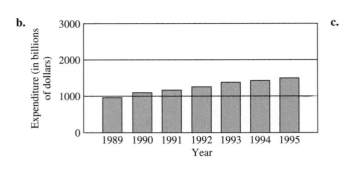

5. Aphrodite **7.** Atalanta Planitia **9.** Theia Mons **11.** Sedna Planitia
13. Terra **15.** Telegraph Hill **17.** Embarcadero **19.** Ferry Building
21. Old Mint Building **23.** Coit Tower **25.** Eva Mikalson
27. Terry Shell **29.** Laurie Pederson **31.** Hannah Becker
33. Beverly Schaap

35.

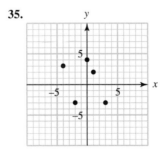

37.

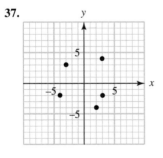

39.

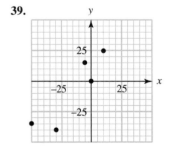

41.

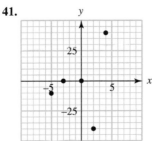

43.

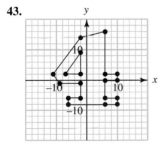

45. (2, 9), (3, 5), (−2, 5), (1, 10), (5, 11), (5, 10), (8, 10), (9, 7), (4, 6), (5, 2), (8, 0), (5, −1), (4, −3), (4.5, −5), (2, −7), (4, −7), (5, −10), (−4, −7), (−3, −6), (−7, −7), (−9, −10), (−10, −6), (−8, −4), (−5, −5), (−5, −1), (1, 5) **47.** They all lie on the same line.
49. a. Infinitely many **b.** 2

51.

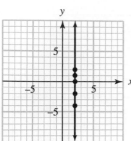

53.

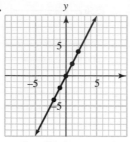

57. F **59.** F

11.2 Functions, p. 554

3. function **5.** function **7.** not a function **9.** function **11.** function **13.** not a function **15.** $f(4) = 18, f(6) = 22,$
$f(-8) = -6, f\left(\frac{1}{2}\right) = 11, f(t) = 2(t + 5)$ **17.** $f(4) = 12, f(6) = 14, f(-8) = 0, f\left(\frac{1}{2}\right) = 8\frac{1}{2}, f(t) = t + 8$ **19.** $M(4) = 17, M(6) = 37,$
$M(-8) = 65, M\left(\frac{1}{2}\right) = 1\frac{1}{4}, M(t) = t^2 + 1$ **21.** $g(4) = 7, g(6) = 11, g(-8) = -17, g\left(\frac{1}{2}\right) = 0, g(t) = 2t - 1$ **23. a.** 8 **b.** -16
25. a. 200 **b.** -50 **27. a.** -1 **b.** -31 **29. a.** 6 **b.** $2m - 8$ **31. a.** 30 **b.** -60 **33. a.** -4 **b.** $8u + 4$ **35. a.** 10
b. $\pi^2 + 1$ **37. a.** 5 **b.** $\frac{\pi}{2}$ **39. a.** 2.46 **b.** 0.6π **41. a.** $-t^2$ **b.** $m^2 - t^2$ **43. a.** 300 **b.** $3\pi^2$ **45. a.** $10m$ **b.** $6u + 4m$
47. a. 64 **b.** 96 **c.** 128 **d.** 256 **e.** 512 **49.** 512 ft/s **51. a.** $(0, 2000)$ **b.** $(6, 860)$ **c.** $(10, 100)$ **53. a.** $\{(a, e), (e, b), (b, c),$
$(c, e), (d, e)\}$ **b.** It is a function. **55.** F **57.** T **59.** F

11.3 Lines, p. 562

3. a. A horizontal line is a line that is parallel to the x-axis. **b.** The graph of the line with equation $x = 5$ is a vertical line. *Ordered
pairs in Problems* 4–15 *may vary.* **5.** $(0, -1), (1, 1), (-1, -3)$ **7.** $(0, -4), (1, -3), (-1, -5)$ **9.** $(0, 1), (1, 2), (-1, 0)$
11. $(0, 1), (1, -2), (-1, 4)$ **13.** $(0, 1), (1, 4), (-1, -2)$ **15.** $(0, 2), (2, 1), (-2, 3)$

17.

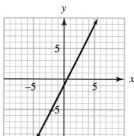

19.

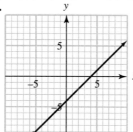

21.

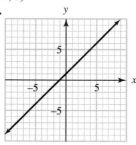

23.

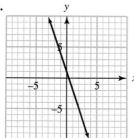

25.

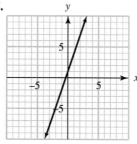

27.

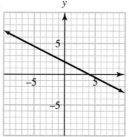

29.

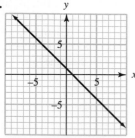

31.

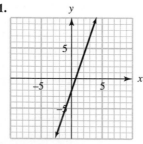

33.

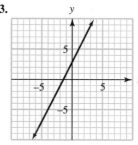

35.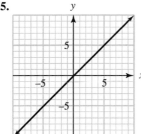

37.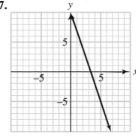

39.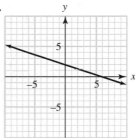

41.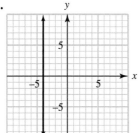

43.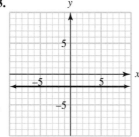

45.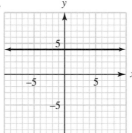

47.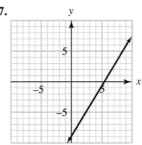

49.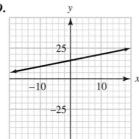

51.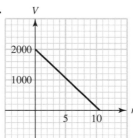

53.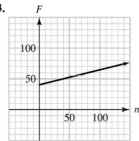

55. F   **57.** F   **59.** F

11.4 Systems and Inequalities, p. 569

1.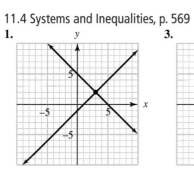

(3, 2)

3.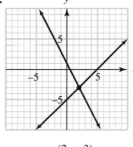

(2, −3)

5.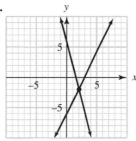

(2, −2)

7.

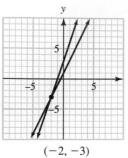

$(-2, -3)$

9.

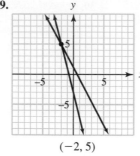

$(-2, 5)$

11.

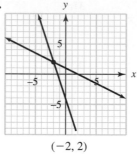

$(-2, 2)$

13.

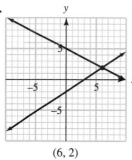

$(6, 2)$

15.

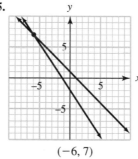

$(-6, 7)$

17.

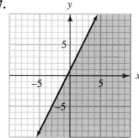

19.

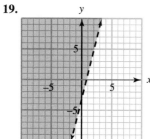

21.

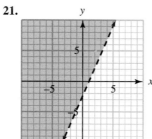

23.

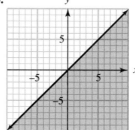

25.

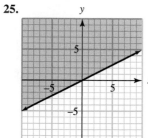

27.

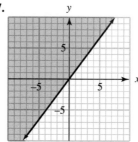

29.

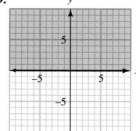

31.

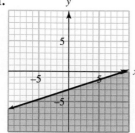

33.

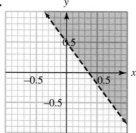

35. Option A: $c = 30 + 0.4m$; Option B: $c = 50$
37. They are the same for 50 miles.

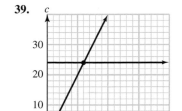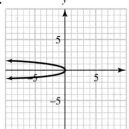

39.

41. $4.00 **43.** $4.00 **45.** $25 **47.** Option A if she drives less than 80 miles
49. T **51.** F **53.** F **55.** T **57.** F **59.** T

11.5 Graphing Curves, p. 576

3.

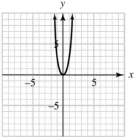

5.

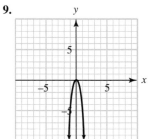

7.

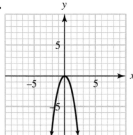

9.

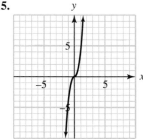

11.

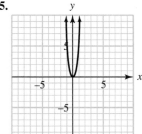

13.

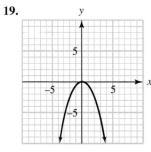

15.

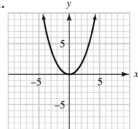

17.

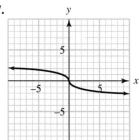

19.

21.

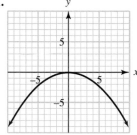

23.

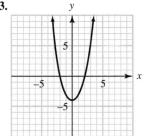

25.

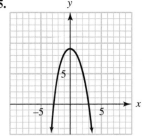

27.

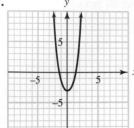

29.

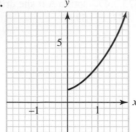

31.

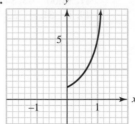

33.

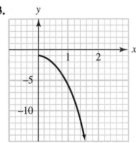

35.

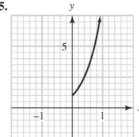

37.

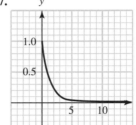

39.

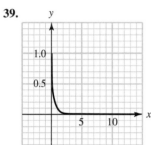

41.

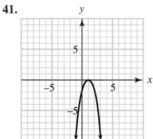

43.

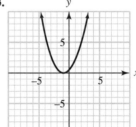

45.

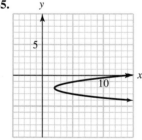

47.

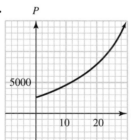

49.

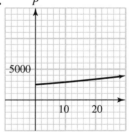

51.

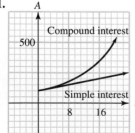

53. a.

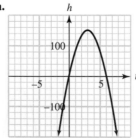

b. downward   **c.** no   **d.**

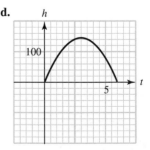

55.

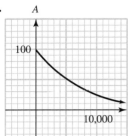

57.

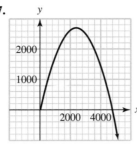

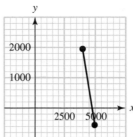

Yes, he will make it. **59.** T

Chapter 11 Review Questions, p. 583

1. a. Plotted points vary.

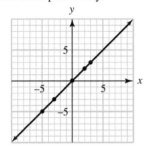

b. Plotted points vary.

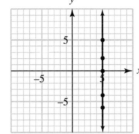

3. a. 20 **b.** −3 **c.** 75 **d.** 5

5.

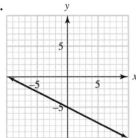

7.

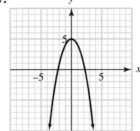

9.

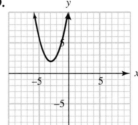

11.

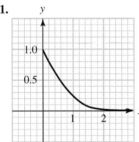

13.

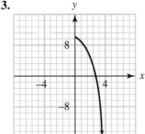

15.

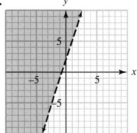

17.

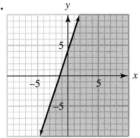

19.

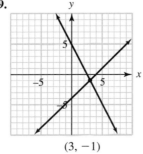

$(3, -1)$

21.

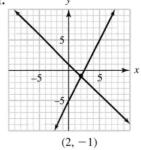

$(2, -1)$

23.

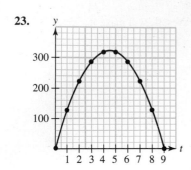

25.

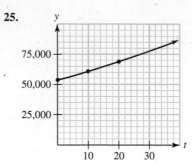

INSTRUCTOR'S ANSWER SECTION

This section is available only in the *Annotated Instructor's Edition*. Instead of printing a separate *Instructor's Manual,* we've included all of the answers next to the problems throughout this edition. However, there are many places where the answers would not fit in the available space, and a reference such as *See IAS* was given in the text. Those answers are included here so that all of the answers to questions in the book are available to instructors.

CHAPTER 1
PROBLEM SET 1.8, p. 64

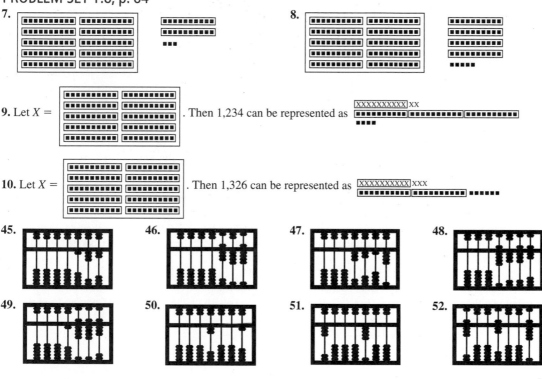

7. **8.**

9. Let $X =$. Then 1,234 can be represented as

10. Let $X =$. Then 1,326 can be represented as

45. **46.** **47.** **48.**

49. **50.** **51.** **52.**

CHAPTER 1 REVIEW QUESTIONS, p. 78

2d.

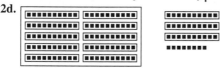

INDIVIDUAL PROJECTS, p. 79

1.1. Answers vary. If you are serious about your students keeping a journal, you need to assign this problem, and then periodically check your students' progress.

1.2. Answers vary. Many students believe that mathematics is dead and all that is known about the subject was discovered many years ago. We know, of course, that is not true, and by assigning this problem you will encourage them to investigate some of the recent mathematical discoveries.

1.3. Answers vary; there are many possible answers; one possibility is

$$1 + 2 + 3 + 4 + 5 + 6 + 7 + 8 \times 9 = 100$$

1.4. Imagine that you have written down all of the numbers from 1 to 1,000,000 and you have done this by aligning the columns as follows:

1,000,000
999,999
999,998
999,997
999,996
999,995
999,994   The number of zeros in the units column: 100,000   This is $\frac{1}{10}$ the number in the digits' column.
999,993   The number of zeros in the tens column: $100,000 - 9$ Nine missing at the bottom of the tens
999,992   The number of zeros in the hundreds column: $100,000 - 99$ column.
999,991   The number of zeros in the thousands column: $100,000 - 999$
999,990   The number of zeros in the 10,000s column: $100,000 - 9,999$
  ⋮   The number of zeros in the 100,000s column: $100,000 - 99,999$
900,001   Thus, the total number of digits is: $600,000 - 111,105 = 488,895$
900,000
899,999
  ⋮

3
2
1

1.5. a. 100 ft (It is dropped from a height of 100 ft.)   **b.** $\underbrace{100 \text{ ft}}_{\text{down}} + \underbrace{\frac{1}{2}(100) \text{ ft}}_{\text{up}} + \underbrace{\frac{1}{2}(100) \text{ ft}}_{\text{back down}} = 200 \text{ ft}$ **c.** $100 + 50 + 50 + 25 + 25 = 250$ ft

d. $100 + 2(50) + 2(25) + 2(12.5) = 275$ ft   **e.** $100 + 2(50) + 2(25) + 2(12.5) + 2(6.25) = 287.5$ ft
f. It looks like it will bounce a total distance of 300 ft.

1.6. Encourage your students to look for a pattern. When they get to part **f** and conclude that $\frac{9}{9} = 0.999\ldots$, get them to think about the fact that 1 is *exactly* equal to 0.999 . . . . Many will think you are playing games with them, but these are, indeed, equal.

1.7. We continue with the pattern of numbers:

0, 1, 2, 10, 11, 12, 20, 21, 22, 100, 101, 102, 110, 111, 112, 120, 121, 122,
200, 201, 202, 210, 211, 212, 220, 221, 222, 1000, 1001, . . .

Explanation: The pattern on the units column is: 0, 1, 2, 0, 1, 2, 0, 1, 2, . . .; the pattern on the next column (moving from right to left) is:

0, 0, 0, 1, 1, 1, 2, 2, 2, 0, 0, 0, 1, 1, 1, 2, 2, 2, . . .

The pattern on the next column is:

0, 0, 0, 0, 0, 0, 0, 0, 0, 1, 1, 1, 1, 1, 1, 1, 1, 1,
2, 2, 2, 2, 2, 2, 2, 2, 2, 0, 0, 0, 0, 0, 0, 0, 0, 0,
1, 1, 1, 1, 1, 1, 1, 1, 1, 2, . . .

1.8. Answers vary. Just write the problem as you would have done in elementary school. For example, consider 43×11:

```
      2  4
  ×   1  1
  ─────────
      2  4
   2  4
  ─────────
   2  6  4
   ↑  ↑  ↑
first digit │ last digit
   Sum of the two digits.
```

TEAM PROJECTS, p. 81

T1. I've found this problem is worth its weight in gold. The classroom dynamic is enhanced considerably when the students feel comfortable with each other and this problem requires at least 30 minutes getting to know each other. Yes, I do give 30 minutes of classroom time for this activity. The paper is secondary to this interaction.

T2. There are $60 \times 60 = 3,600$ sec/hr and

$$3,600 \times 24 \approx 4,000 \times 20 = 80,000 \text{ sec/day}$$

Estimate 1,000,000,000 seconds to be

$$1,000,000,000 \div 80,000 \approx 100,000 \div 8$$
$$\approx 12,500 \text{ days}$$

Actually it is

$$1,000,000,000 \div (3,600 \times 24) \approx 11,574 \text{ days}$$

or if we divide this by 365 we find it is approximately 32 years.

T3. Imagine that you have written down all of the numbers from 1 to 1,000,000 and you have done this by aligning the columns as follows:

1,000,000
999,999
999,998
999,997
999,996
999,995
999,994
999,993
999,992
999,991
999,990
⋮
900,001
900,000
899,999
⋮
10,000
9,999
⋮
100
99
98
⋮
10
9
⋮
3
2
1

The number of digits in the units column:	1,000,000
The number of digits in the tens column:	$1,000,000 - 9$
The number of digits in the hundreds column:	$1,000,000 - 99$
The number of digits in the thousands column:	$1,000,000 - 999$
The number of digits in the 10,000s column:	$1,000,000 - 9,999$
The number of digits in the 100,000s column:	$1,000,000 - 99,999$
The number of digits in the millions column:	$1,000,000 - 999,999$
Thus, the total number of digits is:	$7,000,000 - 1,111,104 = 5,888,896$

The total number of digits is 5,888,896 and the required time is about 68 days.

T4. Here are the first 10 digits as four fours, but remember to check your students' answers because answers are not unique.

$1 = \dfrac{4}{4} + 4 - 4 \quad 2 = \dfrac{4}{4} + \dfrac{4}{4} \quad 3 = \dfrac{4 + 4 + 4}{4} \quad 4 = 4 + \dfrac{4 - 4}{4} \quad 5 = \dfrac{4(4) + 4}{4}$

$6 = 4 + \dfrac{4 + 4}{4} \quad 7 = \dfrac{44}{4} - 4 \quad 8 = 4 + 4 + 4 - 4 \quad 9 = 4 + 4 + \dfrac{4}{4} \quad 10 = \dfrac{44 - 4}{4}$

It is possible to extend this to the first 100 numbers. One time, I challenged the class to do this and I wrote the answers on a back bulletin board. After the first few days, many of the numbers were filled in, but after that, when someone in the class found a new entry, I made a big deal of announcing the "discovery" and had the person sign his/her name next to the entry on the bulletin board.

CHAPTER 2
INDIVIDUAL PROJECTS, p. 131

2.1. Answers vary. If you assigned journals to your students at the beginning of the course, then you should encourage them to continue in this endeavor, which is the purpose of this problem.

2.2. Answers vary. There are so many sources for this project that it is a good place to start for students who do not have a great deal of experience in working with sources on the World Wide Web.

2.3. What the students are led to notice is that it does not matter how many steps, the rise and the run remain the same. The total length of the segments is the sum of the rise (1 in.) and the run (1 in.), namely, 2 in.

2.4. Answers vary. **a.** 1.454554555455554 . . . **b.** 0.534567891011 . . . **c.** $\frac{1}{11} = 0.\overline{09}$ (rational) and $\frac{1}{10} = 0.1$ (rational); one possibility is 0.09009000900009 . . .

2.5. Put it diagonally in a box with dimensions 3 ft by 4 ft.

TEAM PROJECTS, p. 132

If you assign these problems, suggest to your students that they form a pattern with construction paper. They can then manipulate the pieces until they verify the Pythagorean theorem—namely, that the sum of the areas of the two smaller squares equals the area of the larger square.

T5.

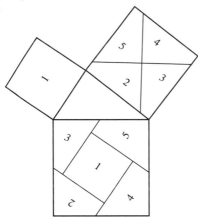

T6.

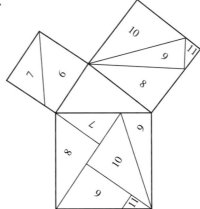

CHAPTER 3
PROBLEM SET 3.7, p. 174

13. a.

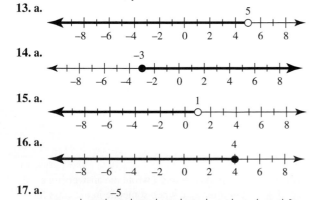

14. a.

15. a.

16. a.

17. a.

18. a.

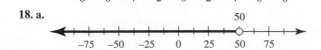

b.

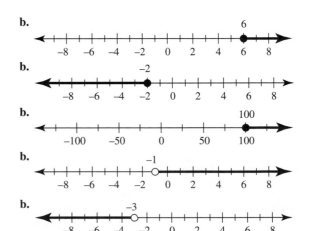

b.

b.

b.

b.

b.

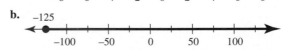

19. a.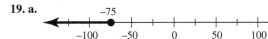
−75 (number line, closed dot at −75, shaded left; marks −100, −50, 0, 50, 100)

b. −30 (number line, open dot at −30, shaded left; marks −75, −50, −25, 0, 25, 50, 75)

20. a. 45 (number line, closed dot at 45, shaded left; marks −75, −50, −25, 0, 25, 50, 75)

b. −40 (number line, open dot at −40, shaded both directions; marks −75, −50, −25, 0, 25, 50, 75)

21. a. −50 (number line, closed dot at −50, shaded right; marks −75, −50, −25, 0, 25, 50, 75)

b. 100 (number line, open dot at 100, shaded left; marks −100, −50, 0, 50, 100)

22. a. 6 (number line, open dot at 6, shaded right; marks −8, −6, −4, −2, 0, 2, 4, 6, 8)

b. 100 (number line, open dot at 100, shaded right; marks −100, −50, 0, 50, 100)

23. a. 8 (number line, open dot at 8, shaded right; marks −8, −4, 0, 4, 8, 12)

b. 8 (number line, open dot at 8, shaded right; marks −8, −4, 0, 4, 8, 12)

24. a. 80 (number line, open dot at 80, shaded right; marks 0, 25, 50, 75, 100, 125)

b. −80 (number line, open dot at −80, shaded right; marks −125, −100, −75, −50, −25, 0, 25)

INDIVIDUAL PROJECTS, p. 181

3.1. Notice that in the last step, the hippopotamus divides both sides by $H - p - w$, but since $H = p + w$, we see that $H - p - w = 0$. Since we can't divide by zero, that step is not allowed and the conclusion is not valid.

3.2. First we note that this problem needs the formula $d = rt$, which says that the distance traveled is equal to the product of the rate and time. We begin by making a statement about distances.

$$2 \text{ (DISTANCE TRAVELED BY LOIS)} = \text{DISTANCE TRAVELED BY CLARK}$$

$$2(50)(2) = \text{RATE} \left(\frac{10}{60} \right)$$

$$200 = \frac{1}{6} \text{ RATE}$$

$$1{,}200 = \text{RATE}$$

Clark's (Superman's) rate is 1,200 miles per hour.

TEAM PROJECTS, p. 182

T7. Answers vary.

T8. Answers vary.

CHAPTER 4

INDIVIDUAL PROJECTS, p. 212

4.1. Let $x = $ AMOUNT THAT I HAVE WITH ME ORIGINALLY. Amount after the first store is

$$x + x - 10 = 2x - 10$$

Amount after the second store is

$$(2x - 10) + (2x - 10) - 10 = 4x - 30$$

Amount after the third store is

$$(4x - 30) + (4x - 30) - 10 = 8x - 70$$

Now, after the third store, the man has no money:

$$8x - 70 = 0$$
$$8x = 70 \qquad \text{Add 70 to both sides.}$$
$$x = \$8.75 \qquad \text{Divide both sides by 8.}$$

The man had $8.75 to start. Let's check:

   $8.75 + $8.75 = $17.50 from the first store, and then spend $10 so the amount the man has after the first store is $7.50.

   $7.50 + $7.50 = $15.00 from the second store, and then spend $10 so the amount the man has after the second store is $5.00.

   $5.00 + $5.00 = $10.00 from the third store, and then spend $10, so the amount the man has left is nothing. Answer checks.

4.2. This is an example of a problem that is easy if you take a step back and look at the big picture. She started with 32 gallons of undiluted soft drink. At the end, she had 1 pt of undiluted soft drink. Thus, the amount served was 31 gallons, 3 quarts, and 1 pint.

TEAM PROJECTS, p. 213

T9. This is an example of a problem that is easy if you look at the big picture. They spent $270 on the room *minus* the $20 tip equals $250. The hotel received $250 *plus* the bellboy received $20 which equals $270. All the money is accounted for and there is no "extra" amount of $10.

T10. Answers vary.

CHAPTER 5
PROBLEM SET 5.1, p. 221

9.

10.

11.

12.

13.

14.

15.

16.

17.

18.

19.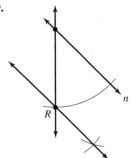

20.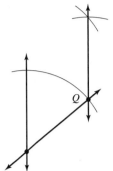

21.

22.

23.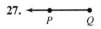

24.

25.

26.

27.

28.

29.

30.

31.

32.

33.

34.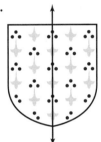

35.

38.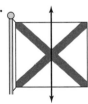

39.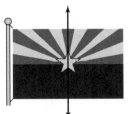

40.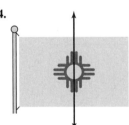

41.

42.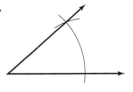

43.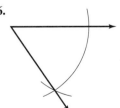

44.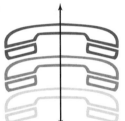

45.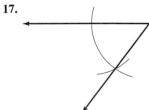

PROBLEM SET 5.2, p. 230

15.

16.

17.

18.

19.

20.

PROBLEM SET 5.3, p. 238

23.

24.

25.

26.

27.

28.

35.

36.

37.

38.

39.

41.

42.

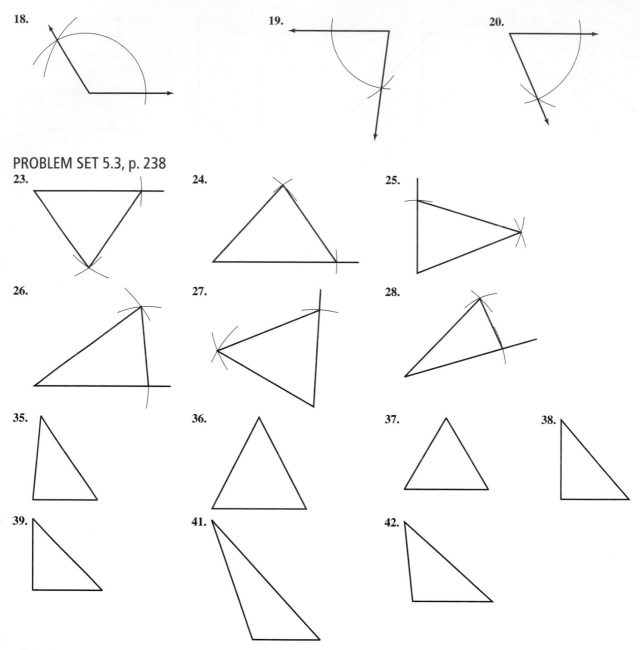

INDIVIDUAL PROJECTS, p. 262

5.1. To do this you need to change your frame of reference to allow the lines you draw to go past the boundaries of the nine dots.

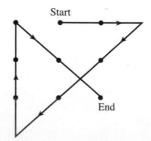

5.2.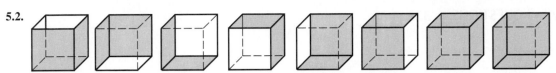

5.3. $m\angle 1 + m\angle 2 + m\angle 3 = 180°$; $m\angle 4 + m\angle 5 + m\angle 6 = 180°$; thus, $m\angle 1 + m\angle 2 + m\angle 3 + m\angle 4 + m\angle 5 + m\angle 6 = 360°$
For a pentagon, three triangles would be formed, so the sum of the angle measures is $3(180°) = 540°$.
For an octagon, six triangles are formed, so $6(180°) = 1,080°$.
Note the pattern: triangle (3 sides), multiply $180°$ by 1; quadrilateral (4 sides), multiply by 2; pentagon (5 sides), multiply by 3; polygon with 8 sides, multiply by 6; thus, we suspect that if there is a polygon with n sides, we need to multiply $180°$ by $(n - 2)$.

5.4. Let x be the distance between Venus and the sun. Then, by definition of sine,

$$\sin 47° = \frac{x}{92,900,000}$$
$$x = 92,900,000 \sin 47°$$
$$\approx 67,900,000$$

The distance is about 67,900,000 miles.
Let y be the distance between Venus and the earth. Then, by definition of cosine,

$$\cos 47° = \frac{y}{92,900,000}$$
$$y = 92,900,000 \cos 47°$$
$$\approx 63,400,000$$

The distance is about 63,400,000 miles.

5.5. Answers vary; the paper should be at least a page and include references.   **5.6.** Answers vary.

TEAM PROJECTS, p. 264

T11. The number is 0 since it is reasonable to assume that there is at least one completely bald person in New York City. Remember, the product of any number and 0 (bald person) is 0.

T12.

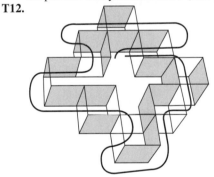

CHAPTER 6
PROBLEM SET 6.6, p. 314

19. $\frac{9}{1,760}$ mi; 27 ft; 324 in.   **20.** $\frac{1}{10,560}$ mi; $\frac{1}{6}$ yd; $\frac{1}{2}$ ft   **21.** 7,040 yd; 21,120 ft; 253,440 in.   **22.** $\frac{5}{2,112}$ mi; $4\frac{1}{6}$ yd; $12\frac{1}{2}$ ft   **23.** 0.009 km; 0.09 hm; 0.9 dkm; 90 dm; 900 cm; 9,000 mm   **24.** 0.00006 km; 0.0006 hm; 0.006 dkm; 0.06 m; 0.6 dm; 60 mm   **25.** 40 hm; 400 dkm; 4,000 m; 40,000 dm; 400,000 cm; 4,000,000 mm   **26.** 0.0015 km; 0.015 hm; 0.15 dkm; 1.5 m; 15 dm; 1,500 mm   **27.** $1\frac{31}{32}$ qt; $3\frac{15}{16}$ pt; $7\frac{7}{8}$ c   **28.** $1\frac{3}{4}$ qt; 7 c; 56 oz   **29.** 2 qt; 4 pt; 64 oz   **30.** 10 pt; 20 c; 160 oz   **31.** 0.000063 kL; 0.00063 hL; 0.0063 dkL; 0.063 L; 0.63 dL; 6.3 cL   **32.** 0.0035 kL; 0.035 hL; 0.35 dkL; 35 dL; 350 cL; 3,500 mL   **33.** 0.08 kL; 0.8 hL; 80 L; 800 dL; 8,000 cL; 80,000 mL   **34.** 0.31 kL; 31 dkL; 310 L; 3,100 dL; 31,000 cL; 310,000 mL   **35.** $\frac{1}{500}$ T; 64 oz   **36.** $\frac{3}{1,000}$ T; 6 lb   **37.** $\frac{21}{8,000}$ T; 84 oz   **38.** 9,000 lb; 144,000 oz   **39.** 65 hg; 650 dkg; 6,500 g; 65,000 dg; 650,000 cg; 6,500,000 mg   **40.** 0.096 kg; 0.96 hg; 9.6 dkg; 960 dg; 9,600 cg; 96,000 mg   **41.** 52.5 hg; 525 dkg; 5,250 g; 52,500 dg; 525,000 cg; 5,250,000 mg   **42.** 45 hg; 450 dkg; 4,500 g; 45,000 dg; 450,000 cg; 4,500,000 mg

CHAPTER 6 REVIEW QUESTIONS, p. 323

25.

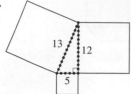

INDIVIDUAL PROJECTS, p. 327

6.1. Answers vary.

6.2. California is about 1.586×10^5 mi$^2 \approx 4.42 \times 10^{12}$ ft^2; divide this by the world population of 6.6 billion:

$$\frac{1.586 \times 10^5 \text{ mi}^2}{6.6 \times 10^9} \approx \frac{4.42 \times 10^{12} \text{ ft}^2}{6.6 \times 10^9}$$

$$\approx 670$$

The best answer listed is D.

6.3. a. $\dfrac{1 \text{ person}}{50 \text{ ft}^2} = \dfrac{x \text{ people}}{(2.8 \times 10^7 \text{ ft}^2)/\text{mi}^2}$

$$x = \frac{2.8 \times 10^7 \text{ ft}^2}{50 \text{ ft}^2} \frac{\text{people}}{(\text{mile})^2}$$

$$\approx 5.6 \times 10^5 \text{ people per square mile.}$$

b. $(6.6 \times 10^9) \times 50 \text{ ft}^2 = 330 \times 10^9 \text{ ft}^2$

$$= 3.3 \times 10^{11} \text{ ft}^2$$

The entire population would need about 11,900 mi^2. This is about the size of Maryland. In other words, the whole world could move to Maryland, each person with about the size of a prison cell, and the rest of the world would be uninhabited by people.

c. $(5.2 \times 10^7) \times 640$ acres; divide this by the population 6.6×10^9 and the result is about 5.0 acres per person!

6.4. $\frac{1}{2}$ mi $= 2,640$ ft; volume of box is $(2,640 \text{ ft})^3 \approx 1.8 \times 10^{10}$ ft^3.

This box could accommodate about $\dfrac{1.8 \times 10^{10} \text{ ft}^3}{2 \text{ ft}^3} = 9.2 \times 10^9$ people.

This box would easily contain the present population.

$$\frac{6.6 \times 10^9}{9.2 \times 10^9} \approx 0.7174$$

This present population would fill only about 72% of the box.

TEAM PROJECTS, p. 328

T13. To answer these questions look at Figure 6.40.

a. A triangular pyramid has 4 sides.

b. A quadrilateral pyramid has 5 vertices.

c. A pentagonal pyramid has 6 sides.

d. A regular tetrahedron has 6 edges.

e. A cube has 6 sides and 8 vertices.

f. A regular octahedron has 8 sides and 12 edges.

g. A regular dodecahedron has 12 sides and 20 vertices.

h. A regular icosahedron has 20 sides and 12 vertices.

A formula for this problem is:

NUMBER OF SIDES $+$ NUMBER OF VERTICES $=$ NUMBER OF EDGES $+$ 2

T14. This is a fun exercise, but will probably need some class time to assign.

T15. The solution of this problem depends on the formula for the circumference of a circle. Let r be the radius of the earth (in feet). Then $r + 6$ ft is the radius of the earth with the band. Let C be the circumference of the earth and let C' be the radius of the earth with the raised band. The amount of extra material is $C' - C$, which is easy to calculate using the formula for the circumference of a circle.

$$C' - C = 2\pi(r + 6 \text{ ft}) - 2\pi r$$
$$= 2\pi r - 2\pi r + 12\pi \text{ ft}$$
$$= 12\pi \text{ ft}$$

The amount of extra material is about 38 ft.

T16. The edges of the two triangles and two trapezoids do not really form a diagonal in the new rectangle. Instead, they form a flat parallelogram whose area is exactly one square centimeter.

CHAPTER 7
PROBLEM SET 7.1, p. 338
54. First, find the sale price of the living room set:

$$s = pc \qquad \text{Sale price formula}$$
$$= \$2,550(0.60) \qquad \text{Complement: } 1 - 0.4 = 0.6$$
$$= \$1,530.00$$

However, don't forget the tax. Since they have $1,600 to spend, the sales tax should not exceed $70. Let r be the sales tax rate and t the tax, so that

$$t = pr$$
$$\$70 = \$1,530r$$
$$\frac{\$70}{\$1,530} = r$$
$$0.046 \approx r$$

If the tax rate is 4.6% (or less) then they will be able to afford the living room set.

PROBLEM SET 7.4, p. 360
52. Previous balance method, $P = \$3,000$

$$I = Prt \qquad \text{Simple interest formula}$$
$$= \$3,000(0.18)\left(\frac{1}{12}\right)$$
$$= \$45.00$$

Adjusted balance method, $P = \$3,000 - \$300 = \$2,700$

$$I = Prt \qquad \text{Simple interest formula}$$
$$= \$2,700(0.18)\left(\frac{1}{12}\right)$$
$$= 40.50$$

Average daily balance method, $P = \dfrac{\$3,000 \times 14 + \$2,700 \times 17}{31}$

$$\approx \$2,835.48$$

$$I = Prt \qquad \text{Simple interest formula}$$
$$= \$2,835.48(0.18)\left(\frac{31}{365}\right)$$
$$\approx \$43.35$$

CHAPTER 7 REVIEW QUESTIONS, p. 390
25. Cost of driving the Hybrid:

$$\text{COST OF CAR} = \$22,600$$
$$\text{COST OF GAS} = (\text{NUMBER OF GALLONS})(\text{COST PER GALLON})$$
$$= \frac{100,000}{37} \cdot \$2.90$$
$$= \$7,837.84$$

$$\text{TOTAL COST OF DRIVING HYBRID} = \$22,600 + \$7,837.84 = \$30,437.84$$

Cost of driving the LX (gasoline car):

$$\text{COST OF CAR} = \$17,760$$

$$\text{COST OF GAS} = (\text{NUMBER OF GALLONS})(\text{COST PER GALLON})$$

$$= \frac{100,000}{23} \cdot \$2.90$$

$$= \$12,608.70$$

TOTAL COST OF LX (GASOLINE CAR) = $\$17,760 + \$12,608.70 = \$30,368.70$

The cost of driving the hybrid for 100,000 miles is $69.14 more than for driving the LX.

INDIVIDUAL PROJECTS, p. 392

Answers varies since all the projects in this chapter are papers. Each should be thoughtful and present relevant information as well as opinions.

7.8. Answers vary. This problem is related to a very famous problem in mathematics, known as the Königsberg Bridge problem. Even though the mathematical solution of this problem (first done by Leonhard Euler) is beyond the scope of the course, these students can proceed by trial and error. It is not possible to trace out the roads in the Santa Rosa street problem without retracing some road.

TEAM PROJECTS, p. 393

T17. a. Answers vary.

b. Notice that 120 bags per hour is 2 bags per minute. This means that if you purchased 8 bags, this is 4 minutes labor. The bagger earns $12.00/hr, which is $0.20/min. This means that 4 minutes labor is $4 \times \$0.20 = \$0.80$. Thus, the savings is less than a dollar, hardly "a bundle."

c. $0.80 is what percent of $200, or 0.4%.

T18. Answers vary, but it is necessary that you keep correct, accurate records of your investment journey.

T19. Answers vary.

CHAPTER 8

PROBLEM SET 8.2, p. 405

Improper subsets in boldface for Problems 15–22.

15. $\varnothing$, $\{y\}$, $\{o\}$, $\{u\}$, $\{y, o\}$ $\{y, u\}$, $\{o, u\}$, $\{\boldsymbol{y, o, u}\}$ **16.** $\varnothing$, $\{a\}$, $\{r\}$, $\{e\}$, $\{a, r\}$, $\{a, e\}$, $\{r, e\}$, $\{\boldsymbol{a, r, e}\}$ **17.** $\varnothing$, $\{b\}$, $\{i\}$, $\{g\}$, $\{b, i\}$, $\{b, g\}$, $\{i, g\}$, $\{\boldsymbol{b, i, g}\}$ **18.** $\varnothing$, $\{3\}$, $\{6\}$, $\{9\}$, $\{3, 6\}$, $\{3, 9\}$, $\{6, 9\}$, $\{\boldsymbol{3, 6, 9}\}$ **19.** $\varnothing$, $\{2\}$, $\{4\}$, $\{6\}$, $\{2, 4\}$, $\{2, 6\}$, $\{4, 6\}$, $\{\boldsymbol{2, 4, 6}\}$ **20.** $\varnothing$, $\{4\}$, $\{8\}$, $\{9\}$, $\{4, 8\}$, $\{4, 9\}$, $\{8, 9\}$, $\{\boldsymbol{4, 8, 9}\}$ **21.** $\varnothing$, $\{m\}$, $\{a\}$, $\{t\}$, $\{h\}$, $\{m, a\}$, $\{m, t\}$, $\{m, h\}$, $\{a, t\}$, $\{a, h\}$, $\{t, h\}$, $\{m, a, t\}$, $\{m, a, h\}$, $\{m, t, h\}$, $\{a, t, h\}$, $\{\boldsymbol{m, a, t, h}\}$ **22.** $\varnothing$, $\{1\}$, $\{2\}$, $\{3\}$, $\{4\}$, $\{1, 2\}$, $\{1, 3\}$, $\{1, 4\}$, $\{2, 3\}$, $\{2, 4\}$, $\{3, 4\}$, $\{1, 2, 3\}$, $\{1, 2, 4\}$, $\{1, 3, 4\}$, $\{2, 3, 4\}$, $\{\boldsymbol{1, 2, 3, 4}\}$ **27.** $\varnothing$, $\{1\}$, $\{2\}$, $\{3\}$, $\{4\}$, $\{1, 2\}$, $\{1, 3\}$, $\{1, 4\}$, $\{2, 3\}$, $\{2, 4\}$, $\{3, 4\}$, $\{1, 2, 3\}$, $\{1, 2, 4\}$, $\{1, 3, 4\}$, $\{2, 3, 4\}$, $\{1, 2, 3, 4\}$ **32.** $\varnothing$, $\{6\}$, $\{7\}$, $\{8\}$, $\{9\}$, $\{6, 7\}$, $\{6, 8\}$, $\{6, 9\}$, $\{7, 8\}$, $\{7, 9\}$, $\{8, 9\}$, $\{6, 7, 8\}$, $\{6, 7, 9\}$, $\{6, 8, 9\}$, $\{7, 8, 9\}$, $\{6, 7, 8, 9\}$

41.

$U = \{\text{people}\}$

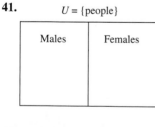

42.

$U = \{\text{people}\}$

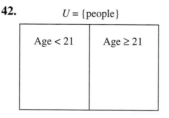

43.

$U = \{\text{shop tools}\}$

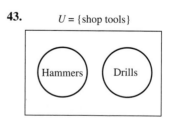

44.

$U = \{\text{animals}\}$

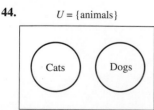

45.

$U = \{\text{people}\}$

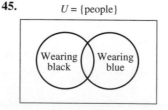

46.

$U = \{\text{people}\}$

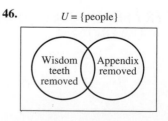

47. $U = \{\text{animals}\}$

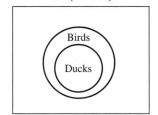

48. $U = \{\text{vehicles}\}$

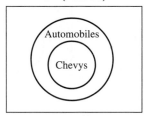

49. $U = \{\text{vehicles}\}$

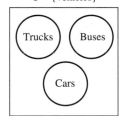

50. $U = \{\text{objects with first letter } f\}$

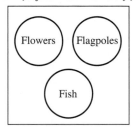

51. $U = \{\text{athletes}\}$

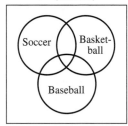

52. $U = \{\text{people in a classroom}\}$

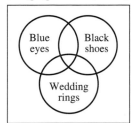

53. $U = \{\text{people}\}$

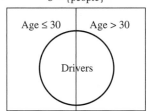

54. $U = \{\text{Olympic swimmers}\}$

55. $U = \{\text{quadrilaterals}\}$

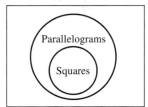

56. $U = \{\text{rational numbers}\}$

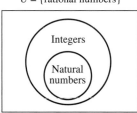

PROBLEM SET 8.3, p. 410

31.

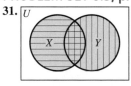

32.

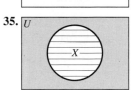

33.

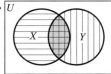

34.

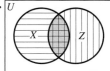

35.

36.

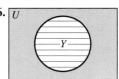

43.

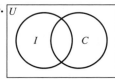

48.

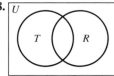

PROBLEM SET 8.4, p. 417

1.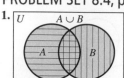

2.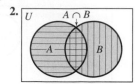

3.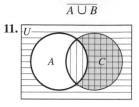

7.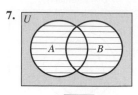

$\overline{A \cup B}$

8.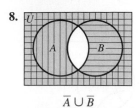

$\overline{A} \cup \overline{B}$

9.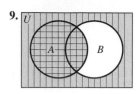

10.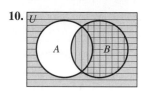

11.

12.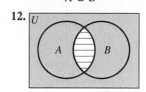

13.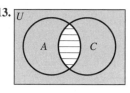

14.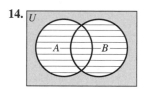

15.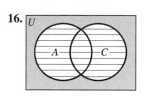

16.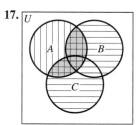

17.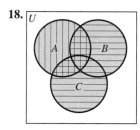

18.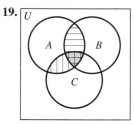

19.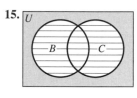

20.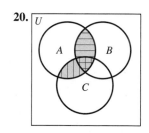

21.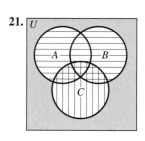

22.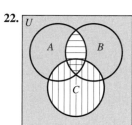

23.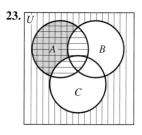

24.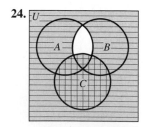

25.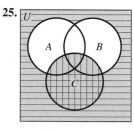

26.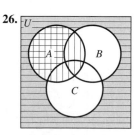

52.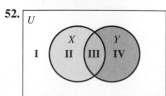

Let U = {students from Liz's school}
X = {those accepted at public university}
Y = {those accepted at private college}
If $|X| = 50\%$ and $|Y| = 50\%$ but $|X \cap Y| = 20\%$, then only 80% are accounted for in regions II, III, and IV.

53.

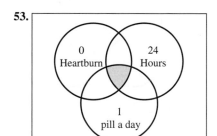

The desired message is that those who take 1 pill a day will provide some users with complete relief from heartburn that will last all day. The problem with the Venn diagram in the advertisement is that it has no region to show the intersection of all three sets.

PROBLEM SET 8.5, p. 423

17.

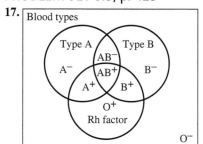

18.

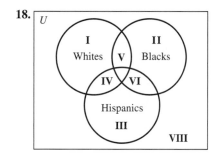

Region I (two white parents)
Region II (two black parents)
Region III (two Hispanic parents)
Region IV (white/Hispanic)
Region V (white/black)
Region VI (black/Hispanic)
Region VII (not labeled) empty
Region VIII (other parents)

58. Use the given information to construct a Venn diagram.

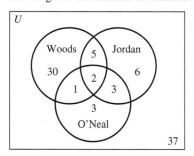

If we add the number of respondents we see there were 50 who did not respond or picked other athletes. Matt's data did not add up because according to his data there were only 87, not 100, accounted for. I would not hire Matt because he did not follow the directions.

PROBLEM SET 8.6, p. 431

23.

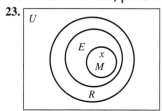

valid

24.

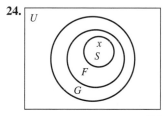

valid

25.

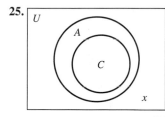

valid

26.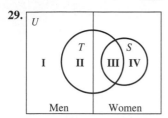

valid

27.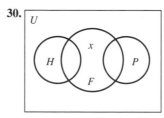

valid

28.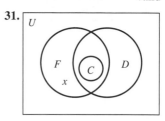

valid

29.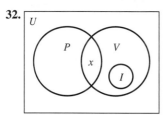

not valid

30.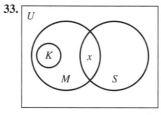

not valid

31.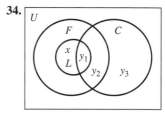

not valid

32.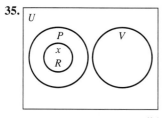

not valid

33.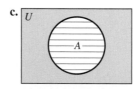

not valid

34.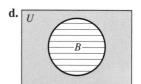

not valid

35.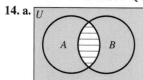

valid

CHAPTER 8 REVIEW QUESTIONS, p. 442

14. a.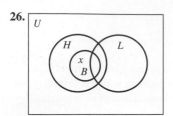

b.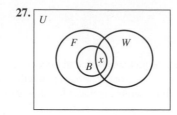

c.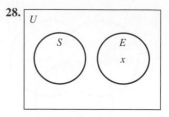

d.

15. a.

b.

c.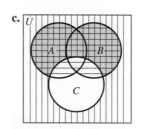

d.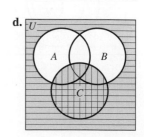

19. There are two statements for De Morgan's laws. (Either one is acceptable.)

Left side   Right side

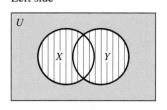 =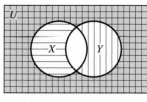

$$\overline{X \cup Y} \qquad\qquad \overline{X} \cap \overline{Y}$$

Thus, $\overline{X \cup Y} = \overline{X} \cap \overline{Y}$

Left side   Right side

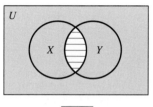 =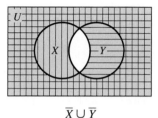

$$\overline{X \cap Y} \qquad\qquad \overline{X} \cup \overline{Y}$$

Thus, $\overline{X \cap Y} = \overline{X} \cup \overline{Y}$

22. 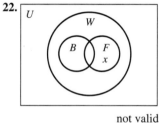   **23.** 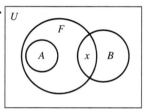   **24.** 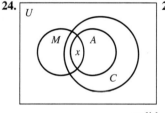   **25.**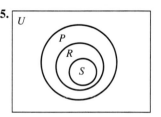

not valid   not valid   valid   valid

INDIVIDUAL PROJECTS, p. 444

8.1. Begin by drawing a Venn diagram, with the regions labeled as indicated. If someone is in the circle labeled "Whites" (Region I) but not in the other circles, then that person has two white parents. If someone is in the intersection of the circles labeled "Whites" and "Blacks" (Region V), then that person has one white parent and one black parent. For this problem we are assuming that the region overlapping all three circles is also empty.

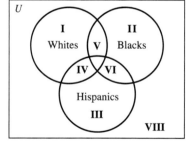

Region I (two white parents): $0.72(263) \approx 189.4$ or 189, rounded to the nearest million.

Region II (two black parents): $0.115(263) \approx 30.2$ or 30, rounded to the nearest million.

Region III (two Hispanic parents): $0.09(263) \approx 23.7$ or 24, rounded to the nearest million.

Region IV (white/Hispanic): $0.01(263) \approx 2.6$ or 3, rounded to the nearest million.

Region V (white/black): $0.005(263) \approx 1.3$ or 1, rounded to the nearest million.

Region VI (black/Hispanic): $0.02(263) \approx 5.3$ or 5, rounded to the nearest million.

Region VIII (other): Use your calculator to carry out the above calculations without rounding to find 10.52 or 11, rounded to the nearest million.

8.2. We proceed by trial and error. Remember, the only possible answers for the letters A through I are 1 through 9.

If $A = 1$, then $B = 8$, and if $B = 8$, then $C = -1$; this is not correct.

If $A = 2$, then $B = 7$, and if $B = 7$, then $C = 0$; this is not correct.

If $\boldsymbol{A = 3}$, then $\boldsymbol{B = 6}$, and if $B = 6$, then $\boldsymbol{C = 1}$; this is possible.

If $B = 6$, then $E = 8$.

If $E = 8$, then $G = 9$.

No clues for H, so we look at $F + I = 11$.

If $F = 2$, then $I = 9$; this has been used.

If $F = 4$, then $I = 7$ and $D = 5$.

This leaves one letter and one number unused: $H = 2$.

Thus, the answer is: $A = 3$, $B = 6$, $C = 1$, $D = 5$, $E = 8$, $F = 4$, $G = 9$, $H = 2$, and $I = 7$.

By the way, there is one other possibility, and that is when $F = 7$. If this value is used, then $D = 2$, $I = 4$, which forces $H = 5$.

8.3.

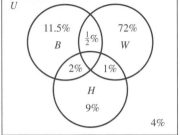

Region I (white): $0.27(0.72)(263) \approx 51.13$,

Region II (black): $0.14(0.115)(263) \approx 4.23$,

Region III (Hispanic): $0.13(0.09)(263) \approx 3.08$

Use by blacks and Hispanics is: $4.23 + 3.08 = 7.31$

which is only 14.3% of the usage of that of whites.

You cannot add percents.

8.4. Yes, answers vary. For example, place three lumps in Cup #1; place five lumps in Cup #2; finally place the last two lumps in Cup #3. NOW place Cup #1 (with its 3 lumps) inside of Cup #3. Now, there are an odd number of lumps in each cup.

8.5. Pour the contents of glass 5 into glass 2.

TEAM PROJECTS, p. 445

T20. This is a research project. The student should systematically investigate each side of the argument.

T21. This is a research project. The named mathematicians are all associated with some paradox, and the students should uncover that common thread.

T22. a.

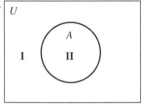

b.

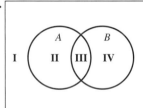

c.

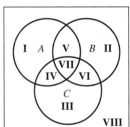

d.

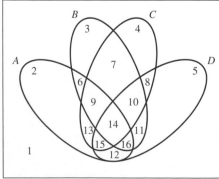

e.

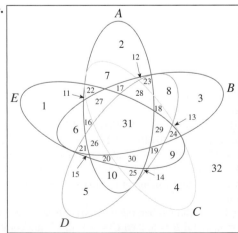

T23. Imagine a long list of the numbers:

$$1, 2, 3, \ldots, 999{,}999,\ 1{,}000{,}000,\ 1{,}000{,}001,\ 1{,}000{,}002, \ldots$$

Suppose we asked for the millionth positive integer on this list—that's easy. It is 1,000,000. Do you understand what is meant by "perfect squares" and "perfect cubes"?

Perfect squares: $1^2 = 1$; $2^2 = 4$, $3^2 = 9$; $4^2 = 16$; 25; 36; 49; 64; 81; ...
Perfect cubes: $1^3 = 1$; $2^3 = 8$; $3^3 = 27$; $4^3 = 64$; 125; 216; 343; 512; ...

Now, suppose we cross out the perfect squares; for each number crossed off, the millionth number in the list changes. That is, cross off 1 and the millionth number is 1,000,001; cross off 1 and 4 and the millionth number is 1,000,002. In this problem, we need to cross out all the perfect squares *and* perfect cubes. *After* we have done this, we look at the list and find the millionth number.

It should be clear that we need to know how many numbers are crossed out.

Let $U = \{1, 2, 3, \ldots, 1{,}000{,}000\}$
$\quad S = \{\text{perfect squares}\}$
$\quad C = \{\text{perfect cubes}\}$

(1) We wish to find the number of elements in S, written as $|S|$: We know that $1{,}000{,}000 = (10^3)^2$ so there are $10^3 = 1{,}000$ perfect squares less than or equal to 1,000,000. Therefore, $|S| = 1{,}000$.
(2) Next, find $|C|$: We also know that $1{,}000{,}000 = (10^2)^3$ so there are $10^2 = 100$ perfect cubes less than or equal to 1,000,000. Therefore, $|C| = 100$.

If you think about crossing out all of the perfect squares and then all of the perfect cubes, you must notice that some numbers are on both lists. That is, what numbers are in the set $S \cap C$? These are the sixth powers:

$$S \cap C: 1^6 = 1; 2^6 = 64; 3^6 = 729; 4^6 = 4{,}096; \ldots; 10^6 = 1{,}000{,}000$$

There are 10 perfect sixth powers, so $|S \cap C| = 10$.

We use the formula from this chapter to find $|S \cup C|$:

$$|S \cup C| = |S| + |C| - |S \cap C|$$
$$= 1{,}000 + 100 - 10$$
$$= 1{,}090$$

If you cross out 1,090 numbers, then the millionth number not crossed out is 1,001,090.

The answer 1,001,090 is not necessarily correct because we crossed out perfect squares, cubes, and sixth powers up to 1,000,000. But each time we crossed out a number, the end number was extended by 1. Thus we need to know whether there are any perfect squares, cubes, or sixth powers between 1,000,000 and 1,001,090 (the target range). Let's check the next number on each of our lists:

Perfect squares:

$$1{,}001^2 = 1{,}002{,}001 \text{ so it is not in the target range;}$$

Perfect cubes:

$$101^3 = 1{,}030{,}301 \text{ so it is not in the target range;}$$

Perfect sixth powers:

$$11^6 = 1{,}771{,}561 \text{ so it also is not in the target range.}$$

The millionth number that is not a perfect square or perfect cube is 1,001,090.

CHAPTER 9
PROBLEM SET 9.1, p. 455

28.

	1	2	3	4
1	(1, 1)	(1, 2)	(1, 3)	(1, 4)
2	(2, 1)	(2, 2)	(2, 3)	(2, 4)
3	(3, 1)	(3, 2)	(3, 3)	(3, 4)
4	(4, 1)	(4, 2)	(4, 3)	(4, 4)

CHAPTER 9 REVIEW QUESTIONS, p. 487

8.

	G_1	G_2	G_3	R_1	R_2	Y
G_1	GG	GG	GG	GR	GR	GY
G_2	GG	GG	GG	GR	GR	GY
G_3	GG	GG	GG	GR	GR	GY
R_1	RG	RG	RG	RR	RR	RY
R_2	RG	RG	RG	RR	RR	RY
Y	YG	YG	YG	YR	YR	YY

$P(\text{same color faces}) = \frac{14}{36} = \frac{7}{18}$

INDIVIDUAL PROJECTS, p. 489

9.1. Answers vary. Enter 5,480,523,297,162 into your calculator and then divide by 50 (jumps per minute). Next, divide by 60 (minutes per hour), divide by 8 (hours per day), divide by 5 (days per week), divide by 50 (weeks in a year), divide by 100 (years in a century). The result shows the display: 9134.20549527
The estimate is a bit over 9,000 centuries.

9.2. Answers vary. Enter 6,077 into your calculator and then multiply by 12 for the total number of links. Since there are 20 students working on this project, divide the result by 20. Next, divide by 30 (number of links per day is the same as the number of minutes per day at work on project), divide by 5 (times per week). The result shows the display: 24.308
The estimate is a bit over 24 weeks (or about 1/2 of the school year).

9.3. The number must be 0 because there is at least one person with a completely bald head, and we know that the product of any number and 0 is 0.

9.4. Answers vary.

TEAM PROJECTS, p. 491

T24. Answers vary. This is an application of the birthday problem (see Project T25). Assuming there are more than 12 persons in the class, the chances of a birthday match are more than 50%. The results of this problem are counterintuitive since most people would guess a probability much less than 50%.

T25. a. Answers vary, but the chances of a match for a group larger than 23 is more than 50%.
 b. In order to reach 1, there must be 367 people (don't forget that a leap year has 366 days).

T26 and T27. Answers vary, but every time I've done this class with a class, I've seen totally unexpected results, which have led to some interesting discussion. I've found this exercise worth the time it takes in class.

T28. Draw the different pairwise outcomes.
A game with dice A and C:

C\A	0	0	4	4	4	4	
2	(2, 0)	(2, 0)	(2, 4)	(2, 4)	(2, 4)	(2, 4)	
2	(2, 0)	(2, 0)	(2, 4)	(2, 4)	(2, 4)	(2, 4)	
2	(2, 0)	(2, 0)	(2, 4)	(2, 4)	(2, 4)	(2, 4)	← A wins 16 out of 36
2	(2, 0)	(2, 0)	(2, 4)	(2, 4)	(2, 4)	(2, 4)	
6	(6, 0)	(6, 0)	(6, 4)	(6, 4)	(6, 4)	(6, 4)	
6	(6, 0)	(6, 0)	(6, 4)	(6, 4)	(6, 4)	(6, 4)	← C wins 20 out of 36

$P(A \text{ winning}) = \frac{4}{9}$ and $P(C \text{ winning}) = \frac{5}{9}$.

A game with dice A and D:

D\A	0	0	4	4	4	4	
1	(1, 0)	(1, 0)	(1, 4)	(1, 4)	(1, 4)	(1, 4)	
1	(1, 0)	(1, 0)	(1, 4)	(1, 4)	(1, 4)	(1, 4)	
1	(1, 0)	(1, 0)	(1, 4)	(1, 4)	(1, 4)	(1, 4)	← A wins 12 out of 36
5	(5, 0)	(5, 0)	(5, 4)	(5, 4)	(5, 4)	(5, 4)	
5	(5, 0)	(5, 0)	(5, 4)	(5, 4)	(5, 4)	(5, 4)	
5	(5, 0)	(5, 0)	(5, 4)	(5, 4)	(5, 4)	(5, 4)	← D wins 24 out of 36

$P(A \text{ winning}) = \frac{1}{3}$ and $P(D \text{ winning}) = \frac{2}{3}$.

A game with dice B and C:

C\B	3	3	3	3	3	3	
2	(2, 3)	(2, 3)	(2, 3)	(2, 3)	(2, 3)	(2, 3)	
2	(2, 3)	(2, 3)	(2, 3)	(2, 3)	(2, 3)	(2, 3)	
2	(2, 3)	(2, 3)	(2, 3)	(2, 3)	(2, 3)	(2, 3)	← B wins 24 out of 36
2	(2, 3)	(2, 3)	(2, 3)	(2, 3)	(2, 3)	(2, 3)	
6	(6, 3)	(6, 3)	(6, 3)	(6, 3)	(6, 3)	(6, 3)	
6	(6, 3)	(6, 3)	(6, 3)	(6, 3)	(6, 3)	(6, 3)	← C wins 12 out of 36

$P(B \text{ winning}) = \frac{2}{3}$ and $P(C \text{ winning}) = \frac{1}{3}$.

A game with dice B and D:

D\B	3	3	3	3	3	3	
1	(1, 3)	(1, 3)	(1, 3)	(1, 3)	(1, 3)	(1, 3)	
1	(1, 3)	(1, 3)	(1, 3)	(1, 3)	(1, 3)	(1, 3)	
1	(1, 3)	(1, 3)	(1, 3)	(1, 3)	(1, 3)	(1, 3)	← B wins 18 out of 36
5	(5, 3)	(5, 3)	(5, 3)	(5, 3)	(5, 3)	(5, 3)	
5	(5, 3)	(5, 3)	(5, 3)	(5, 3)	(5, 3)	(5, 3)	
5	(5, 3)	(5, 3)	(5, 3)	(5, 3)	(5, 3)	(5, 3)	← D wins 18 out of 36

$P(B \text{ winning}) = \frac{1}{2}$ and $P(D \text{ winning}) = \frac{1}{2}$.

Finally, a game with dice C and D:

D\C	2	2	2	2	6	6	
1	(1, 2)	(1, 2)	(1, 2)	(1, 2)	(1, 6)	(1, 6)	
1	(1, 2)	(1, 2)	(1, 2)	(1, 2)	(1, 6)	(1, 6)	
1	(1, 2)	(1, 2)	(1, 2)	(1, 2)	(1, 6)	(1, 6)	← C wins 24 out of 36
5	(5, 2)	(5, 2)	(5, 2)	(5, 2)	(5, 6)	(5, 6)	
5	(5, 2)	(5, 2)	(5, 2)	(5, 2)	(5, 6)	(5, 6)	
5	(5, 2)	(5, 2)	(5, 2)	(5, 2)	(5, 6)	(5, 6)	← D wins 12 out of 36

$P(C \text{ winning}) = \frac{2}{3}$ and $P(D \text{ winning}) = \frac{1}{3}$.

We now summarize these probabilities:

My choices		A	B	C	D
			Opponent Chooses		
	A	—	$\frac{2}{3}$	$\frac{4}{9}$	$\frac{1}{3}$
	B	$\frac{1}{3}$	—	$\frac{2}{3}$	$\frac{1}{2}$
	C	$\frac{5}{9}$	$\frac{1}{3}$	—	$\frac{2}{3}$
	D	$\frac{2}{3}$	$\frac{1}{2}$	$\frac{1}{3}$	—

This means I would want to choose second.

If my opponent chooses die A, then I pick die D.
If my opponent chooses die B, then I pick die A.
If my opponent chooses die C, then I pick die B.
If my opponent chooses die D, then I pick die C.

If I make these choices, then my probability of winning is $\frac{2}{3}$.

CHAPTER 10

PROBLEM SET 10.1, p. 503

7.

Wages	Tally	Frequency		Wages	Tally	Frequency
14	I	1		30	II	2
16	I	1		35	I	1
18	II	2		50	I	1
20	I	1		60	I	1
25	III	3				

8.

Number of Cars	Tally	Frequency
0	I	1
1	IIII	4
2	IIII III	8
3	II	2
4	I	1

9.

Height	Tally	Frequency
63	II	2
64	IIII	4
65	III	3
66	III	3
67	IIII	5
68	III	3
69	IIII	4
70	III	3
71	II	2
72	I	1

10.

Temperature	Tally	Frequency	Temperature	Tally	Frequency
39	I	1	50	IIII	4
40	I	1	51	I	1
41			52	II	2
42			53	II	2
43	II	2	54	II	2
44	I	1	55	II	2
45	II	2	56		
46			57	II	2
47	I	1	58	II	2
48			59	I	1
49	IIII	4			

11.

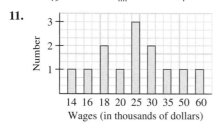

Wages (in thousands of dollars)

12.

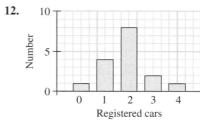

Registered cars

13.

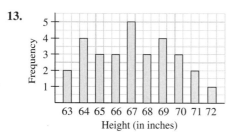

Height (in inches)

14.

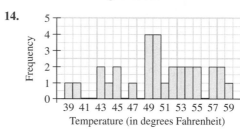

Temperature (in degrees Fahrenheit)

15.

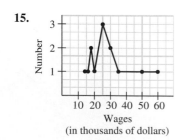

Wages (in thousands of dollars)

16.

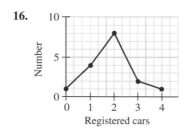

Registered cars

17.

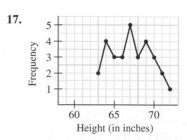

Height (in inches)

18.

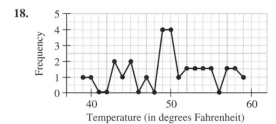

20.

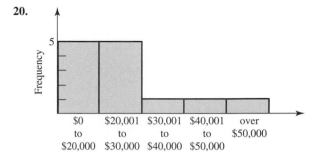

45.

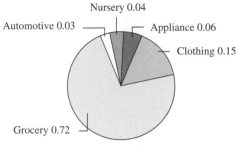

Sales
(by department)

46.

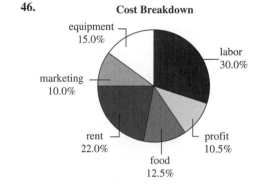

Cost Breakdown

47.

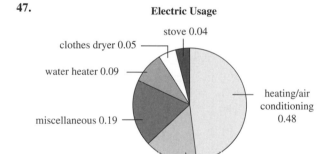

Electric Usage

48.

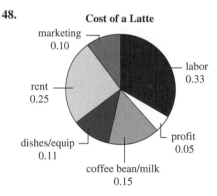

Cost of a Latte

49.

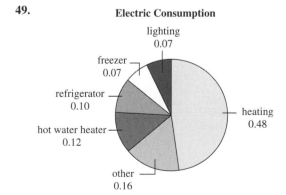

Electric Consumption

50.

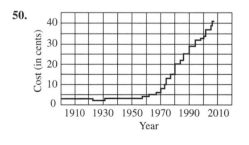

51.

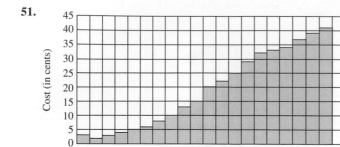

52.

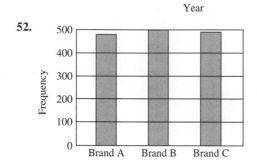

53.

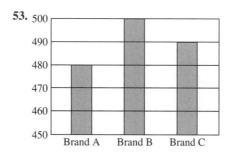

PROBLEM SET 10.4, p. 522

40.

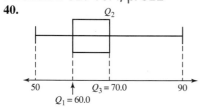

44.

48.

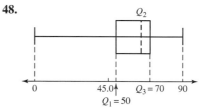

52.

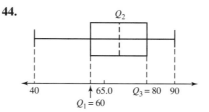

CHAPTER 10 REVIEW QUESTIONS, p. 538

1.

No.	Tally	Frequency
6	II	2
7	IIII	4
8	IIII	5
9	III	3
10	I	1

2.

Party	Tally	Frequency
Democrat	IIII IIII IIII IIII IIII IIII IIII IIII IIII IIII IIII IIII	60
Republican	IIII IIII IIII IIII IIII IIII II	32
Federalist	IIII I	6
Dem.-Rep.	IIII IIII IIII	15
Whig	II	2
American	I	1
Total		116

3.

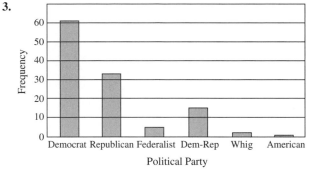

4.

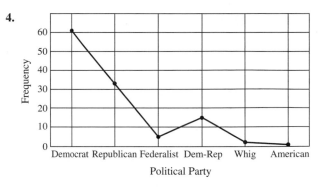

5. a.

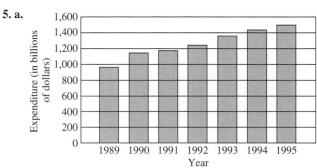

b.

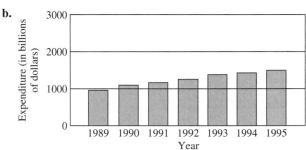

c.

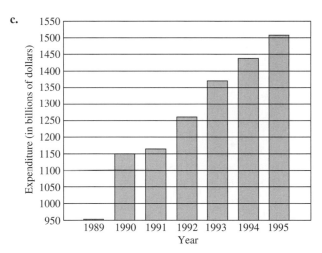

INDIVIDUAL PROJECTS, p. 539

10.1. Encourage your students to have some fun selecting 50 families. Give them this warning: "BE CAREFUL! Don't select 50 people in your circle of friends. Try to figure out how to select 50 people randomly."

10.2. The students are expected to actually assemble these boxes and repeat this experiment 20 times.

10.3. Suppose the coin lands heads 60% of the time. This means that tails comes up 40% of the time. Heads–tails has probability $0.6 \times 0.4 = 0.24$, and tails–heads has probability

$$0.4 \times 0.6 = 0.24$$

10.4. Be sure the students clearly define what they intend to measure before they decide how to select the 100 people. Again, we give the warning that they should not select people from their own neighborhood or circle of friends, unless that is part of the definition of what they are attempting to measure.

10.5–10.9. These problems provide ideas about possible classroom reports.

TEAM PROJECTS, p. 541

T30. For the last project in the book, the students are asked to conduct a survey. I've found that the more freedom I give the students, the better the results. Be there as a resource, not a director.

CHAPTER 11
PROBLEM SET 11.1, p. 549

3.

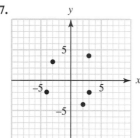

35.

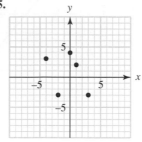

36.

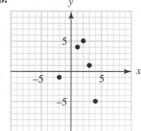

37.

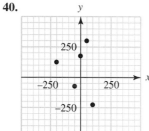

38.

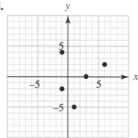

39.

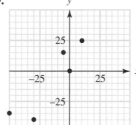

40.

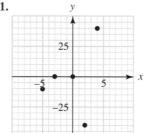

41.

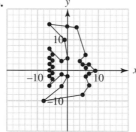

42.

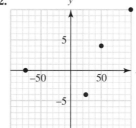

43.

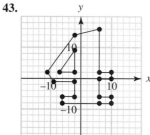

44.

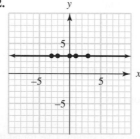

45. $(2, 9)$, $(3, 5)$, $(-2, 5)$, $(1, 10)$, $(5, 11)$, $(5, 10)$, $(8, 10)$, $(9, 7)$, $(4, 6)$, $(5, 2)$, $(8, 0)$, $(5, -1)$, $(4, -3)$, $(4.5, -5)$, $(2, -7)$, $(4, -7)$, $(5, -10)$, $(-4, -7)$, $(-3, -6)$, $(-7, -7)$, $(-9, -10)$, $(-10, -6)$, $(-8, -4)$, $(-5, -5)$, $(-5, -1)$, $(1, 5)$

51.

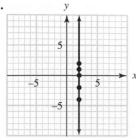

52.

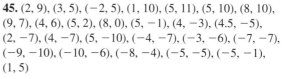

53.

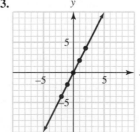

54.

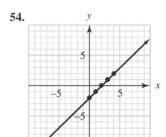

PROBLEM SET 11.2, p. 554

54. $d = 16t^2$ where d is the distance the object has fallen after t seconds.

Since 1 mi = 5,280 ft, $5{,}280 = 16t^2$ Replace d by 5,280.

$$330 = t^2 \qquad \text{Divide both sides by 16.}$$

$$\sqrt{330} = t \qquad \text{Definition of square root (it is positive).}$$

$$18.2 \approx t \qquad \text{By calculator}$$

It would be about 18 seconds to the bottom.

PROBLEM SET 11.3, p. 562

16.

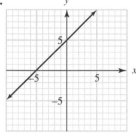

17.

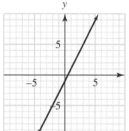

18.

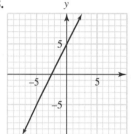

19.

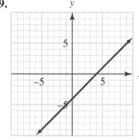

20.

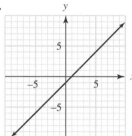

21.

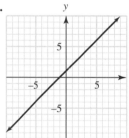

22.

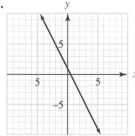

23.

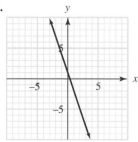

24.

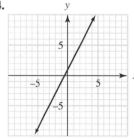

25.

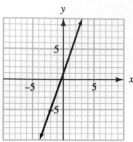

26.

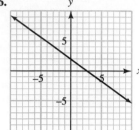

27.

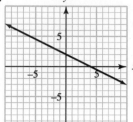

28.

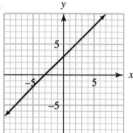

29.

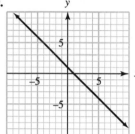

30.

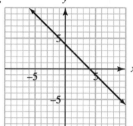

31.

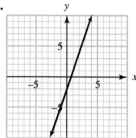

32.

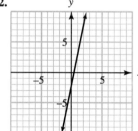

33.

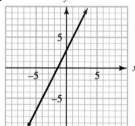

34.

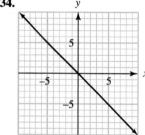

35.

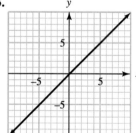

36.

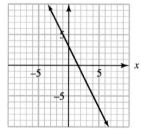

37.

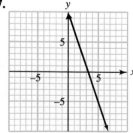

38.

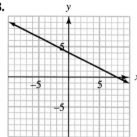

39.

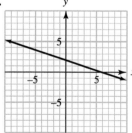

40.
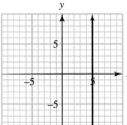

41.
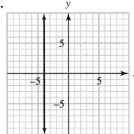

42.
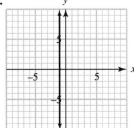

43.
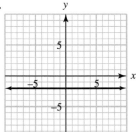

44.
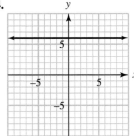

45.
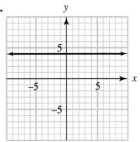

46.
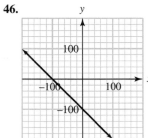

47.
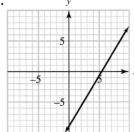

48.
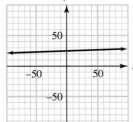

49.
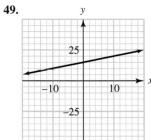

50.
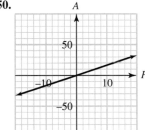

51.
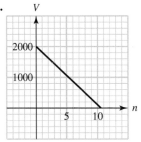

52.
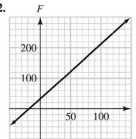

53.
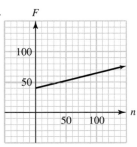

PROBLEM SET 11.4, p. 569

17.

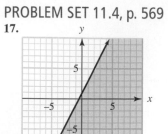

18.

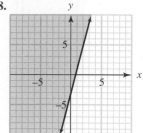

19.

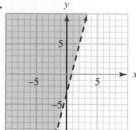

20.

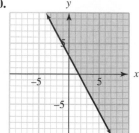

21.

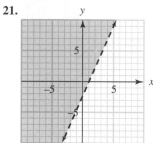

22.

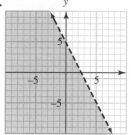

23.

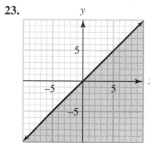

24.

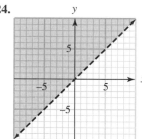

25.

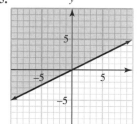

26.

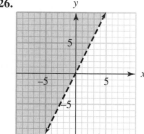

27.

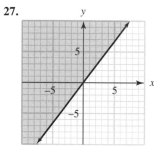

28.

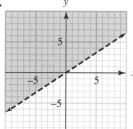

29.

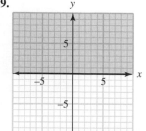

30.

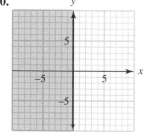

31.

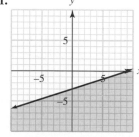

32.

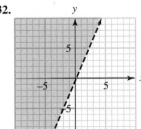

33.

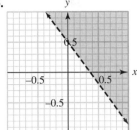

34.

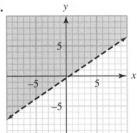

36.

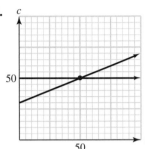

39.

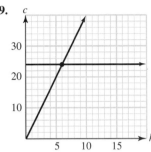

PROBLEM SET 11.5, p. 576

3.

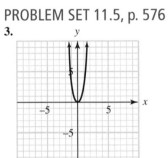

4.

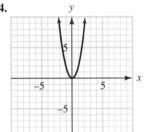

5.

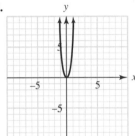

6.

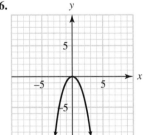

7.

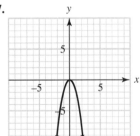

8.

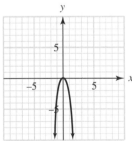

9.

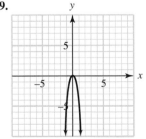

10.

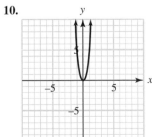

11.

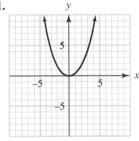

12.

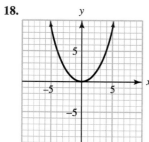

13.

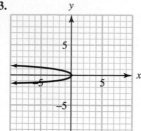

14.

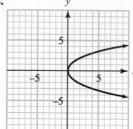

15.

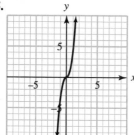

16.

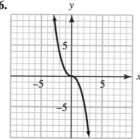

17.

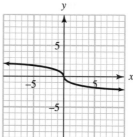

18.

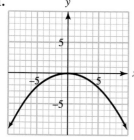

19.

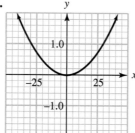

20.

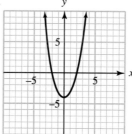

21.

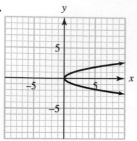

22.

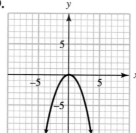

23.

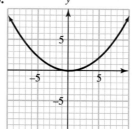

24.

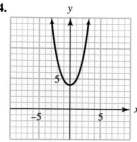

25.

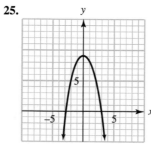

26.

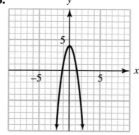

27.

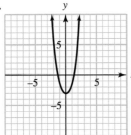

28.

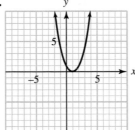

29.

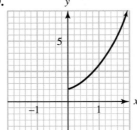

30.

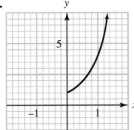

31.

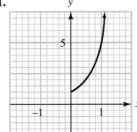

32.

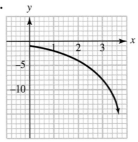

33.

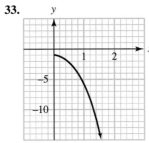

34.

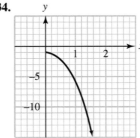

35.

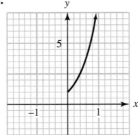

36.

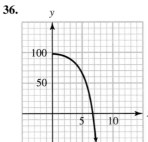

37.

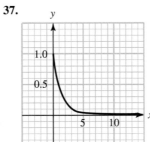

38.

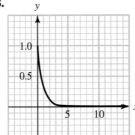

39.

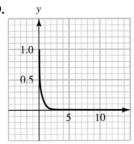

40.

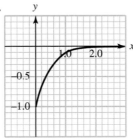

41.

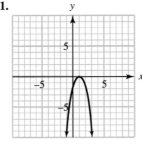

42.

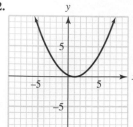

43.

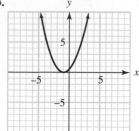

44.

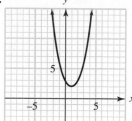

45.

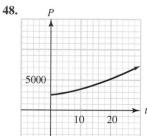

46.

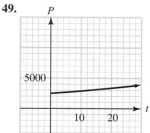

47.

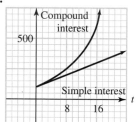

48.

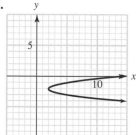

49.

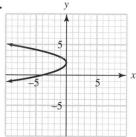

50.

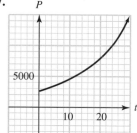

51.

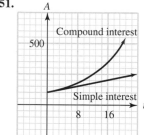

52.

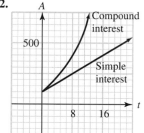

53. a.

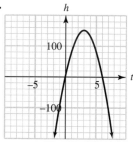

53. d.

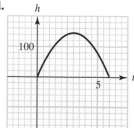

54. a.

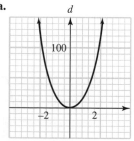

54. d.

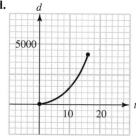

55.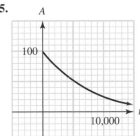

57.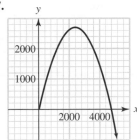

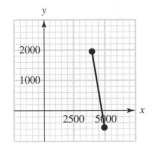

CHAPTER 11 REVIEW QUESTIONS, p. 583

1. a. Plotted points vary.

b. Plotted points vary.

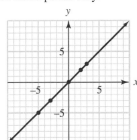

b. Plotted points vary.

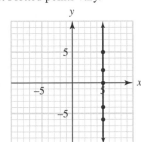

4.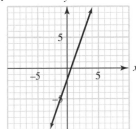

5.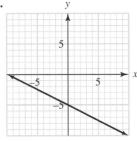

6.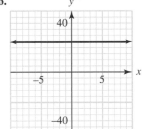

7.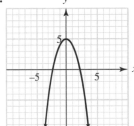

8.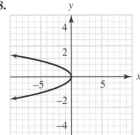

9.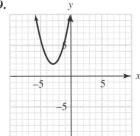

10.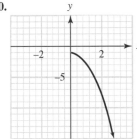

11.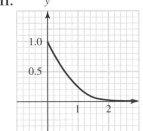

12.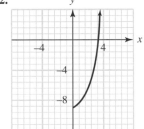

13.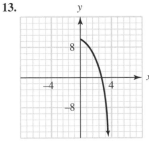

14.

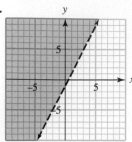

15.

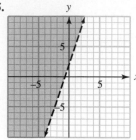

16.

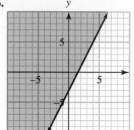

17.

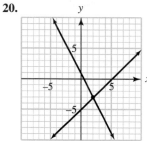

18.

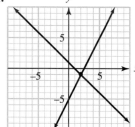

19.

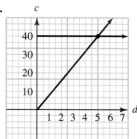

20.

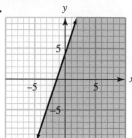

21.

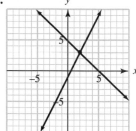

22.

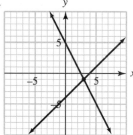

23.

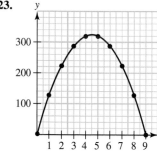

24.

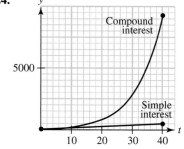

Compound interest

Simple interest

25.

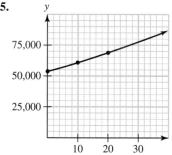

INDEX